the earth

an introduction to physical geology

HOLT, RINEHART AND WINSTON, INC.
New York • Chicago • San Francisco • Atlanta • Dallas
Montreal • Toronto • London • Sydney

JOHN VERHOOGEN, Francis J. Turner, Lionel E. Weiss, Clyde Wahrhaftig,
University of California at Berkeley
William S. Fyfe, *University of Manchester*

the earth

an introduction to physical geology

Library of Congress Catalog Card Number: 77-96846
SBN: 03-079655-5
Printed in the United States of America
0 1 2 3 4 19 9 8 7 6 5 4 3 2 1

PREFACE

The purpose of this book is to present a summary of what is known of the constitution of the earth and of the processes that have shaped its evolution. Unsolved problems and divergence of opinion have been stated in the hope that the reader will be as interested in what remains to be done as in what has already been accomplished in geology.

Although the treatment is not elementary, the book is meant, as the title implies, to *introduce* the reader to physical geology. There is no room in a book of this size to treat any single geologic topic exhaustively—in fact, there is barely space for introducing all those that are important. Weight has been given to topics that, though not necessarily essential to understanding other material in the book, are nevertheless indispensable as introductions for further study at higher levels. Thus more is said, for example, of mechanics of deformation of solids (in Chapter 9) than of the rock structures that require interpretation in the light of this information. Preference, on the whole, has been given to topics and material that are not adequately treated or readily available in other books. For example, certain classical aspects of geology relating to surface processes and sedimentation are well-treated in several recent texts, and for this reason have here been given less space than they would receive in a truly balanced treatment of geology. Other topics are less accessible or have been to some degree neglected in general texts, and to these we have allotted more space (as in much of Chapters 2, 6, 9, and others). No book of this kind can achieve complete balance of presentation. If other accounts seem to us to dwell too much on processes and events operating on the surface, our own views will seem to others to overemphasize what goes on and what has happened in the earth's interior. A book of the same title, written today by any other group of authors, would certainly have a very different approach and content. Perhaps others may be encouraged to attempt presentations of their own.

On the whole, wherever it has been possible, we have preferred an analytical to a completely descriptive approach. This requires of the student a deeper background in the physical sciences than many possess as they first approach the science of geology. No apology is made. The subject matter demands a sound physical background, and we believe that without it the student will find his further progress severely limited. The more important geological discoveries and innovations of the past twenty years have come from the more analytical branches of geology, which many call geophysics and geochemistry. One purpose of this book is to weave such subjects and their underlying physical and chemical concepts into the pattern of thinking of future geologists. Field observations and measurements, such as geological mapping, oceanographic measurements, and seismometry, still provide the essential geological data. But to interpret these to the fullest the geologist must think along lines familiar to the physicist and the chemist.

It may be regretted that the earth evolved and continues to change without regard to how its evolution can be organized as the subject matter for courses. This fact and indeed the very nature of physical geology make it possible that this book may be pronounced unsuited to some current orthodox teaching curricula. We present it as suitable for second- and third-year students in American universities. It is intended to provide background for the development of specific courses at this level (for example, in mineralogy,

v

general geophysics, structural geology, petrology, and tectonics) and a starting point for courses on similar topics at the graduate level. It could be used also for an integrated one- or two-year course covering physical geology. We do not claim that this book contains all that a graduating student of geology should know; but we believe that much that he requires is presented, and little of it is irrelevant. Obviously what we have written must be expanded and critically discussed by the professor who uses it as course background; and field and laboratory work are an indispensable complement. We make no attempt to describe technique or to expound the full variety of common minerals, rocks, structures, and geological phenomena with which the student of geology must become familiar through his own and his teachers' observations and experience.

The scope of the student's interest in geology is by no means uniform. With this in mind we have tried to arrange the subject matter so that the reader may find most of what he is particularly interested in without having to study the whole of it; a student with special interests in chemistry, for instance, might want to read Chapters 1, 2, 5, 6, 10, and 14 while omitting chapters with a more physical flavor (4, 9, 11, 12). Chapter 3 is mainly descriptive and could be referred to only insofar as the student wishes to know the meaning of descriptive terms used elsewhere.

It is notoriously difficult and hazardous to write on subjects that are rapidly growing, and this applies to many of the more interesting aspects of geology. Our presentation of "sea-floor spreading," for instance, is likely to be out of date before it appears in print. If publication had been three or four years earlier, the topic (one of the most stimulating in present-day geology) might not have been mentioned.

Obviously most of the material here presented is drawn from other sources. A book of this kind becomes tedious if cluttered by the innumerable references that would be necessary to acknowledge adequately the authors of our source material; in this general acknowledgment to so many of our predecessors and our living colleagues, we remind those whose names have not been specifically cited that this testifies to the general acceptance and significance of their work. Tables and figures copied or adapted from other publications are acknowledged individually. Here we thank authors and publishers collectively for permission to make use of this material.

We are especially grateful for help and advice of our colleagues in Berkeley and elsewhere, and for invaluable criticism of anonymous reviewers who have read various parts of the manuscript at different stages. Some who criticized our earlier drafts will see that their advice has significantly affected the final presentation. Professors B.A. Bolt, I.S.E. Carmichael, and G.H. Curtis have kindly given useful suggestions and provided important material. Fanchon Lewis has been an extraordinarily patient, good-humored, and skillful typist.

Berkeley, California
November, 1969

J.V.
F.J.T.
L.E.W.
C.W.
W.S.F.

CONTENTS

the earth
an introduction to physical geology

1

THE EARTH AS A WHOLE

THE PURPOSE OF THIS BOOK is to present an account of the earth, of what is known of its constitution and evolution, and of the processes by which this evolution proceeds. The subject is generally known as "physical geology."

When describing the functioning of any complicated object such as the human body or the earth, it is hard to know where to start; for no part of it is independent of the rest of it, and no natural process is understandable without reference to other processes. The purpose of this first chapter is to present a bird's-eye view of the subject, and thereby help the reader to place subsequent chapters in their proper contexts.

By human standards, the subject of our study is an object of rather large size[1] and great age. This object must first be properly described. Thus geology begins in the field, with observation of the materials that form the earth (minerals and aggregates of minerals called rocks), and of their geometric or "structural" arrangement; it continues with the study of the temporal relationships than can be deduced from these observations. These relationships, which establish a sequence of events in time and outline a pattern of change, must then be accounted for in terms of experimentally verifiable physical laws.

A word of caution is in order regarding the meaning of "observation." Most of the earth is hidden from view. All we can see of it, on the surface or in the deepest boreholes (about 6 km), is an insignificant fraction of its total volume. Many observations, and processes deduced therefrom, refer to a remote past, to events that occurred long before the advent of human observers. Much of geology is therefore inferential. When we state that "it is observed that the earth has a dense core with a radius of approximately 3400 km," we mean that from a large number of observations, particularly of the travel times of seismic waves, we *infer* that the earth has a core—although no one has yet seen it, any more than anyone has ever seen an electron. Nevertheless, observations are so compelling that we consider it a fact that the earth has a dense core. We feel much more confident about this statement than we do about the statement, also inferred from multiple and rather complicated observations (Chapter 4), that the earth is approximately 4.5 billion years old; for we have not yet dated every bit of the earth and cannot be certain that a rock may not yet be found that is even older. Statements about geology, especially those that refer to large-scale phenomena,

---

[1] The mean radius of the earth is 6371 km.

vary greatly as to their degree of certainty. On many subjects opposite viewpoints can be defended with equal logic. Evidence is of its very nature almost always circumstantial, and much remains to be discovered.

Partly because of our ignorance and partly because of the nature of the subject of our study, only very few completely rigorous statements can be made. The difficulty here lies in the variety of materials and the variety of processes that operate on them. No two continents are identical; no two volcanoes ever erupt in identical fashion. Rocks rarely have exactly the same composition and texture any more than two human beings are ever identically alike. Human biology makes progress because there are many human beings, to which statistics can be applied to determine longevity, average height, and so forth. There is, however, only one earth with only five continents and four oceans; there has been only one course of geological evolution: the one that actually happened. This is poor statistical material, which makes it difficult to distinguish between phenomena resulting from the operation of laws and phenomena resulting from random or accidental causes. (By "law" we mean a statement to the effect that a geological event of kind A is necessarily linked to a geological event of kind B, much as a force is linked to an acceleration by Newton's law.) Regular laws of physics lead to irregular geological effects mainly because of the multiplicity of variables involved. A similar situation prevails in other natural sciences. In meteorology, for example, although the physical laws that govern the behavior of the atmosphere are well understood, weather remains largely unaccountable and unpredictable.

In dealing with smaller-scale phenomena at and near the earth's surface, especially where the time scale involved is also small, we are on firmer ground. The stuff of which the accessible part of the crust is made is rock. Rocks are aggregates of minerals. Every mineral is a chemical compound, whose composition can be expressed by a chemical formula—such as quartz (SiO_2), pyrite (FeS_2), calcite ($CaCO_3$), and many others. Minerals, moreover, are crystalline; so that the study of the earth on a small scale begins with crystallography, which leads through mineralogy to the study of the rocks themselves and of their modes of origin. Here we are entering a field (petrology) in which scales of size, distance and time are broader, and the science correspondingly more speculative. But at the starting point, crystallography, we confront some of the most orderly phenomena in nature: the periodic arrangement of atoms in space governed by mathematical principles of symmetry.

The Earth in the Solar System

The earth is one of a group of planets that revolve around the sun while they spin on their own axes. A remarkable feature of the system is that angular momentum vectors for orbital motion and spin are in most cases almost parallel; that is, the planets and most of their satellites move in the same sense in the same plane, while also spinning in the same sense. Planetary distances to the sun measured in astronomical units (one astronomical unit equals the mean earth-sun distance) also obey approximately the Titus-Bode law

$$r = 0.4 + 0.3 \times 2^n$$

where $n = -\infty$ for Mercury, 0 for Venus, 1 for the earth, 2 for Mars, 3 for the asteroid belt, 4 for Jupiter, and so on. These regularities in the system suggest that its parts must have been formed by the same process from the same starting material and, presumably, at almost the same time. Even though we still do not know how the solar system came into existence, some information regarding the earth might come from an examination of the planets.

The latter fall into two very distinct categories: the "terrestrial" or inner planets (from Mercury to Mars) and the "major" or outer planets (from Jupiter outwards). The outer planets are considerably more massive than the earth.[2] The inner ones are smaller, and their mean densities are also similar to that of the

---

[2] Except Pluto which is generally considered to be an escaped satellite rather than a planet, even though it is at approximately the distance predicted by the Titus-Bode law for $n = 7$.

earth (for example, 5.52 g/cm³ for the earth, 5.1 for Venus, 4.1 for Mars, but 0.7 for Saturn). The low density of the outer planets is explained as an effect of their mass and high escape velocity (see Chapter 11) which has enabled them to retain a larger proportion of the lighter elements (hydrogen, helium). Thus, presumably, the average composition of the earth might be somewhat similar to that of the inner planets.

There is no single planet at the distance corresponding to $n = 3$ in the Titus-Bode law; instead there is at approximately the right distance a belt of small objects, called asteroids, which may be fragments of one or several disrupted planetary bodies or fragments that failed to agglomerate to form a planet. Meteorites, which are solid objects that fall occasionally on the earth from orbits around the sun, may be asteroids that were pulled out of their orbits by the gravitational disturbance of other planets, or by collisions. Considerable attention has been devoted to meteorites, on the grounds that their composition might be similar to that of the earth. Thus much of our thinking about the composition of the earth has been conditioned by the study of meteorites.

METEORITES

Meteorites fall into two large groups, the "irons" and the "stones." The former consist essentially of metallic iron with some alloyed nickel and smaller amounts of a few other metals. The stones consist mostly of silicates of magnesium and iron, with some metal (meteorites with about equal amounts of metal and silicate are also known). Stones can further be subdivided into chondrites and achondrites according to whether they contain or lack chondri, which are small, rounded bodies composed of magnesium silicates that perhaps were formed by crystallization of drops of melt. Both chondrites and achondrites are variable in composition. The rare "carbonaceous" chondrites consist largely of hydrous silicates, olivine, carbonates and sulfates of magnesium and calcium, iron oxides, and a few percent of carbon compounds. There has been much debate as to whether these carbon compounds include any

biogenic material; it has not yet been demonstrated that they do.

THE MOON

The moon has a mean density of 3.34 g/cm³, which is not unlike that of stony meteorites. Because of the small size of the moon, lunar gravity is also small, so that the pressure inside the moon (see Chapter 11) is nowhere greater than about 50,000 bars and cannot very much affect the density. This suggests that the earth might also consist in part of material with a density (at ordinary pressure) of about 3.3 g/cm³. (Part of the earth's higher mean density of 5.52 g/cm³ is due to gravitational self-compression, as explained in Chapter 11.)

Instrumental readings from Surveyor spacecraft landed on the moon indicate that the sampled lunar rocks are composed mainly of silicates, including significant quantities of aluminosilicates. These surface samples are not exactly analogous to common meteorites (irons and chondrites). Their composition may be consistent with a volcanic origin, but it is perhaps unlikely that lunar rocks will be either uniform in composition or strictly comparable with any common terrestrial volcanic rock.

Gross Structure of the Earth

As explained in later chapters, information regarding the internal structure of the earth accrues from measurements of gravity on its surface, from its rotation and motions from which its moments of inertia can be deduced, from the period of its free oscillations, and, mostly, from the propagation of seismic (or earthquake) waves through it. It has a dense core with a radius of some 3400 km and a lighter "mantle," some 2900 km thick. It was suggested long ago, by analogy with meteorites, that the core corresponds in composition to irons while the mantle corresponds broadly to stones. This suggestion is essentially consistent with modern data.

Overlying the mantle and separated from it by a rather sharp discontinuity known as the

Mohorovičić discontinuity (or "Moho," for short) is the highly heterogeneous "crust," consisting mostly of silicates. The crust is the stuff on which we live and grow our food, and from which we derive all our resources, minerals, metals, and fuels.

Analyses of a large number of rocks indicate that the uppermost crust (the only accessible part of it) consists mainly of just eight elements which together form 98.5 percent of it by weight. These are, in order of decreasing abundance, oxygen (46.6 percent), silicon (27.7 percent), aluminum (8.1 percent), iron (5 percent), calcium (3.6 percent), sodium (2.8 percent), potassium (2.6 percent), and magnesium (2.1 percent). (See Table 14–2.)

A major object of geology is to determine exactly what the crust, mantle, and core, consist of, and how and when this tripartite structure came into existence.

THE CRUST

A glance at a map of the world shows it to consist of continents and oceans. Continents, which constitute about one third of the earth's surface, stand above sea level at an average elevation of some 800 m. They extend seawards into a "continental shelf," which is a platform generally a few tens of kilometers wide (Figure 1–1) lying at shallow depth below sea level (~200 meters). From the outer edge of the shelf, the continental margin drops down gradually ("continental slope") towards the oceanic depths.

The characteristic feature of continents is that they consist of rocks of relatively low density (the average density of continents is probably close to 2.8 g/cm³) as compared with the earth as a whole or with the underlying mantle. As gravity shows (see Chapter 11), it is precisely because of this low density that continents stand high; they float, so to speak, on the denser mantle like ice on water. The thickness of the low-density continental crust in most places ranges between 30 and 50 km; it is related to the height of the continent above sea level, the continental crust being generally but not always thicker under high mountain ranges (isostasy).

Granite is a characteristic continental rock, not found in the oceanic realm. It is an igneous rock (that is, one formed by crystallization of a silicate melt) consisting essentially of quartz, feldspars, and mica. Chemically, it consists mostly of SiO_2 (65 to 70 percent by weight), with Al_2O_3 being the next most abundant constituent. For this reason, the term *sial* (silicon–aluminum) is used as a short-hand notation to designate the composition of the continental crust, as opposed to *sima* (silicon–magnesium) which is more characteristic of oceanic rocks and presumably of the mantle. On continents one also finds great volumes of other igneous rocks rich in silica and alumina (andesites, rhyolites), ubiquitous volcanic basalts, and a thin and irregular cover of sedimentary rocks. The bulk of the continents seem to consist of metamorphic rocks, which are igneous or sedimentary rocks that have recrystallized in the solid state.

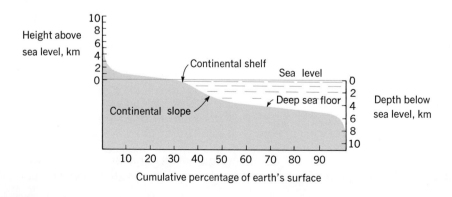

Height above sea level, km

Continental shelf

Sea level

Deep sea floor

Continental slope

Depth below sea level, km

Cumulative percentage of earth's surface

Fig. 1–1 *Height above sea level (or depth below sea level) of the earth's solid surface plotted against cumulative percentage of the earth's surface. Continents, including the adjacent continental shelves, occupy a little more than 30 percent of the earth's surface. The average depth of the sea is about 4.0 km; ocean basins, excluding the continental shelf and slope, have an average depth of 4.8 km.*

The oceans have an average depth below sea level of some 4.8 km. Much of the ocean floor is rather monotonously flat. Great mountain ranges ("ridges" or "rises") rise from it, forming an impressive worldwide system to which much study is presently being devoted. Greatest oceanic depths occur in "trenches," which are narrow, elongated, and arcuate troughs generally bordering continents; the greatest known depth of water (11 km) occurs in the Mariana trench, just east of the Mariana Island arc. Islands that rise from the oceanic floor are typically volcanic and consist dominantly of basalt. The oceanic crust is thin (6–8 km), so that the Mohorivičić discontinuity in oceanic areas lies only 10 to 12 km below sea level.

A major objective of geological inquiry is to discover how continents came into existence and into their present configuration, and to unravel the history of the sea floor. A great advance of the last few years has been to demonstrate that, as suggested long ago, continents move in relation to each other ("continental drift") and that the ocean floor itself partakes in a general pattern of motion ("sea-floor spreading") by which new oceanic crust is produced from the mantle along the crests of oceanic ridges, moves away from its source and down again into the mantle, while continents are rafted along on top. Typical rates of motion are of the order of a few centimeters per year. The motion is almost certainly related to large thermal "convective" disturbances in the underlying mantle, the upper few hundred kilometers of which evidently participate in the motion.

This participation of the mantle in crustal affairs is a recent and very important discovery. For want of adequate observational tools, the attention of geologists had for many decades been focused exclusively on the more readily observable continental masses. These, as well as the oceanic basins, were generally assumed to be permanent and immovable features of the earth's surface, and the source and explanation of observable geological processes were sought mainly, but not very successfully, in the crust itself. The mantle, about which very little was known as late as 30 years ago, was long thought to be essentially uniform, homogeneous, inert, and geologically quite uninteresting. Recent progress in instrumentation (mostly geophysical and oceanographic) gradually led to the contrary view: The mantle (or, at least, the upper mantle) is heterogeneous; it constantly interacts with the crust that it moves and with which it mixes, as new crustal material (oceanic and continental) is formed from it while "old" crustal material sinks back into it. Seen in this light, the time-honored distinction between continents and oceans loses much of its significance, as the dynamic units in the mantle are in some measure independent of it. This is shown, for instance, by gravitational features such as the undulations of the geoid (see Chapter 11) which seem to disregard continental boundaries.

Geologic Processes

To analyze the complicated sequence of events from which the present configuration of the earth has emerged, it is convenient to consider separately a small number of district processes, none of which is entirely independent of the others.

EROSION

Chemical reactions (hydration, oxidation, solution) between water precipitated from the atmosphere and rocks exposed at the surface, assisted by various physical and biological processes, lead to the breakdown of rocks ("weathering") and the formation of soil, that loose and discontinuous layer which supports vegetation and from which we derive our food. An important product of weathering, and a major component of soil, is a group of minerals referred to as clays (hydrated alumino-silicates) which have interesting structural and physical properties. Products of weathering vary with climate; so that something of the nature of past climate conditions may be inferred from ancient weathering products.

Loose material tends naturally to move downhill under the effect of gravity; thus rock detritus produced by weathering generally moves from high points (mountains) to low points (the sea floor). This process of transportation is greatly enhanced by the action of running water and more locally by wind and ice. Weathering and transportation lead to efficient mechanical and chemical sorting. Fine particles, such as clay, generally travel faster and farther than coarser grains, such as sand grains consisting of quartz (SiO_2). Soluble salts—for example, sodium carbonate and calcium bicarbonate—are carried by rivers and end up in the sea.

Erosion obviously has the effect of lowering the surface of the land. A typical rate of lowering may be of the order of a few centimeters per thousand years, although it varies greatly with climate and average elevation. Clearly, at this rate, continents that stand, on the average, only some 800 meters high, would be reduced to sea level in a matter of some 10^7 years. Since they are much older than that, there must be other processes that make them rise, or which build up the relief. The shape of the topographic surface at any moment of earth history, the pattern of hills and valleys, and many other features of the landscape, essentially express the instantaneous balance between erosion and processes (such as volcanism and deformation) that build up the land.

The study of landscape evolution is called geomorphology. One important conclusion that emerged early from such studies is that recently (that is, within the last few million years) there were rather drastic climatic changes culminating in the recurrence of "glacial" episodes during which great masses of ice accumulated in middle and high latitudes. The ice caps of Greenland and Antarctica are surviving examples of these once extensive ice sheets. These recent glaciations have left their prominent mark on the landscape, and have also produced some interesting geophysical disturbances, such as sinking of the surface under the load of ice and its slow recovery after melting. Current estimates of the viscosity of the upper mantle—an essential parameter in all discussions of the dynamics of the earth—are based on the observed rate of postglacial recovery. The point is mentioned to illustrate the somewhat devious paths geologists must follow to obtain the information they need, and also how closely are related branches of geology that at first seem markedly different.

SEDIMENTATION

Loose material carried downward accumulates in low points (for example, valley floors, the continental shelf, or the bottom of the ocean) where it is deposited in flat-lying sedimentary layers. Fluctuating changes in conditions of deposition and in the nature and supply of rock waste are reflected in bedding or stratification so typical of sediments deposited from water or from the air. With passage of time, pressure induced by the increasing load of superposed material, combined with chemical reactions in which entrapped water participates, causes a compaction and induration of initially loosely aggregated sediments. These processes collectively are called diagenesis, and the final products are sedimentary rocks.

The main constituents of sedimentary rocks are grains of chemically durable minerals (notably quartz), fine-grained clay minerals, rock fragments, and calcite ($CaCO_3$) in the form of shell fragments and other organic remains and marine precipitate. The commonest sedimentary rocks are shales—fine-grained aggregates of clay minerals and admixed finely divided quartz. Sandstones, as the name implies, are composed of larger grains, mainly quartz, which bulk largely in the composition of beach sands. Conglomerates are still coarser. They consist of gravel or pebbles set in a sandy or shaly matrix. Prolonged water transport rapidly reduces the size of pebbles by mutual impact and abrasion. Thus conglomerates rarely form very far from their source. They are typical of river-laid deposits in areas close to mountain ranges—for example, along the north margin of the Los Angeles basin, Southern California, and in south-central Chile west of the Andes. Limestones are composed mainly of fragmented skeletons (for examples, shells) of marine organisms. Some are formed almost exclusively of calcium carbonate precipitated directly from seawater. Other chemically precipitated sedimentary rocks include beds of rock-salt (NaCl), gypsum ($CaSO_4 \cdot 2H_2O$), and other chlorides and sulfates—the residue of evaporation from seawater isolated in enclosed basins in regions of semiarid warm climate.

Shales and sandstones, although essentially of inorganic origin, locally contain biogenic material. Notable in this connection are fossils, which are imprints or skeletal remains of once-living organisms. Shells, coral remains, fish teeth, and plant imprints are familiar examples. Organic limestones are the commonest but by no means the only rocks composed mainly of biogenic material. Coal is a rock composed of chemically reconstituted remains of terrestrial vegetation. Petroleum, though hardly a rock, is a distillate from organic remains trapped in sedimentary rocks; after concentration and migration under gravity it eventually becomes stored in porous and permeable sedimentary beds, or reservoir sands. Cherts are sediments composed of silica that has been directly precipitated from seawater or secreted in the skeletons of microscopic organisms. Many deep-sea "muds," phosphate beds, and some sedimentary iron deposits are largely, or at least in significant part, biogenic. Life has contributed considerable variety and interest to sedimentary rocks.

Sedimentary rocks make up only a small fraction of the earth's crust. On the ocean floors they form a layer only a few hundred meters or a kilometer thick; this small thickness, when compared to rates of deposition, provides evidence of the relative youth of the underlying oceanic crust. Sediments form a much thicker mantle on the continental shelf. Large parts of the continents are covered with a veneer of older sedimentary rocks a few kilometers thick. There are local belts (geosynclines) hundreds of kilometers long in which the pile of ancient sedimentary rocks is much thicker: 10 km to 30 km. Many such rocks are demonstrably of shallow-water origin; some indeed were deposited under terrestrial conditions. Clearly deposition in these troughs must have been accompanied by synchronous sinking to keep pace with accumulation in a continuously maintained shallow-water environment. Curiously enough, most of these areas in which the crust continuously sagged downward apace with sedimentation eventually developed into mountain ranges. The classic example is in the Appalachian Mountains along the eastern seaboard of the United States.

IGNEOUS ACTIVITY

VOLCANISM Volcanism, from the human viewpoint one of the most spectacular and destructive of all geological phenomena, consists of surface eruption of molten rock matter and gas. The general term for rock melts is magma. Generation, movement, and eruption of magma collectively constitute what is called igneous activity; volcanism is its surface manifestation. Magma emerging at temperatures in the range of 850°C to 1200°C from a surface vent flows outward under gravity as lava, whose ultimate products of solidification are the volcanic rocks. Discharge of gas may be concentrated in sporadic bursts of great violence called explosions. Volcanic gas (chiefly water and carbon dioxide) when violently expelled is commonly charged with fragmented volcanic material—congealed glass, clotted crystals blown out of the frothing magma—and fragments of rocks torn from the walls of the vents itself. These rain down and coat the surrounding land surface or sea floor as pyroclastic deposits, whose fragmental nature, rough bedding, and sorting recall corresponding features characteristic of normal sedimentary rocks. The surface accumulation of lava and pyroclastic ejecta around the central vent or fissures is called a volcano. The vent or some relic of it may be preserved at the volcano summit; and this is called a crater.

Most magmas are silicate melts in which SiO_2 varies between values of 45 and 70 percent by weight. The more siliceous magmas, according to established usage based on now outmoded notions of the role of "silicic acid," are termed "acid" in contrast to "basic" magmas low in silica. The commonest lavas (basalts) fall in the basic category, with about 50 percent SiO_2. Acid magmas, on the other hand, are represented at the surface mainly by pyroclastic sheets. But magma of many compositions may be erupted either as lava or as pyroclastic material.

The composition of the lava emitted by a volcano may change with time; there is for instance, a conspicuous difference in composition between the lava erupted by Vesuvius at different times. Occasionally a single volcano may erupt alternately or nearly simultaneously different types of lava (for example, the basaltic and acid material at Newberry, a now probably extinct volcano in Oregon). The composition of the lavas from one volcano may be conspicuously different from those of another volcano just a few miles away, as in the case of the central African equatorial volcano, Nyiragongo, and its neighbor, Nyamuragira. More commonly, all volcanoes of a given "province" or area will erupt lavas which, although differing considerably, have persistent chemical characteristics that point to a common origin. How they originate and the reasons for their chemical diversity are among the most important questions of igneous petrology.

Volcanism has occurred, either once or repeatedly, almost everywhere on the earth's surface; but at any one time its geographic distribution has been most restricted. This is the case today: Most active and recently active volcanoes occur along the margins of the Pacific Ocean; the rest are scattered, but localized (in the Mediterranean, the lesser Antilles, Indonesia, the mid-Atlantic, and a few other regions). Volcanism is broadly correlated, but neither coextensive nor strictly contemporaneous, with seismic activity and mountain-building movements. Occurrence of volcanism in space and time seems to be tinged with some degree of randomness.

Seismic evidence at sites of eruption suggests that the immediate sources of magma lie in local reservoirs at depths of the order of 50 km. It is thought that these are pockets of liquid formed by partial fusion of otherwise solid rock in the outer part of the mantle. The precise mechanism by which large quantities of magma could form sporadically in this way and become mobilized into local subcrustal reservoirs is a major unsolved problem.

PLUTONISM   Deep erosion as in old mountain ranges reveals bodies of once deep-seated crystalline rocks, many of very great extent, believed to have formed within the crust by freezing of magma welling up from greater depths. These are the plutonic rocks; phenomena connected with their emplacement, cooling and solidification may be termed plutonism. Plutonic rocks embrace roughly the same compositional range as do volcanic rocks. Similar mineral combinations appear in both classes: quartz with alkali feldspars in acid, pyroxenes with calcic feldspars (plagioclase), and olivine in basic rocks. Common to both classes are certain striking patterns of minor-element concentration—for example, Zr, Nb, Ta, Ti in rocks rich in Na and K relative to Si. There are some persistent, rather minor, chemical differences between volcanic and plutonic rocks, and striking textural differences attributable to differences in rates of cooling and degree of retention of dissolved water under surface versus deep-seated conditions. But the magmatic origin of most plutonic rocks, with the possible exception of some "granites," can scarcely be doubted.

Emplacement of a magma body at some site below the surface of the earth is called igneous intrusion. The processes of intrusion are by no means clearly understood, but the forms of some bodies, especially the smaller ones, and their structural relation to enclosing rocks clearly demonstrate their intrusive nature. Steeply dipping tabular bodies known as dikes cross-cut the bedding of surrounding sediments and may maintain a more or less constant attitude, regardless of structure of the invaded rocks, for many kilometers. Then there are sheets (sills) of plutonic rock that seem to have been injected as magma parallel to the bedding of enclosing sediments. Some of these, basic in composition, are thousands of meters thick and extend laterally for hundreds of kilometers or more. In some places older volcanoes have been eroded to the roots exposing intrusive ring complexes more or less circular in outcrop and commonly 1–30 km in diameter. Typically such a complex consists of several concentric, more or less vertical intrusions, each more or less a hollow cylinder.

Any magma is less dense than an igneous rock of the same composition. Consequently there is a general tendency, statistically speaking, for bodies of magma, once generated, to move upward under gravity. This is especially true for acid magmas, for in general the density of igneous materials diminishes with increase in silica content. However, for reasons that will appear later, intrusive masses of acid magma, forcefully pushing aside the surrounding rocks in their ascent, commonly crystallize and so become frozen to a halt before reaching the surface. They characteristically take the form of very large composite masses (batholiths) compounded of many individual bodies (plutons) each representing a separate surge of magma from below. For example the Sierra Nevada batholith of California, outcropping over an area 600 km $\times$ 100 km with a topographic relief of several kilometers, is made up of perhaps 100 or 200 separate plutons. Though varying considerably in composition, most of these are composed of quartz-bearing acid plutonic rocks loosely termed "granitic." Intrusion of the Sierra Nevada batholith was no sudden event. Radiometric dating shows that plutonic activity was concentrated in at least three episodes spread through an interval of some 100 million years.

Intrusion of a batholith or even of a pluton of smaller dimensions must have been attended by profound disturbances—structural, thermal, and chemical—in the invaded country rocks. Adjacent rocks may be shouldered aside, deformed by plastic flow in the solid state, or fragmented and veined with magma on all scales from that of a hand specimen to that of a geological map. In the vicinity of the intrusive contact, rocks may become recrystallized, chemically changed by introduction of elements borne outward from the cooling pluton by aqueous gases and solutions, or even locally melted. The magma itself participates in such border reactions, and in so doing may become contaminated by material derived from the country rocks.

A side effect of plutonism of great economic interest is the development of ore bodies within or close to igneous intrusions. An ore body is a body of rock in which one or several chemical elements are sufficiently concentrated to allow them to be mined for profit. The processes by which minor constituents of the crust—Cu, Pb, Zn, Au, Ag, Ni, and many others—become concentrated into bodies of economically valuable ore are varied and complex. As examples we note the early separation and concentration of liquid metallic sulfides of nickel and copper in large sheets of basic plutonic rock, and peripheral development of quartz veins carrying gold, silver, and various metallic sulfides deposited from hot aqueous solutions (hydrothermal solutions) circulating through heated country rock bordering cooling granitic plutons.

METAMORPHISM

Vast continental areas are underlain by rocks that can be judged from their mineralogy and texture to be neither purely sedimentary nor igneous. It can be demonstrated that these metamorphic (or transformed) rocks are igneous or sedimentary rocks that have recrystallized while solid. Metamorphism can be induced by heating, or by exposure to high pressure, or both; the effects of heating, for instance, are clearly seen in the "contact metamorphism" that develops around the margins of plutonic intrusions. In general, however, metamorphism is a regional phenomenon that affects very large volumes and cannot be attributed to intrusion of magma.

There is considerable variety in metamorphic rocks, as a number of different mineral assemblages can develop from identical starting material (say, basalt or shale). This variety stems in part from the fact that rising temperature and pressure generally displace chemical equilibrium in opposite senses. Thus high temperature and low pressure lead to mineral assemblages quite different from those formed at low temperature and high pressure. As a result of much field and experimental work, it is now possible to determine broadly the particular conditions of pressure and temperature, and other physical variables, under which a given metamorphic rock has recrystallized.

A striking feature of regionally metamorphosed rocks is the development of a more or less planar foliated or schistose texture. A metamorphic rock called gneiss is mineralogically very similar to an igneous granite, from which it differs mainly by its foliation that induces a more or less planar fissility. Shale may be converted to a highly fissile rock called mica schist. In such rocks there is a tendency for nonequidimensional mineral grains to lie with their greatest dimension in the plane of schistosity; there is also commonly a tendency for most minerals to show a preferred crystallographic orientation. Lamination also results from segregation of minerals (for example, mica) into thin layers parallel to the schistosity. Foliated rocks are strongly anisotropic. Such anisotropy can arise by recrystallization in an initially isotropic rock only if the factors causing recrystallization are themselves anisotropic; nonhydrostatic stress is one such factor. Regionally metamorphosed rocks appear in general to have recrystallized while being deformed under stress (see below).

DEFORMATION (ALSO CALLED DIASTROPHISM, OR TECTONISM)

That the earth is a dynamic rather than a static system is also clear from the mechanical deformation evident in many rocks, particularly sedimentary rocks. These, it will be remembered, form in layers or strata that are originally horizontal or nearly so. Sedimentary strata, however, are commonly observed to have been tilted, or to form various patterns of folds (Figure 3–44) which attest to postdepositional deformation. Marine sediments, moreover, are found in many mountain ranges several thousand meters above sea level, indicating again postdepositional uplift. In some areas, repeated surveys clearly show that the surface of the land is moving today, commonly at a rate of a few centimeters per year. Field mapping occasionally demonstrates that large blocks of rocks have been displaced horizontally (or nearly so) over distances measured in tens of kilometers; parts of the western Swiss Alps, for instance, consist of folded sediments that were originally deposited far to the south of their present positions. Such displaced masses

must be bounded, at least on one side, by discontinuities or "faults"—that is, fractures the opposite sides of which have moved relative to each other. Horizontal displacement along the great San Andreas fault of California, for instance, amounts to several hundred kilometers, and is still proceeding today at a rate that again is of the order of a few centimeters per year. Sudden displacement along a fault may be accompanied by earthquakes, the frequency and magnitude of which testify to the intensity of the earth's present tectonic activity. Deformation in rocks is observable or inferred on every scale, from microscopic distortions within single crystals to translation of whole continents.

Not all parts of the earth are equally deformed; at any one time there will be large areas where nothing much seems to happen, while other areas are being subjected to intense deformation, resulting for instance in the formation of great mountain ranges (for example, the great range that stretches roughly east and west from the Alps to the Himalayas and the western Cordillera of North and South America). These localized areas are said to be orogenic belts, the process of mountain-making being known as orogeny. Orogeny is discontinuous in time, as successive episodes of deformation are separated by intervals of relative quiescence. Orogeny is commonly associated, for reasons to be discussed later, with regional metamorphism; it is also broadly associated with volcanic and plutonic activity.

The geologist is faced with three kinds of problems relating to rock deformation: (1) He must first determine, mainly from field mapping, precisely what deformation has occurred, and when and where. (2) He must then infer from the observed pattern of deformation or strain the stresses that produced it. Since the observed strains are, by definition, permanent strains (that is, irreversible and hence nonelastic), he is faced here with all the intricacies of the nonelastic behavior of solids (Chapter 9), a complicated subject made even more difficult by the length of the geological time scale involved (see Chapter 4). (3) He must then discover a mechanism to produce the inferred stresses. Few geologists doubt that geological stresses are essentially thermal in origin—that is, that they are mainly produced by differences in temperature between various parts of the earth and by differences in the rate at which the temperature changes. Just how a temperature field generates a stress field is a complicated matter; in particular the part played in the earth by thermally driven convective motion has not yet been fully elucidated (Chapter 12), although it is generally believed that crustal deformation is caused in large part by large-scale convective flow in the underlying mantle.

OTHER INTERNAL PROCESSES

All five processes briefly described in the foregoing paragraphs can be seen or inferred from observations on the surface of the earth. Still other processes undoubtedly occur below the surface, as for example heat generation and heat transfer, as discussed in Chapter 12. That heat is transferred in the earth is clear from measurement of the surface heat flow—of the amount of heat that reaches the surface from sources within the crust, mantle, and possibly also within the core. Heat transfer is, in fact, the most important of all geological processes, since it provides the energy required to drive all the others. Heat is generated within the earth mainly by spontaneous disintegration of radioactive nuclides; but significant contributions may come from other sources, such as tidal friction and gravitational energy.

Mass transfer, or convective motion, also presumably occurs on a large scale in the mantle and core. The evidence for it is indirect, for no one has ever seen the mantle flowing; it is based on (1) theoretical considerations to the effect that convection could occur under certain conditions, and (2) the observed pattern of surface deformation, particularly orogeny, continental drift and sea-floor spreading, which are otherwise difficult to explain. Convection, in brief, is an effect of gravity acting on density differences produced by differences in temperature; hotter and thus lighter substances generally tend to move up while cold and dense substances tend to move

downward. Convection is also an efficient mechanism of heat transfer.

Relatively little is known about large-scale migration of elements within the earth. We have already seen that weathering and sedimentation are efficient mechanisms for transfer and sorting of some elements. Transport of other elements presumably has taken place on a large scale within the earth and may still be occurring today; transfer of water, carbon dioxide, and other gases from the mantle to the atmosphere via volcanoes may serve as an example. Some chemical elements of low average abundance (for example, rare earths and metals such as Cu, Au, Hg) are found to be locally concentrated by a very large factor in relatively small portions of the crust. Clearly, the concentration process must have involved transfer of such elements over considerable distances. As examples on a yet larger scale, one could mention the formation of the earth's core and its separation from the mantle; for all we know, this process might still be going on at present. There is also indirect evidence for upward concentration of some elements, particularly U, Th, and K.

James Hutton and the "Uniformitarian" Principle

Fundamental to the interpretation of geological phenomena is a principle first proposed and abundantly illustrated by James Hutton, Edinburgh physician, in the later years of the eighteenth century. Hutton attributed all geological phenomena—mountain ranges such as the Alps, deep canyons and integrated river-valley systems, the soil, the very rocks themselves—to natural observable processes, such as those seen in operation today.

"There are two ways in which we may look for the transactions of time past, in the present state of things, upon the surface of this earth, and read the operations of an ancient date in those which are daily transacted under our eyes. The one way is to examine the soil. . . . In this studying the soil, we shall learn the destruction of the solid parts; and though, by this means, we cannot form an estimate of the quantity of this destruction which had been made, we shall upon many occasions, see a certain *minimum* of this quantity which may perhaps astonish us.

"The second method here proposed, is to examine the solid part of the earth, in order to learn the quantity of matter which had been separated [eroded] from this mass. Here also we shall not be able to compute the quantity of what had been destroyed; but we shall find everywhere a certain *minimum* of this quantity, which will give us an extensive view of the operation of the elements and seasons upon the surface of the earth." (*Theory of the Earth*, vol. 2, pp. 242–243, 1795)

"From the top of those decaying pyramids [Mt. Blanc and surrounding peaks] to the sea, we have a chain of facts which clearly demonstrate this proposition.[3] That the materials of wasted mountains have travelled through the rivers; for in every step of this progress, we see the effect, and thus acknowledge the proper cause. We may often be witness to this action; but it is only a small part of the whole progress that we may thus perceive, nevertheless it is equally satisfactory as if we saw the whole; for throughout the whole of this long course we may see some part of the mountain moving some part of the way. What more can we require? Nothing but time." (*ibid.*, p. 329)

Hutton's doctrine that the present is the key to the past, was expounded and illustrated by Charles Lyell as the "principle of uniformitarianism." This is a rather unfortunate term; for there is nothing in Hutton's writings to suggest that rates of natural processes have necessarily been uniform throughout geological time, or that uniformity is a characteristic of geological phenomena in general. The essence of Hutton's thesis is evolution—successions of events and changes—controlled by natural observable processes. It is a doctrine of actual causes consistent with physical laws. Strict adherence to

the uniformitarian principle, especially with respect to erosion rates, has led to some grossly erroneous conclusions. One of these is the restricted span (less than 100 million years) once generally accepted for geological time.

Geologic Time

GEOLOGY, A HISTORICAL SCIENCE

Geology is a historical science. It deals with successions of events in *time*, and with geological processes whose roles are determined by their *rates*. Nowhere is the fundamental role of time in geology more strikingly apparent than in the revolution in scientific thought occasioned by Hutton's proposal of the uniformitarian principle and the accompanying emphasis which he placed on time:

"What more can we require? Nothing but time. It is not any part of the proofs that will be disputed; but after allowing all the parts, the whole will be denied; and, For what?—only because we are not disposed to allow that quantity of time which the ablution of so much wasted mountain might require." (*Theory of the Earth*, p. 239, 1795)

"The great system upon the surface of this earth is that of valleys and rivers; . . . however this system shall be interrupted and occasionally destroyed, it would necessarily be again formed in time, while the earth continued above the level of the sea." (*ibid.*, p. 538)

At Siccar Point, on the southeastern coast of Scotland, almost undisturbed sedimentary strata lie on a plane surface (unconformity) truncating folded beds of an older sedimentary series (Fig. 1–2). Here, as Hutton first realized, is the tangible record of a sequence of events that collectively must have covered an immense interval of time: (1) accumulation; (2) folding and elevation above sea level; (3) partial erosion of the lower series of sediments; (4) deposition of the upper series; and (5) uplift of both above sea level. But this is only part of the implied span of time; for accumulation of the lower strata implies simultaneous erosion of a yet older rock mass with its own now unrecorded history.

---

[3] Put forward to refute the "hypothesis of violent causes" and "supposition of a great debacle" current among geologists of Hutton's day.

FIG. 1–2 *The unconformity at Siccar Point, Scotland, made famous by Hutton. Nearly vertical Silurian strata are covered unconformably by gently dipping upper old Red Sandstone (Devonian).*

Hutton is acknowledged as the father of modern geology not for the uniformitarian doctrine alone. He also freed geological thinking once and for all from the cramping influence of clerical teaching—hitherto unchallenged for over a thousand years—to the effect that time, inaugurated at the Creation, occupied the excessively narrow span of some 6000 years. Geology owes its peculiar and singular flavor to the pervasive role of time, whose total span, compared with that of written history, is vast.

Sequences of events, evolutionary trends, correlation of simultaneous events, rates of processes—these are the ingredients of geological thought and theory. Much of current geological research effort is concentrated on determination of process rates both from direct observation in the field and by laboratory experiment. Information of this kind, as we shall see later, has made it possible to build up a system of earth chronology expressible in large but standard time units—*millions of years* (*m.y.*). Radiometric dating—based on known rates of decay of radioactive nuclides in mineral crystals—places the age of some rocks of the crystalline continental crust as far back as 3½ billion (3.5×10^9) years. Just as with human history, it is the later part of geological time (the last 500 m.y.) that is most completely recorded in the exposed rocks of the crust.

THE STRATIGRAPHIC COLUMN AND THE GEOLOGIC TIME SCALE

The crystalline basement of the continental crust is covered, over large areas, by veneers of sedimentary rocks. In many places it is possible to study and to measure continuous sequences of sedimentary strata aggregating hundreds or even a few thousands of meters in thickness. It seems a truism to say that in any vertical sequence of sedimentary strata the beds are successively younger from below upward. Yet this was first stated clearly only 300 years ago. Formulated as Steno's *law of superposition*, this principle became the foundation stone on which was later erected the science of stratigraphy—the study of stratified rocks and events recorded in them. Stratigraphy in turn is the basis of geological chronology.

Some sedimentary beds, especially in marine sections, contain fossil remains of once-living animals and plants. These are fragmentary relics of extinct faunas and floras. Their upward succession in a stratigraphic section gives a picture, incomplete but still legible, of the development of life and the geographic migrations of faunas with passage of time. In one respect the picture is unambiguous. Faunas high in the succession developed or arrived at the site of deposition at some period later than did faunas preserved

TABLE 1-1 *Divisions of geologic time based on stratigraphic column*

Era	Period	Epoch	Radiometric Date (tentative)
Cenozoic	Quaternary	Holocene / Pleistocene	← 3 m.y.
Cenozoic	Tertiary	Pliocene / Miocene / Oligocene / Eocene / Paleocene	← 70
Mesozoic	Cretaceous / Jurassic / Triassic		← 225–230
Paleozoic	Permian		
Paleozoic	Carboniferous	Pennsylvanian / Mississippian	
Paleozoic	Devonian		← 350
Paleozoic	Silurian		
Paleozoic	Ordovician		← 500
Paleozoic	Cambrian		← 600
Precambrian time			← 600–3500

lower down in the section. On the oversimplified assumption that identical faunas at different sites were strictly contemporary, it is possible to construct a composite standard stratigraphic and faunal sequence applicable to regions of continental magnitude.

In spite of obvious difficulties, this was first accomplished late in the eighteenth century by an English surveyor, William Smith. He set up a standard stratigraphic column for marine sediments in southeastern England, and then extended and amplified it to cover England and Wales. Well before the close of last century the standard stratigraphic column as we know it today covered not only Britain and Europe but North America as well. The divisions of the column are defined in terms of rock units—specific local stratigraphic sections at type localities. The main divisions (systems) are limited above and below by recognizable breaks in the succession (unconformities) in the type areas. Each rock system constitutes a record of events connected with sedimentation over a corresponding interval of time. Plants and animals are much more diversified than are sedimentary rocks. Each species and each ecological assemblage of species has the legible stamp of uniqueness. Each sedimentary bed is also unique; but its unique character in most cases is not obvious. Limestones of different ages from different localities may be mutually indistinguishable on the basis of their physical (lithological) character alone. So although each division of geological time is defined in terms of a local stratigraphic sequence, correlated events elsewhere are dated geologically on the basis of fossils.

Table 1-1 lists the principal divisions of geological time corresponding to the standard stratigraphic column. All geological events are discussed in terms of this standard chronology. Provisional radiometrically determined ages, given in the right-hand column, have been added only in comparatively recent years, and are of course open to future revision.

Darwin and Organic Evolution

We have seen that geological chronology is closely intertwined with the progress of life through the ages. Life, like time, flows continuously and is irreversible. The flow of both can be read from the stratigraphic record because the sense of sedimentation in the vertical direction also is unique. It is not surprising, therefore, that the first coherent theories of organic evolution were based on the stratigraphic record of the succession of faunas and floras made legible through application of the law of superposition. The doctrine of evolution of species by natural selection was perhaps the most significant—certainly the most controversial—contribution of nineteenth-century science to philosophy. It is also the most important single concept to emerge from stratigraphy.

Long before Darwin, in the early years of the nineteenth century, the French paleontologist Lamarck propounded a plausible theory of organic evolution. His studies of the successive fossil faunas in almost undisturbed Tertiary strata of northern France convinced him that new species arise, not by multifarious acts of sudden creation, but by continuous modification of preexisting species. It was clear to Lamarck that a major controlling role was played by the pressures of environment. But his conception of environment as a direct influence initiating and propelling evolutionary adaptation is no longer accepted. In Britain, Lyell knew of Lamarck's ideas; but for many years he clung to the then orthodox view that each species arises by independent creation and is endowed with but limited capacity for minor variation.

Charles Darwin had a wider frame of reference. He was a "naturalist" without formal training in mathematics or in medicine—the disciplines that constituted the conventional doorway to science in early nineteenth-century Britain. His scientific education came from observation —geological and biological—in many lands. Most important, as he himself states, was his five years' experience as a young man employed (without remuneration) as naturalist on the voyage of the "Beagle" (1832–1836) to South America and the Pacific. With him went the first edition of Lyell's *Principles of Geology,* which opened his eyes to the possibilities of geological chronology of the progress of life. Darwin's contributions to geology were numerous, diverse, and significant. The most significant of all was his theory of origin of species through natural selection. Darwin realized that variation among species—at that time recognized but scarcely understood—could lead only to random diversification of forms of life, unless channeled into specific courses by some powerful external controlling force. To this role he invoked and assigned the "struggle for existence"—competition between individual and individual, between species and species, under the rigorous selective influence of environment. Darwin saw the survivors emerging as new species, better adapted to environment than their displaced predecessors, but still engaged in endless competitive conflict with their contemporaries. Precisely the same conclusion was reached independently by a younger man, Wallace, on the basis of observations confined to biological fields and under the influence of the grim (and today still timely) essay of Malthus on population.

The doctrine of natural selection could scarcely have survived the hostile climate of Victorian British thinking had it not been for the enormous weight and impressive variety of supporting evidence compiled by Darwin and set out in *The Origin of Species* (1859). Since his return from the "Beagle" expedition, Darwin had examined and collected evidence on the effectiveness of organic evolution from every quarter. The geological contribution is crucial. But in *The Origin of Species* it occupies only two chapters. Darwin not only propounded a mechanism of evolution that is consistent with modern concepts of genetics and heredity, but he proved beyond reasonable doubt the very fact of evolution itself.

Two connected ideas of peculiar interest to geologists emerged from Darwin's work: the time implications of imperfection of the fossil record, and the great duration of geological time.

"The noble science of Geology loses glory

from the extreme imperfection of the record. The crust of the earth with its embedded remains must not be looked at as a well-filled museum, but as a poor collection made at hazard and at rare intervals. The accumulation of each great fossiliferous formation will be recognized as having depended on an unusual concurrence of favorable circumstances, and the blank intervals between the successive stages as having been of vast duration. But we will be able to gauge with some security the duration of these intervals by a comparison of the preceding and succeeding organic forms." (*The Origin of Species*, 6th ed., 1872, p. 667, reprinted 1902)

Reviewing the conclusion of the contemporary physicist W. Thomson that the consolidation of the earth's crust probably occurred not less than 98 or more than 200 million years ago,[4] Darwin found this interval of time too cramped to explain the evolutionary changes recorded in Cambrian and later strata and implied for Precambrian time.

"Mr. Croll estimates that about 60 million years have elapsed since the Cambrian period, but this, judging from the small amount of organic change since the Glacial epoch [Pleistocene], appears a very short time for the many and great mutations of life, which have certainly occurred since the Cambrian formation; and perhaps the previous 140 million years [of Thomson's estimate] can hardly be considered as sufficient for the development of the varied forms of life which already existed during the Cambrian period." (*ibid.*, pp. 447–448)

---

[4] Several different figures are quoted in the literature. W. Thomson (later Lord Kelvin) started from the assumption that the earth had formed as a hot gas, which condensed and cooled, and calculated how long it would take after solidification to reach a state in which it could still be losing heat at the observed present rate. Results of such calculations depend obviously on the assumed temperature at the time of solidification and on the values of certain parameters (for example, thermal conductivity). His earlier results (1862) gave possible ages ranging up to 300 million years. He later revised these estimates and in 1897 considerably shortened the allowed time span to between 20 and 40 m.y. His calculations were later invalidated by the discovery of radioactive heat sources in the earth.

Today mechanisms and trends of evolution are investigated by the combined effort of students of biologically oriented sciences. Among these disciplines, and of special interest to geologists, is paleontology, the study of life as recorded by fossils. In this book it will be pursued no further.

Some Remarks About the Earth

Just as Darwin's theory of evolution required a long span of time for "the many and great mutations of life" that have occurred, many geological processes would be neither observable nor understandable if it were not for the great length of time in which they have taken place. To demonstrate relative displacements of continents at a rate of 1 cm/year requires difficult measurement of distances across an ocean with an accuracy of the order of 1 part in 10^8; yet at that rate they will move 1000 km—a sizable distance—in 10^8 years, which is a relatively short interval of geological time. The slowness of many terrestrial processes—which, as we shall see in Chapter 4, is determined to a large extent by the great size of the earth—is compensated by the length of time available for the operation of these processes. Because of its size and age, the earth is, by human standards, an unusual object.

It is also unusual in the sense that most of it is at temperatures (ranging up to a few thousand degrees; see Chapter 12) and pressures (up to some 3 million bars; see Chapter 11) that exceed the range of most experiments. Chemists know a great deal about the properties of water and aqueous solutions; this knowledge can be applied to, say, the chemistry of the oceans and sedimentary processes. Some geologically important natural fluids, however, have temperatures of the order of several hundred degrees (hydrothermal solutions; see Chapter 5), at which the properties of aqueous solutions are much less well known. Physicists can tell us a great deal about the electrical properties of matter (for example, electrical conductivity) under ordinary or near-ordinary conditions; but very little of this is directly applicable under the conditions of pressure prevailing in the core of the earth, where electric currents flow to produce the earth's magnetic field. Thus geologists, geochemists, and geophysicists must fall back to a large degree on broad generalizations and laws —the laws of thermodynamics, for instance— that determine qualitatively but not quantitatively the kind of things that can happen. Much of our ignorance or uncertainty regarding the earth still stems from the lack of relevant experimental data.

A further, and to the physical scientist somewhat annoying, characteristic of the earth is that, seen through our Cartesian eyes, it tends to be rather "messy." Rocks are not the pure compounds with well-defined properties upon which chemists and physicists like to work; instead they are texturally variable aggregates, in variable proportions, of minerals that are themselves commonly solid solutions of variable components in various proportions, with variable amounts of a dozen or more impurities. Similar rocks rarely have identical sets of physical properties. The crust of the earth is not a homogeneous elastic plate through which seismic waves are propagated as predicted in simple and elegant mathematical developments; seismic records, on the contrary, show unexpected complexities attributable to heterogeneity and irregularites

of all kinds. The geological record itself is, in many respects, ambiguous and incomplete. In many places, absence of rocks of a given age precludes the discovery of what happened there at that time; in other places the record may have been obliterated by later events, such as erosion or metamorphism.

Faced as he is with this natural complexity, the physical geologist must perforce proceed by successive approximations. As a first step he is commonly forced to consider highly simplified and idealized "models," which he investigates theoretically or experimentally; for instance, when studying the transfer of sediments by rivers, he will first make an experiment using a channel of uniform cross section and sediments of uniform grain size and density. He then gradually refines his model by introducing more variables, observing all the while what real rivers do. The petrologist will begin his investigation by taking a simple system with a limited number of chemical components; when the behavior of the simple system is well understood, he will gradually add to its complexity to make it more similar to natural rocks. Needless to say there still is a gap between most theoretical models, or experiments, and the natural environment to which they are supposed to apply. As later chapters will demonstrate, there is still much that we do not understand about the earth.

2
MINERALS

THE SOLID EARTH is made up of inorganic compounds—mostly silicates and oxides—and a few elements, notably metallic iron. These, as they occur in nature, are called *minerals;* natural mineral aggregates are rocks. At surface temperatures and pressures minerals with few exceptions (mercury, water) are solid. They occur in the crystalline state, the long-range atomic order of which is often reflected in their external form and symmetry. All physical and chemical properties (density, elasticity, electrical conductivity, melting temperature, resistance to weathering, and so on) of any portion of the earth depend critically on the particular assemblage of minerals that is locally present. So that the logical starting point in the science of geology is the study of minerals (*mineralogy*).

Most minerals familiar to geologists have formed at or near the earth's surface. Some have been transported upward from the deep levels of the crust or even from the outer mantle by dynamic processes, such as volcanism and mountain building. So minerals found at the surface of the earth may have formed over a considerable range of physical conditions: temperatures of perhaps 0–1500°C, pressures ranging up to 20 kb or more. Every mineral or mineral assemblage bears within itself the imprint of the physical conditions under which it originated. Minerals found in meteorites even

provide information as to possible conditions that prevailed on the planetary body or bodies from which they have been derived. One of the principal aims of mineralogy, then, is to unravel and evaluate evidence bearing on the physical environment of origin of common minerals. Mineral formation can be observed directly—for example, crystallization of the silicate Mg_2SiO_4 (olivine) in basaltic lava, and precipitation of $NaCl$ (halite) on the floors of saline lakes or lagoons. But in many cases clues regarding the physical significance of individual minerals or mineral assemblages are subtle, and the task of extracting the required information is far from simple. It can be accomplished only through appreciation of rather involved principles of structural chemistry, chemical kinetics, and thermodynamics. But the results provide critical data on terrestrial processes that could not be otherwise obtained. For example, the temperature of crystallization and subsequent cooling history of a crystal of alkali feldspar can be read from the degree of order shown by internal arrangement of its component Al^{3+} and Si^{4+} ions. Al_2SiO_5 crystallizes as kyanite in a high-pressure, and as andalusite in a low-pressure, environment. The mineralogical identity assumed by iron oxides, such as magnetite (Fe_3O_4) and hematite (Fe_2O_3), and by sulfides gives information regarding temperatures and partial pres-

18

sures of oxygen in the environment of their origin. Something of the chemistry and temperature of ocean waters a hundred million years ago can be read from the isotopic composition of oxygen in calcite or aragonite (both $CaCO_3$) of fossil sea shells. Thus minerals and mineral assemblages collectively record the whole gamut of terrestrial processes and the manner in which these have varied in space and in time. To read the record we must be acquainted with the chemistry of the solid state, as well as with the forces that bind atoms and the principles that determine their regular arrangement within the crystal structure.

Mineralogy has another and perhaps more practical aspect. Throughout human history, man has learned to use and to exploit with increasing sophistication the mineral resources of nature; first by the selection and shaping of stone implements, then by the extraction of metals from mineral ores and by the use of other minerals (clays) for ceramic purposes, then by the increasing development of metals, ceramic materials, cement, concrete, mineral fertilizers, and even the inorganic mineral fuels (uranium ores) that play so large a part in technological development. Behind all this technological evolution lies progress in the study of minerals with a view to locating and exploiting to the full those that are of importance in human economy. It is not the purpose of this book, however, either to pursue this line of mineralogical study for its own sake, or to evaluate its impact upon human history.

Mineralogy can be divided conveniently into three parts:

1. *Crystallography:* study of the internal and external geometry of crystals.

2. *Chemical mineralogy:* study of the chemical structure and properties of minerals.

3. *Physical mineralogy:* study of the physical properties of minerals.

Nowadays it is difficult to draw hard and fast lines among these various disciplines. The modern crystallographer is concerned with the chemical nature of the atoms in a given crystal, and the crystal physicist is not happy unless he can

relate its observed physical properties to both geometric and chemical properties.

In what follows we discuss all three aspects of the study of minerals: The first section examines crystal symmetry, the second reviews chemical principles governing the structure and properties of minerals, and the third introduces some of the physical properties of minerals important to the earth scientist.

Geometric Properties of Crystals

The solid or crystalline state is characterized by an ordered internal structure in which identical clusters of atoms, ions or molecules are symmetrically and periodically spaced along straight lines. The natural plane faces and straight edges of some crystals express this internal pattern. Our aim is to review some fundamental geometric and symmetric features of crystals and crystal structures on which advanced studies depend.

LATTICES AND UNIT CELLS

An ideal crystal structure is a strictly regular periodic repetition of a motif unit (an atom or group of atoms corresponding to the chemical formula of the material) in a manner governed by chemical properties of the atoms and the physical environment of the crystal. In a real crystal, perfect structural regularity is generally not observed; fields and forces acting on the crystal distort the structure and defects or imperfections (such as missing atoms or dislocations) interrupt it. For the purposes of elementary crystallography the effects of such disturbances are ignored and a perfect crystal is postulated with ideally regular polyhedral shape and perfectly periodic internal structure.

Periodic patterns of perfect crystals can be treated as of infinite extent and have in common with all periodic patterns (such as friezes, wallpapers, honeycombs, and so on) characteristic geometric properties, as follows:

1. If one arbitrary point in the pattern is selected as the origin, an infinite collection of

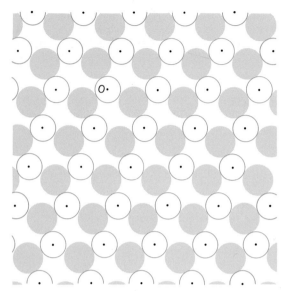

FIG. 2–1 Lattice points (dots) in a two-dimensional pattern. Possible choice of an origin given by O.

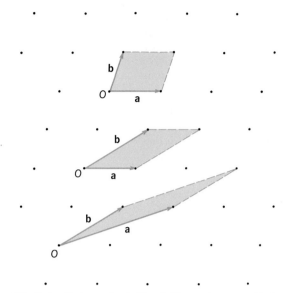

FIG. 2–2 Choices of primitive lattice vectors **a** and **b** for a two-dimensional lattice. Corresponding primitive unit cells are in color.

regularly spaced identical points can be found having the same environment in the same orientation (Figure 2–1, in two dimensions). These points are termed *lattice points*, and the whole collection of points the *space lattice* or *lattice* of the pattern. Different choices of origin define an infinite number of congruent lattices for the same pattern, all related by shifts of origin. Conventionally, a symmetric point in a pattern (such as the center of a spherically symmetric atom in a crystal structure) is chosen as the origin.

2. The position of any lattice point in a three-dimensional lattice is given by a position vector **r** from the origin, where

$$\mathbf{r} = n_1\mathbf{a} + n_2\mathbf{b} + n_3\mathbf{c} \qquad (2\text{-}1)$$

and **a**, **b**, and **c** are vectors from the origin to the three nearest noncoplanar lattice points and n_1, n_2, and n_3 are appropriate integers. All the lattice points in the set are given by the infinite collection of vectors **r** as n_1, n_2, and n_3 take on all possible positive and negative integral values. Vectors **a**, **b**, and **c**, or any other triple of linearly independent vectors for which equation (2-1) locates all points in the lattice, are termed *primitive lattice vectors* (Figure 2–2).

3. The fragment of the pattern contained within the parallelepiped whose volume V is defined by any triple of primitive lattice vectors **a**, **b**, and **c** as

$$V = \mathbf{a} \cdot \mathbf{b} \times \mathbf{c}$$

is termed the *primitive unit cell* of the pattern. For a two-dimensionally periodic pattern the primitive unit cell is a parallel-sided quadrilateral with area $\mathbf{a} \times \mathbf{b}$ (Figure 2–2). Any periodic pattern can be developed from its primitive unit cell by performing all displacements corresponding to vectors **r** in equation (2-1).

A primitive unit cell has lattice points only at its eight vertices (each point being common to eight adjacent cells) and contains the equivalent of one lattice point; but more than one motif unit is generally contained within the cell because these can occur rotated or reflected between lattice points.

4. Triples of lattice vectors may be chosen outlining unit cells an integral number of times larger than primitive cells. For such choices of lattice vectors **a**, **b**, and **c**, the vectors **r** in equation (2-1) do not locate all lattice points; others occur for which some or all of the coefficients

n_1, n_2, and n_3 are fractional. An example is shown in two dimensions in Figure 2–3. Vectors **a** and **b** are nonprimitive lattice vectors and they outline a nonprimitive unit cell (stippled) containing an extra lattice point at its center given by position vector

$$\mathbf{r} = \tfrac{1}{2}\mathbf{a} + \tfrac{1}{2}\mathbf{b}$$

This choice of a centered (c) unit cell reveals an underlying orthogonality in the lattice obscured by all choices of primitive (p) unit cells (such as cells 1, 2, or 3 in Figure 2–3). In certain three-dimensional lattices of crystals, conventional choices of centered nonprimitive cells to reveal underlying symmetry are made as follows:

1. Lattice point at center; body-centered cell, *I*.

2. Lattice points in the centers of one pair of parallel faces; end- or base-centered cell, *C*.

3. Lattice points in the centers of all faces; face-centered cell, *F*.

For example, orthogonal cells can be outlined in four different three-dimensional lattices by suitable choices of one primitive and three centered cells (Figure 2–4). Choices of primitive cells for the three centered lattices would obscure some of their symmetry. Body- and end-centered cells each contain two lattice points (double cells); face-centered cells contain four lattice points (quadruple cells).

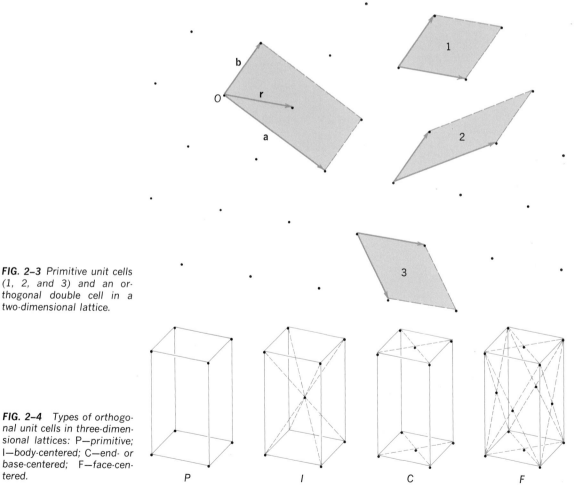

FIG. 2–3 Primitive unit cells (1, 2, and 3) and an orthogonal double cell in a two-dimensional lattice.

FIG. 2–4 Types of orthogonal unit cells in three-dimensional lattices: P—primitive; I—body-centered; C—end- or base-centered; F—face-centered.

P   I   C   F

CRYSTALLOGRAPHIC AXES

The triple of primitive or nonprimitive lattice vectors **a**, **b**, and **c** chosen to specify a unit cell function as a vector basis for the lattice. Through the origin parallel to these unit vectors can be drawn a right-handed triple of reference axes, termed *crystallographic axes* and conventionally designated *x*-, *y*-, and *z*-axes respectively. The angles between positive ends of the axes are designated α, β, and γ, as shown in Figure 2–5, according to various conventions.

Crystallographic axes are useful for specification of the following:

1. Coordinates of lattice points and of other points within unit cells (such as the centers of particular atoms).

2. Orientation of lattice lines through the origin and of crystal edges.

3. Orientation and mutual relationships of lattice planes and of crystal faces.

Coordinates of lattice points are the coefficients of vectors **a**, **b**, and **c** in equation (2-1) for the corresponding position vector. For primitive lattice vectors the coordinates are integral; for nonprimitive lattice vectors (centered cells) some lattice points have half-integral coordinates.

The direction of a lattice line through the origin can be specified by the coordinates of any lattice point through which it passes. For example, the lattice line *LL* in Figure 2–6 passes through lattice points with coordinates of the form $n(021)$ where n has all positive and negative integral values and 021 are coordinates of the first lattice point from the origin with integral coordinates. The symbol [021] is called the *zone symbol* for the lattice line. Note that the symbol [02$\bar{1}$] would serve equally well.

Lattice planes occur in parallel uniformly spaced sets intercepting one or more crystallographic axes. Planes that intercept crystallographic axes only at lattice points are termed *integral intercept planes*. The first such plane from the origin in a set has an equation in intercept form

$$\frac{x}{n_1} + \frac{y}{n_2} + \frac{z}{n_3} = 1 \qquad (2\text{-}2)$$

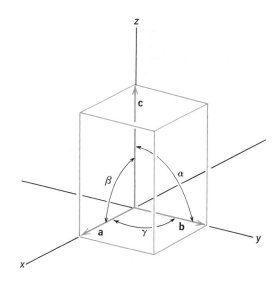

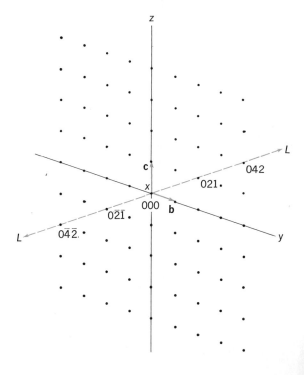

FIG. 2–5 (Above) *Crystallographic axes* x, y, *and* z *and interaxial angles* α, β, *and* γ. **FIG. 2–6** (Below) *Lattice line* [021] *or* [02$\bar{1}$] *in the yz plane of a lattice. Bars over numbers indicate negative coordinates of lattice points.*

where the n's are respective intercepts of the plane on the axes. If m_1 is any factor common to n_2 and n_3 (and similarly with m_2 and m_3) then equation (2-2) can be written with integral coefficients h, k, and l as

$$hx + ky + lz = \frac{n_1 n_2 n_3}{m_1 m_2 m_3} \qquad (2\text{-}3)$$

where $h = n_2 n_3 / m_1 m_2 m_3$, $k = n_1 n_3 / m_1 m_2 m_3$, and $l = n_1 n_2 / m_1 m_2 m_3$. The integers h, k, and l, written as (hkl), are termed *Miller indices* of the lattice plane.

Comparison of equations (2-2) and (2-3) shows that Miller indices are reciprocals of intercepts and can be found simply for a plane with first integral intercepts of, say, 4, 3, and 6, as follows:

1. Find reciprocals of the intercepts; ¼, ⅓, and ⅙.

2. Clear of fractions (multiply by the least common multiple of 4, 3, and 6); 3, 4, and 2.

3. Enclose in parentheses; (342).

Lattice planes making negative intercepts on crystallographic axes are given negative indices (minus sign written above) and planes not intercepting a particular axis have a zero index in the corresponding position.

Miller indices (hkl) can be taken to indicate both a specific lattice plane and a set of parallel lattice planes because all planes in a set have the same ratios between indices. A plane face on a crystal is given the Miller indices of the set of lattice planes to which it is parallel. If faces on a crystal occur in parallel pairs their indices have reversed signs.

Miller indices indicate also the number of lattice planes in a set intercepting the crystallographic axes between lattice points (Figure 2–7). The actual spacing of lattice planes in a set along a line perpendicular to the planes (termed the "d-spacing") can be found from any lattice vector **r** between lattice points in two adjacent lattice planes. The spacing in a set (hkl), $d_{(hkl)}$ is given by

$$d_{(hkl)} = r \cos \phi$$

where ϕ is the angle between **r** and the normal to the planes.

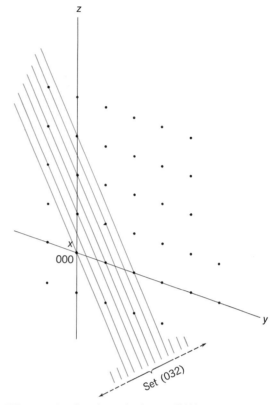

FIG. 2–7 *Lattice planes in the set (032).*

MORPHOLOGY OF CRYSTALS

The following general terms are widely used to describe the morphology of crystals (refer to Figure 2–8):

1. *Face*: a more or less smooth planar bounding surface on the crystal.

2. *Edge:* line of intersection of two faces.

3. *Vertex:* point of intersection of three or more faces.

4. *Form:* a collection of faces related by symmetry operations (see p. 27).

5. *Zone:* a collection of faces that meet, or would if projected, in edges with the same direction, termed the zone axis. Any two nonparallel faces define a zone, but the term is used generally

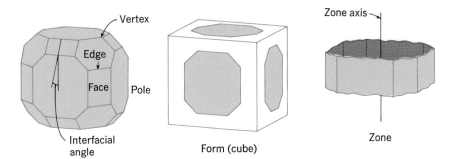

FIG. 2–8 *Morphology of crystals.*

only for collections of three or more faces. Faces in a zone (termed cozonal faces) need not be related by symmetry operations.

6. *Pole:* the direction perpendicular to a face. The poles to all faces in a zone lie in the plane perpendicular to the zone axis.

7. *Interfacial angle:* the angle between two faces measured externally in the plane perpendicular to their edge. It is also the angle between their poles.

In stereographic projection (see Appendix) poles of faces and zone axes plot as points. The poles to all faces in a zone lie on a great circle of the projection, termed the zone circle. Interfacial angles can be measured directly from the zone circle.

If a crystal is viewed as a packing of unit cells it is easy to see that faces and edges (also zone axes) are parallel respectively to lattice planes and lattice lines. The consequences of this control of morphology by internal structure of crystals are conveniently summarized in three interrelated "laws" of morphologic crystallography, which may be stated in simple form, as follows:

1. *Law of constancy of interfacial angle.* In crystals of a given substance the interfacial angles of corresponding faces are always the same.

2. *Law of rational indices.* Miller indices of natural crystal faces and edge or zone symbols are integral (rational with respect to one another).

3. *Bravais law.* Faces developed on natural crystals are those with high or highest density of lattice points (and thus of atoms). The common-

est faces on crystals are observed to be those for which Miller indices are small integers (generally less than 3), particularly those with unit indices—that is, (100), (010), (001), (101), (011), and (111).

Interfacial angles on crystals can be measured and such measurements can be used for the calculation of lattice constants, once symmetry is established and crystallographic axes are chosen. Lattice constants of crystals include the *axial ratio*, calculated from the magnitudes of the lattice vectors as

$$a/b : b/b : c/b$$

and the interaxial angles α, β, and γ. Modern X-ray methods permit cell dimensions and lattice constants of a crystal to be directly determined. Prior to development of these techniques a commonly occurring suitably oriented face (termed the parametral plane) was assumed to have indices (111). From their angular relationships to this face other faces could be indexed and lattice constants found to a first approximation. Such procedures could be applied only to well-formed crystals of suitable size.

CRYSTAL HABIT

The interfacial angles on a given crystal depend entirely upon, and are diagnostic of, lattice properties and internal structure, and are invariant. The size, shape, and spatial arrangement of faces (termed the habit of the crystal) can show great variety in different crystals of the same material. For example, two common habits of the mineral orthoclase are first, elongated in the di-

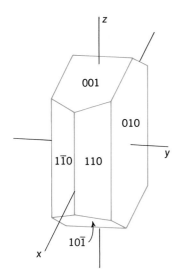

FIG. 2–9 *Orthoclase crystal prismatic in the direction* [001].

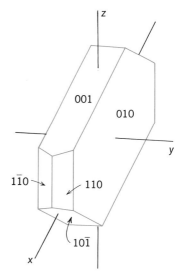

FIG. 2–10 *Orthoclase crystal prismatic in the direction* [100].

rection of the z-axis (Figure 2–9) and, second, elongated in the direction of the x-axis (Figure 2–10). The same faces with the same interfacial angles are generally developed on crystals of the two kinds.

Habit of some crystals is strongly controlled by structure. Amphiboles, for instance, are characteristically strongly elongated in the direction of the x-axis (prismatic habit) reflecting the orientation of the long directions of $[Si_4O_{11}]$ chains in the structure. Similarly, the tabular form typical of mica crystals in the plane (001) reflects the parallel stacking of $[Si_4O_{10}]$ sheets. Other crystals can occur with a large variety of habits which appear to reflect differing physical and chemical conditions at the time of growth.

Twinning is another common feature of crystals generally classed as an aspect of habit. It, too, is partly controlled by structure and partly by conditions of growth, but it can also appear in some crystals as a result of plastic deformation. A twinned crystal consists of two or more identical single crystals bearing a strict geometric relation one to another. Structures in the several parts are geometrically related by a half turn about an axis (termed the twin axis), by a mirror reflection across a plane (termed the twin plane),

or by a combination of the two. Some twinned crystals (contact twins) are in discrete parts joined along a planar surface, the composition plane (Figure 2–11). Others (interpenetration twins) are a complex and patchy intergrowth of two or more crystals and may have a characteristic external shape, typified by the presence of reentrant interfacial angles, in which the individ-

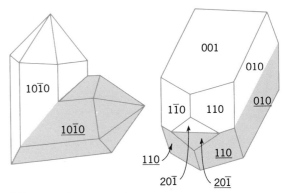

FIG. 2–11 *Contact twins: Left, quartz, twin plane* $(11\bar{2}2)$; *right, orthoclase, twin plane* (001) *(Manebach twin). (After A. C. Bishop, An Outline of Crystal Morphology, Hutchinson, 1967.)*

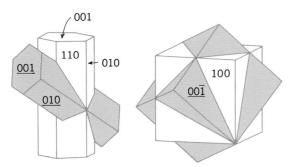

FIG. 2–12 *Interpenetration twins: Left, staurolite, twin plane (232); right, fluorite, twin axis [111]. (After A. C. Bishop,* An Outline of Crystal Morphology, *Hutchinson, 1967.)*

ual crystals appear to be grown together (Figure 2–12). Some minerals form multiple lamellar or polysynthetic twins in which each of the many lamellae is twinned with respect to its immediate neighbors.

Twinning is geometrically possible in crystals because certain lattice planes and lines can perform exactly the same function in crystals of two orientations.[1]

SYMMETRY OF CRYSTALS

Common experience is that certain mathematical or physical entities have geometric properties that permit them to be called "symmetric" or "asymmetric" and that some are "more" symmetric than others or have symmetry of a different kind. Recognition and classification of different types of symmetry are important in crystallography because crystals are classified primarily on the basis of symmetry, and the complexity of many properties in crystals can be fixed once the symmetry type of the crystal is established. Symmetry is defined in terms of certain isometric transformations called symmetry operations.

ISOMETRIC TRANSFORMATIONS Important in many branches of physical science are geometric transformations, termed linear transformations,

---

[1] Note that a symmetry plane in a crystal cannot be a twin plane, and that an axis of evenfold symmetry cannot be a twin axis.

---

in which the coordinates of the new position of a point are linear functions of the coordinates of the old position. A special case of linear transformation important in symmetry theory is the isometric or orthogonal transformation in which all lengths and angles in the transformed point set are preserved. In mechanics isometric transformations describe the motions of rigid bodies. Two kinds are recognized:[2]

1. *Rotation.* Space is turned about a fixed axis.

2. *Translation.* Space is uniformly displaced. Any part of space left unmoved by isometric transformation is termed invariant: rotation leaves an invariant line, the rotation axis; translation leaves no invariant points.

Rotation and translation are proper or performable motions on real bodies. Other isometric transformations exist corresponding to improper motions involving *reflection*. In three dimensions three types of reflection can be distinguished represented by transformations of an initially right-handed triple of vectors r_1, r_2 and r_3 into another triple r'_1, r'_2, and r'_3, as follows:

---

[2] Any isometric transformation in three dimensions with at least one invariant (unmoved) point can be represented by a square matrix of order 3. For a counterclockwise rotation of θ about z-axis viewed from the positive end, for example, this matrix takes the familiar form

$$\begin{pmatrix} \cos\theta & -\sin\theta & 0 \\ \sin\theta & \cos\theta & 0 \\ 0 & 0 & 1 \end{pmatrix} = \mathbf{R}$$

and the transformation of coordinates can be written as the matrix equation

$$x' = \mathbf{R}x$$

where x' are the transformed and x the untransformed coordinates. Matrices for rotations around other axes are similarly established.

Translation cannot be represented by such a matrix but because it is a vector quantity it can be represented as a column matrix $\mathbf{t}$ in an equation of the form

$$x' = x + t$$

The most general rigid body motion is some combination of a rotation and translation and can be expressed by a matrix equation of the form:

$$x' = \mathbf{R}x + t$$

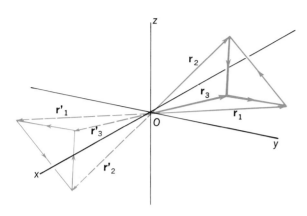

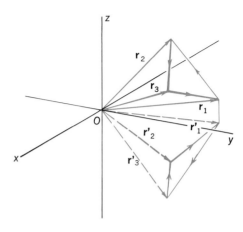

FIG. 2–13 (Above) *Inversion of a right-handed triple of vectors,* r_1, r_2, *and* r_3 *through the origin; triple becomes left-handed.* *FIG. 2–14* (Below) *Reversal of a right-handed triple of vectors,* r_1, r_2, *and* r_3 *through the z-axis; triple remains right-handed.*

FIG. 2–15 *Reflection of a right-handed triple of vectors* r_1, r_2, *and* r_3 *in the xy plane; triple becomes left-handed.*

handed. Repetition by mirror reflection is enantiomorphic.

To each of these transformations there corresponds a transformation matrix the forms of which for various choices of invariant lines and planes are given in Table 2-1. For completeness the identity transformation which transforms a point set into itself is included, denoted by the unit matrix. Because there is no volume change in an isometric transformation the determinants of all the matrices are unity, $+1$ for congruent and -1 for enantiomorphic repetition.

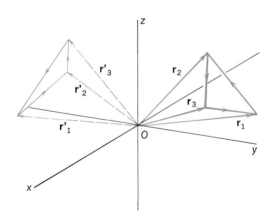

SYMMETRY OPERATIONS The fundamental "units" of symmetry, or symmetry operations, can be defined in terms of isometric transformations, as follows:

A symmetry operation is an isometric transformation that, performed upon an entity, permutes its identical parts by simultaneously bringing them into self-coincidence.

The term "entity" is used in this definition to keep it general. Symmetry operations are most easily visualized where performed upon concrete bodies or their abstract representations (such as perfect polyhedra), but they apply also to physical quantities, properties, mathematical quantities, and many other "entities." Because our concern is presently with crystals, symmetry operations are discussed here with reference to

1. *Reflection in a point (inversion).* After reflection (through the origin in Figure 2–13) the vector triple is left-handed. Repetition by inversion is enantiomorphic.

2. *Reflection in a line (reversal).* After reflection (through the z-axis in Figure 2-14) the vector triple remains right-handed. Repetition by reversal is congruent and is equivalent to a rotation of π about the reflection line.

3. *Reflection in a plane (mirror reflection or reflection).* After reflection (across the xy plane in Figure 2-15) the vector triple becomes left-

TABLE 2–1 Isometric transformations of three dimensions

Type of Motion	Invariant Points	Type of Repetition	Transformation Matrix	Determinant
Identification (proper)	all points	congruent	$\begin{pmatrix} 1 & 0 & 0 \\ 0 & 1 & 0 \\ 0 & 0 & 1 \end{pmatrix}$	1
Reflection (improper)	one plane (reflection plane)	enantiomorphic	reflection plane xy: $\begin{pmatrix} 1 & 0 & 0 \\ 0 & 1 & 0 \\ 0 & 0 & -1 \end{pmatrix}$	−1
Rotation (proper)	one line (rotation axis)	congruent	reversal about z $\begin{pmatrix} -1 & 0 & 0 \\ 0 & -1 & 0 \\ 0 & 0 & 1 \end{pmatrix}$ - - - - - - - - - - - general rotation of θ about z: $\begin{pmatrix} \cos\theta & -\sin\theta & 0 \\ \sin\theta & \cos\theta & 0 \\ 0 & 0 & 1 \end{pmatrix}$	1
Inversion (improper)	one point (inversion point)	enantiomorphic	$\begin{pmatrix} -1 & 0 & 0 \\ 0 & -1 & 0 \\ 0 & 0 & -1 \end{pmatrix}$	−1
Translation (proper)	no points	congruent	—	—

geometric objects such as polyhedra or lattices, and concrete objects such as crystals and crystal structures. Real bodies have no truly identical parts; thus the strict definition of a symmetry operation, as just given, must be relaxed so that, for instance, effectively identical parts (congruently or enantiomorphically related), such as the left and right hands of a human body, or similar faces of a well-formed crystal, can be considered identical.

The possible three-dimensional symmetry operations are clearly the possible isometric transformations listed in Table 2–1 plus any others arising from their combinations. Crystal structures, viewed as infinite periodic patterns, can include translation as a symmetry operation.

TABLE 2–2 *Symmetry operations with invariant points*

	Symmetry Operation	International Symbol	Schoenflies Symbol
"Basic" operations	Identification (identity operation)	1	E or I
	Reflection	m	σ
	Rotation of θ ($\theta = 2\pi/n$, n an integer)	n	C_n
"Composite" operations*	Inversion	$\bar{1}$	i
	Rotation-reflection of θ	$\tilde{n}$	S_n
	Rotation-inversion of θ ($\theta = 2\pi/n$, n an integer)	$\bar{n}$	—

*"Composite" operations, described later, result from simultaneous performance of two "basic" operations.

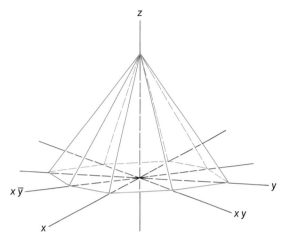

FIG. 2–16 *Ditetragonal pyramid with reference axes.*

The infinite collection of lattice vectors **r** given by equation (2-1) can be viewed also as lattice translations bringing all lattice points (defined as identical points in the structure) simultaneously into self-coincidence. On the other hand, for the identical faces of a polyhedral crystal to be brought into self-coincidence requires that at least one point (the origin of the crystallographic axes) remain invariant, so that translation is not a possible symmetry operation of crystal polyhedrons. For the present we shall consider only operations that leave at least one point invariant. Two conventional symbolisms are in common use for those operations as summarized in Table 2-2. The *international* or *Hermann-Mauguin* symbols are used nowadays by most crystallographers; the older *Schoenflies* symbols are still widely used by chemists and physicists concerned with molecular symmetry, crystal-field theory, and related topics.

SYMMETRY OF POLYHEDRA One statement of the symmetry of a polyhedron is a list of its symmetry operations. For example the pyramid shown in Figure 2–16 (ditetragonal pyramid) has the following symmetry operations (superscripts are used to denote the orientations of rotation axes and poles to planes of reflection according to the scheme in Figure 2–16):

1. Identification: 1
2. Rotation:[3] positive rotation of $2\pi/4$ about z; 4^z
   positive or negative rotation of $2\pi/2$ about z; 2^z
   negative rotation of $2\pi/4$ about z or positive rotations of $6\pi/4$ about z; -4^z
3. Reflections: in plane xz; m^y
   in plane yx; m^x
   in plane bisecting $x \wedge -y$; m^{xy}
   in plane bisecting $x \wedge y$; $m^{x\bar{y}}$
4. Inversion: absent.

The presence of these operations is seen most easily in the stereographic projection of the polyhedron on the xy plane in Figure 2–17. Note how each of the foregoing symmetry operations brings all face poles simultaneously into self-coincidence.

For each operation, and for some combinations of operations, certain collections of points in space remain invariant. These collections are termed *symmetry elements* of the polyhedron and can be of three kinds:

---

[3] A rotation is positive if counterclockwise where viewed along the rotation axis toward the origin.

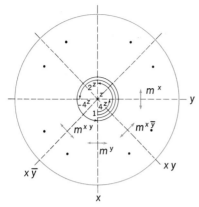

FIG. 2–17 *Symmetry operations of the ditetragonal pyramid as seen in stereographic projection.*

1. The rotations 4^z, 2^z, -4^z and 1 (viewed as a rotation of 2π about the z-axis) all leave the z-axis invariant. This axis (A in Figure 2–18) is termed a *rotational symmetry axis* or *rotation axis* of the polyhedron and the number of operations associated with it is its order. The z-axis is of order 4 and is a fourfold or tetrad rotation axis.

2. Each reflection leaves a unique plane invariant termed a *plane of mirror symmetry* or a *mirror plane*. The pyramid has four mirror planes (P_x, P_y, P_{xy}, $P_{x\bar{y}}$ in Figure 2–18) intersecting in the z-axis and inclined to one another at $\pi/4$.

Inversion (absent in the pyramid) would leave a single point invariant, termed a *center of symmetry*. If all the operations of a polyhedron leave some points invariant these are termed singular points. For the tetragonal pyramid the z-axis is a singular line. The symmetry elements of the tetragonal pyramid are shown in stereographic projection in Figure 2–19.

Because symmetry operations are isometric transformations they can be combined by sequential performance to yield other symmetry operations. By performing all possible combinations of pairs of operations, a "multiplication table" (Table 2–3) can be prepared from which the operation resulting from performing any sequence of operations can be found. The table has the following properties:

1. Every entry is one of the symmetry operations of the polyhedron, no new entries appear.

2. Each row and column contains each operation once and once only.

3. Sequential performance does not necessarily commute, for example (first operation written on the right):

$$m^x \, 4^z = m^{x\bar{y}}$$
$$4^z \, m^x = m^{xy}$$

These features suggest that the collection of symmetry operations of a polyhedron conforms to the mathematical definition of a group.

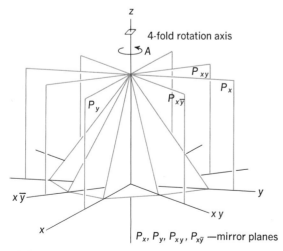

FIG. 2–18 *Symmetry elements of ditetragonal pyramid.*

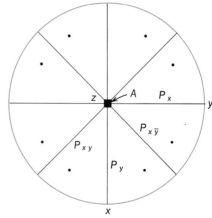

FIG. 2–19 *Symmetry elements of ditetragonal pyramid as seen in stereographic projection.*

TABLE 2–3   *Multiplication table for the ditetragonal pyramid*

First Operation

Second Operation	1	4^z	2^z	-4^z	m^x	m^y	m^{xy}	$m^{x\bar{y}}$
1	1	4^z	2^z	-4^z	m^x	m^y	m^{xy}	$m^{x\bar{y}}$
4^z	4^z	2^z	-4^z	1	m^{xy}	$m^{x\bar{y}}$	m^y	m^x
2^z	2^z	-4^z	1	4^z	m^y	m^x	$m^{x\bar{y}}$	m^{xy}
-4^z	-4^z	1	4^z	2^z	$m^{x\bar{y}}$	m^{xy}	m^x	m^y
m^x	m^x	$m^{x\bar{y}}$	m^y	m^{xy}	1	2^z	-4^z	4^z
m^y	m^y	m^{xy}	m^x	$m^{x\bar{y}}$	2^z	1	4^z	-4^z
m^{xy}	m^{xy}	m^x	$m^{x\bar{y}}$	m^y	4^z	-4^z	1	2^z
$m^{x\bar{y}}$	$m^{x\bar{y}}$	m^y	m^{xy}	m^x	-4^z	4^z	2^z	1

GROUPS OF SYMMETRY OPERATIONS   The meaning of the term "group" is best illustrated by considering a set G of abstract entities $\{A, B, C, D, \cdots\}$ called elements (not to be confused with symmetry elements) with the following properties (group properties) defined under some combination law (binary operation) by which any pair can be combined to form another element (the binary operation is conventionally termed "multiplication" and the result the "product"):

1. The product of any two elements in the set is a unique element also in the set. Following the rule of placing the first element on the right, we have

$$AB = C \qquad (C \text{ in } G)$$
$$BA = D \qquad (D \text{ in } G)$$

This property is sometimes called the closure property. Where all products commute ($C = D$), the group is termed *abelian*.

2. There is one element of the set (conventionally designated E), termed the *identity element*, which multiplies every other element commutatively to leave it unchanged; that is,

$$AE = EA = A$$

3. The associative law of multiplication holds; that is,

$$A(BC) = (AB)C$$

4. For each element of the set there exists another element of the set which multiplies it commutatively to yield the identity element; that is,

$$AA^{-1} = A^{-1}A = E$$

Element A^{-1} is termed the *inverse* or *reciprocal* of A.

These four group properties apply to the set of symmetry operations of the ditetragonal pyramid with sequential performance as the binary operations, as follows:

1. *Closure property:* follows from Table 2–3 because each row and column contains every operation once only. The group is nonabelian.

2. *Existence of an identity element:* the operation 1.

3. *Associative property:* can be established by inspection of Table 2–3.

4. *Existence of an inverse:* for each operation there is another in the group that "undoes" it. Some operations are their own inverses —for example, all reflections and the operation 2^z.

Groups of symmetry operations are termed *symmetry groups.* If the operations of the group leave at least one singular point they are called point groups, and they apply to finite geometric objects such as polyhedra. Groups that include translations as operations are termed space groups; they apply to the symmetry of infinite periodic patterns such as lattices and crystal structures. The number of elements in a group is termed its order. The point groups of crystals are shown below to be of finite order and the space groups of crystals to be of infinite order. Each group of finite order can be, in principle, represented by a multiplication table such as Table 2–3 and by a polyhedron.

Symmetry groups may contain within them subgroups or collections of elements forming a group of lower order. From Table 2–3 the groups of the ditetragonal pyramid is seen to contain, among others, the following subgroups:

$$\{1, 4^z, 2^z, -4^z\}$$
$$\{1, 2^z, m^x, m^y\}$$
$$\{1, m^x\}$$
$$\{1, m^{xy}\}$$

A theorem of group theory states that the order of a subgroup is a factor of the order of a group, so that only subgroups of order 2 and 4 are to be expected in the group of the ditetragonal pyramid (order 8). Note that all subgroups contain the identity element which by itself is said to form a trivial or improper subgroup of order 1.

Conversely, by adding new elements to a group or by combining the elements of two groups, supergroups can be constructed that stand in the same relation to a group as does a group to a subgroup. The elements of supergroups can be of two types, as follows:

1. Elements present in the component groups.

2. Any new elements, not in the component groups, that arise as products. For example, the group of the ditetragonal pyramid can be expanded into a supergroup by adding the operation m^z, a reflection in the plane perpendicular to the z-axis.

The resultant representative polyhedron (the ditetragonal bipyramid) has 16 faces and clearly has in addition the following symmetry operations (Figure 2–20):

1. Reversals (dihedral rotations) about the x- and y-axes (2^x and 2^y, respectively).
2. Reversals about axes bisecting $x \wedge y$ and $x \wedge \bar{y}$, 2^{xy} and $2^{x\bar{y}}$, respectively.
3. Inversion through the origin, $\bar{1}$.

The supergroup so obtained, therefore, includes the following operations:

$$\{1, 4^z, 2^z, -4^z, m^x, m^y, m^{xy}, m^{x\bar{y}},$$
$$m^z, 2^x, 2^y, 2^{xy}, 2^{x\bar{y}}, \bar{1}\}$$

and is apparently a group of order 14. But the group of Table 2–3 must be a subgroup and its order (8) must be a factor of the order of the new group. The new group therefore must be of order 16 and contain two operations as yet unrecognized. The additional operations are the composite operations of Table 2–2 termed improper rotations. They take the form either of a simultaneous rotation and inversion (*rotation-inversion*) or a simultaneous rotation and reflection in the plane perpendicular to the rotation axis (*rotation-reflection*). The two types of rotation are equivalent and only one type—the rotation-inversion (illustrated in stereographic projection in Figure 2–21)—is designated. The two operations needed to complete the group of the ditetragonal bipyramid are therefore the fourfold rotation inversion $\bar{4}^z$ and its inverse $-\bar{4}^z$ (the symbol $\bar{4}$ is pronounced "four-bar").

A given group can always be generated by taking products or powers of a selection of its elements, termed generators of the group. Choice of generators for the group in Table 2–3 include the following:

$$\{4^z, m^x\}$$
$$\{4^z, m^{xy}\}$$
$$\{m^x, m^{xy}\}$$

If a group can be generated from a single element it is termed a *cyclic* group.

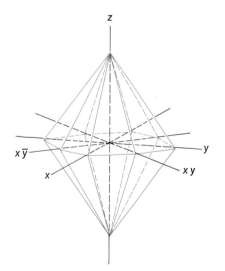

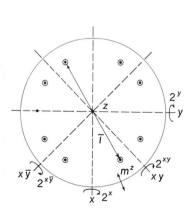

FIG. 2–20 *Ditetragonal bipyramid (left); additional symmetry operations as seen in stereographic projection.*

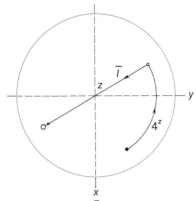

FIG. 2–21 *The operation $\bar{4}^z$ as seen in stereographic projection.*

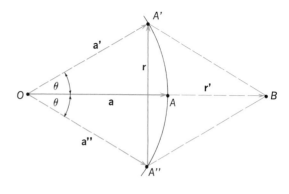

FIG. 2–22 *Combination of rotation and translation.*

Group symbols are constructed from the symbols for typical or generating elements in a symmetry group. In general, such symbols contain more information than generators alone would provide. For example, the conventional symbol for the group of the ditetragonal pyramid is $4mm$, made up of the symbols for one fourfold rotation and one reflection from each of the two classes present. The symbol for the group of the ditetragonal dipyramid is given either as $4/mmm$ or $4/m\ 2/m\ 2/m$. The first or short symbol specifies that there is also a reflection in a plane perpendicular to the axis of the fourfold rotation. The second or full symbol includes also the dihedral rotations, one from each class, about axes perpendicular to the other mirror planes. In what follows we shall use the full symbols.

POINT GROUP OPERATIONS AS ROTATIONS   All point group operations can be viewed as rotations, as follows:

1. *Proper rotations:* the operation of identification 1 is included here as a special case of rotation where $\theta = 2\pi$ about any axis.

2. *Improper rotations:* these are the rotation-inversions of any multiplicity. Special cases are the onefold rotation-inversion $\bar{1}$ equivalent to inversion, and the twofold rotation-inversion $\bar{2}$ equivalent to mirror reflection m in the plane perpendicular to the rotation inversion axis.

All the point groups of crystals can be viewed

as permissible combinations of proper and improper rotations n and $\bar{n}$ respectively, for specific values of the integer n, determined below.[4]

POINT GROUPS OF CRYSTALS   The three-dimensional point groups of space are infinite in number as n runs from 1 to infinity. Few of these can apply to crystals because of a restriction present on rotational symmetry of lattices. The point group operations of crystals must simultaneously permute identical faces and edges of polyhedrons and identical lattice vectors of the underlying lattice. Rotation axes must be perpendicular to lattice planes and in the directions of lattice lines, and mirror planes must be parallel to lattice planes and perpendicular to lattice lines.

Consider a lattice plane with shortest primitive lattice vector **a** (Figure 2–22). Let a rotation operation n (proper or improper) appear at lattice point O with period $\theta = 2\pi/n$. Then vector **a** is rotated by this operation and its inverse into two vectors **a′** and **a″** respectively so that $a = a' =$

---

[4] All point group operations of three dimensions can be represented by square matrices of order 3. The rules set out above for the combination of symmetry operations as products and powers and for their associative and commutative properties hold for the corresponding matrices with matrix multiplication as the binary operation. Point groups of symmetry operations, therefore, can be represented by groups of matrices. Such group representations are of fundamental importance in crystal field theory, quantum mechanics, and other branches of chemistry and physics of the solid state.

TABLE 2–4 *Permissible rotation angles and operations in lattices*

$\cos \theta$	θ	n
1	2π	1
$\frac{1}{2}$	$\frac{\pi}{3}$	6
0	$\frac{\pi}{2}$	4
$-\frac{1}{2}$	$\frac{2\pi}{3}$	3
-1	π	2

a''. Simultaneously the lattice point A, closest to O, is repeated at A' and A''. The vector between A' and A'' is a lattice vector $\mathbf{r}$ with magnitude r given by

$$r = 2a \sin \theta \qquad (2\text{-}4)$$

There must be another lattice point B lying on the line OA given by the vector $\mathbf{r}'$ from the origin, where

$$\mathbf{r}' = \mathbf{a}' + \mathbf{a}''$$

Vector $\mathbf{r}'$ is in the direction of $\mathbf{a}$ and must have magnitude r' of the form

$$r' = ma \qquad (2\text{-}5)$$

where m is an integer. But r and r' are related by

$$r = r' \tan \theta \qquad (2\text{-}6)$$

and by combining equations (2-4), (2-5), and (2-6) we obtain

$$ma = 2a \cos \theta$$

or

$$\cos \theta = \frac{m}{2} \qquad (m \text{ an integer})$$

The permissible values of θ in lattices are therefore those for which $\cos \theta$ is integral (m even) or half integral (m odd). The permissible values are listed in Table 2–4 together with corresponding values of θ and the symbols for the proper rotation operations.

All the point groups of crystals, therefore, can be constructed from the permissible combinations of five proper and five improper rotations, as follows:

Proper rotations: 1, 2, 3, 4, 6
Improper rotations: $\bar{1}$, $m(\bar{2})$, $\bar{3}$, $\bar{4}$, $\bar{6}$

Symmetry elements corresponding to these operations are shown in stereographic projection by the conventional symbols given in Table 2–5.

The point groups of crystals fall naturally in two categories:

1. Groups with all rotations about a single axis, or *monoaxial point groups.*

2. Groups with more than one rotation axis, or *polyaxial point groups.*

TABLE 2–5 *Conventional symbols for symmetry elements*

Order	Rotation Axes	Rotation Inversion Axes	
1	none	○	center of symmetry (not always shown)
2	⬧		plane of symmetry shown by heavy line
3	▲	▲	center of symmetry always present
4	■	◪	resembles a twofold rotation axis
6	⬢	◭	equivalent to 3/m

TABLE 2–6 *Cyclic monoaxial point groups*

Generator n	Generator $\bar{n}$
1	$\bar{1}$
2	$m(\bar{2})$
3	$\bar{3}$
4	$\bar{4}$
6	$\bar{6}$

TABLE 2–7 *Noncyclic monoaxial point groups*

Generators n and $\bar{1}$ (n even)
2/m
4/m
6/m

The monoaxial point groups include two sets of cyclic groups based upon the ten permissible rotations as generators (Table 2–6). Each is specified by the symbol for its generator.

The remaining monoaxial point groups are noncyclic and can be found by including the operation $\bar{1}$ with the proper rotation groups. When n is odd this combination gives $\bar{n}$ and no new groups are obtained; but when n is even the effect of the combination is to introduce a reflection perpendicular to the rotation axis. Only three new groups are obtained; they are given symbols $2/m$, $4/m$, and $6/m$, as in Table 2–7. The monoaxial point groups number 13.

To derive the possible polyaxial point groups the permissible combinations of more than one rotation axis must be determined. This can be done in a number of ways (see, for example, M. J. Buerger's *Elementary Crystallography*) and it is found that only six polyaxial proper rotation groups are possible in crystals. They fall into two categories:

1. Groups with one principal rotation n ($n = 2, 3, 4,$ or 6) and dihedral rotations perpendicular to it (groups 222, 32, 422, 622).

2. Two groups with more than one rotation of order greater than 2 (groups 23 and 432).

From each of the six polyaxial proper rotation groups new point groups can be constructed by including improper rotations. There are many ways of doing this, but all groups can be found in two:

1. The operation $\bar{1}$ is consistent with all other rotations and it can be combined with each of the rotation groups to produce new groups (column 2 in Table 2–8).

TABLE 2–8 *Polyaxial point groups*

Proper Rotation Group	Inclusion of $\bar{1}$	Substitutions $n\bar{n}\bar{n}$	Substitutions $\bar{n}\bar{n}n$	Substitution $\bar{n}n\bar{n}$
223	$2/m\ 2/m\ 2/m$	(2mm)	mm2	(m2m)
32	$\bar{3}\ 2/m$	3m	($\bar{3}\ 2/m$)	($\bar{3}\ 2/m$)
422	$4/m\ 2/m\ 2/m$	4mm	($\bar{4}\ m2$)	$\bar{4}\ 2m$
622	$6/m\ 2/m\ 2/m$	6mm	$\bar{6}\ m2$	($\bar{6}\ 2m$)
23	$2/m\ \bar{3}$	($2/m\ \bar{3}$)	($2/m\ \bar{3}$)	($2/m\ \bar{3}$)
432	$4/m\ \bar{3}\ 2/m$	($4/m\ \bar{3}\ 2/m$)	($4/m\ \bar{3}\ 2/m$)	$\bar{4}\ 3m$

2. Improper rotations can be substituted for the three generating proper rotations. Because the product of these three rotations must be identity an even number (only 2) of substitutions must be made. If the rotation group is $n_1 n_2 n_3$ all possibilities are covered by the substitutions $n_1 \bar{n}_2 \bar{n}_3$, $\bar{n}_1 \bar{n}_2 n_3$, and $\bar{n}_1 n_2 \bar{n}_3$. These substitutions are given in columns 3, 4, and 5 of Table 2–8, the 19 distinct groups and their conventional symbols being without parentheses. The groups in parentheses are equivalent to one of the other groups in the table. The possible point groups of crystals therefore number 32 (13 monoaxial and 19 polyaxial). All crystals have morphologic symmetry elements corresponding to one or other of these groups and are said to belong to 32 *crystal classes* of symmetry.

GROUPS OF TRANSLATIONS AND SPACE GROUPS

The position vectors of lattice points defined as in equation (2-1), can be viewed also as an infinite collection of primitive translations, that is, symmetry operations that bring the origin into coincidence with every other lattice point. Such a set of translations forms a group—the primitive translation group of the lattice—as is shown by examining it for the four group properties with vector addition as the binary operation, as follows:

1. *Closure property:* the sum of any two vectors is another vector in the set. Because vector addition is commutative the group is abelian.

2. *Existence of an identity element:* this is provided by the null or zero vector r_0 where n_1, n_2, and n_3 in equation (2-1) are zero.

3. *Associative property:* vector addition is associative.

4. *Existence of an inverse:* for every vector r in the set there is another vector $-r$ that, added to it, yields the zero vector.

Each of the lattices possible in crystals corresponds to a translation group of this kind. The symmetry of internal structure of crystals is described by groups of operations including both translations and point group operations—the

space groups previously mentioned. Space groups can be constructed by adding to the primitive translation group of a lattice compatible point group operations.

The operations of space groups include translations and rotations (proper and improper), but also a more general type of operation resulting from the combination of a rotation and a translation.[5]

A conventional notation for an operation of this kind (a translation t followed by a rotation R) or vice versa, because the two parts of the operation commute, is

$$\{R/t\}$$

Pure rotations and pure translations can be looked upon as special cases of such operations for which the translation is zero and the rotation is the identity rotation, respectively. The symmetry operations of space groups are thus of three kinds, as follows:

1. Pure rotations (proper or improper) $\{R/o\}$
2. Pure translations $\{E/t\}$
3. Combined rotations and translations $\{R/t\}$

The combined operations $\{R/t\}$ generally correspond to the appearance of rotation operations around translated points in the lattice, so a lattice contains rotation axes, inversion centers, and mirror planes distributed through it in a systematic and periodic way.

But new types of operations arise in certain space groups as follows:

---

[5] Such operations can be represented by matrix equation of the form (see footnote, page 26):

$$x' = Rx + t$$

A second such transformation can be written similarly as

$$x'' = R'x' + t'$$

Performed in sequence the two operations yield

$$x'' = R'Rx + R't + t'$$

where $R'R$ is another rotation matrix and $R't + t$ is another translation. The combination of two general symmetry operations is thus another general symmetry operation.

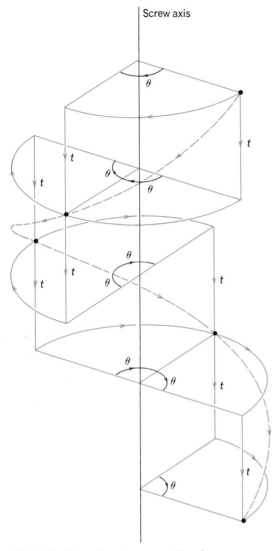

FIG. 2–23 *Operation of screw rotation 4_1.*

order—either 1, 2, 3, 4, or 6—and the nth power of the screw operation must correspond to a rotation of 2π. But the sum of the translational component **t** of the repeated screw motions $\{R/t\}$ must simultaneously equal a primitive lattice vector **r**; that is,

$$\mathbf{r} = m\mathbf{t}$$

where m is an integer. For example, a fourfold screw axis has rotational component $\pi/2$ and its permissible translational components must have the form $(m/n)\mathbf{r}$. The possible values of m/n, since $n = 4$, are:

$$\frac{0}{4}, \frac{1}{4}, \frac{2}{4}, \frac{3}{4}, \frac{4}{4}, \frac{5}{4}, \cdots$$

Only the first four of these are distinct and the permissible translational components of fourfold screw axes expressed as fractions of a primitive translation in the direction of the axis are:

$$0\mathbf{r}, \frac{1}{4}\mathbf{r}, \frac{1}{2}\mathbf{r}, \frac{3}{4}\mathbf{r}$$

The first of these is a pure n-fold rotation axis; the others correspond to distinct types of screw motion. Similar considerations reveal the presence of a number of distinct screw rotations in crystallographic space groups as illustrated in Figure 2–24 and summarized in Table 2–9.

2. A second type of space group operation is found by combining a translation with an improper rotation. For improper rotations $\bar{1}$ (inversion), $\bar{3}$, $\bar{4}$, and $\bar{6}$ all combinations with translations merely generate new improper rotations at different places. But for the rotation $\bar{2}$, a reflection, combination with a translation lying in the reflection plane yields a new operation termed a glide reflection. The operation of a glide reflection is illustrated in Figure 2–25. For a reflection component m and a translation component **t** the second power of the operation $\{m/t\}$ must bring identity so that the only permissible value for **t** is $(\frac{1}{2})\mathbf{r}$ where **r** is a primitive lattice translation. Mirror reflection can be considered to be a special case of glide reflection in which the translational component is zero. Glide reflections are given symbols indicating the directions of their translational components.

1. If a translation or a component of a translation t is in the direction of a proper rotation axis of period n, a point is repeated by sequential or simultaneous performance of those operations according to the screwlike motion illustrated in Figure 2–23. An n-fold rotation axis of this type is termed an n-fold *screw axis* and because it is also a rotation axis it must be of permissible

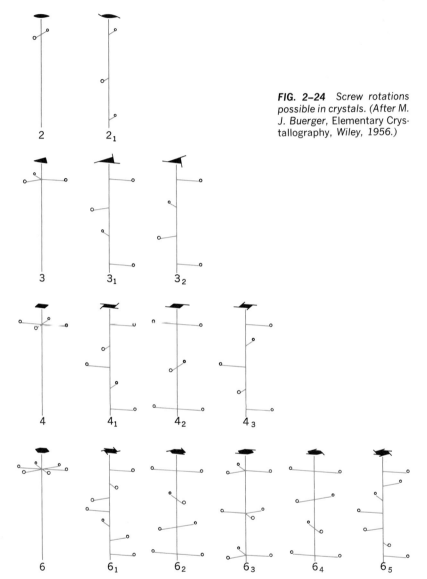

FIG. 2-24 Screw rotations possible in crystals. (After M. J. Buerger, Elementary Crystallography, Wiley, 1956.)

CRYSTAL SYSTEMS AND CLASSES

One effect of the combination of the translation group of a lattice with permissible point group operations is that a lattice has distributed through it mirror planes, rotation axes, or centers of symmetry. As a result, certain points in a lattice—symmetry points—are left invariant by point groups of symmetry operations. For example (Figure 2–26), a lattice point p of a primitive cubic lattice is invariant for the group $4/m \, \bar{3} \, 2/m$ whereas a point p' in the center of a cell face is invariant for the group $4/m \, 2/m \, 2/m$, and a general point such as p'' has no symmetry (group 1). The point groups of all symmetry points in a lattice are subgroups of the group at the lattice points, which is taken as the point group of the lattice. This group of operations performed at

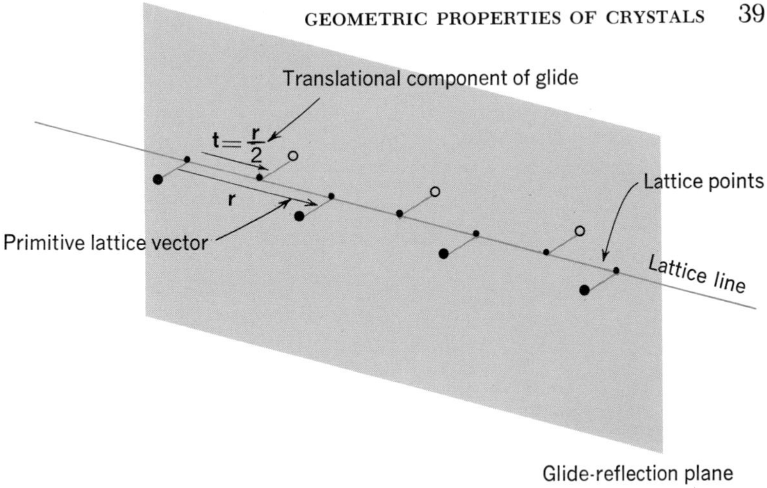

FIG. 2–25 Operation of a glide reflection.

TABLE 2–9 Screw rotations of space groups

n	1	2		3			4				6					
θ	2π	π		$\frac{2\pi}{3}$			$\frac{2\pi}{4}$				$\frac{2\pi}{6}$					
t	0	0	$\frac{1}{2}\mathbf{r}$	0	$\frac{1}{3}\mathbf{r}$	$\frac{2}{3}\mathbf{r}$	0	$\frac{1}{4}\mathbf{r}$	$\frac{1}{2}\mathbf{r}$	$\frac{3}{4}\mathbf{r}$	0	$\frac{1}{6}\mathbf{r}$	$\frac{1}{3}\mathbf{r}$	$\frac{1}{2}\mathbf{r}$	$\frac{2}{3}\mathbf{r}$	$\frac{5}{6}\mathbf{r}$
Symbols	1*	2*	2_1^*	3*	3_1	3_2	4*	4_1	4_2^*	4_3	6*	6_1	6_2	6_3	6_4	6_5

°These rotations are without a sense of screw motion. The pairs linked by arrows are enantiomorphic equivalents.

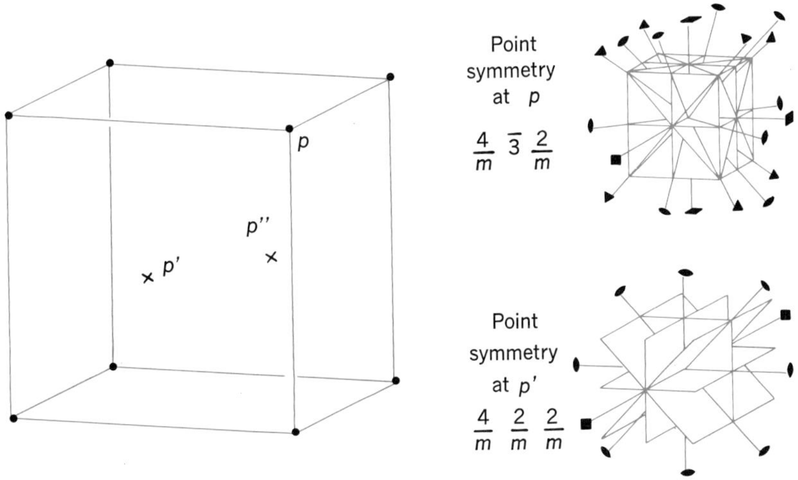

FIG. 2–26 Symmetry operations at points p, p′, and p″ in a primitive cubic lattice.

Point symmetry at p

$$\frac{4}{m}\ \bar{3}\ \frac{2}{m}$$

Point symmetry at p′

$$\frac{4}{m}\ \frac{2}{m}\ \frac{2}{m}$$

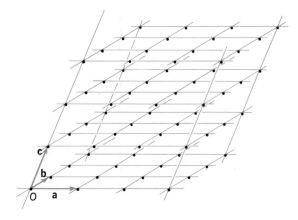

FIG. 2–27 *A three-dimensional lattice as a stack of identical two-dimensional lattices (with the primitive vectors **a** and **b**) spaced according to the third primitive translation **c**.*

FIG. 2–28 *The five two-dimensional lattices (nets).*

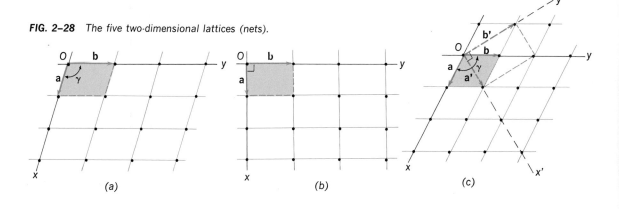

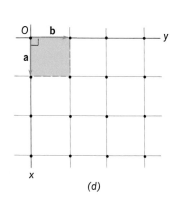

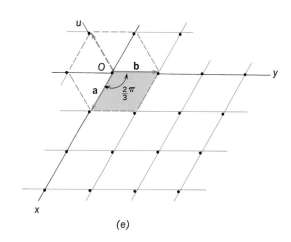

the origin of the lattice brings all other lattice points and the translations relating them into self-coincidence.

The possible point groups of lattices reflect the geometrically distinct lattices that are possible in crystals. One simple way of determining the distinct lattice types is to consider three-dimensional lattices to be stacks of parallel, identical two-dimensional lattices (nets) with primitive lattice vectors **a** and **b** uniformly spaced according to various choices of a third primitive translation **c** (Figure 2–27) and to collect the geometrically and symmetrically distinct results. The geometrically distinct nets are easily shown to be five in number, as follows (Figure 2–28):

1. *Clinonet:* $a \neq b$, $\gamma \neq \pi/2$; unit cell a parallelogram.

2. *Orthonet:* $a \neq b$, $\gamma = \pi/2$; unit cell a rectangle.

3. *Rhombonet:* $a = b$, $\gamma \neq \pi/2$; unit cell a rhombus. Choice of nonprimitive lattice vectors **a′** and **b′** makes the unit cell a centered rectangle.

4. *Tetranet:* $a = b$, $\gamma = \pi/2$; unit cell a square.

5. *Hexanet:* $a = b$, $\gamma = 2\pi/3$; unit cell a rhombus. This lattice is a network of equilateral triangles and each lattice point is situated at the center of a regular hexagon defined by the six nearest lattice points.

Two-dimensional symmetry elements (rotation points, mirror lines, glide lines) are distributed in these nets as shown in Figure 2–29. The point groups of the orthonet and rhombonet are the same, $2mm$; but their space groups are distinct, $p2mm$ and $c2mm$ respectively. Note that symbols for space groups include a statement of the lattice type and thus of the translation group. In space groups $c2mm$, $p4mm$, and $p6mm$ glide lines are present.

In order to illustrate procedure in "stacking" nets to form three dimensional lattices a few examples are considered, as follows (derivation of the remaining lattices by a similar procedure is left as an exercise for the student):

1. Clinonets stacked in a general way so that the stacking vector **c** is oblique to the nets yield a primitive unit cell of parallelohedral shape (Figure 2–30). The only symmetry elements present are centers of symmetry at lattice points and at the center of the cell, and midway along each of the cell edges. Point group symmetry of the lattice is $\bar{1}$ and its space group $P\bar{1}$.

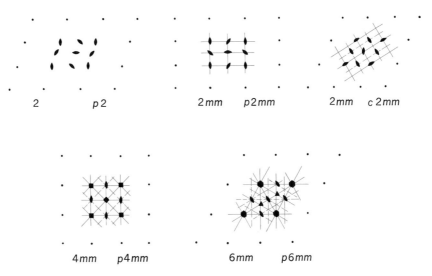

FIG. 2–29 *Symmetry elements in the five nets together with point group and space group symbols. (Mirror lines are shown as full and glide lines as broken lines; centers of symmetry are not shown.)*

2   p 2   2 mm   p2mm   2mm   c 2mm

4mm   p4mm   6mm   p6mm

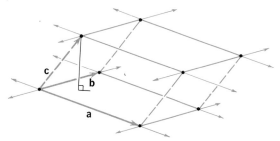

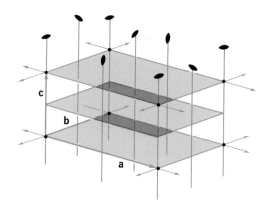

FIG. 2–30 (Above) *General stacking of clinonets.* **FIG. 2–31** (Right) *Stacking of clinonets so that* **c** *is perpendicular to the nets.*

2. The same nets stacked so that the stacking vector **c** is perpendicular to the nets (Figure 2–31) form a primitive unit cell shaped like a right parallelogram prism. Twofold rotation axes appear in the direction **c** and mirror planes are present at and halfway between the nets. Point group of the lattice is $2/m$ and space group $P\,2/m$.

3. Rhombonets stacked so that **c** is perpendicular to the nets (Figure 2–32) yield a right rhombic prism as a primitive unit cell. A base-centered cell C in the shape of a right rectangular prism arises by transformation to nonprimi-

tive lattice vectors **a**′ and **b**′. Twofold rotation axes appear in the **c** direction perpendicular to mirror planes; whereas in the directions **a**′ and **b**′ twofold rotation and screw axes appear perpendicular to interleaved mirror and glide planes with translation components in directions **b**′ and **a**′ respectively. These symmetry elements are shown in Figure 2–33 for one unit cell and in projection on the xy plane with conventional symbols. The point group is $2/m\ 2/m\ 2/m$ and the space group $C\,2/m\ 2/m\ 2/m$.

4. Hexanets stacked with **c** perpendicular to the nets (Figure 2–34) form a primitive unit cell

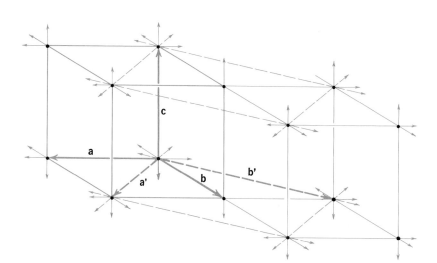

FIG. 2–32 *Stacking of rhombonets so that* **c** *is perpendicular to the nets.*

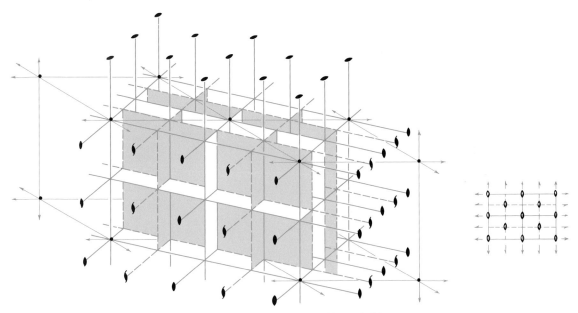

FIG. 2–33 *Symmetry elements for the three-dimensional lattice in Figure 2–32.*

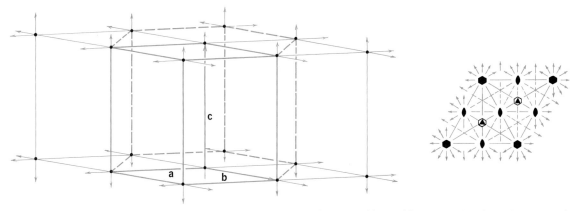

FIG. 2–34 *Stacking of hexanets so that* **c** *is perpendicular to the nets with resulting symmetry elements as seen in projection on the xy plane.*

that is a right rhombic prism. A nonprimitive cell can be outlined with a centered hexagonal base. Symmetry elements are distributed as shown in projection on the xy plane also in Figure 2–34. Point group symmetry at lattice points is $6/m \, 2/m \, 2/m$ and the space group is $P \, 6/m \, 2/m \, 2/m$.

5. Stacking of hexanets so that lattice points (sixfold rotation points) in one fall over the threefold rotation points in the net below destroys the sixfold rotational symmetry present in the nets. A primitive rhombohedral cell R appears extending through four nets (Figure 2–35) with its unique diagonal perpendicular to the nets. The point group is $\bar{3} \, 2/m$ and the space group $R \, \bar{3} \, 2/m$.

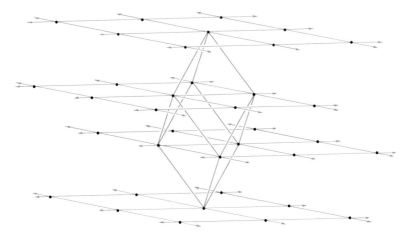

FIG. 2–35 *Rhombohedral lattice by stacking of hexanets.*

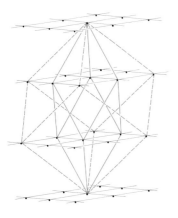

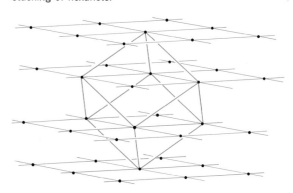

FIG. 2–36 (Left) *Face-centered cubic lattice by stacking of hexanets.* **FIG. 2–37** (Below) *Primitive cubic lattice by stacking of hexanets.*

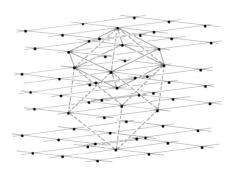

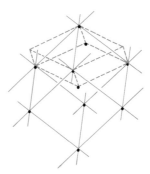

FIG. 2–38 *Body-centered cubic lattice by stacking of hexanets.*

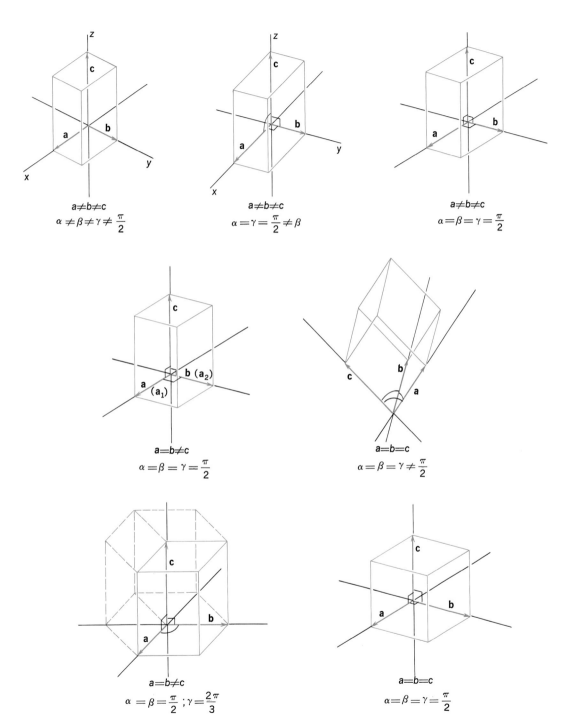

$a \neq b \neq c$
$\alpha \neq \beta \neq \gamma \neq \dfrac{\pi}{2}$

$a \neq b \neq c$
$\alpha = \gamma = \dfrac{\pi}{2} \neq \beta$

$a \neq b \neq c$
$\alpha = \beta = \gamma = \dfrac{\pi}{2}$

$a = b \neq c$
$\alpha = \beta = \gamma = \dfrac{\pi}{2}$

$a = b = c$
$\alpha = \beta = \gamma \neq \dfrac{\pi}{2}$

$a = b \neq c$
$\alpha = \beta = \dfrac{\pi}{2} \; ; \gamma = \dfrac{2\pi}{3}$

$a = b = c$
$\alpha = \beta = \gamma = \dfrac{\pi}{2}$

FIG. 2–39 The seven possible unit cell shapes.

If the spacing of the nets in 5 is changed, the apical angles of the rhombohedral cell change. Where the apical angles are 60° a face-centered F cubic cell can be chosen as in Figure 2–36. The point group becomes $4/m\,\overline{3}\,2/m$ and space group $F\,4/m\,\overline{3}\,2/m$. Apical angles of 90° transform the rhombohedron into a cube—the unit cell of the primitive cubic lattice with point group $4/m\,\overline{3}\,2/m$ and space group $P\,4/m\,\overline{3}\,2/m$ (Figure 2–37). Apical angles of 109° 28′ result in the appearance of a body-centered I cubic lattice extending through six nets (Figure 2–38). Point group symmetry remains $4/m\,\overline{3}\,2/m$; space group symmetry changes to $I\,4/m\,\overline{3}\,2/m$.

Similar stacking procedures for other nets yield a total of only seven unit cell shapes corresponding to seven point groups. Lattice vectors **a**, **b**, and **c** and interaxial angles α, β, and γ for these cell shapes are illustrated in Figure 2–39, with one unit cell for each outlined. These seven cell shapes do not exhaust the list of possible lattices with distinct space group symmetry, however, because the same shape can apply to primitive cells and to cells centered in permissible ways, as described above. In all, 14 distinct lattices (the *Bravais lattices*) can occur in crystals distributed among the cell shapes as shown in Figure 2–40. The point group, space group, and

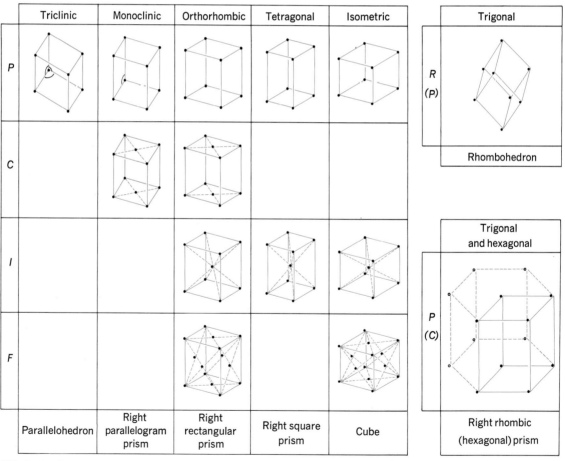

FIG. 2–40   *The 14 Bravais lattices of crystals.*

TABLE 2–10   Symmetry of Bravais lattices

Cell Shape	Symbol	Point Group	Space Group
Parallelohedron	P	$\bar{1}$	$P\bar{1}$
Right parallelogram prism	P C	2/m	P 2/m C 2/m
Right rectangular prism	P C I F	2/m 2/m 2/m	P 2/m 2/m 2/m C 2/m 2/m 2/m I 2/m 2/m 2/m F 2/m 2/m 2/m
Right square prism	P I	4/m 2/m 2/m	P 4/m 2/m 2/m I 4/m 2/m 2/m
Rhombohedron	R	$\bar{3}$ 2/m	R $\bar{3}$ 2/m
Right rhombic (hexagonal) prism	P	6/m 2/m 2/m	P 6/m 2/m 2/m
Cube	P I F	4/m $\bar{3}$ 2/m	P 4/m $\bar{3}$ 2/m I 4/m $\bar{3}$ 2/m F 4/m $\bar{3}$ 2/m

unit cell shape for each lattice are given in Table 2–10.

CRYSTAL SYSTEMS   The seven types of point group symmetry present at lattice points correspond to the seven *holosymmetric* classes of the 32 crystal classes. All crystals are built on lattices with one or other of these point group symmetries and are grouped in *seven crystal systems*. The lattices are referred to distinct sets of crystallographic axes reflecting the geometric properties of the underlying primitive or nonprimitive unit cells. The 32 crystal classes arise because in a real crystal the symmetry of the configurations of atoms, ions, or molecules within the unit cell may not fit exactly the symmetry of the lattice and only symmetry elements common to both the lattice and the internal structure can be symmetry operations of the whole crystal. The general effect of crystal structure, therefore, is to lower the symmetry of the associated lattice to a point group that includes only *some* of the operations of the lattice point group, namely, to one of its subgroups. For example, the possible point groups of crystals built

upon the tetragonal P or I lattices are subgroups of the group of the lattices 4/m 2/m 2/m. These subgroups are shown in Figure 2–41. Other subgroups of 4/m 2/m 2/m do exist (2/m 2/m 2/m, 222, mm2, 2/m, m, 2, $\bar{1}$, and 1) but these are also subgroups of the groups of less symmetric lattices (orthorhombic, monoclinic, and triclinic) and a tetragonal lattice is not necessary or likely in structures with these symmetries.

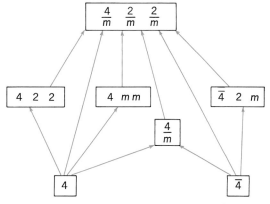

FIG. 2–41   Subgroups of the group 4/m 2/m 2/m.

TABLE 2–11   Distribution of point groups among the crystal systems

Crystal System	Lattice Types	Lattice Point Group	Subgroups (consistent point groups)
Triclinic	P	$\bar{1}$	$1, \bar{1}$
Monoclinic	P, C	$2/m$	$2, m, 2/m$
Orthorhombic	P, C, I, F	$2/m\ 2/m\ 2/m$	$mm2, 222, 2/m\ 2/m\ 2/m$
Tetragonal	P, I	$4/m\ 2/m\ 2/m$	$4, \bar{4}, 4/m, \bar{4}2m$ $4mm, 422, 4/m\ 2/m\ 2/m$
Trigonal	rhombohedral R hexagonal P	$\bar{3}\ 2/m$ $6/m\ 2/m\ 2/m$	$3, \bar{3}, 3m,$ $32, \bar{3}\ 2/m$
Hexagonal	P	$6/m\ 2/m\ 2/m$	$6, \bar{6}, 6/m, \bar{6}m2$ $6mm, 622, 6/m\ 2/m\ 2/m$
Isometric	P, I, F	$4/m\ \bar{3}\ 2/m$	$23, 2/m\ \bar{3}$ $\bar{4}3m, 432, 4/m\ \bar{3}\ 2/m$

Similar investigation of other lattices permits the 32 point groups to be distributed among the seven crystal systems as shown in Table 2–11. One set of classes, 3, $\bar{3}$, 3m, 32, and $\bar{3}\ 2/m$, are

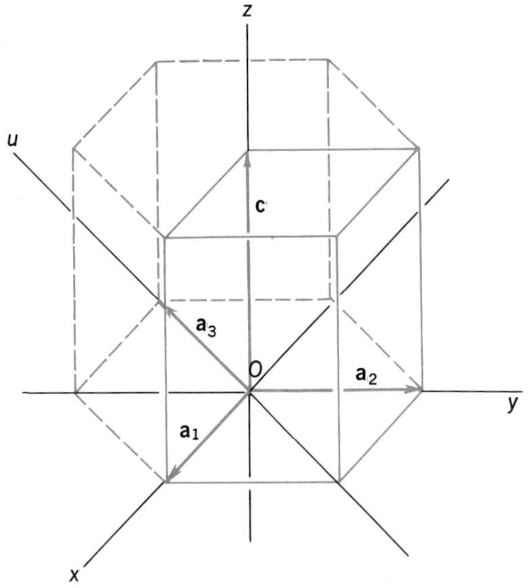

FIG. 2–42   Four-axis system for hexagonal and trigonal crystals.

found to be subgroups of the point groups of two lattices with different symmetry—the rhombohedral R and hexagonal P lattices. Crystals with these point symmetries can be based upon either lattice. All other lattices are consistent with a unique collection of point groups.

The peculiar relationship between the trigonal and hexagonal systems shows up again in the crystallographic axes chosen for these systems. Crystals in both systems can be based upon the same hexagonal P lattice and the same crystallographic axes (hexagonal axes) can be used for both systems. The z-axis is chosen parallel to the unique lattice vector **c**, and x- and y-axes are chosen parallel to the vectors **a** and **b**, perpendicular to **c**, and inclined at $2\pi/3$. For convenience a fourth axis, generally labeled the u-axis, is introduced in the xy plane symmetrically inclined to the x- and y-axes (Figure 2–42). The three lattice vectors parallel to the x-, y-, and u-axes are not linearly independent. Because of the presence of four axes, indices of faces in hexagonal and trigonal crystals have four indices (Miller-Bravais indices) corresponding to four possible intercepts. The first three (reciprocals of intercepts on x-, y-, and u-axes, respectively) are not independent, their sum always being zero

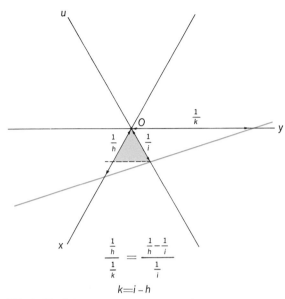

$$\frac{\dfrac{1}{h}}{\dfrac{1}{k}} = \frac{\dfrac{1}{h} - \dfrac{1}{i}}{\dfrac{1}{i}}$$

$$k = i - h$$

FIG. 2–43   *Intercepts on axes x, y, and u.*

(Figure 2–43). Sometimes a dot is substituted for the third index, for example ($hk.l$) instead of ($hkil$).

Some trigonal crystals have rhombohedral lattices, and following usual conventions rhombohedral axes would be used. Because there is no morphologic difference between trigonal crystals with rhombohedral lattices and those with hexagonal lattices, most crystallographers depart from convention and use hexagonal axes, as previously defined, for both. The unique diagonal of the rhombohedral cell is chosen as the z-axis. The x-, y-, and u-axes are chosen parallel to the dihedral rotation axes. Two settings for these (termed obverse and reverse) are possible (Figure 2–44).

In most crystal classes, crystallographic axes can be chosen from the morphologic symmetry elements of crystals. The conventions generally adopted are summarized in Table 2–12. For classes in which symmetry elements cannot be used to locate cell directions, prominent edges of suitable orientation can be chosen as axes.

CRYSTAL FORMS   A collection of faces on a crystal related by the symmetry operations of its point group is termed a *form*, closed if it can totally enclose space (such as the ditetragonal bipyramid), open if its faces are too few or too restricted in orientation to do so (as are those of the ditetragonal pyramid). The collection of faces can be visualized as generated from a given face by the symmetry operations of the group. If the given face is not perpendicular to rotation axes or mirror planes, each operation of the group will repeat the face once into a polyhedron with the same number of faces as there are operations in the group. Such a form is termed a general form. Faces bearing special relationships to symmetry elements can be repeated a fewer

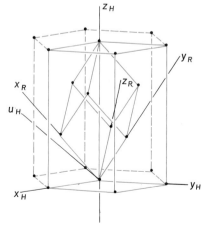

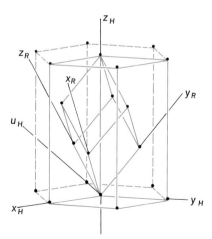

FIG. 2–44   *Reverse (left) and obverse (right) settings of rhombohedral cells.*

TABLE 2–12 *Morphological symmetry and crystallographic axes*

System	Classes	Characteristic Symmetry	Crystallographic Axes
Triclinic	1, $\bar{1}$	identity or inversion only	parallel to prominent crystal edges
Monoclinic	2, m, 2/m	twofold rotation (proper or improper)	*first setting:* twofold rotation axis is the z-axis. *second setting:* twofold rotation axis is the y-axis
Orthorhombic	mm2, 222, 2/m 2/m 2/m	orthogonal twofold rotations (proper or improper)	twofold rotation axes are x-, y-, and z-axes. In class mm2 the proper rotation axis is the z axis
Tetragonal	4, $\bar{4}$, 4/m, $\bar{4}$ 2m, 4mm, 422, 4/m 2/m 2/m	fourfold rotation (proper or improper)	fourfold rotation axis is the z-axis. The x- and y-axes are generally diad rotation axes (proper or improper)
Trigonal	3, $\bar{3}$, 3m, 32, $\bar{3}$ 2/m	threefold rotation (proper or improper)	threefold rotation axis is the z-axis. The x-, y-, and u-axes are generally diad rotation axes (proper or improper)
Hexagonal	6, $\bar{6}$, 6/m, $\bar{6}$m2, 6mm, 622, 6/m 2/m 2/m	sixfold rotation (proper or improper)	sixfold rotation axis is the z-axis. The x-, y-, and u-axes are generally diad rotation axes (proper or improper)
Isometric	23, 2/m $\bar{3}$, $\bar{4}$3m, 432, 4/m $\bar{3}$ 2/m	four threefold rotations in the directions of the long diagonals of a cube	the x-, y-, and z-axes are symmetrical to the threefold rotation axes

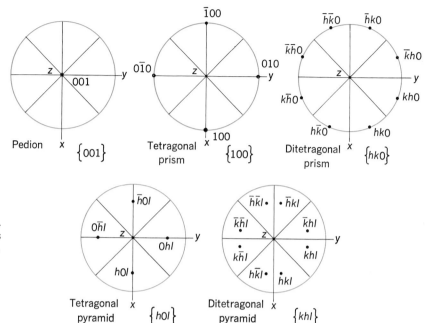

FIG. 2–45 *Stereographic projections of the possible forms in group 4mm (see Table 2–13).*

number of times and give rise to special forms.

In a crystal belonging to a particular point group a variety of forms can exist. For example, in the group *4mm* five distinct forms can be generated by different choices of faces with general or special relationships to symmetry ele-

TABLE 2–13 *Forms in group 4mm*

	Form Symbol	Number of Faces (multiplicity)	Name of Form
General form	{hkl}	8	ditetragonal pyramid
Special forms	{h0l} {hhl}	4 4	tetragonal pyramids
	{hk0}	8	ditetragonal prism
	{100} {110}	4 4	tetragonal prisms
	{001}	1	pedion

ments. Stereographic projections of the forms are given in Figure 2–45 and the properties of the forms are summarized in Table 2–13. Note that the number of faces in a special form is always equal to or a factor of the number of faces in the general form.

Form symbols such as {*hkl*} stand for the whole collection of faces generated from the given face by the symmetry operations. The number of these is the multiplicity of the form. Similarly, a symbol such as ⟨*uvw*⟩ represents the collection of lattice lines (zone axes) generated from the zone axis [*uvw*] by the operations of a point group. For example, the zone symbol [110] for an isometric crystal in class $4/m\ \bar{3}\ 2/m$ indicates the line bisecting the angle between the *x*- and *y*-axes. The symbol ⟨110⟩ stands for a collection of the six lines identical to [110] (the directions of the twofold rotation axes) related to one another by the symmetry operations of the crystal.

FORMS IN THE 32 CLASSES A table, such as Table 2–13, can be prepared for each of the 32

	Monoaxial Point Groups		
	Generator n	Generator $\bar{n}$	Generators n and $\bar{1}$
Triclinic	Pedial 1 C	Pinacoidal $\bar{1}$ C_i	$\dfrac{1}{m} \equiv m$
Monoclinic	Sphenoidal 2 (second setting) C_2	Domatic $m\,(\bar{2})$ (second setting) C_S	Prismatic $\dfrac{2}{m}$ (second setting) C_{2h}
Trigonal	Trigonal pyramidal 3 C_3	Rhombohedral $\bar{3}$ C_{3i}	$\dfrac{3}{m} \equiv \bar{6}$
Tetragonal	Tetragonal pyramidal 4 C_4	Tetragonal bisphenoidal $\bar{4}$ S_4	Tetragonal bipyramidal $\dfrac{4}{m}$ C_{4h}
Hexagonal	Hexagonal pyramidal 6 C_6	Trigonal bipyramidal $\bar{6}$ C_{3h}	Hexagonal bipyramidal $\dfrac{6}{m}$ C_{6h}

classes. The permissible number of forms in each class depends upon the properties of its point group, particularly upon the order. For example, in classes 1 and $\bar{1}$ a face can occupy no special relationship to symmetry elements, so only one form (also the general form) is possible in each. On the other hand, the class $4/m\,\bar{3}\,2/m$ (the group of the cube and octahedron) with nine mirror planes and 13 rotation axes has six possible special forms and a distinct general form.

The general forms of the classes represent the types of forms possible in crystals and they can occur as special forms in one or more of the other classes. Crystallographic forms are given general names according to the number, shape, or arrangement of faces, and specific names indicating the systems in which they can occur. For example, "prism" is a general name; a "ditetragonal prism" is an eight-faced prism in some classes of the tetragonal system. Following are the most common names for crystal forms:

1. *Pedion:* single-faced form; general form in class 1 and special form in a number of other classes (such as m, $mm2$, and $4mm$).

2. *Pinacoid:* two parallel faces; general form in class $\bar{1}$ and special form in most other nonisometric classes (such as 222, $4/m$, 32, and $6/m\,2/m\,2/m$).

3. *Sphenoid:* two nonparallel faces related by a twofold proper rotation; general form in class 2.

4. *Bisphenoid:* four faces related by orthogonal twofold proper rotations or a fourfold improper rotation. Bisphenoids are general forms in classes 222 (rhombic bisphenoid) and $\bar{4}$ (tetragonal bisphenoid).

5. *Dome:* two nonparallel faces related by mirror reflection; general form in class m.

6. *Prism:* three or more cozonal faces. A four-faced prism is a general form in class $2/m$. Prisms of various kinds are special forms only in all classes of orthorhombic, tetragonal, trigonal, and hexagonal systems, generally with the z-axis as

zone axis (exceptions only in the orthorhombic system).

With the exception of the bisphenoid all the foregoing forms are open.

7. *Pyramid:* three or more faces meeting in a vertex. Pyramids are general forms in classes of the type n, nm, and nmm. They can be special forms in some of the same classes.

8. *Bipyramid, rhombohedron, scalenohedron, trapezohedron:* the remaining general forms of the nonisometric classes can be viewed as repetitions of pyramidal forms, by various combinations of dihedral rotation, reflection, and inversion into closed forms with double the multiplicity of the corresponding pyramids. Various names given to these forms indicate the relationships between the upper and lower pyramidal forms. They occur as general and special forms in the classes with one principal rotation axis and either dihedral rotation axes, xy symmetry planes or both.

9. *Isometric Forms:* the forms of the five isometric classes occur in no other classes and none of the foregoing forms occurs in the isometric classes. Many familiar "endospheric" polyhedrons (such as the cube, octahedron, dodecahedron, and tetrahedron) are forms in most of the isometric classes, and others can occur.

Stereographic projections of the 32 general forms and their symmetry elements are given in Figures 2–46 and 2–47 for the monoaxial and polyaxial point groups respectively. The names of the general forms are taken as the names of the corresponding crystal classes; for example, class $4mm$ is named the *ditetragonal pyramidal class*.

Most crystal forms are not confined to crystals of one class. For example, the cube {100} is possible as a special form in all isometric classes only one of which $(4/m\,\bar{3}\,2/m)$ has full cubic symmetry. Differences between arrangements of atoms on the faces of cubes in different classes can be sometimes demonstrated by etching with suitable solvents. Pits are etched around imperfections in the crystal structure, the general shape of which is a guide to the symmetry of the arrangement of atoms. Such etch pits in cubic crystals from the five isometric classes might appear

FIG. 2–46 (Opposite) *General forms in the 13 monoaxial point groups (dot—upper hemisphere face; circle—lower hemisphere face; black line—mirror plane).*

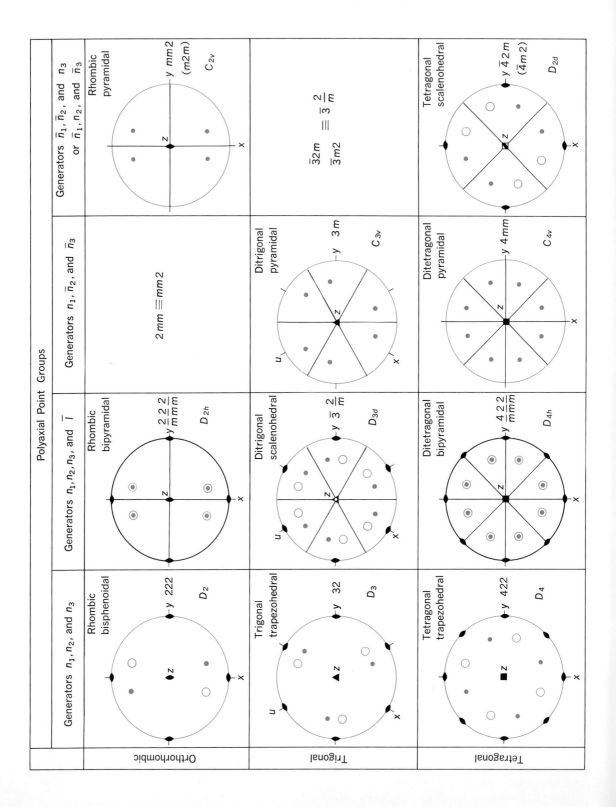

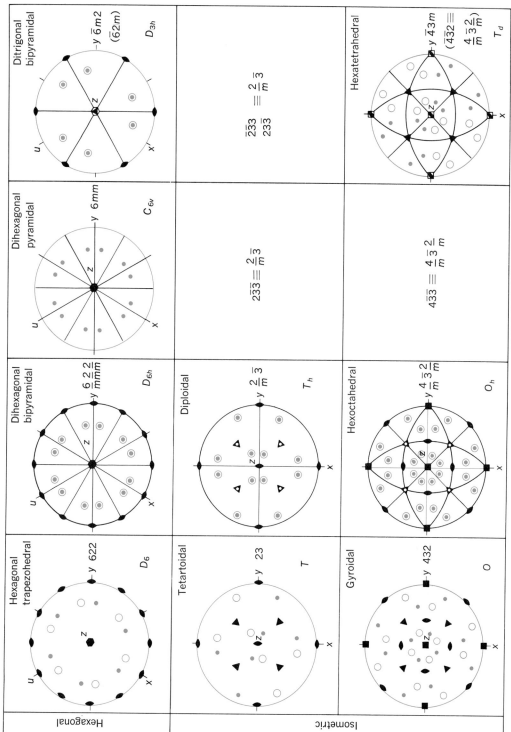

FIG. 2-47 General forms in the 19 polyaxial point groups (dot—upper hemisphere face; circle—lower hemisphere face; black line—mirror plane).

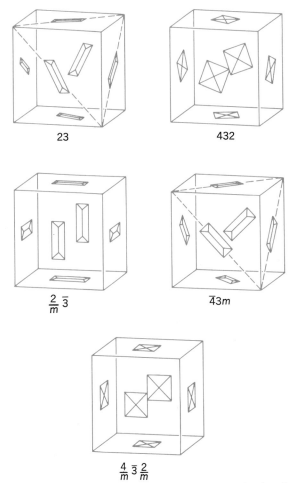

FIG. 2–48 *Typical etch-figure patterns on cubes developed in the five isometric classes. (After M. J. Buerger,* Elementary Crystallography, *Wiley, 1956.)*

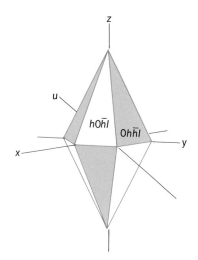

FIG. 2–49 *Apparent hexagonal bipyramid in class 32.*

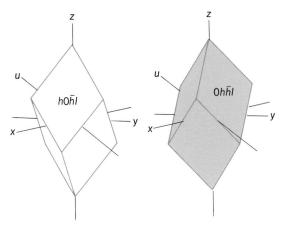

FIG. 2–50 *Positive and negative rhombohedra in class 32.*

as shown diagrammatically in Figure 2–48. The shapes of the pits indicate clearly the presence or absence of rotation axes or mirror planes perpendicular to the faces, and show also the symmetry operation by which the faces are related.

Similar problems arise in crystals in which development of a combination of two forms can simulate a more symmetric form. For example, a crystal of class 32 (such as quartz) might have the shape shown in Figure 2–49, apparently the hexagonal bipyramid $\{h0\bar{h}l\}$. But the hexagonal bipyramid is not a permissible form in class 32

and examination shows that the pyramidal faces comprise two separate forms, unrelated by symmetry operations: the "positive" rhombohedron $\{h0\bar{h}l\}$ and the "negative" rhombohedron $\{0h\bar{h}l\}$, each with six faces (blank and colored, respectively, in Figure 2–50).

In classes with only proper rotations in their point groups (1, 2, 3, 4, 6, 222, 32, 422, 622, 23, and 432) some forms can exist in enantiomorphic pairs reflecting an enatiomorphism (left- or right-handedness) in the actual crystal structure. Quartz (class 32), for example, has a right-handed

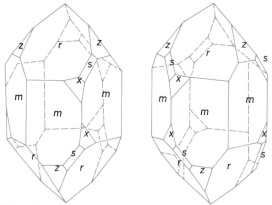

FIG. 2–51 *Left-handed and right-handed quartz crystals. (After E. S. Dana, A Textbook of Mineralogy, revised by W. E. Ford, 4th ed., Wiley, 1955.)*

and left-handed structure that can be expressed in characteristic combinations of forms on natural crystals (Figure 2–51).

Full discussions, including clinographic drawings, of the possible polyhedral forms of crystals and their indices are to be found in the references at the end of this chapter.

SYMMETRY OF STRUCTURE   Some aspects of the atomic structure of a crystal are indicated by its point group symmetry. The unit cell shape, for example, is fixed uniquely by point group symmetry for all but trigonal crystals, but not whether or not the cell is primitive. A complete statement of the structural symmetry of a crystal is given only by its space group, which includes operations of the type $\{R/t\}$, particularly screw rotations and glide reflections. The translational parts of these operations are smaller than lattice translations and the operations appear morphologically as pure rotations and mirror reflections, respectively, so each space group is isogonal with one of the 32 point groups. For example, in a crystal of class 2 with a primitive lattice, two space groups are possible: $P2$, containing only proper twofold rotations, and $P2_1$, containing only twofold screw rotations. Similarly, two space groups are isogonal with class m, Pm and Pa where a stands for glide reflection in the plane (010) with translation direction [100]. Screw axes and glide planes in a structure are always parallel

to rotation axes and mirror planes left invariant by its point group. The translation component of a screw rotation is always in the direction of the screw axis; but glide reflections can have translational components in the direction of any primitive lattice vector lying in the glide plane.

There are a total of 230 space groups distributed among the seven crystal systems, as shown in Table 2–14. Direct space group determination, possible by advanced X-ray methods, is essential to a full understanding of the atomic structure of a crystal, since it is the space group that defines the symmetrical arrangements of motif units (atoms, ions, or molecules) that comprise the crystal structure. A few space groups with only rotations or screws can exist in enantiomorphic pairs—for example, $P4_132$ and $P4_332$. Such pairs cannot be distinguished by any known means.

EQUIVALENT POSITIONS IN STRUCTURES   We saw earlier that one view of a crystal form is as a collection of faces arising by repetition of a given face by the symmetry operations of a point group. In the same way, the symmetry operations of a space group repeat any point in the structure into a set of "equivalent positions." The order of a space group is infinite and so is a collection of equivalent positions; but only a finite integral number of equivalent positions will

TABLE 2–14 *Distribution of space groups among the crystal systems*

System	Number of Space Groups
Triclinic	2
Monoclinic	13
Orthorhombic	59
Tetragonal	68
Trigonal	25
Hexagonal	27
Isometric	36
Total	230

be in one unit cell, termed the rank of the equivalent position.

Points in different parts of a unit cell are, in general, repeated into sets of equivalent positions with different ranks for the same reason that forms with different numbers of faces can be present on a crystal of one class: Certain points have special relationships to symmetry operations and may be left invariant by them. By analogy with the notions of special and general forms therefore, special and general equivalent positions are recognized in a unit cell. The rank of the general equivalent positions is the same as the number of space group operations within the cell.

In tables of space groups, typical special and general equivalent positions and their coordinates, referred to a vertex of the unit cell as origin, are generally listed along with the point group symmetry of the positions and their rank. Figure 2–52 is an adaptation from the *International Tables for X-ray Crystallography* (Volume

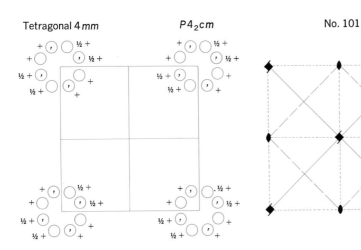

Tetragonal 4 mm $P4_2cm$ No. 101 $P4_2cm$

C_{4v}^3

Origin on 4_2

FIG. 2–52 *The space group $P4_2$cm. (Adapted from International Tables for X-ray Crystallography, Vol. 1, Kynoch Press, 1965.)*

Rank of equivalent positions	Point group symmetry at equivalent positions	Coordinates of equivalent positions	
8	1	x,y,z; $\bar{x},\bar{y},z$; $x,\bar{y},\frac{1}{2}+z$; $\bar{x},y,\frac{1}{2}+z$; y,x,z; $\bar{y},\bar{x},z$; $y,\bar{x},\frac{1}{2}+z$; $\bar{y},x,\frac{1}{2}+z$	General equivalent positions
4	m	x,x,z; $\bar{x},\bar{x},z$; $x,\bar{x},\frac{1}{2}+z$; $\bar{x},x,\frac{1}{2}+z$	Special equivalent positions
4	2	$0,\frac{1}{2},z$; $\frac{1}{2},0,z$; $0,\frac{1}{2},\frac{1}{2}+z$; $\frac{1}{2},0,\frac{1}{2}+z$	
2	mm	$\frac{1}{2},\frac{1}{2},z$; $\frac{1}{2},\frac{1}{2},\frac{1}{2}+z$	
2	mm	$0,0,z$; $0,0,\frac{1}{2}+z$	

I, Symmetry Groups) of the description of the Space Group $P4_2cm$, one of the space groups isogonal with point group $4mm$ of Table 2–3.

The rank of equivalent positions is important in determinations of crystal structure. The number of molecules or motif units in a unit cell can be easily computed once the cell dimensions, chemical composition, and density are known. The molecules must then occupy equivalent positions of rank equal to the number of molecules in the cell. Such considerations limit the possible arrangements of motif units in a crystal structure.

Chemical Mineralogy

GENERAL SCOPE

Crystallography can be treated, as we have just done, purely in terms of geometry, because the possible classes of crystal symmetry can be derived from pattern theory alone. Many of the properties of mineral crystals, such as geometric form and certain physical properties, depend entirely or partly on symmetry. But the identity and behavior of minerals depend on much more than symmetry. To understand the character and properties of mineral crystals we must leave the abstract world of crystal symmetry and enter a more realistic and complex field in which the unit cells of the crystal lattice become populated with atoms. Not only does an atom of each element possess certain specific and unique properties, but in different structural environments under the influence of adjacent atoms of the same or different elements, it becomes endowed with other specific properties. It may for example assume one or more positive or negative electric charges in which case it is called an ion—for example, Na^+, Fe^{2+}, Fe^{3+}, Cl^-, O^{2-}. The unique properties of all such modified atoms sharply limit the number of stable symmetrical patterns in which atoms of different elements combine as minerals. The natural combination of Zn and S atoms, for example, is the compound ZnS, which exists in nature in only two forms (mineral species): the

common mineral sphalerite, isometric class $\overline{4}3m$, and the rare mineral wurtzite, hexagonal class $6/m\,2/m\,2/m$.

Standard tables list about 80 elements (excluding rare gases and short-lived radioactive elements) as occurring in the crust. Only eight of these collectively account for 99 percent of the crust: (weight percentages) O, 46.6%; Si, 27.7%; Al, 8.1%; Fe, 5%; Ca, 3.6%; Na, 2.8%; K, 2.6%; Mg, 2.1%. The commonest minerals, therefore, are silicates (including SiO_2) and aluminosilicates of Fe, Ca, Na, K, and Mg and Fe oxides; on these in their various crystalline forms we shall focus most attention. All are light elements (atomic weight $<$ 56; atomic numbers between 8 and 26) appearing in periods 2 to 4 of the periodic table. Also highly significant in mineralogy are a number of light, reactive, minor nonmetallic elements—C, F, P, S, Cl—and the element H with unique properties. These add to the variety of common mineral species—carbonates, chlorides, sulfides, phosphates, and so on. Such minerals, crystallizing over a wide range of temperature and pressure accommodate a great variety of minor elements in concentrations sufficiently high to rank as exploitable ores; for instance, our supply of the common metals (such as Pb, Zn, Cu) comes mainly from sulfide ores.

CHEMICAL BONDING IN MINERAL CRYSTALS

The definitive characteristics of each mineral species are its chemical composition and its crystal structure. The two are interrelated and share a symmetry that is reflected in the physical properties of the mineral compound. To discuss composition and structure we must first understand something of the forces that hold the component atoms in their regular symmetrical configuration—that is, the nature of chemical bonding in mineral crystals.

Bonding in mineral crystals is most commonly either ionic, or covalent, or partly both. An ionic crystal is held together by the electrostatic attraction between oppositely charged ions (for example, Na^+ and Cl^- in halite, NaCl). The electrostatic energy of an electric charge q_1 at

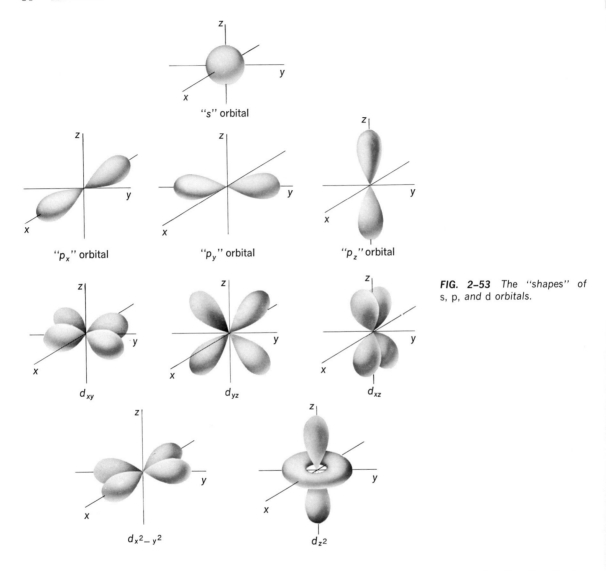

FIG. 2–53 The "shapes" of s, p, and d orbitals.

a distance r from a charge q_2 is simply q_1q_2/r; it is negative (attraction) if the charges are of opposite sign or positive (repulsion) if they have the same sign. Ionic bonds have no directional properties; for a given value of r the energy has the same value regardless of direction. Covalent bonding, on the contrary, is directional. It arises from the interaction between spins, not charges, and its energy depends on the geometrical shape of the wave functions or "orbitals" that describe

the properties, and in particular the distribution in space of the electrons of the bonded atoms. Each orbital is a particular solution of the Schrödinger wave equation to which are attached particular values of the energy and angular momentum. These orbitals have definite symmetries: "s" orbitals, for instance, are spherically symmetrical about the nucleus, while the three possible "p" orbitals of the same energy stretch out in space in three mutually perpen-

TABLE 2–15 *Electronegativity (on a scale devised by Pauling) and ionization potential of mineralogically significant elements, arranged as in the periodic table, with ionization potentials (in volts) in parentheses*

							C (11.26) 2.5	N (14.5) 3.0	O (13.6) 3.5	F (17.4) 4.0
Na (5.1) 0.9	Mg (7.6) 1.2					Al (6.0) 1.5	Si (8.1) 1.8	P (11.0) 2.1	S (10.4) 2.5	Cl (13.0) 3.0
K (4.3) 0.8	Ca (6.1) 1.0	Fe (7.9) 1.65	Co (7.9) 1.7	Ni (7.6) 1.7						

dicular directions (Figure 2–53). Covalent bonding can occur when orbitals of the bonded atoms overlap sufficiently. Note that the number of covalent bonds that an atom can form is limited by the number of electrons with unpaired spins.

ELECTRONEGATIVITY OF ATOMS   Whether bonds in crystals consisting of atoms of at least two kinds are ionic or covalent can be explained broadly in terms of the *electronegativity difference* of the bonded atoms. Electronegativity may be defined in terms of two measurable atomic properties, *ionization energy, I,* and *electron affinity, E.* Both these quantities are usually expressed in electronvolts (eV).[6] The ionization energy is the energy of the reaction by which one electron e is removed to infinity from the outer electron shell of the atom:

$$X = X^+ + e$$

The atom X is thereby converted into a positively charged ion X^+. The value of I shows a strong tendency to increase from left to right in any horizontal row (period) of the periodic table; it is, for instance, 5.36 eV for Li and 17.42 eV for F. I is usually determined from spectroscopic data.

Less readily measured, but known for some elements, is the electron affinity, E, defined as the energy of the reaction

$$X + e = X^-$$

by which an element X becomes a negatively charged ion X^-. E again tends to increase from left to right in any row of the periodic table.

Pauling has assigned to each element an empirical *electronegativity* (also measured in electronvolts) such that the difference in electronegativity of two elements will be related to the difference between the actual energy of a bond between these elements and the energy of this bond if it were purely covalent; the latter is taken to be simply the arithmetic mean of the single bond energies for the two elements. Mulliken has pointed out that the average of I and E should also be a measure of the electronegativity of an element:

$$x = \frac{I + E}{a}$$

where a is a numerical factor chosen so as to give the same electronegativity value as assigned empirically by Pauling.[7] The value of x, like that of I, increases from left to right in any row of the periodic table, as from Li (1.0) to F (4.0). Typical values of x and I are listed in Table 2–15. This scale of electronegativity gives a useful though rough measure of the ionic character of bonds; thus Pauling has plotted an empirically derived "percentage of ionic character" (0 in covalent bonds, 100 in ionic bonds) against electronega-

[6] An electronvolt is the energy required to move one electronic charge across a potential difference of one volt: 1 eV = 1.6×10^{-12} erg = 23,060 cal/g atom. The ionization energy, since it refers to a single electron, has the same numerical value as the *ionization potential,* expressed in volts.

[7] $a = 130$ if I and E are expressed in kcal/mole.

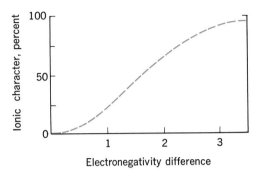

FIG. 2–54 *Ionic character of bonds as a function of electronegativity difference.*

tivity difference as shown in Figure 2–54. This curve is to be interpreted as follows: If two elements have very different electronegativities, or tendencies to gain or lose electrons, electron transfer takes place and bonding occurs by electrostatic attraction between oppositely charged ions. If, on the contrary, the two elements have similar electronegativities, bonding is covalent, and occurs by sharing rather than by transfer of electrons. According to Figure 2–54, the Si-O bond, of fundamental importance in mineralogy, would be about 50 percent covalent; the Mg-O bond would be 70 percent covalent. Actually, many physical properties of minerals as for instance their index of refraction (see page 101) can be accounted for by bonds considerably more ionic than the electronegativity differences would suggest.

ATOMIC SIZE, INTERATOMIC DISTANCE, AND BONDS
Concepts relating to the nature and relative strengths of crystal bonds are inseparable from implications regarding relative "sizes" and distances of mutual separation of the bonded atoms. It is only through the idea of atomic spacing at regular intervals that the geometric laws of crystallography can be applied to real crystals. And it is the mean values of these interatomic distances that are measured by X-ray diffraction (see page 113).

An isolated atom has no definite size, as the probability of finding one of its electrons in an element of volume dv, which is proportional to $\psi^2\ dv$, can be zero only at infinity where the wave function ψ itself is zero. In a crystal, however, the electrons of any atom are constrained by the electrons of all the other atoms. It thus becomes possible to assign to each atom a "radius" such that the sum of the radii of two adjacent atoms equals the observed interatomic distance. These radii depend, of course, on the electronic configuration of each atom; one expects, for instance, the radius of Na^+ to be smaller than that of Na, and that of O^{2-} to be larger than the radius of O. Covalent radii will differ markedly from ionic radii for the same elements.

Interatomic distances in crystals or molecules must be such that they minimize the sum of all the energy terms involved. There will in general be at least two such terms: One must account for the bonding (for instance, electrostatic attraction in ionic crystals), and the other must express the observed fact that most solids are hard to compress, since when the interatomic distance is decreased below a certain value, repulsive forces set in to keep the atoms apart. The energy of the crystal plotted against interatomic distance r will thus in general have the form shown in Figure 2–55a, in which the energy is taken to be zero when the atoms are at an infinite distance from each other. Such a curve prescribes an "equilibrium" interatomic distance r_0 at which the energy has a minimum value E_0 ("lattice energy"). (Note that the repulsive energy rises rapidly as r is reduced below r_0; it is said to have a "hard" character, consistent with the relative incompressibility of solids as compared, say, to gases.)

With rising temperature, thermal energy (heat) added to the crystal goes mostly or exclusively into vibrational energy; atoms now oscillate about their mean position and the mean interatomic distance increases as shown by the broken curve of Figure 2–55b. At temperatures close to the melting point, the volume of a crystal may commonly be 7 or 10 percent larger than at $0°K$; the interatomic distance is then 2 to 3 percent larger than at absolute zero.

Although interatomic distances and crystal structures are not easy to predict, two general rules are helpful. The first of these rules refers to charge correlation. It asserts on electrostatic grounds that the structure of an ionic crystal

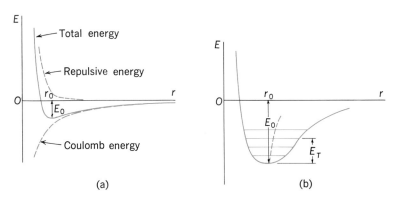

FIG. 2-55 *(a) Lattice energy of an ionic crystal as a function of separation of ions. (b) Effect of temperature on interionic distance. Thermal energy E_T causes an ion to oscillate between the two positions corresponding to the same energy. The mean interionic spacing thus increases with increasing temperature.*

must be such as to place ions of the same sign as far apart from each other as possible, whereas ions of opposite sign tend to be as close to each other as possible. The second rule, or spin correlation rule, refers to the tendency for single electrons to pair with, and remain close to, another electron of opposite spin, whereas electrons with the same spin tend to avoid each other. We remember that charge correlation implies no directional preference or limit, other than their size, on the number of next neighbors, whereas spin correlation (covalent bonding) implies directional properties as well as saturation as the number of bonds is restricted to the number of unpaired electrons.

SIMPLE IONIC STRUCTURES

IONIC RADIUS We have just stated that in an ionic crystal such as NaF, the sum of the ionic radii of Na+ and F− must equal the measured interatomic distance of 2.31 Å [one angstrom (Å) = 10^{-8} cm]. Both ions have the same structure ($1s^2\ 2s^2\ 2p^6$) and the same total number of electrons (10), but the Na nucleus has a higher charge (11) than the F nucleus (9). Pauling reasoned that the radius of Na+ should be smaller than that of F− because of the difference in electrostatic (or "Coulomb") attraction of the two nuclei. The attraction that the nucleus exerts on an outer electron is, however, screened by the intervening electrons of the inner shells, which reduce the apparent charge of the nucleus to an "effective" charge $Z_{eff.}$. This effective charge can be calculated from quantum mechanics or derived empirically from atomic spectra. Pauling proposed that the ratio of the ionic radii of Na+ and F− be taken as the inverse ratio of the effective charges; this gives Na+ = 0.95 Å and F− = 1.36 Å for this structure. Similar procedure applied to other ionic crystals give, for instance, K+ = 1.33 Å, Rb+ = 1.48 Å, Cl− = 1.81 Å, and so on. Some ionic radii applicable to oxides, silicates, and halides are listed in Table 2-16.

Since mineral crystals commonly depart from the ionic model and show some degree of covalency, it would be futile to apply these values uncritically to the structure of complex crystals such as feldspars ($NaAlSi_3O_8$ or $KAlSi_3O_8$) or alkali pyroxenes ($NaFeSi_2O_6$ or $NaAl_2O_6$). Among common elements, the pairs Na—O,

TABLE 2-16 *Ionic properties of common elements in oxides, silicates, and halides*

Element	Atomic Number	Electronegativity (Pauling scale)	Ionic Charge	Ionic Radius
H	1	2.1	1+	
Li	3	1.0	1+	0.60
C	6	2.5	4+	0.11
Na	11	0.9	1+	0.95
Mg	12	1.2	2+	0.65
Al	13	1.5	3+	0.50
Si	14	1.8	4+	0.41
K	19	0.8	1+	1.33
Ca	20	1.0	2+	0.99
Rb	37	0.8	1+	1.48
Ba	56	0.85	2+	1.35
O	8	3.5	2−	1.40
F	9	4.0	1−	1.36
Cl	17	3.0	1−	1.81

K—O, Ca—O, and Mg—O have sufficiently high electronegativity differences (see Table 2–15) to warrant, in general, use of ionic radii. Less certain is the significance of the ionic radii of Fe^{2+} (0.74), Al^{3+} (0.51), and Si^{4+} (0.41), whose electronegativities approach more closely that of O^{2-}.

LATTICE ENERGY   As mentioned, the energy of an ionic crystal can be expressed as the sum of an electrostatic energy and a "hard" repulsive term, which increases rapidly as the interionic distance r decreases. This repulsion is mainly the electrostatic repulsion between electrons of adjacent ions as they begin to overlap. In general, too many electrons are involved to allow an accurate calculation of the energy involved, which we represent by an empirical term of the form b/r^n, where b and n are constants to be determined. Thus the energy u of a pair of ions of opposite sign can be written as

$$u = -\frac{z_1 z_2 e^2}{r} + \frac{b}{r^n}$$

where $z_1 e$ and $z_2 e$ are the charges on the cation and anion, respectively, and b and n are constants. We neglect thermal energy, assuming the temperature to be $0°K$.

The energy ("lattice energy") per mole of a crystal of volume V containing N molecules or ion pairs can then be written as

$$E = -\frac{NA z_1 z_2 e^2}{r} + \frac{B}{r^n} \qquad (2\text{-}7)$$

where A and B are new constants, and N is Avogadro's number (6.02×10^{23}). A is known as the Madelung constant; it is a lattice sum expressing the sum of the electrostatic interactions between all ions in the crystal. The calculation of A is generally quite complicated, as it involves calculating the distances between all pairs of ions; if, for instance, the distance r_{ij} between ions i and j anywhere in the crystal is written as

$$r_{ij} = p_{ij} R$$

where R is the nearest-neighbor separation, A can be written as

$$A = \sum_j (\pm) p_{ij}^{-1}$$

where the summation is over all the ions in the crystal except i and the minus sign is applicable to ions of sign opposite to that of ion i. A simple one-dimensional example will illustrate this sum: Imagine a line of equally spaced ions alternatively positive and negative with charge e

$$+ \ - \ + \ - \ + \ - \ + \ - \ + \ - \ + \ -$$

Starting from the central cation, and remembering that the electrostatic energy is positive for charges of like sign and negative for charges of opposite sign, this energy is

$$-e^2 \left(\frac{2}{R} - \frac{2}{2R} + \frac{2}{3R} - \frac{2}{4R} + \cdots \right)$$

$$= -\frac{2e^2}{R} \left(1 - \frac{1}{2} + \frac{1}{3} - \frac{1}{4} + \cdots \right)$$

$$= -2\frac{e^2}{R} \ln 2$$

so that the Madelung constant for this case is $2 \ln 2$, or 1.384. The Madelung constant for the NaCl structure (Figure 2–56) is 1.7475.

Since the energy is minimum when the ionic separation is r_0, the constant B in (2-7) can be determined from the condition

$$\frac{\partial E}{\partial r} = 0 \qquad \text{for } r = r_0$$

This gives

$$B = \frac{NA z_1 z_2 e^2}{n} r_0^{n-1}$$

and the energy will depend on r as

$$E = -\frac{NA z_1 z_2 e^2}{r} \left[1 - \frac{1}{n} \left(\frac{r_0}{r} \right)^{n-1} \right] \qquad (2\text{-}8)$$

The minimum of the lattice energy corresponding to the equilibrium separation r_0 is easily obtained by substituting r_0 for r in this relation. Figure 2–55a is a plot of E versus r.

To determine the constant n, we recall that at $T = 0°K$, pressure P is given by

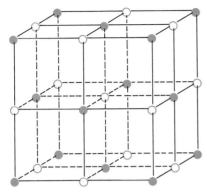

FIG. 2-56   *The halite (NaCl) structure.*

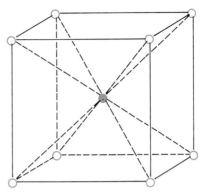

FIG. 2-57   *The cesium chloride structure.*

$$P = - \frac{\partial E}{\partial V} \qquad (2\cdot9)$$

where V, the volume, is related to r as $V = cNr^3$, where c is an appropriate constant depending on the crystal structure. For the halite structure, for instance, $c = 2$ (Figure 2–56). Since the compressibility β is defined as

$$\beta = - \frac{1}{V}\frac{\partial V}{\partial P} = 1/V\frac{\partial^2 E}{\partial V^2}$$

its value can be calculated from equation (2–8). For the halite structure ($z_1 = z_2 = 1$, $c = 2$) one gets

$$\frac{1}{\beta_0} = \frac{(n-1)e^2 A}{18 r_0^4} \qquad (2\cdot10)$$

where β_0 is the "initial" compressibility when $r = r_0$. Assuming β_0 to be known from experiment, the value of n may be calculated from equation (2–10). In general it turns out to lie between 8 and 10.

The lattice energy, it will be recalled, is the energy necessary to "evaporate" the crystal and disperse it into widely separated ions. As such it can also be calculated from thermodynamic data on heats of sublimation, ionization energy, electron affinity, and heat of formation. The two values of E agree within a few percent for many substances, which can therefore be considered to be ionic. Good agreement is also obtained for substances (for example, sulfides of Zn, Pb) that chemists would hesitate to call ionic.

We notice from equation (2–8) that, other things being equal, the most stable structure will be that for which A is maximum. The cesium chloride structure shown in Figure 2–57, for which $A = 1.7627$, would therefore be more stable than the NaCl structure for the same values of r_0 and n. The stability of the NaCl structure arises from its smaller value of r_0, which is the sum of the ionic radii of the constituent atoms. This brings us to a consideration of the effect of ionic size on determining crystalline structure.

RADIUS RATIO AND COORDINATION NUMBER   The coordination number of an atom in a crystal is the number of its closest neighbors. In ionic crystals, charge correlation requires that an ion (for example, a cation A with radius r_A) be surrounded at the shortest possible distance by a maximum number of ions of opposite sign (for example, anions B with radius r_B). It is easy to see that this number of closest neighbors depends on the ratio r_A/r_B, for we can obviously pack more anions around a big cation than around a small one; on the other hand, the number of anions that can be packed around a cation of given size is limited by the size of the anions themselves. Figure 2-58 illustrates several important configurations corresponding to certain values of the radius ratio r_A/r_B.

The point can be illustrated by referring to Figure 2–59a, which shows four anions B surrounding a central cation A so that they all touch. (These anions could be four of six anions in "octahedral coordination," the other two being

R_A/R_B	Coord. no.	Configuration		Example
0.155- 0.225	3	Trigonal planar 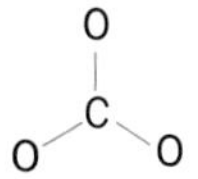		$CO_3{}^{2-}$
0.225- 0.414	4	Tetrahedral 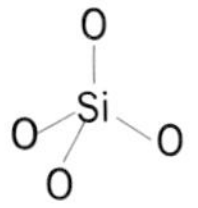		SiO_2
0.414- 0.732	6	Octahedral 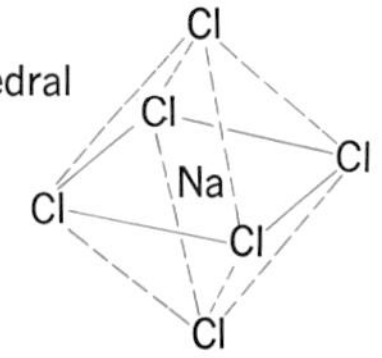		NaCl
0.732- 1.0	8	Cubic 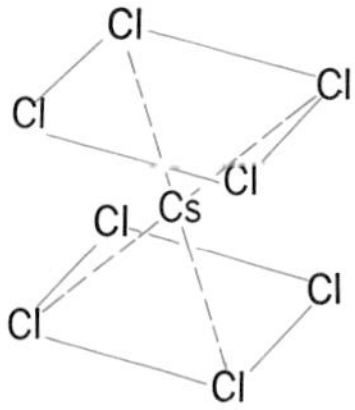		CsCl

FIG. 2–58 *Some radius ratios and corresponding coordinations.*

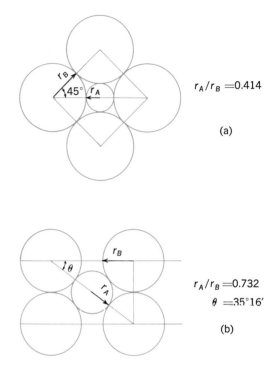

FIG. 2–59 (a) *Limiting radius ratio for octahedral (6) coordination.* (b) *Limiting radius ratio for cubic (8) coordination.*

respectively above and below the cation.) It is readily seen from the figure that

$$\frac{2r_B}{2(r_A + r_B)} = \sin 45° = 0.7071$$

and thus $r_A/r_B = 0.414$. If r_A were smaller than this in relation to r_B, all four anions would not touch the cation, and the anion–cation distance would not be a minimum. For any coordination r_A/r_B is minimal when the distance between centers of the larger ions is $2r_B$, as in Figure 2-59a.

As r_A/r_B increases beyond 0.414, the distance between anions becomes greater than $2r_B$. When the radius ratio reaches 0.732, the cubic configuration with 8-coordination shown in Figure 2-58 becomes possible. From the geometry of Figure 2–59b, a diagonal vertical section through the cube of 8-coordination, drawn for minimum r_A/r_B, can be determined as follows:

$$\tan \theta = \frac{2r_B}{2r_B/0.7071} = 0.7071$$

$$\theta = 35°16'$$

$$\frac{2r_B}{2(r_A + r_B)} = \sin 35°16' = 0.5774$$

whence

$$\frac{r_A}{r_B} = 0.732$$

Coordination patterns shown in Figure 2-58 are represented in crystalline mineral and artificial compounds. They comply with the requirements of ionic bonding; and in some cases— where electronegativity differences between cations and anions are high—bonding probably closely approaches that of the ionic model. Particular instances are illustrated in greater detail, with no attempt to portray relative size of ions,

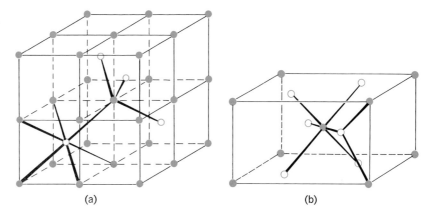

Fig. 2–60 (a) The fluorite (CaF$_2$) structure. (b) The rutile (TiO$_2$) structure.

(a)   (b)

in Figures 2–57 and 2–60. The observed structures are those to be expected from r_A/r_B alone, with the added restriction that the crystal must be electrically neutral.

Halite, NaCl: $r_A/r_B = 0.525$ both Na+ and Cl− in 6-coordination (NaF, with $r_A/r_B = 0.70$, has an identical structure).

CsCl: $r_A/r_B = 0.93$; both Cs+ and Cl− in 8-coordination.

Rutile, TiO$_2$: $r_A/r_B = 0.486$; Ti⁴⁺ in 6-coordination; O²⁻ in 3-coordination.

Fluorite, CaF$_2$: $r_A/r_B = 0.728$. The r_A/r_B value is slightly lower than the limit for 8-coordination. However, the combination Ca²⁺ in 8-coordination and F− in 4-coordination gives closer packing of Ca²⁺ ions than the alternative coordination numbers 6 and 3; so the 8-4 combination is that observed in fluorite.

Two of the examples shown in Figure 2-58, while complying with radius-ratio and coordination requirements of ionic crystals, nevertheless depart from the pure ionic model. The first example is Si⁴⁺−O²⁻ whose constant tetrahedral coordination in a host of silicate minerals is in perfect agreement with the accepted value of $r_A/r_B = 0.293$. Another case is C⁴⁺−O²⁻ in the [CO$_3$]²⁻ grouping characteristic of carbonates. We shall return to this question after considering the nature of the ideal covalent bond.

ELECTRONS, CHARGE, AND SYMMETRY   In a purely ionic crystal the properties and behavior of every ion are spherically symmetrical. We can neglect complexities connected with motion of individual electrons, overlap of adjoining electron clouds, and diversity in spatial properties of electrons in the outer subshells. The hard sphere of the co-ordination model can be considered simply as a nucleus enclosed by electron shells and subshells of finite radius.

The charge on the ion is determined by the propensity for an electropositive atom to lose its outer electrons and for an electronegative atom to accommodate them in its own outer shell. As is well known to chemists, a particularly stable resulting electronic configuration is one in which the *s* and *p* subshells of the outermost occupied shell become filled to capacity with an electron octet s^2, p^6. Thus in period 3 of the periodic table, we find, with increasing atomic number, Na+, Mg²⁺, Al³⁺, Si⁴⁺ cations, all with an electronic configuration $1s^2\ 2s^2\ 2p^6$; and P³⁻, S²⁻, Cl⁻ anions, all with $1s^2\ 2s^2\ 2p^6\ 3s^2\ 3p^6$. The structure as a whole is kept electrically neutral by a strictly maintained numerical atomic ratio: Na+/Cl⁻ = 1, Al³⁺/O²⁻ = 2/3, Si⁴⁺/O²⁻ = 2. The charge on an ion is neutralized to an equal degree by like contributions from its coordinated neighbors of opposite charge. Every cation is equally bonded to each surrounding anion, and vice versa. In halite there is no hint of an NaCl molecule—only an infinite array of Na+ and Cl−

ions, each surrounded by six of the other kind in octahedral coordination.

SIMPLE COVALENT STRUCTURES

GENERAL CONDITIONS   When atoms of identical or similar electronegativity are brought close together, bonding may occur by sharing rather than by transferring outer electrons. The result is one or more covalent bonds; and aggregates so bonded have molecular properties that are foreign to the strictly ionic crystal. The necessary conditions for covalent bonding are these:

1. Each atom must have one or more singly occupied orbital or unpaired electron. The number of covalent bonds an atom can form is often but not always equal to the number of unpaired electrons in its ground state, as described later.

2. Atoms that become bonded must approach closely enough to permit considerable overlap of their respective singly filled orbitals. When overlap exceeds some limiting value, two electrons of opposite spin, one from singly filled orbital of each atom, become paired in a single orbital that has a molecular character in that it is related to both nuclei. Sulfur in the ground state has the electronic structure $1s^2\ 2s^2\ 2p^6\ 3s^2\ 3p^4$. Two of the $3p$ orbitals are singly occupied. In molecular sulfur each of these has become fully occupied. The orbital so formed has a configuration that is equally related to two adjacent atoms; the result is a connecting covalent bond. The molecule S_8 of orthorhombic sulfur is a ring of eight atoms linked by covalent bonds.

HYBRID ORBITALS   Carbon has the ground structure $1s^2\ 2s^2\ 2p^2$ with only two singly occupied $2p$ orbitals. Yet carbon commonly has a valence of 4, and in some compounds or forms such as methane (CH_4) or diamond (C), each carbon is held by four bonds of equal energy to four neighboring atoms in tetrahedral coordination. The molecular structure of methane has symmetry $\overline{4}3m$. This can be explained as follows. First the carbon atom is excited to the state $1s^2\ 2s^1\ 2p^3$ by transferring one of its $2s$ electrons to the hitherto unoccupied $2p$ orbital. The $2s$ and three $2p$

orbitals are then mixed, or "hybridized" to form a new set of four equivalent sp^3 orbitals.[8] The sum of the energies of the *four* covalent bonds that may now form more than compensates for the energy required to raise the carbon atom from its ground state to the excited state. In mathematical form, the wave function of a hybrid sp^3 orbital is written as

$$\psi_{\text{hybrid}} = \psi_{2s} + \sqrt{3}\psi_{2p}$$

In some compounds, such as the common carbonate mineral $CaCO_3$, the carbon atom is tied by three covalent (or partly covalent) bonds to three surrounding oxygen atoms in a triangular planar configuration. In these bonds $2s$ orbital of carbon has hybridized with two of the $2p$ orbitals to give three equivalent sp^2 hybrids, leaving a single $2p$ orbital perpendicular to the plane that is available to form a covalent bond of a different character (π bond) with similarly directed $2p$ orbitals of the adjacent oxygen atoms.

Another possibility, exemplified by the CO_2 molecule, is formation of a pair of sp hybrids.

PROPERTIES OF COVALENT BONDS   In a crystalline nonmetal such as orthorhombic sulfur or diamond, half the mean distance between nuclei of neighboring atoms gives a *covalent radius*. The magnitude of this depends, of course, on the configuration of covalently bonded atomic groups. The covalent radius of C, for example, has three different values one for each state of hybridism of $2s$ and $2p$ orbitals: 0.722, sp^3; 0.665, sp^2; 0.602, sp. There is no obvious relation between covalent radius, number of nearest neighbors, or bond strength (the energy required to break one covalent bond—for example, Cl—Cl or C—C). Some relevant data are given in Table 2–17.

Metallic bonding   In metallic crystals electrons are shared not just by two, but by all atoms. They represent the extreme of the collective electron model. In crystals of metallic elements atoms of uniform size are involved and three

---

[8] A property of the Schrödinger wave equation is that if ψ_a and ψ_b are two solutions of it, $\psi_a + c\psi_b$ is also a solution, c being an arbitrary constant.

TABLE 2–17   Some properties of covalent bonds

Element	Atomic Number	Covalent Radius, A	Number of Near Neighbors	Bond Strength, kcal/g atom
H	1	0.30		
B	5	0.88		
C	6	0.66	3	
		0.77	4	
O	8	0.66		
F	9	0.64		
Si	14	1.17	4	42.2
P	15	1.00	3	51.3
		1.10	4	
S	16	1.04	4	50.9
Cl	17	0.99	4	58.0

structural types are commonly observed as illustrated in Figure 2–61. In face-centered cubic (fcc) packing each atom is identically coordinated to twelve others and the symmetry of the unit cell is $4/m \bar{3} 2/m$. In body-centered cubic (bcc) packing the cell shape and symmetry are the same but the coordination number is 8. In hexagonal close packing (hcp) the coordination number is again 12 but the arrangement is less symmetric than in fcc. High coordination and close packing in typical metal structures testify to general delocalization of bonds.

Additional influences in mineral structures   In all this discussion of bonding we have referred to only the simplest of mineral structures, such as halite and diamond. This is because most minerals, and especially common constituents of the crust such as silicates, carbonates, and oxides cannot be treated in terms of any simple model of bonding. In other words, the present state of atomic and molecular theory is an unsatisfactory

basis for predicting the structure and behavior of mineral crystals. The structures can be determined and the properties and behavior of minerals observed. To some extent the mineralogist rationalizes these in terms of current concepts of atomic structure and of the nature of chemical bonds. To predict on this basis how structure and bonding may be expected to change or develop under conditions prevailing deep within the earth is by no means unprofitable; but caution must be exercised in view of the complicating factors that influence bonding and so also the structure of common minerals. We shall now examine some of these factors.

OXYGEN COORDINATION OF SILICON AND CARBON
Silicates are the most abundant constituents of the crust and mantle, so the bonding relation of Si to O merits special attention. Because the electronic configurations of the Si and the C atom have much in common, and because carbonates are important minerals of sedimentary rocks, it is interesting to compare the oxygen coordinations of the two elements in common minerals. The radius ratio C^{4+}/O^{2-} is 0.11; Si^{4+}/O^{2-} is 0.30 (Table 2–16). As predicted from Figure 2–57, silicon has a coordination of 4. On the other hand, carbon, whose radius ratio is consistent with 2-coordination, consistently appears in mineral structures with a coordination of 3 in a trigonal planar $[CO_3]^{2-}$ anion. Electronegativity differences (see Table 2–15)—(O—Si) = 1.7, (O—C) = 1.01—suggest that bonding in carbonates is not far from the pure covalent model, while in silicates the bonds should share covalent and ionic properties almost equally.

The $[CO_3]^{2-}$ anion of carbonates is explained, as we have just seen, in terms of sp^2 orbital hy-

FIG. 2–61 Common metallic structures. (a) Face-centered cubic structure. (b) Body-centered cubic structure. (c) Hexagonal close-packed structure.

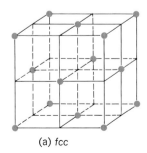
(a) fcc

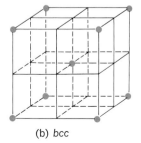
(b) bcc

(c) hcp

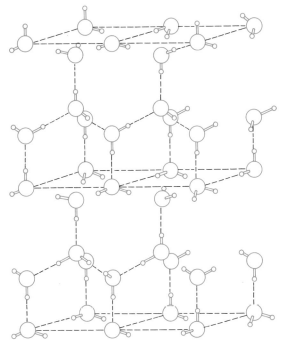

FIG. 2–62   *The structure of ice (after L. Pauling).*

bridism. The carbon atom is tied to each oxygen neighbor by a covalent bond utilizing one of these orbitals; the remaining single *p* orbital is spread as a double bond between all three oxygens.

The $[SiO_4]^{4-}$ group that is the basic unit of all crustal silicates (including SiO_2 polymorphs) is consistent with a model of symmetrical *sp³* orbital hybridism just as in carbon of compounds such as methane. But one may ask, does this fit a part-ionic, part-covalent model? And why is the length of the Si—O bond always about 1.6 Å instead of 1.81 (Table 2–16) or 1.83 Å (Table 2–17)? It has been said that Si may use some of its unoccupied *3d* orbitals to add a small contribution of double bonding. This may sound a little vague; but the extremely high-pressure SiO_2 polymorph stishovite does indeed consist of $[SiO_6]$ groups with Si in octahedral coordination.

Thus at the outset we see that predictions relating to bonding and coordination in complex mineral crystals depend upon subtle and imperfectly understood factors as well as on the stan-

dard models of the simple ionic or covalent bond. It is legitimate perhaps to raise the possibility that, under high pressures favoring higher coordination, carbon might assume a coordination number 4 and build $[CO_4]^{4-}$ groups comparable with the $[SiO_4]^{4-}$ groups of silicates. This cannot, however, be predicted with any certainty; and until they may be produced experimentally, $[CO_4]$ compounds remain hypothetical.

THE HYDROGEN BOND   In an ice crystal oxygen atoms are arranged in an essentially tetrahedral structure, with one hydrogen atom between any two adjacent oxygens (Figure 2–62). Of the four hydrogen atoms surrounding any oxygen atom, two are close to it and two are farther away. The tetrahedral configuration suggests development of four *sp³* hybrid orbitals in the oxygen atom. Two of these are utilized for covalent bonding with two separate hydrogen atoms; and these are held close to the oxygen nucleus. The remaining two *sp³* orbitals constitute two "lone pairs" not involved in covalent bonding.

In ice, then, we may consider any oxygen and its two closest hydrogen neighbors (in effect, a water molecule) as consisting of two positive charges at the H nuclei, and two negative charges situated near the oxygen atom. The electrostatic interaction between charge on the molecule and the charges on all the other molecules is mainly what holds the crystal of ice together. The term *hydrogen bond* is used to describe this kind of attraction. Hydrogen is essential as the link because it possesses two favorable properties: its atomic radius is small (0.3 Å), and it has only one electron. Thus the adjacent molecules can approach very closely without the appearance of the usual hard repulsion due to overlapping of electronic inner shells. Hydrogen bonds can form only between atoms one of which must be sufficiently electronegative. The strength of the electrostatic bond is weak (5 kcal/g atom) compared with that of ionic and covalent bonds.

Many minerals contain hydrogen either as $[OH]^-$ ions or as H_2O molecules. Some of these, such as the clay silicates, have important physical properties and chemical attributes that depend on the existence of the relatively weak hydrogen bond in the structure. Outside the field of mineralogy, water plays a unique role in geological just as in biological processes. Its unique properties are due to persistence of hydrogen bonding and loosely knit tetrahedral structure in the liquid phase.

CRYSTAL-FIELD THEORY AND THE TRANSITION METALS Among metals of the first transition series (21 to 30: Sc, Ti, V, Cr, Mn, Fe, Co, Ni, Cu, Zn), iron is not only one of the common elements in the crust and mantle, but also the principal constituent of the core. The others are widely distributed as minor or trace elements in common crustal minerals and as principal constituents of economically valuable oxide and sulfide ores. Their behavior in mineral compounds and their effects upon the properties of such minerals depend largely on the fact that the atoms of all these metals except zinc have a partially occupied $3d$ or $4s$ electronic energy level.

In simple crystal-field theory we consider the influence of an array of point charges representing the neighboring anions on the five d orbitals of a central cation. In an isolated metal ion the $3d$ orbitals with unique spatial distribution have identical or almost identical energies (they are *degenerate*). Consider what happens when an ion such as Ti^{3+} ($3d^1$) is placed in a regular octahedral field. From Figure 2–63 it can be seen that two of the "d" orbitals (namely, $d_{x^2-y^2}$ and d_{z^2}) point at the surrounding ligands and the three others (d_{xy}, d_{yz}, and d_{xz}) occupy regions in space between the anions. It is clear that electrons in these two kinds of orbitals will not suffer the same repulsion from the anions and the degeneracy of energy in the free ion will be partially removed. Figure 2–63, showing the xy-plane of a regular octahedron, indicates how this difference will arise. Figure 2–64 is the energy-level diagram for a regular octahedral field. The five d orbitals are split into two sets of high and low energy, respectively, and the energy difference, Δ, can easily be measured by finding the energy required to excite an electron from the lower to the higher group. In the case of Ti^{3+} (and most transition-metal compounds) this energy corresponds to a quantum in or near the visible region of the spectrum, and such excita-

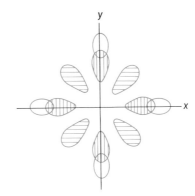

FIG. 2–63 *Schematic representation of orbitals in the xy plane of a transition element in octahedral (6) coordination. The empty ovals correspond to orbitals of surrounding anions. Shaded ovals are, respectively, the $d_{x^2 y^2}$ orbital (on the x and y axes) and the d_{xy} orbital (between axes), of the central cation.*

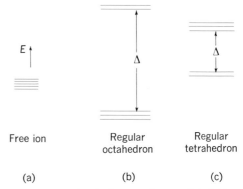

FIG. 2–64 *Energy-level diagram for crystal field splitting of a degenerate level, showing the five degenerate 3d levels of the free ion (a) and the splitting of these levels by octahedral (b) and tetrahedral (c) fields.*

tion and the corresponding absorption of light leads to the colors of many transition metal compounds.

The splitting pattern in a regular tetrahedral field is also shown in Figure 2–64. For each geometrical variation of the field, a distinct pattern of splitting is seen and can be determined by a study of the spectrum. Changes in the magnitude of Δ may lead to drastic changes in the electron configuration. In Figure 2–65 we show the situation with a ferrous ion ($3d^6$) in fields where Δ is small and where Δ is large. In general electrons tend to keep as far from each

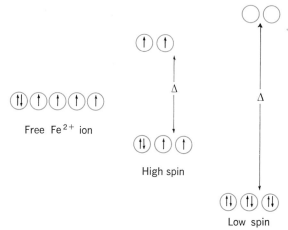

Free Fe²⁺ ion

High spin

Low spin

FIG. 2–65 *"High-spin" and "low-spin" configurations. The "low-spin" configuration may occur when the energy splitting Δ is large.*

other as possible and thus occupy or are spread over all five of the "d" orbitals. But if the energy difference between the split orbitals becomes large relative to electron–electron repulsion, the electrons may occupy only the low energy states. Thus with the ferrous ion, we see a change from a paramagnetic ion ("high spin" configuration) with four unpaired spins to a diamagnetic ion ("low spin" configuration) with no unpaired spins.

The important feature of such changes is that transition metal ions may loose their spherical symmetry when placed in the electrical fields of their neighboring anions. We shall turn to some additional consequences of this phenomenon as we proceed.

In Figure 2–66 are shown the bond lengths in oxides of formula M-O which we may consider to be made from M^{2+} and O^{2-} ions, and in which the metal M occurs in 6-coordination (octahedral coordination). It will be noted that as we proceed from CaO to VO the distance grows shorter, as would be anticipated from screening rules. The nuclear charge is increasing faster than the inner-electron screening, so the nuclear attraction is greater. From Ca to V, electrons are entering the low energy "d" orbitals situated between the anions. When we reach Mn, two electrons have entered the orbitals pointing at the anions and the distances increase. The pattern is then

repeated as we proceed from Mn to Zn. This simple consideration of which orbitals are being progressively occupied allows us to rationalize this rather odd pattern of distances. We would need to consider the same features to understand the lattice energies of these oxides.

The sulfides MnS_2 and FeS_2 also show the drastic changes imposed by a change from high-spin to low-spin configuration (Table 2–18). If we measure the interatomic distances in the oxides MnO and FeO we find that we can assign a radius of 0.80 Å to Mn^{2+} and 0.76 Å to Fe^{2+}. Both oxides have magnetic properties indicating the high-spin state. We would anticipate that in general ferrous compounds would have distances about 0.04 Å shorter than manganese compounds. But the interatomic distances in the disulfides show that the ferrous ion has shrunk by about 0.3 Å and this shrinkage can be correlated with the diamagnetism of FeS_2. If we refer back to Figure 2–53 it is not difficult to explain the shrinkage. In the high-spin state, electrons occupy all five $3d$ levels, including the ones that point towards the adjacent anions. In the low-spin state, on the contrary, electrons are mostly between the anions, thus allowing them to move in closer to the cation, whose size appears to collapse. It would be predicted that since such low-spin ions are smaller, high pressure should favor their formation and lead to a spin-change polymorphism. This phenomenon has been observed in the mineral gillespite ($BaFeSi_4O_{10}$) at 50 kb and it seems likely that ferrous ions deep within the earth would all achieve this state of low spin.

Interatomic distances in some disulfides are

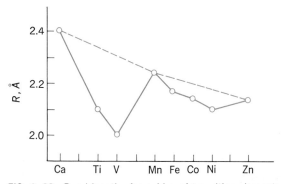

FIG. 2–66 *Bond lengths for oxides of transition elements.*

TABLE 2–18   Interatomic distances in transition-metal disulfides

	MnS$_2$ (hauerite)	FeS$_2$ (pyrite)	CoS$_2$ (cattierite)	NiS$_2$ (vaesite)	S^{2-}
Ionic radius (A)	0.80	0.76	0.74	0.72	1.84
M^{2+}–S distance (estimated)	2.64	2.60	2.58	2.56	
M^{2+}–S distance (observed)	2.59	2.26	2.32	2.40	
Contraction	0.05	0.34	0.26	0.16	
Unpaired electrons	5	0	1	2	

given in Table 2–18, and from these it can be seen that from Fe to Co to Ni the "apparent" radius of the metal ion increases in contrast to the trend shown in most tables of ionic radii.

A comparison of two ions such as Fe$^{3+}(d^5)$ and Mn$^{3+}(d^4)$ reveals an important difference between them in octahedral coordination. With Fe^{3+} an electron can occupy each orbital and spaces along and between all axes are occupied. On the other hand, Mn^{3+} can have an electron in the xy-plane or along the z-axis, but not both. Because of the lower symmetry of these configurations, distortion (so-called Jahn-Teller distortion) of the regular coordination octahedron occurs, so two of the coordinated ions are at a longer or shorter distance and the regular octahedron becomes a tetragonal bipyramid. This distortion occurs particularly with d^4, d^6, and d^9 configurations and is observed commonly in compounds of Mn^{3+} and Cu^{2+} and sometimes in compounds of Fe^{2+}. Such ions prefer distorted sites.

The most common cause of color in minerals is absorption of visible radiation by d electrons of transition metals. The study of the absorption spectrum can provide a wealth of information concerning the geometry of the crystal field, oxidation states of the metals, distribution of ions over various lattice sites, and so on. If the crystal field is not highly symmetric, absorption of polarized light can be anisotropic and the phenomenon of pleochroism is observed; that is, the mineral has different colors in transmitted light for incident polarized rays with different vibration directions (see below). There are many other causes of coloration in minerals, including lattice defects which color the alkali halides, the presence of bands of electrons (in graphite and

sulfides), photochemical oxidation–reduction, or electron exchange (for example, between Fe^{2+} and Fe^{3+} ions in biotite).

POLYMORPHISM

Some combinations of elements in fixed proportions—for example, CaCO$_3$ or Al$_2$SiO$_5$—can exist in two or more structurally distinct forms each with its characteristic symmetry and properties. These are called *polymorphs*. Closely correlated with crystalline structure are the thermodynamic properties—heat of formation, entropy, density, and so on—that determine the stability of a polymorph under given conditions of temperature and pressure. Dense structures, as we shall see later (page 236), are favored by high pressure, and the stability of high-entropy forms increases with rising temperature. Every polymorph, therefore, has a limited temperature–pressure range over which it is the most stable form of the compound in question. Take the case of SiO$_2$. At atmospheric pressure there are five well-known stable polymorphs: α-quartz (trigonal, class 32) up to 573°C; β-quartz (hexagonal, class 622), 573°–870°C; tridymite (hexagonal, $6/m\ 2/m\ 2/m$), 870°–1470°C; cristobalite (isometric, $4/m\ \bar{3}\ 2/m$), 1470°–1713°C (melting temperature). Where two polymorphs show only minor differences in structure, inversion of one form to the other, with appropriately changing physical conditions, is rapid. That is why β-quartz does not survive cooling below 573°C in volcanic rocks. Inversion between polymorphs whose respective structures are radically different involves breaking of chemical bonds, building of new bonds, and diffusion of atoms in a solid medium. A process of this kind may be so slow as to become inappreciable in dry rocks at temperatures less than 100–200°C. This makes possible the survival of sillimanite, the high-temperature form of Al_2SiO_5, without inversion to low-temperature forms, andalusite or kyanite, in rocks that have undergone metamorphism at high temperature. Survival of high-temperature, high-pressure minerals during cooling and unloading of once deep-seated rocks is of great importance to geologists. Such minerals provide what clues we possess to the mineral constitution of the deep crust and the mantle.

POLYMORPHISM OF CARBON   There are two mineral polymorphs of carbon—diamond (isometric, $4/m\ \bar{3}\ 2/m$) and graphite (hexagonal, $6/m\ 2/m\ 2m$). Diamond occurs only in rocks (kimberlite) that are believed to have been transported with explosive violence from the outer mantle, itself—an environment of high pressure. Graphite crystallizes in nature, mainly in metamorphic rocks, at pressures ranging from perhaps 1 to 10 kb.

The diamond structure is tetrahedral (Figure 2–67a). Each atom is held to its neighbor by a single covalent bond to build a giant molecule whose size is that of the crystal itself. The structure completely fits a model of sp^3 hybridization with four singly occupied orbitals. One is shared with each neighboring atom, and the tetrahedral symmetry that results is comparable with that shown by the CH_4 molecule, methane.

In the graphite structure (Figure 2–67b) the unit is an infinitely extensive sheet of carbon atoms arranged in trigonal configuration. This is consistent with a model of sp^2 hybridism. Each atom utilizes one of the three sp^2 orbitals to form a covalent bond with each nearest neighbor. The third $2p$ orbital projects normal to the sheet on both sides and overlaps similar orbitals of neighboring atoms by lateral rather than by end-on juxtaposition. In this way a continuous orbital is formed that extends throughout the crystal and which actually consists of N very closely spaced energy levels forming a "band." The electrons are not localized on or between any pair of atoms but spread over the whole crystal in this band, thus accounting for the high electrical conductivity and optical absorption of graphite (diamond is an insulator).

In diamond the component atoms are closely packed throughout—the covalent radius being 0.77 Å. Packing within individual graphite sheets is even tighter (0.665 Å); but the sheets are mutually separated by much greater distances (3.37 Å). Diamond is much the denser and harder of the two polymorphs. Graphite has a ready cleavage parallel to the sheet structure, whereas in diamond the cleavage is tetrahedral.

POLYMORPHISM OF SiO_2   Table 2–19 lists six geologically significant polymorphs of SiO_2, together with properties—density and entropy—that control their fields of stability. Transient metastable phases that have no field of true stability are also known. The silica polymorphs illustrate a general tendency among crystalline

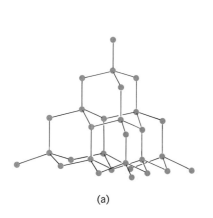

(a)

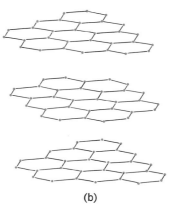

(b)

FIG. 2–67 (a)   The structure of diamond. (b)   The structure of graphite.

TABLE 2-19 *Polymorphs of silica, listed in order of decreasing stability temperature, with critical properties (measured at 25°C, and P = 1 bar)*

Polymorph	Entropy, cal/mole°	Density	Crystal Symmetry
Cristobalite	10.38	2.334	cubic $\frac{4}{m}\bar{3}\frac{2}{m}$
Tridymite	10.50	2.265	hexagonal $\frac{6}{m}\frac{2}{m}\frac{2}{m}$
β-quartz*			hexagonal 622
α-quartz	9.88	2.648	trigonal 32
Coesite	9.30	2.911	monoclinic
Stishovite	6.63	4.287	tetragonal

° Properties virtually identical with those of α-quartz from which it differs very slightly in structure.

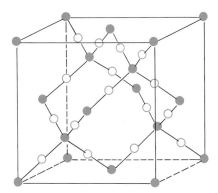

FIG. 2–68 *The structure of cristobalite.*

tetrahedral configuration; hence the great increase in density.

SOLID SOLUTION, MIXING, ORDERING

In any system of two solid phases, just as in a solid–liquid system, there is a tendency for mutual mixing in solid solution (see Chapter 5). Phase A contains a certain proportion of B, and phase B some different proportion of A in solution at the ionic or atomic level. Mutual solubility may be almost zero, or it may have any value up to 100 percent miscibility. Since solution involves increase in entropy (entropy of mixing), solubility of one phase in another increases with temperature. To develop a solution model as a basis for predicting solution behavior in minerals we must turn to thermodynamics. This is done later in Chapter 5. But to understand the range and variability of chemical composition among mineral species, we must first consider solid solution empirically as a common condition in mineralogy. The only general applicable rule is that like dissolves like. In this connection "like" implies similarity with respect to atomic size, interatomic forces, and crystal structure.

The simplest case is mixing of two crystalline phases having identical or closely similar structures, and consisting of atoms or ions that have similar dimensions and identical electric charge. These conditions are met in many common minerals. Take, for example, olivine—a continuous series of solid solutions between the end mem-

solids for inverse correlation between density and entropy (page 237). With some exceptions the high-entropy polymorphs have high symmetry.

All polymorphs except stishovite have the same basic structural unit: the [SiO₄] tetrahedron, familiar in silicate minerals. Silicon is in 4-coordination, oxygen in 2-coordination; and bonding is described as part-covalent, part-ionic. Bond distances, except in stishovite, are 1.61 ± 0.02 Å, and density differences merely reflect relative closeness of packing of the [SiO₄] tetrahedra. The structure that can be most clearly grasped from a diagram is that of cristobalite (Figure 2–68), in which the Si atoms are arranged very much as are C atoms in diamond. Other structures can be understood only through the medium of three-dimensional models. The anomalously high density of stishovite, and its markedly different symmetry, reflect a change from 4- to 6-coordination. Each Si atom now occupies the center of an octahedral group of O atoms, and the structural unit is [SiO₆]. Although the Si—O bond is longer than in 4-coordinated Si, the octahedral configuration of O atoms permits much closer packing than is possible with the bers forsterite Mg_2SiO_4 and fayalite Fe_2SiO_4, represented by the generalized formula $(Mg,Fe)_2SiO_4$. End members have identical structure. Ionic radii are Mg^{2+} 0.65 Å and Fe^{2+} 0.76 Å, both ions being in 6-coordination. Both end members have orthorhombic symmetry (class $2/m\ 2/m\ 2/m$). Unit cell dimensions are: Mg_2SiO_4, a 4.76 Å, b 10.20 Å, c 5.98 Å; Fe_2SiO_4 a 4.82 Å, b 10.48 Å, c 6.11 Å. There is another, though much rarer, mineral with the same structure, tephroite Mn_2SiO_4. The ionic radius of Mn^{2+} is 0.80 Å; the cell dimensions of tephroite are a 4.86–4.9 Å, b 10.60–10.62 Å, c 6.22–6.25 Å. There is a continuous solid solution series of iron-manganese olivines $(Fe, Mn)_2SiO_4$, but these can hold only limited amounts of Mg_2SiO_4 in solution.

More complex is solid solution involving mutual substitution of ions carrying different charges. To maintain electrical neutrality there must be simultaneous mutual substitution of other differently charged ions, or else some sites in the structure must be left vacant. Two examples from mineralogy are:

$NaAlSi_3O_8 + CaAl_2Si_2O_8$
  albite   anorthite
$\rightarrow (Ca, Na)_1(Al, Si)_2Si_2O_8$
        plagioclase

$NaAlSi_2O_6 \cdot H_2O + Ca_{1/2}AlSi_2O_6 \cdot H_2O$
  analcime°   wairakite
$\rightarrow (Na, Ca_{1/2})_1AlSi_2O_6 \cdot H_2O$

° Analcime is also commonly called analcite.

In the second example the product contains more cation sites than cations, and such substances may exhibit facile ion exchange in aqueous media; for example,

$NaAlSi_2O_6 \cdot H_2O$ (solid) $+ \frac{1}{2}Ca^{2+}$
                    (aqueous)
$\rightarrow Ca_{1/2}AlSi_2O_6 \cdot H_2O$ (solid) $+ Na^+$
                                    (aqueous)

Limited solid solution is almost universal in minerals. High-temperature minerals, such as those of igneous rocks, exhibit the general tendency for mutual solubility of end members to diminish with falling temperature. Alkali feldspars crystallizing from magmas at temperatures of perhaps 700°C are solid solutions, in any proportions, of $KAlSi_3O_8$ and $NaAlSi_3O_8$. At temperatures that are lower, miscibility becomes much more limited, and there is a tendency for the once-homogeneous alkali feldspar to unmix to two phases: $KAlSi_3O_8$ with limited Na, and $NaAlSi_3O_8$ with limited K.

In an ideal solid solution, the mutually replaceable atoms have random distribution in the available sites. Unmixing is an ordering process. Ordering of a rather different kind is also possible; for example, in the $KAlSi_3O_8$ structure a specific number of sites are equally available for Al and Si atoms. At low temperatures these tend to be occupied in a precisely ordered manner, but at high temperatures distribution of Al and Si in the available sites tends to be random. Ordering is a process very sensitive to temperature change, and there is usually a range of only a few tens of degrees separating essentially random from essentially ordered phases. Such a relation—a type of polymorphism—is termed a *second-order* or order–disorder transformation. It is shown for example, by $KAlSi_3O_8$:

microcline $\rightleftarrows$ sanidine
ordered: triclinic   disordered: monoclinic

End members of solid-solution series are *isomorphous* in that they have the same crystal structure, symmetry, and form. In the olivines we speak of isomorphous substitution of Fe^{2+} for Mg^{2+}. But there are some isomorphous pairs that show no tendency for solid solution—for example, $NaNO_3$ and $CaCO_3$, both trigonal $\bar{3}\ 2/m$, and similar in cell dimensions. There are no simple rules to predict the degree of mutual solubility of isomorphous compounds.

COMMON MINERALS: COMPOSITION AND STRUCTURE

For systematic information on the composition, properties, and chemical variety of minerals the reader is referred to standard texts. To illustrate the geological significance of common minerals, our treatment here is limited to a few examples drawn from the following categories:

1. Common rock-forming minerals of the crust, mostly silicates, aluminosilicates, and oxides.

2. Minerals that may have special significance in rocks of the mantle.

3. Minerals formed by local concentration of minor elements by surface and near-surface processes: carbonates, sulfates, phosphates, borates.

4. Sulfides, mostly significant as constituents of metallic ores.

Many of these mineral compounds are a good deal more complex than the simple minerals cited as examples in our discussion of crystal chemistry and structure. It is the rule rather than the exception to find tetrahedral and octahedral configuration of oxygen and other atoms distorted from ideal symmetry. Moreover, coordination numbers do not always agree with values predicted from generally accepted ionic and covalent radii. Even the radii themselves, and metal–oxygen bond lengths in complex structure such as silicates may depart considerably from standard values measured in simple halide and oxide structures.

SILICATE STRUCTURES   Silicates, including aluminosilicates, are by far the most important minerals of the crust and the mantle. They exhibit great structural variety, and there is a very close correlation throughout the whole class between structure, symmetry, and physical properties. Almost without exception, silicates and the SiO_2 polymorphs are built of $[SiO_4]$ tetrahedra—a central Si atom in 4-coordination with respect to O atoms. An interesting exception is the SiO_2 polymorph stishovite, an extremely rare

product of shock compression in meteor craters. Its unique $[SiO_6]$ structure and corresponding very high density might possibly be typical of unknown silicate phases in the deep mantle.

The great variety of natural silicates is due in no small part to two influences: polymerization of $[SiO_4]$ and substitution of Al^{3+} for Si^{4+}. Such substitution is limited. The proportion of $[AlO_4]^{5-}$ to $[SiO_4]^{4-}$ tetrahedra is commonly 0.25, more rarely 0.5. The corresponding formula is written $X(AlSi_3O_8)$ or $X(Al_2Si_2O_8)$; but no such "aluminosilicate" anions exist in the structure. Polymerization involves linking of tetrahedra by means of one common oxygen to build linear, sheetlike, and other geometric types of giant anions. These are neutralized electrically and tied into coherent crystal structures by essentially ionic bonds linking oxygen atoms of the tetrahedral units to interspersed cations—Ca^{2+}, Mg^{2+}, Fe^{2+}, and others—in 6-, 8-, or even higher coordination with respect to oxygen.

The degree of polymerization of the silicate ion controls most of the important properties of mineral silicates and provides the generally accepted basis of their systematic treatment and classification:

1. *Orthosilicates* (Figure 2–69a), $X^{4+}[SiO_4]^{4-}$, with nonpolymerized $[SiO_4]$ groups.[9] Examples are

---

[9] X is used to denote any appropriate combination of cations—such as $2Mg^{2+}$, $Ca^{2+}Mg^{2+}$—with a total charge shown by the superscript. To bring out the structural character of a silicate, we sometimes bracket the Si and Al atoms in 4-coordination.

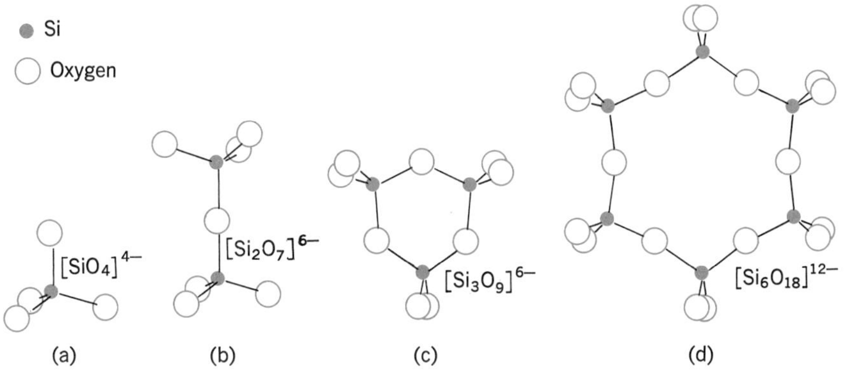

FIG. 2–69   The structure of silicates. (a) Orthosilicate. (b) Sorosilicate. (c) 3-tetrahedron ring silicate. (d) 6-tetrahedron ring silicate. (After L. Bragg, G. F. Claringbull, and W. H. Taylor, Crystal Structures of Minerals, Cornell University Press, 1965.)

● Si
○ Oxygen

$[SiO_4]^{4-}$ $[Si_2O_7]^{6-}$ $[Si_3O_9]^{6-}$ $[Si_6O_{18}]^{12-}$

(a)   (b)   (c)   (d)

Olivines: (Mg, Fe)$_2$SiO$_4$
Garnets: (Ca, Mg, Fe)$_3$(Al, Fe)$_2$(SiO$_4$)$_3$
Zircon: ZrSiO$_4$

2. *Sorosilicates* (Figure 2–69b), $X^{6+}[Si_2O_7]^{6-}$. The [SiO$_4$] groups are paired by linking through a common O atom. Silicates of this class are relatively unimportant. One example is the melilite solid-solution series between Ca$_2$Mg[Si$_2$O$_7$] and Ca$_2$Al[AlSiO$_7$].

3. *Ring Silicates (Cyclosilicates)* $X^{2n+}[SiO_3]^{2n-}$. A small number—3, 4, or 6—of tetrahedra are linked via common oxygen atoms to give a closed ring (Figure 2–69c, d).

One of the simplest such examples is beryl, BeAl$_2$(Si$_6$O$_{18}$), whose hexagonal ring structure is reflected in hexagonal crystal symmetry (6/m 2/m 2/m).

4. *Chain Silicates (Inosilicates)* (Figure 2–70a, b). Chain structures $X^{2+}[SiO_3]^{2-}$ and band structures $X^{6+}[Si_4O_{11}]^{6-}$. In the simpler type giant anions are formed by endless chains of [SiO$_4$] tetrahedra, each linked to its neighbor by a common oxygen atom. The more complex band structure results from linking of two such parallel chains through a common atom in every alternate tetrahedron. Examples are

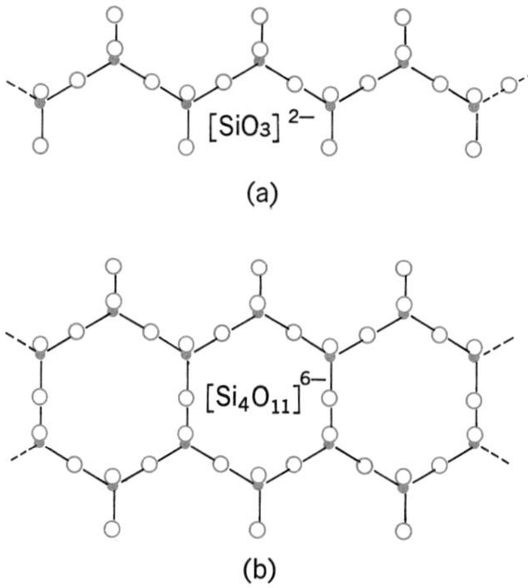

[SiO$_3$]$^{2-}$

(a)

[Si$_4$O$_{11}$]$^{6-}$

(b)

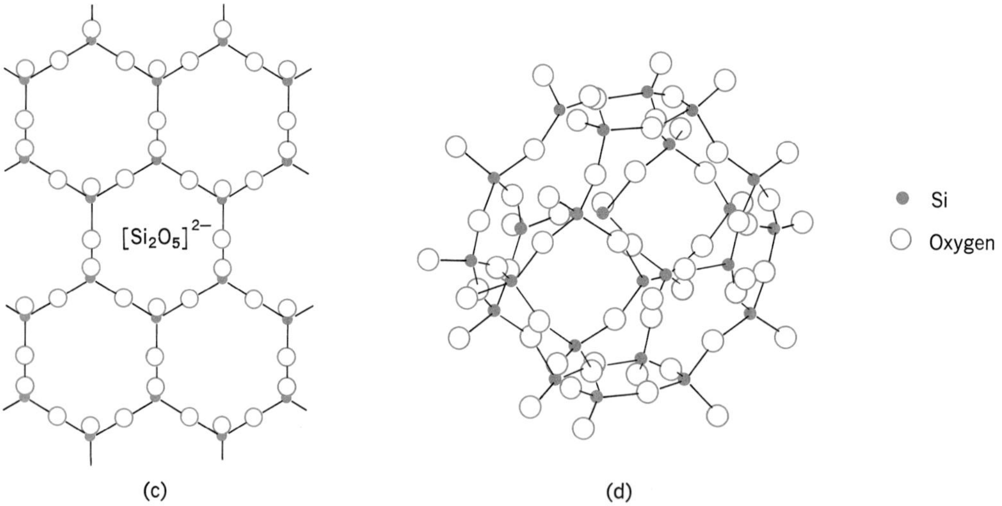

[Si$_2$O$_5$]$^{2-}$

(c)

(d)

● Si
○ Oxygen

FIG. 2–70 The structure of silicates. (a) Chain silicate. (b) Band silicate. (c) Sheet silicate. (d) Framework silicate. (After L. Bragg, G. F. Claringbull, and W. H. Taylor, Crystal Structure of Minerals, Cornell University Press, 1965.)

Pyroxenes: enstatite $MgSiO_3$,
   diopside $CaMg(Si_2O_6)$
Amphiboles: tremolite
   $Ca_2Mg_5(Si_8O_{22})(OH)_2$

5. *Sheet Silicates (Phyllosilicates)* (Figure 2–70c), $X^{6+}(Si_4O_{10})^{4-}(OH)_2^{2-}$, $X^{7+}(AlSi_3O_{10})^{5-}(OH)_2^{2-}$, $X^{12+}(Si_4O_{10})^{4-}(OH)_8^{8-}$. Every tetrahedron shares three oxygen atoms with three neighbors. The result is a continuous sheet of $[SiO_4]$ and $[AlO_4]$ groups, each of which retains a single unshared oxygen. Most phyllosilicates are hydrous. Here belong a large number of important rock-forming minerals, among them micas, chlorites, and aluminous clay silicates. Examples are

Kaolinite (a clay mineral): $Al_4(Si_4O_{10})(OH)_8$
Talc: $Mg_3(Si_4O_{10})(OH)_2$
Muscovite (white mica): $KAl_2(AlSi_3O_{10})(OH)_2$
Chlorite series: $(Mg, Fe)_6(Si_4O_{10})(OH)_8$ to
   $(Mg, Fe)_5Al(AlSi_3O_{10})(OH)_8$

6. *Framework Silicates (Tectosilicates)* (Figure 2–70d), $X^{1+}[AlSi_3O_8]^{1-}$; $X^{2+}[Al_2Si_2O_8]^{2-}$. Extreme linkage of $[SiO_4]$ tetrahedra, so that each shares all four oxygen atoms with four neighbors gives SiO_2 as represented by quartz and other polymorphs (page 74). There are also many aluminosilicates in which Al^{3+} substitutes for a fixed proportion of Si^{4+} ions, leaving a corresponding number of free negative charges on the coordinated oxygen atoms. These are balanced by accommodating an appropriate number of cations, mostly Na^+, K^+, and Ca^{2+}, in the aluminosilicate structures. Examples are

Feldspars: $K(AlSi_3O_8)$, $Na(AlSi_3O_8)$,
   $Ca(Al_2Si_2O_8)$
Nepheline: $Na(AlSiO_4)$
Leucite: $K(AlSi_2O_6)$
Analcime: $Na(AlSi_2O_6) \cdot H_2O$

Cation substitution is general in mineral silicates. Common patterns are

$(Mg, Fe, Mn, Ni)^{2+}$
(Ca^{2+}, Na^+) with compensatory (Al^{3+}, Si^{4+})
$(Al, Fe, Cr)^{3+}$

There are many hydrous silicates containing the $(OH)^-$ anion. Fluorine, when present (for example, in micas and amphiboles), takes the form of F^- substituting for $(OH)^-$. Some silicates have additional oxygen—for example, andalusite, kyanite, and sillimanite, the three polymorphs of $Al_2O(SiO_4)$. In spite of their great chemical and structural variety, silicates consistently conform to some general rules relating to charge and bonding: Charge balance tends to be maintained between near-neighbor ions. Electron pairs in covalent bonds are contributed from near neighbors; movement of electrons is restricted to short distances.

FRAMEWORK SILICATES   *Feldspars*   Feldspars, the most abundant and widely distributed minerals of the accessible crust, are aluminosilicates of potassium, sodium, and calcium. The three principal end members are $KAlSi_3O_8$, $NaAlSi_3O_8$, and $CaAl_2Si_2O_8$. As might be expected from the marked difference with respect to charge and size between Ca^{2+} and K^+ ions, solid solution between $KAlSi_3O_8$ and $CaAl_2Si_2O_8$ is negligible. At temperatures close to the melting range, there is complete solid solution, on the other hand, in two series: the plagioclase feldspars $CaAl_2Si_3O_8$–$NaAlSi_3O_8$, and the alkali feldspars $KAlSi_3O_8$–$NaAlSi_3O_8$. At lower temperatures solid solution is more restricted and unmixing tends to occur on a microscopic or smaller scale.

At room temperature the distribution of Al and Si atoms among available sites in feldspar structures is highly ordered, even though the individual homogeneous ordered domains may be of microscopic or submicroscopic extent. At temperatures of a few hundred degrees disorder becomes significant, and reaches a random state at temperatures close to the melting range. Ordered and disordered feldspars are sometimes designated "low" and "high" respectively—the reference being to temperature.

Plagioclase series (albite $NaAlSi_3O_8$–anorthite $CaAl_2Si_2O_8$). As it crystallizes from the melt, plagioclase forms a continuous solid-solution series between the two end members. Standard terminology arbitrarily defines compositional ranges based on molecular percentages of anorthite (An) and albite (Ab); as follows:

Albite	An_0–An_{10}
Oligoclase	An_{10}–An_{30}
Andesine	An_{30}–An_{50}
Labradorite	An_{50}–An_{70}
Bytownite	An_{70}–An_{90}
Anorthite	An_{90}–An_{100}

As in other feldspars the $[SiO_4]$ and $[AlO_4]$ tetrahedra build a loosely knit three-dimensional framework with large cavities that house the Ca^{2+} and Na^+ ions in 6-coordination. Al and Si atoms in high-temperature plagioclase are distributed at random among available sites. The symmetry is triclinic, class $\bar{1}$. The structure of low-temperature plagioclase is complicated in two respects. In the first place the structure becomes ordered. In low albite four kinds of (Al, Si) sites can be distinguished by X-ray diffraction, and their respective populations by Al atoms are 0.8, 0.0, 0.2, 0.1. Moreover, several structural modifications, all with triclinic symmetry, develop for limited ranges of composition. On a submicroscopic scale, distinguishable only by X rays, the initially homogeneous plagioclase unmixes into two phases. For example, oligoclase An_{20} unmixes to nearly pure albite An_0 and oligoclase, An_{22}–An_{30}. Between An_{30} and An_{100} there are several limited solid-solution series. A minor element that readily substitutes for Ca^{2+} (radius 0.99 Å) in plagioclase is Sr^{2+} (radius 1.13 Å); the Ba^{2+} ion (radius 1.35 Å) is too large to be similarly accommodated.

Alkali-feldspar series ($KAlSi_3O_8$–$NaAlSi_3O_8$). The high-temperature disordered form of potassium feldspar, *sanidine*, has monoclinic symmetry. The K^+ ions are in 9-coordination with oxygen, the bond length K—O being variable, 2.698–3.129 Å, as compared with 2.73 Å derived from values given in Table 2–16. The most completely ordered low-temperature form, *microcline*, is triclinic. K^+ remains in 9-coordination, but the Al populations of the four available (Si, Al) sites are 0.56, 0.25, 0.07, and 0.08. *Orthoclase* is a term widely used for monoclinic $KAlSi_3O_8$ with partial ordering of (Si, Al) distribution. At temperatures of crystallization from melts alkali feldspars form a continuous solid-solution series $(K, Na)AlSi_3O_8$. The common potassic feldspars of this series have monoclinic symmetry. As

sodium increases, at a composition corresponding to 63 percent albite, the structure suddenly changes and the symmetry becomes triclinic. These triclinic sodic alkali feldspars are called *anorthoclase*. Solid solution at lower temperatures becomes limited. An alkali feldspar with more or less equal amounts of sodium and potassium would crystallize from the melt as homogeneous monoclinic sanidine. Cooling slowly under deep-seated conditions, as in the plutonic rock granite, these crystals usually unmix on a microscopically visible scale. The products of unmixing at the same time tend to assume a more ordered state with respect to (Si, Al) distribution. So the ultimate product, *perthite*, is a mixture of two phases: triclinic "low" albite with minor K^+ substituting for Na^+ and triclinic microcline (or partially ordered monoclinic orthoclase) with significant Na^+ substituting for K^+. Minor elements with large ionic radius (Ba^{2+}, 1.35 Å; Rb^+, 1.48 Å), if present, become accommodated in alkali feldspars by substituting for K^+(1.33 Å). In some potassic feldspars ferric iron (Fe^{3+}, 0.64 Å) replaces 10 percent or more of the aluminum ions (Al^{3+}, 0.5 Å).

Feldspathoids Potassium and sodium of crustal rocks is mostly held in feldspars and micas. Some igneous rocks unusually rich in alkalis with respect to silica contain other aluminosilicates in which $(K + Na)/Si$ exceeds the ⅓ ratio characteristic of alkali feldspars. These are somewhat loosely termed *feldspathoids;* they include several structurally distinct mineral series. The $[SiO_4]$ and $[AlO_4]$ tetrahedra are even more loosely packed than in feldspars. This makes it possible for the interspersed structural cavities to accommodate the large number of Na^+ and K^+ ions required by feldspathoid compositions. There is one feldspathoid group, including sodalite $Na_4(Al_3Si_3O_{12})Cl$, in which the crystal structure is open enough to hold large anions, notably Cl^- and $[SO_4]^{2-}$, not normally found in silicate minerals.

Nepheline, Na_3K $(Al_4Si_4O_{16})$, is the commonest feldspathoid. The structure resembles that of tridymite (Figure 2–71a), in which $[SiO_4]$ tetrahedra build continuous sheets of hexagonal rings normal to the z-axis, with apexes alternately di-

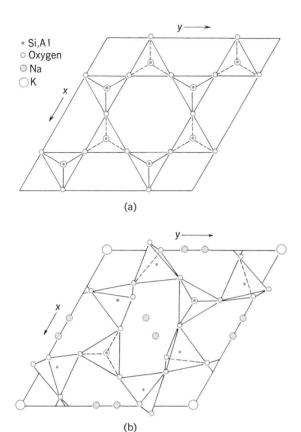

Si,Al
Oxygen
Na
K

y ⟶

x

(a)

y ⟶

x

(b)

FIG. 2–71 (a) Structure of tridymite projected on the (0001)-plane. (b) Structure of nepheline projected on the (0001)-plane. (After W. A. Deer, R. A. Howie, and J. Zussman, Rock-Forming Minerals; vol. 4, Framework Silicates, Wiley, 1963.)

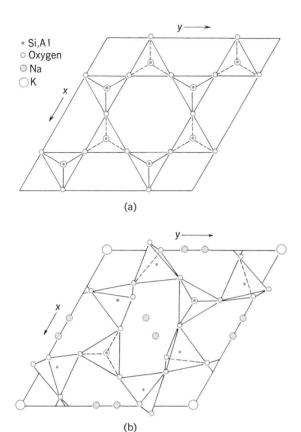

K^+ between their characteristic sites is possible, so that analyses show some variation in Na/K. At higher temperatures mutual substitution of K^+ and Na^+ is more extensive. Ultimately the structure becomes reorganized, and above 900°C new polymorphs become stable before melting sets in.

Leucite, $K(AlSi_2O_6)$, is the feldspathoid of highly potassic volcanic rocks. Above 600°C it is isometric (class $4/m \bar{3} 2/m$); at lower temperatures the structure is slightly different and the structure is tetragonal. The $[SiO_4]$ and $[AlO_4]$ tetrahedra are loosely packed so that the molar volume (88.4 cm³) is high compared with equivalent volumes of nepheline (82.5 cm³), tridymite (79.6 cm³), or albite (75.15 cm³). In a section normal to a tetrad symmetry axis of the isometric structure—parallel to {100}—the tetrahedra form rings of four enclosing a central unoccupied cavity (Figure 2–72a). Sections normal to any triad axis—that is, parallel to {111}—show hexagonal rings of tetrahedra, each enclosing a larger cavity occupied by a K^+ ion in 12-coordination (Figure 2–72b).

Zeolites Zeolites include a large number of aluminosilicate minerals that have several distinctive characteristics in common: The principal cations are Ca^{2+} and Na^+, but barium zeolites are known, and some contain significant potassium. The structure is unusually open, and the density correspondingly low (molar volume high). The $[SiO_4]$–$[AlO_4]$ network is crossed by continuous channels connecting large cavities such as those we have already seen in the leucite structure. Water penetrates freely along these channels and becomes loosely held in the larger cavities. It can be continuously expelled from some zeolites, and later reabsorbed, at least to some degree, without destroying the essential structure. Bonding energy of water in zeolites obviously is low; removal of liquid water from analcime $Na(AlSi_2O_6)$ · H_2O at room temperature and pressure is accompanied by an entropy increase of only 2.6 cal/mol°. The corresponding value for dehydration of brucite $Mg(OH)_2$—which involves severing hydroxyl bonds—is three times greater (8.1 cal/mol°). Cations transported in aqueous solu-

rected in opposite senses along z. In nepheline this structure is somewhat distorted (Figure 2–71b); Al and Si are ordered in that the apexes of the $[AlO_4]$ tetrahedrons point in one sense, those of $[SiO_4]$ in the opposite sense along z. This configuration is reflected in reduced symmetry of nepheline (hexagonal, class 6) as contrasted with tridymite (hexagonal, class $6/m\ 2/m\ 2/m$), and also in its slightly higher molar volume. In the nepheline structure there are two kinds of cation sites: two are relatively large and are occupied by K^+ ions in 9-coordination, the K—O bond being 2.9 Å; six smaller sites accommodate Na^+ ions in 8-coordination, the Na—O bond being 2.65 Å. Limited interchange of Na^+ and

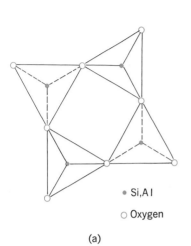

• Si,Al

○ Oxygen

(a)

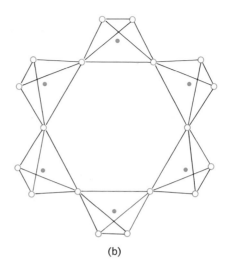

(b)

FIG. 2–72 *Leucite structure, simplified. (a) section parallel to [100]. (b) section parallel to [111]. (After W. A. Deer, R. A. Howie, and J. Zussman, 1963.)*

tions along structural channels can readily exchange with Na^+ ions of the zeolite structure encountered en route. Thus analcime $Na(AlSi_2O_6) \cdot H_2O$ can be converted by silver nitrate solution to an artificial silver analcime $Ag(AlSi_2O_6) \cdot H_2O$. Sodium zeolites have been used similarly as water softeners to remove Ca^{2+} ions from hard water.

In zeolites, solid solution is widespread. The cation sites are large and can accommodate ions that differ significantly in size. Some of them, normally unoccupied, can hold an additional Na^+ ion when this is needed to neutralize the total charge. Patterns of isomorphous substitution are

$$Ca^{2+}Al^{3+} \rightleftharpoons Na^+Si^{4+}$$
$$2Na^+ \rightleftharpoons Ca^{2+}$$
$$K^+ \rightleftharpoons Na^+$$
$$K^+Si^{4+} \rightleftharpoons Ba^{2+}Al^{3+}$$

Some of the commoner zeolites that may be significant constitutents of volcanic rocks and of rocks that have been metamorphosed at low temperature and high pressure are:

Analcime $Na(AlSi_2O_6) \cdot H_2O$
Laumontite $Ca(Al_2Si_4O_{12}) \cdot 4H_2O$
Heulandite $(Ca, Na_2)(Al_2Si_7O_{18}) \cdot 6H_2O$
Natrolite $Na_2(Al_2Si_3O_{10}) \cdot 2H_2O$

Analcime is structurally similar to leucite and has the same symmetry (isometric, $4/m \ 3 \ 2/m$). But the structure is more open and the molar volume

($97.5 \ cm^3$) is correspondingly larger than in leucite ($88.39 \ cm^3$). The set of large structural cavities that accommodate K^+ ions in leucite hold water molecules in analcime. Of the smaller cavities, all unoccupied in leucite, two thirds contain Na^+ ions in analcime, and the rest are vacant. In the structurally similar calcium zeolite wairakite $Ca_{1/2}(AlSi_2O_6) \cdot H_2O$, only one third of these sites are occupied by Ca^+ ions.

SHEET SILICATES In common phyllosilicates there is a giant anion in the form of an infinite layer of $[SiO_4]$ and $[AlO_4]$ tetrahedra with an internal hexagonal ring structure (Figure 2–70c). The unshared oxygen atom of every tetrahedron points in the same direction. More or less at the same level with these, in the middle of each hexagonal ring is an $(OH)^-$ ion. Electric charge is largely or completely neutralized by cations—Al^{3+}, Mg^{2+}, Fe^{2+}—in 6-coordination. They build octahedral layers interspersed between the tetrahedral $[(Si, Al)O_4]$ layers to which they are linked by oxygen atoms in common, the unshared oxygens of the $[(Si, Al)O_4]$ tetrahedra. So the structural unit is a compound sheet consisting of either two (tetrahedral plus octahedral) or three layers (tetrahedral–octahedral–tetrahedral). The hexagonal structure of the component layers is reflected in pseudohexagonal symmetry of crystal form, and in some minerals optical properties as well (some phyllosilicates are optically uniaxial; cf. page 102). But the true symmetry, as revealed especially by X-ray diffraction, typically is reduced because successive sheets, stacked parallel to the z-axis, are staggered or skewed. Differences in stacking patterns are reflected in corresponding symmetry variations and in widely prevalent polymorphism.

Micas   The commonest micas are muscovite (white mica) $KAl_2(AlSi_3O_{10})(OH)_2$ and biotite (brown or black mica) $K(Mg, Fe)_3(AlSi_3O_{10})(OH)_2$. Both are widely distributed in metamorphic rocks. Biotite is an essential constituent, muscovite less common, in plutonic rocks of the granite family.

Muscovite and similar micas in which only two of the three available octahedral cation sites per formula unit are occupied (by Al^{3+}) are termed dioctahedral. Biotite is trioctahedral in that all three sites are occupied (by Mg^{2+} and Fe^{2+}). The structural unit in micas is a three-layer sheet (Figure 2–73a) with a negative residual charge:

$$[Al_2(AlSi_3O_{10})(OH)_2] \text{ in muscovite}$$
$$[(Mg, Fe)_3(AlSi_3O_{10})(OH)_2] \text{ in biotite}$$

The charge is neutralized and the sheets held in coherent stacks by interspersed K^+ ions in 12-coordination. The linkage is weak and is expressed physically in perfect cleavage parallel to {001}.

Muscovite and biotite of igneous and high-temperature metamorphic rocks may approximate the simple ideal compositions expressed above. But isomorphous substitution of ions is common. For example in metamorphic muscovites the ratio Si/Al in the tetrahedral sheets may be greater than 3, and the charge is balanced by compensating substitution of $(Mg, Fe)^{2+}$ for Al^{3+} in the octahedral layers. Again lithium, concentrated in residual fractions of granitic melts, may enter significantly into the composition of muscovite crystals of pegmatites (page 126). The Li^+ ion (radius 0.60 Å) replaces Al^{3+} (radius 0.50 Å) in the octahedral layers, and this necessitates a higher-than-normal Si/Al ratio in the tetrahedral layers. There are even trioctahedral lithium micas, such as $K(Li_{1.5}Al_{1.5})$

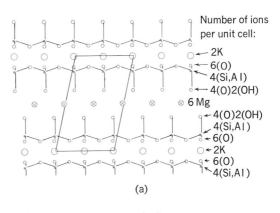

Number of ions per unit cell:

← 2K
← 6(O)
← 4(Si,Al)
← 4(O)2(OH)
⊗ 6 Mg
← 4(O)2(OH)
← 4(Si,Al)
← 6(O)
← 2K
← 6(O)
← 4(Si,Al)

(a)

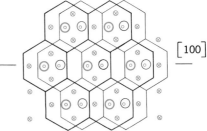

[100]

⊗ Octahedrally coordinated cations; mainly MgAl or Fe
○ Additional hydroxyl ions
⊙ X ions below bottom layer (K,Na,Ca)
⊙ X ions above upper layer (K,Na,Ca)
   Thick lines: bottom Si_2O_5 layer
   Thin lines: upper Si_2O_5 layer

(b)

FIG. 2–73 Structure of mica. (a) View along y-axis with simplest unit cell outlined. (b) Stacking of Si_2O_5 layers. (After W. A. Deer, R. A. Howie, and J. Zussman, Rock-Forming Minerals; vol. 3, Sheet Silicates, Wiley, 1962.)

$(AlSi_3O_{10})(OH, F)_2$, a member of the *lepidotite* group. Muscovites crystallizing at low temperatures in some metamorphic rocks may contain significant Na^+ substituting for K^+. They may even coexist with a sodium mica $NaAl_2(AlSi_3O_{10})(OH)_2$ containing minor K^+ in place of Na^+; for these two micas are capable of only limited mutual solid solution. Finally we must note that in many micas, especially the magnesian biotites and lepidotite, F^- substitutes extensively for $(OH)^-$. The pure magnesian trioctahedral mica phlogopite has a composition $KMg_3(AlSi_3O_{10})[(OH), F]_2$.

The symmetry of a single three-layer mica sheet is monoclinic (class $2/m$); for the upper and lower tetrahedral layers are mutually displaced in the [100] direction (Figure 2–73b). But there are several stacking possibilities. Two or more three-layer sheets that together comprise a unit cell may be mutually displaced by one O—O distance along one or more hexagonal edges in the {001} plane, which thus defines a stacking vector. Many polymorphs thus are possible; and each has its own symmetry. The three commonest are

1M: Unit cell of one sheet; symmetry monoclinic, $2/m$

2M: unit cell of two sheets; stacking vector parallel to one edge at 60° to [100]. Symmetry monoclinic, $2/m$

3T: unit cell of three sheets; stacking vector parallel to alternate hexagonal edges at 60° to [100]. Symmetry trigonal, 32.

Clay minerals   The most abundant constituents of sedimentary rocks are fine-grained phyllosilicates formed by weathering or hydrothermal alteration of feldspars and other aluminosilicates. These are the clay minerals. They include many structurally and chemically distinct mineral groups; and these are complicated by widely prevalent ionic substitution and by stacking polymorphism. Individual crystals are exceedingly small. So the nature and chemical and structural diversity of clay minerals has been revealed largely through X-ray diffraction, electron microscopy, differential thermal analysis, and use of the electron microprobe. Without minimizing the unique importance of clay mineralogy in geology, soil science, ceramic technology and engineering, we limit our treatment here to brief comments on a few simple representative minerals:

1. *Kaolinite,* $Al_4(Si_4O_{10})(OH)_8$. The unit is a two-layer sheet (Figure 2–74). The tetrahedral sites are occupied by Si^{4+}, and two thirds of the available octahedral sites by Al^{3+} ions. Of the six O^{2-} ions with which every Al^{3+} is coordinated two are shared with Si^{4+} and four form $(OH)^-$ groups. Each double-layered sheet is

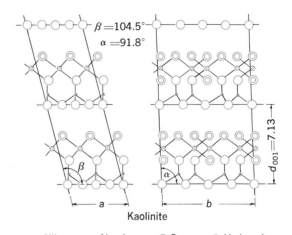

• Silicon   ◎ Aluminum   ◯ Oxygen   ◎ Hydroxyl

FIG. 2–74   *Structure of kaolinite viewed along the y and x axes showing stacking of layers. (From W. A. Deer, R. A. Howie, and J. Zussman, after Brindley: Rock-Forming Minerals; vol. 3, Sheet Silicates, Wiley, 1962.)*

electrically neutral. A continuous crystal structure is maintained by Van der Waals forces, possibly aided by hydrogen bonding. This accounts for the small crystal size and weak cohesion of kaolinite, its polymorphs, and other clay minerals of similar structure. Crystal symmetry is triclinic, 1.

2. *Montmorillonite.* A collective name covering a highly variable group of clay minerals, approximating

$$Al_2(Si_4O_{10})(OH)_2 \cdot nH_2O \quad \text{to}$$
$$(Na, \tfrac{1}{2}Ca)_{0.4}(Al_{1.6}Mg_{0.4})(Si_4O_{10})(OH)_2 \cdot nH_2O$$

The crystal unit is a three-layer sheet. Montmorillonites have the capacity to hold large quantities of adsorbed water and additional cations between the individual sheets, with accompanying very marked swelling of crystals parallel to the z axis.

3. Marine clay minerals with mica structure, but deficient in potassium:

(a) *Illite* $K_{0.5}Al_2(Al_{0.5}Si_{3.5}O_{10})(OH)_2$, the principal constituent of marine shales.

(b) *Glauconite* $K_{0.75}(Mg, Fe)_{0.5}(Al, Fe)_{1.5}$ $(Al_{0.25}Si_{3.75}O_{10})(OH)_2$, the chief constituent of distinctive marine sediments known as greensands.

Chlorites The chlorites are a complex mineral series with compositions ranging between $(Mg, Fe)_6(Si_4O_{10})(OH)_8$ and $(Mg, Fe)_4(Al_2Si_2O_{10})(OH)_8$. Ferric iron may substitute for part of the aluminum. Reduced to its simplest terms the structure of the nonaluminous member approximates a stack of alternating sheets of two kinds:

1. Three-layer sheets $Mg_3(Si_4O_{10})(OH)_2$. Their structure and composition are those of another phyllosilicate, talc. Octahedral sites are occupied by Mg^{2+}, tetrahedral sites by Si^{4+} ions.

2. Single-layer sheets $3Mg(OH)_2$, whose structure and composition are those of the hydroxide mineral brucite.

Linkage between the sheets, which individually are electrically neutral, is effected by weak Van der Waals forces and hydrogen bonds. This is reflected in the softness and perfect {001} cleavage of chlorites.

Talc has monoclinic symmetry, $2/m$; brucite is trigonal, class $\bar{3}\ 2/m$. Alternating layers in chlorite are stacked with a symmetry plane in common, so that chlorites like talc are monoclinic, class $2/m$. As with micas chlorites show polymorphism due to differences in stacking pattern. Chlorites are prominent constituents of low-temperature metamorphic rocks and of the clay fraction of sediments.

Serpentines There are several serpentine $Mg_6(Si_4O_{10})(OH)_8$ minerals, possibly polymorphous, but perhaps distinct mineral species each with its specific chemical character (for example, one may differ from another with respect to specific limits in Fe/Mg). Pure magnesian serpentine and nonaluminous chlorite are polymorphs with radically different structures. The unit in serpentine is a double sheet with all available octahedral sites occupied by Mg^{2+} ions. It thus resembles the kaolinite structure; in terms of the $Mg_3(Si_2O_5)(OH)_4$ formula, however, serpentine is trioctahedral but kaolinite is dioctahedral.

The platy crystal habit so typical of phyllosilicates is characteristic, too, of some serpentine minerals (*antigorite*). But others, notably *chryso-tile* (*asbestos*), crystallize as long fibers that at first sight seem incongruous. The electron microscope has resolved this anomaly. Chrysotile fibers prove to be tubes formed by axial curling of the structurally defined sheet. This is also true for certain other fibrous phyllosilicates—for example, clay minerals allied to kaolinite.

CHAIN SILICATES The commonest ferromagnesian silicates of igneous and metamorphic rocks have the chain structure that characterizes inosilicates. They fall into two groups, each comprising several structurally and chemically distinct isomorphous series. These are the *pyroxenes* and the *amphiboles*.

Pyroxenes These have a single-chain anion (Figure 2–70a) $[(SiO_3)^{2-}]_n$ consisting of linked $[SiO_4]$ tetrahedra, each with two unshared oxygen atoms. Limited substitution of Al^{3+} for Si^{4+} is characteristic of some pyroxenes. The $[SiO_3]_n$ chains are aligned parallel to the z crystal axis, in patterns that depend largely on ionic radii of the linking cations. In most pyroxenes these occupy two kinds of site: the smaller cations, Mg^+ and Fe^+, in 6-coordination with unshared oxygen atoms of the $[SiO_3]_n$ chains; the larger ions, Ca^{2+} and less commonly Na^+ in 8-coordination with O atoms, two of which are shared by adjacent $[SiO_4]$ tetrahedra. Order–disorder phenomena are thus possible and indeed are well-recognized among pyroxenes. Symmetry is monoclinic, class $2/m$, except in one group (*enstatite–hypersthene* series, where $(Mg, Fe)^+$ ions impartially occupy both cation sites, and symmetry is orthorhombic, class $2/m\ 2/m\ 2/m$).

Solid solution is the general rule; but there are natural pyroxenes that closely approximate these end members:

$CaMgSi_2O_6$	*diopside*
$CaFeSi_2O_6$	*hedenbergite*
$Mg_2Si_2O_6$	*enstatite*
$NaAlSi_2O_6$	*jadeite*
$NaFe^{3+}Si_2O_6$	*acmite*

The common solid-solution series are:

Diopside series: $Ca(Mg, Fe)Si_2O_6$

Augites: (Ca, Mg, Fe)(Mg, Fe^{2+}, Fe^{3+}, Al, Ti)[(Si, $Al)_2O_6$]. Substitution of (Mg, $Fe)^{2+}$ for Ca^+, and of Al^{3+} for Si^{4+} is significant, but limited; so that the general composition of augite is rather close to that of diopside–hedenbergite

Aegirine: $NaFeSi_2O_6$

Aegirine–augite: essentially an aegirine–diopside solid-solution series

Pigeonite series: (Mg, $Fe)_2Si_2O_6$ with limited substitution of Ca^{2+} for Mg^{2+}; monoclinic

Enstatite–hypersthene series: (Mg, $Fe)_2Si_2O_6$; orthorhombic. The pure end member $FeSiO_3$ is unstable, but many hyperthenes are rich in iron

Jadeite series: Na(Al, $Fe^{3+})Si_2O_6$

Omphacite series: (Ca, Na)(Mg, Fe^{2+}, Al, $Fe^{3+})(Si_2O_6)$

Amphiboles There are close chemical analogies between pyroxenes and amphiboles. The latter, however, are more complex and chemically diversified. The structure unit is the $[Si_4O_{11}^{6-}]_n$ anion, with $[(OH), F]^-$ playing an essential role reminiscent of that in micas. Symmetry is monoclinic, class $2/m$, except in nearly pure magnesian amphibole, *anthophyllite*, which like its pyroxene counterpart enstatite is orthorhombic ($2/m\ 2/m\ 2/m$).

Although free ionic substitution is the general rule, we again find naturally occurring minerals not far removed from ideal end members:

$Mg_7(Si_8O_{22})[(OH), F]_2$: *anthophyllite*
$Ca_2Mg_5(Si_8O_{22})[(OH), F]_2$: *tremolite*
$Na_2Mg_3Al_2(Si_8O_{22})(OH)_2$: *glaucophane*
$Na_2Fe_3^{2+}Fe_2^{3+}(Si_8O_{22})(OH)_2$: *riebeckite*

The commonest amphibole series are

Tremolite–actinolite:
   $Ca_2(Mg, Fe)_5(Si_8O_{22})[(OH), F]_2$
Hornblendes, highly complex aluminous amphiboles: (Ca, $Na)_{2-3}(Mg, Fe^{2+}, Fe^{3+}, Al)_5[Si_6(Si, Al)_2O_{22}][(OH), F]_2$
Glaucophane series: $Na_2(Mg, Fe)_3(Al, Fe)_2(Si_8O_{22})(OH)_2$
Anthophyllite series: (Mg, $Fe)_7(Si_8O_{22})[(OH), F]_2$

Cummingtonite series: (Fe, $Mg)_7(Si_8O_{22})[(OH), F]_2$

Amphibole structure can be illustrated by reference to the relatively simple species actinolite $Ca_2(Mg, Fe)_5(Si_8O_{22})(OH)_2$. Just as in the pyroxene structure the Ca^{2+} ions are in 8-, the Mg^{2+} ions in 6-coordination. Here, however there are four types of cation sites, and corresponding possibilities regarding disordering and variety in the geometry of chain patterns. The broad array of sites and flexibility of chain arrangement must play a significant part in the extreme chemical tolerance of these minerals—a tolerance probably exceeded by no other structure except that of silicate liquids where the site array is even greater.

RING SILICATES The $[SiO_4]$ tetrahedra are linked in closed rings, so that each tetrahedron has two unshared oxygens. The anion is thus $[(SiO_3)^2]_n$, where n is 3, 4, or 6. Examples are

Beryl: $Be_3Al_2(SiO_3)_6$ is hexagonal, class $6/m\ 2/m\ 2/m$ (Figure 2–69c)
Tourmaline: Na(Mg, Fe, Li, $Al)_3Al_6(Si_6O_{18})(BO_3)_3[(OH), F]_4$; trigonal, class $3m$
Cordierite: $Al_3(Mg, Fe)_2(Si_5AlO_{18})$; orthorhombic, class $2/m\ 2/m\ 2/m$

Beryl crystals frequently contain water and inert gases, which can be considered trapped inside the large cavity within the ring. The rings are stacked in a staggered configuration, thus partially blocking escape. Fluid trapped in this and other ways in a crystal may provide some clues about the chemistry of the solution from which the crystal grew.

ORTHOSILICATES Si-O-Si linkages are completely lacking in orthosilicates. The anion is thus an isolated $[SiO_4]^{4-}$ tetrahedron, and oxygen atoms are correspondingly closely packed. Orthosilicates, therefore, are dense minerals, and doubtless are important constituents of the mantle.

Olivine In olivine (Mg, $Fe)_2SiO_4$, oxygen atoms approximate hexagonal close packing in the {100} plane. Mg^{2+} and Fe^{2+} ions in 6-coordination occupy two kinds of site. Mg—O distances vary between 2.07 and 2.17Å, as compared with the ideal value 2.05 Å derived from Table 2–16.

Garnets   There are two solid-solution series in garnets, both with isometric symmetry, class $4/m\,\bar{3}\,2/m$:

$(Fe^{2+}, Mg, Mn)_3Al_2(SiO_4)_3$
$Ca_3(Al, Fe^{3+}, Cr)_2(SiO_4)_3$

Garnets approximating various end members are well known:

$Fe_3Al_2(SiO_4)_3$:   *almandine*
$Mn_3Al_2(SiO_4)_3$:   *spessartite*
$Ca_3Al_2(SiO_4)_3$:   *grossularite*

Magnesian garnets of the first series, sometimes called pyrope, may contain significant calcium.

Trivalent ions are in 6-coordination. The Ca^{2+}, Mg^{2+}, and Fe^{2+} ions are in unusually high coordination with oxygen (8), and this is reflected in high density of the whole garnet series. Water plays an unusual role in certain garnets, for it may enter the structure by exchange of $[(OH)_4]^{4-}$ for $[SiO_4]^{4-}$. There is thus a complete grossularite–hydrogrossular series from $Ca_3Al_2(SiO_4)_3$ to $Ca_3Al_2(OH)_{12}$. This raises the possibility that corresponding "hydropyropes" $Mg_3Al_2(OH)_{12}$ might exist as potential sources of water in the mantle. For that matter, why should there not be dense "hydroolivines" $Mg_2(OH)_4$ in the same high-pressure environment?

Zircon   In zircon, $ZrSiO_4$, symmetry tetragonal, class $4/m\,2/m\,2/m$, both Si^{4+} and Zr^{4+} ions are in 4-coordination. The ionic radius ratio Zr/O is 0.57, a value consistent with 6-coordination for zirconium; and indeed this is the configuration typical of zirconium in zirconosilicates. Herein may be a partial explanation of the tendency for structural disintegration of zircon to the structureless *metamict* state, in spite of its great chemical stability. A contributing factor is self-irradiation resulting from radioactive decay of thorium and uranium, which may substitute in minor amounts for zirconium. Since small amounts of zircon are widely distributed in granitic and metamorphic rocks and as a detrital mineral in sandstones, it has particular significance in radiometric dating by the U-Th-Pb method (Chapter 4).

Al_2SiO_5 polymorphs   Three polymorphs of Al_2SiO_5, all orthosilicates, are familiar constituents of aluminous metamorphic rocks:

Andalusite: symmetry orthorhombic, class $2/m\,2/m\,2/m$
Sillimanite: symmetry orthorhombic, class $2/m\,2/m\,2/m$
Kyanite: symmetry triclinic, class $\bar{1}$

Kyanite is notably denser than the other two and is the form that is stable at high pressures. Stability relations are discussed in Chapter 10.

NONSILICATES   *Carbonates*   Carbonates of calcium, magnesium, and iron are the main constituents of certain rocks formed near or on the earth's surface: limestones and their metamorphic equivalents (marbles), vein fillings that have been chemically affected by carbon dioxide solutions at high temperatures, and even rare igneous rocks (carbonatites) that have crystallized from carbonate-rich melts. Ionic radii of the principal cations in carbonate minerals are: Ca^{2+}, 0.99 Å; Mn^{2+}, 0.80 Å; Fe^{2+}, 0.76 Å; and Mg^{2+}, 0.65 Å. The difference in size between the commonest of these —Ca^{2+} and Mg^{2+}—accounts for limited ionic substitution following these patterns:

(Ca, Mn, Fe, Mg): Total substitution of other ions for Ca^+ seldom is as great as 20 percent; Mn^{2+} substitutes much more readily than Mg^{2+}.

(Mg, Fe, Mn): Almost complete mutual substitution of Mg^{2+} and Fe^{2+}; Mn^{2+} substitution more limited.

Most mineral carbonates, including rarer species, such as $SrCO_3$ (strontianite) and $PbCO_3$ (cerussite), conform to one or other of the two common polymorphs of $CaCO_3$—*calcite* and *aragonite*. In all the anion is a planar trigonal $[CO_3]^{2-}$ group.

The calcite structure (Figure 2–75) is a distorted version of that of halite. The large size and nonspherical symmetry of the $[CO_3]^{2-}$ anion, as contrasted with its Cl^- counterpart in halite,

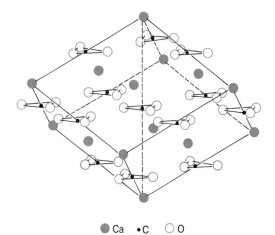

●Ca   •C   ○O

FIG. 2–75   *Structure of calcite (CaCO$_3$).*

reduce the symmetry to trigonal, class $\bar{3}\ 2/m$. Identical in structure and symmetry are other carbonates with cations of radius <1 Å, such as *siderite* FeCO$_3$ and *magnesite* MgCO$_3$. *Dolomite* Ca(Mg, Fe)(CO$_3$)$_2$ is isostructural. But it is a highly ordered double carbonate whose cation layers, parallel to {0001} are composed alternately of Ca^{2+} and Mg^{2+} ions. This reduces the symmetry to trigonal, class $\bar{3}$.

Aragonite has orthorhombic symmetry class $2/m\ 2/m\ 2/m$. But the cations approximate hexagonal close packing in the {001} plane, so microscopic twinning on {110} is common and yields pseudohexagonal units. Packing of oxygen ions is denser than in the calcite structure. This is reflected in the higher density of aragonite, which at room temperature becomes truly stable only at pressures greater than about 5 kb. Carbonates with large cations (for example, strontianite) are stable in the aragonite structure even at low temperatures.

In carbonates and structurally similar nitrates the planar anion is in motion, the freedom and amplitude of which increase with rising temperature. Oscillation, at first through limited angles in the [CO$_3$] plane—{0001} in calcite—increases in amplitude, changes to complete rotation, and ultimately gives way to a free tumbling motion with statistically spherical symmetry. Consequent changes in symmetry and structure with rising temperature are expressed in enhanced possibili-

ties of polymorphism. Indeed several other polymorphs of CaCO$_3$ have been formed by laboratory experiment at high temperatures and high pressures.

Oxides   Geologically important oxides, in addition to SiO$_2$, include

Fe$_3$O$_4$:   *magnetite*
FeTiO$_3$:   *ilmenite*
Fe$_2$O$_3$:   *hematite*
Al$_2$O$_3$:   *corundum*
TiO$_2$:   *rutile*

Others, structurally interesting, and valuable as ores are

Cu$_2$O: *cuprite*
FeCr$_2$O$_4$:   *chromite*

There are several mineral hydroxides with layer structures in which hydrogen bonds play a dominant part in the interlayer and stacking geometry:

Mg(OH)$_2$:   *brucite*
Al(OH)$_3$:   *gibbsite*
AlO(OH):   *diaspore*

These same structures we have already encountered at the unit-cell level in the fundamental makeup of clay silicates and chlorites.

The iron and iron–titanium oxides are the most abundant minerals with magnetic properties on which is based the whole important field of paleomagnetism (Chapter 13). They are significant too as controls ("buffers") for oxidation–reduction reactions connected with the broad processes of magmatic crystallization, metamorphism, and ore deposition.

Of particular interest is the spinel structure $X^{2+}Y_2^{3+}O_4$, in which X may be Mg, Fe, or Ti, and Y may be Fe, Al, or Cr. Symmetry is isometric, class $4/m\ \bar{3}\ 2/m$. The basic structure (Figure 2–76) is an array of oxygen atoms. These enclose potential cation sites of tetrahedral and octahedral configuration in the numerical ratio 1:2. In "normal" spinels divalent ions occupy tetrahedral sites, whereas trivalent ions occur in 6-coordinations. There is something of an anomaly here: The very reverse would be predicted from ionic radius ratios, such as Mg^{2+}/O^{2-}, 0.464, octahedral; Al^{3+}/O^{2-}, 0.357, tetrahedral.

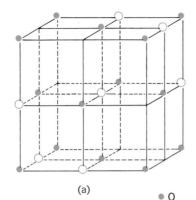

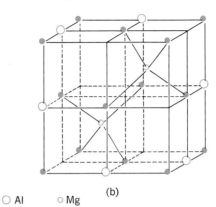

FIG. 2-76 Structure of spinel. (a) Octahedral sites occupied by Al. (b) Tetrahedral sites occupied by Mg.

(a)

(b)

● O   ○ Al   ○ Mg

There are also "inverse" spinel structures with divalent ions in octahedral sites, and trivalent ions distributed over both types. Crystal-field effects appear to exert a dominant influence. At high temperatures there is a tendency for random distribution of cations without regard to valence or to coordination sites. Solid solution is prevalent and comparatively unrestricted.

Also characteristic of the spinel structure is exceptional tolerance of site vacancies. *Maghemite*, a form of Fe_2O_3, has a "defect" spinel structure in which Fe^{3+} occupies both tetrahedral and some octahedral sites, leaving one sixth of the octahedral sites vacant.

The germanium analog of olivine, Mg_2GeO_4, possesses the olivine structure. But corresponding nickel and cobalt compounds, Ni_2GeO_4 and Co_2GeO_4, have the structure of spinel. This has led to the prediction that at high pressure olivine might invert to the spinel structure with a consequent increase in density of some 10 percent. It has now been demonstrated experimentally that fayalite Fe_2SiO_4 and fayalite–forsterite solid solutions invert to the spinel structure at sufficiently high pressures, and it has been suggested that this transition does indeed occur in the mantle (Chapter 11).

Sulfides   Many rocks—igneous, sedimentary, and metamorphic—contain minor amounts of sulfides, especially FeS_2 in the form of *pyrite* (isometric, $2/m\ \bar{3}$) or *marcasite* (orthorhombic, $2/m\ 2/m\ 2/m$). Sulfides also are the principal sources of many important metals. Some of these are

ZnS: *sphalerite*, isometric, $\bar{4}3m$
PbS: *galena*, isometric, $4/m\ \bar{3}\ 2/m$
CuFeS$_2$:   *chalcopyrite*, tetragonal, $\bar{4}2m$
MoS$_2$:   *molybdenite*, hexagonal,
      $6/m\ 2/m\ 2/m$
HgS: *cinnabar*, trigonal, 32
Sb$_2$S$_3$:   *stibnite*, orthorhombic,
      $2/m\ 2/m\ 2/m$

Electronegativity differences between these metallic elements and sulfur are less than 1; and bonding in the sulfide minerals approaches the covalent model, in some cases through development of hybrid orbitals involving *d* orbitals in sulfur. Sulfides also show a transition towards metallic behavior with a considerable contribution from delocalized electrons, whose freedom of movement in sulfides is to some degree reminiscent of that in metallic crystals. Sulfides and metals indeed have some physical properties, such as metallic luster (page 93), in common.

Symmetry of sulfide crystals, like that of metals, is generally high. Many sulfide structures are analogous to those of simple alkali halides or of diamond. Thus pyrite has a halite structure with the S_2^{2-} anion taking the place of Cl^-—hence the reduced symmetry of pyrite (Figure 2-77). Molybdenite (Figure 2-78) structurally resembles graphite and has the same symmetry; hexagonal sheets of molecular composition MoS$_2$ are weakly linked by Van der Waals forces. Consequently molybdenite, like graphite, is endowed with properties (easy cleavage, softness) that make it economically useful as a high-temperature lubricant.

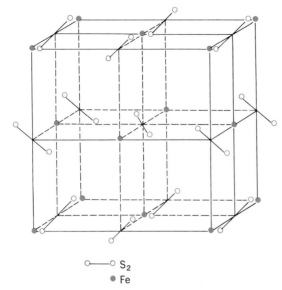

$\circ\!\!-\!\!\circ$ S₂
● Fe

FIG. 2-77 *Structure of pyrite.*

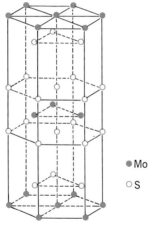

● Mo
○ S

FIG. 2-78 *Structure of molybdenite.*

Miscellaneous ionic compounds Only brief mention can be made of the many minerals—halides, sulfates, phosphates, and others—identical with regard to composition and structure with compounds familiar in the chemical laboratory. Among these are

NaCl: *halite*
KCl: *sylvite*
CaF₂: *fluorite*

CaSO₄: *anhydrite*
BaSO₄: *barite*
CaSO₄ · 2H₂O: *gypsum*
Ca₅(PO₄)₃[F, Cl, (OH)]:   *apatite*
Na₂B₄O₅(OH)₄ · 8H₂O: *borax*
NaNO₃: *soda-niter*

Some, such as apatite, are very common minor constituents of rocks of all kinds. Others—such as sylvite, borax, and soda-niter—are confined to rocks of special composition and origin, in this case *evaporites* (saline residues from evaporated water). Many have great economic importance; and others again such as apatite and monazite, (Ce, La, Y, Th)PO₄ are of special geological significance because they contain radioactive elements in high enough concentration to be useful for radiometric dating of events connected with their origin and subsequent history (Chapter 4).

Physical Properties of Minerals

Rocks are polycrystalline aggregates of minerals, and an understanding of their physical properties depends upon some knowledge of the physical properties of their component mineral crystals. Our aim in the present section is to introduce some principles governing the simpler physical properties of crystals important in the study of rocks.

A physical property can be determined by suitable measurements, and in general gives a relationship between two physical quantities. Thus, for example, to measure the thermal conductivity of a material a temperature gradient is established and the heat current density is measured in the same direction. It is convenient to look upon the temperature gradient as an "influence" acting upon the material and the rate of heat flow as an "effect" resulting from the interaction of the material and the influence. For some selections of influence a given effect is found to be unique and a relationship can be written

$$\text{effect} = P(\text{influence}) \qquad (2\text{-}11)$$

with a functional role played by the physical property P. Thermal conductivity in a solid is an example of such a unique relationship given by

$$\mathbf{q} = -K \operatorname{grad} T \qquad (2\text{-}12)$$

where $\mathbf{q}$ is the heat current density, grad T is the temperature gradient, and K, a scalar constant, is the thermal conductivity of the material.

Some physical properties of minerals, such as optical and elastic properties, are of this kind and are particularly suitable for description in relatively simple mathematical terms. Other physical properties, equally important from a geologic viewpoint, are of a different kind and do not uniquely relate physical quantities. For example, the plastic properties of a crystal cannot be defined as are the elastic properties in terms of a unique relationship between stress and strain (Chapter 9); they must be individually measured and depend upon the previous history of the crystal, the nature of imperfections present within it, and other factors.

From the preceding discussion of the geometric properties of crystals it is evident that for samples similar in size to its unit cell a crystal is not structurally homogeneous. Most physical properties, however, are examined for samples of crystal very large compared to a unit cell, and for many of these properties a crystal can be treated as a homogeneous and continuous body and the intrinsically discontinuous and heterogeneous nature of the crystal structure can be ignored. Properties defined in this way may be termed "continuum properties" and they include most optical, thermal, electrical, and some mechanical properties. Some physical properties, however, such as crystal plasticity and X-ray diffraction, become comprehensible only if the lattice structure present in all crystals is taken into account. For a complete understanding of *any* property a theory based upon the atomic structure of solids must ultimately be developed.

The first part of what follows is concerned with continuum properties of crystals and the discussion is at a "phenomenological" level, at which the existence of atoms spaced according to a lattice structure is ignored and the crystal is treated as a homogeneous continuum. The point group symmetry of a crystal cannot be ignored, however, so we must consider not the single

homogeneous continuum current in elementary physical and engineering theories of solids, but 32 homogeneous continua generated by attributing to each point in a continuum one of the 32 crystallographic point groups. In this fashion we are defining what might be termed the 32 space groups of "crystallographic continua" by combining each of the 32 crystallographic point groups with the group of arbitrary translations for which n_1, n_2, and n_3 in equation (2-1) can take on the values of all real numbers. In these groups periodic translations are replaced by arbitrary translations so that glide reflections and screw rotations disappear and only translations and point group operations remain.

On thermodynamic grounds the continuum properties can be classed as static or equilibrium properties and dynamic or steady-state properties. Equilibrium properties, such as elasticity and thermal expansion, are thermodynamically reversible and the effects disappear when the influence is removed. Dynamic (also called transport) properties apply to systems through which quantities such as heat, mass, or electric energy flow steadily under the influence of physical gradients. The example of thermal conductivity has already been given; electrical conductivity and diffusion are other examples. These properties are thermodynamically irreversible and are generally described in terms of suitably chosen "fluxes" and "forces" corresponding respectively to effects and influences.

Ideally, all possible influences that act upon a crystal are related by way of some physical property to all possible effects. For a given influence a particular effect is generally most pronounced or obvious; for example, strain is generally taken as the principal effect of stress. But other "coupled effects" are also generated defining additional physical properties. Thus a stressed crystal not only can show a strain determined by its elastic properties but also can develop electric charges determined by its piezoelectric properties, a change in temperature indicating piezocaloric properties as well as more complicated effects, such as changes in optical properties indicating photoelastic behavior. Some of these coupled effects are small or absent for certain

FIG. 2–79 *Quartz crystals; black and white divisions on the scale each 1 cm.*

crystals; others are extremely large and important.

Because of the coupling of the various influences and effects it is important that the way in which a given property is measured be specified. For example, the existence of the piezocaloric effect results in the production of heat in a stressed crystal. The measurement of strain to determine elastic properties can then be made under either isothermal or adiabatic conditions, the two results generally being different.

We begin the discussion of physical properties by referring to some simply defined physical properties used widely by geologists to aid in rapid identification of minerals.

SIMPLE PHYSICAL PROPERTIES OF MINERALS

Minerals have a few obvious physical properties that aid the geologist in rapid identification, particularly during fieldwork. A skilled observer with no more equipment than a hand lens and a pocket knife can identify many of the common rock-forming minerals even where they occur in rocks as small grains.

Examples of these simple but diagnostic properties are:

1. *Form and habit.* Some clue to the general structure of a mineral is sometimes given by its morphology. Well-formed crystals, in particular, can give information about the point group of a mineral by means of forms developed. Habit commonly suggests the structural type, especially in silicates. Even minerals that occur in a not obviously crystalline form commonly develop a characteristic mode of aggregation. For example, the mineral hematite Fe_2O_3 can occur in a "specular" form as brilliantly lustrous flakes or it can occur as a dark red chalky variety or as spheroidal reddish gray bodies of metallic hue and concentric structure. Some minerals such as quartz occur widely in large well-formed crystals growing into cavities in rocks (Figure 2–79). Other minerals are rarely seen with well-developed crystal faces, are structurally amorphous, or, like the large family of clay minerals, are aggregates of such minute crystals that only by studies with X rays or the electron microscope can their crystalline nature be established.

2. *Cleavage and fracture.* Their manner of brittle fracture can be characteristic of particular minerals or groups of minerals. In particular, many minerals break most easily on smooth, plane surfaces, termed cleavage surfaces. These surfaces are structurally controlled, being parallel to lattice planes, and are characterized by weak atomic cohesion. Their number and orientation are controlled by the same symmetry considerations that control the developments of possible forms in crystals, and any set of identical cleavage surfaces is always a possible form in a crystal and is specified by Miller indices of one cleavage enclosed in the form symbol. Thus calcite $CaCO_3$ of class $\bar{3}\ 2/m$ has cleavage $\{10\bar{1}1\}$ parallel to the faces of the unit rhombohedron (Figure 2–80). Because the point group of calcite includes the operation $\bar{1}$, the faces of the six-faced rhombohedron are in parallel pairs and the symbol $\{10\bar{1}1\}$ indicates only three orientations of cleavage surface. Because they are related by symmetry operations, these cleavage surfaces are identical in every respect. The three cleavages of albite $NaAlSi_3O_8$, on the other hand, are not related by symmetry operations and are denoted by three distinct form symbols: $\{001\}$, $\{010\}$ and $\{110\}$.

FIG. 2–80 *Cleavage rhomb of calcite; black and white divisions on the scale each 1 cm.*

FIG. 2–81 *Cleavage of mica (biotite); black and white divisions on the scale each 1 cm.*

In the crystal class $\bar{1}$, in which albite belongs, these three forms are pinacoids (pairs of parallel faces) and only one cleavage is denoted by each symbol. The differences between these cleavages is further illustrated by the differences in the ease with which albite can be cleaved on the three surfaces. Cleavage {001} is described as very good, since the crystal cleaves along it with ease; cleavage {010} is described as good; and cleavage {100} is described as poor, meaning that the crystal can be cleaved along it only with difficulty. Recognizable cleavages in minerals range from very poor or imperfect—in minerals such as analcime—to very good or perfect—in minerals of the mica family (Figure 2–81).

Even minerals with natural cleavage surfaces commonly break on other surfaces, and some minerals have no recognizable cleavages. The nature of fracture surfaces other than cleavages can also be diagnostic of particular minerals. Quartz, for example, has no clear cleavage surfaces and breaks instead on randomly oriented shell-like curved surfaces (conchoidal fracture) reminiscent of the fracture surfaces observed in glass (Figure 2–82). Other types of fracture generally given somewhat fanciful names are observed in most minerals.

3. *Color and luster.* Color can be a guide to the identity of a mineral, particularly its color in finely powdered form, termed the "streak" of the mineral. Many minerals show a wide variety of colors in hand specimens, and color alone is not usually a diagnostic property. Closely related to color is the property of luster, which describes the way light is reflected from the surfaces of the mineral. Luster cannot be quantitatively measured, and the terms used to describe it are based on somewhat subjective comparisons to the light-reflecting powers of familiar materials. Some of these terms are, however, useful; they include vitreous (glassy), waxy, resinous, adamantine (diamondlike), metallic, earthy, and many others in less common use.

FIG. 2–82 *Conchoidal fracture in quartz; black and white divisions on the scale each 1 cm.*

4. *Hardness*. Another useful but imprecisely defined property of a mineral is its "hardness." It is measured in an empirical way by the ability of a smooth flat surface on one crystal to be scratched by a sharp edge on another. An arbitrary nonlinear scale of hardness—Moh's scale—has been in use by mineralogists for many years.

More accurate and reproducible determinations of hardness according to different scales can be made by means of hardness testers, which generally measure the load required to indent the mineral with a hard (generally diamond) point. Hardness in some minerals is found to depend on direction.

5. *Density*. The densities of minerals vary widely. The common rock-forming silicates range in density only from 2.65 for quartz to about 4.37 for olivine. These densities vary with temperature and pressure.

Though a "simple property," density, unlike the other properties just discussed, expresses a unique relationship between volume and mass and is one of the more precisely defined "continuum properties" now to be examined.

ANISOTROPY IN CRYSTALS

For a homogeneous body, equation (2-12) is a statement of Fourier's law of heat flow. The quantity K, the thermal conductivity, is a scalar relating two vectors $\mathbf{q}$ and grade T, which must therefore be in the same direction. In such a homogeneous body, in other words, heat flows in the direction of the negative temperature gradient.

Equation (2-12) can be written in component form with respect to a right-handed system of orthogonal Cartesian coordinate axes as

$$q_x = -K\frac{\partial T}{\partial x}$$

$$q_y = -K\frac{\partial T}{\partial y} \qquad (2\text{-}13)$$

$$q_z = -K\frac{\partial T}{\partial z}$$

In equations (2-12) and (2-13) it is assumed that the homogeneous material conducts heat

in the same fashion in all directions given by the value of the constant K; that is, the material is *isotropic* with respect to heat conduction. We have seen from earlier discussions, however, that crystals are not *structurally* isotropic but have directions in them unrelated by symmetry operations,[10] along which the arrangements of atoms can be very different. There is no reason to assume, a priori, that thermal conductivity in a homogeneous crystal is the same in all directions. The simplest departure from isotropy in thermal conductivity, and one which to a first approximation is found in crystals, is that the two vectors $\mathbf{q}$ and grad T are not necessarily in the same direction and related to each other by a fixed constant, but that each component of $\mathbf{q}$ is a linear function of all of the components of grad T and that the coefficient of thermal conductivity relating each pair of components is unique. For this picture, equation (2-13) becomes

$$q_x = -K_{11}\frac{\partial T}{\partial x} - K_{12}\frac{\partial T}{\partial y} - K_{13}\frac{\partial T}{\partial z}$$

$$q_y = -K_{21}\frac{\partial T}{\partial x} - K_{22}\frac{\partial T}{\partial y} - K_{23}\frac{\partial T}{\partial z} \qquad (2\text{-}14)$$

$$q_z = -K_{31}\frac{\partial T}{\partial x} - K_{32}\frac{\partial T}{\partial y} - K_{33}\frac{\partial T}{\partial z}$$

Equation (2–14) is a restatement of Fourier's law of heat flow for a material in which the magnitude of the conductivity coefficient is dependent on direction—that is, for a material *anisotropic* with respect to thermal conductivity. The nine coefficients can be conveniently written as a square matrix

$$\begin{pmatrix} K_{11} & K_{12} & K_{13} \\ K_{21} & K_{22} & K_{23} \\ K_{31} & K_{32} & K_{33} \end{pmatrix} = \mathbf{K} \text{ or } K_{ij}$$

called the thermal conductivity matrix. It can be shown that this matrix is always symmetric (that is, $K_{ij} = K_{ji}$), so for the most general situation only six of the components are independent. For

---

[10] A structurally isotropic material is defined as one in which *all* directions are related by symmetry operations. Such a material would have the point group symmetry of a sphere which, as we saw above, is forbidden in crystals.

a crystal with many directions related by symmetry operations the number of independent components can decrease still further; for a spherically symmetric material, such as a glass or a rock consisting of randomly oriented crystals, in which all directions are related by symmetry operations, the components become equal and equation (2-14) reduces to (2-13) for an isotropic material.

Crystals cannot be spherically symmetric and are thus "potentially anisotropic" with respect to properties that relate a directionally dependent influence to a directionally dependent effect, and the nature of the anisotropy depends upon the complexity of the related quantities. Density, for example, is denoted by a scalar and is nondirectional; it expresses a unique relationship between two other nondirectional quantities, mass and volume. Thermal conductivity, on the other hand, relates two vectors (each with three components) and according to equation (2-14) must be a quantity with nine components, of which only six are distinct. The property of elasticity relates stresses to infinitesimal strains. All three of these quantities have nine or more components and belong to the family of mathematical quantities called *tensors* that includes scalars and vectors as its simplest members. Tensors have the same value in any coordinate system but the magnitudes of their components depend upon the choice of coordinate system.

The complexity of a tensor depends upon the number of its components, which determines its *rank* or *order*. Tensors of rank zero have one component and are scalars; tensors of rank one have three components and are vectors. A tensor such as the thermal conductivity tensor is of second rank and has nine components. In three dimensions, therefore, the number of components is given by 3^n where n is the rank of the tensor. (Most tensors have symmetry of some kind and the number of *independent* components is generally reduced by equivalence between some of them.)

In an equation relating tensor quantities there are strict relationships between the ranks of the tensors. For example, density relates volume and mass according to

$$m = \rho v$$

where all three quantites are tensors of zero rank (scalars). The thermal conductivity equation for an anisotropic body is given in matrix form by

$$\begin{pmatrix} q_x \\ q_y \\ q_z \end{pmatrix} = \begin{pmatrix} K_{11} & K_{12} & K_{13} \\ K_{21} & K_{22} & K_{23} \\ K_{31} & K_{32} & K_{33} \end{pmatrix} \begin{pmatrix} \dfrac{\partial T}{\partial x} \\ \dfrac{\partial T}{\partial y} \\ \dfrac{\partial T}{\partial z} \end{pmatrix}$$

in which two first-rank tensors (vectors) are related by a second-rank tensor. In the general equation for the elasticity of an anisotropic body two second-rank tensors (stress and infinitesimal strain) are related by a fourth-rank tensor, the elasticity tensor, which has $3^4 = 81$ components.

Thus tensors of rank two or more have algebras resembling those of scalars and vectors. For example, the sum of two second-rank tensors (found by adding corresponding components) is another second-rank tensor. It can be shown, moreover, that if an influence represented by a tensor of rank m is linearly related to an effect represented by a tensor of rank n, then the relationship is represented by a physical property tensor of rank $m + n$. The tensor nature of a quantity is identified by the way in which its components change under transformation to a new coordinate system.[11] Upon this basis also

---

[11] Each rank of tensor has a different transformation law. A scalar s for example has the same value in any coordinate system and its transformation law can be written

$$s' = s$$

A vector $\mathbf{v}$ transforms according to

$$\mathbf{v}' = \mathbf{A}\mathbf{v}$$

where $\mathbf{A}$ is a transformation (rotation) matrix such as the matrix $\mathbf{R}$ introduced on page 26. It can be shown that a second-rank tensor $\mathbf{t}$ obeys the transformation law

$$\mathbf{t}' = \mathbf{A}\mathbf{t}\mathbf{A}^{-1}$$

where A^{-1} is the inverse of the transformation matrix (because rotation matrices are orthogonal, the transpose, A^T, of A can be used instead of A^{-1}). The transformation laws for tensors of higher rank are correspondingly more complex.

tensors can be classified as polar if the components do not change their sign for any transformation or as axial if the components change their sign for an improper rotation (see page 26).[12]

Any coordinate transformation that leaves the components of a tensor invariant is by definition a symmetry operation for that tensor. If the generators of a group leave the components of a tensor invariant then the tensor has at least the symmetry of that group. The symmetry groups of tensors are point groups because the origin remains invariant during a coordinate transformation. They can be of a type—the limiting point groups—not specifically examined in the previous discussion of point groups because they are not possible symmetry groups of crystals. Most of the crystallographic point groups have a principal rotation axis of order n (restricted to $n = 1$, 2, 3, 4, or 6) with or without dihedral rotation axes perpendicular to it. If the crystallographic restriction on the order of the principal axis is removed, an infinite number of point groups arise as n increases by integral steps and most of the limiting point groups are those for which $n = \infty$. Two other point groups arise with ∞-fold axes (the spherical or isotropic point groups) as limiting groups to the endospheric (isometric and icosahedral) point groups, giving a total of seven limiting point groups. In Table 2–20 the full international and Schoenflies symbols for these

---

[12] For example, the angular momentum of a point is a vector **J** defined as

$$\mathbf{J} = \mathbf{r} \times \mathbf{p}$$

where **r** is the position vector of the point referred to the origin and **p** is another vector, the linear momentum. **J** is therefore a vector product and has a sign given by the "right-hand rule." An improper rotation that changes the hand of the coordinate axes clearly reverses the sign of this product so that its transformation law becomes

$$\mathbf{J} = \pm\mathbf{AJ}$$

where the plus sign holds for a proper and the minus sign for an improper rotation represented by the matrix **A**. A vector that transforms in this way is called an "axial vector" or "pseudovector" in contradistinction to a vector transforming according to the law in the last footnote which is a "polar" or "true" vector. Similar relationships hold for tensors of other ranks.

groups are given, together with the crystallographic point groups for which they are limiting groups as $n = \infty$ and the form of figures that represent them. Some of these groups are important also as symmetry groups of rock fabrics.

The simpler influences that act on crystals, such as magnetic field strength and electric field strength are vectors (axial or polar) and have symmetry ∞/m or ∞mm. Other influences and effects such as stress and strain and many of the simpler property tensors are polar second-rank tensors and have symmetry groups $\bar{1}$, $2/m$, ∞/m, $2/m\ 2/m\ 2/m$, $\infty/m\ 2/m\ 2/m$, or $\infty/m\ \infty/m$ ∞/m.

Polar second-rank tensors are commonly symmetric across their leading diagonals and, if so, they can be referred to principal axes by a suitable coordinate transformation to give

$$\begin{pmatrix} t_1 & 0 & 0 \\ 0 & t_2 & 0 \\ 0 & 0 & t_3 \end{pmatrix}$$

where t_1, t_2, and t_3 are *principal components*. Symmetric tensors of this kind can have only the three symmetry groups $2/m\ 2/m\ 2/m$, ∞/m $2/m\ 2/m$, and $\infty/m\ \infty/m\ \infty/m$ according to possible equivalences between the principal components.

Where a symmetric second-rank tensor is referred to its principal axes, it is easy to obtain a geometric image of it by constructing the quadric surface

$$\frac{x^2}{t_1{}^2} + \frac{y^2}{t_2{}^2} + \frac{z^2}{t_3{}^2} = 1$$

This surface is a real ellipsoid (termed the "magnitude ellipsoid") whose principal radii are equal to the principal components of the tensor. For tensors of symmetry $2/m\ 2/m\ 2/m$ the magnitude ellipsoid is triaxial, for tensors with symmetry $\infty/m\ 2/m\ 2/m$ it is a spheroid, and for isotropic tensors with symmetry $\infty/m\ \infty/m\ \infty/m$ it is a sphere.

Another graphic representation of a tensor of this kind, used particularly for the stress and infinitesimal strain tensors is the Mohr diagram (see Chapter 9) which is a two-dimensional quantitative representation of great usefulness.

TABLE 2–20 *Limiting point groups*

Limiting Point Groups		Crystallographic Groups for Which These Groups Are Limiting Groups	Representation Figure
Full International Symbol	Schoenflies Symbol		
∞	C_∞	n	left- or right-handed right circular cone
$\dfrac{\infty}{m}$	$C_{\infty h}$	$\bar{n},\ \dfrac{n}{m}$	rotating right circular cylinder
∞mm	$C_{\infty v}$	nmm	right circular cone
$\infty 22$	D_∞	$n22$	left- or right-handed right circular cylinder
$\dfrac{\infty}{m}\dfrac{2}{m}\dfrac{2}{m}$	$D_{\infty h}$	$\bar{n}\dfrac{2}{m},\ \bar{n}2m,\ \dfrac{n}{m}\dfrac{2}{m}\dfrac{2}{m}$	right circular cylinder
$\infty\ \infty\ \infty$	K_∞	$23,\ 432$	left- or right-handed sphere
$\dfrac{\infty}{m}\dfrac{\infty}{m}\dfrac{\infty}{m}$	$K_{\infty h}$	$\dfrac{2}{m}\bar{3},\ \bar{4}\,3m,\ \dfrac{4}{m}\bar{3}\dfrac{2}{m}$	sphere

NEUMANN'S PRINCIPLE

Many physical properties can be represented to a first approximation by tensors uniquely and linearly relating two other tensors representing the influence and effect. These physical properties possess an intrinsic symmetry that must be present also in the tensors that represent them. In particular, the symmetry of a property tensor is dependent upon the point group symmetry of the material to which it belongs in a fashion governed by *Neumann's principle* which can be stated simply in the following form:

The point group of a property tensor must include all the symmetry operations of the point group of the material in the same orientation.

An alternative way of stating this principle is to say that the point group of a crystal is a subgroup of the point groups of all its physical prop-

erties. Note that the principle places restrictions only on the *lower* limit of the order of a point group of a property tensor.

In practice, Neumann's principle means that, provided the orientation of rotation axes is correctly chosen with respect to the coordinate system to which a property tensor is referred, the components of a property tensor are invariant for all coordinate transformations corresponding to symmetry operations of the crystal. The principle can be used, therefore, to establish the form of a property tensor for a crystal of a given point group. To illustrate the procedure, consider the form of a polar second-rank symmetric property tensor (such as thermal conductivity K_{ij}) for crystals of different symmetry. The possible symmetry groups of such a tensor are $2/m\ 2/m\ 2/m$, $2/m\ \infty/m\ \infty/m$, and $\infty/m\ \infty/m$ ∞/m. By inspection, the symmetry of the tensor in isometric, hexagonal, trigonal, and tetragonal crystals cannot be $2/m\ 2/m\ 2/m$ because the point groups of these crystals are not subgroups of this group. Likewise, an isometric crystal cannot have a property tensor with point group $\infty/m\ 2/m\ 2/m$ because none of the isometric groups is one of its subgroups. We can immediately see, therefore, that isometric crystals have a property tensor referred to principal axes of the form

$$\begin{pmatrix} K_{11} & 0 & 0 \\ 0 & K_{11} & 0 \\ 0 & 0 & K_{11} \end{pmatrix}$$

and are isotropic for properties represented by symmetric second-rank tensors.

Hexagonal, trigonal, and tetragonal crystals are less symmetric in their properties and it can be shown that the thermal conductivity tensor in crystals of these systems belongs in the point group $\infty/m\ 2/m\ 2/m$ and referred to principal axes has the form

$$\begin{pmatrix} K_{11} & 0 & 0 \\ 0 & K_{11} & 0 \\ 0 & 0 & K_{33} \end{pmatrix}$$

Crystals of the remaining systems (orthorhombic, monoclinic, and triclinic) have point groups that are all subgroups of $2/m\ 2/m\ 2/m$, and the corresponding property tensors are found to have this symmetry, and only three principal components are needed for their specification. But the principal axes of the tensor are uniquely fixed by crystallography only for orthorhombic crystals where they coincide with the three crystallographic axes x, y, and z (2-fold rotation axes). In monoclinic crystals only one of the principal axes is fixed by the 2-fold rotation axis of the crystal (the y-axis, in the second setting) and an additional "component" is needed in the form of an angle between a principal axis and either the x- or the z-crystallographic axes. In triclinic crystals the orientation of the principal axes is arbitrary with respect to crystallographic axes, and three additional "components" (such as three Eulerian angles) are needed to specify the orientation of the principal axes.

Some of the physical properties of crystals with which geologists are most concerned are represented to a first approximation by tensors of

this kind. Examples include thermal conductivity, compressibility, thermal expansion, diffusion, certain optical properties, and many others. Diagrammatic representations of such properties represented by magnitude ellipsoids, spheroids or spheres are given for crystals in different systems in Figure 2–83.

Similar principles govern the forms of property tensors of higher rank representing more complex properties, such as piezoelectricity and elasticity. Because of Neumann's principle certain properties must vanish in crystals of certain classes. Any noncentrosymmetric property (such as optical activity or piezoelectricity) cannot be present in a centrosymmetric crystal or Neumann's principle would be violated. On the other hand, as we have seen with respect to thermal conductivity, the presence of a centrosymmetric property in a noncentrosymmetric crystal such as thermal conductivity in a crystal of class 222 does not violate Neumann's principle because group 222 is a subgroup of $2/m\ 2/m\ 2/m$.

COMPRESSIBILITY

The isothermal compressibility β_T is defined as

$$\beta_T = -\frac{1}{V}\left(\frac{\partial V}{\partial P}\right)_T$$

where the minus sign is introduced to make β_T positive, since $(\partial V/\partial P)_T$ is always negative in a stable phase (see Chapter 5). The bulk modulus K_T is the reciprocal of β_T

$$K_T = -V\left(\frac{\partial P}{\partial V}\right)_T = \rho\left(\frac{\partial P}{\partial \rho}\right)_T \quad (2\cdot15)$$

where ρ is density.

An isotropic material subjected to pressure variation changes its volume (or density) without changing shape. In an anisotropic material, pressure causes different length changes in different directions and the shape of the body changes. The *linear compressibility* measures relative change in length in a particular direction. Its value can be calculated from the appropriate elastic compliances (see below). The relative magnitude of linear compressibility in different

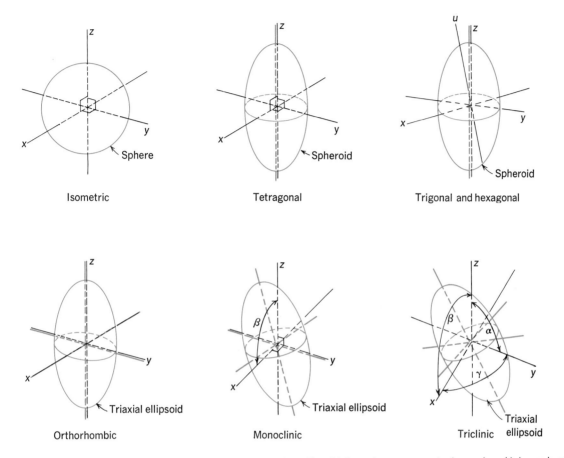

FIG. 2–83 *Diagrammatic representation of the "magnitude" ellipsoid for a tensor property (second rank) in each of the seven crystal systems. For isometric crystal magnitude ellipsoid is a sphere; for trigonal, tetragonal, and hexagonal crystals it is an ellipsoid of revolution (a spheriod) with its unique axis in the direction of the z crystallographic axis; for an orthorhombic crystal it is a triaxial ellipsoid with principal axes along the crystallographic axis; for a monoclinic crystal it is a triaxial ellipsoid with one principal axis along the y crystallographic axis (second setting); for a triclinic crystal it is a triaxial ellipsoid of arbitrary orientation with respect to crystallographic axes (the principal axes of the ellipsoids are indicated by colored lines and the crystallographic axes by black lines).*

directions in crystals of various systems is represented diagrammatically by Figure 2–83. Thus, for example, a sphere cut from an orthorhombic mineral when placed under pressure becomes a triaxial ellipsoid with its principal axes in the directions of the crystallographic axes. A sphere cut from an isometric mineral remains a sphere.

Compression of a substance generates heat and the temperature of an isolated body subjected to an increase in pressure rises. Since a rise in temperature also causes a change in volume the *adiabatic compressibility* measured in a thermally insulated specimen is usually smaller than the isothermal compressibility. The adiabatic bulk modulus K_S is defined as

$$K_S = \rho \left(\frac{\partial P}{\partial \rho} \right)_S$$

where the symbol S refers to entropy.

The velocity of propagation of an elastic wave is controlled by K_S, not K_T. The difference between these two quantities (generally of the order of a few percent) is important in the interpretation of the speed of propagation of seismic waves through the earth (see Chapter 11).

The bulk modulus of most minerals and rocks under ordinary conditions is generally slightly less than one megabar (1 megabar = 10^{12} dynes/cm²). If it did not depend on P, integration of equation (2-15) would give

$$\rho = \rho_0 \exp\frac{P}{K}$$

where ρ is density at pressure P and ρ_0 is density at $P = 0$ or, closely enough, at $P = 1$ bar. Since the pressure in the core of the earth is of the order of several megabars, the ratio ρ/ρ_0 would be large. It is observed, however, that K increases with increasing P as substances tend to become stiffer with increasing compression; dK/dP is typically of the order of 3 to 4. K decreases with increasing temperature as substances become less stiff with heating (quite generally, increasing pressure and temperature have *opposite* effects on physical properties). The precise determination of the variation of K_T and K_S with pressure and temperature over the full range in these variables encountered in the earth still remains a major geophysical problem.

The bulk modulus measures essentially the repulsion term in equation (2-8) for the lattice energy of a crystal. It was shown on page 65 how the exponent n is, in fact, determined from the compressibility. The change in K with pressure, or density, reflects the increasing repulsion as atoms or ions are squeezed more closely together.

THERMAL EXPANSION

Thermal expansion α is defined as

$$\alpha = \frac{1}{V}\left(\frac{\partial V}{\partial T}\right)_P$$

In an anisotropic substance a second-rank tensor arises, relating pure strain (change in volume and shape)—which is itself a second-rank tensor—to temperature change ΔT, a scalar. Referred to its principal axes, the tensor takes the form

$$\begin{pmatrix} \alpha_1 & 0 & 0 \\ 0 & \alpha_2 & 0 \\ 0 & 0 & \alpha_3 \end{pmatrix}$$

where α_1, α_2, and α_3 are principal coefficients of linear expansion. In an isometric crystal $\alpha_1 = \alpha_2 = \alpha_3$, and a sphere cut from such a crystal remains a sphere when uniformly heated. The thermal expansion tensor must from Neumann's principle contain all the symmetry operations of the crystal so that a uniform change in temperature that does not result in polymorphic changes does not change the symmetry of the crystal.

Thermal expansion is generally positive, although cases where it is negative are known (for example, water between 0° and 4°C). For a few minerals (for example, calcite and beryl) some linear coefficients are negative, indicating shortening in some directions on heating.

The thermal expansion of most minerals under ordinary conditions falls in the range of 1 to 5 $\times$ 10^{-5} deg^{-1}; thus a change in temperature of 100° causes a change in volume of less than one percent. The coefficient depends strongly on temperature, being zero at 0°K. Increasing pressure reduces α in a manner related to the change of β_T with temperature since it follows from the definitions of α and β_T that

$$\left(\frac{\partial \alpha}{\partial P}\right)_T = -\left(\frac{\partial \beta_T}{\partial T}\right)_P \qquad (2\text{-}16)$$

Thermal expansion finds its origin in the "anharmonicity" of the lattice vibrations briefly mentioned in Chapter 4—that is, in the fact that the force pushing a displaced atom back to its equilibrium position is not strictly proportional to the displacement. This fact results in vibration of atoms about displaced positions and therefore changes the lattice dimensions. The effect increases with increasing amplitude of the vibrations—that is, with increasing temperature. This is why the thermal expansion becomes zero at $T = 0$°K.

BIREFRINGENCE

In an isotropic material such as glass an electric field **E** induces an electric displacement **D** according to

$$\mathbf{D} = \varepsilon \mathbf{E}$$

where ε is the dielectric constant. The quantities **D** and **E** are vectors, and in a generally anisotropic material we can see that the quantity ε is a symmetric second-rank tensor, which can be referred to its principal axes to obtain the three principal dielectric coefficients ε_1, ε_2, and ε_3. At optical frequencies the refractive index n in an isotropic material is defined as

$$n = \sqrt{\varepsilon} = \frac{c}{v}$$

where c is the velocity of light in a vacuum and v is its velocity in the material. In a generally anisotropic material, three principal refractive indices corresponding to the three principal dielectric coefficients are to be expected. The refractive indices of an anisotropic medium are best visualized in terms of a quadric surface (the optical indicatrix) of the form

$$\frac{x^2}{n_1^2} + \frac{y^2}{n_2^2} + \frac{z^2}{n_3^2} = 1 \qquad (2\text{-}17)$$

which is a real ellipsoid with its principal radii equal to the principal refractive indices referred to the principal axes of the dielectric tensor. Most silicated minerals have refractive indices in the range 1.45–1.80; the difference $n_3 - n_1$, called the *birefringence*, rarely exceeds 0.1.

From Neumann's principle it follows that the indicatrix is a triaxial ellipsoid in crystals of the triclinic, monoclinic, and orthorhombic systems (related to the crystal axes as shown in Figure 2–83); a spheroid whose unique principal axis coincides with the principal rotational symmetry axis in the hexagonal, trigonal, and tetragonal systems, and a sphere in the isometric system.

A ray of light entering an isotropic solid from vacuum is bent (refracted) according to Snell's law (Chapter 11)

$$n = \sin i / \sin r$$

where n is the index of refraction of the solid and i and r are the respective angles between the normal to the interface and the incident and refracted (transmitted) rays. In anisotropic crystals the situation is more complicated. It follows from Maxwell's laws (the proof, which is not trivial, can be found in appendix H of the book by Nye listed at the end of this chapter) that not one, but two waves of different velocity may in general be propagated through a crystal with a given wave normal (the wave normal is the direction normal to the "wave-front," or surface of equal phase). This is *double refraction*. The two waves are plane polarized, and the value of c/v for each wave is called the refractive index of that wave. These refractive indices can be found as follows. Consider a direction OP (the wave normal) and the section of the indicatrix normal to OP. This section is an ellipse with a minor semi-axis OA and a major semi-axis OB, say. These semi-axes are the two refractive indices for the two waves with wave normal OP. The displacement vector **D** for the plane-polarized wave with index OA vibrates along OA; that for the wave with index OB vibrates along OB. Note that **D** is not in general parallel to the electric field vector **E** which lies in the plane containing **D** and the wave normal. The *ray direction*, which is normal to **E** and to the magnetic vector **H** of the electromagnetic light wave, is not in general parallel to the wave normal. The *ray direction* is that in which the energy. **E** × **H** is propagated. The angle between the wave normal and the ray direction, which is equal to the angle between **D** and **E**, is seldom greater than a few degrees.

Because the two waves have different refractive indices, they are also refracted by different amounts as they enter or leave the crystal. Thus a black dot seen through a parallel-sided plate of calcite appears as two dots; hence the name, double refraction.

In crystals of the triclinic, monoclinic, and orthohombic systems, the three principal axes of the indicatrix are denoted α, β, γ, or X, Y, Z. Corresponding refractive indices are $n_\alpha < n_\beta < n_\gamma$. The indicatrix has two circular sections intersecting in the β (Y) axis and symmetrically disposed toward α (X) and γ (Z). The normals to

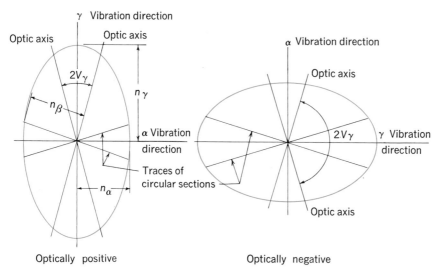

FIG. 2–84 *Section through $\alpha\gamma$ plane of the biaxial indicatrix for an optically positive and optically negative crystal.*

these two circular sections are called optic axes. The two waves whose common wave-normal is normal to a circular section travel with equal velocity; there is no double refraction along the optic axes. Crystals of these classes, then, are optically *biaxial*. The acute angle $2V$ between the optic axes is determined by the magnitudes of n_α, n_β, n_γ. Crystals are said to be optically positive when γ (Z) is the acute bisectrix, negative when α (X) is the acute bisectrix of the axial angle (Figure 2–84). A useful geometric property of the optic axes is as follows: Imagine the traces, upon a plane normal to the direction of propagation, of two planes, each of which contains the wave normal and an optic axis. The two vibration directions for that wave normal are the bisectors of the angle between these two traces.

In crystals of the hexagonal, trigonal, or tetragonal systems, where the indicatrix is a spheroid, for any direction of propagation the vibration direction of one ray ("ordinary" ray) is normal to the principal rotational symmetry axis of the crystal. The vibration direction of the second or "extraordinary" ray lies in the plane containing the direction of propagation and the principal rotation axis. There are two principal refractive indices, n_o and n_e, corresponding to vibrations respectively normal (ordinary ray) and parallel (extraordinary ray) to the principal rotation axis. The indicatrix has a single circular section normal to the principal rotation axis, which is thus a unique direction of no double refraction, that is, an optic axis. Crystals of these symmetry classes thus are *uniaxial*—positive when $n_e > n_o$, negative when $n_e < n_o$. For uniaxial positive crystals the indicatrix spheroid is prolate, for negative crystals oblate.

For isometric crystals the indicatrix is a spheroid. The refractive index has the same value for all directions of vibration. There is no double refraction, and crystals are optically isotropic.

Refractive indices generally depend on wavelength of the light; this is called *dispersion*. Absorption also depends on wavelength (color) and on the vibration direction. Some anisotropic colored minerals exhibit a different color (*pleochroism*) depending on the orientation of the plane of polarization of light with respect to crystallographic axes. Three different colors may be seen in a single biaxial crystal, but only two colors in uniaxial crystals. The petrographic (polarizing) microscope is used to determine refractive indices, color and pleochroism, birefringence, optic axial angle and sign, dispersion, and the relation of indicatrix axes to observable crystallographic directions (cleavage traces, twin axes, directions of elongation). Most rock-forming minerals are readily identified by these properties.

Consider briefly how refraction and birefringence are related to atomic structure and crystal chemistry. The electric field of a light wave impinging on a crystal exerts a force on all electric charges present. Ions are too heavy to oscillate at the high frequency of visible light, but electrons are not. The electric field thus induces a rapid oscillation of the electron clouds surrounding each atomic nucleus. Displacement of a charge $(+e)$ by a distance x is equivalent to addition of a charge $(-e)$ at the original position and a charge $(+e)$ at the displaced position. Such charges are in effect equivalent to the addition of a dipole ex. If polarization p is defined as the vector sum of all the dipoles induced per unit volume by an electric field E, the dielectric constant is by definition $\varepsilon = 1 + 4\pi p/E$. The dielectric coefficient in a particular direction, therefore, measures the relative ease with which electron clouds can be deformed in that direction. The deformability or "polarizability" of an atom or ion in a crystal depends in the first place on how firmly the electrons are held to their respective nuclei; this, in turn, depends on the charge of the nucleus, the number of electrons surrounding it, and their spatial distribution, which reflects the type of bonding as between, say, covalent or ionic. The polarizability depends also on the nature and geometric arrangement of neighboring atoms or ions whose electric field may tend to decrease or enhance the deformation. For example, the strong birefringence of calcite $(CaCO_3)$ and of carbonates in general arises from the fact that the trigonal planar $[CO_3]^{2-}$ group is more readily deformed when the electric field lies in the plane of the group than when it is normal to it. Good agreement is generally obtained between observed and calculated polarizabilities of many minerals, confirming in general their ionic nature and the commonly adopted values of the ionic radii (see Table 2–17).

ELASTICITY

So far, the properties examined have been representable by symmetric second-rank tensors. Most of the simple continuum physical properties of crystals are of this kind. We now look briefly at a more complex property, elasticity, which expresses a unique relationship between two second-rank tensors (stress and infinitesimal strain) and is thus represented by a fourth-rank tensor. Stress and strain tensors are defined in Chapter 9.

As a general statement of elastic behavior, Hooke's law, which states that stress is proportional to recoverable strain, can be extended into a linear relationship between the six independent components of stress and the six independent components of infinitesimal pure strain (Chapter 9). In a crystal no assumptions can be made concerning isotropy in elastic response and we must write each component of stress as a linear function of all the components of pure strain and vice versa to give two sets of six equations, which can be written in matrix form as

$$\boldsymbol{\sigma} = \mathbf{C}\boldsymbol{\varepsilon} \qquad (2\text{-}18)$$

or

$$\boldsymbol{\varepsilon} = \mathbf{S}\boldsymbol{\sigma} \qquad (2\text{-}19)$$

Equation (2-19) written out more fully becomes

$$\begin{pmatrix} \varepsilon_x \\ \varepsilon_y \\ \varepsilon_z \\ \varepsilon_{xy} \\ \varepsilon_{yz} \\ \varepsilon_{xz} \end{pmatrix} = \begin{pmatrix} c_{11} & c_{12} & c_{13} & c_{14} & c_{15} & c_{16} \\ c_{21} & c_{22} & c_{23} & c_{24} & c_{25} & c_{26} \\ c_{31} & c_{32} & c_{33} & c_{34} & c_{35} & c_{36} \\ c_{41} & c_{42} & c_{43} & c_{44} & c_{45} & c_{46} \\ c_{51} & c_{52} & c_{53} & c_{54} & c_{55} & c_{56} \\ c_{61} & c_{62} & c_{63} & c_{64} & c_{65} & c_{66} \end{pmatrix} \begin{pmatrix} \sigma_x \\ \sigma_y \\ \sigma_z \\ \tau_{xy} \\ \tau_{yz} \\ \tau_{xz} \end{pmatrix}$$

$$(2\text{-}20)$$

and there is a corresponding expansion of equation (2-18). The matrices $\mathbf{C}$ and $\mathbf{S}$ each contain 36 components (respectively c_{ij} and s_{ij}: $i, j = 1, 2, 3, 4, 5,$ and 6) and are inverse to each other so that

$$CS = I$$

where I is a unit matrix. The components c_{ij} are called "elastic stiffnesses" or "moduli" and the components s_{ij} "elastic compliances."

Strictly, the elasticity tensor has 81 components, relating the nine components of stress to the nine components of pure strain; however, by limiting discussion to the symmetric stress components and the tensor components of pure strain (see Chapter 9) this number can be reduced to 36. It can further be shown that the matrices C and S are symmetric across their leading diagonals so that the number of independent components is further reduced from 36 to 21.

The most generally anisotropic solid, therefore, has 21 independent elastic components. Triclinic crystals with symmetry 1 or $\bar{1}$ fit this condition. In other crystals symmetry operations reduce still further the number of independent components according to the scheme in Table 2–21. For an elastically isotropic solid (group ∞/m ∞/m ∞/m), the number of independent coefficients reduces to 2.

Most rock-forming silicates are low-symmetry crystals (triclinic and monoclinic) and their elastic properties are so complex that it is difficult or impossible to determine them. We shall see later that rocks can be elastically isotropic or anisotropic in simple or complex ways, depending upon the nature and arrangement of the mineral crystals of which they are composed.

As for compressibility, compliance and stiffness constants may be measured isothermally or adiabatically; the difference usually is not important.

In isotropic bodies the two remaining independent constants are c_{11} and c_{44}; the former is identical to the bulk modulus whereas the latter is usually called the shear modulus or "rigidity" (see Chapter 9).

Elastic constants play in the propagation of elastic waves a role not unlike that of the dielectric constant in the propagation of light. It can be shown that only two types of elastic wave can be transmitted through an isotropic solid; they travel at different velocities, which are independent of the direction of propagation. In aniso-

TABLE 2–21　*Elastic components of crystals*

Systems and Classes	Number of Independent Coefficients
Triclinic (all classes)	21
Monoclinic (all classes)	13
Orthorhombic (all classes)	9
Tetragonal (classes 4, $\bar{4}$, 4/m) Trigonal (classes 3, $\bar{3}$)	7
Tetragonal (classes 4mm, $\bar{4}$2m, 422, 4/m 2/m 2/m) Trigonal (classes 3m, 32, $\bar{3}$ 2/m)	6
Hexagonal (all classes)	5
Isometric (all classes)	3

tropic substances there are generally three types of wave motion for a given direction of propagation corresponding to different directions of particle motion; all three have different velocities, which generally vary with the direction of propagation. An interpretation of seismic records (that is, records of elastic vibrations propagated through the earth from an earthquake focus) is generally made on the assumption that the earth is elastically isotropic, which may not be true everywhere.

PLASTICITY

Many lines of evidence suggest that the solid rocks of the crust and mantle can flow cohesively without rupture. Initially horizontal sedimentary strata are found bent into intricately contorted forms without visible signs of fracture and the metamorphic rocks of the crust commonly exhibit structural features explicable only in terms of intense and repeated deformation in the solid state (see Chapter 3).

Although this flow seems to be of several different kinds (see Chapter 9), some observed structural features indicate that crystals of rock-forming minerals can have the capacity to distort or "flow" mechanically in response to stress; thus the deformation, unlike elastic deformation just described, is not reversible and is not governed by Hooke's law. Such deformation is generally termed *plastic* or *ductile* if it requires shearing stresses higher than those that can be borne elastically, and *creep* if it is a time-dependent flow at stress levels that would cause only elastic reactions if present for periods of short duration (see Chapters 4 and 9).

Much of modern engineering technology depends upon the fact that many crystalline materials (particularly metals) are ductile and can be "formed" plastically without rupture. Most of the solid materials deformed for various purposes by engineers are, like most rocks, polycrystalline aggregates and their behavior depends largely upon the plastic properties of the crystals of which they are built. Although deformation and flow of metals has been the main preoccupation of experimenters in the field of crystal plasticity, recently much attention has been given to the plastic properties of crystals of other types (particularly ionic crystals), partly in response to a developing ceramics industry and partly in attempts by earth scientists to understand the conditions and mechanics of flow of minerals and rocks in the earth.

All experimental studies of "plastic" flow of solids fall into two broad groups (see also Chapter 9). The older and most general types of study are of "phenomenological plasticity," in which experiments are conducted to determine empirical relationships between stress and incremental strain, no account being taken of the actual physical processes involved. The mathematical theory of plasticity—a continuum mechanical theory of isotropic media much used by engineers—is the theoretical basis for these studies. Recently, theories of solid plasticity have arisen that are physical in their basis and take into account the atomic structure and inherent small-scale mechanical anisotropy of crystalline solids. Such theories are still in their infancy, particularly as applied to complex crystals other than metals; but already much information has been obtained about plastic deformation in single crystals and a little has been learned about the behavior of polycrystalline bodies of a simple kind.

In what follows we outline briefly a few of the important facts that have been learned about plastic deformation of crystals—particularly mineral crystals. Our aim is to examine the flow of rocks under natural conditions, so we shall consider also plasticity at elevated temperatures and pressures.

PLASTIC FLOW   Some single crystals cut into a cube or cylinder and polished and loaded at atmospheric pressure and room temperature in an engineer's testing machine can be permanently lengthened or shortened by small amounts without rupture. Other crystals, particularly most silicates, must be placed under high confining pressure and temperature before the same effect can be achieved. In most experiments of this kind it is found that after deformation the polished surfaces of the crystal are no longer smooth but are crossed by one or more sets of striations. Study of such surfaces with a microscope reveals that the striations are generally "steps" on the surface of the crystal and represent the outcrop patterns of thin laminar zones of concentrated deformation separating effectively undeformed plates. What is more, the laminar zones along which deformation is concentrated are commonly parallel to rational planes in the crystal, commonly those with simple Miller indices. Such experiments were long ago taken to show that plastic deformation of a crystal takes place by the sliding of layers of atoms one over the other along particular planes (*slip planes*) and in particular directions (*slip directions*). Both are controlled by the atomic structure of the crystal and are, in general, simple crystallographic planes and lines along which atoms have close or closest packing. From the Bravais law these planes are also common crystal faces. After such slip (Figure 2–85) the crystal structure is still intact and the only visible evidence that slip has occurred is the appearance of the aforementioned "steps" on the outside of the crystal. For small amounts of deformation only part of the crystal is generally deformed and striations (slip bands) can be seen on a polished surface. But if deformation is relatively homogeneous, no obvious effects of deformation are seen other than change of shape.

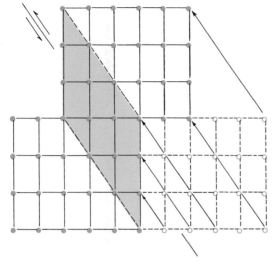

FIG. 2–85 *Slip in a crystal (diagrammatic).*

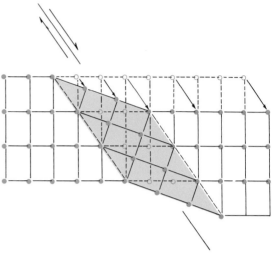

FIG. 2–86 *Mechanical twinning (diagrammatic).*

In some crystals only one slip plane and direction (a combination termed a *slip system* or *glide system*) appear to be active; in others several intersecting sets operate, apparently at the same time. Which slip systems are active in a particular crystal appears to reflect two factors. The first of these is stress distribution. To initiate plastic deformation in a crystal, a particular value of shearing stress must be reached on a potential slip plane in the slip direction. If this stress (termed the yield stress) is not reached, no slip occurs. For a crystal with two potential slip systems with different yield stresses, slip may even begin on the one with the *highest* yield stress if it has a more favorable orientation with respect to principal stresses than the other. The second factor is crystal symmetry. If there exists a slip system on planes and in directions that are repeated by the point group operations of a crystal, then other slip systems are also present; because all of these systems are related by symmetry operations, they have equal yield stress for slip. Thus, if in a high-symmetry crystal slip occurs on one suitably oriented system, then any other systems related to it by symmetry operations are also slip systems of the crystal. For example, if in a crystal of class $4/m\ \bar{3}\ 2/m$ (such as copper) slip is observed on the plane (111) in direction [1$\bar{1}$0], then the crystal will slip with equal ease

on all four planes of the form $\{111\}$ in three directions in each plane, given by the form of lines $\langle 1\bar{1}0 \rangle$, yielding a total of 12 physically distinct slip systems.[13] In a low-symmetry crystal such as one belonging to group $\bar{1}$, the same observed slip system would be unique. We would expect, therefore, high-symmetry crystals to be in general more ductile than low-symmetry crystals. Most metals are in fact high-symmetry crystals. Much of their ductility as aggregates depends on the fact that each grain generally contains a large number of slip systems; thus, for almost any stress distribution, some of these will be suitably oriented for slip. Also, close-packed atomic planes and directions (preferred for slip because the atomic spacing and thus the slip vector is shorter) are present in *fcc* and *hcp* metals, whereas they are generally absent in the relatively open structures of some of the common low-symmetry silicates, such as quartz and feldspar.

Most rock-forming silicates crystallize in the monoclinic or triclinic systems and only one sys-

---

[13] Not all 12 of these slip systems are independent. Combinations of certain of them cancel to give zero deformation; combinations of others yield a rigid-body rotation. It can be shown that only five of the slip systems are truly independent and that these can be chosen from the 12 in 384 different ways.

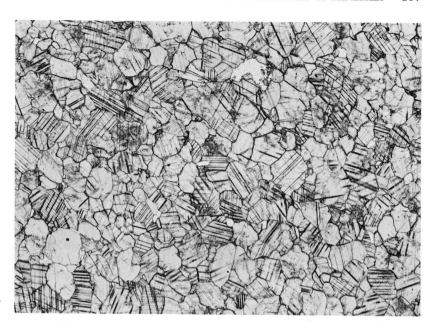

FIG. 2–87 Plastically deformed dolomite crystals showing {02$\bar{2}$1} lamellae, as seen in thin section.

tem of relatively easy slip is to be expected. For this reason most silicates are not markedly ductile, although some can be plastically deformed at elevated temperatures and pressures where slip systems not active under normal conditions can operate. Some nonsilicate rock-forming minerals—particularly calcite, halite, ice, and gypsum —are extremely ductile under conditions of low or moderate temperature and pressure.

More careful study of the laminar domains of slip in naturally and experimentally deformed crystals shows that not all of them fit the simple picture of slip introduced above, and in fact three other types of behavior occur, as follows:

1. *Mechanical twinning.* Each successive lattice layer is displaced by slip through a specific fraction of an interatomic distance. In this way a strained lamella is built up with its lattice in twinned relation to that of the unstrained crystal, as shown simplified in two dimensions in Figure 2–86. Strain in a twinned lamella is strictly limited by the geometry of twinning. Mechanical twinning has been produced naturally and experimentally in many minerals—calcite, {01$\bar{1}$2}; dolomite, {02$\bar{2}$1} (Figure 2–87); diopside {001}.

2. *Kinking.* Kinks or kink bands are lamellar strain domains within which the active slip plane is steeply inclined to the domain boundary (Figure 2–88). Ideally a kink is bounded by a plane surface symmetrically inclined to the respective attitudes of the slip system in the kink and in the host crystal. Departures from this ideal orientation are common. Kinks, like twin lamellae, are optically recognizable by virtue of changed crystallographic orientation. They are familiar indications of strain in crystals of mica, kyanite, brucite, enstatite (Figure 2–89), and other minerals.

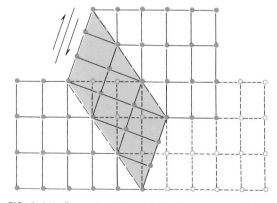

FIG. 2–88 Formation of a kink band (diagrammatic).

FIG. 2–89 *Kink bands in naturally deformed hypersthene crystals: width of kink, about 1 mm.*

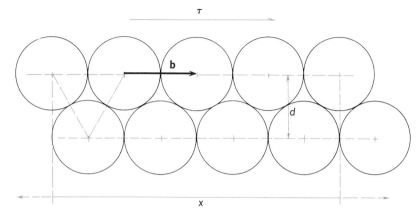

FIG. 2–90 *Close packing of atoms.*

3. *Shear transformation.* Kinklike structures formed experimentally in some minerals contain a polymorph of the initial crystal. The shear strain in the domain is accomplished by an actual phase change of the mineral to a new form. For the transformed part to remain continuous with the untransformed part the interface between them must remain effectively an invariant plane (that is, a plane of little or no distortion in the transformed lattice) as it does also in twinning and kinking. Such transformations are sometimes called "coherent" transformations because of this property. The best-documented case in crustal rocks is the transformation in kinks of enstatite (orthorhombic) to clinoenstatite (monoclinic). This transformation, first produced experimentally at high strain rate, has recently been found in intensely deformed ultrabasic rocks from central Australia. Such transformations may be significant in the mantle.

These three types of plastic deformation coupled with simple or multiple slip enormously increase the possibilities for flow in crystals and polycrystalline aggregates.

DISLOCATIONS   The foregoing view of plastic deformation, which we might term the "card-deck" model, is adequate for many purposes. But simple calculations based on knowledge of crystal structure showed long ago that it does not fit some features of plasticity in crystals, particularly the observed values of yield stresses for initiation of slip. For example, consider part of a simple structure, such as a metal crystal, consisting of atoms of equal size, uniformly close packed (shown in two dimensions in Figure 2–90). Let a shear stress τ tend to slide the upper layer of atoms over the lower. During such progressive shear displacement, the force acting will vary periodically about zero in a manner that can be taken for simplicity as sinusoidal. Thus the shear stress to displace the layer a distance x can be written (after Frenkel)

$$\tau = P \sin \frac{2\pi x}{b} \qquad (2\text{-}21)$$

where b is the magnitude of **b**, the lattice vector in the displacement direction, and P is a constant depending on the shear modulus μ for the material (see page 489). For the first slip increment (elastic deformation), $\tau = \mu x/d$, where d is the interplanar spacing of the atomic layers and, from equation (2-21),

$$\frac{\mu x}{d} = P \frac{2\pi x}{b}$$

and

$$P = \frac{\mu b}{2\pi d} \qquad (2\text{-}22)$$

Substitution of equation (2-22) into (2-21) yields

$$\tau = \frac{\mu b}{2\pi d} \sin \frac{2\pi x}{b}$$

The shear stress τ has a maximum value when $\sin 2\pi x/b = 1$; that is,

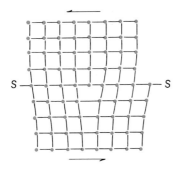
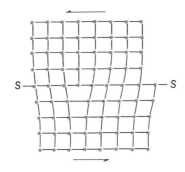

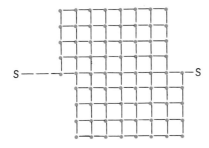

FIG. 2–91 *Motion of a dislocation along a slip plane SS.*

$$\tau_{\max} = \frac{\mu b}{2\pi d}$$

For the model shown in Figure 2–90,

$$\frac{b}{d} = \frac{2}{\sqrt{3}} \qquad \text{and} \qquad \tau_{\max} = \frac{\mu}{\sqrt{3}\,\pi} \cong \frac{\mu}{5.5}$$

This result (and a more accurate result, based on a more realistic model, of $\tau_{\max} \cong \mu/30$) is in marked disagreement with experiments on metals in which $\tau_{\max} \cong 10^{-3}$ to $10^{-4}\,\mu$. Ductile crystals are in fact several orders of magnitude weaker than is to be expected from the simple model of slip.

This conflict was resolved theoretically by Taylor and others. They suggested that the atoms in a displaced layer, instead of all moving to the next equilibrium position simultaneously, were displaced one at a time as an imperfection in the crystal structure, termed a *dislocation*, traveled along a slip plane in the slip direction—much as shown in two dimensions in Figure 2–91 for a simple cubic lattice. The force required to move such a dislocation can be shown to correspond to a much lower shear stress for slip than is required by the slip model, and the net effect, once the dislocations have traveled the whole length of a slip plane, is the same. Although postulated initially on theoretical grounds, the existence of dislocations has been amply confirmed by experiment, and modern techniques exist by which they can be directly observed. A voluminous and complex literature has grown up on the subject of dislocations, their geometric and mechanical interactions, and the effects that these have on the properties and growth of crystals.

A dislocation is a line imperfection which is most easily visualized as separating the slipped from the unslipped parts of a crystal in a slip plane. In fact, a dislocation can move ideally in either sense so that this distinction is arbitrary. The line of a dislocation can terminate at the boundaries of a crystal or it can form a closed loop in a slip plane entirely within a crystal. Because the direction and amount of its unit movement is fixed by lattice vectors, a dislocation has associated with it a vector **b** (called the Burgers

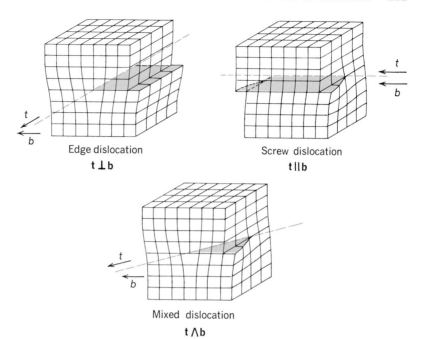

Edge dislocation
t ⊥ b

Screw dislocation
t ∥ b

Mixed dislocation
t ∧ b

FIG. 2–92 *Types of dislocations.*

vector) which defines the amount and direction of movement of the dislocation during displacement of atoms from one site to the next. If the local direction of the dislocation line itself is given by a unit vector **t**, then three types of dislocation can be recognized (refer to Figure 2–92), as follows:

1. A dislocation in which **b** is perpendicular to **t** is called an *edge* dislocation and corresponds to a missing row of atoms.

2. A dislocation in which **b** is parallel to **t** is called a *screw* dislocation and has the effect of connecting parallel planes of atoms into a helical surface around the dislocation as axis.

3. A dislocation in which **b** is oblique to **t** is called a *mixed* dislocation and can be viewed as being composed of components of the pure edge and pure screw type.

In a closed dislocation loop in a crystal, the dislocation is of all three types in different places (Figure 2–93).

The Burgers vector of a particular dislocation can be determined by forming a circuit of com-

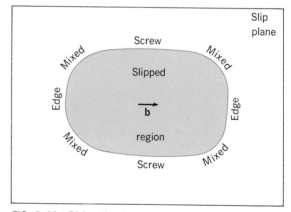

FIG. 2–93 *Dislocation loop.*

plementary lattice vectors around it (the "Burgers circuit"). The vector required to close this circuit is the Burgers vector **b** (Figure 2–94).

Dislocations are thermodynamically unstable, but all natural crystals contain them; indeed, they appear to be fundamental to nucleation and growth of crystals. Most are mobile under stress because they and their Burgers vectors lie in an active slip plane. But dislocations occur (gen-

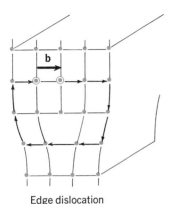

Edge dislocation

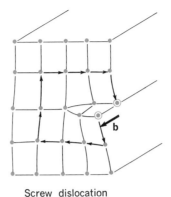

Screw dislocation

FIG. 2-94 *Burgers circuits and vectors* **b** *for edge and screw dislocations.*

erally by growth) that do not have Burgers vectors and line vectors lying in a slip plane. These are immobile (sessile dislocations). The presence and density of dislocations have a striking effect on the mechanical properties of a crystal. The effect on yield stress for slip has already been noted; other effects are strain (or work) hardening and the hardening effects on some crystals of impurity or dispersed atoms—such as, for example, carbon in iron. The first effect results from progressive accumulation of mutually repulsive dislocations of the same sign at obstacles in the slip planes. Not only are dislocations moved by stress, they are also continuously created at dislocation "sources," so dislocation density in a deforming crystal can increase progressively. The second effect results in part from the mutual repulsion of concentric closed dislocation loops that are left behind around foreign atoms by a migrating dislocation: There an increase in the stress is required to propagate each successive dislocation. Fracture of crystals also seems to depend upon local development of large openings at obstacles as a result of the continual introduction of dislocations that propagate no further. This can happen at grain boundaries or within crystals, and cracks are formed that can act as nuclei for large-scale fractures.

A crystal with a high density of dislocations, such as a strongly plastically deformed crystal, has a greatly increased free energy. Such crystals tend to "anneal" or recrystallize more readily than crystals with low dislocation densities. Many crystals in rocks that can be shown on other grounds to have been plastically deformed are commonly annealed completely or "polygonized" —a process by which dislocations in a bent crystal become arranged in relatively stable planes dividing the crystal into segments with slightly different lattice orientations. These processes are thermally activated and diffusional in nature, as is dislocation "climb," by which a dislocation moves from one slip plane to another; they are also probably important in the "creep" of minerals and rocks (Chapter 9). Dislocations are important in diffusional processes and growth processes in general. Remanent magnetization of crystals, so important in paleomagnetic studies (see page 676), resides presumably in dislocations.

All the aforementioned types of plastic deformation can be explained in terms of the motion of dislocations and all have been observed in minerals. But common rock-forming minerals vary widely in their capacity to deform plastically —from calcite, which with six slip systems commonly active at moderate temperatures and pressures is continuously ductile, to garnet, which seems to remain brittle up to high temperature. In between are minerals such as mica, pyroxene, and dolomite, all of which can flow plastically under suitable conditions, and in many of which specific slip systems active in natural deformation have been identified. At present little is known about the properties of dislocations in mineral crystals, because of their complex structures when compared with metals. But dislocations have been photographed in minerals such as quartz by transmission electron microscopy, and are known to increase in density as a result of plastic deformation. Plasticity of quartz is complex and seems to depend on presence of water. Dry quartz remains brittle to very high temperatures and pressures.

DIFFRACTION BY CRYSTALS

The development of modern mineralogy and, indeed, of all branches of the science of the solid state, is closely connected with the development of quantum theory and the recognition of the wave-particle duality. Diffraction of light (defined as any departure of a light path from that prescribed by geometrical optics) by narrow slits has been studied since the early nineteenth century and it early became obvious that to obtain diffraction patterns from sets of such slits or from ruled gratings, their spacings must be close to the wavelength of the light used. In 1912 Max von Laue suggested that the regular three-dimensionally periodic structures of crystals might behave as "diffraction gratings" for radiations with wavelengths close to that of the interatomic distance in solids: these distances were known approximately from Avogadro's number. This suggestion was soon confirmed with X rays; but from the de Broglie relationship describing the wave-particle duality it was obvious that many other types of radiation might be suitable. The de Broglie equation

$$\lambda = \frac{h}{mv}$$

relates wavelength λ to mass m and velocity v (where h is Planck's constant). Thus any stream of particles such as electrons, neutrons, protons, and so on that can be manipulated to yield a λ of about one angstrom unit should also be diffracted by crystals.

Diffraction properties of crystals resemble plasticity in that they become understandable only if the internal structure of the crystal is considered; no diffraction could occur in a truly continuous material. Study of diffraction effects has yielded an enormous body of information on the fine-scale structure and chemistry of crystals and many elegant determinative and other experimental techniques now use diffraction routinely. The choice of radiation used depends upon the particular problem. Electrons and

X rays, for example, are scattered by atoms in proportion to electron density, so heavy atoms tend to scatter more strongly than light atoms. Further, electrons can be easily focused and manipulated to give any desired wavelength. Neutrons, in contrast, are scattered by atomic nuclei and have advantages in locating the protons in a structure; and because of their magnetic moments they interact also with magnetic atoms and can be used to find the orientation of magnetic moments in a crystal. This last property is of use in providing an understanding of the magnetic properties of minerals such as magnetite (Fe_3O_4) which carry a record of the earth's magnetic field.

The diffraction effects most used by mineralogists are those of X rays. Modern crystallography is concerned largely with the analysis of crystal structures (including space group determination) by techniques involving interpretation of vast numbers of diffraction data, generally with the aid of computers. We look briefly now at the simple principles upon which some of these techniques are based.

DIFFRACTION OF X RAYS BY CRYSTALS

If a collimated beam of "white" X rays (unfiltered radiation containing many wavelengths) is allowed to fall on a thin crystal plate placed in front of a photographic film, the beam is diffracted as it passes through the plate into separate beams, which produce a number of spots on the film (Figure 2–95). The positions (but not the intensity) of the spots in this pattern (the "Laue

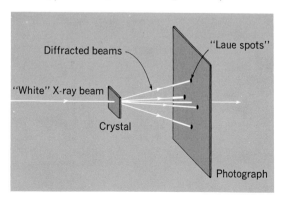

FIG. 2–95 *Formation of a Laue pattern.*

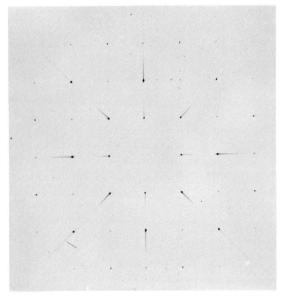

FIG. 2–96 *Laue photograph in the direction [100] in spinel.*

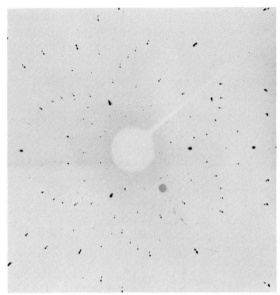

FIG. 2–97 *Laue photograph in the direction [111] in spinel.*

pattern") depend in some way upon the regular arrangement of atoms in the crystal. For example, in Figure 2–96 is shown the Laue pattern obtained from a plate of spinel (point group $4/m\ \bar{3}\ 2/m$) by means of an incident beam directed along the [100] direction of the crystal. The fourfold symmetry of the structure when viewed in this direction is clearly represented in the pattern. Similarly, a beam directed along the [111] direction (Figure 2–97) shows clearly the effect of the threefold symmetry axis lying in this direction. Thus the symmetry of the Laue pattern is a guide to the point group symmetry of a crystal, and by comparing patterns obtained from beams incident on a crystal in different directions the symmetry elements of the crystal can be located.[14] The *intensities* of the spots in a Laue photograph are, in addition, an indication of the electron distribution in a crystal structure.

---

[14] In fact, the presence or absence of a center of symmetry cannot be determined from a Laue photograph and the non-centrosymmetric groups and the groups found by adding to these the operation $\bar{1}$ cannot be distinguished. Thus a crystal can be placed only in one of the 11 groups (the "Laue groups") that correspond to the 11 possible centrosymmetric point groups.

The conditions under which an X-ray beam is diffracted by a crystal can be understood by considering crystals to be made of atoms uniformly packed in evenly spaced parallel planes. In any crystal an infinite variety of such planes could be chosen, but relatively few (those with Miller indices close to zero) have densely packed atoms. For such sets of parallel planes the interplanar spacing or "*d*-spacing" (see page 23) is relatively large. Figure 2–98 represents in two dimensions what happens when a monochromatic X-ray beam with a plane wavefront strikes a plane of atoms. Each atom behaves as an electronic oscillator and reradiates a wave synchronized with the incident wave, but along a spherical wavefront. Because the atoms are evenly and closely spaced a given incident plane wavefront is reradiated as a plane wave as if it were "reflected" from the plane of atoms in a manner obeying the law of optical reflection with θ as the angle of incidence and the angle of reflection. The same type of reflection occurs from all planes in a parallel set of evenly spaced planes, and in general the "reflected" waves are not in phase and will interfere.

For strong reflected or diffracted beams to leave a crystal, as is required to produce a Laue

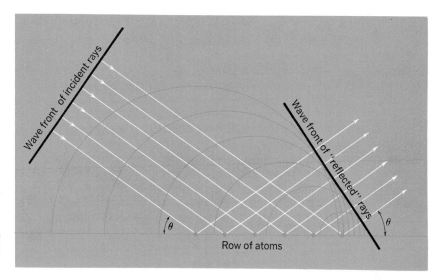

FIG. 2-98 *Monochromatic X-ray beam striking a row of atoms showing "reflection" of wavefront.*

pattern, the reflections from a set of parallel planes must be in phase. For each pair of planes the path length of the wave reflected from the plane farther from the source is larger than that for the nearer plane by an amount $2d \sin \theta$, where θ is the angle between the incident beam and the plane of atoms (the "glancing angle") and d is the interplanar spacing (Figure 2–99). For the two reflected waves to interfere constructively, that is, to be in phase, this increased path length must be an integral number of wavelengths of the incident radiation. Thus the relationship between interplanar spacing, glancing angle, and wavelength of radiation is

$$n\lambda = 2d \sin \theta$$

where n is an integer. This is a statement of *Bragg's law*, upon which most investigation of crystals by X rays is based.

From this relationship we see why the Laue pattern obtained by means of "white" X rays contains many spots. In such a situation there are many combinations of λ and θ that will give strong reflections from different sets of suitably

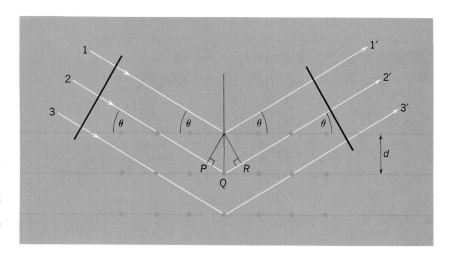

FIG. 2-99 *Bragg's law: Path $2 \rightarrow 2'$ is longer than path $1 \rightarrow 1'$ by 2d sin θ, where d is the spacing of the atomic layers and θ is the glancing angle (angle of incidence).*

spaced atomic planes. Another technique that suggests itself immediately is to use X rays of a single known wavelength (monochromatic X rays) and change the orientation of a crystal placed in the beam until strong reflections are obtained. In practice, a crystal is rotated successively about its major zone axes and the strong reflections determined. From the known orientation of the crystal, the orientation and interplanar spacing of strongly reflecting atomic layers can be found and the lattice dimensions of the crystal directly determined. Such data, coupled with data on the intensities of the reflections, can eventually yield a clear picture of the atomic structure.

Many other techniques have been developed by X-ray crystallographers. Even the presence or absence of space group operations, such as screw axes and glide planes, can be directly established by observing missing reflections. For example, a glide reflection plane requires the presence of an identical but mirror-image atomic layer midway between two like layers. The reflected wave from this mirror-image layer exactly cancels the reflected wave from the like layers, obeying Bragg's law, and no diffracted beam is observed.

A glance at any modern journal concerned with crystal structure determination will indicate the intricacy of the methods used and of the structures they determine.

REFERENCES

There are several excellent books dealing with geometric crystallography at different levels. Morphologic crystallography is covered by **A. C. Bishop** in *An Outline of Crystal Morphology* (Hutchinson, London, 1967). A more complete treatment and an introduction to structural crystallography can be found in **F. C. Phillips**, *An Introduction to Crystallography* (3rd ed., Longmans, London, 1963). Comprehensive accounts of point groups and space groups are to be found in **M. J. Buerger**, *Elementary Crystallography* (Wiley, New York, 1956) and in *International Tables for X-ray Crystallography*, vol. 1 (Kynoch Press, Birmingham, 1965).

An elementary introduction to group theory is given by **P. S. Alexandroff** in *Theory of Groups* (Blackie, London and Glasgow, 1959). Elementary matrix methods are discussed in **J. T. Schwartz**, *Introduction to Matrices and Vectors* (McGraw-Hill, New York, 1961) and more fully by **R. L. Eisenman** in *Matrix Vector Analysis* (McGraw-Hill, New York, 1963).

Many recent books introduce the principles of X-ray diffraction studies of crystals. Examples are **J. B. Cohen**, *Diffraction Methods in Materials Science* (Macmillan, New York, 1966) and **E. W. Nuffield**, *X-ray Diffraction Methods* (Wiley, New York, 1966).

On chemical mineralogy and related chemical topics, the reader is referred to the following works:

Coulson, C. A.: *Valence*, Clarendon Press, Oxford, 1953.

Fyfe, W. S.: *Geochemistry of Solids*, McGraw-Hill, New York, 1964.

Orgel, A. E.: *An Introduction to Transition-metal Chemistry*, Methuen, London, 1966.

Pauling, L.: *The Nature of the Chemical Bond*, Cornell University Press, Ithaca, N.Y., 1960.

Applications of crystal-field theory to mineralogy are discussed by **R. G. Burns** and **W. S. Fyfe** in "Crystal field theory and the geochemistry of transition elements," a chapter in *Research in Geochemistry*, **P. H. Abelson**, editor (Wiley, New York, 1967).

The standard works on descriptive mineralogy are **J. D. Dana**, *The System of Mineralogy*, 7th ed. (C. Palache, H. Berman, and C. Frondel), 3 vols. (Wiley, New York, 1944–1962) and the five-volume *Rock-Forming Minerals*, by **W. A. Deer**, **R. A. Howie**, and **J. Zussman** (Wiley, New York, 1962–1963). An abbreviated *Introduction to Rock-Forming Minerals* by the same authors appeared in 1966 (Longmans, London).

The physical properties of crystals are introduced in excellent books by **J. F. Nye**, *Physical Properties of Crystals* (Oxford, New York, 1960) and by **S. Bhagavantam**, *Crystal Symmetry and Physical Properties* (Academic Press, New York, 1966). Elementary introductions to the same subject are to be found in *Crystals Perfect and Imperfect* by scientists of the **Westinghouse Research Laboratories** (Walker and Co., New York, 1965) and in *The Nature of Solids* by **A. Holden** (Columbia University Press, 1965). A good elementary introduction to dislocation theory is by **J. and J. R. Weertman** in *Elementary Dislocation Theory* (Macmillan, New York, 1964) and a recent advanced treatment in *Theory of Dislocations* by **J. P. Hirth** and **J. Lothe** (McGraw-Hill, New York, 1968).

The best account of physical properties of rocks and minerals is in the *Handbook of Physical Constants*, **S. P. Clark**, editor (Geological Society of America, Memoir 97, 1966).

An introduction to crystal optics can be found in several texts representative of which are *Crystal Optics* by **P. Gay** (Longmans, London, 1967), *Crystals and Light* by **E. A. Wood** (Van Nostrand, Princeton, N. J., 1964), *A Textbook of Mineralogy* by **E. S. Dana**, 4th ed. revised by W. E. Ford (Wiley, New York, 1932), and **A. N. Winchell**, *Elements of Optical Mineralogy*, Part I (5th ed., Wiley, New York, 1961).

3
STRUCTURE AND FORM OF GEOLOGIC BODIES

THE GEOLOGIST, like the engineer, deals with compound bodies whose properties and behavior are determined not by chemical composition and related characteristics alone, but as well by internal structure, external geometric form, dimensions, and mutual relationships in space. These aspects of geologic bodies are the subject matter of *structural geology*. Within this field, uniquely geological concepts and methods have been developed, conforming to the dictates of peculiarly geological conditions: the nature of geological materials, the length of the geological time scale, and the great range of dimensions involved—for geologic bodies exist on all scales from that of a crystal to that of a continent.

Structural geology includes geometric description of the form and internal structure of geological bodies of every size, and use of these data to reconstruct modes of origin and evolution in terms of physical processes operating in the earth. In this chapter we concentrate on the descriptive aspects of geologic structures and some of the methods by which they can be investigated. Genetic implications are examined more fully in later chapters, and methods of graphical representation are introduced in the Appendix. Structure on the smallest scale, as exemplified within crystals, has already been

covered. At the opposite end of the dimensional scale, study of the structure of the earth as a whole is the province of the seismologist and the solid-earth geophysicist. Here we discuss the structure and form of bodies that make up the accessible crust.

In geology the word "structure" has the familiar dual connotation of ordinary usage: (1) the interrelation of parts in an organized whole; (2) an entire complex structural entity (for example, an edifice). Thus the spatial arrangement of crystals in a rock specimen defines its internal structure, which in turn influences the properties of the rock as such. On a larger scale the sedimentary rock sequence overlying a basement of metamorphic rocks, as exposed near the bottom of the Grand Canyon of the Colorado River (Figure 3–1), can be considered as a major unit whose component parts are individual rock layers. Each layer is sufficiently uniform in character to be so designated in the geological section (Figure 3–1). Each is separated from its neighbors by a recognizable surface of discontinuity. The rock layers, their surfaces of separation, and the sharp surface of contact between the sedimentary sequence and the underlying basement are the major structural components of the body of sedimentary rocks.

A more complex situation as seen on a larger scale is illustrated in another vertical cross section in Figure 3–2. A sedimentary sequence initially comparable to that of Figure 3–1 has been deformed by folding and faulting and cut by intrusive bodies of igneous rock (injected as magma from below). Structural features of the whole section include the geometric relationships and forms of folded layers and intrusive igneous bodies, attitudes of faults and displacements upon them, and many features on a scale too small to be shown in the figure. Each individual fold can itself be called a structure in the second sense noted above.

On whatever scale he may be working, the geologist recognizes, measures, and records the distribution of geologic bodies having some degree of homogeneity, and the surfaces of discontinuity or "contacts" that separate them. Homogeneity is relative, and depends on scale. A major sedimentary layer in Figure 3–1 may be homogeneous to the extent that it is dominantly sandstone rather than shale. Its form is essentially a flat-lying sheet. It can be considered—and is so shown in Figure 3–1—as a large-scale body with recognizable attributes of form, dimension, composition, and related properties (color, porosity, and so on). Seen on a smaller scale this same body is no longer homogeneous. It is divisible into smaller units, the distribution and configuration of which define its *internal structure*. Recognizable internal features include thin beds of somewhat shaly character; and these may show local minor fracturing and folding resulting from rather uneven deformation during and immediately following deposition of beds in what still remains an essentially flat-lying major unit. On a smaller scale still, internal structure can be further refined. A sandstone specimen from any constituent bed of the major unit is microscopically heterogeneous. Its own internal structure is defined by the nature, shape, and distribution of component mineral grains (for example, quartz, feldspar, and clay) and microscopic rock fragments. In general, the external boundaries of small-scale bodies are components of the internal structure of bodies studied on any larger scale.

Geological Mapping

Geological investigation begins in the field. Growth of geology as a science received its first great impetus in the later years of the eighteenth century when Smith was constructing his first geological maps and Hutton was observing and pondering the significance of effects of erosion, mountain building, and igneous intrusion as recorded in rock outcrops and the landscape. Today any geological study worthy of the name begins with field observation; and this centers on the nature, form, structure, and spatial relations of geologic bodies. The general nature of the component rocks is determined with the simplest of equipment—a hammer and a hand lens. Attitudes of structural surfaces such as bedding planes are measured with a combination compass–clinometer.[1] The same instrument is used to locate stations at which observations are made and specimens collected. These data are recorded, with other pertinent information, in a notebook and plotted directly on a topographic map or on an air photograph to yield a geologic map. The most important concept underlying geologic mapping is that of a "mappable" rock unit or *formation*. There is no strict definition of a formation other than that it is a body of rock with sufficient internal uniformity in composition and structure and with sufficiently discrete surfaces of contact with surrounding rocks that it can be recognized in the field and that its boundaries can be followed and represented on a map of suitable scale by a line (the contact line of the formation) delineating its aerial extent. In general a formation is a genetically distinct unit formed under one set of geological conditions, and not uncommonly a formation is of the same age throughout, or it was formed through a definite period of time. But time uniformity is not a necessary property of a mappable body and some formations clearly transgress time boundaries as shown by variations in their fossil content or radiometric ages from place to place (see Chapter 4).

---

[1] Most generally used in the United States is the Brunton Pocket Transit.

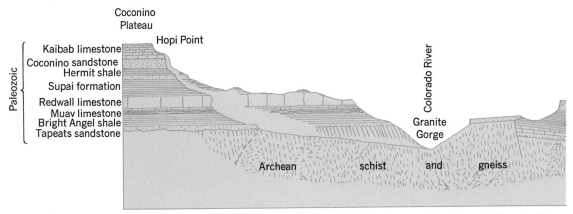

FIG. 3–1 (Above and facing) *Vertical cross section through part of the Grand Canyon of the Colorado River in Arizona showing boundaries between main formations.*

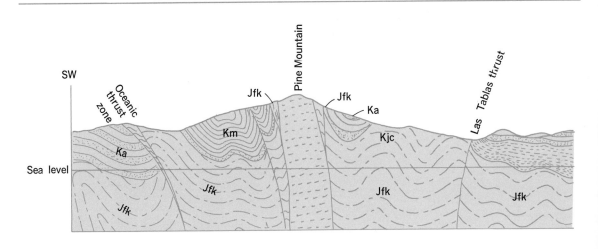

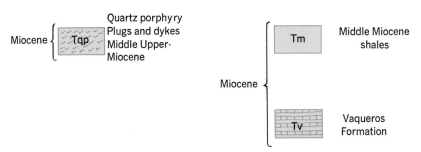

FIG. 3–2 (Above and facing) *Vertical cross section through part of the Santa Lucia Range, California, showing folding, faulting, and igneous intrusion. (After N. L. Taliaferro, Cretaceous and Paleocene of Santa Lucia Range, California, Am. Assoc. Petrol. Geol. Bull., 1944.)*

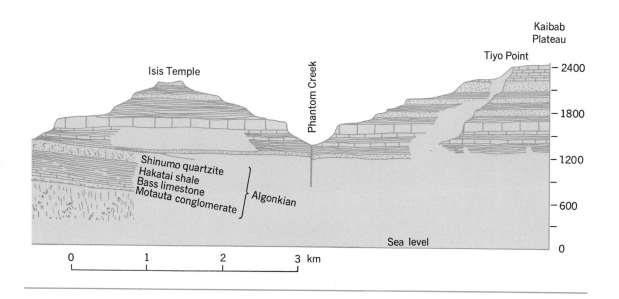

Isis Temple

Phantom Creek

Kaibab
Plateau

Tiyo Point

— 2400

— 1800

— 1200

Shinumo quartzite
Hakatai shale
Bass limestone
Motauta conglomerate

Algonkian

— 600

Sea level

0

0   1   2   3 km

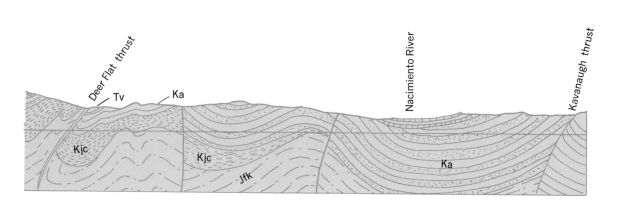

Deer Flat thrust

Tv   Ka

Nacimiento River

Kavanaugh thrust

Kjc

Kjc

Jfk

Ka

Unconformity

Upper
Cretaceous

Ka   Asuncion
Group

Lower
Cretaceous

Km   Marmolejo
formation

Unconformity

Unconformity

Kjc

Upper
Jurassic

Jfk   Franciscan-Knoxville Group
Undifferentiated, Structure
generalized. All intrusions
omitted

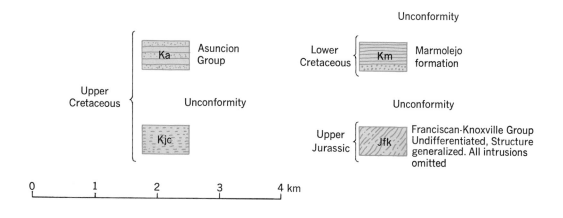

0   1   2   3   4 km

A geologist selects formational boundaries to map in a particular region on the basis of several factors the most important of which are the nature of the rocks and the scale upon which the map is to be made. A map of an area made on the scale of 1:100,000 must necessarily show fewer formational contacts than a map of the same area made on the scale of 1:10,000. Commonly a geologic map is published on a scale smaller than the one at which it was prepared, and many of the formations mapped in the field have to be combined and simplified for publication. Some bodies are so heterogeneous in their compositional and structural properties on a small scale that they cannot be subdivided and thus they are mapped as one "undifferentiated" formation in spite of the fact that many different rock types are present.

The primary aim of the field geologist is to place contact lines between formations as accurately as possible on a map. But no geologic map is an adequate representation of a geologic body unless it supplies information on the composition, internal structure, and relative ages of the formations. This information must be gathered by the geologist and incorporated into the finished map. From such a map, together with information obtained by laboratory investigation of selected samples, emerges a geologic picture of a part of the earth's crust. By mapping, and correlating formations in, larger and larger areas the geologist discovers structural patterns too large to be observed directly. Structural units much more extensive than formations become evident, and the lines placed on maps become progressively more general. Such tectonic units can range in size from relatively small features a few kilometers in extent up to the largest identifiable tectonic divisions of the crust —the continents and ocean basins.

We have seen that the geologist begins his investigations on a small scale—on hand specimens and on exposures that he can observe directly. Few areas of the earth's surface have continuous exposure of crustal rocks (most are discontinuously covered by a veneer of superficial deposit, weathered material, vegetation, water, or ice; others are inaccessible) and the

geologists must interpolate between his direct observations to make a geologic map. In a single exposure structural features can generally be observed in three dimensions. As the scale of observable structures increases with growth of the map, there is some corresponding increase in the geologist's view of form and structure in relationship to depth; but, in the absence of data from borings, mines, or geophysical investigation, this is limited by the degree of topographic relief. Extrapolation again becomes necessary—this time downward by geometrical projection from the surface. Now the geologic picture becomes somewhat obscured by the subjective element in geologic interpretation and speculation. In fact, even though two competent geologists may produce almost identical maps of a given area, they may arrive at significantly different but equally defensible conclusions as to the three-dimensional structural picture. Faced with several possible interpretations, the geologist will usually choose the simplest—always being prepared to abandon his choice should new data favor an alternative model.

A simple initial classification of structures is based upon size or scale. The geologist generally investigates the structure of rocks on three different scales. His closest view of rocks is in the hand specimen and through a microscope. The most important feature of rocks on this scale is their polycrystalline nature, and many of the structural features visible in hand specimens can be tied directly to the arrangements of grains.

On a larger scale, structures of limited size can be observed directly in exposures, generally in three dimensions. These minor structures (bedding surfaces, small folds, faults, and so on) are of great importance as indicators of the large scale or major structures of the crust, which can be observed only indirectly by mapping.

This division of the structural features of the crust is arbitrary and reflects the dimensions of the average geologist and the way in which these force him to work. In fact, no clear distinction between the microscopic, minor, and major structures of the crust can be made, and essentially identical structures (for example, folds) can occur on all three scales. Some of the largest structures—for example, the continents—are, however, unique.

Rocks as Polycrystalline Aggregates

Most rocks are aggregates of mineral crystals ("grains") of one or more kinds closely packed into a coherent structure with or without voids. A few exceptional rocks depart from this definition: For example, obsidian consists partly or wholly of glass formed by the chilling of a silicate melt during sudden volcanic eruption at the earth's surface, and conglomerates, breccias, and similar rocks consist partly or wholly of fragments of older rocks.

The range in mean grain diameter of rocks consisting dominantly of discrete crystalline grains is very large. The finest grained sedimentary rocks, clay and mudstones, contain clay particles less than 0.005 mm in diameter. A typical medium-grained igneous rock has a grain size from 1 to 5 mm and certain very-coarse-grained igneous and metamorphic rocks contain crystals several centimeters or more in largest dimension. A hand specimen (say, about 500 cm^3) of an "average" medium grained rock with grains close to 1 mm in diameter contains about half a million grains.

A geologist who looks at such a rock specimen with the naked eye is observing the mean appearance of a very large number of relatively small crystals, which may be very different from the appearance of the crystals themselves. For example, medium-grained granites are commonly pink or red as seen in a hand specimen. Study with a hand lens reveals that the component minerals vary widely in color and luster from the vitreous dark quartz and pink potash feldspar that compose the bulk of the rock through generally white or glassy plagioclase feldspar to the black of biotite or hornblende commonly found in such granites. Similarly, the bulk physical properties of a rock (such as density or thermal conductivity) express the mean properties of very large numbers of crystals, none of which may agree exactly with those of the rock. Some ("monomineralic") rocks contain only one mineral species. But even these have properties differing slightly from those of a pure mineral crystal because the crystals do not fit together in crystallographic continuity. In such rocks, spaces and other imperfections are present along the boundaries between misoriented crystals (otherwise the "rock" would be a giant single crystal) and those physical properties that are directionally dependent in crystals are not uniform throughout the rock on a microscopic scale.

The structure of a hand specimen of a rock, therefore, has two aspects. First is the nature and interrelationship of individual grains; this aspect is generally termed *texture*. Second, a structurally homogeneous body of rock that is heterogeneous on a smaller scale has a *fabric* defined by the regular geometric repetition of elements such as crystal lattices, grain aggregates, beds, and cleavages. Both of these aspects depend primarily upon the physical processes that initially formed the rock and have subsequently modified it. So characteristic, for example, are the textures of igneous, sedimentary, and metamorphic rocks that a single glance through a microscope will generally permit a geologist to place a rock in one of these categories.

TEXTURES IN RELATION TO ROCK-FORMING PROCESSES

Readily recognizable in the texture of any rock is the influence of one or another of the four genetic processes upon which the primary divisions of rock classification are based: deposition of suspended grains from a fluid medium; precipitation of crystals from aqueous solution; crystallization of silicate melts (magmas); metamorphism of preexisting rocks.

DEPOSITION The main constituents of most sedimentary rocks are mineral grains or rock fragments deposited from suspension in water, air, or (in a special environment) ice. Under the influence of gravity, a polar vector quantity, grains tend to come to rest with their longest dimensions subparallel to the surface of deposition. Another gravity-controlled effect is sorting of grains according to size, shape, and density as they sink at different rates in the fluid medium of deposi-

FIG. 3–3 *Characteristic textural features of clastic or fragmental sedimentary rock (sandstone). The largest grains are about 2.0 mm in diameter.*

tion. This plays a significant role in the bedding of water- and air-laid sediments. Depositional textures are characteristic, too, of *pyroclastic* rocks —accumulations of volcanic debris deposited from air. Certain igneous textures also show the influence of deposition. Here layers of mineral crystals settling under gravity in static or slowly convecting bodies of magma show textural characteristics analagous to those of water-laid sediments.

Characteristic textural features of most deposited rocks are the lack of correspondence or good fit along grain boundaries, and the common presence of voids or pores between groups of grains (Figure 3–3). Mineral grains either arrive or are formed in the basin of sedimentation with a shape characteristic of their origin (generally as *clastic* grains, broken and sometimes worn and rounded fragments of older crystals and rocks) and the aggregation of these to form a new rock is governed by mechanical positioning and sorting under the relatively weak force of gravity aided by currents in the depositing medium and gradients in the floor of the basin. If the grains in a sedimentary rock are all of similar size and character, the rock is said to be well-sorted; if they vary widely in size and shape the rock is said to be poorly sorted. Some grains are clearly broken and rounded fragments of older minerals and rocks; others are euhedral crystals that have been transported a very short distance from their source area or may have been chemically or or-

ganically precipitated in the basin of deposition.

Most deposited sediments are transformed into coherent rocks by *diagenetic* changes taking place after deposition. These include compaction, the partial closing of pores after burial under the gravitational load of overlying sediments, and cementation, the sticking together of grains at their points of contact by materials generally precipitated from fluids circulating through the interconnected pores of the sediment. In some sediments such precipitation between grains can completely fill the pores to form a very strong and effectively impermeable sedimentary rock. Common cements are calcite, hydrated iron oxides, and silica.

CRYSTALLIZATION FROM MELTS   Textures of igneous rocks are determined partly by the nature and order of crystallization of the component minerals, but mainly by kinetic factors—rates of nucleation and of crystal growth, both strongly influenced by rate of cooling and consequent degree of undercooling of the melt below the temperature of crystal-melt equilibrium. Slow cooling favors slow nucleation and growth of large crystals. Rapid cooling of surface lavas favors strong undercooling and rapid nucleation, with resultant fine-grained textures. Extremely rapid chilling may so increase the viscosity of the melt that crystallization is virtually bypassed and the final product is glass. Viscosity depends on the chemical composition of the melt; it is high-

FIG. 3–4 *Phenocrysts of feldspathoid show-ing crystal faces in fine-grained alkaline vol-canic rock. The phenocrysts are about 0.2 mm in diameter.*

est in siliceous anhydrous melts. Igneous textures show great variety, and an unnecessarily large number of names has been coined to denote and differentiate the many textural variants.[2] Here we note a few widely used terms:

Granitoid, the texture typical of granites and many of the more siliceous plutonic rocks. Slow

cooling and complete crystallization have pro-duced an aggregate of coarse equant grains, some of which (biotite, hornblende feldspar) show partially developed crystal outlines.

Porphyritic, large crystals (phenocrysts) of slowly growing early-formed minerals are en-closed in a fine-grained or partly glassy ground-mass. Outlines of phenocrysts (Figure 3–4) may be sharply defined (euhedral) or corroded by late reaction between crystal and melt.

[2] A recent short textbook on petrography (the microscopic study of rocks) contains 87 entries under "texture" in the index. Few of these are really important.

FIG. 3–5 *Elongated feldspar crystals in a state of preferred orientation in a volcanic rock (trachyte). The prisms of feldspar are about 0.2 mm in length.*

Vesicular texture is characterized by abundance of spheroidal cavities originating as gas bubbles in magma boiling under release of pressure close to the earth's surface.

Flow textures, in which elongate crystals (hornblende, feldspar) have become aligned in subparallel orientation during flow of the enclosing viscous magma (Figure 3–5).

CRYSTALLIZATION FROM SOLUTION   Some sedimentary rocks formed by deposition contain mineral grains precipitated from solution in the transporting medium. One class of sedimentary rocks, the evaporites, form by direct precipitation of crystals, generally on the floor of a basin, and represent the dissolved content of a body of water (generally a lake or inland sea) released by its complete evaporation. Evaporites consist of highly soluble salts (salines), such as chlorides, nitrates, sulfates, borates, and some carbonates, with the minerals halite, anhydrite, and gypsum predominating. These rocks are commonly cyclically laminated as a result of successive periods of evaporation.

Most rocks are at some stages in their histories affected by percolating fluids. New minerals can grow in pores and cracks from materials carried in the fluids (as in cementation), or early-formed and generally unstable minerals can react with dissolved ions in the fluids and be partly or wholly replaced by new minerals. Sometimes the crystallographic habit or form of the old mineral is preserved anomalously in a replacement crystal of a different system or class. Such crystals are termed *pseudomorphs* and are particularly common in igneous rocks that have been affected by late-stage, relatively high-temperature aqueous fluids, left as the unsolidified phase of a crystallized magma.

Associated with many igneous and metamorphic rocks are irregular bodies of rock (veins, dikes, and so on) that appear to have crystallized almost entirely from high temperature solutions rather than from melts. Many of these are rich in unusual elements that do not fit easily into the structures of most common rock-forming silicates, and rare and sometimes economically valuable minerals (ore minerals) are formed. The most spectacular of these bodies are the *pegmatites* associated with granitic intrusions. They are characterized by very coarse grain size: Single crystals in some of them reach a meter or more in length.

METAMORPHISM   Metamorphic textures develop during reconstitution of sedimentary and igneous rocks in the solid state. They are dictated by three factors: (1) composition and texture of the parent rock; (2) physical conditions of metamorphism (temperature, pressure, shearing stresses); (3) interplay of crystal deformation and growth of new crystals. Many though not all metamorphic rocks show textural evidence of deformation by cohesive flow. Individual grains become elongated or bent by plastic flow, internal evidence (Figure 3–6) of which may persist as twin lamellae (as in calcite), kink bands (in mica), or deformation lamellae of complex origin (as in quartz). Grains of more brittle minerals such as garnet or feldspar become fractured and ultimately granulated without losing cohesion—a process termed cataclastic flow (Figure 3–7). The extreme products of rapid cataclasis are hard, flinty-looking, very fine-grained rocks called mylonites. Cohesive flow is by no means entirely a mechanical process. Annealing of highly strained material and recrystallization of old and crystallization of new minerals under stress—a process analogous to hot working of metals—very commonly yield an ultimate product whose grain size is much greater than that of the parent rock. Moreover, recrystallization more often than not outlasts flow so that the individual grains in the final product are then unstrained even though the rock as a whole has been intensely deformed at one or more stages of its metamorphic history.

The most outstanding textural feature of most metamorphic rocks is the tendency for inequant grains to have their long dimensions preferentially oriented (such grains are said to be in a state of *preferred orientation*). Many of the characteristic structures of metamorphic rocks visible in hand specimens (such as the cleavage of a slate or the schistosity of a schist) are expressions of this tendency, which will be considered below with respect to fabrics. In most mica schists, for example, there is a pronounced preferred orientation of the mica crystals tabular in the plane {001}. It is this preferred orientation which gives the schist its characteristic platy structure visible in hand specimens. Not all metamorphic rocks contain inequant minerals in a state of preferred orientation. Some clearly undeformed metamorphic rocks—notably the *hornfelses,* formed by static recrystallization in response to hydrostatic pressure and high temperature—are characterized by a random orientation of tabular or equant mica crystals and more closely resemble most igneous rocks in their textural features.

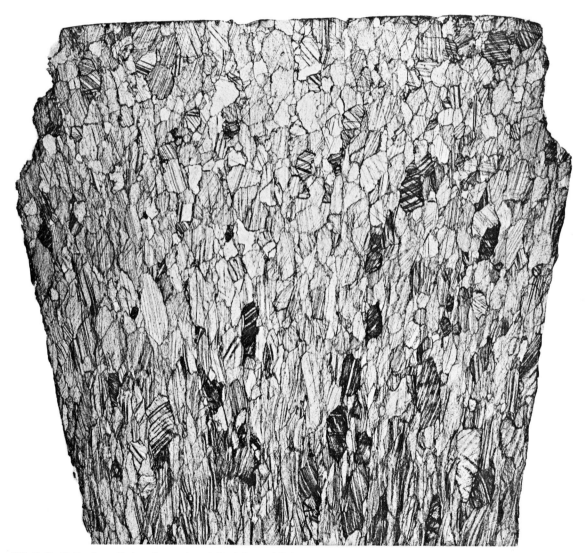

FIG. 3–6 *Half of a cylinder of experimentally deformed Yule marble. The upper part is undeformed; the amount of deformation increases downward as shown by elongation of grains and appearance of mechanical twin lamellae and other structures formed by plastic deformation. The upper part of the specimen is 1 cm wide.*

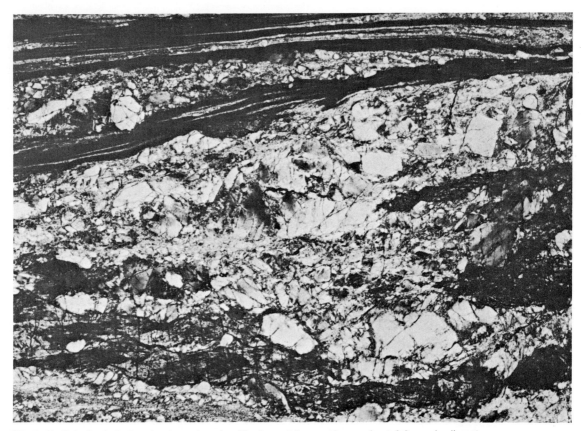

FIG. 3–7 *Cataclastic texture in sheared gneiss. The largest fragments are about 0.3 mm in diameter.*

A common and important textural feature of many metamorphic rocks is the presence of *porphyroblasts*, mineral crystals significantly larger than surrounding grains which have grown in the solid rock (Figure 3–8). Many different minerals, including feldspars, amphiboles, micas, and garnets can grow as porphyroblasts in rocks of suitable composition under appropriate metamorphic conditions. Some are inequant and grow with a state of preferred orientation or randomly. Others are equant; many are euhedral.

Porphyroblasts grow in a solid rock by replacement or displacement of earlier grains, some of which occasionally survive as "inclusions." This texture is useful in establishing sequences of periods of deformation and recrystallization or mineral growth during the history of a metamorphic rock. Some porphyroblasts grown prior to a period of deformation (prekinematic crystallization) enclose structures that have been destroyed elsewhere in the rock. Inside the porphyroblast the earlier structures presumably were protected by the mechanically strong material in which they are embedded. Many garnet porphyroblasts contain strings of inclusions arranged in a spiral pattern explicable only by assuming that the crystals rotated in a flowing matrix as they grew (synkinematic crystallization). In still other porphyroblasts the fact that the pattern of inclusions exactly corresponds to the pattern of similar grains in the surrounding matrix suggests that the large crystals grew after all deformation had ceased (postkinematic crystallization). Much about the history of those

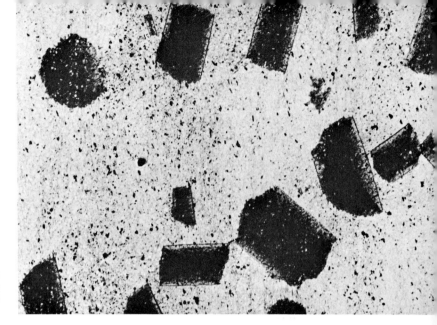

FIG. 3–8 *Porphyroblastic crystals of a metamorphic mineral (ottrelite) grown in a fine-grained schist. Porphyroblasts are about 1.0 mm in diameter.*

metamorphic rocks, called *tectonites*, whose structure is primarily due to deformation can be learned by study of such porphyroblasts.

Similar principles apply to the interpretation of textures in all metamorphic rocks and careful study of the relationships between grains can sometimes uncover a long and complicated history in which periods of new mineral growth and partial recrystallization have alternated with periods of deformation. A knowledge of the history of a rock gained in this way can sometimes aid the geologist in understanding larger scale structures of metamorphic bodies.

ROCK FABRIC AND PREFERRED ORIENTATION OF CRYSTALS A rock may have an internal regularity not unlike that of a crystal, with a unit cell replaced by a representative sample and arbitrary instead of periodic translations. It is said to have a fabric (also termed microfabric or grain fabric). The most important structural feature defining the fabric of a rock is the preferred orientation of grains by shape (as discussed above) or by crystal lattice. Some minerals have a shape or habit controlled largely by crystal structure; for example, mica occurs generally in crystals strongly tabular in the plane {001} (the cleavage plane) and a planar preferred orientation by shape requires that the {001} planes are in the same state of preferred orientation. Rocks with such fabrics are generally foliated in hand specimen to a degree depending

on the proportion of mica in the specimen and the degree of preferred orientation. Other minerals occur generally in equant grains and a preferred orientation of a particular crystallographic direction (for example, the [0001] direction in quartz) is not necessarily expressed in a hand specimen by any visible structure.

A state of preferred orientation by crystal lattice can be established by measuring the orientation of crystals within a representative sample. This can be done with a microscope by noting the orientations in many grains. These orientations are then plotted on an equal-area projection (Appendix) to obtain a fabric diagram that can be contoured to show the density distribution of plotted points (Figure 3–9). Preferred orientations can also be determined by means of X rays and specially constructed cameras. The data are generally recorded on a film from which a fabric diagram can be prepared, preferably with the aid of a computer.

Preferred orientation of grains is not the only factor that contributes to the fabric of a rock; the spatial distribution of grains and groups of grains is also important. In many rocks grains of a particular kind are not uniformly distributed on a microscopic scale but are concentrated into small bodies of inequant but systematic shape, generally with preferred orientations of their long dimensions. These bodies may be layers, lens-shaped clumps, or rodlike and spindle-shaped aggregates. With respect to the hand specimen

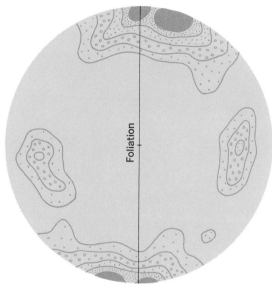

Foliation

FIG. 3–9 *Fabric diagram (equal area projection) showing preferred orientation of [0001]-axes in a quartzite. The diagram is contoured for density distribution of points so that contours enclose regions with 1, 2, 4, 6, and 8 percent of all the points per 1 percent area of the projection (see Appendix).*

these bodies are generally very small, but their preferred orientation commonly imparts to it a prominent linear structure or *lineation*. Similarly, closely spaced fracture or slip surfaces and many similar features contribute to the fabric of a rock provided that they are uniformly distributed throughout a specimen on a very small scale.

Many structural features define the fabric of a given rock containing several different mineral species and no complete study of all of these can be made. A geologist will look only at those features of a fabric that appear to bear upon his particular problem. Thus, for example, in a sandstone or greywacke a geologist might study only the preferred orientation of the long axis of prismatic grains in an effort to determine current directions in the basin of deposition; or in a strongly deformed marble he might study the preferred orientation of [0001]-axis of calcite grains and attempt to correlate what he finds with results from controlled deformation of a similar rock under experimental conditions in-

tended to simulate those of nature. In some rocks different features of the fabric give information about different aspects of the forming process or about different episodes in the history of the rock.

SYMMETRY OF ROCK FABRIC

From the foregoing discussion it is clear that the geologist can learn much about the formation and subsequent history of a rock by studying its microscopic textural and fabric features. The physical properties of a rock must also depend in some way on these features. But it has proved surprisingly difficult to obtain quantitative interpretations of natural structures and physical properties and the most useful feature of fabric in this respect has proved to be its symmetry. This symmetry is related in some way both to the symmetries of the processes that have operated to produce the fabric and the symmetries of the physical properties of the rock.

In Chapter 2 we encountered Neumann's principle as a relationship between the point group symmetry of a crystal and the symmetry of its physical properties. Similar "symmetry principles" can be stated governing the relationships between other functionally related physical phenomena of which the most general governs the relationship between "influences" and "effects." We can consider the development of a rock fabric as the effect of some influence acting either upon the materials from which the rock is made, or upon a preexisting fabric. Thus a functional relationship exists between a fabric and the combined influences and properties that produced it, closely resembling that governing the physical properties of crystals. The general symmetry principle states that the symmetry of an effect cannot be *less* than the combined symmetry of the phenomena that produced it.[3] This principle is best illustrated by a geological ex-

---

[3] This principle, known as Curie's principle, is most succinctly stated as a relationship between "cause" and "effect" as follows: *cause symmetry is a subgroup of effect symmetry*. Thus the symmetry group of an effect can contain the same operations as the symmetry group of cause or more; it cannot contain fewer.

ample. Consider rod-shaped grains sinking under gravity in still water in a basin with a horizontal floor. The phenomena contributing to the formation of the resultant sedimentary fabric are the force of gravity, the isotropic properties of the standing water, and the axially symmetric mineral grains. We can see intuitively that the long dimensions of the settled grains will acquire a horizontal planar preferred orientation and that they will show no tendency towards a linear preferred orientation in this plane. The resultant fabric, defined by the shape orientation of the grains, will be statistically axially symmetric (point group $\infty/m\,2/m\,2/m$) and is more symmetric than the contributing phenomenon with lowest symmetry (the polar force of gravity with symmetry ∞mm, a subgroup of $\infty/m\,2/m\,2/m$). Under no circumstances will the resultant fabric be *less* symmetric than the superposed symmetries of the contributing phenomena, and this is all that the principle states. In Chapter 9 we shall look at the application of this symmetry principle to the interpretation of the fabrics of deformed rocks.

A given rock, therefore, has a definite fabric symmetry, which can generally be determined by examining the preferred orientations of one or two minerals and other internal structures and determining their statistical symmetry. By means of Neumann's principle modified to apply to polycrystalline aggregates we can see that the symmetry of the physical properties of a rock must be related to the symmetry of its fabric. For example, from Neumann's principle we know that quartz is anisotropic with respect to thermal conductivity and that the coefficient in the [0001] direction is unique. A rock (such as a quartzite) made entirely of quartz with strong linear preferred orientation of [0001]-axis can be treated as a physical continuum on a scale where the individual crystals are of insignificant size and it will be anisotropic with respect to thermal conductivity on that scale. We can see intuitively that the direction of preferred orientation of [0001]-directions will have a unique coefficient of thermal conductivity and that the symmetry of this property for the rock as a whole (but not the values) will reflect the symmetry of the preferred orientation of quartz according to Neu-

mann's principle. However, the extreme values of components of a tensor are generally closer together for a rock than for the component minerals, because the anisotropy present in the minerals tends to be reduced by the fact that the grains in a rock do not have exactly the same orientation. In fact, many rocks consist of randomly oriented anisotropic minerals and are structurally isotropic. Thus rocks are in general less anisotropic than the minerals that compose them. But there is no a priori rule giving the symmetry of a physical property in a particular rock as it depends on fabric symmetry; two granites of the same composition, for instance, may have different fabrics and thus different properties.

Rock fabrics have been extensively studied for many years by geologists and relatively few point groups have been established as common in natural fabrics. These groups are listed in Table 3–1 with examples of processes that could form fabrics with the corresponding symmetries. Many other examples could be given.

PERVASIVE STRUCTURES OF ROCKS

Many of the structural features that contribute to the internal structure and fabric of a rock are

TABLE 3–1 *Symmetry groups of natural fabrics*

Symmetry Group	Description	Example of Origin
$\dfrac{\infty\ \infty\ \infty}{m\ m\ m}$	spherical	metamorphism of an isotropic rock under hydrostatic pressure
$\dfrac{\infty\ 2\ 2}{m\ m\ m}$	axial	sedimentation in a stationary medium on a horizontal floor
$\dfrac{2\ 2\ 2}{m\ m\ m}$	orthorhombic	deformation by progressive pure strain
$\dfrac{2}{m}$	monoclinic	deformation by progressive homogeneous shear
$\bar{1}$	triclinic	oblique overprinting of one fabric on another (common in tectonics)

visible also on the scale of a hand specimen or larger. Such features as preferred orientation of grains by shape, preferred orientation of inequidimensional aggregates, presence of closely spaced fracture or slip surfaces, and so on, impart to a hard specimen of a rock obvious planar and linear structures that appear to pervade the whole specimen. In some rocks the planar structures are surfaces of easy breakage as in the examples of the cleavage of a slate and some bedding; in others they are very weakly defined and have no marked effect upon simple mechanical properties.

Such structures can be termed pervasive or penetrative structures and for practical purposes they can be considered to be present at every point in the rock in much the same way as the cleavage of a crystal, controlled by the packing of atomic layers, is considered to be present at every point in a crystal. Examples of such structures are the foliations and lineations of deformed rocks, introduced previously. Similar pervasive planar and linear structures are commonly present also in rocks of sedimentary or igneous origin.

SEDIMENTARY ROCKS   The most important pervasive structures in sedimentary rocks are formed at the time of deposition or soon afterwards, during compaction. These are pervasive bedding and current lineations. Bedding stratification of the kind illustrated diagrammatically in Figures 3–1 and 3–2 expresses changes in source material, rate of supply of sediment, and so on, but it is generally accompanied by microscopic lamination within individual beds and planar preferred orientations of inequant grains, which make most sedimentary beds internally anisotropic. Similarly, currents in the depositing medium tend to align elongated grains (generally parallel to the flow vector during descent and even perpendicular to it if the grains roll slightly on the floor of the basin) and form pervasive linear structures (grain lineations) generally lying in the bedding planes.

IGNEOUS ROCKS   Many volcanic and plutonic igneous rocks contain pervasive planar and linear structures formed by flow in the partly solidified melt during extrusion and intrusion. Inequant grains can acquire preferred orientations, both planar and linear, in the flowing melt, and certain rocks become laminated and banded on a microscopic scale. Terms such as flow lamination, flow banding, flow foliation and lineation have been used to describe these structures.

METAMORPHIC ROCKS AND TECTONITES   The most complex and most widely distributed pervasive structures are found in those rocks formed in response to deformation and metamorphism. Some tectonites contain several generations of pervasive structures formed during successive events. The relative ages of these structures can

FIG. 3–10 Slaty cleavage (steeply inclined) oblique to bedding (gently inclined) in mudstone.

FIG. 3–11 *Foliation in metamorphic rock defined by layers and lenticles cut by incipient secondary foliation (parallel to pencil).*

generally be established by direct inspection or by microscopic study. In some rocks primary pervasive structures have survived deformation and metamorphism. Many terms have been used to describe the pervasive structures of metamorphic rocks. The most general term for all planar structures is foliation and for all linear structures lineation. Some of the commonest types are now described.

Slaty cleavage   A very regular platy fissility found generally in weakly metamorphosed and deformed very fine and fine-grained sedimentary rocks such as mudstones, shales, and siltstones (Figure 3–10). Microscopically it is defined by the preferred orientation of extremely small platy minerals generally oblique to bedding. Rocks with slaty cleavage (slates) split with ease into unusually smooth and continuous tabular plates.

Schistosity   A planar structure resembling slaty cleavage in being defined largely by the planar preferred orientation of platy or prismatic crystals (such as mica and amphibole respectively); it is found, however, in coarser grained rocks such as schists and amphibolites, in which the individual crystals can be seen with the naked eye or a low-power hand lens. Schistosity is commonly emphasized by a tendency for grains of particular compositions to be segregated into very thin laminae or flattened lenticular aggregates as the result of metamorphism (Figure

3–11). Schistosity appears to be gradationally related to slaty cleavage by way of the lustrous foliations of phyllites. These are strongly foliated rocks intermediate in grain size and degree of metamorphism between the slates and the schists. With increasing coarseness of grain and degree of metamorphism, schistosity passes into the foliation of the coarse-grained metamorphic rocks, the *gneisses*. In these rocks equant minerals such as quartz and feldspar generally tend to dominate and the foliation is less marked as a planar preferred orientation of minerals and is not always a surface of easy cleavage. But segregation of light and dark colored minerals into layers is generally more pronounced, and most gneissic foliation is accompanied by a prominent "banding."

Bedding foliation   The growth of inequant minerals and the appearance of segregation laminae and shear surfaces in the plane of sedimentary bedding during metamorphism result in bedding foliation. In strongly metamorphosed rocks it can be difficult or impossible to distinguish bedding foliation from foliations of purely metamorphic origin (many of which form oblique to bedding). Features which help in the identification of bedding foliation are great continuity of the laminae, the presence of continuous concordant layers of peculiarly sedimentary composition (such as a marble layer in a schist), and geometrical correspondence of foliation with mapped formational relationships of clearly sedimentary origin. In general, bedding foliation survives only in metamorphic rocks that have been relatively weakly deformed. Folding and shearing on a small scale (the commonest reaction of layered rocks to deformation) soon obliterates bedding and can destroy stratigraphic continuity on a large scale. Geologists working in metamorphic terrains must be particularly careful not to confuse foliations developed by deformation with bedding. Such confusion can lead to erroneous determination of stratigraphic relationships and misinterpretation of structure and geologic history.

Secondary foliations   We use the term "secondary foliations" to group together foliations which clearly cut and disrupt earlier foliations

FIG. 3–12 *Bedding (inclined downward to the left) undergoing transposition into a vertical foliation.*

or bedding laminations. Many terms—such as strain-slip foliation, fracture cleavage, crenulation cleavage, transposition foliation, and so on—have been used to describe varieties of these structures. The main difference between these foliations and those previously described is that they are less pervasive, being closely spaced sets of relatively discrete surfaces between which are thin laminae preserving the earlier foliation. They are generally associated with folding and bending of the earlier foliation. Secondary foliations vary greatly in character and in the spacing of the foliation surfaces. Some of them appear to be purely mechanical in origin and are closely spaced sharp fracture surfaces or surfaces of shear displacement coated with mylonite into which neighboring grains are bent. Others are clearly associated with growth of minerals and recrystallization. Progressive development of secondary foliation leads to the complete obliteration (transposition) of the earlier foliation or lamination and the disruption of any continuous layers into isolated lens-shaped bodies (boudins) commonly internally folded. The new foliation can become intensified by metamorphism; segregation of new minerals into certain surfaces may even give it a laminated appearance. An example of such a transposition foliation, which is well-developed at the expense of bedding, is illustrated in Figure 3–12. As this process goes to completion a uniformly foliated rock is formed in which the only evidence of the previous existence of an earlier foliation (or bedding) is the local presence of boudins and discontinuous flattened and folded shreds of the transposed layers. Many regular metamorphic foliations appear to have originated in this way, and some rocks can be shown to have undergone several periods of deformation in each of which earlier foliations were folded and transposed.

Lineations   The pervasive linear structures of metamorphic and deformed rocks are referred to as lineations. Like foliations they vary widely in their properties, and many terms have been invented to describe them. They are defined microscopically by such features as linear preferred orientations of inequant grains and groups of grains, intersecting pervasive planar structures (generally bedding and foliation), and microscopic crenulations. A strongly lineated metamorphic rock is illustrated in Figure 3–13.

MAPPING OF PERVASIVE STRUCTURES

Present-day geologists are aware of the important information about the past locked in the pervasive structures of rocks of all kinds, and most field geologists study the nature of these structures and map their positions and orientations as a matter of course. New techniques based on such mapping and accompanying studies of texture and fabric have been developed: In sedimentary formations, for example, analysis of grain lineations and similar structures has led to the determination of paleocurrent directions in long-vanished bodies of water and in the ancient atmosphere; in igneous rocks, the patterns of flow during extrusion and intrusion have been established; in deformed rocks, different episodes of deformation and metamorphism have been detected and placed in time sequence and related to local and large-scale strains and flow patterns in the crust; in rocks of all kinds, directions of remanent magnetization have been used to obtain information on the past magnetic field of the earth. Many more examples could be given.

Pervasive structures are "mapped" in the field primarily by the determination of their orientation at specific localities. In general, they are curved on a large scale and patchily developed, and measurements are made on planes and lines tangent to the structures in order to determine the patterns of curvature and spatial distribution. This procedure resembles "fabric analysis" on a large scale in that the individual attitudes of the pervasive structures play a role in a large body resembling that of crystallographic planes and lines in a thin section by providing, when suitably plotted, a geometric image of the internal structure.

Geographical coordinates are used also to specify the orientations of planar and linear structures. The attitude of a planar structure (S in Figure 3–14) is specified by two angles: The

FIG. 3–13 *Strong lineation lying in the foliation of a gneiss.*

strike is the azimuth of the horizontal line contained within it and the *dip* is the angle of inclination of the planar structure measured in a vertical plane. The measured attitude at a particular locality is recorded on the map in the same position by some conventional symbol. The most commonly used symbol is the one shown in Figure 3–14. The long line indicates the strike and the number at its upper end the azimuth in degrees east or west of north. If this number is near to zero or ninety, the letter E or W can be added to avoid confusion. The short line and number determine the direction and amount of dip (special symbols are sometimes used for vertical and horizontal planar structures). If the atti-

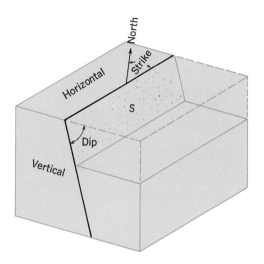

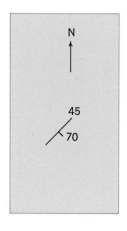

FIG. 3–14 Attitude of a planar structure S expressed in terms of two angles: the strike, the azimuth of the horizontal line contained within it; and the dip, the angle of inclination of S measured in a vertical plane. At right is shown a conventional map symbol for a planar structure striking N45°E and dipping 70°SE.

tudes of several different planar structures are being shown on the map the short line can be replaced by other directional ornaments such as a double line, a rectangle, and so on.

The attitude of a linear structure (L in Figure 3–15) is also specified by two angles: The *trend* is the strike of the vertical plane containing the linear structure and the *plunge* is the inclination of the linear structure in this plane (these quantities correspond respectively to declination and inclination of the magnetic field). The most generally used map symbol is the arrow shown in Figure 3–15. The upper number gives the trend and the lower number the plunge.

Although introduced with respect to pervasive structures, the same terms can be used for *any* planar and linear geologic structures; thus, for example, a geologist will speak of the strike and dip of a fault or of the trend and plunge of a fold hinge.

Geologic Structures

Geologic structures may have the same geometric properties on all scales. Direct study of small structures on the outcrop or in the laboratory assumes great importance since their geo-

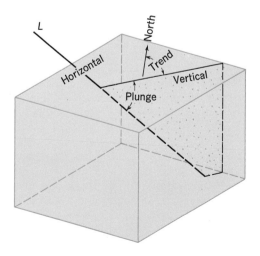

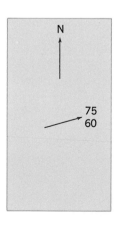

FIG. 3–15 Attitude of a linear structure L expressed in terms of two angles: the trend, the strike of the vertical plane containing L; and the plunge, the inclination of L in this plane. At right is shown a conventional map symbol for a linear structure tending N75°E and plunging 60°.

metric features are a guide to those of the largest tectonic features whose very size makes observation difficult.

POLAR STRUCTURES IN SEDIMENTARY ROCKS

The outstanding structural characteristic of sedimentary rocks on a large scale is the bedding stratification described above. A pile of sedimentary layers is a partial or complete record of conditions at the surface of a basin of deposition and, sometimes, in the surrounding areas of erosion from which the sediments are derived. The structure and composition of the layers show the variations in these conditions with time. Some sedimentary sequences are remarkably uniform throughout thicknesses of thousands of feet indicating long periods of uniform physical conditions in the basin and uniform supply of sediment. Others show cyclic or irregular changes from layer to layer indicating corresponding variations in conditions with time. Most layers vary somewhat laterally, showing also that conditions were not uniform throughout the basin at any one time.

Although most sedimentary bodies are layered, they vary markedly in shape and size. Many are tabular and of great lateral extent when compared to their thickness. Others are linear or prismatic in shape, as a result of rapid and long continued sedimentation in a subsiding trench, or wedge-shaped as a result of one-sided deposition on a slope. Some, such as the bodies of reef limestone, built by corals and other organisms, are of irregular shape and may be of greater vertical than lateral extent.

For a given series of sediments there is no a priori way of determining during what proportion of the period between the beginning and end of sedimentation sediments were actually being deposited. In certain uniform rocks with no marked bedding discontinuities, sedimentation appears to have been uniform and continuous, and if the thickness of the sediments and the length of time required to deposit them are known, the rate of sedimentation can be found simply. But most sedimentary bodies are markedly layered and laminated with rocks of

different composition or structure separated by sharp contact surfaces (bedding "planes"). There can be no doubt that some of these surfaces represent pauses in sedimentation as evidenced by signs of long-continued organic activity at the surface, erosion, and reworking of fragments by bottom currents, and, in some cases, temporary passage from an aqueous to a subaerial environment indicated by sun cracks, rain prints, the tracks of terrestrial animals, and so on. These bedding surfaces commonly represent periods of time during which no sediment was deposited and some may have been removed. The profusion of surfaces of this kind in some sedimentary sequences suggests that the total time represented by such pauses may be vastly greater than the total time represented by sediment accumulation. In some sedimentary sequences a particular surface can be shown to represent a long period of time by differences in the fossils in the rocks above and below it: such a surface is called a disconformity. It may well be that most bedding surfaces in rocks are disconformities to some degree.

The oustanding characteristic of the processes that form sedimentary rocks is that many of them have polar axial symmetry reflecting that of gravity. Many sedimentary bodies actually grow in a polar fashion—*upwards*—and many of the structures formed also have polar symmetry allowing the upward sense of the vertical direction at the time of deposition to be distinguished from the downward sense. Organic evolution is itself a polar process and use is made of this fact in determining the order in which sediments were deposited by studying their fossil content. But most sedimentary rocks lack fossils entirely or contain so few that the field geologist has only a small chance of obtaining a representative selection during the time he has available for making a map.

Some sedimentary series exposed in the crust have been relatively little disturbed since formation and are still in superposed subhorizontal layers, preserving the order in which they were deposited. More commonly the layers have been tilted, faulted, and folded and in some places inverted by earth movements. Some have been

FIG. 3–16 *Graded beds in tuffaceous sediment (each black and white division on scale is 1 cm).*

baked or metamorphosed by igneous intrusions and have had most of their fossils destroyed. In such situations polar structures become the only means of establishing the original order of superposition of the sedimentary layers and their relative ages. A great variety of such structures has been described from sedimentary rocks of different kinds. An example is graded bedding.

GRADED BEDDING   If sediment is supplied at a uniform rate to a stable basin in which the physical conditions are uniform the sedimentary rock that forms is characteristically homogeneous in its properties. In many basins the supply of sediment is irregular in quantity and kind in response to annual or other climatic cycles, to cycles of organic activity, or to local deformation, igneous activity, and like disturbances in the source area of the sediments. Under such conditions there can be at times a sudden inrush of sediments into the basin (generally in the form of a turbidity current; see page 343). A bed is rapidly deposited in which coarser grains at the base are succeeded by finer grains towards the top as a result of the differential rates of settling of grains of different sizes (Stokes' law; see page 219) from the suddenly injected and generally turbulent sedimentary current or slurry. Such beds are termed *graded beds* (Figure 3–16) and they range in size from microscopic laminae to layers many feet thick. Graded beds are particularly common in sediments deposited rapidly along continental margins where earth movements and volcanic activity are dominant. Some of them may be deposited from unstable bodies of wet sediment dislodged from a slight slope by earth tremors or gravitational forces.

Graded beds are polar structures in that their tops and bottoms can be distinguished, and since they occur generally in poorly fossiliferous rocks, which are commonly strongly folded, they are of great importance to the field geologist. Many other such structures have been described from sedimentary rocks (Chapter 8).

SOLE MARKINGS   Other polar structures in sediments are formed by disturbance of the surface of deposition by current-borne objects, organisms, and local movements in the sediments after deposition. The structures are particularly common in the type of sedimentary rock termed *flysch*, a thick succession of marine sediments consisting of layers of fine material such as shales, mudstones, or siltstones, alternating with coarse sediments, generally sandstones. The bedding is commonly graded so that the bottom of a sandstone layer rests generally on a sharp surface at the top of a shale layer, and it is on the lower surfaces or soles of the sandstone beds that the polar structures are best preserved. These structures are generally termed *sole markings*.

EARTH MOVEMENTS IN SEDIMENTARY BASINS
During sedimentation, tilting or shaking of the

newly deposited sediments can cause a segment to break loose and flow in a semicoherent fashion. The slump structures so formed can resemble the sinuous folds produced by flow in solid rocks or can form layers of brecciated and broken material in an otherwise normally bedded sequence. These structures result from minor earth movements. Some of the structures of large sedimentary bodies indicate that gross movements of the crust can occur during sedimentation. The evidence for such earth movements can be indirect; for example, a thick sequence of fine grained or chemical sediments such as limestones may be followed by deposition of a rock composed of coarse angular rock fragments clearly derived from a nearby rugged source area. Such a sequence may indicate relatively sudden uplift of neighboring parts of the crust with consequent acceleration of erosion and change in the nature of the sediment reaching the basin.

More dramatic evidence of diastrophism is given by the presence within many sedimentary sequences of angular unconformities. The fossil record may indicate that no long time break separates two beds, but careful field work may show that an upper bed transgresses laterally onto older formations with a slight angular discordance. Tilting and erosion of the earlier layers must have occurred in the relatively short period before the deposition of the later layer. Strongly angular unconformities between rocks of vastly different age (such as the unconformity at Siccar Point mentioned in Chapter 1) are clear indications of gross earth movements and periods of intense deformation separating two sedimentary sequences (see, for example, the base of the sedimentary sequence in Figure 3–1).

The sedimentary rocks of the crust do not form a continuous sheet but have been deposited patchily in ephemeral basins. In certain parts of the crust—the mobile or geosynclinal belts—great thicknesses of sediment have accumulated in relatively short periods of time. Other parts of the crust, the stable or shield areas, have remained effectively sediment-free for long periods in their history. For sedimentation to take place there must be a basin or low area of the crust to which the sedimentary material can be trans-

ported and there must be elevated areas from which the source material can be derived by erosion. A very close relationship therefore exists between those processes (deformation, uplift and depression, volcanic activity) that tend to change the elevation of the crust and sedimentation—the end product of those processes that tend to restore it to equilibrium. The study of sedimentary rocks and of deformation of the earth's crust are thus intimately linked, and must proceed together, and we shall see below that folds and faults may begin and continue to grow during the formation of a sedimentary body.

FORM AND STRUCTURE OF IGNEOUS BODIES

The geometric properties of igneous rocks are closely tied to their composition and their mode of origin. Silicate melt can solidify to form an igneous rock anywhere within the crust (and probably below it) and upon its surface. We have seen that plutonic rocks solidified below the surface as intrusions are generally medium- to coarse-grained, whereas volcanic rocks erupted on the surface tend to be fine-grained to glassy. Apart from these textural differences the forms of igneous bodies reflect clearly their volcanic or plutonic origins.

VOLCANIC BODIES Basaltic lava flows of low viscosity that are emptied from vents or fissures generally spread out as flat sheets (Figure 3–17) the bottoms of which are generally fine-grained or glassy, whereas the tops are vesicular or irregular. More viscous lavas (andesites, rhyolites, obsidians) tend to form thicker, less extensive flows and even build domes with little lateral flow. Flows emptied under water form characteristic *pillow* structures in which spheroidal bodies of lava are piled one on top of the other. Pyroclastic volcanic rocks have the polar structures typical of sedimentary rocks.

INTRUSIONS Much of the crust is composed of intrusions of plutonic rock. These range in size from granite batholiths a thousand or more kilometers in longest dimension down to diabase dikes with thicknesses measured in centimeters.

FIG. 3–17 Horizontal lava (basalt) flows exposed in the valley of the Columbia River, Oregon.

Many terms have been invented to describe them. Some terms denote size and shape; others the structural relationships of the plutonic bodies to the rocks they intrude ("country rocks").

Geometrically intrusions can be classified most simply as *sheets* and *plutons*.

Intrusive sheets   Generally tabular bodies of medium-grained plutonic rock ranging in thickness from a few centimeters to thousands of meters are referred to as intrusive sheets. The sheetlike form is the result either of concordant intrusion into layered rocks or discordant intrusion along planar or ringshaped fractures. Intrusions of the first kind are known as *sills* and are commonly gently dipping; those of the second kind are known as *dikes*. Dikes are generally intruded along steeply dipping tensional fractures in the crust. They occur commonly in great "swarms," either striking uniformly over a large area or radiating from a center of ancient volcanic activity. Some of these linear intrusions may fill fissure vents from which large volumes of basic lava were erupted.

Plutons   All igneous intrusions of less regular geometric form can be classed together as *plutons*. The shapes and sizes of plutons vary enormously, but the larger ones fall into two main categories, the granitic batholiths of the tectonically mobile parts of the crust and the layered basic intrusions of the more stable areas. The batholiths (or *stocks* as they are called if their aerial extent is less than about 100 km^2) are generally very large, and their true shape is rarely seen. They are commonly pictured as steep-sided bodies continuing downward to great depth. Some smaller granitic plutons have been examined in detail and the shapes of these, generally inferred from the pattern of internal flow structures (foliation and lineation), are generally found to be complex. For example, Figure 3–18 is the structural reconstruction of a pluton at Rattlesnake Mountain in southern California. The exposed aerial extent of the pluton is about 60 km^2 and it is intruded into igneous and metamorphic rocks in a generally discordant fashion. The pluton is basically funnel-shaped with an upper surface in the form of lobes, one of which

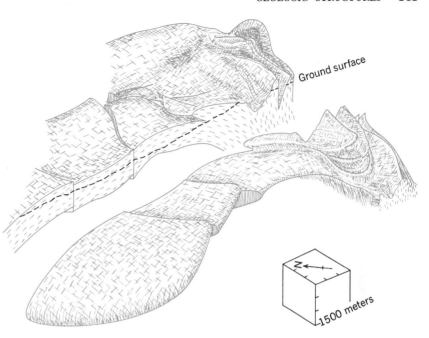

FIG. 3–18 *Orthographic block diagram of the Rattlesnake Mountain pluton in southern California. Form of the pluton (reconstructed above ground surface) is shown. The dashed black lines indicate the local orientation of flow structures. (After R. S. MacColl, Structural geology of Rattlesnake Mountain pluton, Geol. Soc. Am. Bull., 1964.)*

penetrates horizontally a distance of 8 km from the neck. Internal flow structures and laminations are broadly conformable to the funnel. Other plutons of similar size seem to have a much simpler shape but a number have been described that are basically funnel or pear-shaped with a narrow neck at the base.

The great, layered basic intrusions of the ancient stable areas appear to have much greater lateral than vertical extent and to be saucer, funnel, or wedge-shaped, the cross section narrowing downward. Their forms at depths are unknown. A possible vertical section through one such intrusion is shown in Figure 3–19.

Some plutons clearly crosscut structures in the surrounding, generally metamorphic or igneous rocks, and appear either to have replaced material once there or to have entered along irregular fractures which widened as the intrusions grew. Other plutons are remarkably concordant, both in form and internal structure, to the structures in the surrounding rocks and appear to have forcibly pushed the country rocks aside. Boundaries of many granitic plutons are ill-defined, with gradation between plutonic and metamorphic country rock. This implies chemical reaction at the boundary. Possibly the marginal character of some major granitic plutons changes with depth. At the lowest level, where the granitic magma is generated, probably by partial melting of older rocks, the contacts would be diffuse and gradational. The molten material is lighter than the surrounding rocks and begins to rise into the overlying rocks much as a bubble of oil rises in water. At this intermediate level the rising granite is broadly conformable to the surrounding rocks in which it causes deformation and flow as it rises. At the topmost level, as the body nears the surface and cools it moves along fractures in the less ductile rocks and may spread out into a lobate and discordant funnel-shaped pluton.

In fact, the mechanics of igneous intrusion and eruption are not clearly understood except that gravitational instability of a light, fluid body at depth, and the internal pressures from dissolved volatiles in magma are probably the most important factors.

Mapping of igneous intrusions is a relatively simple procedure because of the common sharp-

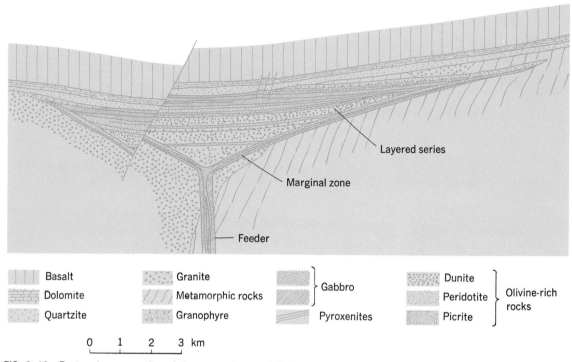

Layered series

Marginal zone

Feeder

Basalt	Granite	} Gabbro	Dunite } Olivine-rich rocks
Dolomite	Metamorphic rocks		Peridotite
Quartzite	Granophyre	Pyroxenites	Picrite

0   1   2   3   km

FIG. 3–19 *Restored cross section of the exposed part of the Muskox layered ultrabasic intrusion, Northwest Territories, Canada. (After T. N. Irvine and C. H. Smith, in* Ultramafic and Related Rocks, *ed. P. J. Wyllie, Wiley, 1967.)*

ness of their contacts with other rocks. But three-dimensional interpretation of their structure is made difficult because simple geometric projections of surface outcrop patterns to depth is not always possible. Simple sheetlike intrusions present no real problems in this respect and some of the remarkable cylindrical intrusions, particularly the "necks" and "plugs" filling eroded volcanic vents seem to maintain constant dimensions through considerable thicknesses of crust. But the structures of large plutons with depth is generally indeterminate without underground or geophysical data.

NATURAL FRACTURES AND RUPTURES

The surface of the earth is intersected on all scales by surfaces of fracture and rupture. The commonest of these occur in regular parallel sets, generally very closely spaced, and show no visible displacements of the rocks on either side. They are termed *joints*. Other fractures occur along which the rocks on one side have been displaced with respect to rocks on the other. Such fractures vary widely in their attitude and character but are usually grouped together as *faults*.

Ruptures of both kinds are a response to distributed forces (stresses) in solid rocks. The stresses may be connected with earth movements and tectonism; they can be thermal stresses connected with the cooling of igneous rocks, or residual stresses in rocks formed at depth and brought to the surface by erosion. In Chapter 9 we shall examine possible causes of joints and faults; in the present discussion we are concerned only with their geometric properties.

JOINTS   Few exposures of rocks at the earth's surface are entirely free of joints, and unless an exposure has been carved by ice or certain types

FIG. 3–20 *Intersecting joint sets in metamorphic rock (note lineation parallel to hammer handle).*

of wave and wind action it generally owes its form to the local joint pattern. Where several sets of joints are developed, rocks tend to break into crudely parallelepipedal blocks (Figure 3–20) the size of which reflects the spacing of joints in the sets and can range from a few millimeters to many meters. Some rocks split along joints in much the same way as they split along a pervasive structure such as bedding or foliation; but that is the only point of resemblance between joints and these structures. Although joints can develop in the same plane as bedding in a sedimentary or flow layering in an igneous rock, they are always finitely spaced discrete surfaces and cannot be classed as pervasive structures.

Joints are very important in the development of landscape, and where one set is well-developed (particularly with occasional prominent "master" joints), can give a marked linear "grain" to an area as seen in an aerial photograph. They are useful to the field geologist in providing natural smooth surfaces on exposures, generally in several directions, on which the internal structures of the rocks can be clearly observed. In some particularly "massive" rocks lacking marked pervasive structures, hand specimens would be difficult to collect were joints absent.

In some massive rocks (particularly granites, gneisses, and sandstones), joint sets subparallel to the topographic surface are commonly developed. They are more closely spaced near the surface and cause the rocks to peel away in successive curved sheets leaving smooth dome-shaped

outcrops. They appear to die out at depth and have been attributed to fracture in response to residual stresses as a result of unloading during erosion.

Particularly in flat-lying bedded sedimentary rocks, sets of planar ("systematic") joints occur with remarkably constant orientation over large areas. They are steeply dipping or vertical and their orientation can be specified adequately by strike alone. They are subperpendicular to bedding and are generally associated with minor ("nonsystematic") joint sets of more variable orientation. In the shales of the Houtzdale quadrangle in the Appalachian plateau of Pennsylvania, for example, the mean strike of such systematic joints is shown by the heavy lines in Figure 3–21 and is grossly transverse to the regional strike of bedding. The mean strike of associated nonsystematic joint sets is given by the fine lines.

Joints are common also in strongly folded and metamorphosed rocks in which they tend to be controlled more strongly by pervasive structures. In tightly folded and lineated rocks, for example, very prominent joints are generally present subperpendicular to the linear structures (cross joints). True profiles of folds can be clearly seen on these joint surfaces. In most bodies of deformed rock, joints have no simple regional patterns. They appear to form with relative ease and many bodies contain joint sets of different orientations formed at different times. Early sets of joints sometimes become faults in a later de-

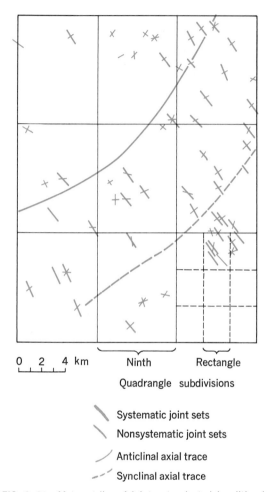

0 2 4 km   Ninth   Rectangle

Quadrangle subdivisions

Systematic joint sets

Nonsystematic joint sets

Anticlinal axial trace

Synclinal axial trace

FIG. 3–21 *Mean strike of joints at selected localities in the Houtzdale quadrangle, Pennsylvania. (After R. S. Nickelsen and V. D. Hough, Jointing in the Appalachian Plateau of Pennsylvania, Geol. Soc. Am. Bull., 1967.)*

formation and are even folded and bent. They are commonly filled with later minerals, particularly quartz and calcite, to form thin veins, and can even become paths for igneous intrusion.

In lava flows, sills, dikes, and other minor intrusions, a unique pattern of jointing that breaks the rock into hexagonal or pentagonal columns commonly perpendicular to the external surface of the igneous body (Figure 3–22) is sometimes present. These columnar joints are formed in response to tensional stresses de-veloped during cooling, and tend to be aligned normal to isothermal surfaces. In most plutons, joints are plentiful and show some systematic relationship to the boundaries of a particular intrusion. They act as channels for the emplace-ment of late-stage pegmatite dikes and seem to result from stresses arising during intrusion or cooling.

Many other types of joints have been de-scribed in rocks of different kinds and it is likely that they are not all formed by the same mechan-ism. Though one of the commonest of all geologic structures, joints remain one of the least under-stood.

FAULTS The fractures in the earth's surface across which the rocks are differentially displaced can be grouped together as faults. They vary widely in their characteristics. Some are discrete surfaces visible in small exposures; others are equally sharp but can be located and traced only by mapping. Many are laminar zones, up to a kilometer or more in thickness, in which there are numerous surfaces of rupture associated with layers of crushed, broken, or mylonitized rock. The observed displacements in faults range from a few centimeters up to distances measured in hundreds of kilometers as on the great San Andreas fault system of California.

Faults can be formed by a variety of mechani-cal processes. Some are sharp surfaces with rela-tively small displacements and seem to have originated by brittle fracture. Others are slip surfaces on which cohesion has not been lost and are more "ductile" in their properties. Some faults are clearly associated with earthquakes, and linear ground breakage along the traces of known faults occurs during some tremors. But whether such fracture is a result or a cause of earthquakes is not established. Other faults are known to move continuously by slow "creep" at rates that can be measured by very sensitive in-struments.

Faults commonly show geometric relation-ships to other structures in the rocks they cut and in some places the relationship seems also to be genetic. There is a close connection, for example, between the folding of horizontally bedded sedimentary rocks and faulting: The patterns of overall displacement indicated by associated folds and faults are commonly similar. In some examples folding precedes faulting; in others the opposite occurs; and in still others the two seem to have proceeded together. Some faults seem to move just once and then "die." Others can be shown to have been repeatedly active over long periods of geologic time, and to have accumulated great amounts of slip.

Many faults follow surfaces of discontinuity, such as joints already present in rocks. Geologic boundaries between rocks of different composition are commonly followed by faults. Such surfaces are planes of stress concentration, and the stress condition required for failure by faulting seems to be reached most easily along them. Thus bedding surfaces between sedimentary formations, metamorphic boundaries, unconformities, and the margins of large igneous intrusions are common sites for faults.

MOVEMENTS ON FAULTS The actual direction and sense of displacement on a particular fault relative to a fixed coordinate system is generally indeterminate. Even to determine relative displacement requires that the separation of once-adjacent points on opposite sides of the fault can be determined. What is generally determined by mapping is an apparent displacement, generally in a horizontal direction. For example, consider the fault F in Figure 3–23, which apparently displaces the layer L a distance h as seen on a horizontal surface. The vector **h** could be the actual displacement if this were along a horizontal line; but the same apparent displacement could be given by displacement **d** in the dip direction of the fault and by an infinite number of inclined displacements such as **o**. Any one of these displacements reversed would make the two parts of L again continuous across the fault. However, if L is one dipping limb of a fold, as shown in Figure 3–24, the displacements **h**, **d**, and **o** would give different outcrop patterns on a horizontal surface, and determination of the position of the hinge line (see page 153) of the fold on both sides of the fault permits determination of the true relative displacement (**t** in Figure 3–24).

FIG. 3–22 Columnar jointing in horizontal lava flows, eastern Oregon.

Even in the most favorable circumstances only the relative displacement vector on a fault can be found. This vector connects the initially adjacent points on opposite sides of the fault but it need not correspond to the actual *path* of displacement by which the points were separated.

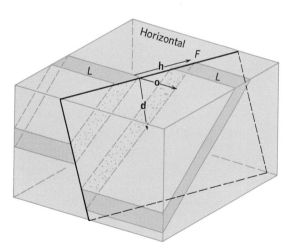

FIG. 3–23 Displacement of a layer L by a fault F as seen on a horizontal surface. **h**, along strike, **d**, along dip, and **o**, oblique, are all possible displacement vectors.

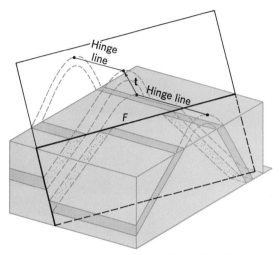

FIG. 3–24 Displacement of the hinge line of a fold by fault F gives unique displacement vector **t**.

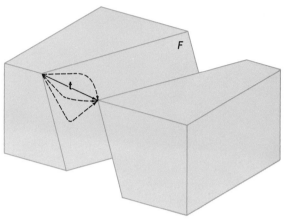

FIG. 3–25 The true displacement vector of a fault F is given by **t**. The dashed black lines are possible paths of motion selected from an infinite number of possibilities.

For example (Figure 3 25), if **t** is the measured displacement vector on a fault, the possible paths of displacement might be any one of those shown or an infinite number of others. Sometimes indications of displacement paths are given by linear structures (slickensides and grooves) formed in a fault surface by differential slip (Figure 3–26). There may be one set of linear structures that agree in direction with the displacement vector determined on other grounds. But many faults show several sets oriented in different directions,

the later sets overprinting and distorting the earlier. Such faults have complex displacement paths as a result of slip in different directions at different times.

Where displacement vectors can be determined in different places on large faults they are generally found to vary in direction and magnitude from place to place and even to change their sense. Some faults die out completely or become folds. The displacements on such faults cannot be exclusively linear, and rotational components must be present. Unless these rotational

FIG. 3–26 Slickensides on an exposed fault surface (the joints are spaced about 1 meter apart).

components (about an axis perpendicular to the fault plane) are obvious they are generally ignored.

Most faults intersect the topographic surface and, if active at the time of formation of the surface, can displace it to give a *fault scarp*. These can be a meter or so in elevation, as are many of the scarps formed by active faults during earthquakes, or they can be mountain walls thousands of meters high like the eastern flank of the Sierra Nevada in California. Such scarps are generally greatly modified by erosion. Some older scarps are purely erosional in origin representing the different resistance to weathering of unlike rocks brought together by faulting.

Some faults can be shown to have been continuously or periodically active during sedimentation or volcanic activity. The sequence of formations can be distinctly different on opposite sides of such faults. Faults that follow natural formational boundaries, particularly boundaries between sedimentary layers, may not displace any visible markers or interrupt stratigraphic successions and can go undetected.

GEOMETRIC CLASSIFICATION OF FAULTS   The most widely used classification of faults is based on orientations of the fault surface and the displacement vector. Most faults are more or less planar features of reasonably constant orientation and they are generally neither vertical nor horizontal. The two sides of a dipping fault are given specific names derived from mining terms: The hanging wall is that above the dipping fault and the foot wall is that below the dipping fault (Figure 3–27). Based upon these terms the following classification is used:

1. *Dip-slip faults* are faults with displacement vectors in the direction of dip of the fault surface; on a *normal fault* the hanging wall moves downward, on a *reverse fault*, also called a *thrust fault*, it moves upward (Figure 3–28). If a fault is vertical there is no distinction between these two types.

2. *Strike-slip faults* have displacement vectors parallel to the strike of the fault surfaces. They are also called *transcurrent*, *lateral*, or *wrench*

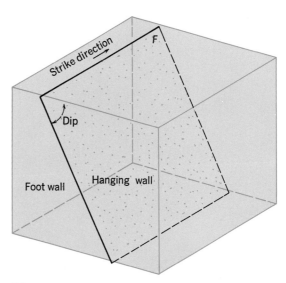

FIG. 3–27 *Hanging wall and foot wall of an obliquely dipping fault.*

faults. They are commonly steeply dipping or vertical and can be classed as right-lateral or left-lateral according to whether the rocks on the side of the fault opposite to that on which an observer stands facing the fault have moved respectively to the observer's right or left (Figure 3–29).

3. *Oblique-slip faults*, the most common faults, have displacement vectors inclined obliquely to the strike and dip directions of the fault surface. The displacement vector can be resolved into strike-slip and dip-slip components (Figure 3–30).

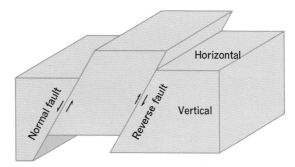

FIG. 3–28 *Dip-slip faults, normal and reverse.*

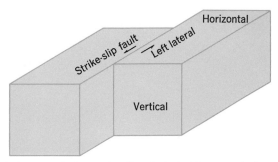

FIG. 3–29   *Left-lateral strike-slip fault (shown vertical).*

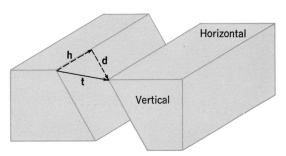

FIG. 3–30   *Oblique-slip fault with displacement vector **t** resolved into strike-slip (**h**) and dip-slip (**d**) components.*

Within this broad geometric classification many specific varieties of faults have been described. Of special note are *low-angle thrust faults*, which appear to have an origin different from that of most steeply or moderately dipping faults. They dip gently or are horizontal and are sharply defined surfaces upon which relatively thin plates of rock have been displaced distances which can reach 100 km or more. They are common in horizontally bedded and weakly folded sedimentary sequences and are usually closely conformable to the bedding stratification (Figure 3–31). Their presence is generally detected only by repetition of sedimentary layers one above the other, by the presence of demonstrably older formations apparently overlying younger formations in stratigraphic continuity, or by superposition of formations of one sedimentary facies (for example, carbonate sediments) on

another (for example, siliceous geosynclinal sediments) of the same age.

The origin of these faults is not fully understood except that it is unlikely that they result from the crustal shortening they at first sight suggest. More probably they arise by the sliding of thin sheets on gently inclined surfaces of weak cohesion under gravity to override similar layers in a different area. In alpine terranes (Figure 3–32) there may be many such thrust surfaces forming slices (*nappes* or *decken*) piled one on top of another or folded together. Some thrust sheets of this kind appear to have slid outward over old erosion surfaces and were themselves eroded during their advance to give coarse conglomeratic sedimentary rocks which in turn were overridden by the moving sheet. Almost complete erosion of such a near-surface thrust sheet can leave isolated patches (*klippen*) of exotic rocks clearly out of their time stratigraphic relationship. The formation of low-angle thrusts is closely bound up with folding.

DEFORMATION STRUCTURES

Structures formed in the rocks of the crust by solid flow in response to distributed mechanical forces range in size from microscopic plastic distortions in crystals, such as kink and twin lamellae, to enormous fold-nappes measured in tens of kilometers, such as those present in the Alpine mountains of Europe. The geometric properties and mechanical origins of these structures are as varied as their sizes and, in general, less is known about them than about any of the primary structures reviewed above.

There are two main reasons for the geologist to pay close attention to such deformation structures. First, they yield information on the mechanics of solid flow in rocks and the physical conditions under which it is possible. Second, an understanding of the displacements and strains involved in their formation can establish large-scale patterns of distortion and flow in the crust, from which the deeper phenomena these patterns reflect can be inferred.

In this section we concentrate on the geometric properties of deformation structures. What is known about their origins is reviewed in Chapter 9.

GEOMETRIC PROPERTIES OF FOLDS   Many of the rocks of the earth's crust are bedded, foliated, or otherwise layered and laminated. In most sedimentary and some igneous rocks, these planar structures are subhorizontal when formed and represent a universal "marker" by which to measure subsequent distortions of the crust. In metamorphic rocks, foliations are rarely horizontal when formed but are generally planar, and later distortions of these too can be detected. Few areas of the crust show such planar structures in a completely undistorted form. With progressive deformation they become tilted and folded to an increasing degree, and in some places they are broken and pulled apart, so once-continuous layers are seen as isolated fragments or boudins, and the initial surfaces of bedding and foliation are partially or completely transposed into new sets of surfaces.

The widespread existence on all scales of folds, boudins, and other deformation structures makes the work of the field geologist much more difficult. Many formational contacts, instead of being relatively smooth plane surfaces that can be geometrically projected down their dip to permit determination of structure in three dimensions, are curved and broken. Pervasive structures, such as bedding, foliation, and lineation, are folded and bent in a complex fashion on large and small scales into intricate patterns that at first sight appear to be without order of any kind. But these complexities are important to the geologist both as technical difficulties to overcome in the mapping and three-dimensional geometric interpretation of a geologic body, and because of the insight they give into patterns of distortion and flow in the crust.

The mechanisms by which solid layers and foliated bodies of rock become folded in nature are poorly understood; but the great variety of rock types in which folds are observed, and the great range of geometric properties that the folds themselves exhibit, make clear that more than one mechanism is involved. Apparently, all layered and foliated rocks, from sedimentary sequences containing massive isotropic layers hundreds of meters thick to the most pervasively and perfectly foliated fine grained phyllites and slates, can fold given appropriate physical conditions. However, the folds that form in rocks with very different mechanical properties are geometrically distinct and it is useless to search for a universal mechanism of folding. What is clear is that folds with much the same geometric properties have been formed again and again during the long history of the earth in rocks of the same type, and that the geometric form of a fold is a guide not only to the kinematics of folding, but also to the mechanics. Therefore, prerequisite to an understanding of folding, is accurate geometric description of the form, orientation, and symmetry of common types of folds.

Fortunately for the geologist folds of very different sizes can occur with much the same geometric properties so that careful direct examination of minor folds yields information which aids in the mapping of folds of very large size. For this reason no account of the absolute size of folds is taken in the following discussion.

Geometric elements of a folded surface In folded sequences of rocks, structural surfaces, once plane, are curved. Such surfaces are qualitatively of two kinds. First, in a pervasively foliated rock we can select one particular surface for study knowing that there are no special properties in this surface and that the rocks on either side are foliated in exactly the same way. Second, in a bedded or layered sequence we tend to select a surface separating two distinct rock types such as the upper boundary of a layer. Such a surface is not pervasive and may, in fact, be unique in the body. In either case, the selected surface is curved into a crudely periodic wavelike form in which curvatures of one sense follow more or less regularly on curvatures of the opposite sense (Figure 3–33). In general, these wavelike forms lie somewhere between two ideal regular forms. The first, illustrated in Figure 3–34, consists of effectively planar segments, termed the *limbs* of

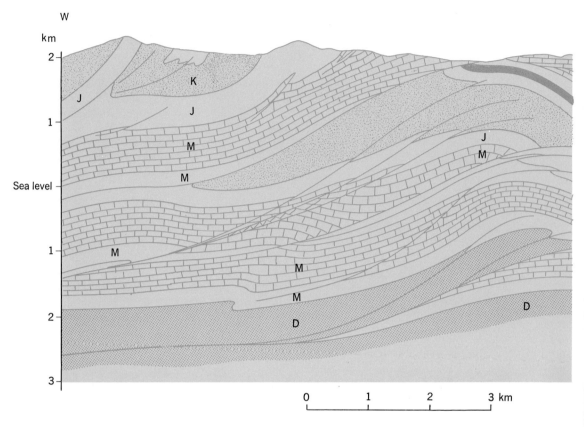

FIG. 3–31 (Above, left and right) *Vertical cross section through the Savanna Creek gas field in Alberta showing low-angle thrust faults. (After F. G. Fox, Amer. Assoc. Petr. Geol. Bull., 1959.) Sedimentary formations of different type and age are indicated.*

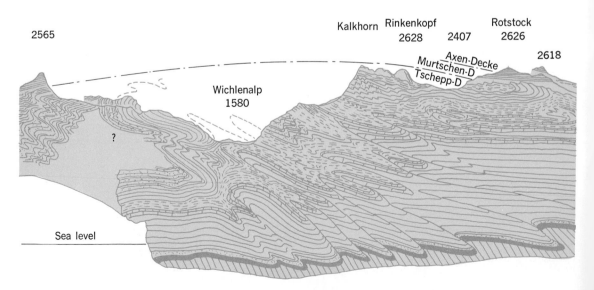

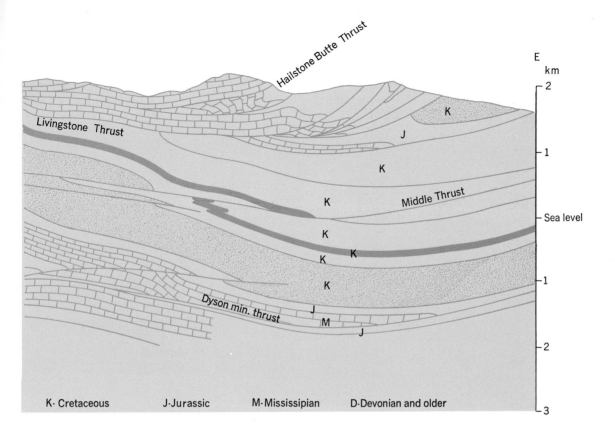

FIG. 3–32 (Below, left and right) *Vertical profile across part of the Glaneralp in Switzerland showing "nappes" and "decken." (After J. Oberholzer,* Geologie der Glaneralpen, Beiträge zur Geologischen Karte der Schweiz, *1933.)*

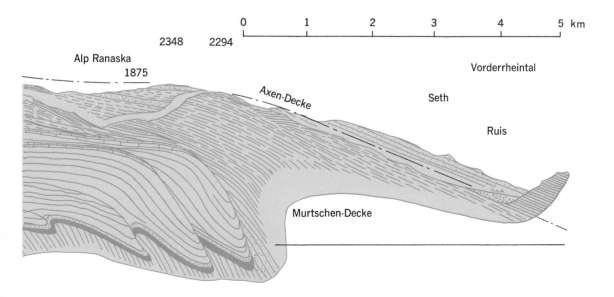

FIG. 3–33 *Wavelike form of a folded surface (schematic).*

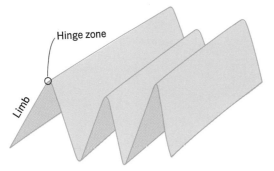

FIG. 3–34 *Folds consisting of interconnected limbs with minor hinge zones.*

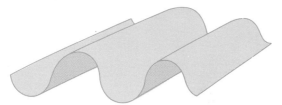

FIG. 3–35 *Folds consisting of interconnected hinge zones with minor limbs.*

the fold connected by sharp angular bends termed *hinges*. Ideally the hinge zones have no extent and such folds consist of interconnected limbs. The second, illustrated in Figure 3–35, consists of a series of concentric arcs with no planar segments. Such folds can be viewed as a series of hinge zones connected by limbs of no extent. Most folded surfaces can be viewed as falling somewhere between these two extremes. For example, the folds shown in Figure 3–36 have well-defined hinge zones connected by segments with much smaller curvatures corresponding to limbs. The division of a folded surface into hinge zones and limbs is an arbitrary process.

In a folded surface seen in three dimensions the following geometric elements can be identified:

1. Somewhere between each pair of hinge zones of opposing curvatures must lie a line which separates curvature of one sense from curvature of the other. This line, the *inflection line,* can be taken as the limit of a single fold in the surface. On some folds, which are "dome" or "canoe" shaped, this line closes completely around the fold; on other folds, more regularly wavelike in form, there are two subparallel lines, which may not meet on the exposed part of the fold (Figure 3–37).

2. Between two inflection lines there is generally another line joining points on the surface

FIG. 3–36 *Small folds in the bedding of metamorphosed chert (Sierra Nevada foothills, California).*

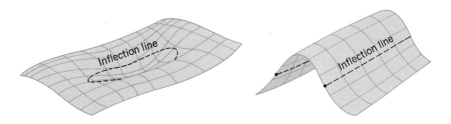

FIG. 3–37 Inflection lines on a folded surface: at left, closed inflection line on a "canoe-shaped" fold; at right, open inflection lines on a simple fold.

with greatest curvature (Figure 3–38). This is termed the *hinge line* of the fold. In some folds a line centrally situated in a uniformly curved hinge zone can be taken as the hinge line.

A set of folded surfaces   A fold is not confined to a single surface but is a three-dimensional structure extending through a foliated or layered sequence. Folded surfaces pervade a well-foliated rock more or less uniformly and a number of suitable, spaced surfaces can be selected to show the orientation and form of the fold. In a layered rock, on the other hand, specific layer boundaries are the most prominent folded surfaces and these are generally selected. For the moment we make no distinction between these extreme examples and consider only the geometric properties of a set of finitely spaced surfaces, or a pair of such surfaces.

The following geometric elements of a fold in a set of surfaces can be recognized (Figure 3–39):

1. A smooth surface can be passed through inflection lines in successive folded surfaces. This *inflection surface* outlines the domain of a single fold in a set of surfaces.

2. A smooth surface can be passed through the hinge lines of successive surfaces. This is

termed the *axial surface* or the *axial plane* of the fold if, as commonly happens, the surface is plane.

Some folds are more complex than the foregoing discussion suggests and may have more than one axial surface with no intervening inflection surfaces. A common fold of this type termed a conjugate or box fold has two axial surfaces of opposite inclination (Figure 3–40).

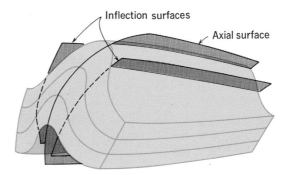

FIG. 3–39   Axial surface and inflection surfaces of a set of folded surfaces.

FIG. 3–38   Hinge lines (dashed black lines) on a folded surface.

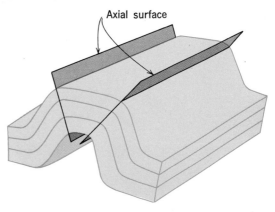

FIG. 3–40   Conjugate or box fold with two axial surfaces.

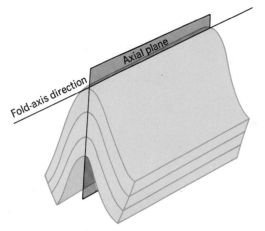

FIG. 3–41   *Plane cylindrical fold.*

Cylindrical folds   Exposed parts of many folds are nested segments of cylinders with a common generating line. This generating line, called the *fold axis*, is parallel to the hinge lines and inflection lines in all the folded surfaces (Figure 3–41). Such folds are termed cylindrical folds. All other folds are noncylindrical; but, if the curvature of the hinge lines is not too marked, noncylindrical folds can be considered to be composed of effectively cylindrical segments of different orientation. If, in addition, a cylindrical fold or segment of a fold has an axial plane it can be called plane cylindrical (Figure 3–41).

Such folds and segments of folds are important because the orientations of their axes and axial planes can be measured and represented on a map by suitable symbols.

Cylindrical folds in profile   A cross section through a cylindrical fold or fold segment drawn normal to the fold axis is called a true profile or profile of the fold. On such sections the true forms of the folded surfaces are clearly displayed: on all other plane sections these forms are to some degree distorted. Folds as seen in profile show great variety in their general and detailed geometric characteristics.

Most geologists classify plane cylindrical folds as seen in profile into two broad groups according to which of two ideal geometrically distinct types they most closely resemble. In the first type, termed a *similar fold*, adjacent folded surfaces have exactly the same form and can be superposed by a simple displacement along the axial plane perpendicular to the fold axis. In such folds, therefore, the distance between a pair of folded surfaces measured in the axial plane (T in Figure 3–42) is constant around the fold. In the second type, termed *parallel* or *concentric folds*, adjacent folded surfaces are concentric curves and their spacing measured normal to the folded surfaces (t in Figure 3–43) is constant around the fold. (See Ramsay's book listed in the References for further discussion of these types.)

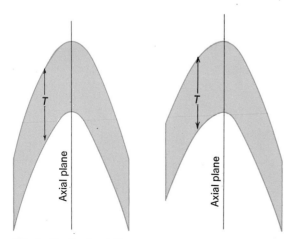

FIG. 3–42   *Similar folds; symmetric (left) and asymmetric (right): distance T constant on folds.*

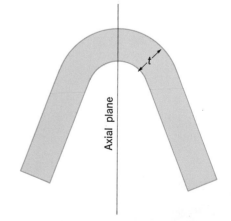

FIG. 3–43   *Parallel or concentric fold: distance t constant on fold.*

FIG. 3-44 *Large kinklike fold in limestone (Lake Lucerne, Switzerland). Scale is given by building on lake shore, lower center left.*

In practice, no real folds correspond exactly to either type, although folds in pervasively foliated rocks tend towards the similar type and folds in mechanically stronger layers enclosed in a weaker matrix tend towards the concentric type. One group of fold types commonly observed in strongly foliated and layered rocks does not fit very easily into the above classification. They are characterized by planar limbs and vanishingly small hinge zones. They are commonly bilaterally symmetric across their axial planes and are variously called chevron, kink, or zig-zag folds. They are commonly associated with and appear to be genetically related to box or conjugate folds mentioned above which generally consist of pairs of kink folds with oppositely inclined axial planes.

Although most obvious as minor folds in pervasively foliated rocks, kink and conjugate kink folds occur also in massive layered and bedded sequences on all scales so long as the layers and beds are thin relative to the size of the fold. An example of such a large fold in bedded sedimentary rocks at Lake Lucerne, Switzerland, is given in Figure 3-44. Much larger examples occur.

Orientation of folds The oldest terms used to describe the approximate orientation of folds indicate the sense in which a fold "closes"—that is, the sense in which the hinge points, upward or downward. The terms are stratigraphic in origin and apply satisfactorily only to uninverted series of sedimentary rocks in which fold axes are horizontal or gently plunging and axial planes dip moderately or steeply. A fold that closes upward with older rocks in its core is an *anticline* and a fold that closes downward with younger rocks in its core is a *syncline* (Figure 3-45). For folds with steeply plunging axes or gently dipping axial planes in which the dominant closure of the

FIG. 3-45 *Anticline and syncline. The folds plunge gently in opposite senses. Note that the outcrop patterns of the two folds on a map (the horizontal surface) are the same.*

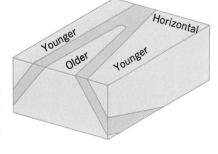

Anticline

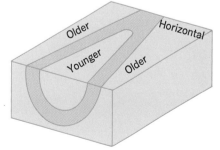

Syncline

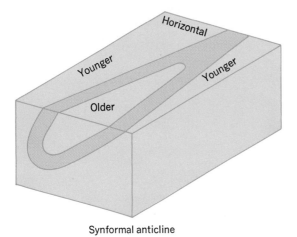

Synformal anticline

FIG. 3–46 *Synformal anticline.*

fold is lateral, the terms can still be used if the stratigraphic succession is known. The terms cannot be used for folds in sedimentary layers of unknown stratigraphic succession or for folds in foliations and layerings of nonsedimentary origin. More appropriate terms for upfolds and downfolds in such structural surfaces are *antiforms* and *synforms* respectively. The two terms can even be combined so that in an inverted stratigraphic succession a fold might be termed a synformal anticline (Figure 3–46). Note that folds with gently dipping axial planes (recumbent folds), steeply plunging axes (vertical folds), or axes that trend at right angles to the strike of their axial planes (reclined folds) cannot be described as antiformal or synformal although stratigraphically they can be anticlines or synclines.

Symmetry of folds   We have already noted that a single fold as seen in profile can be bilaterally symmetric or asymmetric according to whether or not the axial plane is a plane of mirror

symmetry. For any fold, a bisecting surface can be constructed bisecting the interlimb angle. If this surface is parallel to the axial plane, the fold is bilaterally symmetric.

Most folds are part of a wavelike train forming a fold set or system. Two smooth surfaces, called the enveloping surfaces, can commonly be drawn tangential to the fold hinges of opposite sense in a single folded surface (Figure 3–47). A third smooth surface, the median surface, can be drawn through the inflection lines on a folded surface. Various relationships can exist between these surfaces; they can be parallel and equally spaced where folds are of regular amplitude; they can converge or diverge as folds in a surface grow larger or smaller; and they can themselves be folded if the folds are "parasitic" folds on the limb of a larger fold (Figure 3–48).

For a small group of folds the enveloping surface is commonly plane, and its relationship to the axial planes of the folds is another guide to the symmetry of the folding process. For example, if the enveloping surface is perpendicular to the axial planes, the fold group can be termed symmetric, whereas if these two surfaces are oblique, the fold group is asymmetric (Figure 3–49). These relationships are extremely important to the field geologist examining minor folds in a region where major folds are present, particularly in well-foliated rocks without prominent mappable boundaries. The presence of large folds may not emerge from mapping, but the approximate position of their hinge zones can sometimes be located by careful determination of the symmetry properties of the minor parasitic folds. Thus, in Figure 3–50, the hinge area can be detected by a region of symmetric minor folds ("*M*-folds") lying between two regions of asymmetric folds with "left-handed" and "right-handed" forms as viewed down the fold axes in a constant sense

Enveloping surface

Median surface

Enveloping surface

FIG. 3–47 *Enveloping surfaces and median surface of a group of folds (shown in two dimensions).*

Enveloping surface

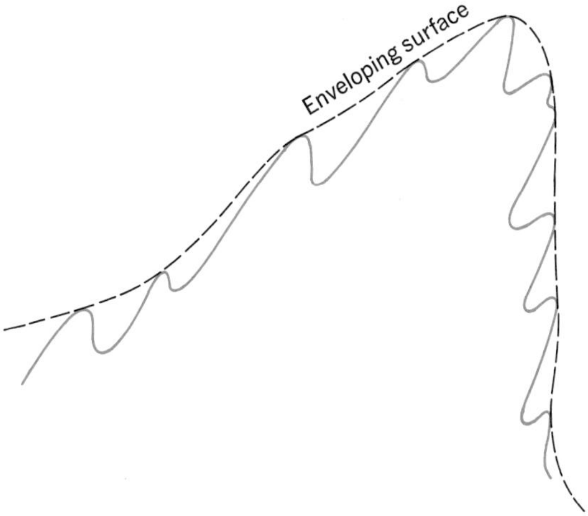

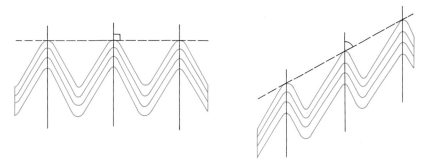

FIG. 3–48 Parasitic small folds on a large fold with a folded enveloping surface (shown in two dimensions).

FIG. 3–49 Symmetric (left) and asymmetric (right) groups of folds. Enveloping surfaces, dashed black lines; axial planes, solid black lines.

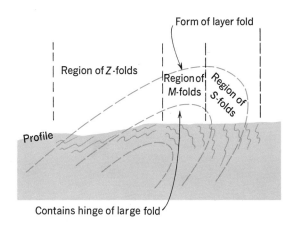

Form of layer fold
Region of Z-folds
Region of M-folds
Region of S-folds
Profile
Contains hinge of large fold

FIG. 3–50 Use of symmetry of parasitic folds to determine the form of a large fold.

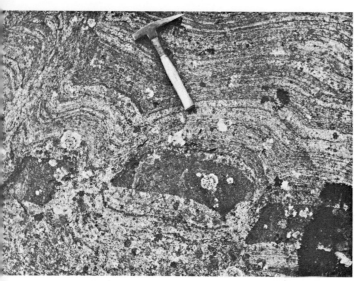

FIG. 3–51 *Angular boudinage of amphibolite in gneiss (Scotland).*

("S-folds" and "Z-folds," respectively). Study of the symmetry properties of small folds becomes particularly fruitful in bodies that have been deformed more than once.

FIG. 3–52 *"Ductile" boudinage of quartzofeldspathic layer in micaceous gneiss (Kenya).*

BOUDINAGE   In general, folds are a result of shortening of a body in the plane of the layering or foliation. Structures called *boudins,* closely related to folds, are a result of lengthening. They are observed most commonly in layers of one kind enclosed in a matrix of another, and they appear to represent the inherent instability of an extended ductile prism or layer which gives rise to the phenomena of "necking" and "ductile fracture," well known from the tensile tests of engineers.

In fact, the observed forms of boudins suggest that all failure phenomena, from brittle fracture to true ductility, can be involved in their formation. Some boudins have sharp angular outlines and the separated fragments can be fitted together again in imagination to reconstitute the boudinaged layer (Figure 3–51). Others are intensely deformed and elongated and have clearly flowed in the solid state during the process of boudinage (Figure 3–52). Some boudins contain internal "rootless" folds and appear to be the disrupted fragments of a once continuous folded layer. In many instances it can be shown that deformation proceeded in two stages—shortening followed by elongation of a layer—especially where bedding or layering has been transposed into a secondary foliation.

In three dimensions boudins are commonly elongated, loglike bodies related to one set of separation surfaces. But extension of a layer in all directions can result in what has been called "chocolate tablet" structure, by which a layer is separated into rhomboidal boudins (Figure 3–53). The converse of this process (shortening in all directions) leads to noncylindrical folding (basin and dome structure).

Careful mapping of the occurrence, nature, and symmetry of boudinage, and of its relationship to folding can yield information on large-scale strains in a deformed body.

DIMENSIONAL MARKERS   The flow and distortion responsible for the formation of folds and boudins is obvious primarily because it is heterogeneous: These structures have appeared as a result of differential deformation. In some deformed rocks (notably the tectonites in which differential

FIG. 3-53 *Discoidal boudinage of siliceous layer in micaceous rock formed by extension in all directions in the layer (published with permission of A. G. Sylvester and J. M. Christie). The slab is about 40 cm long.*

strains and displacements are distributed on the granular and intergranular scale) distortion is not heterogeneous on all scales, and in some small exposures and hand specimens deformation has been so homogeneous that no folds, boudins, or similar structures have appeared. Planar structures have remained plane and linear structures have remained unbent. Fortunately, many rocks contain primary structures of characteristic shape that, when homogeneously deformed, act as dimensional markers recording the magnitude and orientation of components of strain. In sedimentary rocks, for example, crudely spherical microscopic bodies termed ooliths (of concretionary origin, generally in limestones) can acquire a strongly ellipsoidal shape as a result of deformation (Figure 3–54) and are clear indicators of the pure strain component of deformation. Likewise, fossils, pebbles, ripple marks, and so on, of known initial shape become deformed and yield infor-

mation on the state of strain (examples of a deformed fossil and of deformed pebbles are given in Figure 3–55). In volcanic rocks deformed pillows and vesicles can play a similar, if less conclusive, role. These structures form the basis for attempts to determine orientation and magnitude of local principal strains in rocks (see Chapter 9); but they must be used with discretion, since the state of strain of a whole rock may not correspond exactly to the state of strain of enclosed bodies of the kind described.

RELATIONSHIPS BETWEEN DEFORMATION STRUCTURES Most bodies of deformed rock include many different types of deformation structure, and characteristic relationships occur among them.

Axial-plane foliation This is a younger plane foliation more or less parallel to axial planes of

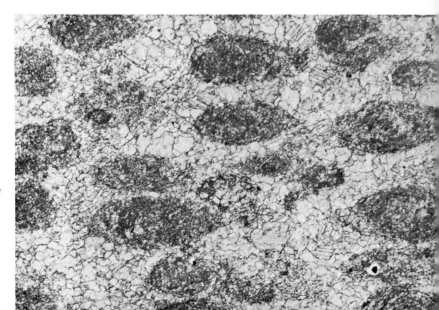

FIG. 3-54 *Deformed ooliths (ellipsoidal bodies) in a limestone (eastern California). The long dimension of the largest ellipsoid is about 1.5 mm.*

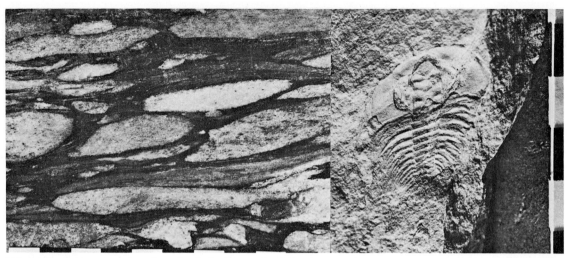

FIG. 3–55 *Deformed markers in rocks. Left, deformed pebbles in a conglomerate (Panamint Valley, California); right, deformed fossil (trilobite, Ollenus, from Inyo Mountains, California). Each black and white division on the scale is 1 cm.*

folds in an earlier set of surfaces; for example, slaty cleavage cutting folded bedding, or a new plane schistosity cutting an earlier folded one. Axial plane foliation may be exactly parallel to the axial planes of folds or it may form a "fan" across the fold, either convergent or divergent toward the inner arcs.

The reasons for these differences are not understood; but convergent fans seem to be characteristic of foliations such as slaty cleavage developing across the bedding in sedimentary rocks, whereas divergent fans are more commonly observed in incipiently developed secondary foliations of the "strain-slip" or "crenulation" variety (particularly in micaceous schists). True axial-plane cleavage (Figure 3–56) with parallel surfaces can be observed in many rock types, but such cleavage is characteristic particularly of uniform, strongly deformed metamorphic rocks in which transposition of earlier surfaces is well-advanced.

Where associated with deformed dimensional markers, axial-plane foliations (including fanlike forms) tend to lie in principal planes of local strain and seem to correspond to a "flattening" normal to foliation. In rocks consisting of layers of markedly different mechanical properties the foliation may be absent in some layers and strongly developed in others, or it can change orientation abruptly at layer boundaries (Figure 3–57). Such "refraction" of foliation can be probably correlated with changes in the orientation of principal strain axes from layer to layer.

Although rarely exactly parallel to the axial planes of associated folds, these foliations can assist the geologist in locating the hinges of large and poorly exposed folds during mapping. For example, in Figure 3–58, the relative orientations of bedding and foliation in isolated exposures in a simply folded sequence indicate that antiformal and synformal hinges must lie as shown. Also, the direction of the fold axis is given by the line of intersection of bedding and foliation which is generally easily seen on both surfaces as a lineation.

Lineations in folded rocks Many folded rocks, and particularly, metamorphic rocks, contain pervasive linear structures. If older than the folds these can be either primary structures such as current lineations in sedimentary rocks or earlier deformation structures. They generally have no special geometric relationship to fold axes and become bent during folding of the sur-

FIG. 3–56 Axial-plane foliation (parallel to hammer handle) in folded schist (Sutter Creek, California).

FIG. 3–57 Change of orientation ("refraction") of slaty cleavage at the boundaries of a coarser layer (Couer d'Alene, Idaho).

faces in which they lie. The manner in which linear structures are so bent has proved to be an important indicator of the folding mechanism, and extensive studies of the patterns of bending have been made by geologists in recent years.

Most lineations in folded rocks are a direct result of the deformation that caused the folding. The commonest is the intersection of axial-plane foliation with the folded surface, parallel to the fold axis. Lineations defined by elongated grains or elongated bodies such as ooliths and rock fragments can form with a variety of inclinations to associated fold axes. Where axial-plane foliation is also developed, these lineations tend to lie in the foliation in which they probably define the direction of greatest extension

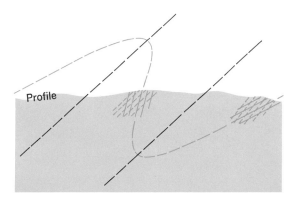

FIG. 3–58 Use of relative orientation of axial-plane foliation (dashed color lines) and bedding (full color lines) to locate hinges of major folds.

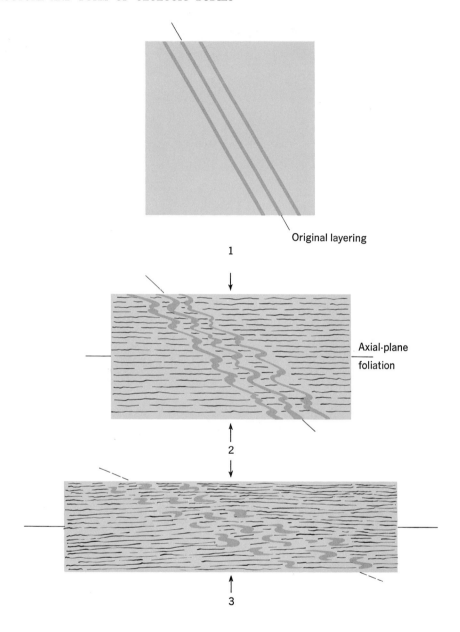

FIG. 3–59 *Transposition of a layering into an axial-plane foliation. Stage 1 is undeformed; three layers (beds) are present in a weaker material. By stage 2 the body has been shortened 30 percent in the direction shown (overall deformation is taken as homogeneous) and the layers are folded and incipiently boudinaged. An axial-plane foliation is well-developed. By stage 3 there is intense boudinage and the direction of continuity of the layers (broken line) is lost. The layering is now transposed into the axial-plane foliation as flattened folds and boudins, all discontinuous (see also Figures 9–69 to 9–71).*

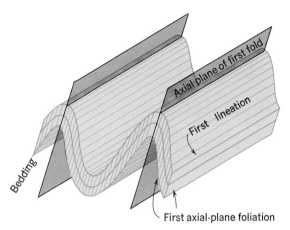

FIG. 3–60 *First generation of folds in bedding with axial-plane foliation and axial lineation.*

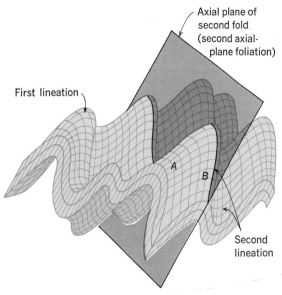

FIG. 3–61 *Superposition of a second generation of folds on the fold shown in Figure 3–60 (schematic). The second folds have constant orientation of axial planes. A second foliation forms in this direction and a second axial lineation. In locality A cylindrical first folds survive; in locality B, cylindrical second folds appear.*

during deformation. This direction can lie along the fold axis or be oblique or perpendicular to it.

Folding and transposition   The close relationship between folding and transposition of foliation has already been noted. The end product of most minor folding associated with development of axial-plane foliation is generally obliteration of the folded surface by transposition into the axial-plane foliation. Boudinage of initially continuous layers plays an important part in this process, destroying their continuity by a sequence of changes such as those shown diagrammatically in Figure 3–59. Major transposed contacts can be mapped on a large scale, but may not be detectable locally in single exposures where they are generally oblique to bedding. The directions of transposed contacts can be determined locally in regions of minimum deformation by the enveloping surfaces of surviving trains of folds in some layers.

REPEATED DEFORMATION   Many noncylindrical folds are formed in a single progressive deformation of a complex heterogeneous kind; but others are clearly a result of repeated deformation in which successive generations of folds, foliations, and lineations develop, forming complex patterns of superposition and "overprinting." Consider an initial system of plane cylindrical folds in bedding with axial-plane foliation and a prom-

inent lineation in the fold axial direction (Figure 3–60). Such structure is typified by a sequence of folded mudstones with prominent slaty cleavage. A later deformation unrelated geometrically now forms a second generation of structures of the same kind, as shown in Figure 3–61. The following features of the resulting structure can be noted:

1. The cylindrical nature of the first folds is destroyed except in small segments (locality *A*).

2. New folds in bedding appear with subparallel axial planes. These folds are cylindrical where formed on planar limbs of the first folds (locality *B*); but, as a whole, the second generation of folds forms a plane noncylindrical system.

3. The axial-plane foliation of the first folds becomes cylindrically folded with the same axial plane as the second folds in bedding.

4. The axial-plane foliation of the second folds is uniformly oriented throughout and is a "secondary" foliation since it cuts the cleavage or schistosity formed by the first deformation.

5. The lineation in the axial direction of the first folds becomes bent around the second folds in a manner controlled by the mechanism of the second folding (locality *B*).

6. The lineation in the axial directions of the second folds in bedding curves around the first folds but always lies in a plane (the axial plane of the second folds—locality *A*).

7. A third lineation uniformly oriented forms as the line of intersection of the first and second axial plane foliations. Other lineations may form depending upon the mechanisms of folding.

This simple example illustrates the increase in structural complexity resulting from the superposition of a second generation of structures on a first. In some deformed regions superposition of

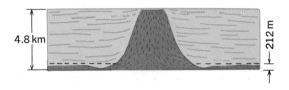

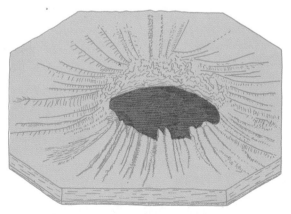

FIG. 3–62 *Diagram to illustrate probable cross section and structural features of Grand Saline Salt Dome, Texas. (After R. Balk, Structure of Grand Saline Salt Dome, van Zandt County, Texas, Amer. Assoc. Petrol. Geol. Bull., 1949.) Upper: cross section on salt dome rising about 5 km above hypothetical source layer (stippled). Dashed black line indicates probable top of source layer before flow into dome. Area on top of dome is "cap rock" (insoluble residues left by solution of rising salt). Dome is surrounded by Eocene and earlier sediments. Lower: structure of salt layers near base of salt dome.*

four or even five distinct generations of structures resulting in extreme complexity has been described. But patient investigation by the geologist in such regions, especially by means of techniques of geometric analysis involving equal-area projections (see Appendix), generally leads to an unraveling of the structure and an understanding of the sequence of events responsible for its development. However, if a later deformation is sufficiently intense, all early foliations may be transposed into a single foliation and all early folds disrupted by boudinage. Intensive metamorphic reconstruction of such a rock can lead to a uniformly foliated and laminated gneiss of deceptively simple structure. Such a sequence of events may have occurred in parts of the ancient metamorphic substructure of the continents.

The presence of superposed minor folds in hand specimens and exposures is generally a clue to the existence of similar phenomena on larger scales. In mapping an area containing such structures the geologist must pay particular attention to the orientation and symmetry of the minor folds and must try to place these in their respective generations by noting their relationships to associated deformation structures, such as foliations and lineations, and to assemblages of metamorphic minerals. The development of radiometric dating techniques has made possible, in favorable circumstances, the absolute age determination of structures of different generations. But structural analysis of repeatedly deformed geologic bodies is never simple.

Further complications are added to the simple picture given above by possible contrasts in "amplitude" of two successive generations of folds. Where the first folds are of large size and the second folds are small (probably the commonest situation), the symmetry of minor (second) folds may no longer be a guide to the location of the major (first) hinges. In other regions the situation is reversed, but the simple rules for locating large hinges from the symmetry of small folds (see Figure 3–50) may be equally invalid. In many regions first and second generation folds occur on all scales, so in some localities the large folds are first and in other localities they are second generation.

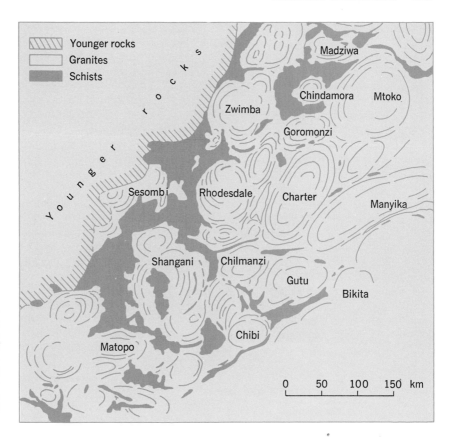

FIG. 3–63 *Domelike gneissic granite batholiths in Rhodesia separated by tightly synformal screens of schist. (After A. M. Macgregor, Some milestones in the Pre-Cambrian of Southern California, Geol. Soc. South Africa Trans. and Proc., 1951.)*

DIAPIRIC STRUCTURES In regions where a deeply buried body of light, weak material is overlain by rocks of significantly greater density, gravitational instability can result and the lighter material can flow upward as a series of lobes to intrude the overlying rock. The possibility that many plutons are emplaced by a similar rise of hot, fluid magma was mentioned earlier. But evidence suggests that solid rock, under suitable circumstances, can rise in the same fashion to form *diapirs* or *diapiric structures*. The commonest and best-known examples of these structures are salt domes—dome or pipe-shaped bodies, generally of halite and anhydrite, that intrude overlying rocks. Structures surrounding these bodies indicate forceful intrusion by which a buried layer of salt and other evaporites pierces the overlying, generally conformable, sediments and penetrates as a stock or sill-shaped lobe even

to the surface, where it may spread outward as glacierlike flows. The structures of salt domes and the surrounding wall rocks are particularly well known for two main reasons. First, salt domes are economically valuable sources of salt; second, salt is relatively impermeable and the surrounding strata are generally deflected upward against their margins (Figure 3–62) so that they act as natural "traps" for the accumulation of petroleum. The internal layering (initially bedding) of a salt dome is complexly folded into tight, sinuous folds. Because the initially horizontal layering is shortened in all directions by the pattern of intrusion (which resembles industrial "extrusion"), the folds tend to acquire very steep axial plunges, particularly in the central part of the intrusion. The patterns of folding are commonly noncylindrical, forming very sharp pointed domes and basins, and closely resemble those of some very intensely metamorphosed rocks that may also have been folded as a result of upward flow and extension.

Diapiric intrusion of solid or semisolid bodies seems, in fact, to occur in association with certain types of intense metamorphism. "Basement" rocks of essentially granitic composition made ductile or weakly creep-resistant by high temperature, dissolved fluids, and other factors appear to rise as domelike bodies "intrusive" into an overlying blanket of generally less easily deformed and denser metamorphic rock. Such "gneiss domes" are found most frequently in the deeply eroded ancient metamorphic substructures of the continents exposed, for example, in parts of the Baltic and African "shields." Maps of such regions show a characteristic pattern of rounded gneissic bodies wrapped by conformable sheaths of strongly foliated and folded metamorphic rock (Figure 3–63). Similar patterns of ring-shaped or mushroom-shaped outcrops are typical also of regions affected by more than one period of folding.

Gross Structure of the Crust

Our present view of the largest-scale structure of the upper layers of the earth rests upon a century or more of painstaking investigation, largely by field geologists, reinforced in more recent years by the findings of geophysicists and oceanographers using indirect methods of observation. From the confusing body of data so obtained there has within the last few years emerged a new picture of crustal structure and evolution that has reconciled many apparently conflicting observations. Moreover, it has provided earth scientists, for the first time since the abandonment of the contraction theory, with a theory of global tectonics that at the same time fits most of the observed facts and provides grounds for testable predictions to be made. The final data on which this theory rests have come, surprisingly, not from the continents on which geologists have patiently labored to obtain a detailed structural picture, but from the ocean basins, which—by the criteria of the field geologist—are

still remote and unknown. In what follows and in Chapter 13 we shall attempt to resolve this paradox by showing the fundamental differences between these two major structural divisions of the crust with respect to the information each provides about the present state and the history of the upper parts of the earth and of the crust in particular.

One problem of dealing with the larger structural features of the earth is that relatively few general statements about them can be made. This problem arises partly because observations become less direct and are consequently subject to more than one interpretation, and partly because the fundamental uniqueness of each geologic structure and event becomes more obvious. One can speak with some validity, for example, of a "typical" fold or fault. It makes much less sense to speak of a "typical" continent or ocean basin, since each of these presently on the earth is unique in its structure and development, and the most that can be done in the way of generalization of their features is to indicate points of resemblance between them.

The lower boundary of the crust is placed conventionally at the Mohorovičić (or M) discontinuity, a world-wide feature indicated by a change in the velocity of seismic P waves (see Chapter 11). In the upper crust V_P is about 6.1 km/sec, increasing downward to 6.8 or 7.0 km/sec at the M discontinuity across which it changes abruptly to about 8.0 km/sec below. The average thickness of the crust so defined is 35 km under the continents, and about 6 km under the oceans. Many seismologists recognize a second (Conrad) discontinuity locally under the continents at a depth of 20 to 25 km, thought to separate an upper crust of essentially granitic composition (density about 2.7) from a lower crust of essentially basaltic composition (density about 3.0). This lower crust may pass under the edges of the continents into the oceanic crust, which appears to have somewhat similar properties. The whole crust is covered discontinuously by a veneer of relatively recent sedimentary rocks—filling "basins" or depressions on the continents, in thick wedges along many of the continental margins and as a thin (about 1 km) uniform layer over much of the ocean floor. Floods of basic volcanic rock cover parts of the continents and have been erupted from centers and fissures in the oceanic crust.

The structure of the crust, as we shall see, is comprehensible only if some of the properties of the upper part of the mantle are considered. These are described in detail in Chapters 11 and 12; but one important feature must be mentioned here. The mantle immediately below the Mohorovičič discontinuity has a relatively high S-wave velocity of about 4.7 to 4.8 km/sec. Beginning at an uncertain depth (put by seismologists generally between 50 to 100 km) and extending perhaps for another 200 km is a layer in which V_S is distinctly lower (falling possibly to 4.3 km/sec). This "low-velocity layer" or "channel" (see also page 616) appears thus to be a region of decreased rigidity, when contrasted with the rest of the mantle. In this layer attenuation of seismic waves (see page 615) is also more pronounced. The presence of this relatively weak layer appears to exercise some control over the nature and velocity of large-scale structural changes in the crust.

Structurally and physiographically the crust is tripartite. First are the continental land masses, with a mean elevation above sea level of about 0.8 km. The rocks are of low density and form broad, relatively flat-lying ancient nuclei bounded and traversed by mountain ranges consisting of strongly deformed and locally metamorphosed rocks of from Cambrian to Recent age. Second are the broad ocean basins—consisting of broad, flat-bottomed depressions of surprisingly uniform depth (about 5 km), traversed locally by underwater ridges, escarpments and deep trenches (up to 11 km or more), and dotted with volcanic islands and sea mounts. Third are the continental margins, where the land masses and the ocean basins join. These vary widely in their physiographic properties from the west Pacific margin, with its seismically and volcanically active arcuate chains of offshore islands, to the seismically and volcanically inactive margins of the South Atlantic Ocean, where ancient continental nuclei cease abruptly without intervening mountain ranges or island arcs.

We look now at the important large-scale tectonic features of these regions.

THE CONTINENTS

The most obvious large-scale structural features of the continents are, first, elongated belts of sedimentary and volcanic rocks folded, locally metamorphosed, and intruded by plutonic rocks since Precambrian times; and, second, more or less equant continental "cores" consisting of dominantly Precambrian igneous and metamorphic rocks. At the present time, therefore, we can distinguish in the continents relatively "stable" regions, termed shields or cratons, which have changed little in their structure since late Precambrian times, and "mobile" regions, termed fold mountain belts or orogens, in which rocks formed largely since Precambrian times have been extensively modified in their structural properties by diastrophic, metamorphic, and igneous activity, commonly in repeated episodes. This distinction is enhanced at present by the general coincidence of the shields with low-lying areas of more or less uniform relief and of the mobile belts with prominent linear or arcuate mountain ranges of extreme relief and ruggedness. The main Precambrian shields and fold mountain belts of dominantly Lower and Upper Paleozoic, Mesozoic, and Tertiary age are shown schematically in Figure 3–64.

FOLD MOUNTAIN RANGES Fold mountains occur generally as narrow linear or arcuate belts, commonly marginal to the stable shields, consisting largely of prismatic bodies of folded, thrust-faulted, and locally metamorphosed sedimentary rocks, clearly once deposited as subhorizontal layers in a basin of deposition. The American geologist James Hall, when working in 1859 in the Paleozoic mountain belt of New York State, was the first to notice that where sedimentary formations of a given age extend out of the folded belt into a relatively undeformed or stable region they become consistently thinner. To explain this phenomenon and the uniform nature of the great thicknesses of sediments observed in the folded regions, Hall suggested the basin of deposition

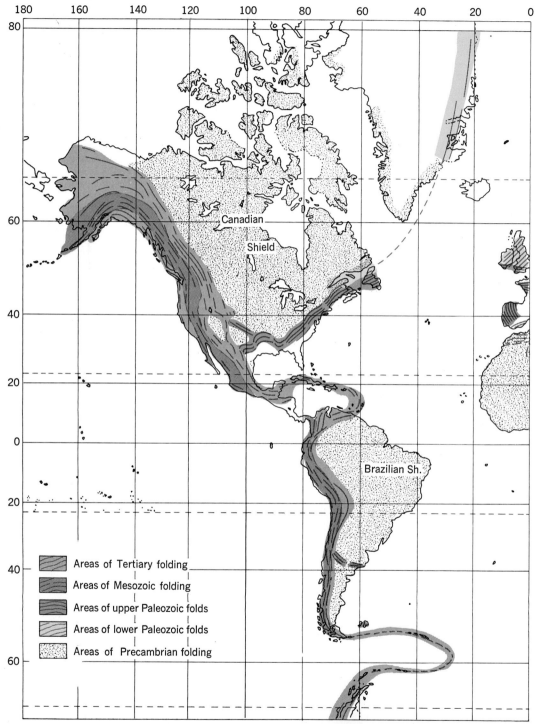

FIG. 3–64 Tectonic units of the continents: shields and orogenic belts. (After J. H. F. Umbgrove, The Pulse of the

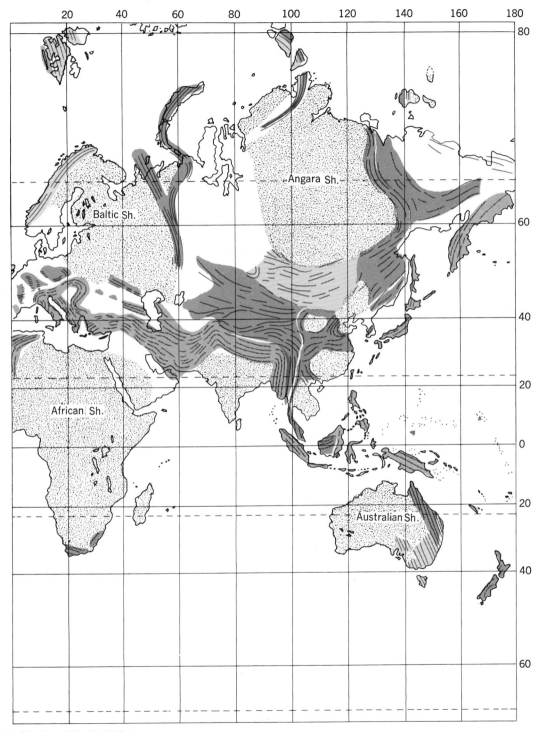

80
20   40   60   80   100   120   140   160   180

Angara Sh.

Baltic Sh.

60

40

African Sh.

20

0

20

Australian Sh.

40

60

Earth, *Martinus Nijhoff, 1947.)*

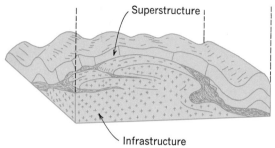

FIG. 3–65 *Mobile infrastructure of migmatite, with its sheath of foliated metamorphic rocks, rising into a superstructure of less mobile sedimentary rocks. (After J. Haller, Bauformen in Migmatit-Stockwerke der Ostgrönlandischen Kalidoniden, Geol. Rundschaus, 1956.)*

must have been steadily subsiding at a rate that matched that of the deposition, and thus more or less constant conditions were maintained in the sedimentary basin over a long period. In this way was born the notion of a *geosyncline* or major basin of unusually thick sedimentation, destined in most cases to become deformed, metamorphosed, intruded by igneous rocks and then uplifted and eroded to form a fold mountain range. The great mountain ranges visible on the earth today are the end products of this process which has been repeated many times in the history of the earth and is undoubtedly proceeding today.

The process of mountain building seems to consist of three main phases, as follows:

1. A pronounced and probably linear depression appears in the crust into which are deposited sediments derived from surrounding subaerially exposed parts of the crust. This first, geosynclinal phase is commonly accompanied by extrusion and intrusion of basic volcanic rocks within the basin, generally as pillow basalts.[4] Sedimentation continues in a more or less steady state, as evidenced by the uniformity in overall composition of the sediments, for very long periods of time, even extending over more than one geologic era. Sediment is generally not uniform over the whole basin in either composition or thickness, and reflects factors such as variations in depth of water, proximity to source area, and so on. In the shallower parts of the basin, rocks such as limestones and sandstones tend to predominate and, in the deeper parts, a much thicker sequence of "flysch" type sediments is generally found. It is in this deeper and presumably most actively subsiding part of the geosyncline that basic volcanic activity is generally concentrated. These differences from place to place in sedimentary type or "facies" are most useful to the geologist in helping him to reconstruct the form of the ancient basin, or, conversely (as has been possible in the Alpine ranges), to establish directions and amounts of relative movement that have taken place during folding and thrusting. The shallower "shelf" part

---

[4] Lava extruded under water commonly forms globular masses (pillows) a meter or so in diameter.

FIG. 3–66 (Below and facing) *Gravitational gliding nappes in the Glarnisch region of Switzerland. (After J. Oberholzer, Geologie der Glaneralpen, Beitr. Geol. Karte Schweiz, 1933.) The fold nappes have come from a region of basement uplift to the south.*

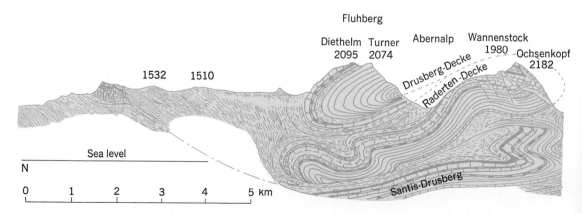

of the geosyncline, with its typical thinner epicontinental sediments, is sometimes distinguished as the "miogeosyncline" and the deeper part, with its thicker shale, graywacke sequence, and associated volcanic rocks, as the "eugeosyncline."

2. The second (tectonogenic or diastrophic) phase involves strong deformation of the sediment-filled basin. Most estimates of the duration of this phase suggest that it is relatively short. But it does not seem to proceed smoothly, and there may be several "false starts" followed by distinct phases of intense activity. The structures formed in this phase are in detail unique to each geosyncline; but commonly occurring features are, first, widespread formation of folds ranging in size from minute crenulations to enormous recumbent folds with amplitude of many kilometers, and second, thrust faulting in many scales, the largest faults moving flat-lying slices many kilometers in extent for very long distances. The folding and low-angle thrusting are intimately related and seem to proceed together.

The structures formed in the diastrophic phase reflect fairly closely the part of the basin involved. The deeper levels, including generally some of the preexisting crust in which the basin developed, become sites of intense metamorphism and are commonly invaded by granite bodies. At the upper and marginal levels, metamorphism is less intense or absent and the rocks seem to behave in a less "fluid" fashion, but the preorogenic basement can become involved in the deformation and appear as lobes or slices of crystalline rock, generally in the cores of large folds in the covering sediments. In the lower levels large bodies of granitic magma appear, which tend to rise into the overlying folded cover. Late in the diastrophic phase these may penetrate upward, even into the essentially non-metamorphic upper parts of the folded sedimentary pile, and form cross-cutting plutons. The lower part of the geosynclinal filling becomes mechanically weak or mobile during metamorphism and can rise, together with similarly mobilized older crystalline crust, to form diapiric domelike folds that push into the upper, less-metamorphosed rocks. Such structures are well-exposed in the lower Paleozoic fold belt of east Greenland, where a highly mobile, lower metamorphic complex or "infrastructure" has been emplaced in a presumably less mobile "super-structure" as great mushroom-shaped folds (Figure 3–65). During these changes a general thickening and rising of the deformed prism of rock occurs and some of the upper folded layers seem to become detached from it and slide under the influence of gravity down the steepening flanks to form a cascade of sinuous folds; or extensive thrust sheets are formed and move out over the less deformed parts of the margin of the geosyncline even onto the undeformed "foreland" (Figure 3–66).

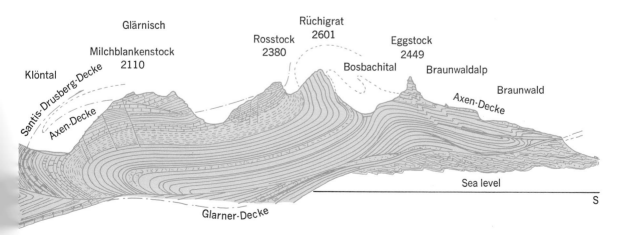

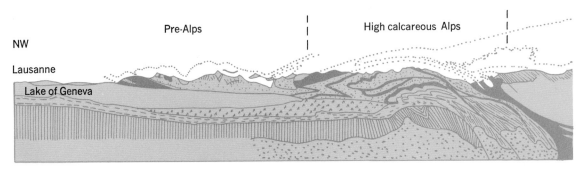

FIG. 3–67 (Above and facing) *Profile across the Alps of Switzerland. On it can be seen the Pennine Alps, large nappes of metamorphic rock; the High Calcareous Alps, dominantly unmetamorphosed folded sedimentary rocks cascading to the northwest; and the pre-Alps, material slid to the northwest over undeformed "foreland."*

3. The last stage is the orogenic or true "mountain-building" phase, in which a general uprising of the deformed geosynclinal filling, and commonly also of the more stable surrounding part of the crust, occurs. Immediately preceding and accompanying this phase there is some renewed volcanic activity, generally involving the extrusion of andesitic lavas, and some high-angle faults appear, cutting across the folds and low-angle thrust faults typical of the diastrophic phase. Sometimes during the latter part of the diastrophic and orogenic phases, marginal and intermediate depressions form that fill rapidly with coarse sediments ("molasse") formed by rapid erosion of the rising mountain range. Some of the later flat-lying fold nappes and thrust sheets gliding under the influence of gravity are even carried out over the molasse deposits formed by erosion at an earlier stage.

The foregoing discussion is a simplification, by no means universally accepted, of the evolution of a mountain range. When a structural geologist examines the ranges presently exposed on the earth, he sees, in different places, different parts of the deformed geosynclinal belt in different stages of development. A young mountain range such as the Alps of Europe preserves most of its levels and stages. In Switzerland it is an asymmetric mountain range, in which most of the displacement of fold nappes and thrust slices

has been to the northwest. It contains, first, an axial zone (the Pennine nappes) of intensely deformed and metamorphosed rocks forming the lowest level; second, a marginal cover of less deformed sedimentary rocks (the Helvetic nappes) in the form of great continuous recumbent folds and cascades of gravity folds; and, third, a molasse basin (The Swiss Plain) into which some of the more deformed rocks have been carried by thrusting and gliding (Figure 3–67). Older mountain ranges, such as the Caledonian (lower Paleozoic) Highlands of Scotland and Scandinavia retain only deeply eroded and dominantly metamorphic roots separated by marginal belts of thrusting (such as the Moine thrust of the northwest Highlands) from stable regions of older rock. As we shall see, in the ancient shields of the continents are preserved the scars of long vanished ranges of many different Precambrian ages, forming an intricate pattern of repeated orogenic episodes throughout the history of the earth.

Not all mountain ranges presently on the earth are geosynclinal in origin; neither do all sedimentary basins within or marginal to continents develop into geosynclines. Ranges like the Jura mountains in Switzerland and France are relatively thin skins of well-bedded sedimentary rock, weakly folded and thrust-faulted with no nappe development or igneous or metamorphic activity. Similarly, high regions such as the

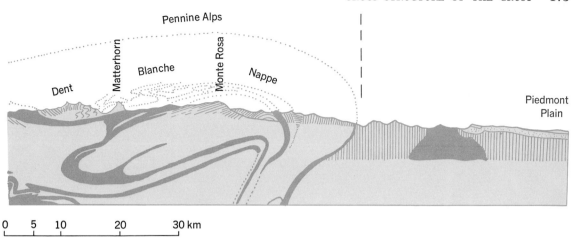

Colorado Plateau have great thicknesses of sediment, laid down over immense periods of time, that show no sign of folding or mountain building of the kind described above. Some mountain ranges have been elevated purely by faulting, and others are dominantly volcanic in origin.

SHIELDS   At first sight, a tectonic map of the earth's surface (Figure 3–64) suggests that the shields are indeed stable, permanent, and fundamentally different from the orogenic belts that wrap around and traverse them. These belts appear to be added to the margins of the shields or to be sandwiched in between them. This pattern has led some geologists to propose a theory of "continental accretion" (see also, page 664), which proposes that the continents have grown throughout geologic time by having generally marginal orogenic belts progressively added to their stable cores. But detailed study of the shields tends to show that they are in no way different in origin from the orogenic belts and that there is no reason to suppose that they have grown significantly in size.

Study of shields is difficult for two main reasons. First, the rocks are largely metamorphic and igneous and of exceedingly complex structure generally as a result of repeated episodes of deformation and metamorphism. Most simple sedimentary structures, which are the main guide to the nature and extent of deformation, are greatly modified or obliterated. Gneissic layering commonly of purely deformational origin is widespread and many areas are flooded by granites. Second, even in the least deformed parts, no fossils useful in either age determination or correlation are preserved and, as is true of all Precambrian rocks, the course of structural development and relative age of different parts of the shields must be established by other means. For these reasons the histories of the Precambrian rocks of the shields have long remained obscure and a subject for sometimes heated debate and argument. Only within the past few decades have radiometric methods of dating and techniques of structure analysis enabled geologists to begin the enormous task of tracing the history of the continents in Precambrian times as preserved in the continental shields.

It is now clear that the shields are complex bodies built of overlapping and intersecting belts of deformed and metamorphic rocks, which appear to be the roots or scars, in various stages of modification and obliteration, of successive orogenic belts. There appears, in fact, to be little special about Cambrian and younger structures, except that they are more clearly preserved and exposed than their ancient precursors, and that their fossiliferous rocks have permitted detailed structural developments and correlations to be established. Gradually, the remnants of the Precambrian orogenic bodies are similarly being

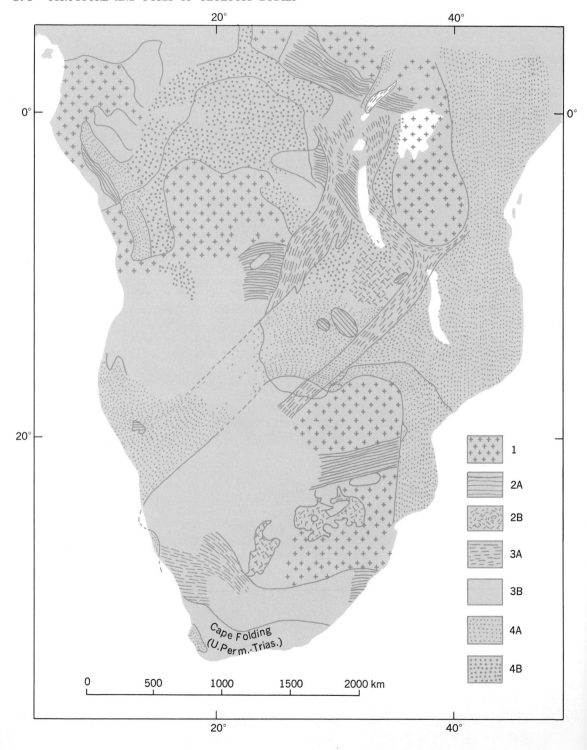

Cape Folding
(U.Perm.-Trias.)

+ + +	1
≡≡≡	2A
⁖⁖⁖	2B
---	3A
	3B
·.·.·	4A
✦✦✦	4B

0   500   1000   1500   2000 km

placed in sequence by radiometric dating, and their structural features established by detailed mapping.

As an example of the complexity of a "stable shield," consider the simplified map of Africa south of the equator shown in Figure 3–68. With the exception of the Upper Paleozoic fold belt of the Cape of Good Hope, the whole region is part of a shield, but at least four major periods of folding and metamorphism have been established within it. Rocks formed in these periods are found in linear regions of definite structural grain, probably representing the roots of the orogenic belts, and as tabular or weakly folded bodies of rock deposited simultaneously on the parts of the continent that remained relatively stable in each orogenic episode.

In most other shields geologists are beginning to recognize similar features, and the oldest shields appear to be composed of the eroded scars and superficial debris of past orogenic belts dating back at least 3.5 billion years and perhaps beyond. The continents, therefore, seem to preserve almost all stages in the evolution of the crust, the remoter events being more poorly represented. We shall see that this feature may be the one that most distinguishes the continents from the ocean basins.

Many other large-scale structures of importance exist on the continents. Perhaps the most striking of these, and certainly the largest, is the great "rift system," a faulted trough or graben extending from Mozambique across most of the length of Africa into the Anti-Taurus mountains of Asia Minor (Figure 3–69). This great linear depression, extending around more than one sixth of the earth's circumference, varies greatly in its width, character, and age. It is widest in the Red Sea (250–500 km), of intermediate widths in continental Africa (30–65 km), and narrowest in the Levant. The Red Sea sector

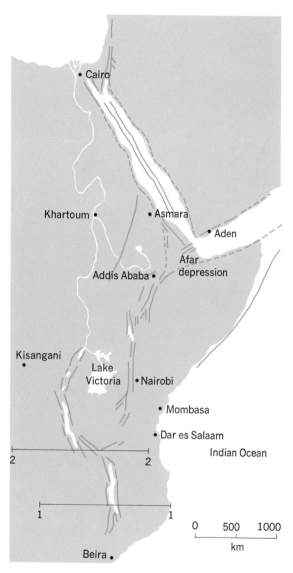

FIG. 3–69 *African part of the great rift system showing major faults (full lines) and depressed troughs (between broken lines).*

FIG. 3–68 (Facing) *Outline structural map of Africa south of the equator showing main orogenic belts and associated tabular stable region deposits. Four main periods of orogenic activity are obvious (there are probably many more) as shown: (1) Regions folded and metamorphosed 2500 m.y. ago or earlier. (2A) Belts folded and metamorphosed 2100 to 1950 m.y. ago. (2B) Tabular beds corresponding to 2A in age. (3A) Belts folded and metamorphosed 1300 to 1100 m.y. ago. (3B) Folded or tabular beds corresponding in age to 3A. (4A) Belts folded and metamorphosed 730 to 600 m.y. ago (later events—as young as 450 m.y.—have also occurred in these belts). (4B) More or less tabular beds corresponding in age to 4A. (After L. Cahen and N. J. Snelling,* Geochronology of Equatorial Africa, *North-Holland, 1966.)*

consists of a broad downwarp, partly filled with sediments and with some localized marginal faulting and a deep axial trough 20–70 km in width containing igneous intrusive rocks. The Gulf of Aden branch appears to include a submarine volcanic ridge offset by right lateral strike-slip faults, and to contain crust of oceanic type. The rift system within Africa consists of the broad triangular fault-bounded Afar depression, where the Red Sea, Gulf of Aden, and African sectors join, and, to the south, the rift systems of Ethiopia, Kenya, Uganda, and Tanzania, which are chains of complex faulted troughs passing locally into broad zones of steplike faulting. In east Africa the rift splits into an eastern and a western branch around Lake Victoria, joining again in southern Tanzania. The western rift is the deepest and most clearly defined, but it is complicated by the presence of enormous upfaulted blocks of Precambrian basement, like the Ruwenzori range. In most places the rift is asymmetric in form and is not a simple flat-bottomed strip bounded by a pair of normal faults (a graben). In southern Kenya, for example, the floor is laced with many small, steep normal faults. The rift system traverses high ground, which has been formed by repeated uplifts. The amplitude of motion between the floor of the rift and the margins may be as much as 5 km. By way of the Gulf of Aden the rift system is connected to the mid-Indian Ocean ridge, to which it may be genetically related. Tertiary and Recent volcanism is common in the rift, which is also a zone of seismic activity.

Many sedimentary basins are locally developed on the shield areas. These sometimes represent marine transgressions, but they are sometimes lacustrine or terriginous (deposited subaerially). Some of these are weakly folded or faulted; others remain undeformed over immense periods of time. Some are partly removed by erosion, and it is likely that many such deposits have existed during the long histories of the individual continents, only to be removed entirely by erosion during the continuing cycles of uplift, depression, and warping to which even the most stable parts of the continental crust seem to be periodically subject.

THE OCEANIC REGIONS

The ocean basins can be divided into two main parts: the deep basins and the continental margins. We shall see that the properties of these two regions are intimately connected.

THE DEEP BASINS Away from the continental margins and the arcuate island chains of the west Pacific, the most obvious physiographic feature of the ocean floor is a deep, flat-bottomed basin termed the "abyssal plain." This plain forms most of the ocean floor at a surprisingly uniform depth of about 5 km and is a relatively level surface covered by a thin (less than 1 km) layer of young sediment probably carried into regions remote from land partly by turbidity currents from the surrounding ridges of sediment at the continental margins. From this plain rise isolated "hills," singly or in groups, in the form of sea mounts, guyots,[5] and other volcanic structures, such as oceanic islands with their fringing coral reefs, and atolls where only the reefs now reach above sea level from subsided volcanic islands. Some of the piles of volcanic rock built upon the plain are of great size. The Hawaiian Islands, for example, rise about 10 km from the abyssal plain making them one of the most striking topographic features on the earth. Most of the volcanic bodies, such as the several thousand sea mounts known in the Pacific Ocean alone, are relatively small.

Despite its uniformity the abyssal plain is traversed by two distinct sets of physiographic and structural features, as follows (Figure 3–70):

Ridges or rises The most prominent and continuous structural feature of the oceans (and of the crust as a whole) is a system of broad ridges or rises, forming a connected world-encircling system over 40,000 km in length. The most obvious and best known branch of this system is the mid-Atlantic ridge, which follows closely the median line between the two shores of the At-

[5] Sea mounts are conical abyssal mountains that are clearly volcanoes. Guyots are similar, but are apically truncated by a flat wave-cut platform. After being so beveled, some guyots have sunk to depths as great as 3 km below the present sea level.

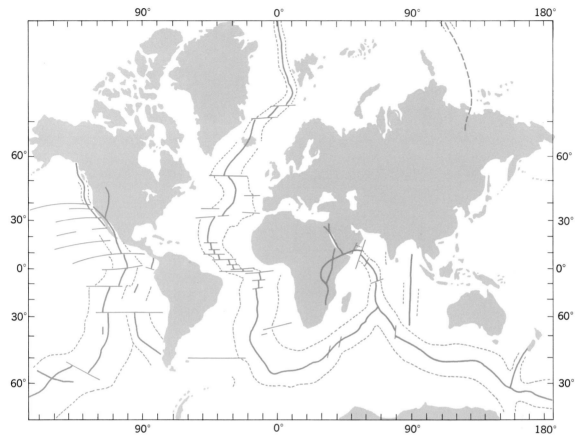

FIG. 3–70 *Oceanic ridges or rises (between dotted lines). The median lines of the ridges, sometimes defined by a faulted trough or graben, are shown by a heavy line. The fracture zones that offset the ridges are shown by fine lines (from various sources).*

lantic Ocean. In detail, the ridge does not curve, but consists of a series of north–south sections, apparently displaced, stepwise, in both senses by a system of what appear to be strike-slip faults. Other rises occur in the east Pacific, the Indian and Arctic Oceans to form an almost continuous line. Through the Gulf of Aden the mid-Indian Ocean ridge passes into the great African rift system, which appears to be part of the same global tectonic feature (Figure 3–70). This notion is supported by the detailed topography of the oceanic ridges. They are broad swells locally with a well-defined graben or rift-valley following their crests. Their profiles somewhat resemble

profiles across the east African part of the great rift (Figure 3–71). The only other places where oceanic ridges pass into land masses are, first, where the east Pacific rise passes into North America by way of the Gulf of California, where the same steplike offsets of the ridge are observed; and second, on Iceland, which appears to be a great plate of oceanic volcanic rocks straddling the northern part of the mid-Atlantic ridge.

The oceanic ridges are sites of seismic and volcanic activity, and anomalously high rates of heat flow have been recorded on them (Chapter 12).

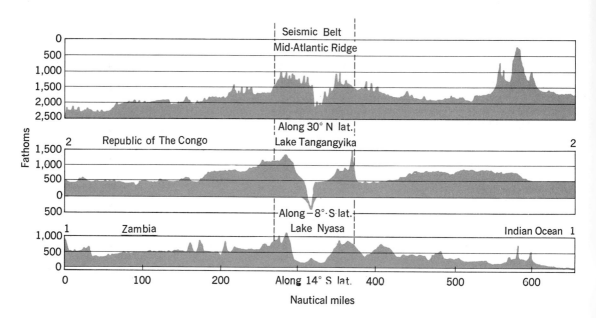

FIG. 3–71 Comparison of a profile across the mid-Atlantic ridge in the north Atlantic (upper) with two profiles across the east African rift along lines 1 and 2 on Figure 3–69. (After B. C. Heezen, in Continental Drift, S. K. Runcorn, ed., Academic Press, 1962.)

FIG. 3–72 The circum-Pacific region showing the great fracture zones (dotted) and trenches (black) following the island arcs of the west Pacific and the coasts of Central America and Chile. (After H. W. Menard, Marine Geology of the Pacific. Copyright 1964. Used by permission of McGraw-Hill Book Co.)

Fractures or faults   Locally the abyssal plain is traversed by long, straight, steplike ridges, which appear to be uneroded escarpments parallel to large fractures or faults in the oceanic crust. The faults that apparently offset the oceanic ridges belong to this system, as do others, such as the unusually continuous east–west escarpments in the northeast Pacific (Figure 3–72). Several lines of evidence confirm that these fractures are sites of local strike-slip displacements. The offset of the oceanic ridges has already been mentioned; other evidence is the offset of parallel bands of magnetic anomaly in the crust (Chapter 13) and evidence of lateral displacements from studies of first motions from earthquakes centered along the faults (Chapter 9).

THE CONTINENTAL MARGINS   Around most continents the continental crust extends under the marginal sea in the form of a gently sloping "shelf." The width of this continental shelf varies greatly from zero to about 1000 km, with an average width of about 50 km. It is covered with shallow water deposits of variable thickness. Beyond the continental shelf at water depths varying from 150 to about 700 meters, a break in slope occurs and a relatively narrow and more steeply inclined slope, called the continental slope, carries the ocean floor to a depth of about 3 km, where an extensive but gentler slope, the continental rise, connects it to the abyssal plain. The continental crust proper ends near the edge of the continental shelf, over which relatively thin, shallow water sediments pass gradually into a thick wedge of deeper water sediments that compose the lower part of the continental slope and the continental rise. From these great wedges of sediment, turbidity currents carry material to the abyssal plains, commonly by way of submarine canyons.

Many of the continental margins, such as most of those bordering the Atlantic, are the abrupt terminations of shields or relatively ancient fold mountain ranges. These margins are aseismic, free of volcanic activity, and fit very closely the picture of a continental margin just given. The circum-Pacific margins are structurally very different. They are bordered by young mountain ranges, which are seismically and volcanically active and in places exhibit structural features unlike those of other continental margins. Three structural features are particularly important.

Island arcs   The western margin of the Pacific is formed by a series of arcuate island chains (island arcs), which appear to be part of a young fold mountain belt. From the Aleutians there is a more or less continuous series of arcs, extending through the Kurile, Japanese, and Philippine Islands, which joins with the great Sunda arc of Indonesia and continues north of Australia to sweep around through the Solomon Islands and the New Hebrides toward New Zealand (Figure 3–72). This great chain is a site of present intense volcanic and seismic activity and parts of it show evidence of past folding and thrusting typical of fold mountain belts.

Oceanic trenches   For the most part paralleling the island arc chain on the ocean side is a system of trenches or deep furrows in the ocean floor that can reach a depth of 11 km or more below sea level. Where they are close to land some of these trenches are partly filled with sediments. Trenches occur also off the coast of Chile and along the island arcs of the Greater and Lesser Antilles surrounding the Caribbean Sea (Figure 3–72).

Transcurrent faults   In several places along the Pacific margin there exist on the continents great faults upon which large amounts of strike-slip movement (generally 100 km or more) have been demonstrated. The most important of these are the San Andreas fault along the coast of California, the Atacama fault in Chile, the Philippine fault, and the Alpine fault of New Zealand (Figure 3–73). Slip on the Philippine fault is left-lateral; the others have right-lateral displacement.

GLOBAL TECTONICS

The gross structural features of the continents and of the ocean basins are dissimilar, and have clearly evolved in different ways. Ocean basins were long thought to be permanent and unchanging, apart from some scattered volcanic activity and local uplift and depression, and it

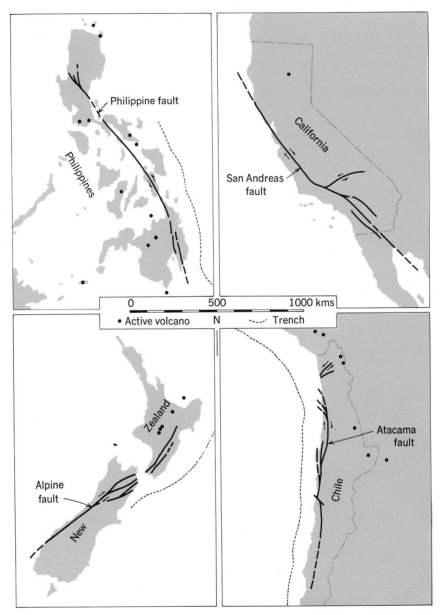

FIG. 3–73 *Large strike-slip faults in four circum-Pacific regions. (After C. R. Allen, Circum-Pacific faulting in the Philippines-Taiwan region, J. Geophys. Res., 1962.)*

was believed that major structural changes occurred only on the continents and at their margins where geosynclines developed periodically to add new mountain ranges. Other geologists believed that the continents drifted slowly over a more or less passive oceanic crust in response to motions in the mantle or some other driving force.

Detailed structural, geophysical, and physiographic studies of the ocean basins have brought recently something of a revolution in global tectonics and have provided the basis for a new dynamic and kinematic picture of the earth's crust. Some of the evidence for the new theory is provided in later chapters (particularly Chapters 9 and 13), but some of the conclusions are briefly introduced here.

The theory of "sea-floor spreading" states that the oceanic crust, far from being permanent, is in a state of continuous and relatively rapid motion (relative displacements of up to a few centimeters per year are postulated), during which it is continually created by volcanic activity along the ocean ridges (sources). From these ridges it spreads laterally to be resorbed under certain continental margins (sinks), where deep sea trenches and island arcs may be an expression of the descending crust. In order for this process to occur, an improbably high rigidity must be attributed to the 5-km oceanic crust. Many geophysicists believe, therefore, that a relatively rigid plate consisting of perhaps the upper 100 km of the mantle (which, together with the crust, is termed the "lithosphere") is involved in this motion over the weaker "low-velocity layer" of the upper mantle, termed the "asthenosphere." A number (perhaps six) of relatively rigid major plates of lithosphere, including continental crust, seem to control the tectonics of the earth by moving with respect to one another (see Figure 13–14). The plates move as a whole except at the ocean ridges, where they are being created, and at the trench and island arc systems, where they are being resorbed into the mantle by turning downward and being thrust or sinking under a continental margin (such as, for example, the eastern margin of Asia). Some continental margins, such as those bordering the south Atlantic, may be part of the same moving plate as the adjacent crust.

The only other places where the plates move past one another are along the fracture zones of the oceans and the great strike-slip faults of the continental margins. Here parts of plates moving in opposite senses slide past one another laterally.

A schematic diagram of the structural features to be expected in such a model of moving plates is given in Figure 3–74. From this model the fractures that offset the ocean ridges and link island arc chains of opposing thrust sense are not simple strike-slip faults; rather displacement is now active only in the segment lying between a pair of ridges where crust is being formed, or a pair of island arc-trench systems, where crust is returning to the mantle. That part of the fault extending beyond this segment is the scar of previously active part of the faults, now no longer moving. Such faults, which develop as shown schematically in Figure 3–75, are called *transform faults* or *transforms*. Note that ridges or trenches are not truly displaced by transform faults. The sense of slip on the faults in their active sector is actually the reverse of that required to give the apparent displacement of the ridges.

During relative motion of the lithospheric plates the area of the earth's surface must be conserved. Thus the rate at which crust is being formed by intrusion and extrusion of basic igneous rocks at the ridges must be balanced by the rate at which it is being resorbed below the continental margins. At the present time, all of the longer oceanic ridges appear to be source regions, but the only major sinks for the spreading

FIG. 3–74 Structural features to be expected for a model of plates of lithosphere moving over a weaker layer, the asthenosphere (after B. Isacks, J. Oliver and L. R. Sykes, 1968). Arrows on lithosphere indicate the relative motion of adjoining plates. Arrows in asthenosphere represent possible compensating flow.

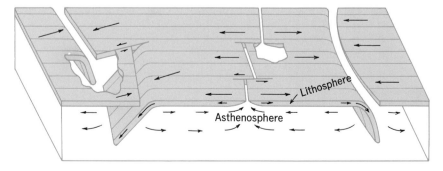

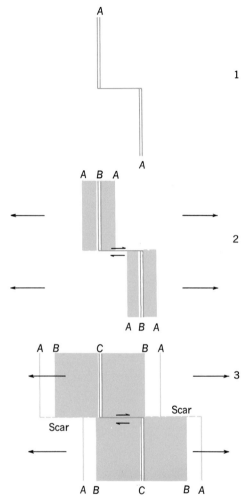

FIG. 3–75 *Schematic representation of development of a ridge-to-ridge transform fault. The double lines represent a ridge along which new crustal material is added, and the single lines represent the transform fault. Three stages are shown: 1, initial fracture; from 1 to 2, addition of material between lines A and A and slip on the fault as shown; from 2 to 3, addition of material between lines B and B. Scars of previously active sections of the fault extend laterally into the surrounding crust. Note that the sense of slip on a transform fault is the opposite of that inferred from the offset of the ridge by conventional strike-slip faulting.*

crust appear to be along the eastern margin of Asia, in the chain of trenches and island arcs that passes round the north and east of Australia (the Tonga and Kermadec region), along parts of the

west coast of South America, and along the south coast of Alaska. In this scheme the San Andreas fault becomes a transform fault of the ridge-to-ridge type, although there are still geological difficulties attached to this view, and the Alpine fault of New Zealand may be interpreted as a transform fault of the arc-to-arc type. The fracture zones off the west coast of North America appear to be the scars of old inactive transform faults left by an earlier period of spreading.

So far we have considered only the structure of the ocean basins and the continental margins. How does the theory of sea-floor spreading and lithospheric plates fit the geologic structure of the continents? At present it is difficult to make very definite statements on this subject; but the theory suggests one fundamental difference between the continents and ocean basins that may exist, and that may be responsible for the apparent complexity and variety of continental structure. If the oceanic crust follows the cycle of creation, lateral spreading, and resorption by the mantle explicit in the theory, then, in view of the rapidity of the process as suggested by geophysical data, the present ocean basins may contain within them records of only the last 100 million years or so of earth history. Ocean basins are, geologically speaking, ephemeral structures that do not remain in existence long enough to acquire the scars of many successive diastrophic episodes. The continents, on the other hand, are clearly not entirely resorbed and regenerated by the processes that seem to affect the oceanic crust, and their history seems to be one of continuous local modification through time. If we look at the younger structures of the continents, notably the Tertiary mountain ranges, we find that they fit well into the patterns of present global distortion deduced from the ocean basins. They occur in a circumpacific belt and may represent the accumulated deformed sedimentary contents of successive basins and trenches formed at the edges of the continents, perhaps by the underthrusting or sinking of the oceanic crust. The belt of Tertiary mountains across Eurasia may similarly be related to the compression of a geosynclinal trough during northward spreading of the Indian Ocean floor since early Tertiary times.

The absence of pronounced fold belts following the Atlantic margin suggests that in this region the oceanic crust may be rigidly coupled to the continental crust, the east and west margins having moved apart since the opening and gradual growth of the Atlantic from a central rift marked by the present mid-Atlantic ridge. On the other hand, the great wedges of sediment locally present along the margins, for example, of the United States and East Africa, may represent infilled depressions, perhaps with trenches, such as those that remain largely empty of sediment along parts of the Pacific margin. Under these circumstances the Atlantic and Pacific margins may represent different stages in evolution of much the same tectonic feature.

The fold mountain belts that lace the continents may be the folded remnants of sediment-filled trenches and platforms formed locally at the edges of moving lithospheric plates of different sizes and shapes that have existed successively on the earth since early Precambrian times. Perhaps the continents are continuously in motion, parting to expose oceanic crust, as appears to be happening in the Gulf of Aden and the Red Sea, and perhaps along the whole rift system of Africa, and then coming together again to deform the wedges of geosynclinal sediments that have gathered along their margins, as may have happened to form the Alpine and Himalayan ranges of Eurasia. In other places, deformation of sedimentary prisms may mark regions of descending oceanic crust as appears to be true along the western margin of the Pacific.

The apparent simplicity of the oceans and the known complexity of the continents may express a difference in the time scale of the two features. The oceanic crust has a short existence and is continuously recirculated; the continental crust is much less involved in mantle affairs and preserves a record of much of its history. Whatever the final verdict on the sea-floor-spreading hypothesis introduced here, the theory has given geologists a new impetus in their study of the continents in the form of a unifying theory of global structure. Much of what is known of the structural detail of the continents, reviewed in the first part of this chapter, must now be re-examined to see if it supports, extends, or demolishes the present theory.

REFERENCES

Recent general textbooks of structural geology are very few in number and are largely descriptive. Good examples are *Structural Geology* by L. U. deSitter (2d ed., McGraw-Hill, New York, 1964) and *Elements of Structural Geology* by E. S. Hills (Wiley, New York, 1963). A more discursive approach to larger scale problems in tectonics can be found in *Basic Problems in Geotectonics* by V. V. Beloussov (translated from the Russian, McGraw-Hill, New York, 1962) and *Tectonics* by J. Goguel (translated from the French, W. H. Freeman, San Francisco, 1962); see also *Geosynclines* by J. Aubouin (Elsevier, New York, 1965).

An excellent introduction to field work is *Manual of Field Geology* by R. R. Compton (Wiley, New York, 1962), and a recent introduction to simple geometric techniques is *Structural Geology* by D. M. Ragan (Wiley, New York, 1968). Detailed accounts of the geometric properties of folds and fabrics are to be found in *Structural Analysis of Metamorphic Tectonites* by F. J. Turner and L. E. Weiss (McGraw-Hill, New York, 1963), and in *Folding and Fracturing of Rocks* by J. Ramsay (McGraw-Hill, New York, 1967).

The literature of regional structural geology is voluminous and it is difficult to single out particular publications for mention. A. J. Eardley, *Structural Geology of North America*, 2d ed. (Harper and Row, New York, 1962) is a good source for information about North America, as is P. B. King, *Evolution of North America* (Princeton University Press, 1959). Important accounts of other structurally important and well known regions are *Bau und Entstehung der Alpen* by L. Kober (Franz Deuticke, Vienna, 1955) and *The Geology of Scotland*, edited by G. Y. Craig (Archon Books, 1965). Many other examples could be chosen.

No better account of the ocean basins exists than that given in H. W. Menard, *Marine Geology of the Pacific* (McGraw-Hill, New York, 1964). Simple accounts of the sea-floor spreading theory are to be found in "Seismology and the new global tectonics," by B. Isacks, J. Oliver, and L. R. Sykes (*J. Geophys. Res.*, vol. 73, page 5855, 1968) and in "Sea-floor spreading," by J. R. Heirtzler (*Sci. Am.*, December 1968).

4
TIME AND GEOLOGY

As POINTED OUT in Chapter 1, time is the essence of geology. Other physical sciences such as chemistry or physics are concerned mostly with the universe as it is today. Geology, on the contrary, is largely concerned with the past. Our knowledge of geological processes is derived mostly from observations of successions of events in time, and is almost entirely based on chronology. Questions most frequently asked by geologists attempting to reconstruct past events are "What happened first?" "What happened next?" "Are these events simultaneous?" As we shall see, the very vastness of geological time helps to account for processes that would be inexplicable on the shorter time scale of a laboratory experiment or a human life.

The passage of time is a familiar experience; the concept of time is, by contrast, hard to define. Philosophers have grappled for centuries with the problem of its nature and definition. Some Greek philosophers denied its existence, as for them it concerned only the past and future, both nonexistent. To Aristotle the essence of time was motion or change: If nothing happens, time does not pass. But since there has always been motion or change, time is uncreated and continues forever. (Aristotle, unlike some other philosophers of his age, thought that the universe was eternal and uncreated.) St. Augustine assigned the be-

ginning of time to the Biblical creation,[1] prior to which concepts of "before" and "after" had no meaning. He considered time to be subjective, existing only through mental processes such as memory (of time past) or expectation (of future time). To Newton, on the contrary, time was objective: "Time, of itself and from its very nature, flows equally."

The modern view of time, as proposed by Einstein, is that time is with length an essential ingredient of four-dimensional space: "When" is inseparable from "where"; simultaneity has no absolute meaning. A moment of reflection shows that indeed this must be true if the speed of propagation of light is finite. Suppose an astronomer on earth E (Figure 4–1) determines that galaxy G is at a distance of 1 billion light-years (one light-year = 9.46×10^{15} meters). He must base his calculations on a signal of some kind—for example, light, received from the galaxy. But the light that reaches the earth now left the galaxy one billion years ago, at a time when the earth was at a different position E'; the galaxy itself is now in some unknown position G'. Thus the distance measured is not really the distance

---

[1] Which most writers prior to the eighteenth century thought to have taken place a few thousand years previously.

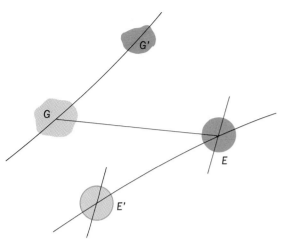

FIG. 4–1 *Measured distance between the earth (E) and a galaxy (G).*

between instantaneous positions of earth and galaxy; it is the distance between the earth now and the galaxy long ago, and is thus a composite of length and time.

The theory of relativity is based on the principle that the speed of light is independent of the respective motions of both the light source and the receiver. There is abundant experimental evidence for this principle, which appears to be a fundamental law of nature. It follows, however, that the length of an object must depend on the velocity (relative to the object) of the coordinate frame with respect to which it is measured; and similarly a time interval measured by a moving clock must be larger than the same interval measured by a clock at rest ("time dilation"). Moving clocks appear to advance more slowly than clocks at rest. This applies to any clock, including radioactive clocks (see page 204); thus, the half-life of a radioactive element depends on its velocity. Fortunately, the velocities involved in geological phenomena are so small, compared to the velocity of light, that the correction is completely negligible (a velocity of 1 km/sec requires a correction to the half-life of less than one part in 10^{10}). As will be explained later, there is also evidence, from pleochroic halos in mineral crystals, that rates of radioactive decay are independent of geologic age, in the sense that one or even

two billion years ago radioactive elements disintegrated at their present rates. Thus it is customary to assume that all physical laws have applied in the past as they apply now (for example, $\mathbf{F} = m\mathbf{a}$ was as true five billion years ago as it is today), although it is not obvious that the numerical value of the constants that appear in these laws have remained unchanged. It has been suggested, for instance, that G, the gravitational constant of equation (11-1), depends on time. At the moment the consensus, based mostly on astronomical evidence, is that G cannot have changed in the past few billion years by more than a few percent, if at all. The matter will be mentioned again in Chapter 13, in connection with the theory of an expanding earth.

The Physical Unit of Time

The numerical value of many physical constants depends on the choice of the unit of time. How can such a unit be defined? A little thought will show that to define a unit of time, we need a regularly recurring phenomenon, the occurrence of which can be counted (cf. Aristotle: "Time is motion that admits of numeration"). Until recently, the rotation of the earth seemed to serve that purpose. Accordingly, since the number of seconds in a 24-hour day is $(24 \times 60 \times 60) = 86,400$, the second has been defined as 1/86,400 of the interval of time ($=$ solar day) between successive passages of the sun in the meridian of an observatory. Note that on this scale the time it takes the earth to make one turn of 360° or 2π radians on its axis is only 86,166 seconds (sidereal day), the difference being due to its motion around the sun (Figure 4–2). Indeed a turn of 360° coupled to an orbital motion of the center of the earth of α degrees brings A to A'; but an observer at A' will see the sun in the same position relative to the local meridian only when the earth has turned on its axis by the additional angle α.

It is now well known that the solar day is not constant. It fluctuates seasonally by a few milliseconds, corresponding to changes in atmospheric circulation; wind-generated stresses on

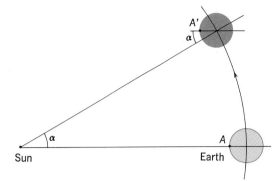

FIG. 4–2 *Difference between solar and sidereal days.*

the surface of the land provide the torque necessary to accelerate or decelerate the earth's rotation.[2] Irregular changes in the length of the day have also been observed.[3] The length of the day around 1870, for instance, was approximately four milliseconds shorter than the mean; by 1910 it was about 3 milliseconds longer than the mean. The cause of these irregular variations is not well understood; is it thought that they have something to do with changes in the intensity of convective motion in the earth's core. The rotation of the earth is therefore not a regularly recurring phenomenon and cannot be used to define precisely a unit of time. Until recently the second was defined in terms of the orbital motion of the earth around the sun, which is thought to be well understood and not subject to irregularity; it is now defined in terms of the period of the radiation emitted in a specified transition of the atom Cs^{133}.

Time and Entropy: Irreversible Processes

The unidirectional flow of time—from the past into the future—is a singular and characteristic property of that elusive quantity that connects it directly to entropy or, more precisely, to the increase in entropy that accompanies irreversible processes.

It is trivial that any isolated system (that is, a system left to itself, without contact or interaction of any kind with the rest of the universe) will evolve spontaneously, though perhaps at a very slow rate, to a state of "equilibrium," in which nothing more happens to it. In that state, the entropy must have the maximum value consistent with the constraints imposed on the system, including its volume and (constant) internal energy; this follows from the first and second laws of thermodynamics. According to the first law, $dU = T\,dS - P\,dV$ (where U = internal energy, T = temperature, S = entropy, P = pressure, and V = volume); hence, if U and V are fixed and constant, $dU = dV = 0$, and therefore $dS = 0$, implying that S is either minimum or maximum. The latter must be the case, for the second law asserts that in an isolated system that neither receives nor loses heat, $dS \geq 0$; the equal sign applies to reversible processes, whereas the inequality applies to irreversible but spontaneous changes. If the system is already in equilibrium, meaning that no further spontaneous process can occur in it with increase in entropy, the entropy must be maximum to begin with. Reversible processes, it will be recalled, imply only infinitesimal departures from the equilibrium conditions; water freezes reversibly to ice only if the temperature is lowered by an infinitesimal amount below the freezing point; and the water-to-ice reaction occurs reversibly only if it also occurs at a vanishing rate. All reactions occurring at a finite rate under conditions (for example, free energy difference) differing by more than an infinitesimal amount for the equilibrium conditions are irreversible, and as such entail the production of entropy above and beyond the amount determined by heat exchange between the system and its surroundings. The rate of production of entropy dS/dt must always be positive, since entropy must increase. This defines, in fact, the positive sense of passage of time: An irreversible process can occur in only one sense in the time dimension, that in which its entropy increases.

The passage of time is thus accompanied, and

---

[2] There is presumably also a daily fluctuation in rate of motion caused by changes in the earth's moment of inertia due to tidal deformation.

[3] From irregularities in the apparent motion of planets, sun, and moon. If the earth does not keep in time properly, the planets, which do, appear to be ahead, or late, as the case may be, on their orbital voyage. The blame can be placed on the earth, not the planets, if—as is actually the case—the time discrepancy is identical for all the planetary bodies.

indeed defined, by an irreversible increase in entropy; in other words, things never are as they used to be. Indeed they aren't; the earth in particular will never again be quite as it is now, nor has it ever been in the past quite as it is today. Of necessity, the earth must be changing and evolving. This is what makes geology fundamentally a historical science. It is concerned mainly with special cases and unique courses of evolution separated in time; whereas physics and chemistry deal with reproducible phenomena in systems as they exist today.

Geologic Time

GEOLOGY AS A HISTORICAL SCIENCE

Traditionally a somewhat arbitrary distinction has been drawn between *historical* and *physical* geology. The former deals with sequences of events, and the latter with their nature, causes, mechanisms (geological processes), and ultimate products (rocks, surface features, continents, ocean basins, and so on). The merits of the distinction are dubious. The nature and rates of processes and the evolutional histories of their tangible products are inferred mainly from the historical record. For example, it is generally believed that some continental masses, now widely separated (such as South America and Africa), were once contiguous parts of a single continent. The inferred physical process of progressive separation with the passage of time is called *continental drift*. But the evidence for the drift process is drawn almost entirely from the data of "historical" geology: observed progressive motion of the virtual geomagnetic poles (a succession of positions recorded in *time*); comparative geological and paleontological *histories* of the continents concerned; recognition of *simultaneous* past events and conditions in what today are separate continents.

Time and the earth itself share the common function that they pervade and connect all aspects of geology. Geological theory progresses by (1) recognition of unique events, (2) placing local events in chronological order, and (3) correlating simultaneous events occurring at points significantly separated in space.

Statistically the materials that concern geologists are extremely heterogeneous. No two oceans, no two continents, no two volcanoes are identical. Individually unique and irreproducible, too, are geological events pertaining to such materials. The evidence for any event is thus circumstantial and open to more than one interpretation. Moreover, in many cases the experimental approach to testing alternative models is excluded by the broad character of the geological time scale (cf. pages 215, 217). Geology is much concerned with processes and successive events of an evolutionary nature, for the earth never was and never will be precisely the same as now. But paradoxically, for reasons just stated, perception of the courses and determination of rates of evolution tend to remain imperfect and open to revision.

TIME–PLACE PROBLEM: HAWAIIAN VOLCANISM

Recognition, comparison, and correlation of geological events tend to be hampered and obscured by a recurrent difficulty inherent in the question: What have been the respective roles of time and place in shaping the observed events? This dilemma, and the manner in which it may be faced and resolved, will be illustrated by considering a single, rather simple case: the volcanic history of the Hawaiian Islands.

The Islands are part of a chain of volcanic summits, extending ESE 1500 km from Midway to Hawaii in the central Pacific (Figure 4–3). Current volcanic activity is concentrated in the large southeasternmost island, Hawaii. Here the volcanoes Mauna Loa and Kilauea, at intervals throughout the short span of historically recorded time, have erupted many flows of lava—all of a distinctive uniform type ("Kilauean basalt"). Indeed both volcanic piles—and the summit of Mauna Loa is 4500 m above sea level—are built of the same kind of lava. On the nearby island of Oahu, the last eruptions of volcanoes now extinct produced lavas of an entirely different character, significantly lower in silica, richer in alkali, and commonly containing nepheline. Another class of lavas, also alkaline but more siliceous, has been erupted from other extinct Hawaiian volcanoes including some on Hawaii itself.

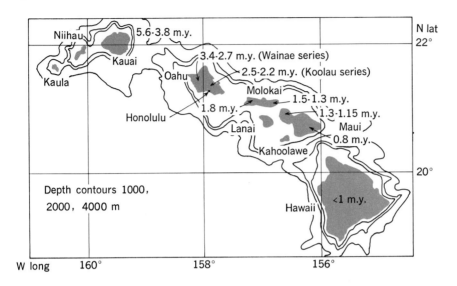

FIG. 4–3 Map of Hawaiian Islands. Radiometric dates (in millions of years) from I. McDougall, Geol. Soc. Am. Bull., vol. 75, pp. 107–124, 1964.

The separate events (eruptions), their products (lavas), and something of their order in time are clear. But do the obvious differences in volcanic behavior express controlling influences inherent in location (for example, fundamental differences in composition of the underlying basement)? Or do they represent different stages of a common pattern of volcanic evolution (in time)? If we accept the second alternative, which is the earliest, which the latest stage?

The older Hawaiian volcanoes have been considerably dissected by erosion. Their individual later histories have been pieced together by the standard geological procedures of mapping and laboratory examination of successive lava units in the volcanic piles. The large amount of varied information so obtained is consistent with a model that assumes a single broad pattern of Hawaiian volcanism. Observed differences are attributed mainly to time; and time has played a dual role:

1. The earlier and principal stages of the life history of any volcano is marked by eruption of flow after flow of lava of the Kilauean type. In the later stages of eruption at the same site lavas become more alkaline. After prolonged tranquility and erosion volcanism may flare up once more (as near Honolulu), the final products being highly alkaline nepheline-bearing lavas.

2. Recent radiometric dating shows that throughout the last few million years there has been a progressive change in the site of volcanic activity along the island chain. Volcanism becomes progressively younger from WNW to ESE. So paradoxically it is the most recent eruptions, those of Kilauea at the southeastern end of the chain, that exhibit the earlier stages of the volcanic cycle.

Still underemphasized, perhaps, is the possible influence of local conditions related to place. Although many Hawaiian lavas are classed as Kilauean basalts, no two flows are chemically and mineralogically identical—even those erupted at different places, levels, and times on Kilauea itself. Still unanswered is the question: To what degree are the unique characters of each flow and each eruption determined by situation in place independent of time?

Geological Chronology

BASIC REQUIREMENTS

Since geology is essentially a historical science, geological effort is continually directed toward problems of chronology. The individual problem may have only local significance: for example, the history of ore deposition in a mining region, the structural evolution of an oil field, or the volcanic history of Yellowstone Park. Or its implications may be much broader: the structural and volcanic history of the Andes, growth of the North American continent, reptilian evolution in Africa. But the basic requirements of any chronology are the same.

1. There should be material evidence of a sequence of events—for example, a stratified sequence of sedimentary rocks, growth rings in a fossil tree trunk.

2. There should be evidence of a unique order of events in time. The upper strata, for example, are younger than the lower; growth rings in a tree trunk are successively younger outward.

3. In the recorded phenomena the influence of time must be distinguishable from that of other factors, notably space. In this respect the local record of events at a single site, though necessarily limited, tends to be clearer than a more complete record compiled from data obtained at several separate sites.

4. For correlation of independent local records to build a regional chronology, each record must bear the imprint of a common event, such as a distinctive layer of volcanic ash or a unique fossil fauna. Difficulties arise concerning (a) the identity of the index event in all records and (b) the possible time interval between its respective manifestations in widely separated places (local records). In (b) we see again the familiar time–place problem.

5. To assign a time span to a sequence of events, or to date any event, in terms of standard physical units (for example, millions of years) we must know the rate (in years) of some process that has left its imprint in the geological record. Two such processes are (a) growth of trees by addition of annual rings to the trunk, and (b) radioactive decay of some nuclides and complementary accumulation of their daughter nuclides in mineral crystals.

STRATIGRAPHIC CHRONOLOGY

STRATIGRAPHY IN RELATION TO GRAVITY AND TIME
The outer skin of much of the exposed crust of

the earth is composed of stratified rocks—sandstones, shales, limestones—whose sedimentary origin is beyond doubt. Enclosed fossils show that these are predominantly of marine origin.

The symmetry of the sedimentary process (page 131) reflects the polarity of gravity (acting vertically *downward*). Moreover, there is a real distinction between the downward and upward senses in any vertical section through a sedimentary sequence. It is scarcely surprising that the significance of this distinction in relation to polarity of the flow of time was first stated by a scientist whose interests included crystallography. This was the seventeenth-century physician Nicholas Steno. He put forward the dual proposition (1) that the attitude of water-laid sediments at the time of deposition is close to horizontal,[4] and (2) that the upward vertical sequence of strata is from older to younger beds. This is the basic principle underlying *stratigraphy*—that section of geology which deals with sequences of events and of physical and biological (ecological) conditions recorded in sedimentary strata. In sediments showing graded or cross bedding— whatever the present atttiude even in folded or overturned beds—it is possible to distinguish the upward from the downward sense normal to the bedding.

Stratigraphy is uniquely important in geology. Most of what we know as to the nature and sequence of events on the earth's surface throughout geological time comes from stratigraphic interpretation of geological maps and drill logs. In this chapter we are concerned only with chronological aspects of stratigraphy. Stratigraphic chronology deals with questions such as these: What are the events that may be read from the stratigraphic record? What is their order in time? What are the relative rates of the processes determining recognizable sequences of events— for example, erosion, transport and accumulation of sediments, relative changes in elevation of crustal blocks, continental drift, mammalian evo-

---

[4] There are known exceptions to this, notably at the advancing front of a delta; but departures exceeding a few degrees are rare.

lution, and so on? The ultimate unattainable goal of classic stratigraphy is to build a complete geochronology covering earth history throughout geological time.

NATURE OF EVENTS Most stratigraphically recorded events are inferred from circumstantial evidence of a more or less statistical nature. The significance of a sandstone bed is read from analysis of composition, size, shape, dimensional variation, and arrangement in space of the constituent grains. These physical properties, together with others such as color and texture, define the *lithology* of the bed. Also amenable to statistical treatment—though usually estimated by simple inspection—are relative abundances of species in fossil faunas. Here is the concrete expression of an event compounded of evolution and migration of animals and plants. Behind any stratigraphically recorded event, there is an implied, though less perfectly perceived, sequence of earlier and in some cases more distant related events. Thus a sandstone outcrop is the record of a local event of sedimentary deposition. Implied are previous erosion of sand grains from some distant source, and transport and sorting of grains by water or air. Some kinds of stratigraphic evidence commonly employed in geochronology are as follows:

1. Vertical variation in lithology indicates changing conditions (in time) at the site of deposition. For example, an upward sequence conglomerate, sandstone, mudstone suggests progressive increase in depth of water and corresponding increase in distance from a retreating shore line.

2. Other lithological changes in a stratigraphic sequence imply events taking place in the source area from which the sediments were derived. An upward transition from sandstones to mudstones may in part reflect changes in climate (and so in weathering conditions) and in topographic relief in the source area. Volcanic debris appearing at a definite horizon in a sandstone region records volcanism, possibly far distant from the site of sedimentation.

3. A recognizable break in the stratigraphic succession indicates a corresponding break in chronology. Uplift, folding, erosion, and resubmergence implied by a major unconformity indicate a time interval (otherwise unrecorded) that may greatly exceed that recorded by the complete exposed succession of beds above and below the break. Even a sudden change in lithology, from one bed to another, may correspond to a time interval that is large compared with that of deposition of either bed. Failure to realize this fully contributed to long prevalent gross underestimation of the absolute time interval represented by the total stratigraphic record—the span of 20 to 200 million years that was generally accepted at the opening of this century.

4. Most thick stratigraphic sequences include some fossiliferous beds. An upward succession of radically different faunas usually expresses corresponding sharp changes in ecology, which in turn reflect fluctuating physical conditions (temperature, depth, turbidity, and so forth) at the site of deposition. This is the interpretation usually placed on alternative appearance, in Lower Paleozoic sections, of graptolitic faunas (deeper water) and assemblages of corals, trilobites and brachiopods (shallower water). Confirmatory evidence is afforded by the nature of the fossiliferous sediments—graptolitic shales, contrasted with sandy sediments typically enclosing coral-trilobite assemblages.

5. The sudden influx of a new element into an otherwise uniform faunal type suggests the opening of a new migration route, possibly distant in place and time from the site of the fauna concerned. For example, giant sloths—widely distributed in Middle Tertiary strata of South America—suddenly appear in North American Pliocene mammalian faunas. The inferred event is opening of a terrestrial migration route between the two continents. It survives today as the Isthmus of Panama.

6. Disappearance of a distinctive genus from a fossil fauna is likely to have a more local time significance. Experience shows that animal genera and species that become extinct in one region may survive elsewhere for many million years. In Europe, mollusks of the *Trigonia* group, abundant in Jurassic and Cretaceous rocks, do not

survive the Mesozoic era. Yet in Australia they still persist in the Tertiary and Recent marine faunas. Archaic fishes of a type otherwise restricted to mid-Paleozoic times have recently been found surviving in the ocean depths off the African coast.

7. More gradual progressive changes in an upward sequence of faunas of a single ecological type at a given site are considered to express trends of organic evolution in time. Well-known examples are the series of morphological changes in certain sea urchins (such as *Micraster*) recorded at progressively higher levels in the late Cretaceous Chalk of southeastern England, and in the ammonite *Baculites* in rocks of similar age in North America. The evolutionary nature of such events can scarcely be doubted when closely similar sequences are observed in widely separated localities.

LITHOLOGY, FOSSILS, AND TIME IN STRATIGRAPHY

The stratigraphic record contains two independent elements of chronological significance. Most obvious is an upward sequence of lithological changes, which commonly is found to vary notably in detail in the lateral sense. Less variable in this respect, but usually less complete, is an upward sequence of changes in fauna. Stratigraphic chronology can thus be expressed in terms of two kinds of time units: those based on rock type and those defined by fossil faunas.

At a given site we see parallel sequences of lithological and faunal changes in time. At separate sites within an area of a few hundred square kilometers it is usually possible to recognize broadly similar relations between lithology, fauna, and stratigraphic level. For example, a particular limestone formation may everywhere contain the same kind of fossil fauna. Indeed it was when William Smith, in the last decade of the eighteenth century, established such a correlation in southern England, that stratigraphy first became practicable. But lithological–faunal relations at separate sites are seldom *identical* and in some cases they may differ radically over distances as small as 10 km. So it is current practice to draw a sharp distinction between time scales based respectively on lithological and on faunal entities. Some confusion arises from use of identical terminology to denote individual units in both scales. Thus we may speak of Jurassic rocks, laid down in Jurassic time, and containing fossil remains of Jurassic life. Such confusion of terminology is inescapable; for it is only within the past 30 years that the independent time connotations of lithology and of fauna have been generally recognized. The accepted terminology of stratigraphically defined time units on the other hand developed during the previous century.

The fundamental sedimentary rock unit of a geological map or of a well log is a laterally extensive continuously mappable sheet of strata, in many cases perhaps 10 to 100 meters thick, called a *formation*. Within it less extensive units may be identified in neighboring drill logs or in limited sectors of the map. These are termed *members*. So at any site the stratigraphic record can be described in lithological terms as a vertical sequence of formations and their component members.

To introduce the connotation of time we must turn to a well defined sequence of strata at some designated type locality. These then constitute a *time-stratigraphic* unit such as a system or a series. The Jurassic *system*, as it is recognized today, is represented by a thick sequence of fossiliferous marine sediments in southern England. This type Jurassic section includes a sequence of lithologically identifiable units—formations and groups of formations—which define individual *series*. These units, in the first instance arbitrarily selected, can now be used as standards for part of a world-embracing time scale. The Jurassic *period* covers the time interval between the beginning and close of deposition of the strata that make up the Jurassic system in southern England. A distinctive unit in the upper part of the Jurassic system is the Great Oolite *series*. The time interval of its deposition is the Great Oolite *epoch*.

It is possible to construct independently a stratigraphic column based on the fossil faunas of critical beds. Here the units are *biostratigraphic*. The one most widely employed has a relatively short vertical range and is termed a *zone.* This is a bed or group of beds, characterized throughout by some distinctive fossil fauna. A zone is named after a selected index fossil in the faunal assemblage. The corresponding time unit, similarly named, is a *secule.* Such are the *Epithyris oxonica* zone and secule in the middle of the Great Oolite series of England (named after a brachiopod species absent from overlying and underlying strata).

Some units that are widely used in stratigraphic chronology are shown in Table 4–1, in decreasing order of magnitude.

TABLE 4–1   *Units in stratigraphic chronology*

Time-stratigraphic Units	Time Units	Biostratigraphic Unit
	era	
System	period	
Series	epoch	
Stage	age	
	secule	zone

At this point we have been able to define objectively the units of a worldwide time scale. But these units are tied to type localities and to restricted areas. To apply the chronological scale to other events in other regions we must devise some system of correlation. And here we must necessarily make assumptions whose validity cannot be proved. This seems to be, and indeed is, a formidable task. But it has been successfully accomplished to the extent that an enormous quantity and variety of stratigraphic and paleontological data are surprisingly consistent with a single standard chronological model. This model moreover, as we shall see later, has survived the severe test of radiometric calibration.

LITHOLOGICAL CORRELATION   It is by its lithological character and stratigraphic position that a formation is identified and traced from outcrop to outcrop or in closely spaced drill logs. On a geological map the legend is shown as a vertical sequence of formations. This is the basis for a local time scale whose units (time-stratigraphic) are defined lithologically. Its significance in terms of absolute time units (10^3 or 10^6 years), and even of biostratigraphic units, is variable both laterally and in a vertical sense. Aspects of this variability are as follows:

1. Rates of sedimentation are extremely variable. In general, silts accumulate more slowly than do sands. But exceptions and fluctuations are numerous. Within a few kilometers the thickness of a formation may thin from 1000 to 100 meters. There is no guarantee that successive lithologically similar beds of the same thickness represent similar intervals of time.

2. Formations that extend over large regions obviously have potentialities for stratigraphic correlation. It is unlikely, however, that the respective time intervals recorded by one formation at points 50 or 100 km distant will be either equal or synchronous. The Chalk of southern England and northern France (Figure 4–4) records an event of great geological significance: maximum submergence of a continental segment, some thousands of square kilometers in area, beneath an advancing late Cretaceous sea. The Chalk is a massive unit. It is several hundred meters thick, and accumulated (as shown by fossil and radiometric evidence) over a lengthy span of time—some 30 million years. To recognize the Chalk in a distant section—for example, in Northern Ireland—is not without chronological value, but the scale of correlation is crude. The base of the chalk might be selected as a more refined index of time. Here, however, we encounter another problem concerning an unknown rate. Continental submergence in the latter part of Cretaceous time presumably was a gradual process. Chalk deposition must have been initiated on a slowly advancing front conditioned by deepening sea and increasing distance from a retreating shore. We know little as to the rates of such processes. It is not unreasonable to suppose that in Cretaceous sections 200 km distant the base of the Chalk might represent points significantly different—possibly several million years apart—in time.

The ideal lithological time index would seem to be a thin, rapidly deposited, extensive sheet of some distinctive sediment. Only rarely does a formation meet these specifications—for exam-

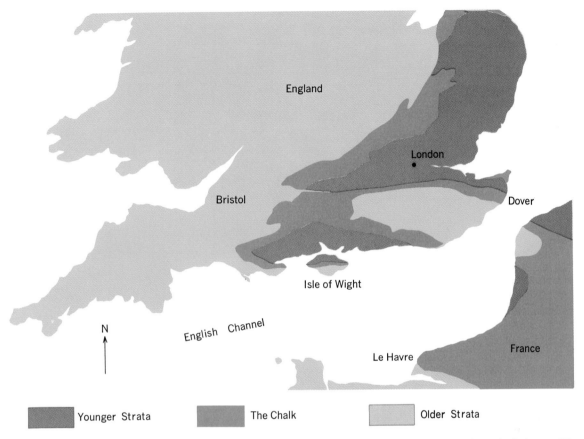

Younger Strata	The Chalk	Older Strata

FIG. 4–4 *Distribution of the Chalk in the type area, England and France, as shown on an early geological map (W. Phillips, 1821).*

ple, a sheet of distinctive volcanic tuff in continental strata.

CORRELATION BY FOSSILS Paleontology is the most important asset of the stratigrapher. Since the day of William Smith the identity of lithologically defined formations and members has been confirmed and amplified by specifying the more obvious features of enclosed fossil faunas. These faunas may maintain their identity, even in thin biostratigraphic units, over distances of hundreds or even thousands of kilometers. Zones defined by successive stages in evolution of late Cretaceous ammonites maintain the same order of appearance in the Rocky Mountains region from the Gulf of Mexico to the Arctic Ocean.

Over comparable distances formations thicken, thin, or die out altogether.

The field geologist must know something of the nature, time significance, and characteristic environments of the main groups of fossil organisms; for example, he should be able to recognize graptolites and ammonites, and should know that these groups are limited respectively to earlier Paleozoic and to Mesozoic times. Detailed sifting of fossil evidence is left to the specialist. But every geologist should be aware of certain general assumptions and questions that lie behind expert paleontological opinion on matters of correlation:

1. Living species and genera are defined by

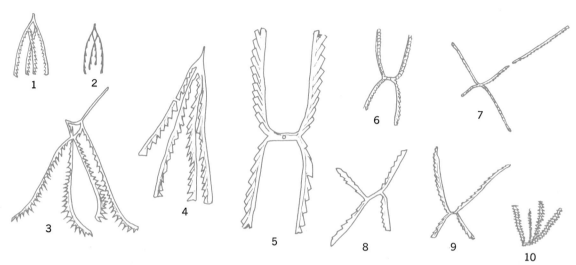

FIG. 4–5 *Various species of Lower Ordovician graptolites identified as Tetragraptus. (1) Victoria, Australia. (2), (3), (5), (6), (10) New York and Quebec. (4), (8) Southwestern New Zealand. (7), (9) Lake district, Western Britain.*

morphological criteria. Specification of these is to some degree subjective; for no two of the multitude of individuals that comprise a species are identical. In paleontology there is an additional difficulty: Most fossil remains—a shell, a bone, an imprint of more or less durable tissue—present a highly incomplete picture of the whole organism. So morphological criteria for defining and recognizing extinct species and genera are correspondingly limited. Are we justified in placing four-branched graptolites from Australia, New York, and Wales in a single genus *Tetragraptus* (Figure 4–5)? The biological implication would be that these and all other species classed as *Tetragraptus* have evolved from a common ancestor. The ammonite species *Oxynoticeras oxynotum*, characteristic of a zone in the Lower Jurassic of England, has been recorded also in France and in Mexico. This simply means that ammonite shells from all three regions have been pronounced by specialists to be identical. It is not surprising that identification and nomenclature of fossil species is under constant revision. Nevertheless, there is sufficient agreement for the data of paleontology to be presented in terms of morphologically defined units (species, genera, orders, and so on) that on the whole have proved adequate for the purpose of correlation.

2. To make chronological use of such information we must identify some feature of each fossil fauna that expresses an event in time. Most widely used are faunal characteristics of vertically limited but laterally extensive biostratigraphic units, such as zones. The fauna of a zone records the existence of a community of species at one or more sites. This is the event used for correlation. Other kinds of events have also been used: the first appearance, or the maximum profusion (acme), or the total span of existence of an index species or genus; or again the sudden influx of a group of species. Where the local record is unusually complete, lineages of gradually evolving species can be traced upward through the stratigraphic succession. Each stage of evolution in such a lineage is a chronologically significant event.

3. Next we must assume that some apparently identical events recorded at separate sites were synchronous. This is the crux of the correlation problem. The validity of the assumption clearly depends on the nature of the events and the distance between sites at which they occurred. Faunal events are shaped by processes whose rates differ mutually and are individually subject to strong variation. These include morphological

evolution and geographic migration of species, as well as changes in local environments. Let us consider briefly two contrasted cases:

(a) In strata comprising the Ordovician system in the type area of Wales and the adjoining Lake District of England, a sequence of zones can be recognized on the basis of distinctive graptolite faunas. In the state of New York and province of Quebec, and again on the opposite side of the world, in Australia and New Zealand, there are also graptolite faunas that, with certain exceptions, closely resemble those of the lower zones in Wales (Figure 4–6). In all three regions similar zones appear in the same stratigraphic order. The enclosing rocks, moreover, are everywhere lithologically similar—silty sediments suggesting deposition in open water far from shore. On these grounds, and from the delicate branching forms of the fossil remains, it is generally thought that graptolites were floating creatures of the open sea. Migration and geographic dispersal were likely to be rapid compared with the slow process of morphological evolution. For these reasons geologists feel confident in placing the graptolite zones of the Southern Hemisphere in the earlier divisions of the Ordovician period of time. Faunal similarities between Australian and New Zealand zones amount almost to identity. It can scarcely be doubted that corresponding events, at sites now 2000 km apart, were synchronous within limits of error of even the most refined geological time scale. Differences between Welsh and antipodean faunas are more obvious and the order of certain successive minor events may even be inverted. Here the scale of correlation is correspondingly coarser; geographic distance has made the rate of faunal migration a significant factor.

(b) The most familiar and widely distributed fossils of Tertiary strata, all the world over, are shells of marine mollusks (clams and snails). Even the layman can see obvious similarities between forms collected from regions as far apart as the Paris and Vienna basins of Europe and the Pacific lands of California and New Zealand. Yet worldwide correlation on the basis of Tertiary molluscan faunas has proved impossible except on the crudest scale. Most Tertiary strata were deposited in relatively shallow basins and on continental margins. Most clams and snails are bottom-living, not floating, forms. Geographic dispersal was therefore both limited and slow. The chief value of Tertiary molluscan faunas in stratigraphy is for correlation over limited distances in local provinces. Even there it may be difficult to disentangle the relative roles of time and of habitat (environment) in determining faunal similarities and dissimilarities.

CONFLICTS IN CORRELATION   Over a few hundred kilometers, a continuous lithologically identified formation is but a crude index of time. Over a similar distance, in rocks of the same lithology (environment of deposition), the time significance of a zonal fauna usually is more precise. Herein lies the explanation of an increasingly recognized situation: intersection of formational boundaries and faunally defined time surfaces. In the Cambrian sequence of the Grand Canyon, a basal sandstone formation (Tapeats Sandstone) is followed upward by a shale formation (Bright Angel Shale) some 200 meters thick. At the western end of the section (Figure 4–7) are two faunal zones, each marked by a distinctive trilobite genus, in the Bright Angel Shale: a basal *Olenellus* zone (early Cambrian), and an upper *Glossopleura* zone (middle Cambrian). About 200–300 km to the east only the *Glossopleura* zone is present; and it occupies a *basal* position in the Bright Angel Shale. The duration of the Cambrian period may have been 100 million years (page 217). So the same kind of event— change from sandstone to shale lithology—took place in the west some 20 to 40 million years earlier than at sites 300 km to the east.

CHRONOLOGICAL SIGNIFICANCE OF UNCONFORMITY AND OROGENY   An unconformity expresses an interval of time not locally recorded by sedimentation. Its duration, which may be tens or even hundreds of millions of years, is estimated by dating faunas respectively above and below the unconformity. Lithological and structural differences between the two sets of strata tell something of the nature and the time sequence, but not the individual duration, of geological events

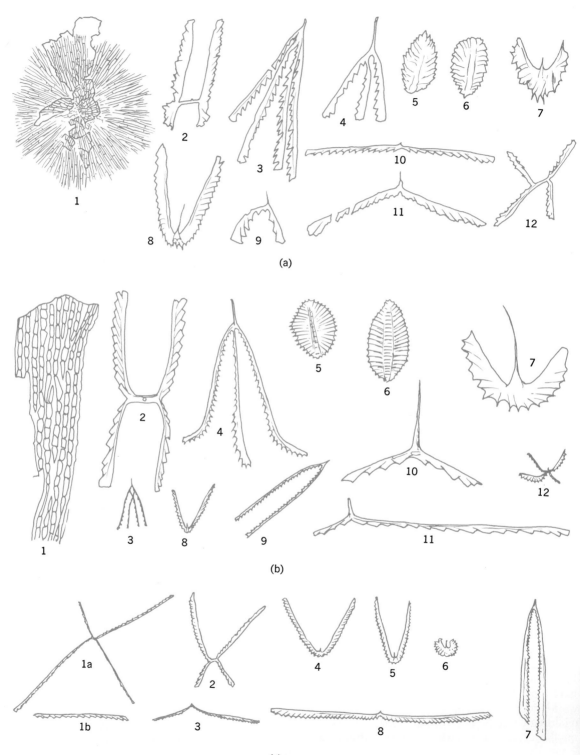

(a)

(b)

(c)

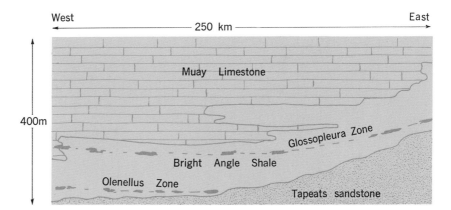

West — 250 km — East

400m

FIG. 4-7 Vertical east-west section of lower part of Cambrian strata, Grand Canyon, Arizona. (After E. D. McKee, Geol. Soc. Am. Mem. 39, 1939.)

Muay Limestone

Glossopleura Zone

Bright Angle Shale

Olenellus Zone

Tapeats sandstone

collectively spanning the stratigraphically unrecorded interval of time. A sequence commonly inferred is (1) deformation and uplift, and (2) erosion of the older strata, followed by (3) depression and resubmergence of the erosion surface (surface of unconformity). Within the first event it may be possible to decipher several episodes of folding and to relate these to possible incidents of metamorphism and/or emplacement of granitic plutons. Here the evidence is of a geometric and mineralogical nature. Each episode and each major event has its own significance in time. Here, then, is potential material for chronology and correlation. The main problem is to determine the degree to which similar events at mutually distant sites were synchronous.

Early stratigraphers, still influenced by the pre-Huttonian doctrine of catastrophe, were prone to regard the unconformity as an expression of some regional convulsion of relatively short duration. Major stratigraphic units such as

systems, on the other hand, were seen as the documented record of intervening lengthy periods of crustal tranquility and steady sedimentation. It is to these men that we owe the standard stratigraphic column and correspondingly named scale of chronology. It is not surprising, therefore, that some trace of the catastrophic doctrine still lingers in geological thought. Today, however, the stratigrapher is less prone to use the unconformity as a single index for correlation. Instead he attempts to correlate by specific events such as the earlier deformational and the later erosional incidents. Meanwhile, as we shall see later, isotope analysis provides additional information (which sometimes complicates rather than clarifies the issue) on events connected with plutonism and metamorphism.

Regional folding and uplift of older strata constitute an event called *orogeny*. The surface of unconformity records a later event of erosion. Both may be traced, though seldom without in-

FIG. 4-6 (Facing) Lower Ordovician graptolites. The fossils are impressions (in slate) of delicate branching skeletons.
(a) Preservation Inlet, southwestern New Zealand (W. N. Benson and R. A. Keble, 1936): (1) Dictyonema macgillivrayi (×1/6). (2) Tetragraptus approximatus (×2). (3) Tetragraptus fruticosus (×2). (4) Tetragraptus fruiticosus 3-branched (×2). (5), (6) Phyllograptus ilicifolius (×2). (7), (8) Isograptus caduceus (×2). (9) Didymograptus artus (×2). (10) Didymograptus nitidus-patulus (×2). (11) Didymograptus bartrumi (×2). (12) Tetragraptus quadribrachiatus (×2).
(b) New York and Quebec (R. Ruedemann, 1947): (1) Dictyonema murrayi (×1). (2) Tetragraptus lavalensis (×4). (3) Tetragraptus pendens (×1). (4) Tetragraptus fruticosus three-branched (×1). (5) Phyllograptus anna (×2). (6) Phyllograptus ilicifolius (×2). (7) Isograptus caduceus (young specimen) (×4). (8) Isograptus caduceus (×1). (9) Didymograptus identus (×1). (10) Didymograptus serratulus (×5). (11) Didymograptus serratulus var. juvenalis (×5). (12) Tetragraptus similis (×1).
(c) Lake District, east Britain (G. L. Elles and E. M. R. Wood, 1901–1918): (1) Tetragraptus quadribrachiatus (×1): (1a) Complete specimen; (1b) Fragment of one branch. (2) Tetragraptus amii (×1). (3) Didymograptus simulans (×1). (4), (5), (6) Didymograptus gibberulus (×1), (Equals Isograptus caduceus). (7) Didymograptus murchisoni (×1). (8) Didymograptus hirundo (×1).

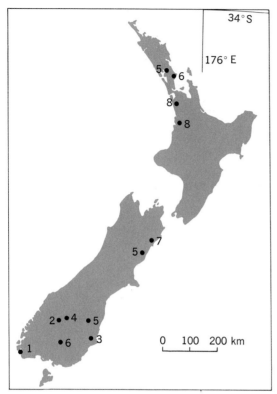

FIG. 4–8 *Locality map showing sites of unconformity between Pre-Cretaceous and younger strata, New Zealand. See text.*

terruption, over distances of 100–1000 km or more. It is customarily assumed that the onset of orogeny, and even specific recognizable episodes within it (such as first folding), were everywhere virtually synchronous. Orogenies are assigned names that, like time-stratigraphic units, have a connotation of age. The Nevadan orogeny of western America has been postulated to account for the folded and metamorphosed state of Jurassic and earlier strata that are unconformably overlain in the Sierra Nevada by unaffected Lower Cretaceous and younger rocks.

It is less generally assumed that the late incident of erosion was everywhere synchronous. Certainly this cannot be said of the final event, resubmergence. The ages of strata immediately overlying a surface of unconformity may range through several epochs or periods of geological time. Thus the unconformity that cuts across the metamorphic Dalradian series in Scotland and Ireland is covered with Devonian strata at many points, but elsewhere by rocks of early Ordovician age (page 573). If the submergence event tends to be piecemeal and to have only local chronological significance, how sound is the argument that orogeny tends to be regionally synchronous? Today's experience in mobile sectors of the crust, such as the western margins of the Americas, suggests that at least in some instances orogeny is the integrated product of small disconnected episodes spread over a long period of time.

With these possibilities in mind we turn briefly to the possible implications of a particular uncomformity and orogeny in New Zealand. Everywhere in this country there is a conspicuous unconformity that conforms to a single general pattern. The older rocks beneath it are marine sediments and some volcanic formations whose age, as shown by fossils, ranges from Carboniferous to later Jurassic. They "look old." They are everywhere folded and highly indurated; effects of metamorphism are widespread but variable. The overlying strata "look young." They are structurally simple, loosely consolidated, nonmetamorphic marine sediments whose abundant fossils indicate ages ranging from mid-Cretaceous to mid-Tertiary. In places the surface of unconformity, partially stripped of its cover, is exposed continuously as an erosion surface along the summits of extensive upfaulted block mountain ranges. New Zealand geologists refer to the deformation event as the Rangitatan orogeny. The unconformity surface is designated post-Rangitatan. The ages of rocks below and above the unconformity in different parts of the country vary greatly. Some representative combinations (located by similarly numbered points in Figure 4–8) are as follows (the horizontal line denotes unconformity):

$$(1) \quad \frac{\text{Lower Cretaceous}}{\text{Ordovician}^{[5]}}$$

---

[5] Strongly metamorphosed, cut by granite plutons.

$$(2) \quad \frac{\text{Lower Tertiary}}{\text{Permian}[6]}$$

$$(3) \quad \frac{\text{Upper Cretaceous}}{\text{? Paleozoic}[7]}$$

$$(4) \quad \frac{\text{Mid-Tertiary}}{\text{? Paleozoic}[7]}$$

$$(5) \quad \frac{\text{Lower Tertiary}}{\text{Mid-Triassic}[6]}$$

$$(6) \quad \frac{\text{Mid-Tertiary}}{\text{Mid-Triassic}[6]}$$

$$(7) \quad \frac{\text{Lower Mid-Cretaceous}}{\text{? Triassic–Jurassic}}$$

$$(8) \quad \frac{\text{Mid-Tertiary}}{\text{Upper Jurassic}}$$

The model of a single Rangitatan orogeny has the advantage of simplicity and is not inconsistent with radiometric dating of connecting metamorphic and igneous events (140–100 m.y.). Suppose, however, that orogeny were not everywhere identical in pattern nor synchronous in time. Repeated deformation and metamorphism could conceivably have occurred locally in Triassic and Jurassic times (combinations 3, 4 above) while sedimentation was proceeding elsewhere (combinations 7, 8). In other sectors deformation and burial metamorphism may have been in progress in Triassic and Permian beds at the base of a sedimentary pile, whereas marine sediments were being continuously deposited in the upper levels late into Jurassic time (combinations 6, 8). Here orogeny could even have continued to the end of the Cretaceous. These alternatives are put forward, not with a view to modifying accepted ideas on New Zealand geochronology, but rather to illustrate the kind of uncertainties that attend chronological use of unconformity and orogeny.

THE STRATIGRAPHIC COLUMN

HISTORICAL BACKGROUND   Stratigraphy was born in Britain. Methods and principles employed

---

[6] Incipiently metamorphosed.
[7] Strongly metamorphosed, with repeated folding.

universally today were conceived and developed mainly by British geologists during the first three decades of the eighteenth century. It was they who first constructed a generalized stratigraphic column compounded of partially overlapping, vertically restricted local segments. And it was in terms of this column that universally applicable divisions of a geological time scale were erected and named. So the geologist of today must be familiar with the broad outlines of British stratigraphy. He must realize, moreover, that stratigraphic chronology is still tinged with the imprint of British thought in the days before Darwin. More sophisticated notions of the stratigraphic significance of fossil faunas, however, stem independently from French paleontologists, contemporaries of Hutton and Smith. While mapping and extension of the stratigraphic record proceeded in Britain, French effort in the first decades of the nineteenth century was directed to the successive faunas themselves, as revealed in the younger rock series of northern France. Thus was born modern paleontology, the rise of which is associated especially with the names of Cuvier and Lamarck. With it came revolutionary ideas of faunal change through evolution, although these were unknown, or treated with skepticism, in Britain for another half century.

DEVELOPMENT OF THE COLUMN   Stratigraphy was made possible when Smith realized that the surest means of recognizing a formation was through its distinctive fossils. The first regional geological maps (Smith, 1815; Phillips, 1821) cover all England and Wales (Figure 4–9). Their gross features differ scarcely at all from those that figure in modern textbooks. Charles Lyell (*Elements of Geology*, 1839, pp. 159–196) set out clearly and simply the essential stratigraphic principles: superposition of strata in order of decreasing age; use and limitations of lithology and of fossils in identification and correlation of stratigraphic units; the significance of unconformities. His generalized column of "fossiliferous strata" then adopted throughout Britain, France and Germany already includes familiar names still retained in modern chronology:

Tertiary	{ Newer Pliocene Older Pliocene Miocene Eocene	
Cretaceous	{ Chalk Greensand Wealden	
Oolitic	{ Upper Oolite Middle Oolite Lower Oolite Lias	

		German equivalents:
Upper New Red	{ Upper New Red Sandstone Muschelkalk	Keuper Muschelkalk Bunter sandstone
Lower New Red and Carboniferous	{ Lower New Red Sandstone Magnesian Limestone Coal strata Old Red Sandstone	Zechstein
Primary fossiliferous	{ Upper Silurian Lower Silurian Cambrian and older fossiliferous strata	

KEY FOR FIG. 4-9

Formations		Age on Modern Time Scale
LC	{ Diluvial Beds, Upper Marine, Freshwater Beds London Clay (LC), Plastic Clay	} Tertiary (London Clay, Eocene)
C	{ Chalk (C), Chalk Marle and Green Sand, Weald Clay, Iron Sand	} Cretaceous
L	{ Purbeck and Portland or Aylesbury Limestone and Kimmeridge Clay, Coral Rag and Calcareous Grit, Oxford or Clunch Clay, Cornbrash Forest Marble and Great Oolite, Inferior Oolite and Sandy Beds, Lias (L)	} Jurassic
	{ New Red Sandstone, Magnesian Limestone	} Jurassic and Permian
	{ Coal, Millstone Grit and Limestone Shale, Carboniferous or Mountain Limestone, Trap of Coal and Mountain Limestone	} Carboniferous
	{ Old Red Sandstone	} Devonian
	{ Transition Limestone, Slates Greywacke Clay Slate	Older formations Metamorphic and Plutonic rocks

FIG. 4–9 *Early geological map of a part of Britain (W. Phillips, 1821). (From* History of the Earth *by Bernard Kummel. W. H. Freeman and Co. Copyright © 1961. Second edition.) See key, lower opposite.*

TABLE 4–2   *Stratigraphic column*

System	Time Units			
	Epoch	Period	Era	
Quaternary	Holocene* / Pleistocene	Quaternary		
Tertiary	Pliocene / Miocene / Oligocene / Eocene / Paleocene	Tertiary	Cenozoic	
Cretaceous		Cretaceous		
Jurassic		Jurassic	Mesozoic	
Triassic		Triassic		
Permian		Permian		
Pennsylvanian		Pennsylvanian		
Mississippian		Mississippian		
Devonian		Devonian	Paleozoic	
Silurian		Silurian		
Ordovician		Ordovician		
Cambrian		Cambrian		
Local systems series and time units recognized but not correlated on a worldwide basis.			Precambrian	

* Also termed Recent.

It took time to unravel the mutual relations of the structurally complex older rock units of Wales and southwestern England. But by 1880 it was accomplished. The three oldest systems, named after Wales and her ancient tribes, had been established: Cambrian, Ordovician, Silurian. The Old Red Sandstone in Devonshire was found to be a component formation of a more comprehensive system; and this was named Devonian. Further modifications and additions reflect the growing realization that certain systems are more fully developed outside than within Britain. Mississippian and Pennsylvanian systems of America replaced the more limited Carboniferous of Europe. The Permian (Urals) and tripartite Triassic (Germany) were substituted for equivalent New Red Sandstone and associated strata of Britain. Because of abundance of equivalent fossils in the Jura Mountains, the earlier lithologic name Oolitic was dropped in favor of Jurassic. Meanwhile the early divisions of the Tertiary, originally defined by Lyell on the basis of increasing abundance of what were thought to be still-living species, were redefined and modified to their present pattern. So finally emerged a stratigraphic column, still universally accepted as the basis of a corresponding geological time scale (see Table 4–2).

WORLDWIDE UNITY OF THE COLUMN   Early stratigraphers found it convenient to postulate catastrophic upheavals and accompanying annihilation of preexisting life as events that could be used for correlation on a regional scale. Lyell, the exponent of uniformitarianism, would have none of this. He recognized that even major unconformities used to delimit stratigraphic systems have local rather than transcontinental significance. Faunal change in time he regarded as slow and spontaneous, while discounting any mechanism of evolution such as had long been in vogue in France. But he also appreciated the role of migration in the abrupt upward changes in fauna so commonly observed in stratigraphic sections. Lyell taught that worldwide implementation of a stratigraphic time scale could become possible only through patiently piecing together mutually overlapping data of many local records. To this principle most geologists adhere today. There is little support for the idea that alternating periods of continental uplift and submergence on a global scale provide the basis for continental or worldwide correlation by orogeny and unconformity.

Worldwide application of a stratigraphic time scale based essentially on sections in western Europe hinges on this question: Can we recognize, as identical and synchronous, events recorded both in Europe and in distant continents? A century's experience justifies an optimistic answer. Certain spectacular events—faunal innovations, evolutionary trends, extinctions—that mark the progress of life from Cambrian times onward in Europe, are parallelled in distant regions. *Their relative order everywhere is identical.* There is thus an overwhelming body of evidence, which by its internal consistency, points to certain worldwide faunal events as valid indices of time.

Customary procedure today is to establish in detail, for any sizable continental segment, a local stratigraphic column, and a local faunal succession. By use of faunal indices of worldwide validity, the local column may now be calibrated broadly in terms of standard chronology. Refinement of correlation decreases with increasing distance from the type locality of the standard stratigraphic unit employed. Thus Jurassic sections in North America and in central France are correlated stage for stage (that is, at the level of *age* units on the time scale) with the standard British column. But New Zealand geologists, while recognizing five faunally defined stages, group these into two series: Herangi series, early Jurassic *epoch*; Kawhia series, middle and late Jurassic *epoch*.

PRECAMBRIAN CHRONOLOGY   When Darwin in 1859 conclusively demonstrated the origin of species through slow evolution he severely jolted geological thinking based on the writings of Lyell. Upward faunal changes in conformable strata imply a much greater interval of time than that required for deposition of the sedimentary beds. Formational boundaries presumably express major time intervals unrecorded by sediment. But of all breaks in the sedimentary record that at the base of the Cambrian now assumed profound significance. The earliest Cambrian faunas include many diversified forms of life. Some, notably the trilobites, were complex forms in an advanced stage of evolution. Precambrian time, therefore, must have been of vast duration. A century after Darwin its total span has been shown to exceed 80 percent of all geological time.

In spite of the great duration of Precambrian time and the great extent of Precambrian rocks in continental shields, it has proved impossible to set up a corresponding worldwide time scale on the basis of stratigraphy. Precambrian rocks are largely unfossiliferous. Where fossils have been found they prove to be primitive forms with little obvious time significance as yet. The Precambrian record moreover has been obscured by repeated episodes of orogeny, metamorphism, emplacement of granitic plutons, and prolonged erosion. It is possible, nevertheless, to reconstruct, by conventional means, the broad sequence of local events. This has been done, for example, in the Lake Superior region of the Canadian shield, in northwestern Scotland, in the Baltic shield, and in parts of Australia.

Mapping in the Lake Superior district first revealed a detailed stratigraphic record. The lowest rocks comprising the "Archaean" system of earlier writers are for the most part strongly metamorphosed folded sediments and intrusive granitic and other plutonic bodies. Separated from these by a regional strong unconformity are less metamorphosed folded sediments of the "Algonkian" system. Each system was divided into recognizable stratigraphic series. For a long time Precambrian rocks from other parts of the Canadian shield, and even from distant localities such as the Grand Canyon section of Arizona were correlated with the Archaean or the Algonkian of the Great Lakes. It was even general practice to speak of supposedly equivalent time intervals as the "Archaeozoic" and "Proterozoic" eras. But it has become abundantly clear that any such general correlation is completely unwarranted. Degree of metamorphism is no criterion of the relative age of rocks in different provinces. General practice today is to designate local stratigraphic divisions simply as upper, middle, and lower Precambrian. And there is always the possibility that the middle Precambrian of one province may correlate in time with the upper or the lower Precambrian of other districts.

RADIOMETRIC CHRONOLOGY

HISTORICAL BACKGROUND   By 1900 many geologists were convinced that the total span of geological history was between 20 and 100 million years. This interval, it was thought, could account for the estimated thickness of sediment in the geological column and for progressive accumulation of salt in a once fresh-water ocean. The lower limit seemed to be demanded by the supposed thermal history of the earth (later to be drastically revised when radioactivity was discovered). The ghosts of Darwin and Lyell might well have been uneasy at the general consensus, for both men had postulated a minimum of 200 m.y. to account for the complexity and diversity of life. Once again, however, geological opinion on time received a severe jolt, this time at the hands of physicists. In 1905 Rutherford demonstrated the relation of radioactivity to atomic disintegration. And he realized at once that in his hands was a potential geological chronometer. From the uranium and helium contents of an analyzed mineral crystal he placed its age at not less than 500 million years. The age of radiometric dating in geology had begun. At Yale, Boltwood saw the significance of lead as a daughter element springing from radioactive decay of uranium. Immediately he used Pb/U ratios in analyzed minerals to assign absolute ages to several periods: Carboniferous, 340 m.y.; Devonian, 370 m.y.; most startling of all, Precambrian crystals from three continents in the range of 1025–1640 m.y. All this had happened before 1910.

Geologists were now divided. The majority—and among them some geochemists—rejected the new data on the grounds that the basic analyses were suspect. But there were champions of the newly enlarged concept of time. Foremost was Arthur Holmes, a man destined to become the most eminent geologist of his day, who at the age of twenty-one (in 1911) wrote a classic—and, to many, shocking—paper "The association of lead with uranium in rock-minerals, and its application to the measurement of geologic time." He had the company of older men, among them stratigraphers: at Yale, Barrell, in 1917, reopened and convincingly argued the case for equating seemingly minor stratigraphic breaks with unsuspectedly lengthy unrecorded intervals of time.

Meanwhile chemists concentrated on improvement of analytical technique and on evaluating the relative merits of He/U and Pb/U ratios as indices of absolute age. The period 1935–1950 was marked by great advances in fields related to radiometric chronology, especially in isotope chemistry, mass spectrometry, and radioactive behavior of minor isotopes of some common elements, notably C^{14}, K^{40}, and Sr^{87}. The flood of new data proved for the most part to be internally consistent. By 1950 radiometric dates were generally accepted as a most significant element in the geological time scale. Radiometric scales will of course be subject to future modification and refinement. Current controversy centers on such topics as the nature of the dated events and apparent conflicts between radiometric and stratigraphic data. Today, however, no geologist doubts that the history of our planet extends back through several thousand million years. And this conclusion rests on radiometric data.

STATEMENT OF THE PRINCIPLE   Radioactivity covers various kinds of spontaneous changes affecting the respective numbers of protons and neutrons in certain inherently unstable nuclides. The unstable nuclide decreases in abundance with time and a more stable daughter nuclide increases in corresponding numbers. By-products of various patterns of decay are α-particles (helium nuclei), β-particles (electrons), and energy (γ-radiation) in various combinations. Radioactive decay, at the level of an individual atom, is a random process. So its rate depends upon the number of atoms N, present at a given instant (Figure 4–10). It can be expressed in terms of a decay constant λ which is a unique property of each nuclide—the proportion of atoms that decay in any small interval of time

$$\lambda N = -\frac{dN}{dt} \qquad (4\text{-}1)$$

from which

$$N_t = N_0 e^{-\lambda t} \qquad (4\text{-}2)$$

or

$$\frac{N_0}{N_t} = e^{\lambda t} \qquad (4\text{-}3)$$

where N_0 is the initial number of parent atoms and N_t is the number surviving at time t.

Radiometric dating in geology involves determining the time t since a radioactive nuclide becomes fixed in a system such as a crystal or a rock sample. A more convenient expression for

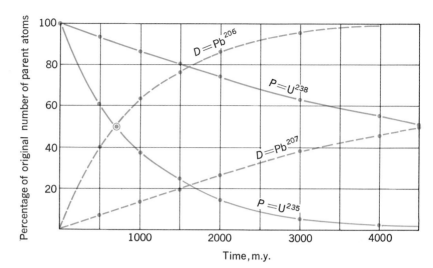

this purpose, from equation (4-3), is

$$t = \frac{1}{\lambda} \log_e \frac{N_0}{N_t} \qquad (4\text{-}4)$$

A rate of decay is readily visualized in terms of a related quantity, the *half-life*, T, of the decaying nuclide. This is the time taken to reduce the number of parent atoms by one half:

$$T = \frac{1}{\lambda} \log_e 2 = \frac{0.69325}{\lambda} \qquad (4\text{-}5)$$

Experimentally determined decay constants are available for nuclides used for radiometric dating. Mass spectrometry permits determination of atomic proportions of parent (P) and daughter nuclides (D) in a mineral or rock sample. Equation (4-4) becomes

$$t = \frac{1}{\lambda} \log_e \left(1 + \frac{D}{P}\right) \qquad (4\text{-}6)$$

where t is the radiometric date, in years, of an event recorded in the sample (for example, crystallization of hornblende in andesite).

Daughter nuclides of decay reactions that are used for radiometric dating are isotopes of common elements, among them lead, strontium, calcium, and argon. So there is always a problem concerning the amount of the daughter nuclide that may have been present in the dated material

at zero time, t_0. There is also the possibility that the sampled system may have been to some degree open to parent or to daughter nuclides over some interval of time since t_0. This can be checked by concordance or discordance between dates obtained by different methods from the same sample. Finally decay constants are changed slightly from time to time as required by new and more refined data. Radiometric dates therefore are open to constant revision as errors connected with these problems become reduced in the light of new techniques and data.

DECAY SCHEMES The nuclides and decay schemes most commonly used for radiometric dating are as follows:

1. U^{238}. U^{238}, the most abundant of the naturally occurring isotopes of uranium, decays to Pb^{206} by a complex series of nuclear transformations in which 14 short-lived nuclides are successively produced and eight α-particles are emitted; the entire sequence can be summed up as $U^{238} \rightarrow Pb^{206} + 8He^4$. (Check that $238 = 206 + 8 \times 4$). The decay constant $\lambda_{238} = 1.537 \times 10^{-10}/\text{yr}$, corresponding to $T = 4.53 \times 10^9$ yr.

2. U^{235}. U^{235}, which occurs at present in the fixed ratio of 1 atom of U^{235} for 137.8 atoms of U^{238}, decays (also in steps) as follows:

$$U^{235} \rightarrow Pb^{207} + 7He^4$$
$$\lambda_{235} = 9.72 \times 10^{-10}/yr$$
$$T = 0.713 \times 10^9 \, yr$$

3. *Th²³²*. Stepwise decay of Th²³² leads to formation of the stable isotope Pb²⁰⁸ as follows:

$$Th^{232} \rightarrow Pb^{208} + 6He^4$$
$$\lambda_{232} = 4.99 \times 10^{-11}/yr$$
$$T = 13.89 \times 10^9 \, yr$$

4. *Rb⁸⁷*. The Rb⁸⁷ isotope of rubidium (27.85 percent of natural Rb) decays by β-emission to Sr⁸⁷. The decay constant is somewhat uncertain; a value $\lambda = 1.39 \times 10^{-11}/yr$ is commonly used. The correspondong value of T is 4.99×10^{10} yr.

5. *K⁴⁰*. The isotope K⁴⁰ (0.119 percent of natural K) decays in two ways. By β-emision, 89 percent of K⁴⁰ decays to Ca⁴⁰, and the remaining 11 percent form A⁴⁰ by electron capture. The decay constant for the combined process is $5.305 \times 10^{-10}/yr$.

6. *C¹⁴*. Neutrons produced in the upper atmosphere by cosmic radiation and reacting with N¹⁴ form a radioactive isotope of carbon C¹⁴. This decays by β-emission back to N¹⁴ and has a half-life of 5750 years (a value of 5568 years was much used prior to 1961).

CONSTANCY OF DECAY RATES   Radiometric dating is predicated on the assumption that, throughout the span of earth history, rates of radioactive decay (that is, values of λ) have remained constant. Here is uniformitarian thinking in the most rigid sense. Is it warranted? Has every radioactive nuclide proceeded on a rigid course of decay at a constant rate? The energy released in the spontaneous decay of a nuclide is so large—compared, say, to thermal energy kT—that it is unlikely that the rate of decay could be sensibly affected by any change in temperature or pressure likely to have occurred in terrestrial history. Yet, could the fundamental physical laws, or the numerical values of the basic physical constants (for example, Planck's constant, or the velocity of light) have changed so as to alter decay constants? These are questions significant to the geologist and physicist alike. There is long-familiar mineralogical evidence, in the form of "pleochroic haloes" to suggest that decay constants have indeed not changed.

Crystals of biotite and other minerals in granitic or metamorphic rocks commonly enclose minute specks of minerals (sphene, monazite, xenotime, zircon, and so on) containing uranium or thorium. The α-particles emitted at high velocity by the disintegrating nuclides interact, because of their charge, with electrons of surrounding atoms which slow them down until they finally come to rest in the host mineral at a distance from their source that depends on their initial kinetic energy and the density and composition of the host. Where they finally stop they produce lattice distortions and defects, which generally result in discoloring or darkening. Thus each of the eight α-particles emitted in the course of the disintegration of U²³⁸ to Pb²⁰⁶ produces in biotite a dark ring around the radioactive inclusion, each ring having its own characteristic radius (of the order of a few microns) in a given mineral (for example, biotite). This radius measures the kinetic energy, hence the probability of emission of the corresponding α-particle, therefore also the half-life of the parent nuclide (Geiger-Nuttall law[8]). Radii of such "pleochroic haloes" are found to be identical in biotites of all ages, implying that the rate of decay has remained constant.

URANIUM–LEAD DATING   A complete U-Th-Pb analysis yields data which, by substitution of appropriate values in equation (4-6), yield several independent values for a single date. The most sensitive time indices, after correction for contamination by common lead, are the ratios Pb²⁰⁶/U²³⁸ and Pb²⁰⁷/U²³⁵. Much less sensitive, because of the long half-life of thorium, is Pb²⁰⁸/Th²³². In a system that has remained closed since the dated event the two Pb-U dates should be concordant; that is, the two isotopic ratios should plot on the theoretical "concordia curve" XY in Figure 4–11. Commonly this is not the case. Many analyses of zircon samples from Precambrian rocks yield markedly discordant

---

[8] The Geiger-Nuttall law is an empirical relation between the half-life of an α-emitter and the range in air of the emitted α-particles. It can be justified theoretically on quantum-mechanical grounds.

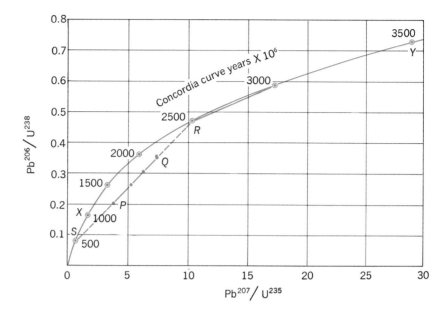

FIG. 4–11 *Concordia curve for Pb/U isotope ratios. Calculated for λ constants cited in text. PQ hypothetical experimentally determined points indicating date of origin R (2500 m.y.) and possible disturbance by a later event at S (500 m.y.).*

Pb^{206}/U^{238} and Pb^{207}/U^{235} values. This is attributed to late leakage of lead. In such cases, however, the discordant values obtained from different samples in the same general area commonly fall on a straight line, such as *PQ*. This line is thought to represent a specific pattern of departure from a point *R*—the upper intercept of *PQ* on *XY*—that represents the true date of the event in question. In some, but not in all cases, disturbance of the system can be traced to a late independently recorded event whose date is given by the lower intercept, *S*, on *XY*.

RUBIDIUM–STRONTIUM DATING The geochemical properties of rubidium and strontium are such that any mineral containing Rb is likely to contain also small amounts of inherited Sr (Sr^{86} and Sr^{87}) in addition to Sr^{87} produced by decay of Rb^{87}. To obtain a correct age for the mineral, the amount Sr^{87}_0 initially present must be deducted from the present amount of that isotope. Equation (4-6) becomes, accordingly,

$$t = \frac{10^{11}}{1.39} \log_e \left(\frac{Sr^{87}_t - Sr^{87}_0}{Rb^{87}_t} + 1 \right) \qquad (4\text{-}7)$$

Since Sr^{86} is nonradiogenic and stable, in any

closed system $Sr^{86}_t = Sr^{86}_0$. Thus,

$$t = \frac{10^{11}}{1.39} \log_e \left[\frac{(Sr^{87}/Sr^{86})_t - (Sr^{87}/Sr^{86})_0}{(Rb^{87}/Sr^{86})_t} + 1 \right]$$

$$(4\text{-}8)$$

The rate of decay of Rb^{87} is so slow that the first term inside the bracket is usually very small. Thus only a very small error is introduced when replacing equation (4-8) by

$$t = 10^{11} \left[\frac{(Sr^{87}/Sr^{86})_t - (Sr^{87}/Sr^{86})_0}{1.39(Rb^{87}/Sr^{86})_t} \right] \qquad (4\text{-}9)$$

where $(Sr^{87}/Sr^{86})_0$ is unknown. To determine this ratio, isotope ratios are determined separately on several systems with the same presumed history (for example, separated fractions of biotite, microcline, or hornblende from the same rock, or two different rocks from the same pluton). If the ratio $(Sr^{87}/Sr^{86})_0$ was the same for all samples, which all became closed to diffusion of rubidium and strontium at the same time t_0, a plot of $(Sr^{87}/Sr^{86})_t$ against $(Rb^{87}/Sr^{86})_t$ for the several samples (Figure 4–12) will yield a straight line, called an isochron, with slope $t \times 1.39 \times 10^{-11}$; its intercept on the (Sr^{87}/Sr^{86}) axis defines $(Sr^{87}/Sr^{86})_0$.

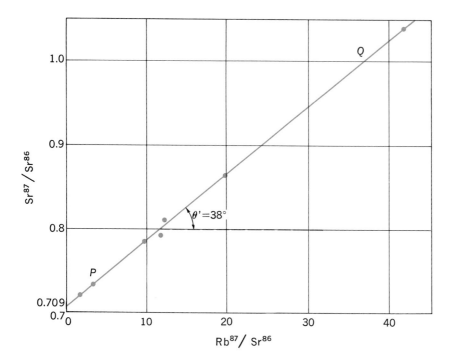

FIG. 4–12 Rubidium/strontium whole-rock isochron for seven specimens of Northbridge granite, Massachusetts. (After S. Moorbath, M.I.T. Report NYO-3943, 1962, p. 8.)

POTASSIUM-ARGON DATING The dating equation (4-6) for potassium-argon becomes

$$t = \frac{10^{10}}{5.305} \log_e \left(1 + \frac{A^{40}}{0.11K^{40}}\right)$$

The decay to Ca^{40} is not used for dating, because nonradiogenic Ca^{40} is generally present initially in potassium-bearing minerals. Since argon is not a common constituent of minerals, errors due to the presence of initial A^{40} are usually (but not always) small.

Argon produced by decay of K^{40} tends to diffuse out of the host; above 300°C the rate of diffusion is appreciable in most minerals. Loss is most serious from microcline, less so from micas and sanidine, and even less from pyroxenes and hornblende, which, however, generally have a very low content of K^{40}. Whole-rock analyses of rocks such as basalts yield reliable dates only if the rock has suffered no alteration. The dated event is the time of final cooling below approximately 300°C.

RADIOCARBON DATING C^{14} generated in the upper atmosphere mixes rapidly with ordinary atmospheric and oceanic carbon (C^{12} and C^{13}) and is taken up by plants and other organisms. Exchange between the atmosphere and the organism generally ceases with the death of the latter. Thereafter C^{14} decays at its characteristic rate. The time at which exchange ceased is determined by measuring the amount of C^{14} now present in the remains of the organism (for example, wood).

Radiocarbon dating depends on the assumption that the C^{14} content of the air or seawater when exchange ceased was the same as it is today. This assumption may not be quite correct. In the first place, the burning of fossil fuels (which no longer contain any C^{14}) has added in the last 200 years a measurable amount of C^{12} and C^{13} to the atmosphere. In the second place, the C^{14} concentration in the atmosphere depends on the rate at which it is produced by cosmic rays. Insofar as cosmic rays consist of charged particles (protons), they are deflected by the earth's magnetic field, which serves as a shield. As the intensity of the latter is known from paleomagnetic observations to have fluctuated by a factor of about 4 in the last 10,000 years, slight errors in C^{14} dating are likely.

Because of its short half-life, C^{14} obviously cannot be used for dating much beyond 40,000 years.

EARLY TERRESTRIAL EVENTS *The "age" of the earth and of meteorites* A minimum age for the crust of the earth is the oldest measured on any rock; at the moment this is about 3.5 b.y. (1 b.y. = 10^9 years).

An approximate maximum age for the earth can be determined in several ways. As noted on page 205, U^{235} disintegrates faster than U^{238}; the ratio U^{235}/U^{238}, which is now $1/137.8$ must decrease with time. Arguments of nuclear physics suggest that the abundances of these two isotopes must have been originally nearly the same. The time t_0 at which this ratio was 1 is easily found for equation (4-2)

$$t_0 = \frac{\log_e 137.8}{\lambda_{235} - \lambda_{238}} \simeq 6 \times 10^9 \text{ yr}$$

More precise determinations are based on isotopic ratios of lead. In addition to radiogenic Pb^{206}, Pb^{207}, Pb^{208} (the *initial* amounts of which are unknown), there exists, in a small amount, a nonradiogenic stable isotope Pb^{204}, the abundance of which is presumably constant. Thus abundances of the other isotopes can conveniently be expressed in terms of isotopic ratios Pb^{206}/Pb^{204}, and so on. Suppose now a reservoir in which uranium disintegrates, starting at time t_0. At a later time t, the radiogenic lead is extracted from the system and crystallized as, say, galena containing no uranium, so that from time t to the present the isotopic composition of the galena does not change. The isotopic ratio in the galena is then

$$\frac{Pb^{207}}{Pb^{206}} = \frac{U_0^{235}}{U_0^{238}} \frac{1 - e^{-\lambda_{238}(t_0-t)}}{1 - e^{-\lambda_{235}(t_0-t)}}$$

$$= \frac{1}{137.8} \frac{e^{\lambda_{238}t_0} - e^{\lambda_{238}t}}{e^{\lambda_{235}t_0} - e^{\lambda_{235}t}}$$

which is constant for given t regardless of the original amount of uranium. The amount of radiogenic Pb^{206} is, however, the present amount a minus the original amount x, and similarly for Pb^{207} (b and y, respectively). Thus the left-hand side of the last equation must be replaced by $(b - y)/(a - x)$, where x and y are unknown. The problem can, however, be solved as explained for the rubidium–strontium method of dating. If values of a and b for samples of the same age are plotted, they fall on a straight line (isochron) which passes through the point (x, y) and whose slope is a function of t_0. Results obtained by this method tend to scatter rather badly, presumably because the history of terrestrial galenas is not as simple as postulated here. Stony meteorites yield a value of t_0 close to 4.5 b.y.; in agreement with the value 4.45 b.y. obtained from Rb-Sr isochrons (Figure 4–13).

The present isotopic composition of lead in minerals varies greatly, reflecting differences in age, in uranium and thorium content, and in past history. An average isotopic composition for modern lead can, however, be obtained by extracting the very minute amounts of lead that precipitate on the sea floor and which represent lead of all ages leached from all continents by weathering and carried by rivers to the sea. It is also possible to guess roughly the average ratio of uranium to Pb^{204} in rocks. It is then possible to calculate a maximum age for the crust on the assumption that all Pb^{207} in modern lead is radiogenic. This gives about 5.5 b.y.

Calculations could be refined if the original ratios x and y were known. Iron meteorites whose age, determined by other methods, is of the order of 4.5 b.y. contain practically no uranium and very small amounts of lead whose isotopic composition is therefore presumably the original one (ratios of Pb^{207}/Pb^{204} and Pb^{206}/Pb^{204} in meteoritic lead are uniquely low). Comparing this primeval lead to modern lead gives for the earth an age of about 4.5 b.y. The same value is derived from an isochron for modern oceanic lead, lead from recent basalts, and several Tertiary lead ores which are so young—25 to 30 m.y.—that they may for the present purpose be considered modern.

It thus seems at the moment that meteorites

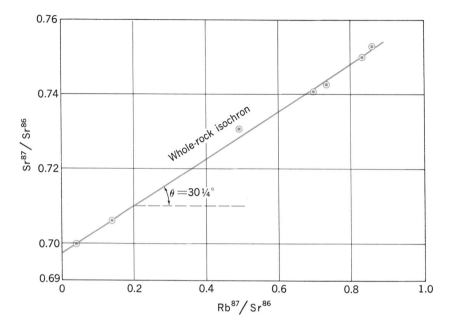

FIG. 4–13 *Rubidium/strontium whole-rock isochron for seven stony meteorites. (After R. M. Shields, W. H. Pinson and P. Hurley, M.I.T. Report 138–13, 1965, p. 141.)*

and the earth must have come into existence as separate bodies some 4.5 b.y. ago. J. H. Reynolds has adduced evidence from meteorites to suggest that this event occurred not very long after nucleosynthesis. Some meteorites contain an excess of Xe^{129} probably formed by decay of I^{129}, which must have been present in these meteorites. I^{129} has a half-life of only 17 m.y. If these meteorites had formed long after nucleosynthesis of I^{129}, there would not have been enough of it left to account for all the X^{129} found in them; Reynolds thus sets an upper limit of about 300 m.y. for the interval between the formation of iodine (and presumably all other heavy elements in the solar system) and crystallization of these meteorites. The moon's surface also is very old.

The "age" of the continents In a closed reservoir containing Rb^{87}, the ratio Sr^{87}/Sr^{86} must increase with time at a rate depending on the Rb/Sr ratio. Suppose that at some time differentiation occurs and much of the rubidium is removed to form a new system with a higher Rb/Sr ratio. In this new system, the Sr^{87}/Sr^{86} will increase with time faster than in the original one. By measuring the Sr^{87}/Sr^{86} ratio in the new

system at various times, it is possible to determine when separation of the new system occurred.

If the composition of the mantle resembles that of meteorites, the Rb/Sr ratio of mantle material is probably close to 0.04. In modern oceanic basalts, which come from the mantle, Sr^{87}/Sr^{86} is generally in the range of 0.702–0.705, corresponding to an initial ratio, 4.5 b.y. ago, of about 0.698. The Rb/Sr ratio in crustal rocks (granites and gneisses) is much higher than in the mantle, as would be expected from the geochemistry of rubidium which, like potassium, becomes concentrated in low-melting silicate fractions. Correspondingly, continental rocks generally have a higher Sr^{87}/Sr^{86} ratio than modern basalts. By measuring this ratio on continental rocks of various ages, it should be possible to determine when they separated from the mantle. One calculates, for instance, that if the continental crust, with an average Rb/Sr ratio of, say, 0.25, separated from the mantle 3 b.y. ago, its Sr^{87}/Sr^{86} ratio should now be about 0.735.

From a careful review of a large number of analyses, Hurley and his colleagues have concluded that there has been a *continuous* generation of crustal material from mantle sources, causing the continents to grow. They estimate the rate of areal growth to be about 7000 km²/m.y. for North America; this rate seems to have been operative over most of geological time. If their conclusion of continuous creation of continental crust is correct, no definite age can be assigned to the continents. The lead isotope data, on the contrary, have been interpreted to indicate that continents have not grown substantially in the last few billion years. To resolve this dilemma, Armstrong has proposed a model by which the volume of the crust remains nearly constant, although crustal material is recycled through the mantle. The matter will be further mentioned in Chapter 12.

PRECAMBRIAN CHRONOLOGY Precambrian events that can be dated radiometrically relate to crystallization and cooling of igneous bodies, to metamorphic recrystallization of rocks in general, and to episodes of rock deformation. It is only when the radiometric date can be related to strong deformation—usually accompanied by regional metamorphism and subsequent uplift implied by unconformity—that the dated event can be termed an orogeny. In most Precambrian terranes of great extent, such as the Canadian and Brazilian shields and northwestern Scotland, there are clearly defined, sharply separated tectonic provinces. Each province has its own stratigraphy. Each has its peculiar structural and metamorphic pattern. Radiometric dating makes it possible to establish a chronology of events for each province and, where such exist, to correlate events in common. But there is one complicating feature that, though not confined to problems of Precambrian time, is of particular importance in this field. The older Precambrian rocks are likely to have undergone repeated deformation, metamorphism, and plutonic invasion. How are we to disentangle the confused memory of a succession of events retained in radioactive and daughter nuclides in these ancient rocks?

The general problem can be illustrated by reference to a single well documented example. The Canadian shield (Figure 4–14), covering

4,000,000 km², comprises seven tectonic provinces, each with its own stratigraphic and structural history. The easternmost Grenville province is separated from the two adjoining provinces—Superior and Churchill—by a sharply defined line, known as the Grenville front. This runs northeastward from Lake Huron for 2000 km to the coast of Labrador. In places it is a fault, in places a shear zone. Everywhere it marks a sharp change in style and grade of metamorphism and deformation. Long ago the spectacular changes where rocks of the Huronian system in the Superior province abut against the Grenville front north of Lake Huron were described thus:

"The Huronian formations have . . . a total length from west to east of 500 miles. At the eastern end they attain their greatest thickness, comprising quartzites, conglomerates, graywackes, and limestone that aggregate 23,000 feet in thickness. Then they vanish. A definite and fairly straight line can be traced [the Grenville front] . . . on one side of which are these sediments, and on the other a vast expanse of granitic and gneissic rocks . . . [within the Grenville province]."[9]

In spite of conspicuous differences in pattern of metamorphism and, as we shall see later, of radiometric age, some stratigraphic units can be traced eastward across the Grenville front far out into the Grenville province. Such are the younger iron formations of the Labrador Trough (Churchill province), which because of their distinctive lithology can be recognized as strongly folded disrupted masses in the adjacent metamorphic complex of the Grenville province.

Many K-A dates, mostly determined on micas and feldspars, are available for all three provinces. Independent age values from U-Pb and Rb-Sr analyses of various minerals are mostly but not invariably concordant with K-A dates. The regional distribution of K-A values is remarkably constant (Figure 4–15). Clearly each province has a unique radiometric age pattern. In each the grouping of K-A values records a termi-

[9] T. T. Quirke and W. H. Collins, The disappearance of the Huronian, Geol. Survey Canada Mem. 160, p. 1, 1930.

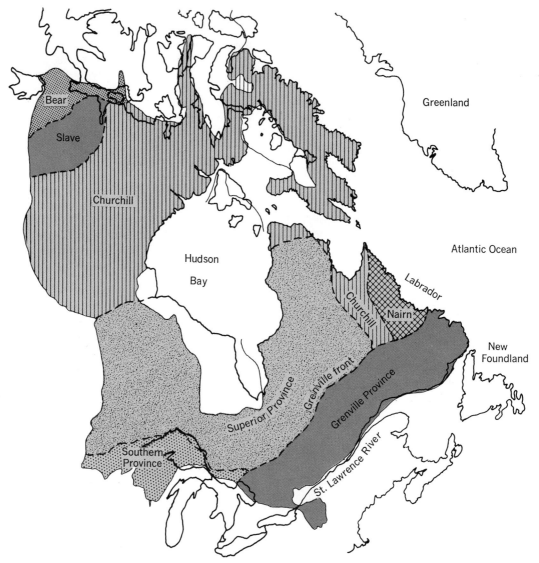

FIG. 4–14 *Tectonic provinces of the Canadian shield. (After C. H. Stockwell, Geol. Surv. Canada, Dept. Mines and Technical Surveys, Paper 63–17, 1963.)*

nal event currently identified among Canadian geologists with orogeny. Note that precision in most cases is ±100 m.y. Each regional "event" may really be several local events clustered in time.

1. Kenoran orogeny, 2500 m.y., was determined for basement rocks ("Archaean") of the Superior province. This would mark the end of a tectonic cycle that must have started a very long time earlier. The earliest K-A dates so far re-

corded in Canada include 2735 m.y. obtained from muscovite of a pegmatite dike cutting folded metasediments of the basement.

2. Hudsonian orogeny, 1750 m.y., involves numerous measurements on granitic and metasedimentary rocks in the Churchill province. This event is also recorded in the Superior province—for example, dates obtained from granitic rocks intruding Huronian sediments close to the Grenville front immediately north of Lake Huron.

3. Grenville orogeny, 950 m.y., was the sole event recorded by K-A dates throughout the Grenville province. It has left virtually no imprint on rocks of the two adjoining provinces.

The age pattern of K-A dates is so clear and the coverage so full that certain far-reaching conclusions have been drawn regarding the evolution of continental shields and the division of

Precambrian time. In brief it has been suggested that each province is the product of a single tectonic cycle: sedimentation and volcanism; folding plutonic intrusion and metamorphism; uplift and erosion. The shield has been pictured as growing outward by addition of peripheral provinces (such as the Grenville) after the life cycle of the nucleus (Superior province) had run its full course. Not all geologists have accepted this model. Some see the Grenville province as an ancient basement partially covered with late Precambrian sediments, the whole having been metamorphosed and reworked during the 950 m.y. orogenic event. This second model receives strong support from recent whole-rock analyses for Rb-Sr. The analyzed rocks are metasedimentary gneisses and intrusive granites collected at distances up to 300 km southeast of the southern end of the Grenville front. The Rb/Sr ratio of the

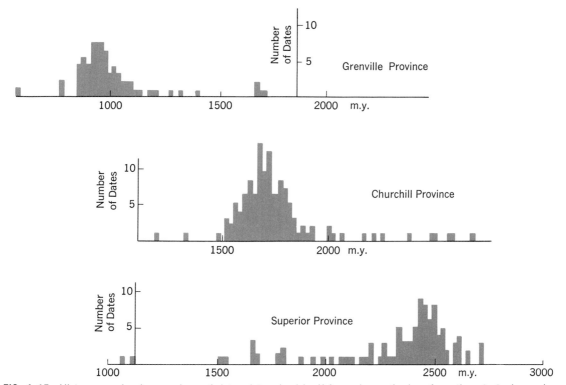

FIG. 4–15 *Histograms showing numbers of dates determined by K-Ar analyses of micas from three tectonic provinces of the Canadian shield. (After J. A. Lowdon, Geol. Surv. Canada, Dept. Mines and Technical Surveys, Paper 63–17, 1963.)*

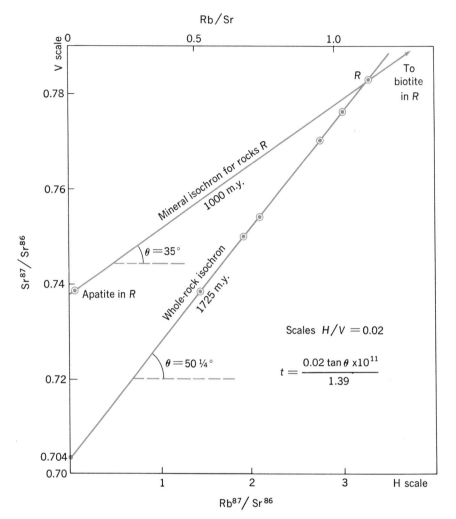

Rb/Sr

V scale   0   0.5   1.0

0.78

0.76

Sr⁸⁷/Sr⁸⁶

0.74   Apatite in R

0.72

θ = 35°

θ = 50 ¼°

Mineral isochron for rocks R
1000 m.y.

Whole-rock isochron
1725 m.y.

R

To biotite in R

Scales $H/V = 0.02$

$$t = \frac{0.02 \tan\theta \times 10^{11}}{1.39}$$

0.704
0.70

1   2   3   H scale

Rb^{87}/Sr^{86}

FIG. 4–16 *Rubidium-strontium isochrons for granite of French River, Grenville province (Ontario). (Modified from T. E. Krogh and coauthors, Carnegie Inst. Washington Year Book, vol. 66, 1966–1967, p. 530, 1968.) The Rb^{87}-Sr^{86} scale has been computed to fit the isochron ages cited by Krogh et al.*

granites varies sufficiently to permit drawing isochrons. One example, from a pluton some 60 km inside the Grenville province, is shown in Figure 4–16. A whole-rock isochron gives the age of crystallization as 1725 m.y., with Sr^{87}/Sr^{86} initially 0.704. But an isochron drawn for one rock sample R and its constituent biotite and apatite gives 950 ± 50 m.y.[10] and an initial Sr^{87}/Sr^{86} ratio of 0.738. This last is the age of the Grenville

orogeny, during which the rocks of the pluton were finally homogenized with regard to Sr and Rb isotopes. Since the granites must be younger than the rocks which they invade, the metamorphic basement of the Grenville province must be more than 1750 m.y. old. Isochrons drawn for whole-rock samples of hornblende-biotite-rich and feldspathic layers in metasedimentary gneiss show that the layering itself was fully developed between 1750 and 1900 million years ago. Here perhaps we see the imprint of the Hudsonian orogeny.

It can scarcely be contested that Canadian

---

[10] 1000 m.y. for apatite and whole rock; somewhat less for biotite and whole rock.

geologists have established three index events in the history of the Canadian shield. Moreover, the stratigraphic record covering intervals of time prior to, between, or after each event have been compiled for one or other tectonic province or subprovince. Do we know enough to set up a provisional stratigraphic–radiometric time scale for the Canadian shield? And can such a scale be used for the rest of North America and perhaps extended to other continents as well? With due caution, attempts in this direction seem justified. It is not even necessary to draw the boundaries of time divisions at recognizable major unconformities. Certainly we cannot assume that any unconformity is a worldwide or even continent-wide phenomenon. But to divide time on the basis of sharply defined local events, and to place events recognized elsewhere in proper chronological relation to these, is normal stratigraphic procedure. Accordingly we accept tentatively the major chronological divisions, *eons*, established radiometrically in Canada. We cannot expect to find precisely corresponding orogenies in other continents. But such as are recognized elsewhere can be placed approximately in one or other of the eons of Canadian geochronology (Table 4–3).

Using such a system of chronology it would be possible to make statements such as these: The history of the Churchill province goes far back into Archaeozoic time; for over large parts

of it Rb-Sr and U-Pb dates show the imprint of an event synchronous with the Kenoran orogeny. Isochrons drawn for Rb-Sr analyses of rocks from northeastern Brazil reveal a regional early Proterozoic orogenic event at about 2000 m.y.; locally, near the mouth of the Amazon, this has been overprinted by the effects of orogeny at or immediately after the close of Proterozoic time.

PHANEROZOIC CHRONOLOGY The peculiar interest of radiometric dating of Cambrian and subsequent events lies in the mutual overlap between radiometric and classical stratigraphic chronologies. Each system provides a severe test of the validity of the other. Mutual consistency is remarkably close; serious discrepancies are few. Some general conclusions—all subject to future modification and refinement—are already justified: The length of the Phanerozoic eon is of the order of 600 m.y., or somewhat less than one fifth the recorded history of the earth's crust. Certain points on the Phanerozoic time scale have been calibrated to within a few million years (many more such are needed). Some stratigraphic periods (for example, Ordovician and Cretaceous) were of long duration compared with others (for example, Silurian and Jurassic). The history of man—some 3 m.y.—is much more lengthy than was once supposed. We have already reached a point where it is possible to correlate, even on a continent-wide or worldwide basis,

TABLE 4–3 *Major divisions of time*

Eon	Subdivision	Canadian Orogeny	Radiometric Date
Phanerozoic	Cenozoic era Mesozoic era Paleozoic era		
			600 m.y.
	Late	Grenville	950 m.y.
Proterozoic	Middle	Hudsonian	1750 m.y.
	Early	Kenoran	2500 m.y.
Archaeozoic			>3200 m.y.

certain events of orogeny, eruption, or plutonism, whose relation in time could scarcely have been guessed on a purely stratigraphic basis.

These and future achievements must nevertheless be viewed with caution. Inherent in every radiometric technique are possible errors arising from slight uncertainty as to values of decay constants, and from inaccuracy in sampling and in purification and analysis of the sample. Any natural system, too, departs to some degree from the ideal dating model: argon leaks from biotite, micas contain inherited Sr^{86}, and so on. So there is always the problem of setting an order of preference on dates independently determined by different means. We shall not attempt to review all possibilities. Both K-A and Rb-Sr methods have been used to cover most of Phanerozoic time. The latter is inaccurate for dates of 10 m.y. or less; but K-A dating of volcanic rocks and of fresh crystals of potassium feldspar in tuffs has provided points extending even through Pleistocene time, overlapping finally the 40,000-year span of reliable radiocarbon dating. To illustrate the possibilities and limitations of radiometric dating in Phanerozoic time we now turn to a few specific examples:

1. Phanerozoic time starts with the beginning of the Cambrian period. So the base of the Cambrian system has a particular significance in stratigraphy. The Cambrian system in the type region of Wales is a thick but incomplete sequence of poorly fossiliferous strata. Consequently most European geologists today refer the Cambrian system to type sections in the Baltic region, where there is a clear sequence of zones defined by distinctive trilobite faunas. The lowest zones contain *Olenellus* and allied trilobites. Here and in many other parts of the world the Cambrian rocks rest unconformably on folded and metamorphosed Precambrian rocks. Elsewhere, however, as in South Australia and the mountains of southeastern California, Lower Cambrian strata with *Olenellus* and *Archaeocyathus* are underlain, with no major break, by great thicknesses of unfossiliferous essentially nonmetamorphic sedimentary rocks. Where is the base of the Cambrian? It can be defined as the base of

one of the fossiliferous Baltic sections. Or we can fix some date consistent with radiometric dating of various Cambrian events. Either procedure is arbitrary. Significant radiometric dates include the following:

Blue clay of Baltic section (taken by some geologists as the arbitrary base of the Cambrian system), 517 m.y.; K-A analysis of glauconite. This, because of possible leakage of argon, is considered a minimal date.

Murray shale, Tennessee, U.S.A., early Lower Cambrian, 584 ± 30 m.y.; Rb-Sr analysis of glauconite.

Vire-Carolles granite, Normandy, France, between late Precambrian and middle Lower Cambrian, 553 m.y.; K-A analysis of biotite.

Following Kulp's time scale of 1961, we may place the base of the Cambrian, consistent with the foregoing and similar radiometric data, at 600 m.y. But it is still impossible to determine the base of the Cambrian in those sections where significant thicknesses of nonfossiliferous strata conformably underlie Lower Cambrian beds containing *Olenellus*.

2. Two mutually distant localities where the Devonian–Carboniferous boundary has been fixed by fossil evidence are Tennessee, U.S.A., and Victoria, Australia. Both are remote from the type Devonian section of Britain. The index fossils used for correlation are very different— microfossils called conodonts in Tennessee, freshwater fishes in Australia. In Tennessee the critical formation—Chattanooga shale—contains two members that have been dated radiometrically, both with Late Devonian faunas. The upper is a black uranium-bearing shale bed, the lower a thin layer of siliceous tuff. In Australia radiometrically dated siliceous lavas lie between Upper Devonian and Lower Carboniferous freshwater sediments, both with distinctive fish faunas. Radiometric data are as follows:

Chattanooga shale, upper black bed, 350 ± 10 m.y., U^{238}/Pb^{206} analysis of shale; considered to be a reliable minimal value.

Chattanooga shale, lower tuff bed, 340 ± 6 m.y.; K-A analysis of biotite (note that the older bed gives a slightly younger age).

Snobs Creek rhyolite, Australia, 350 ± 2 m.y.; six analyses of biotites from different specimens.

Considering the diversity of the evidence, agreement is remarkably close. The Devonian–Carboniferous boundary is placed at approximately 350 m.y.

3. More than 50 satisfactory radiometric dates are available for the various epochs of Tertiary time. Most are based on K-A analyses of glauconite from sediments, and of biotite from volcanic lavas and tuffs. Some sanidine, plagioclase, and whole-rock analyses for K-A in igneous rocks are also available. There is good agreement between glauconite and other dates, provided the glauconite samples have been taken from rocks that have never been buried deep enough to be subjected to temperatures sufficiently high to permit loss of argon by heating. Radiometric dates for Tertiary rocks from all over the world are most consistent. We cite a single example. Sedimentary rocks from many countries, classed by fossil evidence as Lower Miocene, have been dated by K-A analyses: New Zealand (glauconite), Patagonia (plagioclase in tuff). Nebraska (biotite in tuff), California (glauconite), Austria (glauconite), Oregon (glass and albite in tuff). The dates so determined range from 19.4 to 25.6 m.y. Other points straddling the Miocene-Oligocene boundary as defined by fossils range from 21.5 to 25.7 m.y. So the beginning of Miocene time is placed at 26 m.y.

Over 30 years ago Holmes was bold enough to draw up a radiometric time scale to cover the periods of Phanerozoic time. In Figure 4–17 we show for comparison the earliest and latest scales of Holmes and those of Kulp and of a recent British symposium now in general use. The principal modification resulting from three decades of radiometric dating, including the birth and development of K-A and Rb-Sr techniques, is to push back the base of the Cambrian from 470 to 600 m.y. Most periods have been correspondingly extended by some 25 to 30 percent—exceptions being the Silurian and the Tertiary.

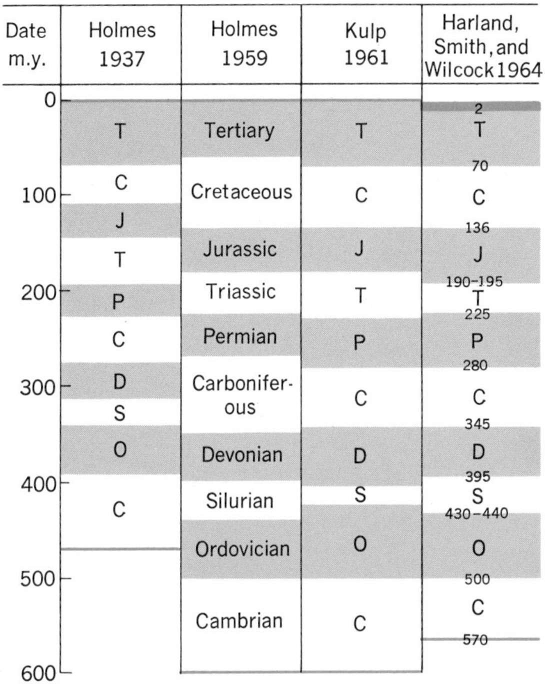

Date m.y.	Holmes 1937	Holmes 1959	Kulp 1961	Harland, Smith, and Wilcock 1964
0				2
	T	Tertiary	T	T
				70
100	C	Cretaceous	C	C
	J			136
	T	Jurassic	J	J
200		Triassic		190–195 T
	P		T	225
	C	Permian	P	P
				280
300	D	Carboniferous	C	C
	S			345
	O	Devonian	D	D
400				395
	C	Silurian	S	S
		Ordovician	O	430–440
500				O
		Cambrian	C	500 C
600				570

FIG. 4–17 Four radiometrically calibrated scales for Phanerozoic time. The Quaternary Period (3 m.y. by recent estimates) is shown as a solid color bar below the zero line.

CHANGES IN THE LENGTH OF THE DAY

We mention here some paleontological observations, to be further discussed in Chapter 13, bearing on the variation of common units of time such as the length of the day or month.

The conical skeletons (epitheca) of corals commonly show transverse striations on two scales (Figure 4–18). The coarser ridges are believed to represent *annual* growth increments reflecting the effects of sunlight and seasonal temperature changes on metabolic rates. Finer ridges, about 50 microns in thickness, are also observed. J. W. Wells counted about 360 finer ridges in a year's growth of a modern coral and suggested that they represent *daily* growth rings. Thus a count of the finer ridges in an annual growth band of an ancient coral would give the

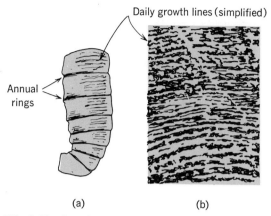

Daily growth lines (simplified)

Annual rings

(a)   (b)

FIG. 4–18 *Growth lines on Devonian corals. (After J. W. Wells, 1963.) (a) Whole skeleton, external aspect, ×0.5. (b) Daily growth lines on part of skeleton, ×12.*

number of solar days in the ancient year. Wells thus found about 400 ± 7 days per year in certain mid-Devonian corals. C. T. Scrutton also observed on other mid-Devonian corals what appear to be monthly bands reflecting the influence of moonlight, or of the height of the tides, on coral growth rates; he counted an average of 30.6 solar days in the Devonian synodical month.

The only factor that could change the length of the year is a change in the gravitational constant G (Chapter 11). Assuming it has remained constant since Devonian times, it follows from the observations that the length of the Devonian day was $(24 \times 365)/400$ or a little less than 22 hours, implying that the earth rotated then faster than it does now. The rate of rotation of the earth is in fact known to be decreasing as a result of lunar tidal forces which dissipate as heat some of the earth's kinetic rotational energy; such dissipation occurs, for instance, in tidal currents and their frictional drag on the sea floor. By the law of conservation of angular momentum, it follows that the moon's distance from the earth must increase; at the same time its angular velocity about the earth must also decrease, and the length of the synodical month increases. The present deceleration of the earth is approximately known from observation of ancient eclipses; it corresponds to

changes in the length of the day of about 20 seconds per m.y. In mid-Devonian times, roughly 365 m.y. ago, the day was thus shorter by about two hours, in agreement with observations on corals. Observations on Pennsylvanian corals (385 to 390 finer ridges per year) and on the shells of other marine invertebrates confirm these findings.

This apparent agreement between the calculated and "observed" length of the Devonian day may, however, be somewhat fortuitous, for it seems unlikely that the deceleration of the earth would have remained constant since that time. Tidal dissipation changes with time because (1) the increasing moon-earth distance decreases the amplitude of the tides raised in the earth by the moon, and (2) part of the tidal dissipation occurs in shallow seas, the extent of which may have changed appreciably through geologic time. The earth's rate of rotation is also affected by changes in its moment of inertia C which could result from changes in the earth's radius, or shape, or internal mass distribution. The gravitational constant G may also have changed with time (Chapter 13). It is no simple problem to determine how each of these factors may have affected the length of the day in the past.

Time and the Physics of Geological Processes

DIMENSIONAL ANALYSIS

Many physical quantities can be expressed in terms of fundamental units of mass (M), length (L), and time (T). A velocity, for instance, is a length divided by time, and has therefore the "dimensions" of L/T. Acceleration (change in velocity with time) has the dimensions of L/T^2. Force, which is mass $\times$ acceleration, has the dimensions MLT^{-2}. Viscosity, which is defined as the ratio of stress to either strain rate or velocity gradient, has dimensions $ML^{-1}T^{-1}$; and so on.

The analysis of a physical quantity in terms of its dimensions is frequently used to check the mathematical expression of physical laws, since all terms in an equation must have the same dimensions. Dimensional analysis is also used to predict the mathematical form of an equation. Consider, for instance, a sphere of radius r and density ρ_1 falling with constant velocity v in a fluid with density ρ_2 and viscosity η. The velocity will reach a steady state when the force of gravity F_g equals and opposes the viscous force F_v. The latter will presumably depend on r, η, and v. We write this

$$F_v \propto r^a \eta^b v^c$$

As the dimensions of both sides of this relation must be identical, it follows that $a = b = c = 1$. On the other hand, F_g is g times the difference in mass between the falling sphere and an equal volume of liquid; hence

$$F_g \propto g(\rho_1 - \rho_2)r^3$$

where g is the acceleration of gravity. Equating the two forces leads directly to

$$v \propto \frac{r^2(\rho_1 - \rho_2)g}{\eta}$$

a relation known as Stokes' law. The proportionality constant, which can be determined from a single and simple experiment, turns out to be $2/9$.

Dimensionless quantities, such as the ratio of two forces, or of a force to the product mass times acceleration, are obviously independent of the actual numbers and units of length, mass, and so on, that characterize the system under consideration and are therefore very useful in expressing general properties. To illustrate by another example from fluid dynamics, the product velocity $\times$ length divided by the kinematic viscosity[11] is dimensionless and is called the Reynolds number. It turns out that regardless of the actual values of these three quantities in any particular experiment, the flow will be laminar if the Reynolds number is small, and turbulent if it is large.[12] These dimensionless numbers are

commonly formed by taking the ratio of two relevant forces, or more generally, of all factors that favor a certain behavior to those that oppose it; for instance, the Reynolds number is essentially the ratio of inertial forces (which favor turbulence) to viscous forces (which inhibit it). The Rayleigh number mentioned in the discussion of convection in Chapter 12 is also the ratio between factors respectively favorable and unfavorable to convection. The length that appears in the Reynolds number is a "characteristic" length of the system under consideration, for instance the diameter of the pipe in which the fluid is flowing; the velocity is similarly a "characteristic" velocity, such as the average velocity.

SIMILITUDE   Dimensional analysis is essential whenever one attempts to study the behavior of a large system by experimenting on a smaller one, or vice versa. Suppose, for instance, that we wish to study the flow of water in a river channel 100 meters wide by experimenting with a laboratory flume 100 cm wide. The model has a characteristic length one hundred times smaller than the river. If water is used in both cases, the viscosity is the same. Thus for the flow to have the same character with respect to turbulence, the velocity in the model will have to be 100 times larger than in the river. If, on the contrary, the experimental velocity is the same as that of the river, the fluid used in the experiment must have a viscosity 100 times lower than that of water.

In general, if an experiment is to reproduce a natural phenomenon by means of a scaled-down model, all properties of the model must be scaled down in the proper ratio given by dimensional analysis. If, for instance, λ is the scaling factor of length (that is, the ratio of length in the model to the corresponding length in the original system), and μ and τ are scaling factors for mass and time, respectively, then all properties of the model involving length, mass, and time must be scaled down in the ratio corresponding to their dimensions. Velocities must be scaled down by the factor $\lambda \tau^{-1}$. Kinematic viscosity must be scaled down by a factor $\lambda^2 \tau^{-1}$. Stress has the dimensions of force per unit area, or $ML^{-1}T^{-2}$; thus the strength of the model, or its elastic co-

---

[11] Kinematic viscosity is the viscosity divided by the density; it has dimensions $L^2 T^{-1}$.

[12] Turbulent flow can be distinguished from laminar flow by the following property: In laminar flow any two particles of fluid that are initially close together will stay together, whereas in turbulent flow they will move apart with time. Turbulent flow is characterized by randomly fluctuating flow parameters (velocity, density, and so forth).

efficients, all of which have the dimensions of stress, must be scaled down by the factor $\mu\lambda^{-1}\tau^{-2}$, and so on.

The requirements of "similitude," as this proper scaling is called, set rather stringent conditions on the kind of geologic experiments that can be validly performed. Suppose, for instance, that we wish to study a natural process involving gravity. The acceleration of gravity has dimensions LT^{-2}. But gravity cannot be altered arbitrarily; the gravity that operates in the laboratory has essentially the same magnitude as that which operates in nature. Hence similitude requires that

$$\lambda\tau^{-2} = 1 \qquad \text{or} \qquad \lambda = \tau^2$$

Suppose now that we wish to reproduce in one day ($\sim 10^5$ seconds) a natural phenomenon that requires, say, 3×10^6 years or, roughly, 10^{14} seconds. Then $\tau = 10^5/10^{14} = 10^{-9}$. Accordingly, we require $\lambda = \tau^2 = 10^{-18}$. The whole earth would be represented in the model by a sphere of radius $6 \times 10^8 \times 10^{-18} = 6 \times 10^{-10}$ cm, much smaller than any atom. Thus the experiment is clearly impossible. The very length of geologic time seems to forbid any experiment in which accelerations are involved.

This difficulty can, however, be partially circumvented. We could, for instance, do the experiment in a centrifuge where the acceleration is many times greater than the acceleration of gravity, so that $\lambda\tau^{-2} \gg 1$; this, however, adds to the experimental difficulties. Alternatively, one can use the fact that observed velocities in many geological systems are very small (of the order of 1 cm/year or less, see below); accelerations are even smaller and can be neglected in many problems. The only large acceleration that need be considered is precisely that of gravity, but it is the force rather than the acceleration of gravity that really matters. Since the force of gravity is proportional to the mass of the system, it can be scaled down in the ratio μ of the masses. Now the condition for dynamical similitude is that the ratio of the various forces acting in the model be the same as the ratio of these same forces in the natural system; for a viscous fluid, for instance, it is sufficient that the Reynolds number be the same. Hence, if the force of gravity is scaled

down by a factor μ, dynamic similitude requires only that all other relevant forces be scaled down in the same ratio.

If we thus neglect accelerations and corresponding inertial forces, and set the scale factor ϕ for forces (including force of gravity) equal to μ, stress which is a force per unit area must be scaled by the factor $\mu\lambda^{-2}$, and the scalar factor for viscosity becomes $\mu\lambda^{-2}\tau$.

A further simplification occurs through the fact that all common solids and liquids have rather similar densities; thus, in general, the scaling factor δ for density is of the order of 1, and since $\delta = \mu\lambda^{-3}$, $\mu = \lambda^3$.

Suppose that for convenience we wish to take $\lambda = 10^{-6}$ (1 cm in the model represents 10 km) and $\tau = 10^{-12}$ (1 minute in the model represents approximately 2×10^6 years). Then the mass of the model will be 10^{-18} times that of the prototype; its strength, which has the dimensions of stress, should be 10^{-6}, and its viscosity 10^{-18} times, those of the prototype. Velocities in the model would be a million times larger than in the original.[13] An extremely viscous earth would be represented by a model of quite ordinary viscosity, and a strong earth would be represented by a very weak one.

This is a very important result. Because the earth is so large, and geologic time so long, the earth behaves as would a model with properties quite different from the measured terrestrial properties. The earth is very viscous and very strong; yet it will behave geologically as would a weak and relatively inviscid body in a laboratory experiment. The behavior of a large body over a long time cannot be simply pictured in terms of that of a small body in a short experiment.

This may be seen in a still simpler example. Imagine a block of granite in the shape of a cube of dimension a; let its density be ρ. The block rests on a table. The total force that the block exerts on the table is $g\rho a^3$. The normal compo-

---

[13] Yet the flow must remain laminar since, by assumption, inertial forces are negligible. Hence the Reynolds number is essentially zero.

nent of stress across the face on which the cube rests is therefore $g\rho a^3/a^2 = g\rho a$. It is clear that this stress can be made very large by making a very large cube; if $a \simeq 10^6$ cm, for instance, the stress would be of the order of the crushing strength of granite. Any larger block would break under its own weight, as one could have surmised from the observation that the maximum relief of the earth's surface is of the order of 10 km. More generally, when a body force (such as gravity) which increases proportionately to the third power of the linear dimension produces a stress, that stress must necessarily increase as the first power of this dimension. This has some bearing on the possibility that small temperature differences, and hence very small density differences in the earth, might cause convection (Chapter 12).

CHARACTERISTIC TIME SCALE OF GEOLOGICAL PROCESSES

It is ordinarily possible to associate with any physical process a quantity having the dimension of time, which serves as a measure of the rate at which the process occurs; the reciprocal of that time, which is a frequency, serves the same purpose. Electromagnetic radiation, for instance, can be described by its period T (duration of an oscillation) or its frequency $\nu = 1/T$ (number of oscillations per unit time). The life span of a human being can be described by an average age at death, which may serve as a characteristic time scale for human life. The time necessary to reduce the number of radioactive atoms to half its initial value ("half-life") is a characteristic time scale for radioactive disintegration. The period of the oscillation of a mass attached to a spring, which depends on the size of the mass and on the physical properties of the material of which the spring is made, is a characteristic time for the mass–spring system. Conversely, given the time scale of a process, it may be possible to draw from it inferences regarding the physical mechanisms involved.

Geologists are concerned with an extraordinarily wide range of time scales, ranging roughly from 10^{-18} to 10^{+18} seconds. The very short time scale (10^{-18}) corresponds to radiation with a wavelength $\lambda = cT = 3 \times 10^{-8}$ cm (c is the velocity of light), falling in the X-ray part of the spectrum. This is the order of magnitude of the wavelength of X rays used in X-ray diffraction (see Chapter 2); clearly, if X-ray diffraction is to give information on the position of atoms in crystals, the wavelength used must be commensurate with the size of the atoms themselves. The long time-scale (10^{18} sec) corresponds roughly to the age of the solar system, or to the half-life of some long-lived radioactive isotopes.

Characteristic times commonly turn out to be indeed so characteristic that we can often guess what a geologist or geophysicist is working on by asking him simply what his time scale is. The following examples may be illustrative. We start at the short-time end of the spectrum, for which it is customary to use frequencies rather than periods.

$\nu \simeq 10^{+18}$ sec^{-1}. X rays; crystal structure (see Chapter 2).

$\nu \simeq 10^{14}$ sec^{-1}. These frequencies correspond to the visible part of the spectrum. Optical properties of crystals in the visible range serve for identification purposes. Absorption spectra of minerals are used to infer the mechanism of chemical bonding as in crystal-field theory (see Chapter 2), and are relevant to the rate of heat transfer by radiation (see Chapter 12).

$\nu \simeq 10^{12}\text{-}10^{13}$ sec^{-1}. Infrared. These are typical frequencies for lattice vibrations in crystals, which are determined by the mass of the atoms forming the crystal and the strength of the interatomic forces as measured, say, by the incompressibility. These lattice vibrations enter prominently into solid-state theories of the thermal properties of solids (specific heat, entropy, free energy, thermal expansion, and so forth). Similar frequencies occur in the theory of transport properties of solids (thermal and electrical conductivity, diffusion, plastic flow) and in chemical kinetics (reaction rates).

$\nu \simeq 10^{-2}\text{-}10^1$ sec^{-1} ($T = 0.1$ to 100 seconds). These are typical frequencies and periods for seismic waves (Chapter 11). In a medium where the velocity is, say, 5 km sec^{-1}, a frequency of 1 sec^{-1} corresponds to a wavelength of 5 km. Seismic waves would indeed be expected to have a wavelength commensurate with the linear dimensions of the source (for example, the break on a fault).

Note that the usual theory of propagation of seismic waves is based on elastic theory (Hooke's law: strain is proportional to stress). In a perfectly elastic medium there can be no dissipation of energy, and elastic waves propagate in such a medium without attenuation. In practice, attenuation of seismic waves is observed in most parts of the crust and mantle, but is small in this frequency range, so that the use of nonviscous elastic theory for oscillations at these frequencies is justified. As we shall presently see, a rather different behavior is observed at lower frequencies.

$\nu \approx 10^{-3}$ sec^{-1}, ($T \approx 10^3$ seconds or up to approximately 50 minutes). These frequencies and periods include free oscillations of the earth (see Chapter 11).

$T \approx 1$ day. Periods of about 12 and 24 hours are characteristic of the tides. The deformation of the solid earth under the effect of the periodic tidal force is measurable and found to agree with calculations based again on the assumption that the earth is elastic. Slight imperfections of elasticity do, however, lead to dissipation of energy and slowing down of the earth, although it is not precisely known as yet whether this dissipation occurs mostly in the oceans and shallow seas or in the solid earth itself. Theories of the past history of the earth–moon system hinge on this.

$T \approx 1$ year. An interesting phenomenon, called the "variation of latitude," consists in a wobble of the earth with respect to its axis of rotation; the rotational pole moves with respect to the earth on a roughly circular path with a radius of the order of a few meters.[14] The motion is found to consist of the superposition of an an-

nual motion (that is, with a period of one year) and a "Chandler wobble," with a period of about 430 days. The former is due to meteorological effects. Great masses of dense cold air that accumulate in winter over the continents of the Northern Hemisphere blow away in summer when the ground warms up. These displacements of mass also displace the axis of maximum inertia around which a body rotates stably (that is, with minimum kinetic energy). The axis of rotation, which remains fixed in space since no torque is involved, no longer coincides with the displaced axis of inertia, which starts to revolve about the axis of rotation; this motion, similar to the wobble of an unbalanced wheel, is annual because the displacement of air masses that cause it is also annual. The Chandler wobble, on the other hand, is believed to be a free oscillation, its period being determined by the mechanical properties of the earth. For a perfectly rigid and undeformable earth, the period of this free oscillation ("Eulerian period") would be the period of its rotation (one day) times $C/(C - A)$, where $(C - A)/C = 1/305$ is the ratio that appears in the theory of the figure of the earth (Chapter 11).[15] Here C and A are, respectively, the greatest and least principal moments of inertia of the earth. The lengthening of the period from the theoretical 305 to the observed 430 is due to the deformation of the earth under the effect of the changing centrifugal force which must at all times be perpendicular to the instantaneous axis of rotation which is itself moving; thus the ratio 430/305 measures the yielding of the earth, which turns out again to be just about what one would expect for an elastic earth. Yet the amplitude of the Chandler wobble appears to be damped in a way suggestive of a serious departure from perfect elasticity. The matter is mentioned here because it is of some importance in assessing the possibility of large polar displacements in the past (see Chapter 13).

$T \approx 10$-100 years. Two phenomena are observed that have characteristic times in the range

---

[14] Since the colatitude of a point on the earth's surface (colatitude is 90° minus latitude) measures the angular distances from that point to the pole of rotation, any displacement of the latter entails a change in colatitude (or latitude) of about a few tenths of one second of arc. An angle of 0.1″ at the center subtends an arc of about 3 meters on the earth's surface.

[15] For a derivation of this result, see, for instance *Berkeley Physics Course*, vol. 1, pp. 250–252 (McGraw-Hill, New York, 1962).

from a decade to a few centuries. One is the irregular change in the earth's rate of rotation (see page 186). The other is the secular variation of the magnetic field (Chap. 11). The time scale of the latter is so different from that of any crustal or mantle process that on these grounds alone it could be safely deduced that its source must lie in the core. Because their time scales are so similar, it is tempting to link secular variation to rotation rates, and mechanisms for doing this have been proposed. Essentially, any change in the pattern and intensity of convection in the core that causes changes in the magnetic field should also result in a change in the distribution of angular momentum and hence in the rate of rotation; in particular, one might expect the irregular changes in the rotation rate to be related to changes in the rate of the westward drift of the nondipole component of the magnetic field (see Chapter 11). This correlation is not obvious in the data, but their accuracy is marginal.

The growth of strain preliminary to a large earthquake also has a characteristic time of a few decades.

$T \approx 10^3$-10^4 **years.** This range of time includes the half-life of C^{14}, the long-period components of the secular variation of the magnetic field, and the isostatic recovery time for glacial unloading. The uplift of Scandinavia in the past few thousand years following the melting of the last Pleistocene icecap will be mentioned on page 357. It is of considerable interest that the latter type of event is clearly one that involves flow (that is, fluid dynamics) rather than elastic theory. The consequences of this observation will be further discussed subsequently.

This same time span of 10^3–10^4 years is that required for the accumulation of one centimeter of deep-sea sediment, and is a characteristic decay time for electric currents and magnetic fields in the core (Chap. 11). It therefore determines the rate at which the magnetic field must, on the average, be produced. Interestingly, it is also the time it takes for the field to reverse its polarity.

$T \approx 10^5$ **years.** This is approximately the cooling time of a small pluton, the life-span of a small volcano, and the duration of a glacial episode.

$T \approx 10^6$-10^7 **years.** This seems to be the order of magnitude of the lifetime of a large volcanic center (for example, the Hawaiian Islands), or the time needed for the accumulation of a substantial thickness of plateau lavas. Successive intrusions of granitic plutons in the Sierra Nevada of California occurred at intervals of about 10^6 years. A major episode of folding may take place in as little as 10^7 years. Evolution in Jurassic ammonites in about 10^6 years was sufficient to lead to recognizable stratigraphic zonation (62 "Oppelian" zones in the Jurassic, the whole of which spans about 50 million years).

The geologic picture at this long time scale becomes somewhat blurred, as it is not easy to define precisely the beginning and end of the more protracted events.

$T \approx 10^8$ **years.** The time required to transfer heat by conduction at low temperature ($< 1500°$K) through 100 km of rock is about 10^8 years (see Chapter 12). The development and filling of a geosyncline takes a time of this order; volcanic activity in a given province lasts somewhat less. Although episodes in intense folding are usually not quite so protracted, deformation as a whole—including uplift, block faulting, and so forth—may last for 10^8 years or so. Horizontal displacement at the rate of 1 cm/yr amounts to 1000 km in 10^8 years.

$T \approx 10^9$ **years.** This is the characteristic time scale for evolution of the earth as a whole—for example, cooling of the whole earth. It is also the half-life of the most important radioactive elements. Since radiogenic heat makes an important contribution to the energy required to drive geologic processes, it may be confidently surmised that 10^{10} years from now the earth will have become a pretty dead body, and most geologic processes will have come to a stop. It might also turn out to be the time required for geologists to begin to understand them.

CHARACTERISTIC TIMES, OR RATES, RELATED TO PHYSICAL DIMENSIONS OF THE SYSTEM

What information can characteristic times, or rates, give on the nature of the processes them-

FIG. 4–19 *A particle in a linear lattice displaced from its equilibrium position.*

selves? Clearly, there must be some relation between the two; there must be some reason why the characteristic frequencies of lattice vibrations are of the order of 10^{12}–10^{13} sec⁻¹, while those of the earth as a whole are about 10^{-3} sec⁻¹. As we shall see, the relationship depends (1) on the physical dimensions of the systems, and (2) on the physical law that causes the process itself.

Start with lattice vibrations. Imagine, to simplify the problem, a one-dimensional lattice consisting of equally spaced atoms (spacing a) of equal mass m. If an atom is displaced an amount x (Figure 4–19) from its equilibrium position, repulsion between its own electrons and those of the adjacent atom will push it back to the left. Assume that this force F is proportional to the displacement x; that is,

$$F = -bx$$

where b is the "force constant"; the minus sign is there because the force is in the sense opposite to the displacement. The equation of motion of the displaced atom is

$$m\frac{d^2x}{dt^2} = -bx$$

a solution of which is

$$x = A \sin \omega t$$

where

$$\omega^2 = \frac{b}{m} \qquad (4\text{-}10)$$

The solution implies that the particle will oscillate about its equilibrium position $x = 0$ with a circular frequency $\omega = (b/m)^{1/2}$, or a frequency $\nu = \omega/2\pi$ and a period $T = 1/\nu = 2\pi/\omega$.

To find the magnitude of ω, consider first b, the force constant, which must intuitively be related somehow to the incompressibility K of the solid, which also measures the repulsion be-

tween atoms. Dimensions of b are force/length, or MT^{-2}; dimensions of K are force/area or $ML^{-1}T^{-2}$; hence b equals K times a length that must reflect some property of the crystal; a natural choice would be to choose for this length the lattice spacing a; thus we try $b = Ka$. For diamond, $a = 0.8 \times 10^{-8}$ cm, $K = 5.5 \times 10^{12}$ g/cm⁻¹ sec⁻², $b = 4.4 \times 10^{4}$ g/sec⁻², m (the mass of an atom of carbon) is 2×10^{-23} gram; hence $\omega = (b/m)^{1/2} = 4.4 \times 10^{13}$ sec⁻¹, which is the right order of magnitude. Needless to say that calculations for a real three-dimensional lattice consisting of N interacting atoms are much more complicated, for it turns out that the possible vibrations, in three dimensions, of a collection of N atoms consist of, or can be described as, the superposition of $3N$ "modes" of different frequencies ranging from zero to a maximum frequency ν_m determined by the elastic constants (such as incompressibility) of the crystal and the lattice spacing; these "modes" are in essence elastic waves, of varying wavelengths, that travel back and forth through the crystal. The energy of these waves, which for sinusoidal oscillations is proportional to the square of their amplitude, represents the heat content of the crystal (their amplitude is therefore zero at $T = 0°$K). As mentioned above, all thermodynamic properties of the solid can be derived if one knows how the $3N$ modes are distributed with respect to frequency (that is, how many modes have frequencies in the range from ν to $\nu + d\nu$, for all values of ν from zero to ν_{max}). Calculations for real crystals with complicated structures are difficult, but approximations as in the Debye theory of specific heat lead to results generally in very good agreement with experiments.

Calculations must be carried out, as for all atomic systems, using quantum mechanics; classical dynamics, exemplified by equation (4-10), are not strictly applicable. This leads to yet another way of accounting for the characteristic frequencies involved in solid-state theory. If quantum mechanics is involved, so is Planck's constant $h = 6.62 \times 10^{-27}$ erg sec. On the other hand, the product of Boltzmann's constant $k = 1.38 \times 10^{-16}$ erg/deg multiplied by the absolute temperature T has the dimensions of energy and is, in fact, an excellent unit in which to measure the kinetic or potential energy of thermal motion; in a monoatomic perfect gas, for instance, each atom has kT units of translational kinetic energy per degree of freedom. The ratio kT/h, which is 6×10^{12} at room temperature, has precisely the dimensions of a frequency (sec^{-1}). Little surprise, then, that this characteristic frequency should turn up, as it does, in all atomic processes in which the thermal energy of the atoms plays a part, as in chemical reaction rates, rates of diffusion, and so on.

Consider now the oscillations of the earth as a whole, more particularly a torsional oscillation such as shown in Figure 11–26. A very obvious calculation would suggest a circular frequency, as in equation (4-10), where b would be again related to the relevant elastic coefficient, in this case the rigidity μ. The appropriate length might be of the order of the circumference of the earth, say 4×10^9 cm; and the relevant mass, that of crust and mantle (the core, having no rigidity, plays no part) is approximately 4.5×10^{27} grams. Taking the average rigidity of the mantle to be of the order of 1.5×10^{12} dynes/cm^2, we find $\omega = 1.15 \times 10^{-3}$ and $T = 2\pi/\omega = 5.5 \times 10^3$ sec $= 90$ min, about twice the period of the gravest observed torsional mode (43 min). The discrepancy is not surprising as our model ignores the true geometrical features of the problem and crudely replaces the laws of elasticity (stress proportional to strain) by the assumption that force is proportional to displacement. Nevertheless, this calculation when compared to the previous one illustrates how the physical dimensions of a system may affect its characteristic time. A similar illustration pertaining to the earth's magnetic field will be given in Chapter 11.

CHARACTERISTIC TIMES RELATED TO PHYSICAL LAWS

Clearly, a characteristic time must also reflect the nature of the forces involved.

Consider, for example, a spherical ball of radius r, density ρ_1, falling in vacuum under the influence of gravity g, its initial velocity being zero (free fall). After time t, the ball will have fallen a distance $h = gt^2/2$, so that the average velocity $\bar{v} = h/t = gt/2$, which is independent of the mass or size of the ball. Conversely, the time t to fall a distance h is $t_h = (2h/g)^{1/2}$.

Consider how the same ball falls through a liquid of density ρ_2 and viscosity η. Its motion is now controlled by gravity *and* viscous forces. The velocity v is given by Stokes' law (see page 219):

$$v = \frac{2}{9} r^2 \frac{(\rho_1 - \rho_2)g}{\eta}$$

and the time t_h required to fall a distance h is $t_h = h/v$. Obviously those two times may be quite different. Observation of t_h will tell us whether viscous forces are important or not; more precisely, it can give us information regarding the viscosity of the fluid.

INFERENCES FROM RATE OF DEFORMATION   It was pointed out earlier that most geophysical observations pertaining to deformation with characteristic times less than about a year (propagation of seismic waves, earth tides, Chandler wobble) can be accounted for, to a first approximation, on the assumption of elastic behavior; observations at longer time scales cannot. In particular, the rates of uplift in Scandinavia and at Lake Bonneville, which are interpreted to represent the effect of unloading (melting of the icecap in the first instance, and evaporation and draining of the lake itself in the second instance) can be used to determine the viscosity of the underlying mantle. We wish to look further into the matter, and particularly into the significance of the characteristic time ($\sim 10^3$ years) at which viscous behavior clearly supersedes elastic behavior.

Viscosity (η) can be defined in a general way as the ratio of a stress σ to the corresponding rate of strain; that is,

$$\sigma = \eta \frac{de}{dt}$$

An elastic coefficient—for example, rigidity μ—is defined as the ratio of a stress to the corresponding strain:

$$\sigma = \mu e$$

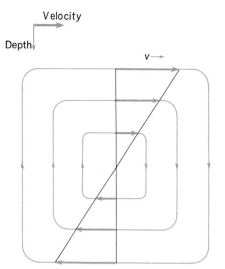

FIG. 4–20 *Hypothetical velocity distribution in a convection cell.*

It follows that viscosity has the dimensions of rigidity × time

$$\eta \approx \mu t_0$$

where t_0 is called a "relaxation" time for the following reason. Imagine a body that combines elastic and viscous behavior, so that the strain in the body is the sum of elastic and viscous components

$$e = e_{\text{elast.}} + e_{\text{visc.}}$$

In any experiment in which the strain is held constant, $de/dt = 0$, and

$$\frac{de}{dt} = 0 = \frac{1}{\mu}\frac{d\sigma}{dt} + \frac{\sigma}{\eta}$$

Integration gives

$$\sigma = \sigma_0 e^{-t/t_0} \qquad (4\text{-}11)$$

where $t_0 = \eta/\mu$. Equation (4-11) shows that an initial stress σ_0 will relax in a characteristic time t_0; that is, it will fall to $1/e$ of its initial value in a time $t = t_0$. A body with this property is called a "Maxwell solid." In such a body, the viscous strain will exceed the instantaneous elastic strain after a time t such that

$$\frac{\sigma}{\eta} t \geq \frac{\sigma}{\mu}$$

or

$$t \geq t_0$$

t_0 may then serve as a measure of the characteristic time at which viscous behavior predominates over elastic behavior.

Take $t_0 \approx 10^3$ years $= 3 \times 10^{10}$ seconds, and $\mu = 4 \times 10^{11}$ dynes/cm², appropriate to the upper mantle. The corresponding viscosity of the upper mantle must then be

$$\eta = 4 \times 10^{11} \times 3 \times 10^{10} =$$
$$1.2 \times 10^{22} \text{ g cm}^{-1} \text{ sec}^{-1}$$

which is of the same order as the viscosity calculated from the observed rate of uplift, even though the upper mantle may not behave exactly as a Maxwell body.

We now go one step further. Can this viscosity account for the observed and inferred rates of horizontal displacement of a few centimeters per year mentioned in Chapter 1?

Viscosity, previously defined as the ratio of a stress to the corresponding strain rate can also be defined as the ratio of a stress to a velocity gradient[16]; for example,

$$\sigma_{xz} = \eta \frac{\partial v_x}{\partial z}$$

Now imagine (Figure 4–20) a convection cell, the surface of which moves with a horizontal velocity $v_x = 10^{-7}$ cm sec⁻¹. Suppose that the velocity decreases linearly with depth, being zero at, say, 400 km, and in opposite sense below that depth. Then

$$\frac{\partial v_x}{\partial z} = 25 \times 10^{-16} \text{ sec}^{-1}$$

_____

[16] That the strain rate is equivalent to a velocity gradient is easily shown for a component of strain such as e_x, defined as $e_x = \partial u/\partial x$ where u is the x-component of the displacement:

$$\frac{\partial e_x}{\partial t} = \frac{\partial}{\partial t}\left(\frac{\partial u}{\partial x}\right) = \frac{\partial}{\partial x}\left(\frac{\partial u}{\partial t}\right) = \frac{\partial v_x}{\partial x}$$

The proof for shear components of strain is longer and will not be given here.

For $\eta = 10^{22}$ g cm^{-1} sec^{-1},

$$\sigma = 25 \times 10^6 \text{ g cm}^{-1} \text{sec}^{-2} = 25 \text{ bars}$$

This is not an unexpected value. Twenty-five bars corresponds to the load $(g\rho h)$ of a layer of rock of density $\rho = 3$ g cm^{-3} and thickness $h = 85$ meters. The gravitational attraction of this layer $(2\pi G \rho h)$ is only 10 milligals. We conclude from this that inequalities in mass or density distribution that would barely perturb the gravity field are sufficient to produce stresses large enough to cause a medium with viscosity $\eta = 10^{22}$ to flow at a rate of a few centimeters per year. Observed rates are therefore quite consistent, as to their order of magnitude, with the observed characteristic time for viscous flow. The hydrodynamic problem of determining precisely what the velocity distribution should be, given a pattern of density perturbations is, of course, considerably more difficult and will not be pursued here.

RATES OF UPLIFT AND EROSION   It was noted that vertical uplift at rates of the order of 1 cm/yr have been observed in several places. Rates of erosion, on the other hand, are very much smaller, generally of the order of a few centimeters per thousand years (Chapter 7). It follows that erosion cannot determine the final elevation of the land; it is the process of uplift itself that must come to an end. How soon? Since elevations greater than 10 km do not occur, it would seem that uplift cannot continue at a uniform rate for more than 10^6 years. Uplift has thus, geologically speaking, a short time scale, much shorter than that of geosynclinal subsidence, which may last for 10^8 years or so. One can infer from this difference that uplift and geosynclinal subsidence are different phenomena, as far as their rates are concerned.

If one assumes that the average elevation of the land does not fluctuate through geologic time by much more than a factor of 2 or 3, a comparison of rates of uplift and erosion indicates that, on the average, areas undergoing uplift must be much smaller, by a factor of 100 or more, than areas simultaneously undergoing denudation. Thus uplift is restricted, at any given time, to a relatively small fraction of the earth's surface, much as volcanic activity.

The cause of uplift is not known and remains a major problem of geology.

THE SEARCH FOR PERIODICITY

Suppose that we have a "historical" record— that is, a record of events in time. This record might consist, for instance, of a list of earthquakes, or of volcanic eruptions, with their time of occurrence, or of a series of observations of the instantaneous position of the pole of rotation at various times, or an alternating sequence of warm-water and cold-water faunas in a deep-sea sediment, or a record of successive diastrophic episodes. Any such sequence of events, called a "geophysical time series," can be analyzed in several ways: We may wish, for instance, to calculate an average, say the average number of earthquakes per year; or we may be looking for "trends" (for example, are earthquakes becoming more or less frequent?), or for periodicities (do earthquakes occur at constant intervals at any one place?), or for randomness (do volcanic eruptions occur at random?). The purpose of an analysis of this type may be to predict the future (when is the next earthquake likely to occur?); more commonly, mean values, trends, and periods or frequencies are used for the information they may yield regarding the nature of the process itself. When, for instance, a "harmonic" analysis reveals that the several components of the tides have periods in exact agreement with those calculated from gravitational theory and the relative motions of the earth, sun, and moon, it can hardly be doubted that the gravitational attraction of the sun and moon is what causes the tides. Similarly, the motion of the poles when properly analyzed (see page 222) turn out to consist of two interposed motions, one having a period of one year (and therefore presumably of meteorological origin) and the other one having a period of 430 days; it is from this number that inferences regarding the yielding of the earth are drawn.

FOURIER SERIES   Consider a function $y = f(t)$ defined in the interval $t = 0$ to $t = 2\pi$. (If the function is instead defined in the interval 0 to T, a new variable $t' = 2\pi t/T$, which varies from 0 to 2π as t varies from 0 to T, may be substituted for t in what follows.) If the function $f(t)$ satisfies a few not very restrictive conditions,[17] Fourier's theorem states that it can be expanded in an *infinite* series of the form

$$y = f(t) = a_0 + a_1 \cos t + b_1 \sin t + \cdots$$
$$+ a_n \cos nt + b_n \sin nt + \cdots$$

where

$$a_0 = \frac{1}{2\pi} \int_0^{2\pi} f(t)\, dt$$

is the average value of $f(t)$ in the interval considered, and

$$a_n = \frac{1}{\pi} \int_0^{2\pi} f(t) \cos nt\, dt$$

$$b_n = \frac{1}{\pi} \int_0^{2\pi} f(t) \sin nt\, dt$$

Alternatively, the expansion can be written as

$$y = f(t) = a_0 + \sum_{n=1}^{\infty} c_n \sin(nt + \varepsilon_n)$$

where c_n and ε_n are, respectively, the amplitude and phase of the nth "harmonic" constituent of $f(t)$. It is easily shown that

$$c_n = (a_n^2 + b_n^2)^{1/2} \qquad \varepsilon_n = \tan^{-1}(a_n/b_n)$$

The function $f(t)$ is not generally known in detail; instead of a continuous record of y we may have only a finite number of y values $y_0 \cdots y_i \cdots y_r$ measured at regular intervals of time. Suppose that any noncyclic trend has been removed, so that $y_0 = y_r$. It can be shown that

$$a_0 = \frac{1}{r} \sum_1^r y_i$$

$$a_n = \frac{2}{r} \sum_1^r y_i \cos nt_i$$

---

[17] It must have a continuous first derivative and, at most, a finite number of maxima and minima in the interval from 0 to 2π.

$$b_n = \frac{2}{r} \sum_1^r y_i \sin nt_i$$

where $t_i = 2\pi\, i/r$ $(i = 0, 1, \cdots r)$. Amplitudes c_n and phases ε_n can thus be computed from the observations y_i. It can be shown that if the time series y_i contains a hidden periodicity near the nth harmonic, c_n will be large compared to the other amplitudes.

RANDOM EVENTS: POISSON DISTRIBUTION   Purely random events have no periodicity at all; there is, for instance, no regularity in the recurrence of heads and tails in successive throws of a coin. To test for randomness in geological events, it may be convenient to compare a number of events per unit time (for example, the number of earthquakes per year) to the number predicted from the Poisson distribution function. The Poisson distribution, which applies particularly to rare events (that is, events with small probability) predicts that if the probability of one event occurring in the interval of time δt is $m\delta t$, the probability of n events occurring in time δt is

$$P(n, \delta t) \quad \frac{(m\delta t)^n e^{-m\delta t}}{n!}$$

Thus if the mean number of eruptions per year of a particular volcano is $1(m = 1)$, the probability of three eruptions occurring in one year is

$$P(3, 1) = \frac{1^3\, e^{-1}}{3!} = 0.0613$$

and that of no eruption at all in a year is

$$P(0, 1) = \frac{1}{e} = 0.3679$$

since $0! = 1$. The probability of no eruption in two consecutive years is

$$P(0, 2) = \frac{1}{e^2} = 0.135$$

Alternatively, the probability $F(t)$ that the interval between two events will be of length t or shorter is

$$F(t) = 1 - e^{-nt}$$

The Poisson distribution applies only to completely independent events, in the sense that the occurrence of an event must in no way influence the probability of the next event. It is therefore somewhat surprising that, as shown by Wickmann, the record of eruptions at a few volcanoes is apparently Poissonian, as if the probability of occurrence of an eruption in a given year or month were independent of what happened during the previous years or months.

All attempts to establish the periodicity of earthquakes have failed. They appear to be uncorrelated events, following more or less a Poisson distribution; but difficulties in the interpretation arise from (1) the presence of aftershocks— that is, a sequence of relatively small shocks which follow closely in a given region a larger shock which apparently starts the sequence—and from (2) their geographical distribution. Since earthquakes do not necessarily recur at exactly the same place, randomness in space may be involved as well as randomness in time. Although it may be possible to predict the total number of earthquakes of given magnitude that will occur all over the earth in a given interval of time, it is as yet impossible to predict when the next earthquake will occur at a particular place.

POWER SPECTRUM   Geological and geophysical processes usually involve simultaneously a large number of independent variables. As a rule, as more variables are involved, the phenomenon itself becomes less predictable, and its record tends to be obscured. Observations are also commonly affected by extraneous factors of a more or less random character; for instance, the observed height of the tide may be affected by the direction in which the wind happens to be blowing. The annual temperature at a point on the earth's surface and its fluctuations in time must be estimated from records that include day–night variations, seasonal variations, and fluctuations associated with the vagaries of the weather. Thus many geological and geophysical time series (that is, a sequence of observations in time) contain some "noise," noise being characterized by irregular or random fluctuations in amplitude and phase. Simple Fourier analysis is not well-adapted to treat such cases, and more elaborate techniques of a statistical nature may be required.

Consecutive stretches of a record involving random components or noise will not, in general, look alike, inasmuch as they may contain peaks of various heights scattered randomly in time. Imagine now that the record of a variable $x(t)$ is cut into pieces of equal length T. Each piece can be analyzed and the amplitude of all its Fourier components (a_n, b_n) determined. These coefficients will differ for different pieces of the record and their significance must be tested statistically. Essentially, we must look for the features that are common to all pieces.

To make the problem more definite let us assume that the time average $\langle x(t) \rangle$ of the variable is zero and that the series is "stationary"—in other words, that its statistical properties (mean, variance) do not vary with time. We develop one piece of the record in a Fourier series

$$x(t) = \sum_{n=1}^{\infty} (a_n \cos 2\pi f_n t + b_n \sin 2\pi f_n t)$$

where $f_n = n/T$, as usual. Let P_n be defined as the square of the nth component:

$$P_n = (a_n \cos 2\pi f_n t + b_n \sin 2\pi f_n t)^2$$

The time average of P_n, denoted by brackets $\langle \ \rangle$ is

$$\langle P_n \rangle = \frac{\langle a_n^2 + b_n^2 \rangle}{2}$$

because

$$\langle \cos^2 2\pi f_n t \rangle = \langle \sin^2 2\pi f_n t \rangle = \frac{1}{2}$$

$$\langle \cos 2\pi f_n t \sin 2\pi f_n t \rangle = 0$$

Searching now for what is common to all pieces of the record, we form the average of $\langle P_n \rangle$ for all pieces of the record, which we write as $\langle \overline{P}_n \rangle$. The "power spectrum" or "spectral density" $G(f)$ in the frequency interval Δf_n from f_n to f_{n+1} is then defined as[18]

$$G(f)\Delta f_n = \langle \overline{P}_n \rangle$$

---

[18] $\Delta f_n = f_{n+1} - f_n = \dfrac{n+1}{T} - \dfrac{n}{T} = \dfrac{1}{T}$

It is not difficult to show that the sum of $\langle \overline{P}_n \rangle$ over all values of n is simply the average of the square of $x(t)$, so that

$$\overline{x^2}(t) = \sum_n \langle \overline{P}_n \rangle = \sum_n G(f) \Delta f_n = \int_0^\infty G(f)\, df$$

from which it appears that G has the dimensions of the variable x squared and divided by a frequency, or multiplied by a time. From the definition of G it is apparent that in order for $G(f)$ to be large at a particular frequency f_m, the average value of $\langle \overline{P}_m \rangle$ must also be large, which implies in turn that the amplitudes a_m and b_m be large in all or most pieces of the record. If this is so, f_m is a significant frequency.

The details of the calculation of the spectral density are complicated and will not be given here. $G(f)$ is closely related to another function, called the "autocorrelation" or "autocovariance" function $C(\tau)$, which also serves to measure the consistency of the record. Suppose that we compare the record $x(t)$ with another record $x(t + \tau)$ obtained simply by displacing the origin of time by a "lag" τ, and form the product of the two. The function $C(\tau)$ is then defined as the time average of the product

$$C(\tau) = \langle x(t)\, x\, (t + \tau) \rangle$$

For each choice of τ, $C(\tau)$ has a different value; its maximum value corresponds to

$$C(0) = \langle x^2(t) \rangle$$

If the record consisted of a pure sinusoidal curve with period T_n, displacing the curve by a time T_n would reproduce the original curve so that

$$C(T_n) = C(0)$$

and is again maximum. The values of τ at which the autocorrelation function is maximum must thus bear some relation to the important frequencies in the record. It can be shown that $G(f)$ can be obtained directly from $C(\tau)$ as

$$G(f) = 4 \int_0^\infty C(\tau) \cos 2\pi f_n \tau\, d\tau$$

GEOLOGICAL APPLICATIONS: ICE AGES   Reference has already been made (Chapter 1) to the recur-rence in the past three million years of alternating "glacial" and "interglacial" phases, which together constitute an "ice age." Glaciation is characterized, at least in the Northern Hemisphere, by the development of enormous continental glaciers forming icecaps similar to the present icecaps of Greenland and Antarctica. Accumulation of ice to form these icecaps requires in the first place that the winter snowfall be greater than the melting of snow during the summer; thus abundant winter precipitation and relatively cool summers should favor the accumulation of ice. Since the temperatures of the ground and atmosphere are determined by the solar radiation (see Chapters 7 and 12), any astronomical effect that might cause a decrease in summer temperature might contribute to the onset of an ice age even if it were accompanied by slightly warmer winters. There are several such effects, all related to the dynamics of the earth–sun–moon systems, and particularly to the perturbations in the motion of the earth caused by its nonspherical shape.

Seasons exist because the axis of rotation of the earth is not perpendicular to the plane of the earth's orbit (ecliptic). The inclination, or "obliquity" is presently approximately 23½ degrees, which is also the angle between the plane of the earth's equator and the ecliptic. The unequal gravitational attraction of the sun and moon on the two sides of the equatorial bulge (the one toward the sun and the one away from it) results in a torque that if applied to a nonrotating earth would cause the obliquity to vanish. Instead, however, the gyroscopic effect of the earth's spin causes the axis of rotation to describe in space a cone about the normal to the ecliptic, thereby causing a change in the time of the year at which the seasons change from winter to spring, or summer to autumn; this is called the precession of the equinoxes. The combined effects of the sun and moon cause in addition a slight periodic change in the obliquity itself. When the obliquity increases, seasonal differences become more marked. Finally, the eccentricity or ellipticity of the earth's orbit oscillates, influencing both the total amount of radiation received from the sun (because of changing the sun–earth distance) and the length of the seasons. These various effects have different periods: 92,000 years for the eccentricity; 26,000 years for the precession of the equinoxes; 40,000 years for the obliquity.

The calculation of the probable variation in insolation at a point on the earth which results from these periodic changes is a difficult problem that has been attacked by Milankovitch and, more recently, by van Woerkom. The frequencies that appear in the insolation curve are the fundamental frequencies of the several astronomical motions and their harmonics (that is, integral multiples), and also sums and differences of these fundamentals and their harmonics. To translate such insolation curves into actual temperature changes of the surface of the land or of the oceans is still another, and much more difficult, problem, inasmuch as these temperatures depend not only on the insolation at the point considered, but also on the whole pattern and intensity of the atmospheric and oceanic circulations that are determined by the innumerable factors governing local climates.

Temperature variations in the oceans in the last few million years may be recorded in deep-sea sediments. The isotopic ratio O^{18}/O^{16} in the shells of various organisms (for instance, pelagic Foraminifera) is known to depend on the temperature of the water during growth of the organism. Use can also be made of the relative abundance in a particular sediment of foraminiferal species that are characteristic of warm or temperate waters, as determined by their latitudinal distribution. If we measure such quantities in a sediment core and plot them against depth in the core, fluctuations that can be subjected to power spectrum or Fourier analysis become apparent. Depth, rather than time, can be used as the variable. If, in addition, some constant rate of sedimentation is assumed, the resulting power spectrum may be compared to the power spectrum of the insolation to see whether the same frequencies or periods appear in both. Figure 4–21 shows the result of such calculations for a deep-sea core from the central Caribbean, on the assumption that the length of the core (1430 cm) represents 360,000 years (with a rate of sedimentation of approximately 4×10^{-3} cm/yr). If the dating is correct, and if other cores showed consistently the same pattern, we would conclude that the temperature fluctuations recorded in the sediments are indeed related to the changing motions of the earth.

It is not implied, however, that these changes actually cause climatic fluctuations such as ice ages. Clearly, the motions of the earth described must have persisted for longer than the few mil-

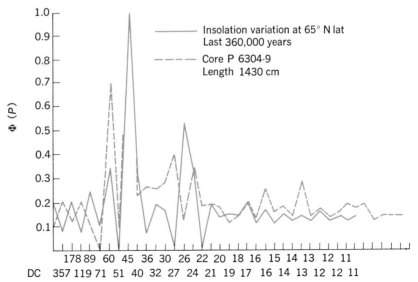

FIG. 4–21 Power spectrum of insolation compared with O^{18}/O^{16} power spectrum for a sedimentary core. (From W. C. Kemp and D. T. Eger, J. Geophys. Res. vol. 72, p. 747, 1967.)

lion years of the Pleistocene ice age, the onset of which must therefore have a still different cause. A number of such causes have been suggested: changes in the sun's output of radiation, changes in mean elevation of the land, local changes in climate due to wandering (relative to the earth itself) of the pole of rotation, and so forth. It is noteworthy that isotopic O^{18}/O^{16} ratios in fossils seem to indicate a continuous decrease in the temperature of the oceans ever since Cretaceous times. It does appear, though, that climatic oscillations, as from glacial to interglacial, may be related to (or controlled by) the bodily motions of the earth.

PERIODICITY IN OROGENY In western Europe, a major unconformity separates early Devonian rocks from the underlying Silurian; another major unconformity separates the Permian from the middle and late Carboniferous. In southern Europe, pronounced deformation has occurred throughout the Cenozoic. Thus, since late Precambrian times three major orogenies have occurred there: Caledonian (about 500–400 million years ago), Hercynian, (also known as Variscan, although the former term refers usually to western, and the latter to central, Europe), about 300 million years ago, and Alpine, with a paroxysm in the late Oligocene and early Miocene, some 30 million years ago. Orogenies in Europe are well-marked events of relatively short duration,[19] irregularly spaced in time. This has given rise to the notion that orogenic deformation might be a periodic phenomenon. Stille thought he could show that orogenies had occurred simultaneously in many parts of the world, making them world-wide or planetary events; expressions such as the "pulse" of the earth have been used.

The search for periodicity in orogenic events is, at best, a most difficult problem. In the first place, to detect with some assurance a period of length T, one needs a record spanning a length of time much greater than T. The record will therefore have to include the Precambrian, which includes the major part of the earth's history but which is, in many respects, less well known; in particular the exact dating of Precambrian orogenic events still presents problems. Radiometric dates refer to the time of crystallization, or recrystallization, of minerals or rocks, not necessarily to the time of their deformation. Because igneous activity (particularly granite intrusion) and metamorphism seem in a few well-documented instances to have accompanied deformation, the latter may perhaps be approximately dated by dating the former, yet it does not follow that the age of a pegmatite dike necessarily represents the date of a major orogeny. In principle, the date of an orogeny is determined by comparing the age of the youngest sedimentary strata that it deforms with the age of the oldest sediments that lie unconformably on the deformed ones. But, as is commonly the case in Precambrian terranes, erosion may have removed all postorogenic sediments.

It is also difficult to assess quantitatively the magnitude of an orogenic episode—that is, to determine the ordinate of a plot of orogeny against time. Minor and local unconformities are common in sedimentary sequences; transgressions and regressions of the sea frequently occur without any sign of deformation other than mild upward or downward movements. The areal extent of the deformation is of some importance, but how should one compare a rather intense deformation of a small area with a milder deformation of a much broader area? What is needed is a quantitative index of the power (energy per unit time) expended on deformation; in the absence of any such index no analysis is possible.

Qualitatively, the picture that emerges from the geological record is that very few places on earth are ever totally quiet at any given time; but relatively few places are undergoing more than mild and slow vertical movements, up or down. In any particular area, it is generally possible to recognize distinct times, and occasionally prolonged, periods of time (for example, the whole of the Jurassic in the western United

---

[19] Radiometric dating shows that the Caledonian orogeny in the type region of Scotland involved repeated episodes of folding, metamorphism, and igneous intrusion collectively spanning over 100 million years.

States, or most of the Cenozoic in California) of more intense deformation, but only rarely can one recognize in any area more than two super-posed intense deformations of very different age, the record of any earlier ones having been ob-literated. Intense deformation may occur at any time in one area without affecting other areas one or two thousand kilometers away, and is not

therefore generally "worldwide"; yet signs of a late-Carboniferous orogenesis are found in so many areas in both hemispheres that it is difficult not to think of it as a global event. No periodicity in orogeny has yet been recognized nor is recog-nition likely because of inherent gaps in the geo-logical record and absence of a suitable quantita-tive index of orogenic activity.

REFERENCES

Aldrich, L. T., G. W. Wetherill, G. L. Davis, and G. R. Tilton: Radioactive ages of micas from granitic rocks by Rb-Sr and K-A methods, *Am. Geophys. Union Trans.,* vol. 39, pp. 1124–1134, 1958.

Arkell, W. J.: *The Jurassic System in Great Britain,* Oxford, New York, pp. 1–37, 1933.

————: *Jurassic Geology of the World,* Oliver & Boyd, London, pp. 3–14, 1956.

  Reviews of the development of the smaller time-stratigraphic, biostratigraphic and time units in stratigraphic chronology, with special reference to the Jurassic system, starting with the ideas of William Smith.

Armstrong, R. L.: A model for the evolution of strontium and lead isotopes in a dynamic earth, *Rev. Geophys.,* vol. 6, pp. 175–199, 1968.

Barber, N.F.: Fourier methods in geophysics, in *Methods and Techniques in Geophysics* (ed. by S. K. Runcorn), Interscience, New York, vol. 2, pp. 123–204, 1966.

Barrell, J.: Rhythms and the measurement of geologic time, *Geol. Soc. Am. Bull.,* vol. 28, pp. 745–904, 1917.

  Revision of ideas in stratigraphic chronology, with emphasis on the significance of breaks in the rec-ord, under the impact of radiometric evidence of the great duration of geological time.

Blackman, R. B., and J. W. Tukey: *The Measurement of Power Spectra,* Dover, New York, 1958.

Chapman, S., and J. Bartels: *Geomagnetism,* Clarendon Press, Oxford, 1940.

  Fourier series are treated in Chapter 16, pp. 543–605.

Curtis, G. H., J. F. Evernden, and J. Lipson: Age de-termination of some granitic rocks in California by the

potassium-argon method, California State Div. Mines Special Rept., no. 54, 1958.

Darwin, C.: *The Origin of Species* (6th and final ed.), J. Murray, London, 1872.

  Two chapters (pp. 366–492 in the reprint of 1902) discuss "the imperfection of the geological record" and "the geological succession of organic beings."

DeSitter, L. U.: *Structural Geology* (2nd ed.), McGraw-Hill, New York, 1964.

  Scale models and similitude are described on pp. 34–62. Periodicity in orogeny is treated briefly in Chapter 35, pp. 474–484.

Eicher, D.: *Geologic Time,* Prentice-Hall, Englewood Cliffs, N.J., 1968.

  An elementary treatment of stratigraphic and ra-diometric chronology.

Faul, H.: *Ages of Rocks, Planets, and Stars,* McGraw-Hill, New York, 1966.

  A concise clear account of the principles of radio-metric chronology.

Folinsbee, R. E., H. Baadsgaard, and J. P. Lipson: Potassium-argon time scale, Rept. Intern. Geol. Congr., 21st session, Norden, 1960, pt. 3, pp. 7–17, 1960.

————:Potassium-argon dates of upper Cretaceous ash falls, Alberta, Canada, *Ann. N.Y. Acad. Sci.,* vol. 91, pp. 352–359, 1961.

  Argument leading to establishment of sharply de-fined points on the radiometric–stratigraphic time scale.

Gilluly, J.: Distribution of mountain building in geologic time, *Geol. Soc. Am. Bull.,* vol. 60 pp. 561–590, 1949.

————: The tectonic evolution of the Western United States, *Geol. Soc. London Quart. J.,* vol. 119, pp. 133–174, 1963.

Glaessner, M. F.: The base of the Cambrian, *J. Geol. Soc. Australia,* vol. 10, pp. 223–239, 1963.

An illustration of difficulties attending attempts to establish the beginning of Phanerozoic time on a stratigraphic basis.

Harland, W. B., A. S. Smith, and B. Wilcock (editors): The phanerozoic time scale, *Geol. Soc. London Quart. J.,* vol. 120S (supplement), 1964.

A series of essays on radiometric dating of the standard stratigraphic column.

Holmes, A.: The duration of geological time, *Nature,* vol. 87, pp. 9–10, 1911.

————: A revised estimate on the age of the earth, *Nature,* vol. 159, pp. 127–128, 1947.

————: A revised geological time scale, *Trans. Edinburgh Geol. Soc.,* vol. 17, pp. 183–216, 1959.

The radiometric time scale as first seen and subsequently revised by Holmes.

Hubbert, M. K.: Theory of scale models as applied to the study of geologic structures, *Geol. Soc. Am. Bull.,* vol. 48, pp. 1459–1520, 1937.

Kittel, C., W. D. Knight, and M. R. Ruderman: *Berkeley Physics Course, vol. 1, Mechanics,* McGraw-Hill, New York, 1962.

Especially Chapter 8: Elementary dynamics of rigid bodies; Chapter 11, Lorentz transformations of length and time (which discusses the time "dilation" of moving clocks, pp. 356–361).

Knopf, A.: Measuring geologic time, *Sci. Monthly,* vol. 85, pp. 225–236, 1957.

Kulp, J. L.: Geologic time scale, *Science,* vol. 133, no. 3459, pp. 1105–1114, 1961.

Discusses radiometric calibration of the stratigraphic time scale and sets up a generally accepted standard scale.

Kummel, B.: *History of the Earth,* W. H. Freeman and Company, San Francisco, 1961.

A comprehensive modern text that treats principles of geochronology, pp. 1–71.

Lomnitz, C.: Statistical prediction of earthquakes, *Rev. Geophys.,* vol. 4, pp. 377–393, 1966.

Lyell, C.: *Elements of Geology,* (6th ed.), Appleton, New York, 1886.

The section "On the different ages of the aqueous rocks" (pp. 92–106) reflects the views of Lyell on stratigraphy after he accepted Darwin's theories of evolution and natural selection.

Munk, W. H., and G. J. F. MacDonald: *The Rotation of the Earth,* Cambridge, New York, 1960.

Chapters 8 to 11 deal with variations in the length of the day and the "Chandler wobble."

Rankama, K.: *Progress in Isotope Geology,* Interscience, New York, 1963.

Savage, D. E., G. H. Curtis, and G. T. James: The potassium-argon dates and the Cenozoic mammalian chronology of North America, *Am. J. Sci.,* vol. 262, pp. 145–198, 1964.

Tilton, G. R.: Volume diffusion as a mechanism for discordant lead ages, *J. Geophys. Res.,* vol. 65, pp. 2933–2945, 1960.

————, **and S. R. Hart:** Geochronology, *Science,* vol. 140, pp. 357–366, 1963.

Toulmin, S., and J. Goodfield: *The Discovery of Time,* Harper & Row, New York, pp. 141–231, 1965.

Van Woerkom, A. J. J.: The astronomical theory of climatic changes, in *Climatic Change, Evidence, Causes, and Effects* (edited by H. Shapley), Harvard University Press, Cambridge, Mass., 1953.

Wells, J. W.: Coral growth and geochronometry, *Nature,* vol. 197, pp. 948–950, 1963.

Wetherill, G. W. (editor): Geochronology of North America, *Natl. Acad. Sci. Natl. Res. Council, Nucl. Sci. Ser.,* Rept. 41, 1965.

Voluminous radiometric data with special reference to the Precambrian.

Wickman, F. E.: Repose period patterns of volcanoes, *Arkiv. Mineral. Geol.,* vol. 4, pp. 291–301, 303–317, 319–335, 337–350, 351–367, 1966.

Woodford, A. O.: *Historical Geology,* Freeman, San Francisco, 1965.

Principles of stratigraphic and radiometric chronology are treated on pp. 45–94, 191–220.

Zeuner, F. E.: *The Pleistocene Period,* Hutchinson, London, 1959.

5

THERMODYNAMIC CONSIDERATIONS

WHEN ATTEMPTING TO DECIPHER the geological record and to interpret it in terms of the geological processes that have been operative, we find ourselves, time and time again, asking such questions as "Under what conditions could mineral X or mineral assemblage Y form?" or conversely, "What minerals or mineral assemblages can exist under such and such conditions?" "Under what conditions, and how fast, will Y transform to Z?" Without the answer to such questions the record of geological history inscribed in minerals and rocks cannot be properly read.

In principle, the answer to all such questions is to be found in the laws of quantum mechanics, statistical mechanics, and thermodynamics. The purpose of this chapter is to provide a brief summary of some of the thermodynamic relations that turn out to be most useful to geologists.

Geologists are much concerned with solutions. The ocean is an aqueous solution of great complexity, the understanding of which is essential to the interpretation of sedimentary processes. Fluids of one kind or another pervade the crust. Many metamorphic reactions proceed in the presence of small amounts of a pore solution filling small openings between grains; this pore solution plays an essential role in the kinetics of recrystallization. Economically important deposits of a large number of metals are formed through the agency of hot, or "hydrothermal," aqueous solutions. A magma is a silicate solution of a large number of components, including H_2O and CO_2. Most common minerals (feldspars, olivines, pyroxenes, micas, and so forth) are solid solutions. Since solutions exist because of the general tendency of things to "mix," as governed by entropy, much of the following discussion will be focused on entropy.

Some Fundamental Relations: Free Energy and Chemical Potential

The Gibbs free energy G,[1] defined in terms of internal energy U, entropy S, volume V, temperature T, and pressure P is

$$G = U + PV - TS$$

It is easily shown from the laws of thermodynamics that in any spontaneous process occurring at constant P and T, the function G must decrease; that is the free energy of the products must be

---

[1] Sometimes called free enthalpy to distinguish it from the Helmholtz free energy F defined as $F = U - TS$. The enthalpy H is defined as $H = U + PV$.

less than the free energy of the reactants or starting material. The change in free energy ΔG of a reaction, defined as the free energy of the products minus that of the reactants, must be negative if the reaction is to proceed spontaneously. If $\Delta G = 0$, reactants and products are said to be in equilibrium.

The first law states that the change in the internal energy U of a system must equal the heat received by the system $(T\,dS)$ plus the work $(-P\,dV)$ done on it; hence $dU = T\,dS - P\,dV$. It then follows from the definition of G that

$$dG = - S\,dT + V\,dP$$

and

$$\left(\frac{\partial G}{\partial P}\right)_T = V \text{ and } \left(\frac{\partial G}{\partial T}\right)_P = -S \qquad (5\text{-}1)$$

Correspondingly,

$$\left(\frac{\partial \Delta G}{\partial P}\right)_T = \Delta V \text{ and } \left(\frac{\partial \Delta G}{\partial T}\right)_P = -\Delta S \qquad (5\text{-}2)$$

$$d(\Delta G) = -(\Delta S)\,dT + (\Delta V)\,dP \qquad (5\text{-}3)$$

where the symbol Δ refers to a difference between products and reactants.

In systems of variable composition, such as a solution, it is convenient to introduce the chemical potential μ_i of component i, defined as

$$\mu_i = \left(\frac{\partial G}{\partial n_i}\right)_{P,T,n_j}$$

where n_i is the number of moles of i, and n_j designates the number of moles of any other component. The chemical potential of i in a solution is thus defined as the change in free energy of the solution when a small amount of i is added to it at constant T and P and without otherwise changing its composition. For a pure substance, μ is the free energy per mole. At constant P and T,

$$dG = \sum_i \mu_i\,dn_i$$

where the summation is over all components.

Now suppose that in a reaction (for example, melting) at constant T and P, a small amount dn_i of component i moves from phase α (for example, a solid) to phase β (for example, a melt).

The free-energy change dG of the reaction is

$$dG = -\mu_i^\alpha\,dn_i + \mu_i^\beta\,dn_i$$

For the reaction to proceed spontaneously, we require $dG < 0$, or $\mu_i^\alpha > \mu_i^\beta$. At equilibrium,

$$dG = 0 \qquad \text{or} \qquad \mu_i^\alpha = \mu_i^\beta$$

Thus a component i moves spontaneously from phase α to phase β if its chemical potential is greater in α than in β. For equilibrium between two phases, it is necessary that the chemical potential of each and every component be equal in the two phases. Obviously the chemical potential bears the same relation to chemical transfer as temperature does to heat transfer.

THE COMMON VARIABLES

The most important variables in geological processes are pressure and temperature. It is clear from (5-2) that raising the pressure will cause a reaction to run in the sense for which ΔV is negative; raising the temperature causes it to run in the sense for which ΔS is positive. High P and high T favor, respectively, phases of low volume (high density) and high entropy. In many substances of geological interest, large volume is associated with large entropy, and vice versa; raising the temperature and raising the pressure thus generally have opposite effects.

The effect of pressure is likely to be, on the whole, more important in the earth than is the effect of temperature. This is because the temperature in the earth is probably nowhere greater than a few thousand degrees, whereas the pressure at the center of the earth is of the order of 3.5×10^6 bars.[2] Consider, for instance, a reaction or transformation with rather typical values of $\Delta S = -0.5$ cal/deg and $\Delta V = -1$ cm³, occurring near the bottom of the mantle where $T = 3000°C$ and $P = 10^6$ bars, say. Compared with the same reaction occurring at the surface $(T = 0°C, P = 1$ bar$)$, the free energy of the reaction in the mantle changes by the amount $0.5 \times 3000 = 1500$ cal, due to temperature, and

_____

[2] 1 bar $= 10^6$ dynes/cm² $= 0.987$ atmospheres.

by an amount -1×10^6 bar cm^3 = $-23,900$ cal, due to pressure.[3] The latter is, in fact, commensurate with a bonding energy, so that we may expect that pressure in the deep earth will induce rather drastic mineralogical changes. In the upper mantle and crust, where P is less than 10^5 bars, the effects of pressure and temperature are generally of comparable magnitude.

OTHER VARIABLES

Because of the earth's gravitational field, the energy of an object of mass m depends on its position. The amount of energy needed to lift it by a length dh is $mgdh$, where g is the local value of the acceleration of gravity (see Chapter 11). Thus the free energy of a phase of mass M containing n_i moles of a component with a molecular weight M_i depends on position as

$$\left(\frac{\partial G}{\partial h}\right)_{P,T} = gM = g\sum_i n_i M_i$$

It follows that

$$\left(\frac{\partial \mu_i}{\partial h}\right)_{P,T} = g M_i \qquad (5\text{-}4)$$

This relation will be used later in connection with the distribution of elements in the earth.

The potential energy of an atom or ion in a solid depends on the number of next neighbors (see Chapter 2). Thus the energy of a particle on the surface, where it has neighbors on only one side, differs from that of a particle somewhere inside the body, and energy is needed to create a new surface. The free energy therefore depends on the surface area A as

$$\left(\frac{\partial F}{\partial A}\right)_{P,T} = \sigma \qquad (5\text{-}5)$$

where σ is the "surface tension," which, in crystals, depends on the crystallographic orientation of the surface. For a given mass or volume of substance, the surface area increases with decreasing grain size. Thus, small grains have a higher energy than larger grains. The effect is

---

[3] 1 calorie = 41.8 bar cm^3.

important in the "nucleation"—that is, in the incipient growth of a phase that forms, for example, by crystallization from solution.

Entropy

As we saw, two important thermodynamic parameters are volume and entropy. The former is easily measured. The latter is less familiar. It can be calculated in several ways, the most common one being by integrating the specific heat or heat capacity C_P at all temperatures between $0°$K and T:

$$S = S_0 + \int_0^T \frac{C_P}{T}\, dT$$

where S_0 is the entropy at $0°$K. The entropy of crystalline substances at $0°$K is generally zero, except in a few special cases. The entropy unit (1 e.u.) is one calorie per degree per mole.

Let us examine the entropy change for the following reactions. (SC means standard conditions of $P = 1$ bar, $T = 298°$K.)

$H_2O \rightarrow H_2O$ (SC) $\Delta S = +28.39$ e.u.
liquid   gas

$H_2O \rightarrow H_2 + \frac{1}{2}O_2$ (SC) $\Delta S = +10.61$ e.u.
gas   gas   gas

$H_2O \rightarrow H_2O$ ($0°$C, 1 bar) $\Delta S = +7$ e.u.
solid   liquid

$Na + \frac{1}{2}Cl_2 \rightarrow NaCl$ (SC) $\Delta S = -21.54$ e.u.
solid   gas   solid

$MgO + SiO_2 \rightarrow MgSiO_3$ (SC) $\Delta S = -0.1$ e.u.
solid   solid   solid

$MgO + H_2O \rightarrow Mg(OH)_2$ (SC) $\Delta S = -36.45$ e.u.
solid   gas   solid

Careful inspection of these data suggests what entropy is about. Entropy increases when we pass from more-ordered states (solid) to less-ordered states (liquid, gas). It may change very little in reactions between solids. If we take one gas molecule and break it up, entropy increases again. Entropy is in some way associated with disorder.

Entropy is also related to volume. For a single phase at constant temperature,

$$\left(\frac{\partial S}{\partial V}\right)_T = \frac{\alpha}{\beta}$$

where α is thermal expansion and β is compressibility. The latter is always, and the former usually, positive, so that in general entropy increases with increasing volume. In many reactions of mineralogical interest (for example, $MgO + SiO_2 = MgSiO_3$), ΔV and ΔS have the same sign; the magnitude of ΔS can be roughly predicted from ΔV and values of α and β. We recall the fundamental property of entropy, mentioned on page 186, that an isolated system of given energy and volume spontaneously tends to reach a state of maximum entropy. Equilibrium is reached when the entropy is maximum.

STATISTICAL INTERPRETATION OF ENTROPY

In statistical mechanics, the entropy of a system is defined as

$$S = k \ln \Omega \qquad (5\text{-}6)$$

where k, the Boltzmann constant,[4] is 1.38×10^{-16} erg/deg, and Ω is the number of quantum states accessible to the system. "Accessible" means consistent with macroscopic constraints imposed on the system, such as its total volume or total energy.

The notion of a quantum state is familiar in the case of the hydrogen atom. The Schrödinger wave equation has many distinct solutions, each of which corresponds to a different "orbital," or distribution in space, of the electron. Most of these solutions, or "quantum states," correspond to different values of the energy; states with the same energy are said to be degenerate states. Each state of the hydrogen atom is defined by a set of three quantum numbers.

For a system of N identical atoms—where N is large, of the order of Avogadro's number (6.02×10^{23})—Schrödinger's equation has $3N$ variables (the three coordinates of each of the N particles). Each solution, or quantum state, is defined by $3N$ quantum numbers, and is asso-

ciated with a definite value of the total energy, although many states may have the same energy. The same total energy may be consistent with a large number of different distributions of energy among the particles that form the system. Each quantum state corresponds to a different distribution of particles in space.

The connection between entropy and number of quantum states follows from the property of entropy that in an isolated system it tends to be maximum. Of unequally probable events, the ones that tend to occur more often are those of greatest probability; thus the statement about entropy can be construed to mean that an isolated system tends spontaneously to a more probable state. But the probability of a state increases with the number of ways, or "configurations," in which this state can be achieved. If two coins are tossed, for instance, the configuration head–tail is twice as probable as either head–head or tail–tail, because head–tail can be achieved in two ways (coin 1 head, coin 2 tail; or coin 1 tail, coin 2 head) whereas the other configurations can be reached in only one way. Thus the most likely state of a system is that in which it has the greatest possible number of configurations, or quantum states.

Quantum states of a system consisting of many particles differ mainly as to the distribution of particles in space, and to the distribution of particles among their possible energy levels. A gas has more quantum states than a solid because the molecules of the gas can be found anywhere within the container, whereas those of the solid are constrained to fixed lattice positions. The entropy of a gas increases with volume because there are more ways in which the molecules can be spatially distributed in a larger volume than in a smaller one. A gas expands into a vacuum because its entropy increases by filling the whole volume accessible to it.

Particles free to move in three directions have more degrees of freedom and more quantum states than particles free to move in one direction only. The number of quantum states also increases with the number of modes in which the energy can be distributed; thus translation, vibration, and rotation all contribute to the entropy.

---

[4] The Boltzmann constant is simply related to R, the gas constant, through Avogadro's number N_a as follows: $R = N_a k$.

In an ordinary crystal at $0°K$ all particles are fixed in space and all have the same vibrational energy. There is therefore only one quantum state accessible to the system, and since $\Omega = 1$, the entropy according to (5-6) must be zero.

The number Ω is thus associated with the number of degrees of freedom of a system—that is, the total number of parameters needed to describe the detailed microscopic behavior of each particle in the system. Any restriction placed on the behavior of the particles (for example, assignment of definite locations in a lattice) reduces the number of degrees of freedom, Ω, and S. High entropy, or lack of restrictions, is thus commonly associated with the idea of disorder, or of randomness. When a deck of cards is shuffled, there is a large number (52!) of ways in which individual cards can be arranged. This number is much reduced if we specify that, for instance, all spades must occur together at one end of the deck. Thus a crystal containing two kinds of atoms (such as Cu and Zn in an alloy) will have a high entropy if both kinds of atoms are distributed randomly among all available sites; the entropy will be lower if each kind of atom is restricted to a particular kind of lattice site. Two substances will mix spontaneously, even if energy is required to do so, simply because of the increase in entropy ΔS_m resulting from increased randomness in the distribution of the two kinds of molecules. This is essentially why solutions form. The only constraint is that the decrease in free energy $-T\Delta S_m$ due to mixing must be greater than, or at least equal to, the increase in internal energy ΔU.

THE BOLTZMANN DISTRIBUTION

Consider now an isolated system of N non-interacting particles with total energy E. Suppose that the energy levels accessible to each particle are $\varepsilon_0, \varepsilon_1, \varepsilon_2, \cdots, \varepsilon_i$; these levels are generally very closely spaced; that is, the difference $\varepsilon_2 - \varepsilon_1$ is very much smaller than E. There are obviously many ways in which the energy E could be distributed among the N particles; they could, for instance, all have the same energy E/N, or alternatively, most of them could have a low energy

while a few have a much higher energy, and so on. Let n_i be the number of particles having energy ε_i. What will the values of $n_0, n_1, \cdots, n_i$ be at equilibrium?

We recall that equilibrium in an isolated system of given E and V requires that S, hence Ω, be maximum. Here Ω is the number of ways in which the particles can be distributed among the available energy levels, since each distribution represents a different quantum state. Thus,[5]

$$\Omega = \frac{N!}{(n_1!)(n_2!) \cdots (n_i!)} \qquad (5\text{-}7)$$

Since the number N and E are fixed, we also require that

$$\Sigma n_i = N$$

$$\Sigma \varepsilon_i n_i = E$$

The value of n_i that makes Ω maximum, subject to these two conditions, is found to be

$$n_i = \frac{N}{f} e^{-\varepsilon_i/kT}$$

where the "partition function" $f = \Sigma e^{-\varepsilon_i/kT}$. The temperature T appears in this result because of the thermodynamic requirement that $(\partial E/\partial S)_V = T$.

If energy is counted from the ground state or lowest level ($\varepsilon_0 = 0$), the number n_0 of particles in the lowest level is

$$n_0 = \frac{N}{f}$$

and

$$n_i = n_0 e^{-\varepsilon_i/kT} \qquad (5\text{-}8)$$

It follows from equation (5-8) that, at $T = 0$,

---

[5] Suppose we wish to arrange four particles in two boxes, one of which will contain three particles and the other will contain one. According to equation (5-7), the number of ways of doing so is

$$\frac{4!}{3!1!} = 4$$

which is obvious, since the single particle in box 2 must be either particle 1, or particle 2, or particle 3, or particle 4. No other arrangement is possible.

$n_0 = N$ and all other n_i's are zero. All particles are in the lowest energy state accessible to them.

The factor $e^{-\varepsilon_i/kT}$ is known as the Boltzmann factor and plays a very important role, particularly in the study of rate processes such as diffusion. If an energy ε_i is required for an atom of a crystal to move from a lattice site (which is, by definition, a position of minimum energy) to an interstitial site, the fraction of all atoms in the crystal that have at any time enough energy to do so is $e^{-\varepsilon_i/kT}$; this fraction determines, therefore, the rate at which diffusion occurs. In general, it will determine the rate of all "activated" processes (chemical reactions, viscous flow, electrical conductivity) in which a particle requires an additional amount of energy (the activation energy) to enter the process.

The partition function f turns out to be an important function, for all thermodynamic properties can be derived from it; the Helmholtz free energy per mole, for instance, is simply

$$F = -RT \ln f$$

Unfortunately, in most systems of interest the energy levels are not sufficiently accurately known to allow a precise calculation of f.

THERMODYNAMIC FUNCTIONS FOR SOLIDS

In crystals the major contribution to Ω and f arises from the lattice vibrations already mentioned in Chapter 4. The energy levels of a "harmonic" oscillator such as described on page 224 are found by solving the appropriate form of the Schrödinger equation. They are simply

$$\varepsilon = h\nu(n + \tfrac{1}{2})$$

where h is Planck's constant (6.62×10^{-27} erg sec), ν is the frequency of the oscillator, and n is any integer from zero to infinity. Thus all thermodynamic properties (E, S, F, G, and specific heat C_v) that arise from vibrations can be calculated if the $3N$ vibrational modes can be properly enumerated. Note that in the lowest state corresponding to $n = 0$, the oscillator still has an energy $\tfrac{1}{2}h\nu$; this is called the "zero-point energy."

In carbonates and nitrates, CO_3 and NO_3 planar groups may oscillate or rotate about an axis normal to the plane of the group. Such rotation contributes to the thermodynamic properties and also increases crystal symmetry.

ORDER–DISORDER   In solids, part of the entropy can also arise from order–disorder and from the formation of defects. The order–disorder effect is clearly seen in albite ($NaAlSi_3O_8$), in which Si and Al are randomly distributed among 4-coordinated sites at high temperatures, but ordered at low temperatures. Disordering increases the entropy by an amount

$$\Delta S = k \ln \Omega$$

If N atoms of Al and $3N$ atoms of Si are randomly distributed on $4N$ lattice sites,

$$\Omega = \frac{(4N)!}{(3N)!\, N!}$$

By Stirling's formula, $\ln(x!) = x \ln x - x$, if x is large. Hence,

$$\Delta S = kN \ln \frac{256}{27} \simeq 2.24R$$

per mole. If, on the other hand, randomness is limited to each unit cell, which is constrained to contain three atoms of Si and one atom of Al, the excess entropy for N cells is

$$\Delta S = kN \ln \frac{4!}{3!\,1!} \simeq 1.38R$$

Since high temperature favors the state of highest entropy, disorder will spread through the crystal as the temperature is raised; at high T, some cells will be found to contain 0, 1, 2, or even 4 aluminum atoms.

The exact calculation of the degree of disorder that will prevail at any temperature T is difficult, as the internal energy U also depends on the degree of ordering (U must be minimum in the ordered state or ordering would never occur). Disorder sets in when the temperature T is sufficiently high for the term $-T\Delta S$ to become larger than the increase in energy ΔU resulting from disordering. If the degree of order can be measured (for example, from the crystallographic parameters of the unit cell, which depend on it) on crystals annealed at a known temperature, measurements on natural crystals may indicate the temperature at which equilibration took place, and serve therefore as natural thermometers.

ISOTOPE SEPARATION A different kind of natural thermometer is provided by the relative abundance of stable (that is, nonradioactive) isotopes in minerals. Isotopes (for example, O^{16} and O^{18}) differ only by their mass. Inasmuch as their electronic structures are identical, they have identical chemical properties and cannot be separated chemically. However, since they differ as to mass, vibration frequencies (see page 224) and hence thermodynamic properties (solubility, vapor pressure, and so forth) are also different. Light water H_2O^{16}, for instance, has a higher vapor pressure than the heavier H_2O^{18}, and rainwater accordingly contains more of the former than the ocean water from which it evaporated.

Consider now two chemically different crystals containing oxygen (for instance, quartz and calcite). At a given temperature, the free energies of SiO_2^{18} and SiO_2^{16} are slightly different, as are also those of $CaCO_3^{18}$ and $CaCO_3^{16}$. Accordingly, the free energy of a quartz (or calcite) crystal containing both O^{18} and O^{16} depends on the ratio O^{18}/O^{16}. This dependence is not identical for quartz and calcite, because the vibration frequencies of oxygen are different in these two structures. Thus transfer of O^{18} out of one phase may lower its free energy by an amount greater than the increase in free energy of the phase into which O^{18} is transferred. When the two phases come to equilibrium (minimum total free energy), the O^{18}/O^{16} ratios in the two phases will, in general, be different, and will depend on temperature. Conversely, the temperature of equilibration may be determined from the measured ratios.

A rule of thumb is that the heavy isotope tends generally to be concentrated in the compound in which it is more tightly held; thus, for instance, the ratio O^{18}/O^{16} will be higher in a crystal of quartz than in the aqueous solution from which

the crystal grew. The effect is more marked for isotopes of elements which have a relatively greater difference in atomic weight. It is, for instance, more marked for O^{18}/O^{16}, with a ratio of $(18-16)/16$, than for Sr^{87}/Sr^{86}, with a ratio of $(87-86)/86$; isotopic separation of heavy elements (roughly beyond sulfur) has not been detected in nature.[6] The effect disappears at high temperature where the energy of an oscillator becomes simply kT, regardless of the mass of the vibrating atom or of the force constant.

An application of the method to the determination of paleotemperatures in the ocean was mentioned on page 231. The use of isotope ratios to determine the temperature of recrystallization of metamorphic rocks is illustrated in Chapter 10.

THERMODYNAMIC PROPERTIES OF SOLUTIONS

Suppose that n_a moles of component A are dissolved in n_b moles of B. The mole fraction x_a of A is defined as $x_a = n_a/(n_a + n_b)$ and $x_b = n_b/(n_a + n_b)$. For simplicity, let $n_a + n_b = n$.

The formation of the solution, or mixing of A and B, entails an entropy of mixing ΔS_m corresponding to the number of possible configurations of $n_a N$ molecules of one kind and $n_b N$ molecules of another kind, where N is Avogadro's number. Thus

$$\Delta S_m = k \ln \frac{(nN)!}{(n_a N)! \ (n_b N)!}$$

which, by Stirling's formula, reduces to

$$\Delta S_m = -R[n_a \ln x_a + n_b \ln x_b]$$

Suppose that there is no heat evolved or absorbed and no volume change during mixing ("ideal" solution). The free energy of mixing is thus simply $-T\Delta S_m$ and the free energy of the solution is

$$G = n_a \mu_a^0 + n_b \mu_b^0 + RT[n_a \ln x_a + n_b \ln x_b]$$

where μ_a^0 and μ_b^0 are, respectively, the chemical potentials of pure A and pure B.

---

[6] Except where it results from radioactive disintegration.

The chemical potential of A in the solution is then[7]

$$\mu_a = \left(\frac{\partial G}{\partial n_a}\right)_{P,T,n_b} = \mu_a^0 + RT \ln x_a \quad (5\text{-}9)$$

Most solutions obey equation (5-9) when they are sufficiently dilute. Solid solutions of albite ($NaAlSi_3O_8$) and anorthite ($CaAlSi_2O_8$), and of forsterite (Mg_2SiO_4) and fayalite (Fe_2SiO_4) are very nearly ideal at all concentrations.

The condition of zero heat of mixing is rarely exactly met, since it implies similarity of bond energies in mixed and unmixed configurations (for example, identity of bond energies for bonds A-A, B-B, and A-B). Equation (5-9) must in general be replaced by the more general expression

$$\mu_a = \mu_a^0 + RT \ln \gamma_a x_a \quad (5\text{-}10)$$

where γ_a is the "activity coefficient" of component A; $\gamma_a x_a$ is known as the "activity" of A. The activity coefficient is a function of concentration, approaching 1 as x_a approaches zero. Regular solutions are solutions in which the heat of mixing is not zero, but mixing is still random. For regular solutions it can be shown that $RT \ln \gamma_a = \alpha(x_b)^2$, $RT \ln \gamma_b = \alpha(x_a)^2$, where α is proportional to the difference in bond energies $(AA) + (BB) - 2(AB)$, provided this difference is less than kT. Regular solutions are stable only above a certain critical temperature T_C below which they unmix to form two solutions the compositions of which depend on temperature (Figure 5–1). The critical temperature $T_C = \alpha/2R$. Solid solutions of K feldspars and Na feldspars, and of ilmenite–hematite ($FeTiO_3$–Fe_2O_3) show this behavior. In the latter, unmixing together with ordering of iron and titanium atoms in the "exsolved" phases may lead to the interesting phenomenon of self-reversal of the remanent magnetization (see Chapter 13).

A further point must be made regarding the form of equation (5-9). Consider, for instance, a solid solution of the two pyroxene minerals

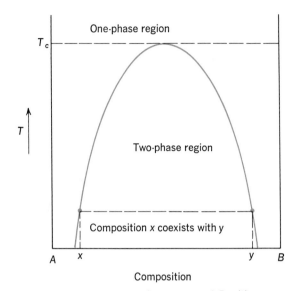

FIG. 5–1   *Phase diagram for a system A-B with nonzero heat of mixing. At high temperatures the positive entropy of mixing leads to complete miscibility, whereas at lower temperatures phase separation occurs.*

jadeite ($NaAlSi_2O_6$) and diopside ($CaMgSi_2O_6$) that occurs in some deep-seated rocks. Random mixing of these two components now implies mixing of *two* ions in each component; in the solid solution both Na and Al are mixed randomly with both Ca and Mg in $4N$ sites; the chemical potential μ_j of jadeite in the solution, assuming it to be ideal, must therefore be written

$$\mu_j = \mu_j^0 + 2RT \ln x_j$$

and similarly for diopside. In general, to apply the solution equations (5-10) or (5-9) to solids a detailed knowledge of site populations is required.

EQUILIBRIUM CONSTANTS   The familiar equilibrium constants, such as solubility products and dissociation constants, used to describe equilibria in solutions arise naturally from the solution equation. Consider, for example, the dissociation of water

$$H_2O = H^+ + OH^-$$
liquid   aqueous   aqueous

and suppose that the dissociation is so limited

---

[7] Noting that $\dfrac{\partial}{\partial n_a} = \dfrac{\partial}{\partial x_a}\dfrac{\partial x_a}{\partial n_a}$.

that the molar fraction of water is essentially 1, while the solution behaves ideally with respect to H+ and OH−. Equilibrium requires that

$$\mu_{H_2O} = \mu_{H^+} + \mu_{OH^-}$$

or, by equation (5-9),

$$\mu_{H_2O}^0 = \mu_H^0 + RT \ln x_{H^+} + \mu_{OH^-}^0 + RT \ln x_{OH^-}$$

Hence

$$RT \ln x_{H^+} x_{OH^-} = \mu_{H_2O}^0 - \mu_{H^+}^0 - \mu_{HO^-}^0 = -\Delta\mu^0$$

say. The terms on the right are constant at constant temperature and pressure; hence,

$$RT \ln x_{H^+} x_{OH^-} = -\Delta\mu^0 \text{ is constant}$$

and

$$x_{H^+} x_{OH^-} = \text{constant at constant } P \text{ and } T$$

DISTRIBUTION COEFFICIENTS Minerals are rarely pure. They generally contain minor amounts of several components. What determines the manner in which such minor components distribute themselves among the several minerals that form a rock?

Let i be a minor component of two minerals α and β assumed to be in equilibrium; thus $\mu_i^\alpha = \mu_i^\beta$. The solution of i in both α and β is supposed to be ideal, which will in general be true because of the small concentration of i. Thus

$$\mu_i = (\mu_i^0)^\alpha + RT \ln x_i^\alpha = (\mu_i^0)^\beta + RT \ln x_i^\beta$$

where $\mu^{0\alpha}$ is the chemical potential of a crystal α consisting of i only; and similarly $\mu_i^{0\beta}$ is the chemical potential of i in form β. Thus the distribution coefficient $D = x_i^\alpha / x_i^\beta$ is simply

$$\ln D = \frac{(\mu_i^0)^\alpha - (\mu_i^0)^\beta}{RT} = \frac{\Delta\mu_i^0}{RT}$$

where $\Delta\mu_i^0$ is the free energy necessary to transform a crystal of pure i from α to form β. If we are considering, for instance, the distribution of Rb in albite (NaAlSi$_3$O$_8$) and orthoclase (KAlSi$_3$O$_8$), $\mu_i^{0\alpha}$ and $\mu_i^{0\beta}$ refer to the free energy per mole of RbAlSi$_3$O$_8$ when it has the crystal structure and unit cell dimensions of albite and orthoclase, respectively. Because the ionic radius of Rb is closer to that of K than to that of

Na, $\Delta\mu_i^0$ will be negative and we expect RB to be more concentrated in orthoclase than in albite. Similarly, the distribution of Rb between orthoclase and mica will be determined by the difference in free energy between pure Rb feldspar and pure Rb mica.

Aqueous Solutions

Practically all mineral reactions in the sedimentary and metamorphic environments occur in an aqueous medium. Since most minerals are inorganic compounds with high degree of polarity in their chemical bonds, they have measurable solubility in water, and water is the common solvent effecting material transport. The nature of solutions at low temperatures is rather well understood; this is not true at elevated temperatures, where so many reactions of geological importance occur. The reasons for this ignorance are in part the difficulty of making many of the simplest physicochemical measurements in water at high pressures and temperatures. Thus measurements of electrical conductivity, optical absorption, electrode potentials, solubility, and so forth, all so fundamental in inorganic chemistry, become increasingly difficult as P and T rise. Part of our problem is simply the lack of suitable containers, for plastics, glass, and even noble metals are destroyed or become too soluble or corroded. Slowly this situation is improving and hard-won data accumulate. As they do, the depth of our understanding of problems such as ore deposition advances rapidly.

WATER

The rather unusual properties of water, such as its large liquid range[8] and high dielectric constant, are related to the ability of water molecules to associate via strong hydrogen bonds (page 70.) The polarity of the water molecule residing in the O-H bonds and the asymmetric lone pairs

---

[8] That is, the large difference between boiling and freezing temperatures.

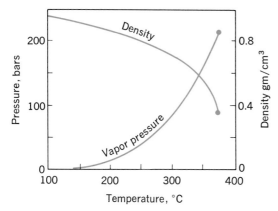

FIG. 5–2 *Variation of the density and vapor pressure of liquid water.*

leads to this bonding and also to the ability of water to interact (solvate) strongly with cations and anions. Without this strong interaction of hydration solubilities would be small, for the solvent–solute forces must compensate for the large binding forces of ionic solids.

Liquid water can exist up to $374.15°C$, where the vapor pressure is 221 bars. This is the so-called critical point of water, beyond which a liquid–vapor boundary is not observed. The vapor pressure and density of liquid water are shown in Figure 5–2.

The patterns of solubility of minerals in water are of two types. The solubility of some solids, like NaCl, increases along the liquid–vapor curve, and critical phenomena disappear. Thus, in the system $NaCl-H_2O$, as long as solid NaCl is present, liquids are observed all the way from the melting point of ice to that of NaCl. The solubility curve is shown in Figure 5–3. Most minerals, however, show the behavior illustrated by the system SiO_2-H_2O. The solubility of quartz decreases along the liquid–vapor curve and approaches zero near the critical point of water which is little disturbed by the presence of quartz. The fact that this critical end point is observed implies that another must be present at the high-temperature end of the system where liquid silica exists. Solubilities in these two regions are shown in Figures 5-4 and 5-5.

Much of the data on aqueous solutions of geologic interest is summarized by Barnes. We should note that many minerals dissolve incongruently; that is, the composition of the solute differs from that of the phase undergoing solution. Albite, for instance, partially dissolves in water by leaving a residue enriched in alumina.

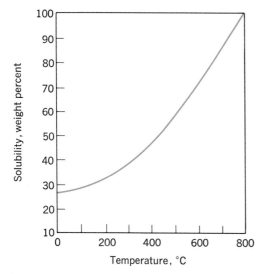

FIG. 5–3 *Temperature variation of the composition of saturated NaCl solutions.*

AQUEOUS SOLUTIONS AT HIGH TEMPERATURE

Our ideas about the properties of simple inorganic aqueous solutions at high temperature tend to be dominated by our knowledge of ionic solutions at ordinary temperature. We know that most simple salts dissolve to produce simple ions, while acids and bases are classified as weak or strong depending on the extent of their dissociation. Do we anticipate that these well-established models will also work at the higher temperatures involved in metamorphic and igneous processes? Whenever we consider the effect of temperature it is well to consider the relevant entropy changes. Some typical values, all for $298°K$, are as follows:

$$\underset{\text{solid}}{NaCl} \rightarrow \underset{\text{aqueous}}{Na^+} + \underset{\text{aqueous}}{Cl^-} \qquad \Delta S^0 = +10.3 \text{ e.u.}$$

$$\underset{\text{gas}}{HCl} \rightarrow \underset{\text{aqueous}}{H^+} + \underset{\text{aqueous}}{Cl^-} \qquad \Delta S^0 = -31.4 \text{ e.u.}$$

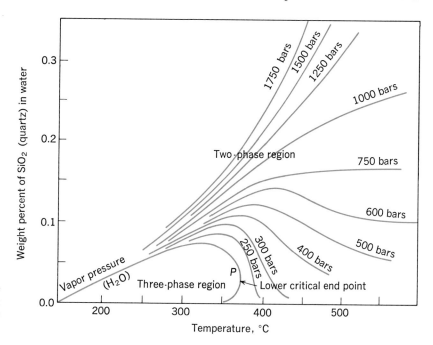

FIG. 5–4 *Isobaric solubility curves of quartz in water at low pressures and temperatures.*

$$\underset{\text{aqueous aqueous}}{HF \rightarrow H^+} + \underset{\text{aqueous}}{F^-} \qquad \Delta S^0 = -28.3 \text{ e.u.}$$

$$\underset{\text{solid}}{CaSO_4} \rightarrow \underset{\text{aqueous}}{Ca^{2+}} + \underset{\text{aqueous}}{SO_4^{2-}} \qquad \Delta S^0 = -34.6 \text{ e.u.}$$

$$\underset{\text{solid}}{Ca_3(PO_4)_2} \rightarrow \underset{\text{aqueous}}{3Ca^{2+}} + \underset{\text{aqueous}}{2PO_4^{3-}}$$

$$\Delta S^0 = -200.0 \text{ e.u.}$$

When these compounds dissociate in water, the energy to disrupt the solid is provided by ion–dipole forces between the water molecules and ions. Thus, while the ions of the solid gain freedom and hence entropy on solution, water molecules become locked to the ions and lose freedom. The more highly charged an ion and the smaller the ion, the more water molecules are likely to be bound. The expected trends are shown clearly in the foregoing figures. In the case of HF, both the proton and fluorine ion react strongly with water molecules and the dissociation process is accompanied by a highly negative ΔS.

If we consider weak acids we see the same trends:

$$\underset{\text{aqueous aqueous}}{HSO_4^- \rightarrow H^+} + \underset{\text{aqueous}}{SO_4^{2-}} \quad \Delta S^0 = -26.2 \text{ e.u.}$$

$$\underset{\text{aqueous aqueous}}{H_2S \rightarrow 2H^+} + \underset{\text{aqueous}}{S^{2-}} \quad \Delta S^0 = -135.6 \text{ e.u.}$$

$$\underset{\text{aqueous aqueous}}{H_2CO_3 \rightarrow 2H^+} + \underset{\text{aqueous}}{CO_3^{2-}} \quad \Delta S^0 = -58.4 \text{ e.u.}$$

Complex ions in water are of two types: those formed from ions and neutral molecules, and those formed from cations and anions.

$$\underset{\text{aqueous aqueous}}{Ag^+ + 2NH_3 \rightarrow} \underset{\text{aqueous}}{Ag(NH_3)_2^+} \quad \Delta S^0 = -12.5 \text{ e.u.}$$

$$\underset{\text{aqueous aqueous}}{Fe^{3+} + Cl^- \rightarrow} \underset{\text{aqueous}}{FeCl^{2+}} \qquad \Delta S^0 = +34.9 \text{ e.u.}$$

$$\underset{\text{aqueous aqueous}}{Hg^{2+} + 4Br^- \rightarrow} \underset{\text{aqueous}}{HgBr_4^{2-}} \qquad \Delta S^0 = +12.2 \text{ e.u.}$$

It is quite normal for neutral molecule complexes to show negative entropies of formation while for cation–anion complexes the entropy change is positive. For the latter the total number of charged species is reduced and, generally, the number of solvating water molecules is also reduced.

We are thus led to suggest that, as tempera-

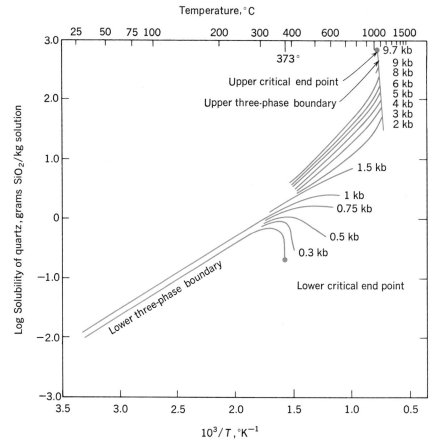

Temperature, °C

FIG. 5–5 *Isobaric solubility curves of quartz in the regions of the two critical points. Note the logarithmic scale of solubility. (After H. L. Barnes.)*

ture is increased, ionization should become less favored, particularly so at high temperature and low pressure, where the solvating water molecules have a much increased entropy compared to ordinary liquid water. We would also anticipate that ion association or complexing might also increase with increasing temperature; in the end, chemistry will become molecular chemistry.

Another important generalization has been made by Brewer: As temperature rises, the complexity of the vapor in equilibrium with a solid increases. At low temperatures, the vapor phase in equilibrium with a solid is generally simple, with only few molecular species present. But as temperature rises, so does the number of different molecules, and it is possible that polymerization also increases. It turns out that the

balance is normally in favor of increased complexity. Thus we expect that high-temperature fluids will be increasingly molecular and that the molecules may become larger as temperature rises.

At present only limited data are available. Tables 5–1 and 5–2 list the data[9] pertaining to the dissociation constants of KCl and HCl which illustrate also the important effect of pressure. The dissociation constant K for KCl describes the equilibrium

$$KCl = K^+ + Cl^-$$

---

[9] From E. U. Franck, *Angewandte Chemie*, vol. 73, 1961, p. 318.

TABLE 5-1   Dissociation constants of KCl

T, °C	Fluid Density, g/cm³		
	0.3	0.5	0.7
	Dissociation Constant K		
450	3.6×10^{-5}	2.8×10^{-3}	4.0×10^{-2}
550	1.0×10^{-5}	1.5×10^{-3}	6.9×10^{-2}
650	6.3×10^{-6}	1.0×10^{-3}	
750	3.7×10^{-6}		

TABLE 5-2   Dissociation constants of HCl

T, °C	Fluid Density, g/cm³		
	0.3	0.5	0.7
	Dissociation Constant K		
400	4.0×10^{-6}	1.1×10^{-4}	7.0×10^{-3}
500	2.7×10^{-6}	6.3×10^{-5}	2.9×10^{-3}
600	1.8×10^{-6}	2.9×10^{-5}	1.0×10^{-3}
700	6.7×10^{-6}	1.4×10^{-5}	

and is given by

$$K = \frac{[K^+][Cl^-]}{[KCl]}$$

where brackets designate concentrations.

A steam density of 0.3 corresponds to a pressure of about 280 bars at 400°C, and of about 1200 bars at 750°C. At 400°C a density of 0.7 corresponds to a pressure of 1000 bars and at 750° a density of 0.5 corresponds to a pressure of 2300 bars. Note that if K is 10^{-4}, then in a solution of KCl of unit molal concentration only 1 percent of the molecules will dissociate to form ions.

The dominance of molecules in high-temperature solutions (particularly those at moderate pressures where the solvent density is much lower than one) leads to much interesting chemistry. For example, reactions such as

$$\underset{\text{solid}}{SiO_2} + \underset{\text{solid}}{2NaCl} + \underset{\text{gas}}{H_2O} \rightarrow \underset{\text{solid}}{Na_2SiO_3} + \underset{\text{gas}}{2HCl}$$

go to completion at low gas pressures and temperatures near 600–700°C. The entropy change of the above reaction is +27 e.u. It will be noted that in this reaction more gas molecules are produced than consumed. Reactions of this type might have some connection with volcanism.

ORE DEPOSITS

A major geological problem is to explain the formation of the relatively large accumulations of nearly insoluble metallic sulfides (Pb, Zn, Cu, and others) that are found, commonly associated with silicates, carbonates, and fluorides, in veins or disseminated patches in country rock surrounding plutonic intrusions. The geological evidence points clearly to an aqueous or hydrothermal origin. However, the solubility product[10] of lead sulfide at room temperature, $K = (Pb^{2+}) (S^{2-})$ is only about 10^{-28}. This means that the number of ions in water in equilibrium with pure PbS is very small indeed. Such low solubilities of many metal sulfides have always raised the important question as to how they can be transported in large quantities in aqueous solutions without the need for gigantic volumes of water. Recently, Hemley, Meyer, Hodgson, and Thatcher have done measurements that may answer the question. They consider the reaction

$$\underset{\text{muscovite}}{KAl_2(AlSi_3O_{10})(OH)_2} + \underset{\text{quartz}}{6SiO_2} + \underset{\text{aq-mol}}{2KCl}$$
$$= \underset{\text{feldspar}}{3KAlSi_3O_8} + \underset{\text{aq-mol}}{2HCl}$$

and show that a significant concentration of HCl is produced by this reaction. This HCl can then react with PbS:

$$\underset{\text{solid}}{PbS} + \underset{\text{aq-mol}}{2HCl} = \underset{\text{aq-mol}}{PbCl_2} + \underset{\text{gas}}{H_2S}$$

Lead chloride is much more soluble than lead sulfide and high concentrations (0.1 molal) of dissolved lead have been measured at temperatures near 500°C and pressures of 1000 bars. The association of metallic sulfide, common silicate minerals, and an alkali halide solution is by no means geologically unusual. Fluid inclusions in

---

[10] The solubility product of a compound is the product of the concentrations (or activities) of its constituent ions in a saturated aqueous solution (see Chapter 8).

minerals commonly contain quite large amounts of halides. Helgeson, using a computer to calculate equilibria involving thirteen species in $NaCl$–HCl–H_2O solutions in equilibrium with galena up to 350°C, has shown that enough lead can be carried by these solutions (from 1 to 600 ppm) to account for hydrothermal ore deposits. The important complexes are $PbCl^+$, $PbCl_4^{2-}$, H_2S, HCl, and $NaCl$.

Equilibrium in Multiphase Assemblages

We now turn to a consideration of some rules governing equilibrium between two or more phases. This includes such geologically relevant topics as phase transformations (for example, graphite–diamond), melting in multicomponent systems (for example, crystallization of a magma), and the varied mineral assemblages found in metamorphic rocks. Two simple thermodynamics rules—the phase rule and the Clausius-Clapeyron equation—can often be usefully applied.

THE PHASE RULE

When examining an assemblage of minerals, as in metamorphic rocks, the question arises as to whether these mineral phases are in mutual equilibrium. The converse problem also occurs: Given the chemical composition of a system, how many phases could be present at equilibrium? The phase rule gives a partial answer to such questions.

Imagine a system of n components or chemical species, somehow distributed among ϕ phases labeled α, β, $\cdots$, ϕ. Let R be the number of possible chemical reactions among the n species.

The phase rule, to be presently derived, states the number of intensive variables that can be fixed arbitrarily in a system in equilibrium; this number is called the variance of the system. Intensive variables, such as pressure, temperature, and the variables describing the composition of each phase, are independent of the quantities of the various phases.

The composition of a phase is adequately described by the mole fraction of each species or component in that phase. Since the sum of the mole fractions must necessarily equal 1, there are $(n - 1)$ compositional variables for each phase. The total number of these variables is thus $\phi(n - 1)$.

If the system is in equilibrium, temperature must be uniform throughout. Otherwise heat would flow from hotter points to colder points with attending increase in entropy, and properties of the system would not be independent of time. Thus one variable suffices to describe the temperature.

Generally one variable will suffice to describe the pressure; for if pressure is not uniform matter will flow (again producing entropy), unless the system has sufficient mechanical strength. In some natural systems (for example metamorphic rocks) all phases need not necessarily be at the same pressure; it is conceivable, for instance, that the fluid—mainly water—that fills interstices in the rock may be at a lower pressure than the solid phases themselves (see Chapter 10). For the moment we shall consider only one pressure variable. The total number of variables is thus $\phi(n - 1) + 2$.

For the system to be in equilibrium, the chemical potential of each species i must be the same in all phases, hence

$$\mu_i^\alpha = \mu_i^\beta = \cdots = \mu_i^\phi \qquad (i = 1 \cdots n)$$

a total of $n(\phi - 1)$ relations. If R distinct reactions can occur, R additional conditions are necessary to prescribe equilibrium.

The variance, or number of degrees of freedom f of the system, is the difference between the number of variables and the number of relations between them

$$f = \phi(n - 1) + 2 - [n(\phi - 1) + R]$$
$$= n - R - \phi + 2 \qquad (5\text{-}11)$$

If $f = 0$, there are just as many variables as equations relating them; it is then theoretically possible to solve the equations and calculate the value of each of the variables. If $f < 0$, there are more equations than variables. The equations cannot, in general, be satisfied and the system cannot be presumed to be in equilibrium. If $f = +1$, one variable can be chosen arbitrarily;

all other variables will then be determined from the conditions for equilibrium. Equilibrium is still possible for any value of this variable.

The number 2 that appears in equation (5-11) is, as will be recalled, somewhat arbitrary, since it applies only to cases in which one pressure variable suffices to describe the mechanical condition of the system. If other variables (electric or magnetic field, surface tension, and so forth) were involved, or if the system were closed—that is, if the mass of each component were specified and constant—the phase rule (5-11) would take a different form. The present form is valid even if some components (for example, n_j) are totally insoluble in some phases (for example, phase γ), since the number of variables is reduced ($n_j^\gamma = 0$) by the same number as the equilibrium relations regarding equality of chemical potential.

The number $n - R$ is commonly called c, the number of *independent* chemical components.

Let us see how the rule works. If the system under consideration consists only of albite ($NaAlSi_3O_8$), $n = 1$, $R = 0$, $c = 1$, $\phi = 1$, and $f = 2$. Albite may be presumed to be stable over a range of pressures and temperatures. Next imagine that albite is in equilibrium with a liquid of the same composition. Again $c = 1$, but $\phi = 2$, and $f = 1$ (systems for which $f = 1$ are said to be univariant). Thus only one variable, pressure or temperature, may be chosen arbitrarily and that choice determines the other variable. On a diagram where P and T are the abscissa and ordinate, respectively, a univariant equilibrium is represented by a single curve, the locus of all values of P and T consistent with equilibrium. This curve divides the PT plane into two fields in which solid and liquid albite, respectively, may exist.

The albite–quartz–jadeite system has $n = 3$, but $R = 1$ because of the possible reaction

$$NaAlSi_2O_6 + SiO_2 = NaAlSi_3O_8$$
$$\text{jadeite} \quad \text{quartz} \quad \text{albite}$$

hence $c = 2$ and $f = 1$ as before. This univariant equilibrium can, as the melting of albite, be represented by a curve describing the equilibrium temperature as a function of pressure (or equilibrium pressure as a function of temperature).

Clearly, in a one-component system, not more than three phases can coexist. They will coexist at a definite P and T (triple point).

A simplified form of equation (5-11) may be used to find the variance of a given assemblage of phases of known and fixed composition. Since the composition of each phase is fixed, there are no compositional variables, and the total number of variables is reduced to two. The number R of relations between them is the number of equilibrium conditions relating the free energies of the phases; this number is equal to the number of possible chemical reactions between them. Thus, simply

$$f = 2 - R$$

which is the same as (5-11) if we define each phase as a "component" and set accordingly $n = \phi$.

To illustrate, consider the assemblage solid and liquid plagioclase. No relation can be written between the free energies of the two phases except at singular points where the free energies and compositions of the two phases are equal (for instance, point E in Figure 6–4a). Thus $f = 2$, except at singular points where $f = 1$. Or consider the mineral assemblage forsterite–calcite–dolomite–diopside–CO_2 (gas). There is one relation expressing equilibrium for the reaction

$$CaMgSi_2O_6 + 3[CaMg(CO)_3]_2 = 4CaCO$$
$$\text{diopside} \qquad \text{dolomite} \qquad \text{calcite}$$
$$+ 2Mg_2SiO_4 + 2CO_2$$
$$\text{forsterite} \qquad \text{gas}$$

and $f = 1$, as predicted from (5-11) with $n = c = 4$ (CaO, MgO, SiO_2, CO_2), and $\phi = 5$.

The phase rule does not predict how many phases will be present in a system of given composition; it merely states the maximum number of phases that could be present at equilibrium. It can be used to prove disequilibrium, as when $f < 0$, but it is not sufficient to prove equilibrium.

Since pressure and temperature are subject to change with time, particularly in the metamorphic environment, it is unlikely that we would ever find assemblages of variance zero, as they would have to develop at precisely fixed values of P and T; any further change in these variables would destroy the assemblage. We thus expect to find in rocks mostly assemblages for which f is at least equal to 2. Assemblages with $f = 1$ or $f = 0$ *might* therefore indicate disequilibrium. We emphasize the italicized word.

THE CLAUSIUS-CLAPEYRON EQUATION

The Clausius-Clapeyron equation gives the relation between pressure of and temperature in univariant equilibria (melting, phase transformations, and so forth). It follows directly from equation (5-3). If two or more phases are initially in equilibrium, $\Delta G = 0$. If they are to remain in equilibrium when the pressure is changed, the temperature must also change so that ΔG remains zero; hence $d(\Delta G) = 0$ and, by (5-3),

$$\frac{dT}{dP} = \frac{\Delta V}{\Delta S} \tag{5-12}$$

In many phase transformations of geological interest, ΔV and ΔS have the same sign,[11] so that melting points or transformation points generally rise with increasing pressure. In transformation involving only solid phases (for instance, quartz–coesite, or kyanite–sillimanite), dT/dP is commonly between 10 and 30 degrees per kilobar at low pressures. The relation is not exactly linear, because ΔV and ΔS both depend on T and P, and the slope of the equilibrium curve tends, at least in the case of melting, to decrease with increasing pressure.

MELTING IN MULTICOMPONENT SYSTEMS

Because of the obvious importance of melting phenomena in the generation and crystallization of magma, we consider melting in some detail, starting with a two-component system of components A and B.

EUTECTIC BEHAVIOR   Suppose first that solids A and B are mutually insoluble, so that the only

solid phases to be considered are pure A and pure B. Suppose further that liquids A and B mix in all proportions to form ideal solutions (no heat of mixing). The superscript l refers to the liquid phase and s refers to the solid phase. A subscript o refers to a pure phase, a subscript m to the melting temperature of a pure phase.

We start with pure A at its melting point T_m. Thus,

$$\mu_{a,o,m}^l = \mu_{a,o,m}^s \tag{5-13}$$

We now add some B to the liquid, the mole fraction of A in the liquid dropping from 1 to x_a. The chemical potential of A in the liquid is now, by (5-9),

$$\mu_a^l = \mu_{a,o}^l + RT_m \ln x_a$$

and is less than $\mu_{a,o}^l$ since $x_a \leq 1$. The liquid is no longer in equilibrium with the solid; to restore equilibrium the temperature must be lowered to a value $T(T \leq T_m)$ which we proceed to calculate, assuming that the entropy of melting of A is independent of temperature, which is not quite correct.

At temperature T, the potential of solid A is

$$\mu_{a,o}^s = \mu_{a,o,m}^s + S_a^s(T_m - T)$$

The chemical potential in the liquid is, at this temperature

$$\mu_a^l = \mu_{a,o}^l + RT \ln x_a$$
$$= \mu_{a,o,m}^l + S_a^l(T_m - T) + RT \ln x_a$$

Equating the two, and using (5-13), we obtain

$$S_a^s(T_m - T) = S_a^l(T_m - T) + RT \ln x_a$$

or, setting $S_a^l - S_a^s = \Delta S_a$ (the entropy of melting of pure A),

$$\ln \frac{1}{x_a} = \frac{1}{RT} \Delta S_a(T_m - T) = \frac{\Delta S_a}{R} \left(\frac{T_m}{T} - 1 \right) \tag{5-14}$$

which gives the composition of the liquid in equilibrium with pure solid A at any temperature $T \leq T_m$. Conversely,

$$T = \frac{T_m}{1 - (R/\Delta S_a) \ln x_a}$$

A similar relation is found for B (note that

---

[11]There are notable exceptions to this statement, such as the melting of ice, or of granite or basalt in the presence of enough water to saturate the liquid.

$x_b = 1 - x_a$). The two curves showing, respectively, the temperature of melting of A and B as a function of the composition of the liquid can be drawn (Figure 6–1). They are found to intersect at a point, representing the eutectic composition and eutectic temperature. Below this temperature, no liquid can exist in this system at the pressure (assumed to constant) considered. Conversely, the first liquid to form when a mixture of A and B is heated, or the last liquid to crystallize when a melt is cooled, will invariably have the eutectic composition.

It is clear from equation (5-14) that if the entropy of melting is small, x_a will be large for a given T/T_m and the eutectic composition will be rich in A. This is why silica, which has a high melting point but a small entropy of melting, becomes concentrated in the last liquid to crystallize. The petrological implications will be further discussed in Chapter 6.

SOLID SOLUTIONS   If A and B are mutually soluble, a different behavior is observed. The solid-liquid equilibrium can still be treated as we have just done, but the notation becomes cumbersome and the derivation will not be given here.[12] If both liquid and solid solutions are ideal, the result is

$$x_a^l = \frac{e^{\lambda_b} - 1}{e^{\lambda_b} - e^{-\lambda_a}} \quad x_a^s = \frac{e^{\lambda_b} - 1}{e^{\lambda_a + \lambda_b} - 1} \quad (5\text{-}15)$$

where

$$\lambda_b = \frac{\Delta S_b}{R}\left(\frac{T_{m,b}}{T} - 1\right) \text{ and } \lambda_a = \frac{\Delta S_a}{R}\left(1 - \frac{T_{m,a}}{T}\right)$$

The "solidus" (beginning of melting) and "liquidus" (end of melting) curves are shown in Figure 6–3. A melting diagram for a system with limited solubility of the solids is shown in Figure 6–4b.

INCONGRUENT MELTING   Suppose that two components A and B form an addition compound

---

[12] It may be found in I. Prigogine and R. Defay, *Chemical Thermodynamics* (Longmans Green & Co., New York, 1954, p. 368).

AB, as when SiO_2 and MgO combine to form enstatite ($MgSiO_3$), a substance with well-defined properties that is not just a solid solution of A and B. It may happen that the temperatures and entropies of melting of A and B are such that the melting curve lies above the melting point of AB, where by "melting point of AB" we mean the temperature at which AB would be in equilibrium with a liquid of the same composition. AB will then be observed to melt "incongruently"— that is, it will decompose or "disproportionate" to form a new solid and a liquid of different composition.

In the system SiO_2–MgO two addition compounds exist: forsterite (Mg_2SiO_4) and enstatite ($MgSiO_3$). The latter melts incongruently to form forsterite + liquid enriched in SiO_2 (Figure 6–7). Conversely, when an enstatite melt cools, forsterite forms first at the temperature T. At T_i the incongruent melting point of enstatite, solid forsterite reacts with the liquid to form enstatite. If the liquid is initially more siliceous than enstatite, crystallization will continue beyond T_i to the eutectic T_E, where enstatite and silica crystallize together.

Orthoclase melts incongruently to form leucite ($KAlSi_2O_6$) + liquid. As in the case of enstatite, melting becomes congruent at high pressure. Incongruent melting plays an important role in the crystallization of some igneous rocks (Chapter 6).

MULTICOMPONENT SYSTEMS   Calculations and the graphical representation of experimental data become rather complicated in nonideal systems of three or more components; but here also considerable progress has recently been made. In such complex cases, the liquid is generally considered to have a definite structure with certain numbers of cation and anion sites. To this liquid "lattice" can be applied the statistical mixing treatment, adding parameters where needed to describe nonideal behavior. A fast computer is necessary to carry out the calculations which are based essentially on the observed behavior of all the relevant binary systems (say A-B, A-C, A-D, B-C, B-D, and C-D, in the quaternary system A-B-C-D). Blander has achieved considerable success in this endeavor, and the day may not be far away when it will be possible to predict the melting behavior of multicomponent petrological systems, such as a magma.

Stability

It is important to keep in mind the distinction between equilibrium and stability.

Equilibrium describes the condition under which the driving force of a reaction or transformation is zero. This driving force, as we recall, depends on the conditions imposed on the system. If the system is held at constant volume and entropy, the driving force for a reaction is the change in internal energy ΔU accompanying the reaction; for constant T and P the driving force is the free-energy change ΔG; and so on. If the system is in equilibrium, nothing happens.

Equilibrium, however, is not necessarily stable. One is reminded here of the analogy of a rounded stone on the top of a hill. Although the stone is initially motionless (in equilibrium), the slightest disturbance will send it tumbling down the hill. The stone is said to be in unstable equilibrium.

A system is said to be stable if any disturbance of external or internal origin (for example, a random fluctuation) will disappear in time, while the system returns spontaneously to its initial configuration.

There is no general criterion of stability covering all possible transformations that could occur in a system; a system may be stable with respect to one reaction, yet unstable with respect to another reaction. At room temperature, quartz is stable with respect to any polymorphic transformation; however, it is unstable with respect to solution in hydrofluoric acid.

A useful distinction can be made between states that differ only infinitesimally from the initial state and states that differ by finite amounts. The former are called "adjacent states." For a solution, for instance, an adjacent state may correspond to an infinitesimal change in composition. A crystal at its melting point and the melt do not constitute adjacent states, since their entropies, volumes, and so forth, differ by finite amounts.

A phase of given composition is said to be unstable if any perturbation leading to either adjacent or nonadjacent states will continue to grow with time. At constant P and T, this statement implies that the free energy of the phase is greater than that of other phases that differ only infinitesimally from it. The phase is *metastable* if its free energy is less than that of any adjacent state, but greater than that of some other nonadjacent phase. The phase is stable if its free energy is less than that of any other possible phase or phases. A stone at the top of a hill is unstable. A stone at the bottom of the valley is stable. A stone at the bottom of a hole halfway up the hill is metastable, for although it will return to its position at the bottom of the hole for any infinitesimal displacement, a sufficiently large thrust out of the hole will send it tumbling down. An undercooled liquid is metastable, for although it is stable with respect to any adjacent state, a disturbance such as the introduction of a nucleus or "germ" of the solid phase will cause it to crystallize. In mathematical language, stability and metastability both require that the free energy be minimum for given P and T. In the first case, the minimum is absolute; in the second case it is a relative or "local" minimum. We note that the conditions for stability depend on the external constraints. For a system at constant volume and energy, stability requires that the entropy be maximum. For a single phase, stability with respect to thermal perturbations requires that the specific heat at constant volume be positive. Otherwise, an infinitesimal fluctuation bringing heat from A to B would cause B to cool and A to warm up, thereby causing more heat to flow from A to B; the perturbation would thus increase with time. It can be shown that mechanical stability requires that $(\partial V/\partial P)_T$ be negative. Stability with respect to composition of a solution requires that $(\partial \mu_i / \partial x_i)_{P,T}$ be positive for all components of the solution; if this condition is not met, different components will diffuse in different directions and the solution will split up into two or more phases of different composition. Unmixing, as in regular solutions (page 242) occurs when the composition and temperature are such that this condition ceases to be satisfied.

Most minerals and mineral assemblages at the surface of the earth, and particularly metamorphic rocks, are metastable. Many are unstable with respect to chemical reactions with the atmosphere.

Kinetics

Even though minerals and rocks may have formed at, or near, equilibrium, many of them are not in equilibrium under the conditions prevailing now where we see them. Magnetite (Fe_3O_4), a common mineral, should react with oxygen in the atmosphere to form hematite (Fe_2O_3). Diamond is unstable with respect to its less dense polymorph graphite, and sillimanite should transform to kyanite. Many metamorphic rocks should revert to their premetamorphic form. High-temperature and high-pressure minerals occur and survive on the surface of the earth only because the reactions by which they should revert to their more stable form are extremely slow. The variety of rocks found at the surface of the earth, and our understanding of the geological processes by which they form, owe much to this slowness.

RATES OF REACTION

Reaction rates, as rates of transport in general (electrical conductivity, viscous flow, diffusion, and so forth), are found to depend exponentially on temperature, the rate K being of the general form

$$K = K_0 e^{-E/RT}$$

where K_0 and E are constants.[13] The form of this relation suggests that the term $e^{-E/RT}$ is a Boltzmann factor (page 240), controlling the number of particles—molecules, ions, electrons, and so on— that have the required energy E to participate in

the process; this energy is called the activation energy. In the comparatively simple process of diffusion in an ionic solid, for instance, the activation energy of a diffusing ion is the energy that an ion must have to leave its initial lattice position and squeeze through the energy barrier formed by the ions that immediately surround and repel it when it approaches too closely. A reaction rate will thus depend on (1) the number of ions, atoms, or molecules that at any time have the required excess energy, and (2) the rate at which these activated particles actually move across the energy barrier. The latter term turns out to be approximately of the form kT/h, where k and h are, respectively, Boltzmann's and Planck's constants (note that the ratio kT/h has the dimension of a frequency). A reaction rate can then be expressed in the general form

$$K = \frac{kT}{h} K^*$$

where K^* measures the concentration of activated ions. Eyring's theory of absolute reaction rates starts from the premise that K^* is determined, as in ordinary chemical equilibrium, by the "free energy of activation" ΔG^*

$$RT \ln K^* = -\Delta G^*$$

where ΔG^* is defined as the difference in molar free energy between activated ions and ions in their equilibrium lattice position or, more generally, in their initial state.

ΔG^* itself can be split into three terms:

$$\Delta G^* = \Delta E^* - T\Delta S^* + P\Delta V^*$$

where ΔS^* and ΔV^* are, respectively, the activation entropy and activation volume. Thus

$$K = \frac{kT}{h}\left(\exp \frac{\Delta S^*}{R}\right)\left(\exp \frac{-\Delta E^*}{RT}\right)\left(\exp \frac{-P\Delta V^*}{RT}\right)$$

$$(5\text{-}16)$$

The precise meaning of ΔS^* is not always clear. For a diffusing ion it would presumably correspond to the additional translational degree of freedom that the ion must acquire to move through the crystal. If the assumption is made that the sign of ΔS^* is the same as the sign of ΔS, the entropy change of the reaction itself, equa-

---

[13] The factor R appears when E represents energy per mole; when E is energy per particle, the appropriate factor is k, the Boltzmann constant.

tion (5-16), explains why reactions are usually much faster in the direction in which entropy increases (for example, melting or vaporization) than in the opposite sense (crystallization or condensation).

HOMOGENEOUS SYSTEMS   The rate of a chemical reaction occurring in a single homogeneous phase (for example, an aqueous solution) can generally (but not invariably) be described by an equation of the form

$$\frac{dc_a}{dt} = Kc_b^m c_c^n \cdots$$

where c_a, c_b, c_c are concentrations of various chemical species, m and n are small numbers, and K is a "rate constant" that depends exponentially on temperature and also on the nature of the solvent. Its value could be given by an expression of the type of equation (5-16).

The same type of equation can be applied to heterogeneous reactions (those involving several phases) taking place through the medium of a solution. Thus when aragonite ($CaCO_3$) transforms at $100°C$ to calcite ($CaCO_3$) by dissolving in an aqueous solution from which the more stable calcite then precipitates, the rate of transformation is found to be proportional to the product of the concentrations of Ca^{2+} and $(HCO_3)^-$ ions in the solution.

HETEROGENEOUS SYSTEMS   Heterogeneous reactions involving two or more phases generally consist of several distinct steps. When magnetite reacts with oxygen gas, the rate of formation of hematite will depend on (1) the rate at which oxygen molecules hit the surface, (2) the rate at which O_2 molecules break up, (3) the rate at which oxygen attaches itself to iron on the surface, with attendant exchange of electrons, and (4) the rate at which either atomic oxygen diffuses inward, or Fe ions diffuse outward, from the crystal undergoing oxidation. The overall rate of reaction is controlled, of course, by the rate of the *slowest* step.

DIFFUSION   Diffusion in solids is commonly a slow rate-controlling step. Diffusion rates are described by means of a diffusion coefficient D defined by[14]

$$\mathbf{q}_i = -D \operatorname{grad} a_i \qquad (5\text{-}17)$$

where $\mathbf{q}_i$ is the flow of diffusing particles of type i crossing a unit surface in unit time (for example, moles per square centimeter per second) and a_i is the activity of i, or its concentration if i forms an ideal solution in the medium through which it diffuses. The minus sign in equation (5-17) reminds us that flow is from regions of high activity to regions of low activity. D, being the ratio of two vectors, is itself a tensor (see page 95), its value depending generally on the particular direction in the crystal in which diffusion takes place. As usual, D depends on temperature as

$$D = D_0 e^{-E/RT}$$

Activation energies for diffusion in silicates are usually in the range 20–100 kcal/mole, or 1.4 to 7×10^{-12} erg/atom (1 to 5 electronvolts). The activation energy generally increases with increasing size and charge of the diffusing ion. In many silicates, diffusion coefficients commonly fall in the range of 10^{-20} to 10^{-6} cm² sec⁻¹ between 500° and 1000°C. Thus diffusion through solids is slow and will rarely account for transfer of matter over distances of more than a few centimeters. We commonly find zoned crystals of garnet, plagioclase, and so on, a millimeter or less in size, in which concentration gradients have survived for millions of years.

NUCLEATION   When a new phase forms—say, by precipitation from a saturated solution—a certain number of molecules of the solute must assemble in a suitable configuration to form a nu-

---

[14] Note the similarity of this equation to the equation of heat conduction (2-12). If the number of diffusing particles is conserved, div $q_i = 0$, and concentration obeys an equation of exactly the same form as for temperature, equation (12-3),

$$\frac{\partial c}{\partial t} = D \frac{\partial^2 c}{\partial x^2}$$

for one-dimensional flow. Thus the time required for a change in concentration increases as the square of the distance over which diffusion occurs and varies inversely as the diffusion constant.

cleus of the new phase. However, because of surface tension, the free energy of a mole of matter in the form of small grains of radius r exceeds that of the same matter in bulk by the amount $\Delta G_\sigma = 2\sigma V/r$, where V is the molar volume. The term $2\sigma V$ is commonly of the order of 10^{-4} to 10^{-2} cal cm/mole, so that if r is, say, 10^{-6} cm, ΔG_σ is important. To form a nucleus, the parent solution must necessarily be supersaturated; otherwise small nuclei would redissolve in it (because of their excess free energy) as fast as they form. A nucleus that forms when a sufficient number of molecules of solute accidentally come together has a short lifetime; it will continue to exist only if it succeeds against heavy odds in growing to the critical size, at which its tendency to redissolve vanishes.[15] The formation of such critical clusters is a rare event and nucleation is a comparatively slow process, as attested by the common occurrence in volcanic rocks of glass that has failed to crystallize. The survival at the surface of the earth of unstable polymorphs (for example, sillimanite and cristobalite) may be due to the slow nucleation rate of the stable form. Relative rates of nucleation probably also account for the commonly observed appearance of phases in a PT field where they are metastable with respect to some other phase. For instance, cristobalite, a high-temperature form of silica, forms more rapidly from solution or from amorphous silica than quartz, even in the temperature range where quartz is stable. Cristobalite may then slowly transform to quartz; in laboratory experiments the transformation often occurs through an intermediate step of another metastable polymorph, silica-K, which is unknown in nature.

POLYMORPHIC TRANSFORMATIONS   Polymorphic transformations are generally slow, except for the so-called "displacive" transformations. In a displacive transformation (for example, the α-β transition in quartz) there is no change in coordination number but only relatively small changes in bond lengths and bond angles. No diffusion is involved, and the surface energy at the interface of the two phases is presumably small, so that nucleation presents no special difficulty. Displacive transitions are fast and reversible. In a sense, one can picture the original crystal as simply "vibrating itself" into the new form.

An example of polymorphic transformation of great geological interest is the calcite–aragonite transformation. Calcite is stable under surface conditions; aragonite, being denser than calcite, becomes stable above 3.4 kilobars at 0°C, the slope of the univariant curve being 16.6 bars per degree C. In oceanic sediments both forms are commonly present and marine organisms may secrete either form or both. In wet sediments, aragonite is rapidly converted to calcite except if protected by an organic membrane such as marine animals secrete to prevent re-solution of their shells. Experimental studies show that it is easy to synthesize either form in aqueous solutions at low pressure; high calcium and bicarbonate concentrations favor calcite, whereas a high concentration of magnesium favors aragonite. In the dry state, the transformation is slow but can be observed around 400°C; in a single crystal of aragonite it is seen to involve a nucleation step followed by a slow migration into the aragonite crystal of the boundary between it and the newly formed calcite. The activation energy is of the order of 60 kcal/mole, which implies that the transformation, which occurs in hours or days at 400°C, would require thousands of years at or below 200°C.

Aragonite forms, and is preserved, in some metamorphic rocks (see page 576) that have, as indicated by their mineralogy, been subjected to pressures of the order of several kilobars; such pressures presumably result from depth of burial. Imagine now (Figure 5–6) calcite-bearing sediments being gradually buried and reaching a depth where aragonite will form. Later uplift or erosion slowly brings these rocks back to the surface while preserving aragonite, which we now find in them. At no time during the upward movement can these rocks have been exposed to temperatures much above 200°C at depths

---

[15] The critical radius r_c is such that $2\sigma V/r_c$ equals the difference in chemical potential between the solute in the supersaturated solution and in solid form.

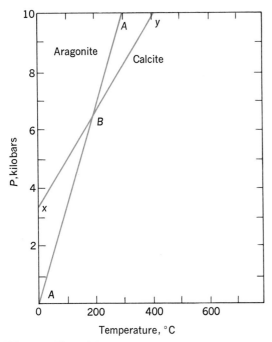

FIG. 5–6 *The calcite-aragonite phase diagram showing the line of equilibrium (xy) and a PT curve corresponding to a crustal thermal gradient of about 10° C/km.*

where calcite is the stable form. The pressure corresponding to 200°C on the univariant curve is 6.7 kb (point *B*). Since 1 kb in crustal rocks corresponds to a depth of roughly 3.3 km, it can be inferred that the temperature did not increase with depth at a rate much greater than about $(200/6.7) \times 3.3 \approx 10°C/km$ (it normally increases much faster than this; see Chapter 12). It is interesting that kinetic considerations may shed light on thermal and tectonic processes.

Irreversible Processes

In the preceding pages, we have considered mainly conditions of chemical equilibrium. Equilibrium implies, as we have noted earlier, a constancy of entropy which must, in fact, be maximum for given *E* and *V*. Equilibrium conditions cannot apply therefore to systems in which an irreversible process, with attendant increase in entropy, is taking place. Heat transfer in a tem-

perature gradient, or material diffusion in a concentration gradient, are examples of irreversible processes. Deductions drawn from equilibrium conditions can still be useful where gradients (of temperature or concentration) are small; a geothermal gradient of 20°/km corresponds in the laboratory to a difference in temperature of only 0.002° between top and bottom of a vessel 10 cm high. Yet, on the scale of the earth, irreversible processes must be important.

All that classical thermodynamics has to say on the matter is that in an irreversible process $dS > dQ/T$. In an isolated system for which the heat dQ exchanged with the surroundings is zero, $dS > 0$. This is an inequality, not an equality; it says nothing of the actual magnitude of dS except that it is positive and larger than the minimum dQ/T corresponding to equilibrium. To deal with irreversible processes it is thus necessary to extend the laws of thermodynamics. A useful additional principle has been proposed: It states that the steady state of a system in which an irreversible process (for example, heat conduction) is taking place is such that the rate of entropy production has the minimum value consistent with external constraints which prevent the system from reaching equilibrium (for example, the temperature differences which are maintained between points in the system).

Without entering into a discussion of the deductions that can be drawn from this and other principles of irreversible thermodynamics it may suffice to state that it leads in a particular case to an important geochemical result: A steady temperature gradient imposed on a solution will generally result in a concentration gradient, and vice versa. This is known as the Soret effect, which is in some ways comparable to the concentration gradient induced by a gravitational field, except that the latter represents an equilibrium state; furthermore, gravity does not displace chemical equilibrium for a reaction in which mass is conserved, while temperature does displace equilibrium in all reactions in which entropy does not remain constant. Thus both gravity and temperature gradients tend to destroy any uniformity in composition that might otherwise exist. We recall that transport of heat is used in the chemical industry in purification processes as, for instance, the separation of isotopes, or the growth of large synthetic crystals of quartz from a hydrothermal solution in which a temperature gradient is maintained.

The theory of the Soret effect is difficult to follow and will not be considered here,[16] except

to mention that in a binary solution in a steady state, the concentration c_1 of component 1 must obey the relation

$$[c_1(1 - c_1)]^{-1} \operatorname{grad} c_1 = -s \operatorname{grad} T$$

where s, the "Soret coefficient," depends on both the material and the thermal diffusion coefficients in the solution. We know of no experimental determination of s in silicate melts. Note that the Soret effect entails an inverse Dufour effect, by which a concentration gradient produces a temperature gradient.

---

[16] It can be found in *Thermodynamics of Irreversible Processes* by S. R. DeGroot (North-Holland Publishing Co., Amsterdam, 1951).

REFERENCES

There are innumerable good books on chemical thermodynamics. A standard text is **G. N. Lewis** and **M. Randall**, *Thermodynamics*, (2d ed., revised by **K. S. Pitzer** and **L. Brewer** (McGraw-Hill, New York, 1961). We also like **K. Denbigh**, *The Principles of Chemical Equilibrium*, (Cambridge University Press, 1957), **E. A. Guggenheim**, *Modern Thermodynamics by the Method of J. W. Gibbs* (Methuen, London, 1933) and *Chemical Thermodynamics* by **I. Prigogine** and **R. Defay** (Longmans, Green & Co., New York, 1954). *Thermodynamics for Geologists* by **R. Kern** and **A. Weisbrod** (Freeman, Cooper and Co., San Francisco, 1967) contains numerous examples of calculations. An Introduction to the subject may be found in Chapters 2, 14, and 17 of **J. F. Turner** and **J. Verhoogen**, *Igneous and Metamorphic Petrology* (2d ed., McGraw-Hill, New York, 1960) and in *Metamorphic Reactions and Metamorphic Facies* by **W. S. Fyfe, F. J. Turner,** and **J. Verhoogen** (Geol. Soc. Am. Memoir 73, 1958), particularly Chapters 2 and 3. *Introduction to Geochemistry*, by **K. Krauskopf** (McGraw-Hill, New York, 1967), and *Principles of Geochemistry*, by **B. Mason** (3d ed., Wiley, New York, 1965) are also very useful.

The Berkeley Physics Course, vol. 5, *Statistical Physics*, by **F. Reif** (McGraw-Hill, New York, 1965) provides an excellent introduction to the statistical description of entropy.

Numerical data are to be found in the *Handbook of Physical Constants*, edited by **S. P. Clark** (Geol. Soc. Am. Memoir 97, 1966), and in **R. A. Robie** and **D. R. Waldbaum**, "Thermodynamic properties of minerals and related substances at 298.15°K (25°C) and one atmosphere (1.013 bars) pressure and at higher temperatures" (*U. S. Geol. Survey Bull. 1259*, 1968).

The theory of reaction rates mentioned on page 253 is developed in *The Theory of Rate Processes*, by **S. Glasstone, K. J. Laidler,** and **H. Eyring** (McGraw-Hill, New York, 1941).

The following works are also recommended:

Barnes, H. L.: *Geochemistry of Hydrothermal Ore Deposits*, Holt, Rinehart and Winston, Inc., New York, 1967.

Bischoff, J. L. and **W. S. Fyfe:** Catalysis inhibition and the calcite—aragonite Problem, *Am. J. Sci.*, vol. 266, pp. 65–79, 1968.

Blander, M.: The topology of phase diagrams of ternary molten salt systems, *Chem. Geol.*, vol. 3, pp. 33–58, 1968.

Brewer, L.: Undiscovered compounds, *J. Chem. Educ.*, vol. 35, pp. 153–156, 1958.

Helgeson, H. C.: *Complexing and Hydrothermal Ore Deposition*, Pergamon Press, Oxford, 1964.

Hemley, J. J., C. Meyer, C. J. Hodgson, and **A. B. Thacher:** Sulfide solubilities in alteration-controlled systems, *Science*, vol. 158, p. 1580, 1967.

Strickland-Constable, R. F.: *Kinetics and Mechanism of Crystallization*, Academic Press, New York, 1968.

6
IGNEOUS PHENOMENA AND PRODUCTS

THE EARTH'S CRUST is primarily the product of repeated volcanism and plutonism. Plutonic rocks of the granite family outcrop continuously over areas of thousands of square kilometers in continental shields. The products of more recent episodes of eruption and intrusion, though local and intermittent, collectively amount to an impressive contribution to a still growing crust. To take a single instance, over half a million cubic kilometers of basaltic lava were poured out in southern Brazil and adjoining states in early Cretaceous times; and most of this was erupted in the relatively short span of 10 million years (130–120 m.y. ago). This was no unique phenomenon, for similar lavas flooded the Deccan plateau of India in Cretaceous times, and large parts of Idaho, Washington, and Oregon during the Tertiary, in each case on a similar grand scale. The Andean geosyncline of northern and central Chile, 3000 km long and 150–200 km wide, is filled with a great stratigraphic thickness (at least 35 km) of Jurassic and Cretaceous rocks, predominantly lavas of intermediate silica content called andesites, and acid pyroclastics.

Of igneous processes we know less than we do of the products—igneous rocks. Plutonism doubtless operates today as in the past at more or less random sites, some of which presumably are located in the depths below surface zones of re-

cent volcanic and seismic activity. But they are inaccessible to direct observation. Volcanism, however, can be studied at first hand; so we start our survey of igneous phenomena with a review of the living processes of volcanism.

Volcanism

VOLCANIC ERUPTIONS

Volcanic eruptions take many forms. In one type melt emerges quietly or turbulently from a crater or from a fissure. It carries in solution dissolved gases, which quietly bubble out as the melt approaches the surface and the pressure on it is reduced, much as CO_2 bubbles out of a freshly opened bottle of soda water. Eruptions of another kind produce mostly gas, which escapes suddenly and with shattering violence. All gradations between these types have been observed. The mode of eruption appears to be related to the viscosity of the magma, which is itself related to its composition. Melts rich in SiO_2 are very viscous, as is liquid SiO_2 itself, because they consist essentially of polymerized assemblages of $[SiO_4]$ units. Escape of gas bubbles is easier if the melt has a low viscosity, as shown by the quiet bubbling that characteristically occurs in basaltic lavas.

The ratio by weight of gas to melt has been measured in a few quiet eruptions of basaltic lavas and found to be of the order of 0.5 to 1 percent. On the other hand, the crater of Nyiragongo, in the Western Rift Valley of Africa north of Lake Kivu, contains a lava "lake"—a pool of incandescent lava at a temperature of about 1100°C—that has existed there since the volcano was first seen by European explorers in the first years of this century. The sole activity consists in the emission of gases that continuously bubble out of the lake and keep it stirred, so that the gas/lava ratio in the products of this volcano is, at the moment, infinite. It is worth noting that the heat radiated at the surface of the lake amounts to 1 cal cm^{-2} sec^{-1}, roughly 10^6 times the normal heat flow at the earth's surface (see Chapter 12). It is not known exactly how this heat is transferred to the surface, the most probable mechanism being thermal convection in the volcanic conduit, aided in some measure by the bubbling gases.

Volcanoes erupt intermittently. The largest Hawaiian volcano, Mauna Loa, has erupted every three to four years during the past two centuries. But previously there must have been a lengthy quiet period, for the prehistoric flows are all deeply weathered. The adjacent volcano, Kilauea, erupts rather more frequently—once every two to three years on the average; the total output of lava, however, is not large (0.1 km^3 between 1918 and 1921 during a recorded cycle of activity 1913–1924). Other volcanoes erupt less frequently. About 1600 years elapsed between the great eruption of Vesuvius which destroyed Pompeii in A.D. 79 and the next manifestation. A single eruption may last anywhere from a few hours to a few years. It is not known how long a volcano remains intermittently active, but the total life-span is probably not more than about 10^6 years.

Volcanic eruption typically is concentrated at localized centers, around which are built volcanoes of the "central type." Basaltic lavas, because of their low viscosity, build "shield volcanoes," whose sides slope outward at less than 10°. Explosive viscous andesitic magmas build steeper volcanoes of the familiar Fujiyama type. On the other hand, eruption of basaltic magma may also occur from fissures on linear zones of crustal weakness. The most extensive recorded eruption of this kind occurred along the 30-km-long Laki fissure of Iceland in 1783, and flooded some 500 km^2 with over 10 km^3 of basalt. Of the 200 eruptions recorded in the long history of Iceland, none was comparable with that of 1783 from the Laki fissure.

NATURE OF THE GAS PHASE

Gases emitted by volcanoes obviously play a dominant role in the mechanism of volcanic explosions; they provide information on the nature of the fluids that may circulate at depth; and as we shall see, they seem to have played a critical part in the development of the atmosphere and hydrosphere, both of which are probably mainly or entirely of volcanic origin (see Chapter 14).

Gases collected directly from volcanic vents, or from cooling lava flows, and small quantities of trapped gas that may be obtained by heating lava specimens *in vacuo* all have approximately the same composition. Main elements are hydrogen, oxygen, carbon, and sulfur. The actual molecular species present in any sample depend on its temperature, because of shifting chemical equilibria. Water is universally present, but tends to limited dissociation into H_2 and O_2 at high temperature. Sulfur may occur as H_2S, as molecular sulfur, or as SO_2, or even as microscopic particles of sulfate (of Ca, Na, K, mainly) carried in suspension in the gas. Carbon occurs as CO and CO_2. From thermodynamic considerations it appears that in a mixture of water-sulfur-carbon in volcanic proportions, sulfur will be present mainly as SO_2 at high temperatures and as H_2S at low temperatures; H_2 will be present in noticeable amounts only at the highest temperatures.

In all instances, H_2O is the main constituent, followed by CO_2. The ratio H_2O/CO_2 (by weight) seems to lie generally between 3 and 10. In addition to sulfur, boron, and nitrogen, argon and other rare gases are also generally present; chlorine and fluorine take the form of HCl and HF. It is not known exactly what proportions of these elements released during an eruption are "juvenile" in the sense that they are reaching the earth's surface for the first time; much of the nitrogen could come from air drawn into the sample either at the time of collection, or previously into the volcanic vent. CO_2 may come in some instances from the thermal decomposition of carbonates, sedimentary or otherwise, through which the ascending magma has penetrated. Some of the water may be rain water that has seeped down and been brought up again in the melt. Certainly much of the water emitted at hot springs in volcanic areas is meteoric, as shown by its isotopic composition (deuterium, O^{18}/O^{16} ratio). Volcanic argon may, as nitrogen, be partly atmospheric; much of it, however, is probably radiogenic A^{40} formed from K^{40} in the mantle.

A surprising number of metals are also present in the gases, as may be noticed by examining the deposits that form around small vents ("fumaroles"), through which gases continue to escape, long after eruption, from massive flows that cool slowly, or from the volcano itself. Iron, copper, zinc, mercury, and a host of other metals have been found. Copper in the form of copper chloride has been identified by its characteristic bands in the spectrum of flames that are occasionally observed in basaltic eruptions, and which are themselves presumably produced by the combustion (oxidation) of sulfur where volcanic gases mix with air. Volcanic gases thus seem capable of carrying many of the elements that typically occur elsewhere in contact metamorphic rocks and in metallic ore veins.

MECHANISM OF ERUPTION

Much of our information regarding the nature of volcanic eruption is drawn from continuous records of activity of the two adjacent Hawaiian volcanoes Mauna Loa and Kilauea. The erupted lava is basalt of low viscosity. Some weeks before an eruption there is a notable increase in frequency of small earthquakes with foci at a depth of 50 to 60 km—well within the mantle, for here the oceanic crust is but a few kilometers thick. The foci gradually rise to shallower depths; and a net of sensitive tiltmeters shows that the whole volcanic edifice is gradually swelling as if liquid were being injected from beneath under pressure. Lava ultimately bursts out in the summit crater or from points on well-defined lines of weakness on the flanks, the sites of repeated eruption in times past. These are interpreted as the surface outcrops of sealed fissures or rifts extending deep into the volcanic edifice. In the first stage of eruption, lava commonly gushes upward in fountains and seems to be carried up by its own momentum. Later, eruption becomes more tranquil, less continuous, and finally dies away.

The composition of lava erupted from a single volcano, as seen in successive flows, may change significantly in time—even over intervals measured in decades. Synchronous flows from closely adjacent volcanoes may differ markedly in composition. Usually there is little correlation in time between eruptions at nearby active centers; such is the case with Mauna Loa and Kilauea, whose craters—both intermittently active—are only 30 km apart. All this suggests that each volcano is fed from some kind of shallow reservoir, within which the magma may be progressively modified—for example, by fractional crystallization—between eruptions. Soviet scientists have found that seismic S-waves (which cannot be transmitted through liquid) generated on one side of the andesite volcano Klyuchevskaya in Kamschatka are unrecorded at stations on the other side. This is consistent with "screening" by an interposing magma-filled reservoir at an estimated depth of 60 km.

Since silicate liquids are less dense than corresponding solids, the upward movement of magma through the solid crust is generally attributed to gravity. Control by gravity, indeed, is demonstrated by the fact that volcanoes do not grow indefinitely upward. Under static conditions the height h to which a column of liquid with density d_l can rise above the base of a column of solid rock, thickness H, is given by

$$ghd_l = gHd_s$$

where d_s is the density of solid rock. Hence,

$$\frac{h - H}{H} = \frac{d_s - d_l}{d_l}$$

For basaltic magma $d_l = 2.8$ g/cm³; d_s for the upper mantle may be close to 3.3; thus $(d_s - d_l)/d_l = 0.15$. Hence $h - H$, the height of the volcano, is $0.15H$. Mauna Loa, in Hawaii, rises about 8 km over the adjacent sea floor. This gives $H = 55$ km, in good agreement with the seismic data. In other words, the hydrostatic pressure of the liquid column equals the pressure at the source due to a load (thickness H) of material with density d_s.

The magnitude of volcanic explosions is astounding, but the mechanism is imperfectly understood. The climactic eruption of the andesitic volcano Krakatao (Indonesia) in 1883 was heard in Australia, nearly 5000 km away; moreover, it produced atmospheric sound waves that traveled around the world. It hurled into the atmosphere an estimated 18 km³ of solid particles of all sizes, some of which remained suspended in the air for more than a year, producing interesting meteorological effects; the energy of the explosion has been estimated at 10^{26} ergs; the height of the volcanic cloud was 20 km. From the observed velocity at which fragments of rock are thrown up, it is possible to infer roughly the gas pressure inside an exploding volcano. This pressure is commonly found to be of the order of 10^2–10^3 bars. How do such pressures develop?

Experiments show that the solubility of water in silicate melts increases roughly as the square root of the water pressure, corresponding presumably to a reaction such as

$$H_2O + O^{2-} = 2(OH)^-$$

gas   melt   melt

At constant pressure, the solubility decreases with increasing temperature, but depends only slightly on the composition of the melt. At 1100°C and at a pressure of 1000 bars, a basaltic melt can contain about 3 percent (by weight) of water; conversely, the partial pressure of water in a gas phase in equilibrium with a basaltic melt containing 1 percent of water would be about 100 bars. If the pressure drops below this value, water will boil out; but under static conditions the pressure developed in the evolving gas cannot exceed 100 bars without the water going back into solution. To create a pressure of 1000

bars inside an andesite volcano would require what seems an excessive amount of water—perhaps 4–5 percent.

Theoretically, high water pressure can develop as a result of cooling and crystallization of magma. As water does not enter the first-formed crystals (olivine, pyroxene, plagioclase, iron–titanium oxides), its concentration in the liquid must increase as crystallization proceeds. Its vapor pressure therefore also increases, and in some systems may reach very high values, of the order of 10^3 bars. When water pressure becomes equal to the external pressure, water will boil from the melt. (This is called retrograde boiling, since it is induced by cooling.) One could thus imagine a batch of magma slowly crystallizing inside a volcanic reservoir so that the water pressure gradually builds up to some value that exceeds the strength of the volcanic edifice and is then released by explosion. Judging, however, from the commonly glassy state of much of the pyroclastic material, such as that expelled in the great eruption of Krakatao, it would seem that explosions may occur while the magma is still essentially liquid. Retrograde boiling by contrast generally occurs only in more advanced stages of crystallization. So the dilemma remains unresolved.

The mechanism of an explosion must surely also be affected by kinetic factors, such as the rate of nucleation of bubbles. The formation of *nuées ardentes* or "glowing clouds" is a related problem in kinetics. A *nuée ardente*, first observed at the eruption of Mt. Pelée, Martinique, in 1902, is a cloud of volcanic solid material and gas at high temperature, which is emitted suddenly from the crater, and because of its high average density flows downward across the surface of the volcano. This cloud sweeps down the slope of the volcano with extraordinary velocity, and is partly self-propelling; apparently each particle as it moves emits gas, creating such turbulence that even relatively dense solid particles are prevented from settling. When they come to rest the particles are so hot that they tend to become welded—and this is the mode of origin generally accepted for welded tuffs ("ignimbrites"). The precise mechanism of *nuée ardente* eruption is still something of a puzzle. But thin sheets of welded tuff of enormous volume and extent, as developed for instance in Nevada and Utah, constitute the main product of acid volcanism—for a characteristic of all ignimbrites is a high content of silica.

GEOGRAPHIC CORRELATION OF VOLCANIC AND SEISMIC ACTIVITY

The number of active volcanoes is about 800, and many more have erupted so recently that they have been but little affected by erosion. Their geographic distribution is by no means random. For example, they are notably absent from continental shields, and are thickly clustered along the "circle of fire" that margins the Pacific Ocean. Here belong the volcanoes of the western Americas, the Aleutians, Kamchatka, the Kuriles, Japan, the Philippines, New Britain, New Zealand, and Antarctica.

There is an obvious gross geographic correlation between recent volcanic and seismic activity. Many active volcanoes lie on or near the seismic belts where epicenters of recorded earthquakes also are concentrated (Figure 9–77). Detailed correlation, however, is far from perfect. The great seismic belts are much more continuous than are "coinciding" belts of volcanism. For example, along the circum-Pacific seismic zone there is a conspicuous 2000-km gap in the "circle of fire" between Lassen, in northern California, and the active volcanoes of central Mexico. Again consider the east–west seismic zone that extends from the western Mediterranean across Turkey, Iran, and the Pamir and Himalaya ranges, and thence along the Indonesian arc. There are some active volcanoes in the Mediterranean—Etna, Vesuvius, and others—a few in the Caucasus, many in Indonesia, but none across Turkey and the high-mountain ranges of south-central Asia. Even where seismic and volcanic zones coincide, correlation tends to break down on a smaller scale. In New Zealand, for example, volcanic eruptions are rarer events than strong earthquakes; and eruptions are confined to a limited area no more than 250 km × 100 km (Wairakei–

Taupo zone, Figure 10–22), while epicenters of severe earthquakes have been pinpointed along zones of dislocation extending 1500 km along the length of both islands. A generally similar relation holds in Chile. Epicenters of many Atlantic earthquakes fall on or near the crest of the Atlantic Ridge; many volcanic islands occur hundreds of kilometers away. In the Pacific, the Hawaiian Islands are the site of continuous volcanic activity that has lasted several million years; but epicenters for large earthquake shocks are conspicuously absent.

Local seismic activity is the normal precursor or accompaniment of volcanic eruptions. But they are minor accessory phenomena. In the great eruption of the Nicaraguan volcano Coseguina in 1835, some 10 km³ of debris was blasted out in a three-day eruption; yet preliminary earthquakes were not severe and were confined to the day preceding eruption. The seismic activity that heralds Hawaiian eruptions is detectable for the most part only by instruments.

Most major earthquakes are not directly associated with eruptions. Yet there are exceptions. On February 20, 1835, while the "Beagle" was visiting Chile, Concepcion and other southern coastal towns were devastated by earthquake. Darwin[1], who was on the spot, records that

> . . . at the same hour when the whole area was permanently elevated, a train of volcanoes situated in the Andes in front of Chile, instantaneously spouted out a dark column of smoke, and during the subsequent year continued in uncommon activity . . . We thus see a permanent elevation of the land, renewed activity through habitual vents, and a submarine outburst [off Juan Fernandez], forming parts of one great phenomenon.

On the basis of this experience Darwin later wrote[2]

> These phenomena appear to me to prove that the

---

[1] C. Darwin, *Journal of Researches* (Hafner, London, 1839, reprinted 1952, p. 380).
[2] C. R. Darwin, *Geological Observations*, 3d ed. (Smith Elder, London, 1891, p. 236).

action by which large tracts of land are uplifted, and by which volcanic eruptions are produced, is everywhere identical.

Southern Chile was again severely affected by earthquake on May 22, 1960. Synchronous volcanic eruption was again observed, but this time on a limited scale. Most volcanoes remained inactive; one of these, Calbuco, in the heart of the seismic area, broke into violent eruption, but not until eight months after the earthquake. Even in Chile the relation between the two kinds of activity is only indirect.

VOLCANIC AND TECTONIC ACTIVITY IN TIME

Going back into the past, one sees again some general geographic correlation between volcanic and tectonic activity. Radiometric dating of igneous events tends to show that correlation in time is less perfect than was once generally thought. In many fold mountain belts there are large volumes of volcanic and plutonic rocks. In some of these, volcanism has been concentrated mainly during the early stage of sinking and filling of the ancestral geosyncline, and in the post-tectonic stage following folding of the filling and elevation of the mountain range. Plutonic intrusion of granitic magma tends to be more capricious, and is usually limited to one or more episodes of short duration.

The continental shields are generally considered as tectonically stable areas, and we tend to project this stability back through Phanerozoic time. For large areas—for example, in Canada, Australia, and Africa there has been no volcanism since Precambrian times. Elsewhere there has been regional rifting of the shields and geographically associated volcanic activity. Thus the Cretaceous flooding of southern Brazil by basaltic flows was accompanied by spectacular cracking and extension of the shield. Outside the basalt-flooded region, the eroded roots of Mesozoic volcanoes, which erupted alkaline magma, pierce the Brazilian shield in the country west and south of Rio de Janeiro. Similar activity is taking place today along the east African Rift Valleys of Kenya and Tanzania. In the Pacific Ocean, volcanic activity has been widespread in times recently past. All the islands within the Pacific basin are volcanic, many with fringing additions of coral growth. The only currently active centers are those of Samoa, the Galapagos, and Hawaii. Perhaps for lack of adequate information, the Pacific basin is not considered to be a region of large-scale tectonism.

ORIGIN OF MAGMA: THE MELTING PROBLEM

Since the melting points of most minerals increase with pressure, it has been suggested that reduction in pressure on rocks close to the melting range might account for generation of magma in the upper mantle. However, no simple mechanism for local reduction of pressure has been proposed. The earth is essentially in a state of hydrostatic equilibrium; therefore, at any given depth, pressure is determined by density of the rock (or magma) and the acceleration of gravity, neither of which can change without corresponding changes in the mass and size of the earth. Moreover, the almost perfect isostatic adjustment of the earth (Chapter 11) precludes local pressure fluctuations of more than say 100 bars at any fixed point in the mantle. The corresponding effect on melting temperatures could not exceed a few degrees.

An alternative possibility is reduction of pressure without significant lowering of temperature in the upward-moving limb of a convection cell operating in the solid mantle. But convection is also proposed as the driving force of tectonic activity; and, as already noted, correlation between magmatic activity such as volcanism, and tectonic events (development of geosynclines, mountain-building, and seismic activity) is far from perfect. It may be that different patterns of convection are involved, and that only under special conditions (for example, of temperature and rate and direction of flow) would large-scale melting become possible. It is conceivable, too, that magma could form during the simple upward movement of a body of mantle material—a solid bubble rising into the crust—without the lateral drag which characterizes much of orogeny. In the absence of critical data, such notions at present belong to the realm of speculation rather than hypothesis. We know that magma forms by melting of rock in the mantle and perhaps in the deep crust. For the mechanics of melting we still have no adequate model.

Crystal–Melt Equilibria in Silicate Systems

All common magmas are silicate melts with minor additional components such as H_2O, SO_2, or HF. Igneous rocks too, volcanic and plutonic, are composed principally of silicates (including quartz). So a crucial role in genesis and evolution of magmas and igneous rocks is played by melting of multiphase silicate systems, and separation of silicates from cooling melts (magmas). A great deal of information relating to crystallization behavior of silicates has come from laboratory experiments in the fields of ceramic chemistry and metallurgy as well as in geochemistry itself. These experimental data are concerned mainly with equilibrium between crystalline phases and melts; and so they can be tested and applied against the background of classical thermodynamics.

THERMODYNAMIC CONSIDERATIONS

EUTECTIC CRYSTALLIZATION In a two-component system A-B, with no tendency toward mutual solution between the solid phases A and B, any melt of intermediate composition can be regarded as a solution of A in B or vice versa. At any given pressure, the molal concentration of A in the melt, x_a at temperature T is given by equation (5-14), which may be written

$$\ln \frac{1}{\gamma x_a} = \frac{\Delta S_a}{R}\left(\frac{T_{m,\,a}}{T} - 1\right) \qquad (6\text{-}1)$$

where $T_{m,a}$ is the melting temperature of component A, ΔS_a its entropy of melting, and γ an activity coefficient denoting departure from ideal behavior (for which $\gamma = 1$).

Such is the system $NaAlSi_3O_8$ (albite)–Fe_2SiO_4 (fayalite) at atmospheric pressure (Figure 6–1). It follows from equation (6–1) that crystalline fayalite can coexist in equilibrium with a melt only in a range of temperatures below its temperature of fusion. Moreover, temperatures on the equilibrium curve must decrease with the fayalite content of the melt. At the other side of the diagram, the melting curve of albite-rich mixtures falls away from the fusion temperature of pure albite. Thus two segments meet at a unique, univariant eutectic point E. Here liquid E can coexist with albite and fayalite crystals at constant minimal temperature. The temperature–composition diagram is divided into four fields within each of which one phase assemblage is stable. The configuration of the FE segment of the liquidus—assuming ideal solution—is determined solely by the temperature and entropy of fusion of fayalite; it is independent of the nature of the "solvent," in this case albite.

For most simple minerals of igneous rocks the melting temperature at room pressure is known

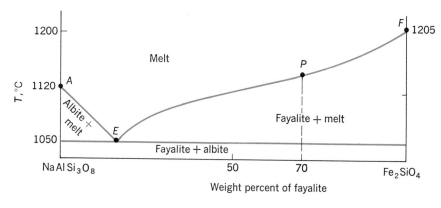

FIG. 6–1 Equilibrium diagram for crystallization of liquids in the system $NaAlSi_3O_8$–Fe_2SiO_4. (After N. L. Bowen and J. F. Schairer. Proc. Natl. Acad. Sci., vol. 22, p. 349, 1936.)

within a few degrees. The second parameter, ΔS_m, can be calculated from the respective heat capacities of the crystalline phase and the glass of the same composition. Alternatively, it can be obtained calorimetrically from differential heats of solution of the crystalline phase and of the glass in some such solvent as HF. But data of this kind for igneous minerals are extremely meager. Some that have been recorded for $P = 1$ bar are:

Diopside	$CaMgSi_2O_6$	13.8 ± 2 cal/mole deg
Anorthite	$CaAl_2Si_2O_8$	16.1 ± 2.5 cal/mole deg
Cristobalite	SiO_2	1.02 cal/mole deg
Albite	$NaAlSi_3O_8$	9.75 ± 0.5 cal/mole deg
Sanidine	$KAlSi_3O_8$	9.98 ± 0.5 cal/mole deg

By contrast, most standard values of ΔS_m for silicates have been computed *in reverse* from experimentally determined melting-point curves in two-component systems. Values for albite and fayalite obtained in this way many years ago by Bowen are respectively 0.75 and 1.3 cal/g atom deg (the value for albite has recently been determined experimentally as 0.75 cal/g atom deg).[3] The relatively low value of ΔS_m for albite, rather than its somewhat lower fusion temperature, is responsible for displacement of E toward the albite composition in Figure 6–1.

Pure silica has an exceptionally low melting entropy (< 0.4 cal/g atom deg) consistent with the complex polymerized structure of silica melts. Also low compared with values for oxides (2 cal/g atom deg for TiO_2 and Al_2O_3) and for simpler silicates (1–1.5 cal/g atom deg for olivines and pyroxenes) are the melting entropies of alkali feldspars. These data impose important strictures on the crystallization behavior of magmas. The final residual liquids developed during crystallization of magma and the first liquid fractions to form when silicate aggregates begin to melt have this point in common: They must be relatively enriched in silica and in alkaline aluminosilicate "molecules."

---

[3] The entropy per gram atom is the entropy per mole divided by the number of atoms in the chemical formula.

INCONGRUENT MELTING   Requirements for congruent and for incongruent melting (page 251) are contrasted in Figure 6–2. Each of the two diagrams depicts a two-component system with SiO_2 as one component and an alkaline aluminosilicate (feldspathoid) as the other. In each there is a possible compound of intermediate composition, an alkali feldspar. In Figure 6–2a both right- and left-hand segments of the liquidus drop to temperatures below the melting point of albite before reaching the composition $NaAlSi_3O_8$. Thus there are two independent simple eutectic subsystems with eutectic points E_1 and E_2 (whose approximate coincidence as to temperature is fortuitous).

Leucite, by contrast with nepheline, has a fusion temperature close to that of silica. But for the intermediate compound $KAlSi_3O_8$, the leucite–silica diagram would have a form such as $LE'S$ (Figure 6–2b), whose eutectic point E' would be displaced toward SiO_2. At a unique temperature R, $KAlSi_3O_8$ melts incongruently to give a liquid of more siliceous composition, plus the less siliceous crystalline phase leucite. The implication is that $KAlSi_3O_8$ would melt congruently at a somewhat higher temperature K, below that for the same composition (F) on LE'; but at K equilibrium between melt and crystals, both of composition $KAlSi_3O_8$, would be metastable. This metastable melting point can be estimated, from equation (6-1), by extending the curve ER to cut the vertical line drawn at $KAlSi_3O_8$; it is close to 1200°C.

In Figure 6–2a, any liquid O intermediate between $NaAlSi_3O_8$ and SiO_2, first cools down OP, then changes down PE_1 with separation of albite, and finally crystallizes to completion at E_1, with simultaneous separation of albite and silica in eutectic proportions. Similarly, any liquid Q in the albite–nepheline subsystem must ultimately attain the composition E_2. The composition of a liquid in one subsystem can never cross over the $NaAlSi_3O_8$ barrier into the other subsystem.

In Figure 6–2b the initial liquid O cools to P and moves down PR with crystallization of leucite. At R, a univariant point, three phases coexist; for leucite begins to dissolve while feldspar $KAlSi_3O_8$ is precipitated in abundance to keep

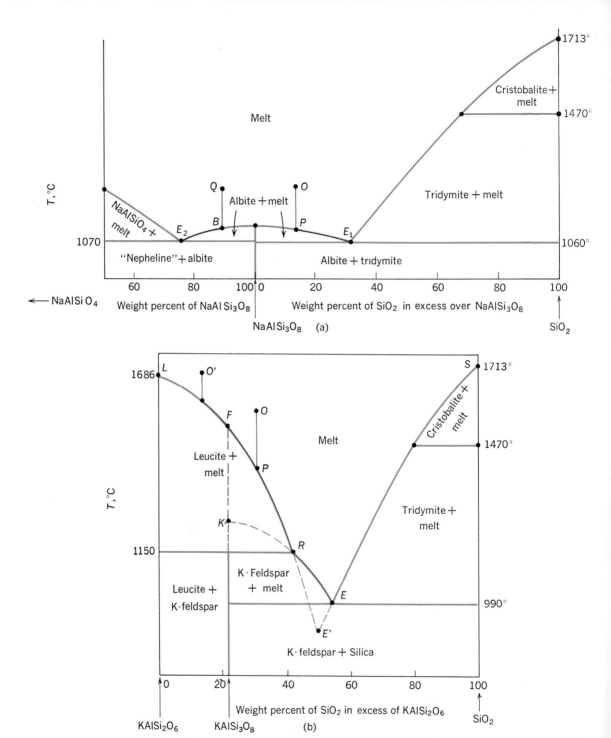

FIG. 6–2 *Equilibrium diagrams for crystallization of liquids in feldspathoid-silica systems. (a) NaAlSiO₄–SiO₂. (After T. F. W. Barth. Simplified by omission of minor solid-solution effects. T. F. W. Barth, Die Eruptivgesteine, in: Die Enstehung der Gesteine. Ein Lehrbuch der Petrogenese. Springer, Berlin-Göttingen-Heidelberg, 1960.) (b) KAlSi₂O₆–SiO₂. (After J. F. Schairer and N. L. Bowen, Proc. Comm. Géol, Finlande, vol. 140, pp. 72–75, 1947.)*

the liquid composition at R. An approximate equation is

$$(2 \text{ KAlSi}_2\text{O}_6 + 5 \text{ SiO}_2) + 3 \text{ KAlSi}_2\text{O}_6 \rightarrow$$
liquid R leucite

$$5 \text{ KAlSi}_3\text{O}_8$$
feldspar

When leucite is eliminated, the liquid then cools along RE with separation of feldspar. Eutectic crystallization of feldspar and silica then ensues at constant temperature E. A most significant twist to the course of crystallization of liquids such as O' in the leucite–feldspar subsystem is given by the incongruent behavior of KAlSi_3O_8. They are forced eventually into the feldspar–silica subsystem and finish crystallization as leucite–feldspar mixtures at R. If, however, all crystalline leucite were removed (crystal fractionation) when the liquid had reached P, this final fraction would thereafter follow the course PRE, just as in the later stages of the initial liquid O. So a parent liquid O', initially deficient in silica, could give rise to late fractions from which free silica would crystallize. In highly potassic volcanic rocks phenocrysts of early-formed leucite are enclosed in a glassy base which does in fact contain excess silica.

CRYSTALLIZATION OF SOLID SOLUTIONS The respective compositions of a solid solution and an associated melt in a two-component system at constant pressure and temperature T are given by equation (5-15), which can be written

$$\ln \frac{x_a^s}{x_a^l} = \frac{\Delta S_a}{R}\left(\frac{T_{m,a}}{T} - 1\right) \qquad (6\text{-}2)$$

$$\ln \frac{1 - x_a^l}{1 - x_a^s} = \frac{\Delta S_b}{R}\left(1 - \frac{T_{m,b}}{T}\right) \qquad (6\text{-}3)$$

where x_a^s and x_a^l are molar concentrations of A in solid and liquid phases; ΔS_a and ΔS_b are molar fusion entropies of a and b, and $T_{m,a}$ and $T_{m,b}$ are melting temperatures of pure components, $T_{m,a} > T_{m,b}$.

Figure 6–3 depicts crystallization in the olivine series, in which A is Mg_2SiO_4 (forsterite) and B is Fe_2SiO_4 (fayalite). Liquid O cools to L, where crystallization of olivine P begins. Both the liquid and the solid phases now change composition continuously with further cooling—from L

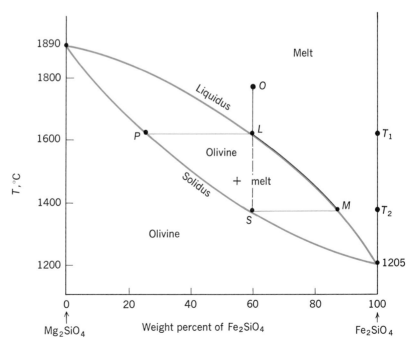

FIG. 6–3 Equilibrium diagram for crystallization of liquids in the olivine system Mg_2SiO_4–Fe_2SiO_4. (After N. L. Bowen and J. F. Schairer, Am. J. Sci., vol. 29, p. 163, 1935.)

to M and from P to S, respectively, as temperature drops from T_1 to T_2. At any instant, equilibrium requires that there be two homogeneous phases, one solid and one liquid. Crystallization ceases as the last fraction of liquid M is eliminated, and the composition of the homogeneous crystalline phase is now S. Maximum divergence between respective compositions of liquid and crystal phases is reached at temperature $(T_{m,a} + T_{m,b})/2$. Strong divergence, from equations (6-2 and 6-3), is favored by a marked difference in the fusion entropies of the two end members.

COEXISTENCE OF FLUID PHASES   So far it has been assumed that melting in polycomponent systems leads to a single liquid phase with which one or more crystalline phases can coexist in stable equilibrium. For silicate systems approximating the compositions of common magmas this indeed is the case. But, as is well known to ceramic chemists, there are simple silicate–oxide systems in which mutual solution is so far from ideal that two liquids can coexist, in some cases with a crystalline phase as well, over a rather wide range of composition. Such is the case in the $CaO—SiO_2$, $MgO—SiO_2$, and $FeO—SiO_2$ systems, for total compositions with more than about 70–80 percent (molar) of SiO_2. Important in the development of certain ore bodies is unmixing of silicate melts with minor dissolved sulfides into two liquid fractions—one essentially silicate (magmatic), the other sulfide enriched in minor elements such as copper, lead, zinc, and silver. There is geologic evidence that under spe-cial conditions a magma may unmix to two liquid fractions, one consisting of silicates, the other of iron oxides.

At high pressures silicate melts can contain significant water. A water content of 5 percent by weight, which is readily tolerated by some silicate melts at water pressures of a few kilobars, corresponds to a molar concentration of perhaps 30 percent. So melting temperatures of pure silicate phases such as albite and anorthite can thereby be lowered by several hundred degrees. If there is sufficient water in the system, there is a P-T field in which crystals and hydrous silicate melt can coexist with a second fluid phase, rich in water and in the supercritical state.

PRESSURE EFFECTS   Melting of silicates is accompanied by increase, ΔV_m, in molar volume. Thus melting temperatures increase with pressure according to the Clausius-Clapeyron equation

$$\frac{dT_m}{dP} = \frac{\Delta V_m}{\Delta S_m} \qquad (6\text{-}4)$$

Some gradients for igneous silicates are listed in Table 6-1. In each case the value dT_m/dP represents the calculated initial slope of the melting curve at atmospheric pressure; $\Delta T_m/\Delta P$ is the measured average rate of change up to 20 kb. The latter is usually less than the initial slope because dT_m/dP generally decreases with increasing pressure.

Since gradients for different minerals differ significantly, observed melting effects in multi-

TABLE 6–1   Effect of high pressure on T_m of silicates

Compound	T_m at 1 bar °K	ΔV_m at 1 bar cm³/mol	ΔS_m at 1 bar cal/mol deg.	dT_m/dP °C/kb calculated	$\Delta T_m/\Delta P$ °C/kb observed; up to 20 kb
Forsterite Mg_2SiO_4	2163	1.308	7.1	4.6	4.5
Pyroxene $MgSiO_3$	1830		8.5	14	9
Diopside $CaMgSi_2O_6$	1664	10	13.8 ± 2	18	12
Albite $NaAlSi_3O_8$	1378	10.226	9.75 ± 0.5	25	10
Muscovite $KAl_2(AlSi_3O_{10})(OH)_2$ plus quartz	1000 (metastable)*				6.5

* Muscovite plus quartz remains stable up to melting temperatures only at pressures greater than 3 or 4 kb.

component systems at room pressure cannot safely be extrapolated to high pressures of the deep crust and the outer mantle. The difference in respective values of dT_m/dP for forsterite and for enstatite result in *congruent* melting of $MgSiO_3$ at no great pressure. This was predicted on thermodynamic grounds and subsequently confirmed by experiment (the pressure at which melting of $MgSiO_3$ becomes congruent is between 2.5 and 5.5 kb). At very high pressures T_m for albite might exceed that of anorthite; and incongruent melting of albite to liquid plus the dense phase jadeite $NaAlSi_2O_6$ is another possibility.

RESULTS OF DIRECT EXPERIMENT

USE OF PHASE-EQUILIBRIUM DIAGRAMS The equilibrium diagrams of Figures 6–1 to 6–3, used to illustrate thermodynamics of melting and crystallization, actually were plotted from the data of direct experiment. For example, the crystallization temperature of a mixture of fayalite and albite in weight proportions 70/30 (point *P*, Figure 6–1) was determined by bracketing the temperatures at which crystals first appear in a cooling melt and finally disappear during heating of a crystalline mixture of the same composition. (In both cases, crystals and liquid coexist over the temperature interval *EP*.) Data similarly determined for three-component systems are plotted on a triangular diagram[4] and isothermals are drawn through points of identical liquidus temperature (Figure 6–7); alternatively a few key temperatures are shown, with arrows indicating the sense of falling temperature on field boundaries (for example, Figure 6–9).

Phase diagrams concisely convey petrologically significant information such as the following:

1. The sequence of phases that successively become stable during cooling of a melt to room temperature. This is usually termed "equilibrium" crystallization—strictly a sequence of stable equilibria.

2. Progressive change in liquid composition when the crystalline fraction is periodically removed during cooling of some specified initial liquid. Removal of crystals initiates a new system whose initial composition is now that of the liquid at the moment of fractionation. Here we are tracing the course of fractional crystallization of any liquid in the comprehensive system.

3. The sequence of successively stable phases or phase assemblages during progressive heating of a crystalline mixture to complete melting. This is the reverse of the two kinds of behavior specified under items 1 and 2. Periodic removal of liquid (differential fusion) with increasing temperature is the reverse of fractional crystallization.

4. Modifying effects of high pressure, addition of other phases (especially water), and variation in partial pressure of oxygen.

Data of petrological interest, mainly the result of half a century's research at the Geophysical Laboratory, Carnegie Institution, Washington, have been summarized in standard texts, and especially in *Geological Society of America Memoir 97* (1966), and *U.S. Geological Survey Professional Paper 440L* (1964). Here we reproduce a few typical diagrams each divided into fields showing the range of composition of melts that can coexist with specified crystalline phases. A liquid in the field labelled "forsterite" can be associated with forsterite crystals; another liquid composition on the forsterite–pyroxene *cotectic* curve (boundary between fields of forsterite and of pyroxene) is in equilibrium with both crystalline phases. Crystallization of forsterite directs the course of the changing liquid composition in a three-component diagram along a straight line drawn from the forsterite point (for example, *L* toward *M* in Figure 6–8).

CRYSTALLIZATION OF FELDSPARS *Alkali feldspars* Crystallization of pure alkali feldspars and of the feldspathoids nepheline and leucite at

---

[4] Thus, in Figure 6–7, point *X* represents a bulk composition $xNaAlSi_3O_8$—$yCaAl_2Si_2O_8$—$zCaMgSi_2O_6$, where x, y, z are weight percentages ($x = y = 20$; $z = 60$). A liquid of this composition begins to crystallize at $1300°C$.

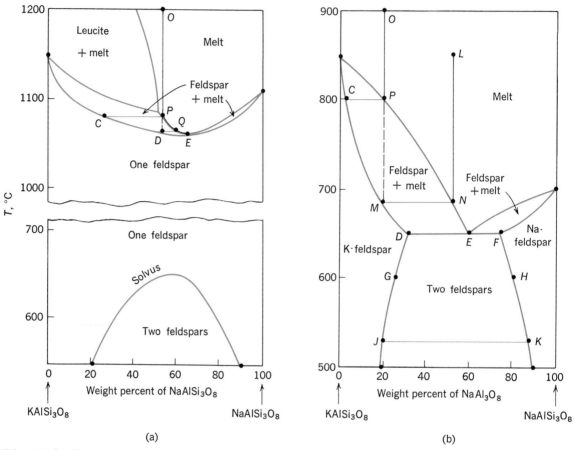

FIG. 6–4 *Equilibrium diagrams for crystallization of liquids in the system KAlSi$_3$O$_8$–NaAlSi$_3$O$_8$. (a) At P = 1 bar. (Modified after N. L. Bowen and O. F. Tuttle, J. Geol., vol. 58, pp. 489–511, 1950.) (b) At P$_{H_2O}$ = 6 kb. (Diagrammatic.)*

atmospheric pressure has already been illustrated in Figure 6–2. There is complete solid solution in the alkali–feldspar series NaAlSi$_3$O$_8$—KAlSi$_3$O$_8$ at liquidus temperatures and atmospheric pressure. The crystallization diagram, Figure 6–4a, shows a minimum temperature E, reflecting departure from ideal mixing in the solid and/or in the liquid. All melts in the system move toward this composition. For example, an initial liquid O first cools from O to P (melt only), and then follows from P to Q (melt plus feldspar $C \to D$); the final product is the homogeneous crystalline phase D. Only a melt of the same composition as E ever crystallizes at that point. But fractionation

progressively displaces the composition of the late liquid and crystal fractions towards E.

At temperatures below the solidus there is no longer complete miscibility in the alkali feldspar series. Feldspars in the medium range tend to unmix into two coexisting solid phases (page 242) whose compositions define an unmixing curve or *solvus*. It is probable but not certain, that as solidus temperatures are depressed at water pressures of a few kilobars, the solvus, which rises with increasing pressure, cuts the solidus as shown diagramatically in Figure 6–4b. In this situation a liquid O cools to P, at which point potash feldspar C starts to crystallize. The two phases now change composition continuously along *PN* and *CM* respectively. Crystallization ceases at *N*. Liquid *L* cools to *N*, when feldspar *M* begins to separate. As the liquid composition changes from *N* to *E*, feldspar also changes from *M* to *D*, the limit of solid solution. At *E* eutectic crystallization of two solid solutions *D* and *F* sets in, and continues at constant temperature until the liquid is exhausted. As the temperature falls below *E* the compositions of stable coexisting phases changes down opposite sides of the solvus *DGJ*, *FHK*. Whether this course of unmixing is actually followed, and whether the intergrowth (perthite) of unmixed phases can be seen under the microscope or detected only by X rays, depends on the kinetics of diffusion of K^+ and Na^+ ions in solid media. Slow cooling under plutonic conditions in nature does normally produce visible perthitic intergrowths in alkali feldspars.

Plagioclase feldspars   At liquidus temperatures the plagioclase feldspars form a con-tinuous solid-solution series $NaAlSi_3O_8$ (al-bite)–$CaAl_2Si_2O_8$ (anorthite). The crystallization diagram for atmospheric pressure, Figure 6–5, resembles that of the olivines (Figure 6–3). Possible courses of cooling liquids are: Liquid $P \rightarrow A$ (cooling melt), $A \rightarrow C$ (melt with crystals, which simultaneously change down the solidus, $B \rightarrow D$). Liquid $Q \rightarrow G$, $G \rightarrow K$ (melt with crystals $H \rightarrow L$). If during the course of crystallization from *P*, the liquid fraction at composition *G* were separated from the crystalline fraction *H*, the liquid line would now follow the second course $G \rightarrow K$, and crystals, beginning to form at *H* would simultaneously change composition along $H \rightarrow L$. The effect of fractional crystallization during cooling of melt *P* is thus to enrich the late liquid and crystalline fractions in albite (as they approach *K* and *L*). At water pressure $P_{H_2O} = 5$ kb, the shape of the diagram is generally similar to Figure 6–5; but temperatures of crystallization are lowered by about 300°C. Plagioclase liquids in contact with water vapor at

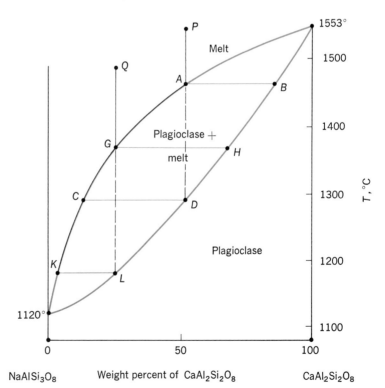

FIG. 6–5 Equilibrium diagram for crystallization of liquids in the system $NaAlSi_3O_8$–$CaAl_2Si_2O_8$. (After N. L. Bowen, slightly modified, Am. J. Sci., vol. 35, p. 583, 1913.)

such pressures (as in laboratory experiments) contain very much more dissolved water (8 or 9 percent by weight) than is possible in magmas. So this effect may have only minor geological significance.

CRYSTALLIZATION OF OLIVINES The main geological implication of the olivine diagram (Figure 6–3) is that late liquid and solid fractions become progressively enriched in iron. Since ferrous silicates in general melt at lower temperatures than their magnesian counterparts (page 269), a characteristic feature of fractional crystallization in all silicate systems is progressive increase in the ratio Fe/Mg in successive liquid fractions.

At atmospheric pressure, the intermediate compound (pyroxene, $MgSiO_3$) in the system Mg_2SiO_4–SiO_2 melts incongruently to give a somewhat more siliceous liquid (R in Figure 6–6) and crystals of Mg_2SiO_4 (forsterite). The equilibrium diagram is similar to that for the leucite–silica system (Figure 6–2b). Much has been made

of its possible significance in providing a mechanism by which silica-poor melts such as P on the forsterite side of the diagram must ultimately yield melts (between Q and R) that, if removed from olivine crystals, must finally crystallize as mixtures of pyroxene and free silica. There is evidence of reaction between olivine and liquid in basalts: Early formed large olivine crystals are commonly corroded as if by later reaction with the melt (see, for example, point R in Figure 6–6). However, as predicted on thermodynamic grounds (page 268), $MgSiO_3$ has been found to melt congruently at pressures above 5 kb; so incongruent behavior has little or no significance in melting and crystallization of magnesian rocks in the outer mantle.

In the system $FeSiO_4$–SiO_2, there is no stable intermediate compound, and crystallization behavior follows the simple eutectic pattern.

CRYSTALLIZATION IN THREE-COMPONENT SYSTEMS WITH PYROXENE $CaMgSi_2O_6$–$CaAl_2Si_2O_8$–

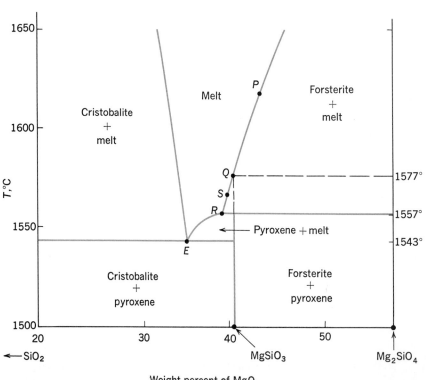

FIG. 6–6 Equilibrium diagram for crystallization of liquids in the system Mg_2SiO_4–SiO_2. (After N. L. Bowen and J. F. Schairer, Am. J. Sci., vol. 29, p. 157, 1935.)

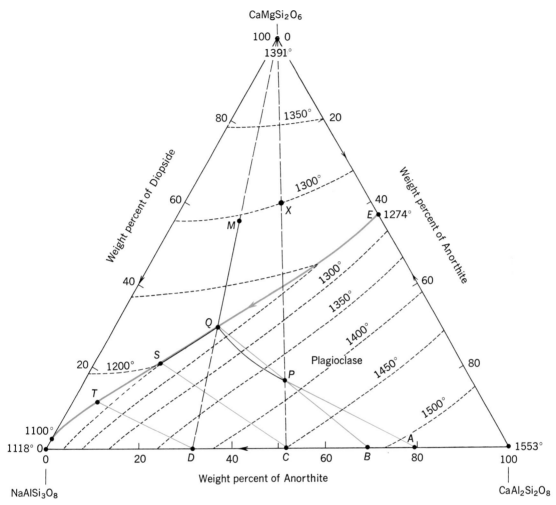

FIG. 6–7 *Equilibrium diagram for crystallization in the system CaMgSi$_2$O$_6$–CaAl$_2$Si$_2$O$_8$–NaAlSi$_3$O$_8$. Weight percentages. Isothermals of crystal–melt equilibrium (dashed, black), degrees C. (After N. L. Bowen, Z. Anorg. Chem., vol. 94, p. 41, 1916.)*

NaAlSi$_3$O$_8$. The phase diagram for the plagioclase–diopside system at $P = 1$ bar is shown in Figure 6–7. Typical of melts in the plagioclase field is composition P (An$_{41}$Ab$_{41}$Di$_{18}$–molar).[5] At 1375°C, plagioclase begins to crystallize; its composition is found to be An$_{79}$. The melt fol-

lows the unique curve PQ, plagioclase changing, as it crystallizes, to B. As the melt cools down the cotectic from Q to S (1200°C), plagioclase finally reaches composition C(An$_{50}$Ab$_{50}$) and the melt is eliminated at S. A liquid M(An$_{12}$Ab$_{28}$Di$_{60}$) yields diopside as it cools down MQ from 1295° to 1216°C. Then, as it follows the cotectic from Q to T, plagioclase crystallizes and progressively changes from B to D(An$_{30}$Ab$_{70}$) where the melt is eliminated. Note that late fractions of all melts are progressively enriched in albite and in total

[5] Compositions of solid solutions are usually given in terms of molar percentage—for example, An$_{81}$Ab$_{19}$. Compositions on experimentally based phase diagrams, such as Figure 6–7, are weight percentages.

plagioclase content. At water pressures of a few kilobars the cotectic is significantly shifted towards the plagioclase edge of the diagram. The anorthite–diopside eutectic at $P_{H_2O} = 5$ kb is $An_{67}Di_{33}$, $T_E = 1095°C$. At atmospheric pressure the eutectic (E in Figure 6–7) is $An_{43}Di_{57}$; $T_E = 1274°C$. In the anhydrous system the effect of pressure is similar but less pronounced. At $P = 20$ kb, E is $An_{70}Di_{30}$, $T_E = 1500°C$.

Pyroxene–olivine–silica systems   The common nonsodic pyroxenes of igneous rocks are the Ca-Mg-Fe clinopyroxenes (augites) and the Mg-Fe pyroxenes (orthorhombic enstatite–hypersthenes, monoclinic pigeonites). The corresponding systems that have been studied in the laboratory are complicated by possible crystallization of olivines and of silica, by the still imperfectly understood polymorphism of the $(Mg, Fe)SiO_3$

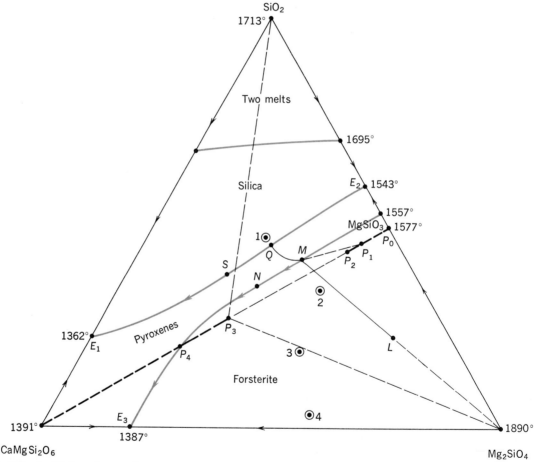

FIG. 6–8 *Equilibrium diagram for crystallization of liquids in the system $CaMgSi_2O_6$–Mg_2SiO_4–SiO_2 (mole percentages). E_1, E_2, and E_3 are binary eutectic points. (Modified from N. L. Bowen; data on pyroxene join from F. R. Boyd and J. F. Schairer, J. Petrol. vol. 5, pp. 280, 281, 296, 1964.) Circled points (1)–(4) are plots of normative pyroxene + quartz or pyroxene + olivine (cf. p. 283) calculated from analyses of some Hawaiian basalts: (1), (2), tholeiitic; (3), (4), alkaline. (G. A. MacDonald and T. Katsura, J. Petrol., vol. 5, 1964; Table 8, no. 4; Table 3, no. 3; Table 8, no. 10; Table 2, no. 7.)*

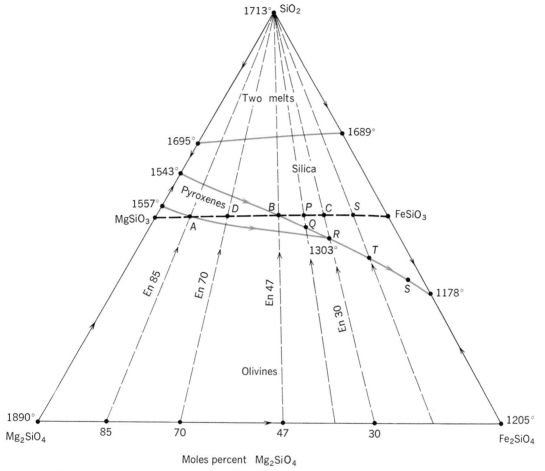

FIG. 6–9 *Equilibrium diagram for crystallization of liquids in the system Mg_2SiO_4–Fe_2SiO_4–SiO_2. (Modified from J. F. Schairer.)*

series, and (where pyroxene is combined with moderate concentrations of silica) by the development of two immiscible liquid phases. Some petrologically significant aspects of crystallization at atmospheric pressure are illustrated in Figures 6–8 and 6–9.

The nonferrous pyroxene solid-solution series is broken, at liquidus temperatures, by a miscibility gap (P_2–P_3 in Figure 6–8) between $Di_{10} En_{90}$ and $Di_{40} En_{60}$. All pyroxenes with a molar percentage of less than 60 diopside (P_4 to P_0) melt incongruently; so the first phase to separate from these is forsterite, which later becomes elimi-

nated as the liquid moves along the boundary between the forsterite and pyroxene fields. The course followed by a liquid L is: L to M with separation of forsterite; M to some point such as N while pyroxene separates and forsterite is used up. Meanwhile the pyroxene, initially of some such composition as P_1 would first move to P_2; thereafter two pyroxenes P_2 and P_3 would crystallize simultaneously, the final crystalline product being forsterite, P_2 and P_3. From a starting liquid M, P_1 would first separate, and the liquid would follow some curving course MQ across the pyroxene field, crystalline pyroxene meanwhile becoming increasingly diopsidic much as just described. From Q the liquid moves to a final and pyroxene composition such as S with separation of silica. The final product must be P_2, P_3, and silica.

Pyroxene–olivine systems   In the Mg_2SiO_4–Fe_2SiO_4–SiO_2 system (Figure 6–9) the behavior of pyroxene melts depends on the Mg/Fe ratio. Pyroxenes more magnesian than $A(En_{85}$, molar) follow the pattern of incongruent melting illustrated in Figure 6–6. Melts between A and $B(En_{85}$ to $En_{47})$ continuously precipitate pyroxene (which becomes richer in iron as the temperature falls) and ultimately yield a single pyroxene of the same composition as the parent melt. But in the range $DB(En_{70}$ to $En_{47})$ the melt at some stage reaches the pyroxene–silica cotectic and moves down BR. Silica is first precipitated at B, along with the changing pyroxene, and later is eliminated completely before R is reached. Iron-rich pyroxene melts with En 30–47 percent (molar)—to right of B—precipitate silica as the first crystalline phase. The melt thus moves to the pyroxene–silica cotectic (for example, along PQ) and then down the cotectic with simultaneous precipitation of pyroxene and silica, until it reaches the unique reaction point R. Here reaction proceeds toward elimination of silica while iron-rich pyroxene and olivine, both of unique composition, crystallize. The end product is a mixture of these three phases. Pyroxene melts with En less than 30 percent (molar) at no stage precipitate pyroxene. They follow courses such as STV with crystallization first of silica (on ST) then of olivine (on TV); the end product is ferrous olivine X plus silica. Equilibrium crystallization of any melt of course involves progressive enrichment of both solid-solution phases in iron as the temperature falls.

APPLICATION TO IGNEOUS PETROGENESIS   Theoretically based and experimental data regarding silicate–melt equilibria impose some strict limitations on any model of igneous petrogenesis. They predict the behavior of common rocks when heated to fusion temperature; the behavior of magmatic melts as they cool to and below crystallization temperature; the temperature and pressure ranges at which common igneous minerals and mineral assemblages can coexist in equilibrium with a melt.

In the following we summarize chemically based specifications for (1) origin of magma by fusion of deep-seated rocks, (2) differentiation of magmas by fractional crystallization, (3) modification of magmas by reaction with surrounding solid rocks.

Origin of magmas   Magmas may originate in two ways:

1. Complete or nearly complete fusion of pre-existing rocks. The most likely parent materials will be either low-melting crustal rocks (graywacke, shale, and granite), or deep-seated rocks (for example, in the mantle), where, regardless of composition, the temperature is close to the melting range.

2. Partial fusion (the reverse of fractional crystallization) by which a low-melting liquid fraction is drawn off from an unfused residue. If we are correct in assuming that the mantle is composed largely of heavy silicates rich in Mg and Fe, basaltic magmas could be derived from mantle material by differential fusion. Alternatively, andesitic or rhyolitic (granitic) magmas could form by differential fusion of basaltic (gabbroic) rocks. In either case we must suppose that the magmatic fraction is much less voluminous than the unfused residue; but the latter is conveniently hidden in the depths and so raises no serious problem.

Differentiation of magmas   It is agreed that the most effective means of magmatic differentiation—the continuous evolution of magmas from a common parent—is fractional crystallization. Other possible mechanisms, such as unmixing of the parent magma into immiscible fractions, or development of strong concentration gradients in still-liquid magmas are generally discounted, but not impossible. For example, development of very specialized magmas consisting largely of carbonate, of silica and ferrous silicates, or of even almost pure iron oxide (magnetite) could well be due to an unmixing process. But for over half a century fractional crystallization and magmatic differentiation, as applied to common rocks, have been thought of by geologists as virtually synonymous.

Restrictions imposed by experimental experience include the following:

1. Early crystal fractions must be composed of high-melting phases: magnesian olivines, pyroxenes with a high Mg/Fe^{2+} ratio, calcic plagioclase. Experiments at high pressures show that the pyroxenes of such fractions formed at great depth are likely to be aluminous; and some may be associated with a spinel, $(Mg, Fe) (Al, Fe)_2O_4$.

2. Successive liquids formed from basaltic magma will be progressively enriched in $(Na + K)/Ca$, in Fe^{2+}/Mg, and in $(Na + K)/Fe^{2+}$. The content of alkali feldspar + quartz (or nepheline) will rise at the expense of ferromagnesian silicates in the low-temperature differentiates (see Figures 6–1 and 6–7).

3. Individual crystals of plagioclase and olivine commonly show concentric compositional zoning: $NaSi/CaAl$ increases outward in plagioclase crystals, Fe^{2+}/Mg in olivine. Normal zoning of this kind is predictable on the basis of experimental data (see Figures 6–3 and 6–5). It implies failure of crystal–melt equilibrium due to slow rates of ionic diffusion in the rapidly growing crystal and in the adjacent liquid. Reversal or oscillation of the normal trend is not uncommon and indicates departure from the simple model of cooling at constant pressure. Crystal zoning changes the compositional trend of the residual melt and so affects the course of differentiation.

4. At an advanced stage of crystallization, water may become concentrated to the point at which hydrous phases such as hornblende and micas appear. Eventually the magma, becoming oversaturated in water at low pressures, may boil to give a second, largely aqueous, fluid phase. Crystallization of hydrous phases postpones the boiling stage.

5. The liquid becomes depleted in trace elements that readily substitute for common elements in the early crystalline phases: Ni for Mg in olivine; Cr^{3+} for Fe^{3+} in silicates and iron ores; Sr for Ca in plagioclase. Trace elements that cannot behave thus will build up in the late fractions. There they may become accommodated in the low-temperature crystalline phases: Ba^{2+} for K^+ in feldspar; Li^+ and Rb^+ for Mg^{2+} and K^+ in biotite. Or they may become concentrated in the aqueous fluid as it boils off in the last stages—for example, B, Be, Ta, Zr, Sn and a large number of others. Some of the controlling factors are discussed later (pages 279–280).

6. The relative quantities of late liquid fractions must steadily diminish in comparison with the volume of parent magma.

7. The scope of differentiation of a high-temperature melt such as basalt, for which the potential temperature range of fractional crystallization is several hundred degrees, will be wider than that of low-temperature magmas such as granite.

His first two decades of experimental work on silicate melts led N. L. Bowen to formulate his comprehensive model of igneous petrogenesis made classic in *The Evolution of the Igneous Rocks*, 1928. Basaltic magma was assigned the parent role; all other magmas, granitic melts included, were treated as products of fractional crystallization of the parent basalt. This was long accepted among English-speaking geologists (with the notable exception of Holmes) as orthodox dogma. Bowen's ideas are consistent with a vast amount of experimental data; and they satisfactorily explain many features of the chemistry and mineralogy of common igneous rocks. Today no one denies the importance of differentiation of basaltic magma by fractional crystallization to produce more siliceous and alkaline secondary magmas, some even in the granitic category. But as a *universal* mechanism of magmatic evolution, differentiation of basalt is no longer generally accepted.

Magmatic assimilation   Once held in general esteem was the rival mechanism of magmatic assimilation. Rising magma, especially in the great granitic batholiths, was pictured as melting its way upward, through crustal rocks, at the same time assimilating into itself the newly generated liquid. There is indeed widespread field evidence of extensive reaction between country rock and magma along the borders of many granitic plutons. But Bowen demolished the previously held idea that these are melting effects. His experiments placed two limitations upon the possibility of melting induced by rising magma already at the point of crystallization:

1. A melt from which high-temperature phases are crystallizing can melt rocks composed of low-temperature phases. At constant pressure the necessary heat of fusion will be supplied by crystallization of a thermally equivalent quantity of those phases with which the magma is already in equilibrium. Thus basalt magma can convert granite or graywacke to a liquid; but at the same time it will precipitate a thermally equivalent quantity of calcic plagioclase olivine or pyroxene. Thereby the remaining liquid fraction, although not augmented in quantity, becomes markedly changed in composition (more "granitic").

2. A melt in equilibrium with low-temperature phases cannot convert a solid aggregate of high-temperature phases to liquid of the same composition. Thus a granite magma from which

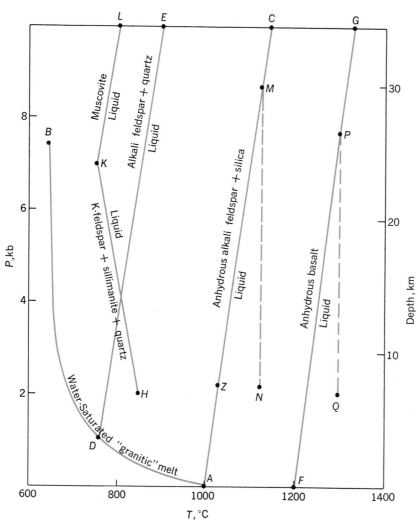

FIG. 6–10 *Approximate melting curves. AB—water-saturated minimum-melting mixtures of albite, potash feldspar, and quartz (ideal granite). DE—a mixture of albite, potash feldspar, and water, undersaturated with water at pressures above 1 kb. AC—anhydrous "granite." FG—anhydrous "basalt." HKL—muscovite or chemically equivalent dehydration products.*

sodic plagioclase and hornblende are crystallizing cannot liquify even a small quantity of basalt. By mutual diffusion between liquid and solid rock, the latter becomes converted to phases (for example, alkali feldspars, hornblende, and biotite) that can exist in equilibrium with granitic liquids. The granitic liquid of course becomes correspondingly depleted in elements such as Na, K, and Si, and enriched in Ca and Mg. Moreover, disrupted fragments and microscopic crystal aggregates pried from the reconstituted wall rock can become mechanically disseminated through the adjacent granite. The latter is thereby contaminated; but the resultant rock was never in an entirely liquid state.

The crux of the problem lies in the amount of heat available in the magma for melting of assimilated material. This "superheat" is the difference between the actual enthalpy of the magma and its enthalpy when it reaches the crystallization range. A liquid in equilibrium with its own crystals has no superheat. On a pressure–temperature diagram, melting curves of specific silicate mixtures (Figure 6–10) have a positive slope of perhaps 8–25°/kb (page 268). So magmas rising rapidly from the depths can clear themselves of crystals and become superheated—for example, along MN or PQ. Such magmas, even granites such as N, can assimilate low-melting materials, especially sediments rich in clay and mica, and metamorphic rocks containing hydrous silicates, such as micas and hornblende. The maximum effect would be achieved in a rather unlikely situation in which the country rock was already very close to its melting temperature. If we assume for both magma and country rock a specific heat 0.25 cal/g deg and a heat of fusion 70 cal/g, then a given volume of magma N, in cooling to its point of crystallization Z, could heat through 50° and then melt about 15–20 percent of its own volume of country rock. However, this value should be reduced to take account of adiabatic cooling of the rising magma.

Most of our knowledge of high-pressure melting phenomena comes from experiments at constantly maintained high water pressure equivalent to total pressure on the system. Much has been made of the "minimum melting curve" of "granite" (quartz alkali–feldspar mixtures), AB in Figure 6–10. The significance of such melts under plutonic conditions is dubious. Most magmas contain much less water than do corresponding melts in contact (as in the experiment) with a separate water-vapor phase.

Chemistry of Separation of Minor Elements

In a crude way the distribution of minor elements in crustal rocks reflects Goldschmidt's classification into siderophile, chalcophile, and lithophile categories (see Chapter 14). Platinum and nickel, siderophile elements presumed to be concentrated in the core, are found in ores associated with deep-seated plutonic rocks. This applies, too, to magmatic sulfide ores of chalcophile elements such as copper. On the other hand, it is in granitic rocks, believed to be products of crustal fusion, that lithophile or oxyphile elements such as tungsten and uranium reach their highest concentration.

Much that has been written on partition of elements between solid and liquid phases during fractional crystallization of magma or fusion of rocks reflects the well-known rules of Goldschmidt:

1. To form a solid solution series two mutually substituting elements must have similar ionic sizes (Mg^{2+}, Fe^{2+} in olivine; Na^+, Ca^{2+} in plagioclase).

2. If two elements of identical charge are similar in ionic size, the early crystalline fraction is relatively enriched in the smaller of the two (Mg^{2+} over Fe^{2+} in olivine).

3. If two ions of similar size differ in charge, the early crystalline fraction will be enriched in that with the higher charge (Ca^{2+} over Na^+ in plagioclase). Obviously, however, there are many exceptions to these rules. For example, any rule that applies to one side of the alkali–feldspar crystallization diagram (Figure 6–5) is contradicted by relations on the other side of the melting-point minimum.

A more realistic approach must take into account the ordered structure of silicate liquids. Since heats of fusion are trivial compared with lattice energies, it is clear that binding forces and structures in liquids must be similar to those in solids. If this were not so, solids would not melt except at enormous temperatures. Most of the properties of melts indicate a close approach to the structures of solids from which the melt is derived, but with breakdown of the long-range order of the solid. The nearest-neighbor environment of an ion in a melt is normally quite similar to that in the solid; but bond lengths tend to be a little shorter, and average coordination numbers smaller in the melt.

Principally through data of spectrography, including γ-ray spectrography (that is, Mössbauer spectra), something is beginning to be known regarding the structure of silicate liquids. This permits a more realistic application of thermodynamics to melting phenomena. It is even becoming possible to explain what otherwise seem to be anomalies and to predict with some confidence the crystallization behavior of complex silicate melts. This situation can be illustrated by brief reference to two cases:

1. The melting temperature of nickel olivine Ni_2SiO_4 is considerably lower than that of common magnesian olivine Mg_2SiO_4. The crystallization diagram for $(Mg, Ni)_2SiO_4$ solid solutions resembles that for $(Mg, Fe)_2SiO_4$ (Figure 6–3) with Mg_2SiO_4 again the high-melting end member. Yet the Ni/Mg ratio of magnesian olivine—the first silicate phase to crystallize from basaltic magma—is notably higher than that of the liquid with which it was in equilibrium (now represented by the fine-grained groundmass). This has been explained in terms of crystal-field theory, taking into account (a) the marked difference between the respective structures of $(Mg, Ni)_2SiO_4$ liquid, and basaltic liquid whose components include alkalis and aluminum, and (b) the preference of Ni for 6-coordinated rather than 4-coordinated sites (see page 71). Such 4-coordinated sites occur in basaltic melts but not in $(Mg, Ni)_2SiO_4$ liquids. Mg has no site preference.

2. Ions with exceptional properties—very large, very small, or having unusual oxidation states—tend to form separate compounds, even at low concentrations. These generally remain in the liquid until the very last stages, when they crystallize as separate phases in pegmatites (the coarse-grained feldspathic vein rocks formed from the final residues of granitic magmas). In this category belong Li, Be, U, Ta, Sn, and others. Their low concentration and slow buildup toward saturation favors slow but perfect growth of large crystals about few nuclei—a situation that has fortunate economic implications. Large crystals perhaps result where the crystal structure has unique interatomic spacings and nucleation consequently tends to be homogeneous. Alternatively nucleation may be induced on crystals of some common phase, in which case small crystals containing the rare element may be dispersed over crystal faces in a large volume of host rock. The fact that uranium is readily leached from granite suggests that some uranium compounds fall in this category.

Igneous Rocks

The tangible products of igneous activity are bodies of igneous rocks. Their nature and origin constitute the subject matter of igneous petrology. Questions of origin and evolution of igneous rocks and their parent magmas are viewed by the petrologist against a background provided by the observed phenomena of volcanism and the chemistry of crystal–melt equilibria in silicate systems.

In spite of their chemical diversity there is a somewhat surprising simplicity in the broad mineralogical patterns of igneous rocks. Most are composed of simple combinations of a few principal phases: feldspars, pyroxenes, olivine, hornblende, biotite, quartz, nepheline (or other feldspathoid), iron-titanium oxides. Some of these phases are mutually incompatible on chemical grounds, notably olivine–quartz and nepheline–quartz. Others show strong tendencies toward mutual association, or on the other hand mutual antipathy, for which there is no obvious chemical explanation. Thus quartz and alkali feldspar are constantly associated in acid rocks, and olivine, pyroxene, and calcic plagioclase in basic rocks. Antipathetic pairs are olivine–orthoclase, quartz–pyroxene, and others. It was Bowen who pointed out the significance of such tendencies. Associated phases are those that have been found by experiment to crystallize over the same temperature ranges in silicate–melt systems. Antipathetic phases have been found in the laboratory to crystallize at widely different temperatures. Herein lies the most convincing evidence supporting the igneous origin of plutonic rocks (granites included, for in these, too, the same generalizations hold good).

CLASSIFICATION AND NOMENCLATURE

Classification and nomenclature of igneous rocks takes into account chemical composition (especially content of SiO_2), mineralogical composition and texture. General correlation between these characteristics again is obvious and simple. Basic rocks are composed mainly of pyroxene, olivine, and calcic plagioclase, and because of the abundance of the first two minerals are dark in color. Acid rocks are light-colored and composed mainly of alkali feldspar, sodic plagioclase, and quartz. Between the two extremes lie other rocks with intermediate characteristics. Among these are the andesites of the Andes to which reference has already been made. Each chemically defined group has a limited range of texture reflecting the nature of the constituent minerals and varied cooling histories.

Paradoxically, in view of such overall simplicity, classifications of igneous rocks in current use—and there are a dozen of these—are unnecessarily and in some instances incredibly complex. They have been framed with a view to accommodating as a separate entity every slight departure from the obvious simple patterns, which are few. With complexity and proliferation of nomenclature has come ambiguity. Even the everyday terms "basalt" and "granite" have no universally accepted precise definition. Another unfortunate result of overclassification lies in arbitrary sharp distinctions that have been drawn between rock types that in nature show every shade of mutual gradation. No matter how

we define basalt and andesite, nor what silica percentage we may arbitrarily set as a line of division between the two, it cannot be denied that in nature no division exists. The great majority of basalts are recognizable as such by any definition; and the same applies to a great many andesites. But there are other lavas, whose silica content hovers between 52 and 54 percent, that are transitional rocks; and these may be the sole ingredient of some volcanoes.

To set up and discuss the main problems of igneous petrology, complex nomenclature fortunately is neither necessary nor desirable. We can limit ourselves to use of a few names in a rather elastic sense that is consistent with the uniqueness of every igneous product and with the mutually gradational nature of many associated rock types. These names are set out in Table 6–2, which is highly simplified and lists only the essential minerals of common rocks of each class. All basalts, for example, contain the listed minerals—labradorite, pyroxene (mainly augite), olivine—together with minor phases, notably iron–titanium oxides and apatite. Every geologist knows this; and he is aware, too, that other minerals may be present. But he is hindered rather than helped by introduction of a score of additional names (with most of which he is unfamiliar) to cover variations in alkali/silica ratio or possible presence of small quantities of other phases such as nepheline, hornblende, biotite, or alkali feldspar.

Finally, it is noted that there is no sharp division between volcanic and plutonic rocks. In rocks of each class the texture and, to a lesser degree, the mineralogy of the rock reflect its cooling history. This is conditioned partly by depth, partly by the size of the magma body. The textures of volcanic rocks normally express rapid cooling and solidification at or near the surface. The typical product is finely crystalline or even glassy, the extreme being almost pure glass (obsidian) developed from highly viscous acid magmas. The glass phase itself is a metastable liquid of extreme viscosity. Many volcanic rocks have a porphyritic texture (Chapter 3). The large well-formed crystals (phenocrysts) in most cases have formed by slow crystallization in the depths prior

TABLE 6–2 Nomenclature of common igneous rocks (Essential silicate phases are listed in parentheses)

	Basic Composition 45% SiO_2				Acid Composition 75% SiO_2
Volcanic Rocks	Basalts (calcic plagioclase, pyroxenes, olivine)		Andesites Dacites (medium plagioclase, pyroxenes, hornblende)		Rhyolites (quartz, alkali feldspar, sodic plagioclase)
		Sodic basalts (with medium or sodic plagioclase)	Trachytes (alkali feldspar, pyroxenes)		
			Phonolites (alkali feldspar, nepheline, sodic pyroxenes)		
	Nephelinites (nepheline, olivine, pyroxenes, minor calcic plagioclase)				
Plutonic Rocks	Peridotites or ultramafic rocks (olivine, pyroxenes)	Gabbros (calcic plagioclase, pyroxenes, olivine)	Diorites (medium plagioclase, hornblende)	Granodiorites (quartz, medium or sodic plagio- clase, potash feldspar, horn- blende, biotite)	Granites (quartz, potash feldspar, sodic plagioclase, biotite, hornblende)
			Syenites (alkali feldspar, hornblende, biotite)		
			Nepheline syenites (with nepheline and sodic pyroxenes)		

to extrusion. They are usually high-temperature phases such as magnesian olivine or calcic plagioclase. Commonly, too, gas bubbles have become frozen in as spherical or ellipsoidal cavities (vesicles). Plutonic rocks for the most part lack all these features. They are coarser and more uniform in grain. Slow cooling after solidification has permitted varied chemical adjustments on the microscopic scale: reorganization of grain boundaries (somewhat as in annealed metal); reaction between adjacent grains of different minerals; unmixing of two components in solid-solution series such as pyroxenes and alkali feldspars. Hydrous minerals such as biotite and hornblende are much more prevalent in plutonic as contrasted with volcanic rocks—presumably because high pressure in the deep environment favors retention of dissolved water in the magma. These generalizations, though open to frequent exception, provide a sound basis for dividing igneous rocks into two mutually gradational major classes: volcanic and plutonic.

In Table 6–2 there is complete gradation between rock types along each horizontal line.

Cross gradations likewise exist. Such are the respective transitions between rather alkaline basalt and oligoclase basalt, between trachyte and sodic rhyolites, and between diorites and syenites. The reader who consults the literature cited at the end of this chapter will encounter many additional rock names.

CHEMICAL COMPOSITION

A sample of igneous rock on any scale is, from the thermodynamic standpoint, a heterogeneous system consisting of a number of phases (minerals and, if present, glass). It can be defined in terms of (1) the nature and relative quantities of the associated phases and (2) its bulk chemical composition. The nature and composition of the phases is commonly known only from optical data, supplemented in recent years by X-ray data and chemical analyses of representative minerals. Chemical analysis of total rocks are expressed in terms of weight percentages of a dozen principal oxides. Some, especially in recent years, are supplemented by spectrographically determined trace-element contents—parts per million of Ba, Sr, Rb, Co, Ni, V, Cr, Zr, Th, and others. Something is becoming known, too, as to isotope ratios for the principal elements, notably Si and O and some radioactive nuclides, Sr^{87}/Sr^{86}. Today there is a vast amount of information regarding the chemistry of rocks, and less extensive but rapidly increasing data on the compositions of igneous minerals.

Rock compositions are usually recorded in any or all of three ways: (1) chemical composition (from analysis); (2) *mode*, expressed in weight percentages of constituent minerals; (3) *norm* expressed in weight percentages of ideal phases as computed from the chemical analyses.

The normative compositions of most igneous rocks are expressed in terms of the ideal phases:

Q	quartz	SiO_2
Or	orthoclase	$KAlSi_3O_8$
Ab	albite	$NaAlSi_3O_8$
An	anorthite	$CaAl_2Si_2O_8$
Ne	nepheline	$NaAlSiO_4$
Di	diopside	$Ca(Mg, Fe)Si_2O_6$

Hy	hypersthene	$(Mg, Fe)SiO_3$
Ol	olivine	$(Mg, Fe)_2SiO_4$
Mt	magnetite	Fe_3O_4
Hm	hematite	Fe_2O_3
Il	ilmenite	$FeTiO_3$
Ap	apatite	$Ca_5(PO_4)_3$

Olivine and nepheline are incompatible with quartz; nepheline also with hypersthene. Rocks with normative quartz are *oversaturated*, rocks with normative olivine or nepheline *undersaturated*, in silica. Hematite in the norm indicates a high oxidation ratio. Relatively rarely additional phases must be included in the norm.

The general compositional range of common igneous rocks is illustrated by a few representative examples in Table 6–3.

Patterns of Igneous Phenomena

IGNEOUS ROCK ASSOCIATIONS

We have seen that igneous activity has always been a local and, to some degree, random phenomenon. So it is possible to recognize specific *petrogenic provinces*, mostly a few thousand square kilometers in extent, within which mutually associated igneous rocks can be assigned to a restricted period—perhaps a few million years—of activity. The rocks of any province usually have chemical characteristics in common, suggesting community of origin. But they also tend to show considerable chemical and mineralogical divergence, implying some kind of magmatic evolution from a parent stock or *primitive magma*, or perhaps independent origin at different times in the same environment. The rocks of a province are generally regarded as the collective product of a unique cycle of igneous activity or temporary disturbance, the broad pattern of which tends to repeat itself; and as a result igneous cycles and their products, as exemplified by individual petrogenic provinces, tend to conform to a dozen or so recognizable patterns.

For half a century, emphasis in teaching and research has been placed upon regularity in igneous petrogenesis. Data have been systematized to the point where ten or a dozen standard rock associations are familiar to every geologist.

TABLE 6–3 *Chemical analyses and norms of some representative igneous rocks (expressed as weight percentages)*

No.:	1	2	3	4	5	6
SiO_2	42.86	48.04	50.02	60.31	66.57	72.80
TiO_2	2.94	1.83	2.23	1.02	0.60	0.46
Al_2O_3	11.46	12.04	15.05	17.53	15.14	13.12
Fe_2O_3	3.34	2.35	3.77	3.30	1.15	1.32
FeO	9.03	8.80	7.37	3.85	1.90	1.62
MnO	0.13	0.17	0.17	0.16	0.06	0.04
MgO	13.61	14.41	7.01	2.59	0.56	0.60
CaO	11.24	8.76	10.17	5.97	1.50	2.20
Na_2O	3.02	1.60	2.05	3.20	4.18	3.63
K_2O	0.93	0.30	0.33	1.20	5.02	3.71
H_2O	0.56	1.63	1.65	0.90	3.01	0.24
P_2O_5	0.52	0.12	0.27	0.14	0.19	0.04
Others	CO_2 0.30				BaO 0.25	BaO 0.06
Total	99.94	100.05	100.09	100.17	100.13	99.84
Q			6.30	19.50	16.9	32.34
Or	5.56	1.67	1.67	7.12	29.5	21.68
Ab	5.76	13.62	17.29	27.04	35.6	30.39
An	15.29	24.74	31.14	28.72	7.0	8.62
Ne	10.51					
Di	29.43	14.20	13.84	0.86		1.83
Hy		27.47	17.72	9.01	3.0	1.79
Ol	20.79	9.51				
Mt	4.87	3.25	5.57	4.78	1.6	1.86
Il	5.62	3.50	4.26	1.93	1.2	0.91
Ap	1.34	0.34	0.67	0.34	0.3	
Total	99.17	98.30	98.46	99.30	95.1	99.42

Explanation of column headings:

1. Highly undersaturated lava of nephelinite family, Honolulu Series, Oahu, Hawaii (H. Winchell, *Geol. Soc. Am. Bull.*, vol. 58, p. 30, no. 13, 1947).

2. Somewhat undersaturated olivine basalt, Haleakala volcano, Maui, Hawaii (G. A. MacDonald and T. Katsura, *J. Petrol.*, vol. 5, p. 122, no. C-122, 1964).

3. Oversaturated basalt (tholeiite) Waianae volcano, Oahu, Hawaii (MacDonald and Katsura, *ibid.*, no. C-27, 1964).

4. Pyroxene andesite, northeastern Japan (Y. Kawano, K. Yagi, and K. Aoki, *Sci. Rept. Tohoku University*, ser. 3, vol. 7, no. 1, p. 32, no. 70, 1961).

5. Trachyte, Main Range, Queensland, Australia (N. C. Stevens, *Proc. Royal Soc. Queensland*, vol. 87, no. 4, p. 46, no. 3, 1965).

6. Hornblende-biotite granodiorite (granite) Mt. Hale, Southern California, Batholith (E. S. Larsen, *Geol. Soc. Amer. Mem.* 29, p. 91, 1948).

Some of the more important of these are listed below.

ESSENTIALLY VOLCANIC ASSOCIATIONS

1. Slightly oversaturated basalts of very great extent and small compositional range, with andesites and rhyolites as minor associates. Similar magmas intruded as shallow sills have subordinate differentiates of granitic composition. The environment is characteristically but not exclusively continental.

2. Basalts, mostly saturated or nearly so in

silica, covering or underlying the sediments of the ocean floors, and building volcanic islands.

3. Alkaline basalts undersaturated in silica, nepheline-bearing basaltic rocks (nephelinite family), and subordinate trachyte, phonolite or sodic rhyolite. These are worldwide in their occurrence. They are represented in continental provinces of all ages and on many midoceanic islands.

4. Andesite (flows and tuffs) and rhyolite (mainly pyroclastic) in geosynclinal fillings (associated with albitized basalts) and repeatedly erupted later during and following the folding and uplift of geosynclincal rocks.

5. Highly alkaline basaltic lavas accompanied and locally dominated by potassic basalts, trachytes, and other lavas in which K_2O/Na_2O is exceptionally high. Provinces of this kind are especially characteristic of continental areas; not uncommonly these are either tectonically stable or affected only by large-scale rifting. But there are a few oceanic islands (for example, Tristan da Cunha) whose lavas are more than normally potassic.

ESSENTIALLY PLUTONIC ASSOCIATIONS

1. Granodiorite *migmatites* of continental shields and deeply eroded older mountain ranges. In migmatite complexes, granodiortic and metamorphic components are intimately associated, though mutually segregated, on all scales from that of a hand specimen to that of a batholith.

2. Discrete batholiths, usually composed of many individual plutons, ranging from gabbro and diorite to granite, but with granodiorite greatly predominant. These commonly invade the folded rocks of geosynclinal terranes.

3. Immense layered sheetlike intrusions of overall basaltic composition. Individual layers include peridotite, pyroxene rock, chromite rock, gabbro (dominant), plagioclase rock (anorthosite) and minor granite.

4. Sheets and lenses of peridotite and its hydrated equivalent serpentine rock (serpentinite), intruded into geosynclinal sediments and lavas in the prefolding and early folding stages. Common associates are siliceous marine sediments (cherts) and albitic basalts.

5. Precambrian batholiths of anorthosite (labradorite rock) with some associated gabbro, pyroxene syenites, and pyroxene granite.

6. Small intrusions of alkaline, often feldspathoidal, plutonic rocks and carbonatite (calcite or dolomite rocks now believed to have crystallized from carbonate melts). These intrusions, of all ages, usually cut through stable areas of Precambrian gneiss and granite. Some are clearly the shallow plutonic equivalent of the alkaline volcanic associations listed as 3 and 5.

MAGMA TYPES

In the first part of this century it was widely held that basalts—the dominant lavas of the world—were essentially uniform in composition and came from a common source, a world-encircling basaltic shell in the lower crust. But intensive study of the Tertiary Scottish volcanic province during the 1920s and early 1930s revealed a range of basalts too diversified to fit so simple a model. To explain the diversity, W. Q. Kennedy invoked two independent basaltic "magma types." One, the *tholeiitic* type, was envisaged as essentially saturated or oversaturated in silica. The other, the *alkaline basalt* (or olivine basalt) magma type was specified to be more alkaline than the tholeiitic type and strongly undersaturated in silica. With but few chemical analyses available, the two types were remarkably distinct.

To keep petrology systematic, the same two magma types were sought, and found, elsewhere—in the Pacific, in Australia, in the United States, and so on. As more rock analyses became available the sharp boundary between tholeiitic and alkaline types became blurred. Departures from the two alternative sets of specifications became obvious. To meet the changing situation and the embarrassing wealth of new analytical data, petrologists today tend to adopt one of two attitudes. Some have so enlarged and refined the original specifications that the line of division between the two magma types is distinguishable only to the geochemist or to a well-instructed computer. Others have invoked additional magma types. Such are the high-alumina magma type found in andesite provinces; the nephelinite magma type of alkaline volcanic terranes; the strange magma type responsible for extremely potassic nonsodic rocks in Leucite Hills, Wyoming; and the oceanic tholeiite magma type, with its extreme Na/K ratio, represented by the most extensive basalts of the world—those of the deep ocean floors. Other magma types, not specifically designated as such, have been brought in to account for rock associations respectively dominated by andesite–rhyolite, by granodiorite, and by peridotite.

Much of research and controversy in petrology today centers on the number, definition, possible modes of origin, and evolution of principal magma types. In this book we stress the uniqueness of every petrographic province, and incline to the view that distinct magma types are many.

MINOR-ELEMENT AND ISOTOPE PATTERNS

The relative concentrations of minor elements and the isotopic compositions of others, such as oxygen, carbon and strontium in common igneous rocks, conform to consistent recognizable patterns reflecting three factors: inheritance from the source rocks of primitive magmas; partition between successive liquid and crystalline fractions during differentiation; and radioactive decay of unstable nuclides, which introduces an element of time into the observed isotope pattern.

The chemistry of a primitive magma sets obvious limits on the composition of the source material. For example, elements such as K, Rb, Li, Th, U, that preferentially enter the liquid phase must necessarily be present in smaller concentrations in the source rock than in any directly extracted magma. On the other hand, partial melting cannot lead to appreciable fractionation of stable isotopes. So the isotopic composition of elements such as O, Si, C, S, should be much the same in source rocks as in derived magmas. The same has been claimed for Sr^{87}/Sr^{86} provided the present value, taking into account the Rb/Sr ratio, is extrapolated back to the time of origin of the magma. There is a possible flaw in this reasoning. Radiogenic Sr^{87} in the source rock occupies misfit sites in mineral crystals and so might become preferentially concentrated into the liquid fraction withdrawn from the unfused resi-

due as new magma. The significance of Sr^{87}/Sr^{86} in primitive magmas is compounded of the dual influence of time and situation.

During differentiation of any magma the minor-element and isotope patterns follow well-established lines determined by partition between successive crops of crystals and liquid fractions (Chapter 5). As the major elements Si, Na, and K increase, and Mg, Fe, and Ca fall off along the liquid line of descent, there is sympathetic increase in some minor elements (Rb, Ba, Li, Th, U, and others) and decrease in others (for example, Ni, Co, V, Cr). Also significant are changing ratios between related elements: Rb/Sr, Ba/Sr, Co/Ni increase, whereas K/Rb decreases markedly in later liquids. The particular pattern in any rock series gives a valuable hint as to the differentiation pattern itself. Heavy depletion in Ni indicates early removal of olivine; sharp decrease in V is correlated with early crystallization of magnetite, itself determined by the state of oxidation of the magma. Concentration of SiO_2 in andesitic magmas has been attributed by some to early separation of magnetite; if this is true we must expect to find the andesitic differentiate cleaned free of vanadium.

Patterns of isotopic fractionation are also beginning to emerge. Thus in differentiation of basaltic magma to granitic liquids $\delta_{S^{34}/S^{32}}$ (relative to standard meteoritic FeS) rises from ± 0.1 per mil to as high as $+7$ per mil; and $\delta_{O^{18}/O^{16}}$ (relative to standard seawater) may rise from $+5.5$ to $> +8$ per mil.[6] Since Rb/Sr rises along the liquid line of descent, then in ancient differentiates Sr^{87}/Sr^{86} will be significantly higher than in rocks representing the contemporary primitive magma. These values should plot on an isochron that dates the event of differentiation.

Profound modification of minor-element patterns can be expected where a primitive magma becomes significantly contaminated by later reaction with country rock. Ratios involving unstable nuclides and daughter nuclides of radioactive decay—for example, Sr^{87}/Sr^{86} and Th/U —will be especially affected when young mag-

---

$^6 \delta_{O^{18}/O^{16}} = 1000 \left[\dfrac{O^{18}/O^{16} \text{ in rock}}{O^{18}/O^{16} \text{ in standard}} - 1 \right].$

mas react with ancient rocks in the deeper parts of the continental crust.

If minor-element patterns observed in primitive magmas set limits on the composition of source rocks, the reverse is equally true. Magmas that habitually show the most "primitive" traits —such as very low K, Rb, Li, minimal Rb/Sr, S^{87}/S^{86} (corrected for age), high K/Rb—are basalts from the deep ocean floor. These characteristics, presumably inherited from the source, give an idea of the composition of the upper mantle, at least beneath the oceans. There are some close analogies with corresponding characteristics of stony meteorites, especially those of the common chondrite class. And this supports a generally prevalent idea based on a variety of independent evidence that the composition of the mantle may be akin to that of chondritic meteorites. There are nevertheless unexplained anomalies; for example, in chondrites Rb/Sr may be much higher (0.17 to 0.30), and Sr^{87}/Sr^{86} somewhat higher, than in many oceanic basalts; and K/U is much higher in chondrites than in most terrestrial rocks (see Chapter 12).

With these and other data of a similar nature in mind, geochemists have stipulated certain characteristics of the minor-element and isotope patterns of igneous rocks as indicating inheritance from a source in the mantle. Hurley, for example, thinks that the present Sr^{87}/Sr^{86} ratio in the mantle source is between 0.702 and 0.705, having increased by 0.004 from a primordial value in 4.5 b.y.; the ratio Rb/Sr is given as 0.02. Isotopic compositions in the mantle, as given by Taylor, are those found both in chondritic meteorites and in most basalts: $\delta_{O^{18}/O^{16}} = +5.3$ to $+6.3$ per mil; $\delta_{S^{34}/S^{32}} = \pm0.1$ per mil; $\delta_{C^{13}/C^{12}} = -16$ to -25 per mil (the value for carbonaceous chondrites is very different, -4 to -11 per mil). K_2O in mantle-derived magmas must be low, but not less than values round 0.11 common in chondritic meteorites; K/Rb should be somewhat below the chondrite value, 300.

It would be a mistake to apply so simple a model universally. It is scarcely likely that the mantle, even the uppermost part, is homogeneous. Moreover, we believe it to be subject to internal disturbance—convection. Locally, at least, there must be patches of mantle rock having a residual character imposed by extraction of more fusible constituents to yield magmas. We should be on the lookout, too, for magmas that have isotopic or minor-element patterns resembling those of the more extreme stony meteorites.

Potential source materials of another kind may be sought in the deeper levels of the continental crust. Possible candidates are ancient granitic gneisses and metamorphic rocks, some of sedimentary origin, such as we see at the surface today in the continental shields. Chemical traits expected to be inherited from sources such as these include high Si, K, Rb, Li, Th, U, and a host of other minor elements. Also to be expected are high Rb/Sr (exceeding 1 in many granites), Sr^{87}/Sr^{86} (averaging 0.71–0.73 in Precambrian sialic rocks and exceeding 0.8 in some ancient granitic gneisses, and $\delta_{O^{18}/O^{16}}$ (+8 to +10 in granitic rocks, as high as +25 in siliceous sediments). Extreme isotopic compositions of sulfur are found in many ancient granites and metasediments ($\delta_{S^{34}/S^{32}}$ close to +30 in some cases). K/Rb values tend to be low, commonly 200–230.

With regard to distribution of minor elements in igneous rocks and isotopic compositions of key elements, our present state of knowledge is still too imperfect to permit confident conclusions as to the exact situations of magma sources, or as to the chemistry of the source rocks themselves. All we can do is to set limits to several alternative possibilities. Today petrologists set up various comprehensive models of petrogenesis, which are then tested for internal consistency and modified or rejected in the light of new data from several independent sources. Still of paramount importance in this connection is information regarding the mutual association and relative volumes of common igneous rocks and their order of appearance in time. Some of this information we shall now examine.

Basaltic Provinces

HAWAIIAN ISLANDS

GEOGRAPHY AND VOLCANIC HISTORY   In the mid-Pacific, between latitudes 20° and 30°N a submarine ridge—mean altitude about 5000 meters below sea level—rises above the ocean floor and extends for more than 2000 km east-southeast from Midway to Hawaii. It is capped intermittently by volcanic islands (Figure 4–3). Those occupying the southeastern 1000 km of the ridge crest are the Hawaiian Islands. They constitute a mid-oceanic basaltic province whose character is illustrated in two of the largest islands, Hawaii at the southeastern end of the chain, and Oahu in the middle, some 200 km northwest.

Hawaii, the largest island, comprises the coalescing summits of five volcanoes (Figure 6–11), whose growth collectively spans less than a million years. All except one, Kohala, continued active into Recent times. The two southernmost —Mauna Loa and Kilauea—have been continuously active through historic times. On Hualalai a single historic eruption occurred early last century. The three volcanic series of Oahu (Figure 6–12) span the Miocene–Recent period; but there are no records of eruptions in historic times.

The largest volcano on Hawaii, Mauna Loa, has a total bulk, allowing for submarine extension over the basement ridge, of the order of 40,000 to 50,000 km³. In form it is a *shield volcano* (Fig-

ure 6–13a), a flat dome whose surface slopes seaward at 7° or 8° from the summit (nearly 4200 meters above sea level). There is a summit *caldera*, a steep-walled, flat-floored depression 3 km wide and 300 meters deep, a principal center of eruption. Smaller calderas ("pits"), also eruptive centers, are aligned on linear radial rifts on the flank of the mountain. Kilauea (Figure 6–13b) is a smaller, though still impressive, shield volcano (summit elevation 1250 meters), with its own caldera and crater-pitted rift zones running southeast and southwest from the summit to the sea. The three northern volcanoes, the highest of which is Mauna Kea (about 4200 meters high) have been deeply dissected. So too have the volcanic piles of Oahu (maximum elevation 1000 meters).

A general scheme of volcanic evolution has been established by comparing the individual histories of the older and more completely developed volcanoes in the northwestern islands, with the younger still developing volcanoes of Hawaii itself which illustrate the earlier stages only (p. 188).

PRIMITIVE HAWAIIAN BASALT   Because of its importance with respect to problems of magma type and petrogenesis, attention has been strongly focused in recent years on the nature of primitive Hawaiian basalt or basalts.

1. The basalt of Kilauea and Mauna Loa is remarkably uniform, and its classification as "olivine tholeiite" is generally accepted. Most flows contain significant but not plentiful magnesian olivine as early-formed, large, corroded crystals. But except where olivine is unusually concentrated, the norm consistently shows abundant hypersthene, minor (but significant) quartz, no olivine or nepheline. The rock composition is tholeiitic by any definition. Minor associates are olivine-enriched basalts, and at the other extreme, hypersthene basalts with but little olivine. Generally similar, and also to be classed as olivine tholeiites, are lavas from the early shield stage on Kohala and on the Waianae and Koolau volcanoes of Oahu (Figure 6–12).

2. There are other Hawaiian volcanoes in

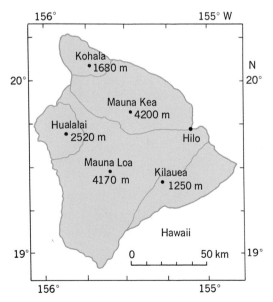

FIG. 6–11 *Map showing locations of main volcanic centers of the Island of Hawaii.*

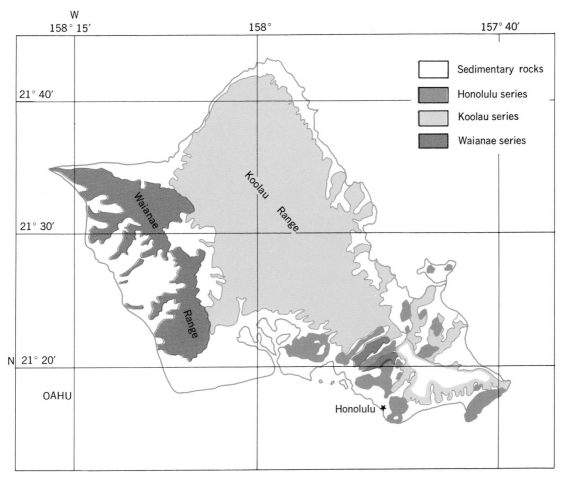

W
158° 15'   158°   157° 40'

21° 40'

Koolau   Range

21° 30'

Waianae

Range

N 21° 20'

OAHU

Honolulu ★

Sedimentary rocks

Honolulu series

Koolau series

Waianae series

FIG. 6–12 *Map of Oahu, Hawaiian Islands, showing distribution of principal eruptive provinces. (After C. K. Wentworth and H. Winchell, Geol. Soc. Am. Bull., vol. 58, p. 51, 1947.)*

which the exposed portion of the primitive shield is composed of basalts distinctly undersaturated in silica. Those of Mauna Kea consistently show about 10 percent of olivine, and some a trace of nepheline in the norm. These rocks cannot be classified as tholeiitic.

3. The lower bulk of most of the Hawaiian volcanoes is built of olivine tholeiite lavas similar to those of Mauna Loa and Kilauea. But there are also large edifices in which the lowest exposed components of the shield are of another type— undersaturated basalt with abundant normative olivine. Highly alkaline basaltic magmas repre-

sented by basalts with normative nepheline, and by nephelinites, are confined to the later stages of some volcanoes and make up a small fraction of the total Hawaiian volcanic pile.

4. Tilley used a graphic plot $(Na_2O + K_2O)$ against SiO_2—a type of variation diagram (see page 292—to demonstrate what was considered 20 years ago to be a sharp chemical distinction between tholeiitic and alkaline basalts (Figure 6–14a). Plotted on the same basis (Figure 6–14b) the much more numerous analyses of Hawaiian basalts that are now available cover the whole field. The line AB, arbitrarily drawn by Mac-

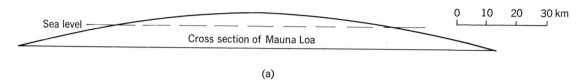

Sea level

Cross section of Mauna Loa

0 10 20 30 km

(a)

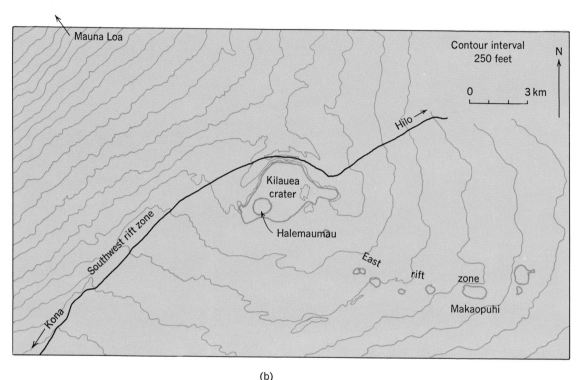

Mauna Loa

Contour interval
250 feet

N

0   3 km

Kilauea
crater

Halemaumau

Southwest rift zone

East

rift

zone

Kona

Makaopuhi

Hilo

(b)

FIG. 6–13 (a) Cross section (true vertical scale) across Mauna Loa, Hawaii. (b) Caldera and rifts Kilauea volcano, Hawaii. (After G. A. MacDonald and J. P. Eaton, U.S. Geol. Surv. Bull., 1061-B, p. 21, 1957.)

Donald, conveys an impression of artificiality; but it occupies an area of minimum density of plotted points (as currently available); and most, though not all, primitive basalts fall in the bottom right sector. This is the basis for the generally accepted view that the primitive magma of Hawaii is "tholeiitic." But this is not the tholeiite that we shall encounter in dominantly basaltic continental volcanic piles and sill swarms elsewhere. And there are major volcanoes such as Mauna Kea in which the postulated olivine tholeiite, if present, is not exposed.

5. If all the Hawaiian basaltic magmas have a common origin then clearly olivine tholeiite is cast for the parental role. Most petrologists today advocate or lean toward this view. But there is an alternative possibility. Each batch of magma supplying material for eruption at any center over a period of about a century may have originated as an independent unit, as suggested by Powers. If so there is no such thing as a uniform parent magma on a regional scale. Marked differences in composition, as between olivine tholeiite, olivine basalt, and nephelinic basalts, may simply reflect differences in time and place. Those who see uniform simplicity in the scheme

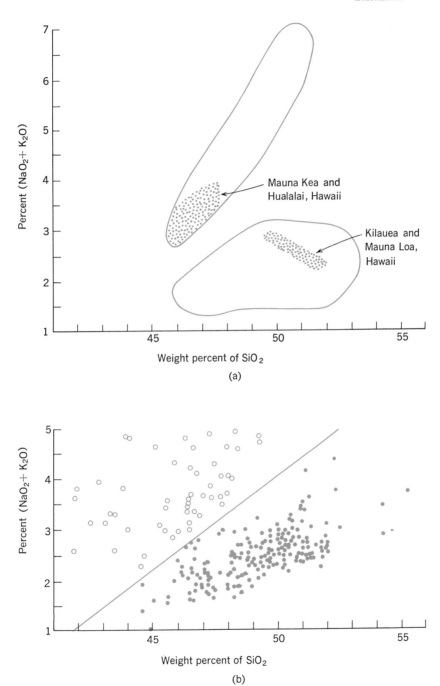

FIG. 6–14 *Alkali–silica diagrams (weight percentages) for Hawaiian basalts. [(a) After C. E. Tilley, Geol. Soc. London Quart. J., vol. 106, p. 42, 1950. (b) After G. A. MacDonald and T. Katsura, J. Petrol., vol. 5, p. 87, 1964.]*

of magma genesis beneath the Hawaiian Islands possibly seek order where little order exists, and neglect an element of randomness that may be real.

DIFFERENTIATION OF HAWAIIAN MAGMAS   Late in their history many Hawaiian volcanoes erupt lavas chemically distinct from the primitive basalts. These include slightly undersaturated basaltic rocks with abnormally sodic plagioclase (oligoclase or andesine), and rather rare trachytes and rhyolites. Compared with the primitive basalts, all these rocks are notably high in $(K_2O + Na_2O)$, lower in $(MgO + FeO + Fe_2O_3)$, and have a higher $(Fe_2O_3 + FeO)/MgO$ ratio; the oligoclase basalts are somewhat higher, the trachytes and rhyolites much more so in SiO_2. These consistent chemical characteristics suggest that the magmas in question are late liquid fractions derived from basaltic magmas by fractional crystallization (differentiation). Most geologists accept this interpretation; and it is consistent too with the small volume and late appearance of the lavas in question.

A commonly used device for illustrating chemical variation in associated igneous rocks is some sort of graphic plot of significantly varying chemical parameters. Such a plot is called a variation diagram. One type has already been used to demonstrate differences in alkali/silica ratios of Hawaiian basalts (Figure 6–14). Another is the *AFM* plot of oxide percentages by weight, in which

$$A = Na_2O + K_2O$$
$$F = FeO \ (Fe^{2+} \text{ and } Fe^{3+} \text{ calculated as FeO})$$
$$M = MgO$$
$$A + F + M = 100$$

This is used in Figure 6–15 to show corresponding variation in the tholeiitic and alkaline basalts and their respective associated lavas in Hawaii. If we are correct in interpreting the more alkaline minor associates as differentiates, then the curves of Figure 6–15 represent the liquid lines of descent (in the directions shown by the arrows) developed in successive fractions drawn off from crystallizing magmas initially basaltic in composition.

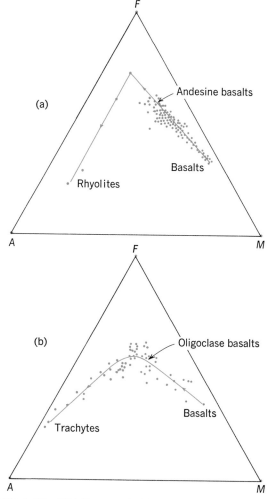

FIG. 6–15   *AFM diagrams (oxides, weight percentages) for Hawaiian lavas. (a) Tholeiitic basalts and differentiates; (b) alkaline basalts and differentiates. (Modified from G. A. MacDonald and T. Katsura, ibid., p. 109.)*

Complementary to late liquid fractions should be crops of early-formed high-temperature minerals. Judging from experimental experience, these might be expected to include magnesian olivine and augite and calcic plagioclase. Some of the basaltic flows indeed are found to contain abundant phenocrysts or coarse-grained aggregates of just these minerals, especially olivine and augite. And olivine phenocrysts in such rocks as well as in the primitive tholeiitic basalts show a tendency to develop rounded "corroded" outlines as if by late reaction with a melt oversaturated in silica (for example, the reaction at R in Figure 6–6 or along MN in Figure 6–8). Mineralogical and textural data alike agree with predictions based on experiment.

Recent eruptions along the southeastern rift of Kilauea from time to time have filled earlier pit craters with lava. Two of these, still partly liquid beneath a thickening frozen crust, and a 75-meter natural section through a completely frozen prehistoric lake, have been sampled in detail. Complete solidification of such lakes takes 40 or 50 years. But even in this short time significant differentiation has been effected by sinking of large, early-formed crystals of magnesian olivine. The prehistoric lake is composed of Kilauean olivine tholeiite whose original composition is preserved in the upper, rapidly chilled crust. This contains 5 to 6 percent of olivine phenocrysts. At a depth of 25–30 meters the olivine content is reduced to 2 percent. The cause is easy to see; for in the basal 25 meters of the section olivine phenocrysts make up between 15 and 20 percent of the rock. Here we see, frozen in, a picture of dense olivine crystals slowly sinking under gravity in a less dense medium—a long familiar mechanism of fractional crystallization. Residual glass separated from the olivine-depleted basalt toward the upper part of the Kilauean lake section has the "granitic" composition ($NaAlSi_3O_8$ + $KAlSi_3O_8$ + SiO_2) predicted long ago by Bowen for late liquid fractions in basaltic systems.

VESTIGES OF THE MANTLE   Alkaline undersaturated rocks of the nephelinite family, all the world over, contain ultramafic rock fragments, up to a few centimeters in diameter, with a most distinctive mineralogical composition: highly magnesian olivine, the pyroxenes enstatite $MgSiO_3$ and diopside $CaMgSi_2O_6$ (both low in iron), and the chrome spinel $(Mg, Fe)(Al, Cr)_2O_4$. Hawaii is no exception. Such fragments are abundant for example in the nephelinites of the Honolulu series. These fragments (*xenoliths*) are truly alien to the magma that encloses them.

Their most likely source is in the mantle itself; and they are generally interpreted as unfused residues of mantle material from which basaltic liquid has already been extracted (page 312). In the tuffs of one small volcano near Honolulu there are plentiful fragments of a rock of very different character. It is composed of garnet and aluminous augite, a mineral combination that has been found by experiment to crystallize from basaltic liquids at pressures of the order of 20–30 kb. If the composition of the mantle locally approaches basalt, garnet–pyroxene would be the stable phase combination at depths of 70–100 km.

Whatever the origin of these xenolithic bodies, it cannot be denied that the source of Hawaiian magmas is in the outer mantle. Here the crust is thin—not more than 10 km—and the focus of seismic activity preceding eruption is much deeper than this. So in the primitive Hawaiian magmas we may expect to find chemical traits inherited from the mantle source rock. In tholeiitic basalts and oligoclase basalts of Hawaii Sr^{87}/Sr^{86} is reported as 0.7041 ± 0.0003; $Rb/Sr = 0.024 - 0.038$. In nephelinites of Oahu Sr^{87}/Sr^{86} is reported as 0.7031. These low values are expectable in the light of earlier discussion. Throughout the full range of Hawaiian lavas, from basalts and nephelinites to trachytes, the ratio Th/U maintains a remarkably constant value, 4.1. This is thought to be an inherited character of the source rock, which in this respect must be uniform beneath the whole province.

MODEL OF HAWAIIAN PETROGENESIS   We conclude with a skeleton model of petrogenesis consistent with those data that appear at the moment to be reliably established:

1. Over the past few million years olivine tholeiite magma has been repeatedly generated at subcrustal depths—50 to 60 km—at numerous centers along the Hawaiian chain. These centers, commonly no more than a few tens of kilometers apart, have maintained their separate identities over this whole period.

2. Each batch of magma supplies the mate-

rial for a limited cycle of activity, a century or two in duration. A new batch develops at the same site, and the cycle is then repeated.

3. At each center, as its full life history draws to a close, the composition of the principal magma changes. Instead of olivine tholeiite, it is now alkaline olivine basalt, or even, after a prolonged interval of inactivity, highly undersaturated nephelinite magma. Such magmas possibly are derived from tholeiitic magma by deep seated differentiation of a nature not yet fully understood. Perhaps more likely is an independent origin, as physical conditions at the source change, also in a manner still unknown (for example, by deepening of the source).

4. Both tholeiitic and alkaline olivine basalt magmas differentiate, mainly by relative movement of olivine in relation to liquid, to fractions yielding lavas with more sodic feldspar. The ultimate product of differentiation in the alkaline line is trachyte. That in the tholeiite line is rhyolite. Both are quantitatively insignificant.

MID-ATLANTIC PROVINCES

MID-ATLANTIC RIDGE The sole volcanic rock along the full length of the mid-Atlantic ridge, as shown by numerous dredge samples, is a slightly oversaturated tholeiitic basalt. The mineral composition is uniform and simple—labradorite, calcic augite and persistent minor olivine. Obvious in most chemical analyses is a feature otherwise found only in some continental basalts (page 299)—unusually high Al_2O_3, between 15 and 20 percent. Many basalts of the deep Atlantic have chemical characteristics (Table 6–4, no. 1) that are unknown among continental basalts, but are matched by many lavas from the floors of the Pacific and the Indian Ocean: exceptionally low K_2O (<0.2 percent), Ti, Rb, Sr, Th, U, Zr; uniquely high Na/K (>10) and K/Rb (possibly as high as 1300); extremely low Sr^{87}/Sr^{86} (0.7016–0.7027) and Rb/Sr (<0.01). Perhaps these features reflect more clearly the overall chemical composition of the suboceanic mantle than do corresponding but less extreme chemical characteristics of Hawaiian lavas. Cer-

tainly they show consistent analogies with the chemistry of some stony meteorites. For such reasons some writers regard the oceanic tholeiites as the most primitive of all basalts, closest of all in composition to upper mantle material, and indeed the parent of all other basaltic magmas (for example, Hawaiian) found in the ocean basins. Alternatively, if there is no direct relation between the various basaltic magmas of oceanic provinces, the source of oceanic tholeiites must lie deeper in the mantle than that of more alkaline basalt magmas.

MID-ATLANTIC ISLANDS Strung out along or close to the mid-Atlantic Ridge are groups of volcanic islands including Ascension, St. Helena, Gough, and the currently active groups of the Azores and Tristan da Cunha. In all these the principal lavas are reminiscent of the late alkaline olivine basalts of the Hawaiian Islands, but are even higher in alkali and more undersaturated in silica (Table 6–4, nos. 2, 3). They typify the alkaline basalt magma type. Late minor associates (differentiates) are highly alkaline trachytes (Table 6–4, nos. 4, 5), phonolites, or sodic rhyolite. The compositional picture resembles that of lavas erupted during the later stage of the Hawaiian cycle, but is even further removed from that of tholeiitic basalts. Variation diagrams for Gough Island lavas are shown in Figure 6–16. Note how the normative compositions (Table 6–4, nos. 2, 4, 5) reflect persistence of the undersaturated condition, rise in alkali (or + ab + ne), depletion in (Mg + Fe) (di + ol) and in Ca (an + di) with progressive differentiation along the basalt–trachyte line. Most unusual among oceanic basalts (though common enough and generally surpassed among alkaline basalts of the continents) is the distinctly high K_2O content of basalts from Tristan da Cunha (Table 6–4, no. 3).

ICELAND Situated on the mid-Atlantic ridge is the volcanic island of Iceland, 50,000 km^2 in area (Figure 6–17). A central northeast–southwest belt of Quarternary lavas, with numerous active centers of eruption, covers an immense thickness of Tertiary lavas now well exposed in the eastern

TABLE 6–4 *Chemical analyses (percent by weight) and norms of some basalts and associated rocks from the mid-Atlantic*

No.:	1	2	3	4	5	6	7	8	9
SiO_2	49.94	47.7	47.5	56.3	61.5	47.07	49.48	60.59	72.4
TiO_2	1.51	3.2	3.8	1.8	0.3	1.66	9.58	1.25	0.18
Al_2O_3	17.25	15.2	16.7	17.8	18.3	14.86	13.12	15.07	11.5
Fe_2O_3	2.01	2.3	3.2	2.9	2.6	4.08	5.63	2.31	0.6
FeO	6.90	8.7	7.4	4.7	2.8	7.20	9.61	5.73	1.3
MnO	0.17					0.17	0.23	0.19	0.06
MgO	7.28	9.7	5.1	2.3	0.2	8.52	5.33	1.73	0.11
CaO	11.86	8.9	9.7	4.7	1.5	11.47	10.41	4.94	0.92
Na_2O	2.76	2.7	4.0	4.8	7.0	2.24	2.99	4.29	4.5
K_2O	0.16	1.6	2.6	4.7	5.8	0.20	0.27	1.59	3.6
H_2O						2.25		1.84	4.9
P_2O_5	0.16					0.18	0.35	0.43	0.03
Total	100.00	100.0	100.0	100.0	100.0	99.90	100.00	99.96	100.10
Q							3.30	15.42	30.5
Or		9.5		27.8	34.5	1.11	1.67	9.45	21.1
Ab		21.9		38.4	48.9	18.34	24.63	36.15	38.2
An		24.5		13.3	1.1	30.30	20.85	17.24	0.6
Ne		0.6		1.1	5.6				
Di		15.8		8.1	5.5	20.70	23.04	4.21	3.5
Hy						14.93	10.79	9.04	
Ol		18.4		3.6	0.1	2.78			
Mt		3.2		4.2	3.7	6.03	7.89	3.25	0.9
Il		6.1		3.5	0.6	3.19	4.71	2.43	0.5
Ap						0.34	0.67	1.01	
Total		100.0		100.0		97.72	97.55	98.20	95.3

Explanation of column headings:

1. Average composition (calculated water-free) of 10 oceanic tholeiites dredged from Atlantic and Pacific Oceans (A. E. J. Engel, C. G. Engel, and R. G. Havens, *Geol. Soc. Am. Bull.*, vol. 76, p. 723, 1965).

2. Alkaline olivine basalt (average of two analyses, calculated water-free) Gough Island, South Atlantic. (R. W. Le Maitre, *Geol. Soc. Am. Bull.*, vol. 73, p. 1328, no. 2, 1962).

3. Alkaline olivine basalt (average of four analyses) Tristan da Cunha (J. C. Dunne, cited by R. W. Le Maitre, *ibid.*, p. 1335, no. 4).

4. Lavas approaching trachytic composition (average of two analyses, calculated water-free) Gough Island (R. W. Le Maitre, *ibid.*, p. 1328, no. 4).

5. Trachyte (average of three analyses, calculated water-free) Gough Island (R. W. Le Maitre, *ibid.*, p. 1328, no. 6).

6. Olivine tholeiite, Thingmuli volcano, Iceland (I. S. E. Carmichael, *J. Petrol.*, vol. 5, p. 439, no. 1, 1964).

7. Olivine-free tholeiite (calculated water-free), Thingmuli volcano, Iceland (I. S. E. Carmichael, *ibid.*, p. 454, no. 4).

8. Andesite, Thingmuli volcano, Iceland, (I. S. E. Carmichael, *ibid.*, p. 442, no. 14).

9. Glassy rhyolite, Thingmuli volcano, Iceland. (I. S. E. Carmichael, *ibid.*, p. 443, no. 23).

and western coastal belts and dipping gently inward beneath the younger rocks. The exposed eastern section is 5 km thick. It consists of hundreds of flows, each 10 meters or so thick, some with a regional extent of over 20 km. Basaltic lavas greatly predominate. Most are oversatu-

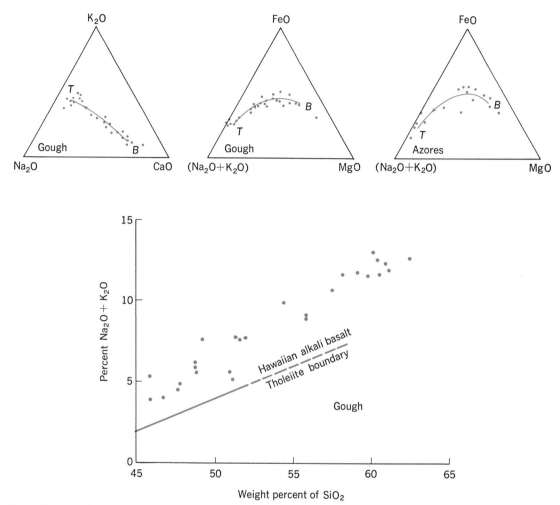

FIG. 6–16 *Variation diagram (oxides, weight percentages) for volcanic rocks of Gough Island and the Azores, mid-Atlantic province: B—basalts, T—trachytes. (After R. W. LeMaitre, Geol. Soc. Am. Bull., vol. 73, pp. 1327, 1337, 1338, 1962.)*

rated olivine-free types, but slightly undersaturated olivine basalts are also prominent. All are tholeiitic. About 10 percent of the total accumulation is composed of rhyolite and andesite (in the ratio 3:1). These more siliceous rocks are virtually confined to a number of central volcanoes, each of which became engulfed in the surrounding regional basaltic pile. Now reexposed and partially dissected by erosion, two of these have been studied in detail by S. P. L. Walker and I. S. E. Carmichael. One, the Thingmuli volcano, some 10 km in diameter,

consists of tholeiite 50 percent, rhyolite 21, andesite 18, fragmental and other rocks, 4 percent. Chemical data are summarized in Table 6–4 (nos. 6–9), and Figure 6–18.

Either olivine tholeiite or tholeiite could qualify for the role of parent magma in three respects: great volume, uniform composition, and once completely liquid state (as indicated by common occurrence as fine-grained lavas). Closely similar values of Sr^{87}/Sr^{86} suggest a common origin for the whole volcanic series. The obvious difficulty regarding the relatively large

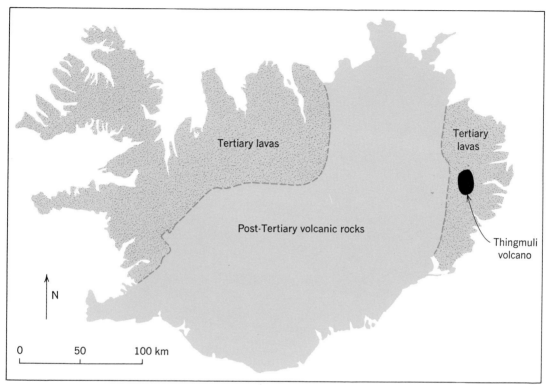

FIG. 6–17 *Map of Iceland showing distribution of Tertiary and post-Tertiary lavas. (After G. P. L. Walker, Geol. Soc. London Quart. J., vol. 114, p. 368, 1959.)*

volumes of siliceous lavas vanishes if we postulate concentration of late differentiates in the surface ejecta at volcanic centers such as Thingmuli. Using this argument Carmichael presents a model of simple differentiation along the line:

$$\text{olivine tholeiite} \rightarrow \text{tholeiite} \rightarrow$$
$$\text{andesite} \rightarrow \text{rhyolite}$$

The course of the liquid line of descent on the *AFM* variation diagram (Figure 6–18c) reflects a complexly changing course of crystallization established independently by microscopic observation:

WX: olivine tholeiites. Crystallization of magnesian olivine is reflected in rising SiO_2 (48.2 → 49.6) and Fe/Mg.

XY: tholeiites and basaltic andesites. Olivine ceases to crystallize; for the first time magnetite crystallizes as an early phase. SiO_2 rises sharply (49.6 → 54.8) and Fe/Mg is almost unchanged. Crystallization of calcic plagioclase causes increase in normative alkali feldspar.

YZ: andesites and rhyolites. Magnetite no longer crystallizes early; so Fe/Mg begins to increase once more in the liquid. Fractionation is dominated by feldspars, with corresponding rise in SiO_2 and in normative alkali feldspar in the final liquid fractions.

CONTINENTAL BASALTIC PROVINCES

In the oceans the primitive magmas are all basaltic; it has even been claimed that there is but one primitive oceanic magma, "oceanic tholeiite." On the continents the situation is different. There are very large areas of andesitic and rhyolitic lavas and tuffs with but minor accompanying basalt. In the plutonic realm rocks of the granodiorite–granite series outweigh rocks of basaltic composition. Yet basaltic lavas are still

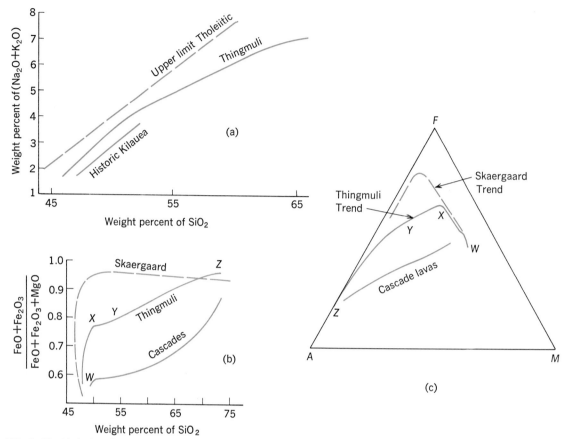

FIG. 6–18 *Variation diagrams for lavas of Thingmuli volcano (Tertiary) Iceland. (After I. S. E. Carmichael, J. Petrol., vol. 5, p. 48, 450, 1964.)*

the most voluminous of continental volcanic rocks. And there are immense plutonic sheets whose parent magma can only have been basalt. In some continental basaltic provinces the primitive magma and its differentiates are analogous in a general way with some of the oceanic series. But the analogy seldom amounts to identity.

FLOOD BASALTS OF THE PACIFIC NORTHWEST, U.S.A. In the states of Washington and Oregon, and adjoining parts of California and Idaho, volcanism from the early Miocene onward was continuous and varied. The products are basalts, andesites, and rhyolites. For long periods, however, volcanism consisted in the outpouring, over

very large areas, of enormous quantities of lava almost exclusively basaltic. Thus the Columbia River Plateau of eastern Washington (Figure 6–19) is a sagging basin, 100,000 km² in extent, filled to an average depth of between 1 and 2 km with nearly horizontal flows of oversaturated tholeiitic basalt (Table 6–5, no. 3). Chemical traits typical of some other continental basalts are high Sr^{87}/Sr^{86} (0.7079)[7] and Rb/Sr (0.18). All this eruption was accomplished in Miocene times,

---

[7] The tholeiitic flood basalts of the Paraná Basin, Brazil, uniformly have a lower initial ratio 0.7057, consistent with direct derivation from the mantle.

the great bulk of it in the last quarter of that period.

Further south, in the plateaus of Oregon and the eastern Cascades, eruption of tholeiitic basalt continued on a similar scale through Pliocene into Recent time. These rocks are chemically distinct from those of the Columbia River province. They are undersaturated to slightly oversaturated in silica and have an exceptionally high content (17 to 19 percent) of Al_2O_3 (Table 6-5, nos. 1, 2). Lavas with similar characteristics are widely distributed in other regions (for example, in Japan), and to accommodate them some petrologists have assigned them to a distinct magmatype—"high-alumina basalt." In the Oregon plateaus, as also in other parts of the world, high-alumina basalts are accompanied by significant, though subordinate, andesites and rhyolites.

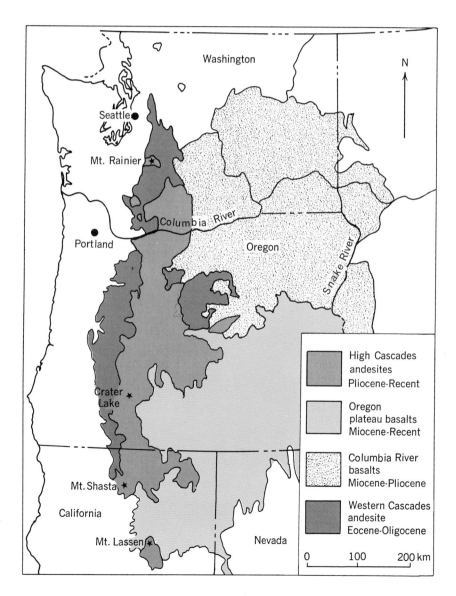

FIG. 6-19 Distribution of Tertiary and Quaternary volcanic rocks in the Pacific Northwest, U.S.A. (After A. C. Waters, op. cit., p. 159.)

TABLE 6–5 Chemical analyses (percent by weight) of some continental basalts, diabases, and associated differentiates

No.:	1	2	3	4	5	6
SiO_2	48.27	49.15	50.0	58.35	53.18	68.94
TiO_2	0.89	1.52	3.2	1.15	0.65	0.79
Al_2O_3	18.28	17.73	13.5	16.27	15.37	11.27
Fe_2O_3	1.04	2.76	1.9	1.01	0.76	3.80
FeO	8.31	7.20	12.5	7.38	8.33	4.03
MnO	0.17	0.14	0.25	0.15	0.15	0.14
MgO	8.96	6.91	4.4	3.07	6.71	0.35
CaO	11.32	9.91	8.3	6.30	11.04	3.20
Na_2O	2.80	2.88	2.9	4.24	1.65	2.50
K_2O	0.14	0.72	1.4	1.75	1.03	3.20
H_2O	0.22	0.65	0.9	0.20	1.12	1.92
P_2O_5	0.07	0.26	0.7	0.18	0.08	0.18
Total	100.47	99.83	99.95	100.05	100.07	100.32

Explanation of column headings:

1. High-alumina basalt, Medicine Lake Highlands, northeastern California. (H. S. Yoder and C. E. Tilley, *J. Petrol.*, vol. 3, no. 16, p. 362, 1962).

2. Average high-alumina basalt, Oregon plateaus. (A. C. Waters, Crust of the Pacific Basin, *Geophys. Mono.* no. 6, p. 165, 1962).

3. Average Yakima basalt (four analyses), Columbia River plateau. (A. C. Waters, *ibid.*, p. 164).

4. Andesite, Newberry volcano, central Oregon (H. Williams, *Geol. Soc. Am. Bull.*, vol. 46, no. 6, p. 295, 1935).

5. Diabase; Tasmania: mean composition of chilled border phase. (I. D. McDougall, *Geol. Soc. Am. Bull.*, vol. 73, p. 294, 1962).

6. Granitic differentiate from diabase, Tasmania. (I. D. McDougall, *ibid.*, p. 297.)

These are generally regarded as differentiates of the predominant basalts, much as in Iceland. Local eruption of rhyolite, without preliminary appearance of andesitic lavas, raises another possibility: it may be that the rhyolitic magmas are of independent origin.

DIABASE SILLS, TASMANIA There are many basaltic provinces in which much or all of the magma has never reached the surface, but has deployed laterally as intrusive sheets, commonly of great thickness and extent. This happened in Jurassic times in Tasmania. Here sills of diabase —a subplutonic basaltic rock with a characteristic coarse microtexture—now outcrop continuously over an area of 15,000 km². Some sheets are several hundred meters thick. The enclosing rocks are porous continental sandstones of low density. Chilled marginal rocks representing the parent magma are oversaturated tholeiites unusually high in silica (Table 6–5, no. 5). As with similar intrusions the world over, the sills of Tasmania show a vertical pattern of compositional variation that is consistent with gravitational settling of early crystals (magnesian olivine and magnesian pyroxene). Near the base these have accumulated to give undersaturated olivine diabase. In the upper levels the diabase is so enriched in silica that quartz appears in the mode as well as in the norm. In compliance with experimentally based theory, the upper quartz diabases have increasingly sodic plagioclase and increasingly ferrous pyroxenes. Alkalis and water here become concentrated to the point where the last phases to crystallize include hornblende and biotite; with these appears alkali feldspar. The final differentiates, squeezed out of the largely crystalline mass into segregation veins and even into local massive roof concentrations 100 meters thick, are granitic rocks (Table 6–5, no. 6) whose chemical and mineralogical evolution (Figure 6–20b) is close to that predicted by experiments on pyroxenic melts. First two pyroxenes coexist: one rich, the other poor in the diopside end member $CaMgSi_2O_6$ (refer to the miscibility break P_2–P_3, Figure 6–8). As fractionation proceeds the ratio Fe/Mg in both phases rises steadily (see the Mg–Fe pyroxene series, Figure 6–9). In the granitic residues the calcium-poor pyroxene cuts out; iron-rich olivine appears (see Figure 6–9, R–T), along with a pyroxene that is steadily approaching $CaFeSi_2O_6$. The liquid then leaves the olivine field, and in the final residue the sole ferromagnesian phase is a pyroxene close to the $CaFeSi_2O_6$ end member.

The minor-element pattern of the diabases and their differentiates is consistent throughout, and unusual compared with that of other diabases and continental basalts. Sr^{87}/Sr^{86} (0.7115), Th/K (4.9×10^{-4}), U/K (1.3×10^{-4}) and Rb/Sr (0.2) are exceptionally high and comparable with

values appropriate to a crustal source. So also is the low value K/Rb (200–220).

CONTINENTAL ALKALINE BASALTS   The great bulk of continental basalts fall within the broad tholeiitic category. But there are many provinces, less extensive but widely scattered across the world, where the most abundant lavas are highly alkaline undersaturated alkali basalts. Their differentiates are trachytes and phonolites much as we have noted in similar associations of mid-Atlantic islands. Some local provinces are characterized by exceptional concentration of K_2O over Na_2O. There are centers or subprovinces in which nephelinites or their rarer potassic equivalents (leucite basalts) are the main or sole basic lavas. And it is here, or in eroded, shallow underlying plutonic ring complexes, that we find the strangest of all igneous rocks, the carbonatites, whose principal constituents are carbonates such as calcite and dolomite. Continental basalts in general have a higher content of K_2O and TiO_2, and are very much higher in Rb, Sr, Ba, Th, U, P,

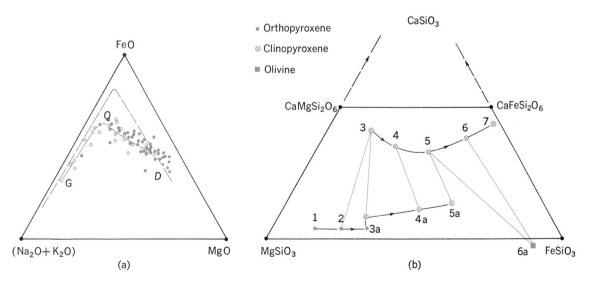

FIG. 6–20 Differentiation of Tasmanian diabase. (a) AFM diagram (oxide percentages) for diabases D, differentiated quartz diabases Q and granitic rocks G. Broken line is trend for similar rocks of Skaergaard gabbro intrusion, Greenland. (After I. D. McDougall, Geol. Soc. Am. Bull., vol. 73, p. 303, 1962.) (b) Course of crystallization of pyroxenes (in direction of arrow) with progressive differentiation from diabase to granitic residue. Colored ties connect co-existing phases. (After I. D. McDougall, ibid., p. 290.)

Zr, Ta, Nb, and related elements, than are oceanic tholeiites. In the alkaline differentiates concentration of such elements may reach extreme values. In fact, carbonatites are extensively mined as ores of Ta, Nb, P, and Ba.

Isotopic compositions of oxygen and carbon in carbonatites suggest very strongly that these have a primary magmatic source, perhaps deep in the mantle: $\delta_O{}^{18}/_O{}^{16}$ is $+6$ to $+8.5$ per mil as in primitive basaltic magmas; but $\delta_C{}^{13}/_C{}^{12}$ has a range of -5 to -8, otherwise unknown in terrestrial igneous rocks but matching that of carbonaceous meteorites (page 313), and not far from that of natural diamond.

PRIMITIVE BASALTIC MAGMAS

The general picture today is like this: There are many igneous provinces in which the magmas that best qualify for primitive status are basaltic. Each recognizable cycle of activity in such a region can be correlated with its uniquely generated magma. Some may be termed tholeiitic, some alkaline, some perhaps nephelinitic. But this in no way implies a common source or even a common origin for magma types similarly designated but separate in place and in time. Among primitive magmas that properly have been called tholeiitic, it is easy to recognize significant variation. No rocks could be more similar than the diabases and their minor granitic differentiates of the mid-Mesozoic sills of New Jersey, South Africa, Tasmania, and Antarctica. All are typically tholeiitic. Yet those of Tasmania have exceptionally high $SiO_2/(K_2O + Na_2O)$ and a unique pattern of minor elements (page 301). Then there are the clearly different, but still tholeiitic, olivine basalts of Kilauea; and again other rocks of a rather similar nature (for example, Thingmuli, Iceland), that are iron-rich and so high in Al_2O_3 that they can be called high-alumina basalt. The great diversity of primitive tholeiitic basalt magmas surely is more significant than the fact that in all the ratio $SiO_2/(K_2O + SiO_2)$ is higher—though in many only just perceptibly so—than in rocks designated alkaline basalts (page 291). There is perhaps even greater diversity—for example, with regard to SiO_2, Na_2O/K_2O, and $SiO_2/(K_2O + Na_2O)$—among the alkaline basalts and nephelinites. In both groups wide variation in minor-element patterns suggests correlated diversity in the source materials from which basaltic magmas are extracted.

Then there is the possibility, perhaps probability, that even within a single province the nature of the primitive magma may change from time to time at the source. Here is room for difference of opinion regarding identity and possible relationships of primitive basaltic magmas in a given province. Hawaiian lavas have been attributed by some writers to differentiation from two primitive types—the familiar "tholeiite" and "alkaline olivine basalt"—of which the second is considered derivative from the first. At the other end of a whole spectrum of ideas is Powers' concept of separate generation (in the mantle) of each batch of magma erupted over a short cycle of 100 to 200 years' duration. The reader must choose his own preferred model. The one we have tentatively adopted leans much closer to Powers' interpretation than to models invoking one or two primitive magmas referable to the whole Hawaiian province over a period of several million years.

Most, if not all, basaltic magmas come from the mantle. There is no reason to specify a homogeneous outer mantle any more than to propose a homogeneous crust. Various source materials for magmas may well be available in the depths. There are probably peridotites analogous in composition to stony meteorites; but there may also be supplies of garnet–pyroxene and garnet–pyroxene–feldspar rock closer to basalt in composition. Partial melting of these over a depth range of 40–100 km, combined with all sorts of fractionation possibilities at various levels, could generate all known varieties of primitive basaltic magmas. Local concentrations of more potassic mantle material, perhaps magnesian micas or hornblendes, could yield minor exotic magmas whose rare surface representatives have highly unusual but surprisingly consistent chemical traits. Such are the extremely potassic leucite-bearing lavas that appear in Leucite Hills, Wyoming, and also in a remote range of hills in western Australia.

It would seem unlikely that the phenomena of magma genesis are simple enough to fit any uniform model of mantle composition, even though it may be legitimate to specify such as a background for exploratory experiments. If every igneous cycle is a unique event, then, strictly speaking, the number of primitive basaltic magma types is infinite.

Andesite–Rhyolite and Granodiorite–Granite Provinces

The principal volcanic rocks of orogenic zones are andesites and rhyolites; plutonic rocks are mainly in the granodiorite–granite range. Apparently unrelated to these are ultramafic bodies to which we shall refer later as being of the "Alpine type." Basaltic lavas also appear in most orogenic belts and may completely dominate some provinces for limited times.

WEST AMERICAN CORDILLERAN SUPERPROVINCE

For the past 200 million years the Pacific margins of the American continents have been the loci of continuous orogenic and igneous activity. The whole belt can be considered as a kind of superprovince, whose individual provinces are a linear series of geosynclines and elongate basins, each with its individual character and history.

ANDEAN PROVINCE OF CHILE One such province, a segment of the South American Cordillera 3000 km long and 100 to 150 km wide, is the Andean geosyncline of northern and central Chile. It is filled to a stratigraphic depth of 30 km or more with Jurassic and Cretaceous sediments and volcanic rocks. The former are of terrestrial or shallow-water marine origin. Volcanic rocks, the bulk of the filling, are mainly andesitic flows and sheets of rhyolitic tuff. Plutonic activity was localized in time. Large plutons of the granodiorite family were emplaced in three separate episodes, each synchronous with a period of orogeny (uplift and erosion): uppermost Jurassic (125 m.y.), middle and upper Cretaceous

(110–90 m.y.), early Tertiary (60–30 m.y.). After folding and uplift of the geosynclinal filling in the Eocene, volcanism was renewed along the Andean crest and continues today. The products in the north (and over into Peru) were enormous rhyolitic tuff sheets covering 70,000 km². In the southern section of Chile, active volcanoes erupt mainly andesite and basalt.

QUATERNARY HIGH CASCADES PROVINCE, NORTHWESTERN UNITED STATES For 1000 km from the Canadian border into northern California, the summit of the Cascade Range is dotted with Quaternary volcanoes, some of which have been active in historic times. From the middle of the state of Washington to the Californian peaks of Shasta and Lassen, ejecta from these volcanoes cover a strip 50–100 km wide parallel to and 150 km inland from the Pacific coast. This is the High Cascades province (Figure 6–19). Dipping beneath the Cascades volcanics along the western margin is a great mass of Tertiary lavas and volcanic debris, mainly andesitic. The eastern margin is somewhat artificially defined; for here the Quaternary volcanoes lie on top of the Pliocene high-alumina basalts of the east Oregon plateau province, where volcanism likewise continued locally into Quaternary times. The southern volcanoes of the Cascades province, Shasta and Lassen, lie directly on a basement of metamorphosed Paleozoic–Mesozoic sediments and intrusive granodiorites.

The volcanoes of the High Cascades are impressive piles of andesite–dacite–rhyolite ejecta, mostly 3000–4000 meters in elevation. Each center of eruption maintains its own individuality. The great northern volcano Rainier is built mainly of andesite. In the southern volcanoes, Shasta and Lassen, dacite and rhyolite became prominent only in the later stages of growth; the earlier lavas were andesite, some grading in composition towards basalt. Mount Mazama, Oregon, in whose collapsed crater lies Crater Lake, was an andesite cone (2500 to 3000 meters high), which exploded within the last few thousand years, blanketing a large area with a volume (estimated as 40 km³) of welded dacite tuff. Basalt is mentioned throughout the classic litera-

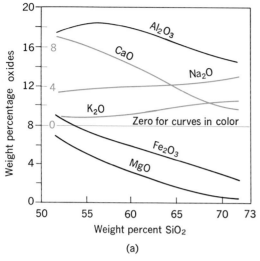

(a)

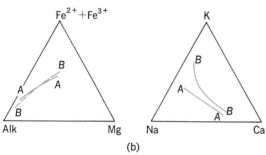

(b)

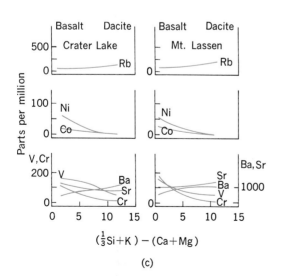

$$(\tfrac{1}{3}Si+K) - (Ca+Mg)$$

(c)

ture as an important component of the Cascades volcanoes. Possibly its role in this province has been overemphasized. Many of the rocks so called are basaltic andesites with 53 to 57 percent SiO_2, such as those predominating in Tertiary–Recent provinces of Central America. (The lavas of the newborn Mexican volcano Paricutin are of just this type.) Andesites in the silica range of 60–63 percent also are very extensive; the andesites that make up the great bulk of Rainier are almost uniformly in this range of composition. Chemical variation is illustrated in Table 6–6 and Figure 6–21. The same broad pattern can be duplicated in many another andesite–rhyolite province. But in detail not only each province, but each volcanic center within it, has individual chemical traits.

SIERRA NEVADA AND SOUTHERN CALIFORNIA BATHOLITHS In California the essentially granodioritic Sierra Nevada and Southern California batholiths outcrop continuously over two extensive areas, each about 600 × 100 km. They invade deformed and regionally metamorphosed geosynclinal sediments and volcanic rocks (mainly andesitic) of late Paleozoic and Mesozoic age that were folded and uplifted in the late Jurassic (Nevadan orogeny). Some of the western plutons that make up the Sierra Nevada batholith, like others still further northwest, have been dated at 140 m.y. (late Jurassic); and some plutons on the eastern flank of the Sierra may be early Jurassic (150–180 m.y.). But the great bulk of both batholiths, as elsewhere along the full length of the western margin of the continent, were emplaced in the earlier part of the late Cretaceous (80–100 m.y.).

In the period 1940–1950 geologists were greatly exercised concerning the origin of granitic rocks, and skepticism was widespread as to the

FIG. 6–21 *Variation diagrams for rocks of High Cascades province. (a) Volcanic rocks of Crater Lake, Oregon. (After H. Williams.) (b) AA—Crater Lake and Mt. Shasta. BB—Mt. Lassen. (After S. R. Nockolds and R. Allen, Geochim. Cosmochim. Acta, vol. 4, pp. 107, 111, 1953.) (c) Crater Lake and Mt. Lassen. (After S. R. Nockolds and R. Allen, ibid., 1953.)*

TABLE 6-6   Chemical analyses (percent by weight) of volcanic rocks of west American Cordilleran provinces

No.:	1	2	3	4	5	6
SiO_2	55.04	58.03	55.83	63.16	68.72	74.24
TiO_2	0.94	0.91	0.84	0.54	0.31	0.20
Al_2O_3	18.82	16.99	18.01	18.22	15.15	14.50
Fe_2O_3	1.92	3.52	2.63	1.36	1.16	1.27
FeO	5.69	4.38	4.07	3.33	1.76	0.67
MnO	0.07	0.16	0.08	tr	0.11	0.06
MgO	5.68	3.50	5.12	2.30	1.28	0.25
CaO	7.17	7.35	7.40	5.24	3.30	0.11
Na_2O	3.88	3.18	3.64	4.06	4.26	3.00
K_2O	0.85	1.71	1.22	1.16	2.78	3.66
H_2O	0.16	0.21	0.98	0.50	0.74	2.04
P_2O_5	0.21	0.09	0.11	0.14	0.09	0.07
BaO				0.05	0.07	0.18
SrO				0.04	0.03	tr
Total	100.43	100.03	99.93	100.10	99.76	100.25

Explanation of column headings:

1. Basaltic andesite, Parícutin, Mexico (H. Williams, *U.S. Geol. Survey Bull.*, no. 965–B, p. 271, 1950).
2. Quaternary andesite, eastern Nicaragua. (H. Williams, *Univ. California Geol. Publ.*, vol. 55, p. 39, no. 11, 1965).
3. Basaltic andesite, Crater Lake, Oregon (H. Williams, *Carnegie Inst. Washington Publ.* 540, p. 149, no. 10, 1942).
4. Pyroxene andesite, Mt. St. Helena, Washington (J. Verhoogen, *Univ. California Geol. Publ.*, vol. 24, p. 293, no. 4, 1934).
5. Dacite (with hornblende and biotite) Lassen, California (H. Williams, *Univ. California Geol. Publ.*, vol. 21, p. 365, no. 28, 1932).
6. Rhyolite, Lassen, California (H. Williams, *ibid.*, p. 300, 1932).

truly igneous nature of rocks of the granodiorite–granite family. It was argued by a considerable number, following H. H. Read, that many "granites" might in fact be metamorphosed ("granitized") sediments to which had been supplied (both from sources and by means unknown) K, Na, Si and other elements necessary for conversion to granitic composition. Today this view is less fashionable. It has nothing to recommend it with respect to undoubtedly intrusive plutons of the Sierran type. There is little evidence of any but localized reaction along the pluton borders, but much of forceful intrusion in a mobile, presumably liquid, state: The long axis of the batholith as a whole is parallel to the regional NW-SE structural trend of the enclosing rocks. At contacts of individual plutons mapping reveals displacements, divergences, and at times demonstrable thinning of country-rock formations, some of which (especially limestones) have yielded to

the force of nearby intrusion by plastic flow. On a smaller scale the same behavior is indicated by lateral veins and dikes of granite injected along fissures in the host rock; by marginal brecciation of both host and partially solidified plutonic rock; and by internal flow structures aligned parallel to contacts but not necessarily parallel to structural trends in the host. Large "roof pendants" and swarms of smaller blocks of country rock, in various stages of metamorphism and assimilative reaction, occur in the upper levels and along the margins of some plutons. These suggest the process of "magmatic stoping"—that is, fracture of the country rock and slow engulfment of the fragments by rising magma.

The compositional range of the Sierran and Southern Californian "granites" moreover parallels that of volcanic dacites and rhyolites, and enters the experimentally defined field of low melting in quartz–feldspar mixtures. So we accept the origin of these particular rocks as truly igneous. In country rocks immediately adjacent to plutonic contacts, and in the dark basic inclusions that occur in local swarms in some plutons, the effects of reaction are just as predicted by Bowen (page 278). The dark xenoliths, for example, have been converted to aggregates of hornblende, biotite, and andesine—phases characteristic, too, of the enclosing granodiorite.

Each of the two great Californian batholiths is compound. In each there are many, perhaps 200 or 300, individual plutons. Each of these is sharply bounded against its neighbors. The outcrop area of a major pluton may be as much as 500 km^2. Some are internally heterogeneous, the central, younger portions being expectably richer in quartz and alkali feldspar than the border zones.

The principal rock of both batholiths belong to the quartz–diorite–granodiorite granite series. Modal quartz is abundant (15–30 percent); modal alkali feldspar is mostly subordinate to plagioclase. Silica percentages are mostly between 60 and 70; total alkali (with Na $>$ K) is 5–7 percent. These rocks are chemically identical to some volcanic andesites and rhyolites. Also present, but except for one large pluton in Southern California subordinate, are dark rocks of gabbro or diorite composition.

A list of analyses or any of the standard variation diagrams shows a very close overall chemical similarity between the rocks of the two batholiths and andesite–dacite lavas such as those of the High Cascades provinces. But there are three striking differences between the plutonic and the volcanic provinces. First, although volcanic and synchronous tectonic activity have been virtually continuous throughout the history of the west American province, plutonism has been confined to a few well-defined episodes. Gilluly, noting that in a much broader region "the volume of the early Late Cretaceous plutons must be several hundred times that of all the other granite masses of the western United States" concludes that "Plutonism must depend on processes whose time-scale is of an entirely different order of magnitude from those of volcanism or tectonism" (*Geol. Soc. London Quart. J.*, pp. 164, 168, 1963).

Equally significant is the mean composition range of the most plentiful rock types. In the neovolcanic regions of Nicaragua, Mexico, and the High Cascades, the most voluminous lavas are basaltic andesites. These are indeed more siliceous—more "andesitic"—than the tholeiitic primitive basalts of other continental regions. But they are notably less siliceous—less "granitic"—than the dominantly granodioritic rocks of the two Californian batholiths. To derive the more siliceous (rhyolitic) lavas of Iceland from tholeiitic basalt is possible. To explain the Quaternary lavas of the High Cascades in similar terms is difficult but, because of abundance of contemporaneous basalt in the adjoining eastern plateau, not impossible. But how can we envisage the vast bulk of the two Californian batholiths as a differentiated residue from a basic parent magma that, in spite of profound postintrusive erosion, still is nowhere exposed in an area whose topographic relief is 4000 meters?

Granodioritic rocks of the Californian batholiths have high values of $\delta_0{}^{18}/0^{16}$ compared with andesites and rhyolites of comparable silica content. This strongly suggests independent lines of magmatic evolution.

SUMMARY There has been significant local variation in the pattern of igneous activity along the western border of the two American continents over the past 200 million years. But, perhaps for lack of fuller information, it is possible to generalize broadly about some significant aspects of the whole Cordilleran superprovince.[8]

1. Volcanic activity was continuous, with local interruptions and variations, during the filling and early folding of the longitudinal geosynclines. The products were mainly andesitic and rhyolitic, each rock type being dominant in particular provinces at particular times. Basaltic lavas are locally important. The original mineral assemblages of deeply buried lavas have been partly obscured by burial metamorphism. For example, plagioclase is widely replaced by albite.

2. Plutonic activity was limited to a few

---

[8] These generalizations should not be applied, unless there is good reason, to andesite–granodiorite provinces elsewhere.

sharply defined episodes. The most important by far occurred within a short span of time (perhaps 20 m.y.) in the early late-Cretaceous. The most voluminous plutonic rocks are broadly granodioritic.

3. During early and mid-Tertiary times volcanism continued, both in continental and in some geosynclinal areas. Although basalt was erupted in great abundance in local provinces (for example, the Olympic Peninsula, northwest U.S.A.) the dominant rocks of the whole superprovince were still andesitic.

4. General uplift at the close of the Pliocene was accompanied by renewed volcanism. The principal lavas now were basaltic andesite and basalt. But more siliceous andesites and rhyolites were ejected in quantity during the later stages of activity of some of the larger volcanoes.

5. Basaltic, basaltic–andesitic, and dacite–rhyolitic magmas seem to have played at least partially independent roles. Perhaps independent too, though possibly connected with dacite–rhyolite petrogenesis, was the granodioritic magma of the great plutonic intrusions.

CALCALKALINE MAGMAS OF OROGENIC ZONES

PROBLEM OF RELATION TO BASALTIC MAGMA Rocks and magmas in the andesite–rhyolite and diorite–granite range are termed "calcalkaline," in contrast with "alkaline," differentiates of some basaltic lineages (trachyte, phonolite, and so on). Opinion is divided as to their origin. It can scarcely be doubted that the andesites of Iceland are differentiates of an iron-rich tholeiite; and subordinate andesites associated with high-alumina flood basalts, as in the Oregon plateaus, may have a similar origin. There are other areas, also dominated by basalt, where contamination of basaltic magma by reaction with the continental crust may account for some calcalkaline magmas, as could also melting of the crust; the fact that such magmas do not occur in oceanic environment may lend support to the view that they are indeed partly or wholly derived from the continents. There is also some evidence, outlined below, that these magmas are formed in the mantle independently of basalt.

ACID CALCALKALINE MAGMAS The very composition of primitive magmas in the granodiorite–granite range places the site of their origin elsewhere than that of basaltic magmas. The most obvious possible site is deep in the crust; and in our model we derive these magmas by wholesale fusion from crustal rocks. Various parental materials have been proposed. Most qualified, for reasons of bulk composition, feasibility, and environment is the graywacke–shale–andesite filling of geosynclines. If this idea is accepted it implies that an important role in the development of granitic magma, at least in the later part of geological time, has been played by preliminary weathering of crustal rocks to provide geosynclinal sediment. During subsequent burial, these rocks become partially dehydrated and mineralogically reconstituted (metamorphism). Such rocks heated at $P_{H_2O} = 2000$ bars (as at depths of say 7–10 km) to 700°–770°C, have been found to yield large liquid fractions in the compositional range granodiorite–granite. On this experimental basis Winkler proposes a simple model in which deeply buried geosynclinal sediments are first metamorphosed and then partially melted to give a large granodiorite magma fraction (see Chapter 14).

Isotopic composition of strontium in many relatively young granites is generally consistent with such an origin. Thus initial Sr^{87}/Sr^{86} values reported for Sierra Nevadan granodiorite are 0.7073. Hurley's estimate for average geosynclinal sediment is not less than 0.708; however, this may be reduced somewhat if account is taken of associated volcanic materials. Data for isotopic composition of sulfur in granitic rocks are few. Extreme values, $\delta_S{}^{34}\delta_S{}^{32} = +10$ to $+30$ per mil, reported for some Precambrian intrusive granites can only be explained by a very large contribution from fused sediments.

A granodioritic magma, once generated thus and moving upward in the crust, could fractionate towards truly granitic liquids whose composition range is found always to be in the field of minimum liquidus temperature in the system quartz–albite–orthoclase (–anorthite). In contact with basic rocks the granodioritic magma, by assimilative reaction, can become somewhat contaminated in the direction of more basic composition.

We have been considering acid magmas in the plutonic setting. But what of the large volumes of acid lavas and tuffs that span more or less the same range of composition? It is tempting to equate the two, especially since massive eruption of dacite–rhyolite debris so commonly is independent both locally and in time from eruption of andesitic lavas in the same provinces. Geochemical evidence tends to support the view that, in some regions at least, the acid volcanic rocks represent magmas derived from or heavily contaminated by fused sediments. Thus there are close and detailed chemical analogies (especially concerning minor elements) between late Quaternary rhyolites and underlying graywackes and shales in the Taupo thermal area of nothern New Zealand. The rhyolites constitute a sheet of debris (ignimbrite) and lava with a total volume of about 15,000 km³. Andesites, which build several spectacular volcanoes, are much less voluminous. The sediments fill a deep basin in which the vertical thermal gradient today is exceptionally high.

ANDESITIC MAGMAS   With respect to volume alone, it can scarcely be doubted that andesitic magmas, which dominate many orogenic provinces and build massive volcanic piles like Rainier in Washington or Ruapehu in New Zealand, are primary. As compared with tholeiitic basalts, these magmas are consistently high in SiO_2, Na_2O, and Al_2O_3; commonly they are significantly lower in K_2O. The more basic types, including the lavas of Parícutin in Mexico and many Nicaraguan volcanoes, are not far removed from high-alumina basalts. Indeed they are commonly placed in this category. So the question is whether the range of primary basic magmas extends unbroken through basaltic–andesite to more typically andesitic magma (SiO_2 around 60 percent). Certainly such rocks have geochemical traits consistent with this proposition. Thus lavas of Parícutin (SiO_2 = 54–58 percent) have low ratios—Sr^{87}/Sr^{86} (0.7040–0.7043) and Rb/Sr (0.014–0.052)—that are even more "primitive" in flavor than corresponding data for continental

tholeiitic basalts. The view is gaining ground that andesites, unlike rhyolites, are too low in K, Rb, Th, U, Li, and rare earths to permit the possibility of significant contribution from granitic sources to primary andesitic magmas.

Many geologists today lean toward the view that andesitic magmas are primary and that their source lies somewhere in the mantle. It has even been suggested that these magmas originate by melting of mantle material along the Benioff zone of deep earthquake foci that slopes beneath the continents from their junction with the oceans. This would imply generation of magma at unusual depths (perhaps 80–200 km); for such is the vertical distance of the inland volcanoes above the Benioff zone. Implied also is a mantle composition under the continental margins, drastically different from that which underlies the thin crust of the ocean basins. All this may well be consistent with the model derived (Chapter 13) from ocean-floor spreading: The earthquake belts that dip under the continents are interpreted as zones in which "old" oceanic crust is being pushed down on the descending limb of the convection cell, which rises along the oceanic ridges to produce "new" oceanic crust. Since the downgoing material is necessarily cold, it may not become reheated to its melting point until it has reached a depth greater than that at which magma would form in an ascending current. At the same time, its composition would differ from that of ordinary basalt by the addition of whatever oceanic sediments might happen to be carried down with the crust. The picture as yet is by no means clear, for it remains to be shown, for instance, that the generation of andesite magma is everywhere synchronous with such motion. We note, for example, that there is at present no evidence for the existence of a descending current (no deep earthquakes) under the High Cascades province.

Ultramafic Rocks in Plutonic Complexes

Major bodies of peridotite consistently appear in one of two situations: (1) as stratified layers of crystal "cumulates" low down in very large intrusive sheets of differentiated gabbro (Bushveld or Stillwater type); (2) as sheets and lenses emplaced during the early stages of deformation in geosynclinal fillings (Alpine type).

STILLWATER COMPLEX, MONTANA

The Precambrian Stillwater complex is a fragment of a tilted sheet whose present outcrop is 50 km long. There is a chilled basal zone of hypersthene gabbro, which preserves the initial composition of the magma at the time of intrusion. As in many but not all major intrusions of this kind, the primitive magma is a highly aluminous saturated tholeiite (comparable with Kuno's "high-alumina basalt"). It is low in both Ti and K. The state of oxidation of iron is extremely low (atomic ratio $Fe^{3+}/Fe^{2+} = 0.033$). Above the basal zone is one of nearly pure enstatite rock (pyroxenite) and enstatite periodite (800 meters), and then a succession of alternating plagioclase-rich (anorthosite) and pyroxene-rich (gabbro) layers totaling 4000 meters. The upper part of this enormous mass has been removed by Precambrian erosion.

The great stratified basic intrusions are interpreted as having been built upward by "sedimentation" of crystals deposited by magma currents slowly creeping across the floor during convection of the cooling sheet. The parallel between the structures preserved in the Stillwater body and those of marine turbidites is incredibly close. Cross-bedding, graded bedding, scour structures, and slump structures are all clearly recognizable. Rocks so formed have been termed cumulates.

We cannot do justice here to the detail of magmatic evolution recorded in the Stillwater and related intrusions. We merely note: (1) that in general the sequence of differentiation can be read from the base of the intrusion upward; (2) that the first crystals to form are magnesian pyroxenes, with olivine (as required by the congruent melting of $MgSiO_3$ at high pressure) playing a relatively minor role; (3) that the lower pyroxenite layers are accumulations of these early crystals; (4) that there is a general upward increase in Fe/Mg, (Na + K)/Ca, and total SiO_2; (5) that the detailed succession of banding

is too complex to be explained completely by the simple mechanism of crystal settling at the base of undisturbed convection cells.

ULTRAMAFIC BELT, SOUTHWESTERN NEW ZEALAND

In the South Island of New Zealand, a great thickness of late Paleozoic and Mesozoic geosynclinal sediments—with some associated basic volcanics—was intensely deformed and folded early in the Cretaceous period. In the earlier stages of sinking and folding, and prior to metamorphism that attended the climax of deformation, an extensive body of ultramafic material was intruded along the length of the geosyncline. At the close of Cretaceous deformation this must have been a more or less continuous sheet 200 to 300 km long, and locally 2 to 3 km thick, dipping steeply parallel to the structural trend of the folded rocks. It was, and still is, confined to a limited level in the stratigraphic section—in lower Permian strata toward the base of the geosynclinal filling. Subsequently, the ultramafic sheet has been disrupted into major northern and southern discontinuous segments, as a result of right-lateral displacement along a major currently active transcurrent fracture zone, the Alpine fault zone (Figure 6–22).

The primary rocks are peridotites composed of four essential phases: olivine (Fo_{90} to Fo_{94}), almost invariably the dominant mineral, 70 to over 95 percent; enstatite (En_{88} to En_{93}), almost ubiquitous, and the principal pyroxene; chromiferous diopside, variable in quantity, and in some rocks absent; a chromiferous spinel always present in minor quantity. Both pyroxenes are significantly aluminous (Al_2O_3 in enstatite 2–4 percent), as in pyroxenes found by experiment to crystallize from magnesian melts at high pressure. Discontinuous compositional layering and crude streaking are widespread, but regular layering comparable with that of proved cumulates is exceptional. Where it does occur, some layers may be feldspathic. Layers or bodies of gabbro are virtually lacking.

The smaller ultramafic bodies and much of the outer portions of the larger intrusions have

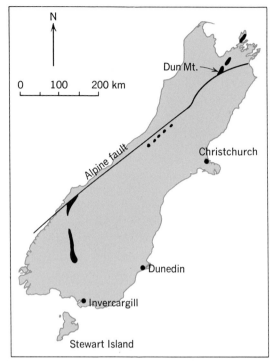

FIG. 6–22 *Ultramafic belt of southern New Zealand. (After R. G. Coleman, New Zealand Geol. Surv. Bull., no. 76, p. 14, 1966.) Ultramatic bodies, solid black.*

been converted to serpentinites—assemblages of one or more serpentine minerals, minor talc, tremolite, and chlorite. Serpentinization, a process of hydration, is almost universal in ultramafic bodies of the Alpine type. It is in no way connected with weathering or ground-water circulation; for distribution of serpentinite is unrelated to surface topography, the relief of which in New Zealand is close to 2000 meters.

It was long argued that Alpine ultramafic bodies must have been emplaced at temperatures much below the magmatic range. High-temperature marginal effects seemed to be totally lacking. The rocks of the New Zealand peridotite belt have been cited repeatedly as typical of low-temperature emplacement. It must be admitted however that initial high-temperature effects might be obscured or eliminated by two processes characteristic of peridotite bodies and ex-

emplified by those of New Zealand: (1) late low-temperature hydration reactions, such as serpentinization within the intrusive body, and replacement of marginal rocks and enclosed fragments by albite or hydrous calcium–aluminum silicates; (2) upward migration of serpentinite masses, under gravity, into a higher and cooler environment. Patient search along the margins of the New Zealand ultramafic bodies has revealed local relics of high-temperature contact effects. Basalts have been converted to plagioclase–diopside–hypersthene–hornblende, an assemblage that suggests temperatures of 700°–800°C.

PROBLEMS OF PETROGENESIS

Still hotly debated, as described in Wyllie's recent collection of essays by many authors, are questions such as these: What is the ultimate source of the Alpine ultramafic intrusions? Have they crystallized from true magmas—ultramafic melts of like composition? What light, if any, do they throw on the composition of the mantle? By what means is serpentinization effected, and whence comes the vast quantity of water locked up in Alpine serpentinites? These questions we shall review briefly in reverse order; for the site of serpentinization presumably is nearer to hand than the ultimate sources of the ultramafic material.

SERPENTINIZATION It is easy to write conventional equations for serpentinization of olivine in closed or in open systems:

$$3Mg_2SiO_4 + SiO_2 + 4H_2O \rightarrow 2(OH)_4Mg_3Si_2O_5$$

olivine   introduced   serpentine

or

$$5Mg_2SiO_4 + 4H_2O \rightarrow 2(OH)_4Mg_3Si_2O_5 +$$

olivine   introduced   serpentine

$$4MgO + SiO_2$$

removed in solution

The first implies a volume increase of 70 percent; the second would occur without change in volume. Other alternatives in which $MgSiO_3$ or CO_2 participate can readily be devised. None necessarily represents what actually happens. Argument, presented in terms of such equations, has centered on the questions of (1) volume change and (2) the source of the water—that is, whether it is magmatic or externally derived from seawater trapped in enclosed sediments. These questions are related. On neither is there general agreement.

Today most geologists admit substantial volume change. There is some structural evidence of this on all scales, and country rocks generally fail to show effects of outward transfer of SiO_2 and MgO on the scale implied by the second of the foregoing equations. Much of the increase in volume could be taken up during slow ascent of a solid ultramafic body synchronous with the serpentinization process. Yet we find a lifelong student of Alpine peridotites, with unrivalled field experience the world over, recently writing this:

> The available chemical and physical evidence leaves little room for argument. I believe, but that serpentinization is essentially a constant volume process which requires removal of about 30 percent by weight of the original bivalent oxides and SiO_2 in peridotite.
>
> (T. P. Thayer, *Am. Mineral.*,
> vol. 51, p. 707, 1966)

The exchange, he believes, is effected partly by brines entrapped in the enclosing geosynclinal filling, partly by waters exuded from the crystallizing parent magma itself.

The isotopic composition of hydrogen and oxygen in nonmetamorphic serpentinites proves to be significant. In North America $\delta_{D/H}$ for hydrogen of meteoric ground water varies consistently with climatic temperature, and so with latitude. Values determined by Wenner and Taylor for geologically young west-coast serpentinites show the same relation ($\delta_{D/H}$ −205 to −150 in British Columbia; −140 to −108 in Washington and Oregon; −108 to −85 in California). The agent of serpentization seems to be deeply circulating meteoric water. Oceanic serpentinites, such as those of the Mid-Atlantic Ridge, on the other hand have a unique combination of heavy hydrogen with light but variable oxygen ($\delta_{D/H}$, −70 to −49; $\delta_{O^{18}/O^{16}}$, +0.3 to +6.6) consistent with participation of seawater in serpentinization. It may be significant too, that serpentinites are consistently richer than peridotites in boron—an element that is stored in seawater.

PRIMARY PERIDOTITE MAGMAS?   Two alternative possibilities keep recurring in the literature dealing with Alpine peridotites:

1. Intrusion of ultramafic magma, rich in water (which later contributed to serpentinization) or extrusion of such a magma on the deep sea floor—for example, at the bottom of a tectonically active ocean trench. Magmatic temperatures would need to be exceptionally high, perhaps 1400°C. This was once considered an insuperable obstacle; for there were few records, until recently, of high-temperature metamorphism at peridotite contacts. Today it finds favor with a good many geologists, for there is increasing evidence of emplacement of Alpine peridotites at high initial temperature (though not approaching 1400°C). Recorded contact effects suggest intrusion temperatures no lower than those of diabase and gabbro sheets (perhaps 1100°C). And "cold" contacts in many cases reflect continued upward migration of the solidified intrusion as a solid body of serpentinite. Moreover, submarine eruption of ultramafic flows or intrusion of such magma as sills in deep-sea sediments could explain the localized stratigraphic distribution of some Alpine ultramafic sheets. Incompatible with emplacement on the sea floor is the consistently aluminous composition of peridotite pyroxenes, indicating crystallization at pressures of the order of 10 kb or more.

2. A view long considered orthodox, and firmly backed by Bowen, postulates origin of all peridotites by gravitational sinking of olivine and enstatite crystals in basaltic magma. Intrusion of Alpine peridotites would be accomplished by upward squeezing of a mobile mush of olivine and enstatite crystals, with an interstitial basaltic liquid to act as lubricant. But field evidence of an

adequate amount of lubricant usually is absent. And why do the olivine–enstatite assemblages of the Alpine peridotites differ consistently in general lithology from the enstatite–pyroxenite and feldspathic peridotites so typical of the proved cumulate bodies? Also why are the pyroxenes of Alpine peridotites significantly more aluminous than those of cumulates? Perhaps these objections have been overemphasized. Many experienced workers in this field minimize apparent differences between peridotites of the Alpine and the Stillwater types. The real difference, they suggest, is one of environment: The Alpine peridotites have acquired their distinctive character during serpentinization, internal deformation, and bodily upward migration along structurally weak zones in orogenic belts. Perhaps we are losing sight of the significance of the almost universal association of Alpine peridotites with albitized submarine basalts and deep-sea siliceous sediments—well-known to an older generation as the "Steinmann trinity." Are Alpine peridotites and submarine basalts simply complementary differentiation products that became separated from crystallizing intrusive bodies of the Stillwater type during the early stages of orogeny in tectonic belts?

ALPINE PERIDOTITES AS MANTLE MATERIAL   A completely different view of Alpine peridotites has been gaining ground over the past two decades, especially among geochemists. This viewpoint envisages Alpine peridotite bodies as slices of solid mantle rock squeezed up by plastic flow in the earlier stages of geosynclinal folding. Olivine and enstatite indeed prove to be relatively ductile at pressures greater than 5 kb and temperatures of 700°–800°C. Moreover, the microstructure of many peridotite bodies indicates intense strain and flow in the solid state. One such is the peridotite of St. Paul Rock, pushed through the ocean floor on the mid-Atlantic Ridge. The aluminous pyroxenes and nonfeldspathic assemblages of Alpine peridotites are consistent with experimentally established stability fields covering high temperature and pressures of perhaps 10 to 30 kb. Even higher pressures

are suggested by the appearance of magnesian garnet in some peridotites, notably those of Norway. And there is a close relation, both in compositions of phases and in the overall phase assemblages, between the peridotites and the olivine–pyroxene–spinel xenoliths, believed to have come from the mantle (page 293), that are so common in nephelinite lavas and in kimberlite. It is the view of Hess and some others that the large serpentinite bodies of some island arcs, notably in the Caribbean, are simply hydrated outcrops of mantle rock, naked of crustal cover.

SIGNIFICANCE OF MINOR-ELEMENT AND ISOTOPE PATTERNS   The relative concentrations of many minor elements and of certain isotopes in peridotites, basic igneous rocks, and the commonest stony meteorites (chondrites, rich in olivine) are closely similar. The implication to some geochemists is that such meteorites probably reflect fairly well the overall chemical composition of the upper mantle. If so, there must be a close genetic connection between the mantle rock, Alpine peridotites, and basic magmas. But no conclusion can be drawn directly from this general argument as to the nature of such connections. Alpine peridotites could be either (a) typical upper-mantle rock, or (b) unfused residue after extraction of basalt liquid from mantle rock, or (c) a crystalline precipitate from mantle-derived basaltic magma (as in the Stillwater complex).

Some persistent chemical traits of Alpine peridotites nevertheless provide clues toward decision among these alternatives. The extremely low concentrations of Na, K, Rb, Sr and relatively low-ratio K/Rb (200–500) compared with corresponding data for basalts of oceanic provinces eliminate Alpine peridotite as a possible source rock for genesis of basalt. The peridotite composition has an unmistakably residual character. So if there are mantle rocks of this composition they must exist as refractory material from which alkalis and strontium were drained upward into the crust at some early stage in terrestrial evolution. In other words, there can well be an upper mantle zone, not necessarily continuous, whose composition is identical with that of Alpine peridotite; but if so, the source of basaltic magmas must lie farther down. Consistently high Sr^{87}/Sr^{86} (0.707–0.725; mean 0.711) as compared with oceanic basalts (0.703–0.705), notwithstanding rather low (but still uncertain) Rb/Sr, implies separation of the peridotite fraction within the upper mantle at some rather remote point in earth history. Thus, despite uncertainties regarding the composition of the mantle, geochemical evidence strongly favors the idea that Alpine peridotites probably make up extensive residual patches in the upper mantle; but these are not the direct source of basaltic magma welling up today from the mantle.

KIMBERLITES The strange ultramafic rocks called kimberlites are insignificant in areal extent; but we must touch on them briefly since all evidence points to a source of kimberlite in the upper mantle. Kimberlites are mica peridotites, strongly affected by serpentinization and carbonate replacement, usually brecciated, and enclosing nodules of peridotite and combinations of high-pressure minerals such as magnesian garnet, diopside–jadeite solid solutions, $(Ca, Na)(Mg, Al)Si_2O_6$, and even the extreme high-pressure mineral diamond. Kimberlites occur as small vertical pipes and dikes cutting ancient crustal rocks in stable continental regions (South Africa, Brazil, Siberia). Common associates in space and time are alkaline basic plutonic ring complexes, in which carbonatite is prominent. Kimberlite pipes characteristically show evidence of explosive emplacement.

Compared with other rocks of mantle origin, kimberlites have some unusual geochemical characteristics: they are high in K_2O (commonly 1 to 2 percent), and with this is correlated exceptional concentration of Rb, Ba, and Cs, and very low Na/K; Sr^{87}/Sr^{86} is expectedly high. Such values of carbon isotope composition as are available are normal; but that of enclosed diamonds is exceptional ($\delta_{C^{13}/C^{12}} = -3$ to -4) and is close to values for carbonatites (-5 to -8) and carbonaceous chondrites (-4 to -10). If we accept a kimberlite source in the mantle, then clearly,

from the great mineralogical variety of enclosed rock fragments, the mantle beneath the continental shields is far from homogeneous and does not conform to any simple model of stony meteorite composition.

General Model of Igneous Petrogenesis

All scientific models are tentative; and any comprehensive scheme of igneous petrogenesis must be especially so. That which we temporarily present involves these essentials:

1. Common igneous rocks are formed from at least two, and probably three, fundamentally distinct series of primary magmas.

2. One series covers the whole range of common basalts—from alkaline to tholeiitic, from high-alumina to low-alumina composition. Each batch of primitive basalt is uniquely generated as a primary magma by differential fusion within the outer mantle. Its composition is determined by local composition of the mantle, by temperature–pressure conditions, and by factors connected with time and mechanics of mobilization and migration toward the surface. It is possible to speculate upon, but difficult to test rigorously, the respective influences of these factors. But comparison of primitive oceanic and continental basalts might bring out consistent chemical differences between upper-mantle rocks underlying the oceanic crust and the continental crust respectively.

3. The second series of magmas covers the granodiorite–granite (equals dacite–rhyolite) composition range. Again each batch of magma is uniquely generated, but in this case by fusion of crustal, mainly geosynclinal sediments. Refusion of older granites and metamorphosed sediments doubtless contributes to the genesis of some younger granites, which will then have notably high Sr^{87}/Sr^{86}.

4. Voluminous andesitic magmas of more basic composition—transitional toward tholeiitic basalt—develop by fusion of deep crustal or

upper-mantle material in orogenic zones of continental borders and island arcs. Not to be excluded is the possibility that these magmas may mix with more acid primary magmas or become modified by reaction with "granitic" rocks in the lower crust.

5. A principal cause of variation among associated igneous rocks is fractional crystallization of basic magmas. The precise mechanism varies. Heavy crystals may sink in the early stages under gravity; residual liquids may be squeezed away from largely crystalline bodies; upward concentration of water may cause upward transfer of alkalis. Common differentiation series include

   (a) Tholeiite → andesite → dacite → rhyolite
   (b) Olivine tholeiite → sodic basalt → rhyolite
   (c) Olivine basalt → sodic basalt → trachyte → phonolite
   (d) Nephelinite → sodic basalt → trachyte → phonolite
   (e) Nephelinite ⟨ nepheline–syenite / carbonatite
   (f) Granodiorite → granite
   (g) Andesite → dacite → rhyolite

6. Magmas may also be modified by assimilative reaction with wall rock in the plutonic environment.

   (a) Basification of border rocks in granitic plutons.
   (b) Modification of basaltic magma toward andesitic composition by deep-seated reaction with crustal rocks (sediments, granites).
   (c) Reaction between alkaline basalt and granite to yield potassic (often leucite-bearing) lavas.

7. Ultramafic rocks of the Stillwater type are accumulations of early-formed crystals "sedimenting" from massive sheets of basaltic magma. Alpine peridotites, on the other hand, come directly from refractory residues locally present in the upper mantle, either as lubricated crystal mushes or as segments of solid mantle rock.

A model of petrogenesis is the logical conclusion of a chapter on igneous phenomena. But this is not the end of the matter. There are obvious implications regarding the possible composition and gross structure of the deep crust and the outer mantle. To these we shall return in the final chapters.

REFERENCES

The problems of igneous petrology as they have appeared to various writers at different times are set out in general works by Harker, Bowen, Daly, Read, Tilley, Turner and Verhoogen, and Barth that appear throughout the lists of references. Most of the cited papers, however, are devoted to specific topics as seen by contemporary workers in petrology. They have been selected with a view to introducing the reader to the broad sweep of problems that confront the student of igneous petrology today, to combinations of new and old approaches toward their solution, and to resulting differences in current opinion on such matters.

Abelson, P.: Annual Reports of the Director Geophysical Laboratory, *Carnegie Institution Year Books,* vol. 64, 1964–1965; vol. 65, 1965–1966; vol. 66, 1966–1967.

   Reports of progress in experimental investigation of melting and crystallization of minerals and rocks by J. F. Schairer, H. S. Yoder, C. E. Tilley and others.

Baird, A. K., D. B. McIntyre, and E. E. Welding: Geochemical and structural studies in batholithic rocks of southern California; Part II, Sampling of the Rattlesnake Mountain pluton for chemical composition, variability, and trend analysis, *Geol. Soc. Am. Bull.,* vol. 78, pp. 191–222, 1967.

Bowen, N. L.: *The Evolution of the Igneous Rocks,* Princeton University Press, Princeton, N.J., 1928.
   Summary of silicate-melt equilibria and their bearing on fractional crystallization of basaltic magmas and magmatic assimilation.

Buddington, A. F.: Granite emplacement with special

reference to North America, *Geol. Soc. Am. Bull.*, vol. 70, pp. 671–747, 1959.

Carmichael, I. S. E.: The petrology of Thingmuli, a Tertiary volcano in eastern Iceland, *J. Petrol.*, vol. 5, pp. 435–460, 1964.

A study of differentiation from tholeiitic basalt to andesite and rhyolite.

Clark, S. P.: *Handbook of physical constants*, Geol. Soc. Am. Mem. 97, 1966.

Especially for data on crystal-melt equilibria and thermodynamic properties of mineral phases.

Daly, R. A.: *Igneous Rocks and the Depths of the Earth*, McGraw-Hill, New York, 1933.

A classic attempt to correlate petrogenesis with a simple model of the crust and underlying rocks as envisaged in 1930.

Dawson, J. B.: Basutoland kimberlites, *Geol. Soc. Am. Bull.*, vol. 73, pp. 545–560, 1962.

Engel, A. E. J., C. G. Engel, and R. G. Havens: Chemical characteristics of oceanic basalts and the upper mantle, *Geol. Soc. Am. Bull.*, vol. 76, pp. 719–734, 1965.

Ewart, A., and J. J. Stipp: Petrogenesis of the volcanic rocks of the Central North Island, New Zealand, as indicated by a study of Sr^{87}/Sr^{86} ratios and Sr, Rb, K, U, and Th abundances, *Geochim. Cosmochim. Acta*, vol. 32, pp. 699–736, 1968.

Gilluly, J.: The tectonic evolution of the western United States, *Geol. Soc. London Quart. J.*, vol. 119, pp. 133–174, 1963.

Includes a discussion of the relations between volcanism, plutonism and orogeny in western United States during Phanerozoic time.

Harker, A.: *The Natural History of Igneous Rocks*, Macmillan, New York, 1909.

The classic starting point of modern igneous petrology.

Härme, M.: On the potassium migmatites of southern Finland, *Comm. géol. Finlande Bull.*, no. 219, 1965.

An account of large-scale intrusion of Precambrian granites and accompanying potassium metasomatism (replacement effects).

Heier, K. S., and J. J. W. Rogers: Radiometric determinations of thorium, uranium, and potassium in basaltics and two magmatic differentiation series, *Geochim. Cosmochim. Acta*, vol. 27, pp. 137–154, 1963.

Hess, H. H.: Stillwater igneous complex, Montana, a quantitative mineralogical study, Geol. Soc. Mem. 80, 1960.

A comprehensive study of differentiation in a thick sheet of basic magma, with an addendum on differentiation in diabase sills.

Hurley, P. M., P. C. Bateman, H. W. Fairbairn, and W. H. Pinson: Investigation of inital Sr^{87}/Sr^{86} ratios in the Sierra Nevada plutonic province, *Geol. Soc. Am. Bull.*, vol. 76, pp. 165–174, 1965.

Origin of granodioritic and related magmas is discussed in the light of Sr^{87}/Sr^{86} and Rb/Sr ratios.

Jackson, E. D.: Primary textures and mineral associations in the ultramafic zone of the Stillwater complex, Montana, U.S. Geol. Surv. Prof. Paper No. 358, 1961.

Kolbe, P., and S. R. Taylor: Major and trace element relationships in granodiorites and granites from Australia and South Africa, *Contrib. Mineral. Petrol.*, vol. 12, pp. 202–222, 1966.

Geochemical demonstration of the origin of acid plutonic rocks by fusion of geosynclinal sediments and subsequent differentiation of the magma so formed.

Kuno, H.: Lateral variation of basalt magma type across continental margins and island arcs, *Bull. Volcan.*, vol. 29, pp. 195–222, 1966.

Le Maitre, R. W.: Petrology of volcanic rocks of Gough Island, South Atlantic, *Geol. Soc. Am. Bull.*, vol. 73, pp. 1309–1340, 1962.

Mineralogical and chemical study of alkaline basalts and their differentiates (culminating in trachytes) in a volcanic island on the mid-Atlantic ridges.

Macdonald, G. A., and T. Katsura: Chemical composition of Hawaiian lavas, *J. Petrol.*, vol. 5, pp. 82–133, 1964.

McDougall, I.: Differentiation of Tasmanian dolerites: Red Hill dolerite-granophyre association, *Geol. Soc. Am. Bull.*, vol. 73, pp. 279–316, 1962.

Moore, J. G., and B. W. Evans: The role of olivine in the crystallization of the prehistoric Makapouhi lava lake, Hawaii, *Contrib. Minerol. Petrol.*, vol. 15, pp. 208–223, 1967.

Page, N. J.: Serpentinization at Burro Mountain, California, *Contrib. Mineral. Petrol.*, vol. 14, pp. 321–342, 1967.

Chemical and mineralogical study of serpentinization in a peridotite body, with thermodynamic discussion of possible equilibria.

Read, H. H.: *The Granite Controversy*, Murby, London, 1957.

A series of addresses on the field occurrence, relation to metamorphism, and origin of granitic rocks, with an emphasis on granitization.

Taylor, H. P.: The oxygen isotope geochemistry of igneous rocks, *Contrib. Mineral. Petrol.*, vol. 19, pp. 1–71, 1968.

Taylor, S. R., and A. J. R. White: Trace element abundances in andesites, *Bull. Volcan.*, vol. 29, pp. 177–194, 1966.

Andesitic magmas are attributed to melting in the subcontinental mantle.

Thayer, T. P.: Serpentinization considered as a constant-volume metasomatic process, *Am. Mineral.*, vol. 51, pp. 685–710, 1966.

Tilley, C. E.: Some aspects of magmatic evolution, *Geol. Soc. London Quart. J.*, vol. 106, pp. 37–61, 1950.

A starting point for development of modern ideas on basaltic and andesitic magmas.

Turner, F. J. and J. Verhoogen: *Igneous and Metamorphic Petrology* (2d ed.), McGraw-Hill, New York, 1960.

The first 450 pages cover igneous petrology with the emphasis on common rock associations and petrogenesis.

Tuttle, O. F., and N. L. Bowen: Origin of granite in the light of experimental studies, *Geol. Soc. Am. Mem.* 74, 1958.

The experimental approach and the emphasis placed on magmas are complementary to the treatment in Read's *Granite Controversy*.

——and J. Gittins: *The Carbonatites*, Wiley, New York, 1967.

Wager, L. R., and others: Symposium on Layered Intrusions, *Mineral. Soc. Am. Spec. Paper no.* 1, 1963.

A series of papers by independent authors dealing with various aspects of major stratified basic intrusions of the Stillwater type.

Wilshire, H. G.: The Prospect alkaline diabase-picrite intrusion, New South Wales, Australia, *J. Petrol.*, vol. 8, pp. 97–163, 1967.

Differentiation by crystal settling and upward transfer of alkalis in a sheet of alkaline basaltic magma.

White, R. W.: Ultramafic inclusions in basaltic rocks from Hawaii, *Contrib. Mineral. Petrol.*, vol. 12, pp. 245–314, 1966.

Wyllie, P. J., and others: *Ultramafic and Related Rocks*, Wiley, New York, 1967.

A series of independent essays on various aspects of ultramafic rocks and carbonatites, with extensive bibliography.

7
GEOMORPHOLOGY

THE NEXT TWO CHAPTERS describe processes that take place on or near the earth's surface. Their products are, on the one hand, sedimentary rocks and, on the other, the landscape itself. The driving force is mostly gravity. Energy comes from different sources: chemical reactions between surface rocks and the atmosphere and hydrosphere; gravitational potential energy of rock masses lifted above sea level by tectonic or volcanic processes; and solar energy. The latter contributes, for instance, to the uplift of water into the atmosphere by evaporation. This water, condensing as rain or ice to form rivers or glaciers, is the effective transporting agent that considerably speeds up the process of moving rock material from high to low points. Inasmuch as running water is not uniformly distributed over the earth's surface, its localized action forms and shapes the landscape, as by carving valleys. Solar energy also controls, through photosynthesis, the amount of plant life, which, in turn, affects erosional processes, as described later; it also powers the winds, which are effective geomorphic agents of erosion and transport.

The sum total of all the activity on the earth's surface—the weather, ocean currents and waves, the hydrologic cycle, biologic activity, weathering, erosion, and deposition—may be thought of as the operation of a great engine fueled largely by solar energy. The solar energy intercepted by the earth is enormous. At the average distance of the earth from the sun, the radiant energy flux is about 2 cal cm^{-2} min^{-1}, or 1.4×10^6 ergs cm^{-2} sec^{-1} at normal incidence, and the total intercepted by the earth is approximately 6000 times the flow of energy from the earth's interior (see Chapter 12). If all this solar energy were retained in the earth and not reradiated back into space, it would be sufficient to melt a layer of granite 1 km thick in about 500 years. The temperature at the surface of the earth has been within the narrow range of tolerance of living matter (roughly between $-50°C$ and $+60°C$) for at least 3 billion years. Therefore there must be complete balance between incoming and outgoing radiation, almost on a year-to-year basis.

The surface of the solid earth is enclosed in two fluid shells that are extremely thin in comparison to its size: an outer continuous gaseous shell, the atmosphere, whose upper limit is indefinite; and an inner discontinuous liquid shell, the hydrosphere, consisting essentially of water. About 71 percent of the earth's surface is covered by oceans; in addition, water stored on the land in the form of ice and snow, or in the process of flowing to the sea in rivers, as well as the ground water that fills all pores and fractures beneath a certain depth in the ground called the *water table*, is also considered part of the hydrosphere. There is continuous exchange of water and atmospheric gases between the hydrosphere and the atmosphere; on the average, the water in the atmosphere in the form of gaseous H_2O amounts to about 25 mm of liquid water per cm^2. Since the average annual rainfall for the world as a whole is close to 1000 mm, the residence time of water in the atmosphere (that is, the average length of time a molecule of water vapor is in the atmosphere between evaporation and subsequent precipitation) is about nine days.

In its passage from a source rock to a newly consolidated sediment, mineral matter passes through a sequence of stages; at each stage it is acted upon by different agents and processes, whose activity is controlled by different sets of conditions; the sequence is as follows:

1. Rock weathering, which involves the chemical and mechanical breakdown of rock to fragments and particles small enough to be handled by agencies of erosion and transportation.
2. Transportation of debris down slopes into the path of running water or ice (slope processes).
3. Transportation of debris in streams of running water or ice, or by wind, and its eventual deposition or delivery to standing water.
4. Movement of debris by currents in standing water.
5. Deposition on lake and sea floors of clastic material, and precipitation from solution or accumulation by organisms.
6. Burial by younger sediments, compaction, diagenesis, and consolidation.

Stages 1 through 5 represent the surficial or visible part of James Hutton's geognostic cycle. The hidden stages of this cycle include metamorphism, anatexis (melting of rock to magma), intrusion and volcanism, and tectonism.

To a limited and local extent, some of the stages in the foregoing sequence can take place independently of others. Streams armed with gravel can erode their beds into unweathered rock, and waves can attack the shore, delivering rock debris directly to the ocean. More generally, however, there is a dependence of each step on the completion of the preceding step: rock must be weathered before it can move downslope; and must move downslope before it can be picked up by streams. The rate of each process may be increased or decreased by altering the conditions under which preceding or succeeding stages take place. For example, a wave of accelerated erosion and gullying, brought on by rapid downcutting of the master streams, may strip the vegetation and soil from parts of a landscape and expose bare rock. In consequence of the resulting lack of organic acids and soil moisture, the subsequent rate of weathering may be greatly reduced on the very areas where erosion was previously most rapid. Or an increase in frost-induced hillside creep in a cold region could conceivably deliver to small streams far more coarse debris than they could handle. They would build up (aggrade) their beds with this coarse debris, carrying away only fine material, and it is possible that the debris could reach such thickness and volume that much of their water would flow underground through the coarse gravel of the stream bed, rather than on the surface as before, and the streams might then be able to transport less material than before. In other words, there may exist positive or negative feedback between the various processes and steps of weathering and erosion. What that feedback will be depends on the rock, topography, climate, vegetation, and possibly other factors as well.

The rates of surficial processes are far from uniform. First, there are cyclic variations in weather, climate, and the condition of the sea caused by rotation of the earth on its axis, the tides, and the passage of the seasons. Superimposed on these are irregular and even random variations in precipitation, temperature, and streamflow. In general rates of erosion and transportation increase markedly with rainfall and stream discharge, so that a flood of the magnitude that occurs only once every 50 or 100 years may be responsible for as much erosion as takes place in the decade preceding or following that flood. With fluctuations of streamflow of a thousand-fold and more during a year, it is difficult at times —assuming such a thing as equilibrium between streamflow and shape and gradient of the channel—to decide with just what discharge the channel is in equilibrium. Problems caused by the wide variation in rates of geomorphic processes in space and time are continually plaguing the geomorphologist in his attempts to measure the rate of weathering and erosion and to determine its dependence on external factors.

An important aspect of the surficial environment is the presence of the biota (plants and animals). Vegetation and animal activity can both help and hinder erosion and are themselves responsible for many sedimentary rocks. On the one hand, organic decay products and respiration of soil organisms and plant roots reduces the pH of soil water and makes the CO_2 content of soil air many times greater than that of the environment. This aids the solution of mineral constituents and speeds weathering. On the other hand, vegetation forms a continuous integument over much of the landscape; its roots bind the soil and its leaves and branches reduce rainfall impact. Thus it slows erosion. The relation between the biota and its inanimate environment is a delicate one. A disturbance of this relationship, either through alteration of the natural environment or a change in the composition of the biological community, does not necessarily bring into play processes that restore the old relationship. An entirely new biological community and a different kind of geomorphology may be the ultimate result of rather small disturbances in the biota or its environment.

An organism that has had an increasing effect on the natural environment in the last 20,000 years is man.[1] Although the changes have been deliberately made, at least lately, the results have not always favored the ends intended. Landslides along roadways and in urban areas, rapid erosion in lumbered and cultivated regions, silt-

ing behind breakwaters and in harbors, and pollution of the air and water supply all attest to changes made in the natural environment without a clear understanding of what these changes would lead to. Barren rocky mountains in countries such as Greece, Asia Minor, Iran, and China, which were once forested, and rivers now either dry or in flood that once had water the year round, are examples of the destruction by a heedless civilization of the very basis for its existence.

This discussion of the general nature of the surficial environment is intended to show that, although a tendency toward equilibrium is inherent in all spontaneous processes, in the short term, and even in spans of time comparable to the age of the earth, equilibrium may not be achieved. We are accustomed to think that any irregularity on the land surface must eventually be erased: that mountains will be reduced to hills, and hills to gentle plains; and geologists have argued that the steeper the slopes the more rapid the rate of reduction; that cliffs and waterfalls are ephemeral features of the landscape that are quickly erased. However, the complexity of the surficial environment, the large number of stages involved in weathering, erosion, and transportation, and the way in which they may affect each other, may lead to the development of steep cliffs, waterfalls, and rugged mountains, that remain virtually unmodified for entire geologic periods. Following the discussion of geomorphic processes, the possible outcomes of geomorphic evolution will be considered—for example, cyclic models, leading to peneplains and pediment landscapes; steady-state models, and still others.

On a smaller time scale, the geologist wishes to evaluate the geomorphic evidence for climatic change, the ecologist or botanist wishes to understand the interrelations of vegetation and environment, the soil scientist may want to know the age of a soil or the length of time that a given hillside or alluvial surface has remained unchanged, and the engineer may wish to know the effect of dam building on erosion or sedimentation or the landslide potential of a highway route. In attempting to answer questions such as these, the geomorphologist must keep constantly in mind

[1] R. H. Meade (*Geol. Soc. Am. Bull.*, vol. 80, pp. 1265–1274, 1969) finds that in rivers of the Atlantic drainage system of the U.S.A. the sediment load is probably four to five times greater than it would be if the area had remained undisturbed by man.

that he is dealing with processes that may affect each other in a variety of ways, some of them quite unexpected. His main contribution to the work of others may be to keep them aware of the complexity of the environment they are studying or attempting to modify.

Atmosphere, Weather, and Climate

The chief agent of geomorphic activity is water. Its availability as liquid or solid (ice) governs the nature and rate of geomorphic processes, and the resulting landforms. Its availability depends on local weather and climate whose diversity accounts in part for the diversity of geomorphic processes and landforms. Climate, and particularly temperature, determine also the nature of the vegetation cover, which, in turn, exerts some control on geomorphic processes.

Climate may be defined as the time integral of weather, which is itself a rather complicated product of atmospheric circulation in which the thermodynamics of water (evaporation, condensation, and so forth) play a large part. Atmospheric circulation is, by and large, the result of unequal heating by the sun; equatorial regions, being closer to normal incidence to solar rays than polar regions, receive more heat. Part of the incoming solar radiation is, of course, reflected; the reflection coefficient, or *albedo*, which for the earth as a whole is estimated to be 30 to 35 percent, depends very much on the nature of the surface: green forests reflect very little (3–10 percent) of the incident sunlight, while fresh snow reflects about 80 percent. That which does actually penetrate into the ground heats it, and the ground then reradiates according to the Stefan-Boltzmann law (see also Chapter 12), mostly at wavelengths in the infrared, which are partially absorbed by atmospheric carbon dioxide and water vapor; this in turn heats up the atmosphere. This heating is seasonal since, because of the inclination (23½°) of the earth's axis to the plane of its orbit, different parts of the earth receive different amounts of radiation at different times ("seasons"); each of the poles, for instance, is completely shielded from the sun for half the year. Heating of the atmosphere is also different over land as contrasted with sea.

Differential heating of the atmosphere causes convective motion, with hot air rising near the equator and moving poleward while cold and denser air sinks near the poles and moves toward the equator. The circulation, however, does not form a single cell; instead it breaks up into three types of subcell as follows:

1. A tropical zone, with hot air rising at the equator, cooling by expansion, and sinking back to the ground in two high-pressure belts at about 30° North and South of the equator. Part of the sinking air flows back towards the equator at ground level.

2. Temperate zones, from 30° to 60° latitude, in which air and thermal energy are transported mainly through convective cells about vertical axes (cyclones and anticyclones).

3. Polar regions, with rising air at about 60° North (and South) and sinking air at the poles.

CORIOLIS FORCE

The general circulation pattern is caused in part by the rotation of the earth and the resulting Coriolis force. This is a fictitious force that acts perpendicular to the displacement and so does no work (Chapter 11). It arises from the fact that our reference frame (the earth) rotates. An object that, according to Newton's laws, must move at constant speed in a straight line (with respect to a fixed, nonrotating observer) when no force is applied to it, appears to move on a curved path when viewed from a rotating frame; the Coriolis force accounts for this apparent curvature. Its magnitude (per unit mass) is simply $2\mathbf{v} \times \omega$, where $\mathbf{v}$ is the velocity and ω the angular velocity of rotation of the earth. Thus at latitude ϕ, an object moving eastward with velocity v_ϕ is subject to a force $2v_\phi\omega \sin \phi$ directed toward the equator; an object moving poleward is deflected eastwards by a force of the same magnitude. For an observer looking in the direction of motion, the deflection is invariably to the right in the Northern Hemisphere and to the left in the Southern Hemisphere. Thus air flowing southwards from 30°N towards the equator appears as a northeast "trade" wind. A curious effect of the Corliolis force is to cause the wind to blow along, rather than normal to, lines of equal pressure or *isobars*. This effect can be visualized as follows: suppose that a nonviscous gas flows at a steady rate in response to a pressure gradient. If the pressure gradient were the only force acting on the gas, it would be continuously accelerated; thus if the velocity is more or less constant the only other force (Coriolis) acting on the gas must be equal and opposite to the pressure gradient. Since, however, the Coriolis force is normal to the velocity, it can oppose the pressure gradient only if the velocity itself is normal to the pressure gradient—that is, if the wind blows along isobars, with the high pressure on the right (in the Northern Hemisphere) of an observer standing with his back to the wind. In this way, the general north–south and south–north pressure gradients give rise to notable east–west components (for example, the dominant "westerlies" of the mid-latitudes and the polar "easterlies"). Similarly, wind rushing toward the center of a low-pressure area (*cyclone*) is deflected and tends to circulate counterclockwise around it (in the Northern Hemisphere); while wind moving radially outward from a high-pressure area (*anticyclone*) moves clockwise in the Northern Hemisphere, and counterclockwise in the Southern Hemisphere.

RAIN

Rising air that does not exchange heat with its surroundings expands adiabatically as it rises (since pressure in the atmosphere decreases upward); it therefore also cools at a rate of roughly 10°C per kilometer. Since water vapor (molecular weight 18) is lighter than either O_2 or N_2, humid air is less dense than dry air at the same temperature and pressure. As humid air rises and cools, water condenses as drops or ice crystals. This may happen, for instance, in a cyclone (low-pressure area of rising air), or where

air is forced upward to pass over mountains, or where a warm and humid air mass rises to override a mass of dense cold air (front). The distribution of rainfall (and snowfall) is thus determined mainly by the general circulation pattern and by relief. That rainfall is associated with rising rather than with sinking air explains, for instance, the occurrence of arid regions forming two belts about 30° north and south of the equator, for these are the "high-pressure" belts where, as we have seen, air moves mostly downward. Water vapor in the atmosphere is derived by evaporation from warm sea surfaces, and by evapotranspiration from land. It is estimated that a polar air mass moving south across the United States towards the Gulf of Mexico, warming and acquiring moisture by evaporation as it goes, carries more water from the continent than does the Mississippi River in the same time interval. The proportion of rainfall that is not returned to the air as evapotranspiration from a landmass constitutes its total "runoff," which returns to the sea as surface-stream or ground-water discharge. For the United States this is only 26 percent and for Australia only 13 percent of precipitation.

THE OCEANS

The role of the oceans in controlling weather and climate must be emphasized. The high specific heat of water (1 cal/g deg, as against 0.2 for most silicate minerals at ordinary temperature) implies that a small change in temperature of the ocean requires exchange of a considerable amount of heat. Furthermore, a much greater mass is involved in the heat exchange, because of the seasonal convective overturning of the upper layers of the ocean. The ocean warms or cools more slowly than land and acts therefore as a temperature stabilizer. Heat is transferred from the ocean to the air partly by conduction across the surface and partly by rising water vapor which releases latent heat to the atmosphere when it condenses as rain. This latent heat contributes greatly to the instability of the atmosphere, for instance, in development of hurricanes.

Ocean currents, driven in part by wind and in

part by differences in temperature between equator and poles, contribute approximately one third of the general poleward transfer of heat. Differences in density resulting from variations in salinity also play a role in the vertical circulation within the ocean. Differences in salinity arise mainly from differences in rates of evaporation of water; where evaporation exceeds precipitation, as in subtropical latitudes, surface waters tend to become more saline and, conversely, salinity is low in the equatorial region, where precipitation is very high.

CLIMATES OF THE PAST

In brief, then, climate is determined by a large number of factors, most of which are mutually dependent, and all of which may have changed appreciably during geologic times: radiation from the sun, inclination of the earth's axis, distribution of land and sea, relief of the surface, nature and extent of the vegetation cover, carbon dioxide content of the atmosphere, dust content of the atmosphere (as resulting, say, from volcanic action or wind transport of erosional debris), and so on. The complexity of meteorological processes, and the large number of factors involved, precludes any detailed analysis or explanation of climatic changes during geologic times.

There is indeed much geological evidence of past climatic changes. The Quaternary glaciation, already mentioned in Chapter 4, will be examined later in this chapter. The late Paleozoic glaciation of "Gondwana land," and its bearing on continental drift, are discussed briefly in Chapter 13. Local climatic changes may also be inferred from the nature of the sediments of a particular age (for example, the Permian red beds and evaporites of the Northern Hemisphere), or from the flora (such as "tropical" early Cenozoic floras in high latitudes). A record of changes in the temperature of the sea and in the volume of the sea is found in the varying isotopic ratio O^{18}/O^{16} of carbonate shells of marine animals. Purely climatic effects are, however, difficult to disentangle from those of polar wandering or continental drift (Chapter 13). Continental drift changes climate locally, as the continent moves

from one climatic belt to another; and it may also produce worldwide effects by modifying the pattern of ocean currents or winds. Polar displacement, in principle, moves all climatic zones that are concentric about the poles without altering their character or size; but again this simple picture could be greatly distorted if a pole moved, say, from a continental to an oceanic area, thereby probably modifying the whole pattern of global circulation.

Weathering

SCOPE

Any section of the exposed land surface is the site of continual reaction within a physical system in perpetual disequilibrium. At atmospheric temperature and pressure internal disequilibrium is the general rule even among the solid phases in the system—the mineral aggregates that make up rocks of all kinds formed over a broad range of temperature and pressure. But near the surface these accidentally encounter one of the most active of all natural chemical agents, meteoric water containing significant quantities of dissolved atmospheric oxygen and carbon dioxide. The surface system, moreover, is far from static. Segments of surface rock are subject to relative displacement on all scales under the influence of tectonic and gravitational forces. Surface water is highly mobile. It is supplied from the atmosphere intermittently. In surface rocks, water is in a state of fluctuating motion—its ultimate destination the ocean or lakes of inland drainage basins.

The complex reaction of rocks to the surface environment of disequilibrium is essentially destructive. Mineral grains suffer some degree of solution or become converted to new minerals such as the clay silicates that are stable in the presence of water at atmospheric temperature and pressure. Water also has a strong catalytic influence, accelerating intermineral reactions that otherwise would be infinitely slow. Closely connected with chemical destruction is mechanical disintegration of rocks on all scales down to that of the individual grain. One or the other may

FIG. 7-1 *Sheeting in quartz–monzonite exposed in a cirque on the northeast side of Chiquito Ridge, Sierra Nevada, California. The sheets are 0.5–1.5 meters thick. (Photograph by N. King Huber, U.S. Geological Survey.)*

dominate under different surface conditions, but in general chemical and mechanical reaction against surface disequilibrium are almost inseparable. The sum total of all such reactions constitutes the broad process termed *weathering*.

Weathering products fall into two categories. Some are removed from the weathering site in solution or by mechanical transport. The principal transporting agent is water; the controlling force, gravity. What is left is a surface residue of weathering products, the *soil*.

MECHANICAL ASPECTS

SIGNIFICANCE OF JOINTS Most rock bodies are cut by systems of joints (Chapter 3). These facilitate weathering in several respects. They augment the total area of reaction surface between rock and water. Small-scale jointing steps up the process of mechanical destruction. Where joints dip steeply, as they commonly do, they provide a ready means of access for surface waters to penetrate to relatively deep levels.

One type of jointing is essentially a surface feature, the response of internally stressed, once-deep-seated rocks to reduced surface pressure. The precise nature of the stress system and of its ultimate release by fracture (jointing) is debatable. But the resulting structures follow a regular and familiar pattern known as *sheeting*. Surface rocks, particularly crystalline plutonic rocks of the granite family, develop regular continuous joints approximately parallel to the detail of the land surface (Figure 7–1). Intervening granite sheets in New England quarries average two or three meters thick at depths down to ten meters. At a depth of 20 to 30 m the average thickness is about 5 m. Sheeting can be considered as a purely mechanical element in weathering—one of the few such in which water plays no role.

FROST RIVING   Freezing of water at atmospheric pressure is accompanied by a volume increase of 10.9 percent. In cold climates the freezing process is a powerful agent of mechanical disintegration of surface rocks and soil. The effect is intensified by surface tension which significantly lowers the freezing point of water in capillary openings. Thus water at a temperature below that of normal freezing can move freely through the finer crevices and pores of surface rocks and so contribute continuously to the enlargement of growing ice crystals. Disintegration by freeze-and-thaw action of ice is called *frost riving*. It is extremely effective in regions of high altitude or high latitude, where at the depth of zero annual temperature fluctuation, rock temperatures are below the freezing point of water. Below this level every rock crevice is permanently filled with ice; the perenially frozen ground is termed *permafrost*. Above the permafrost level surface material shattered by winter freezing disintegrates on every scale as the cementing ice melts in the summer thaw. Frost riving is the mode of origin of the abundant rock debris that litters glacial surfaces and valley floors in glaciated regions. The same process can produce sand and silt particles whose lower size limit is about 0.15 mm.

OTHER EFFECTS   Somewhat analogous to frost riving but much more limited is the disintegration effect of salt crystallizing from solution in rock crevices in regions of seasonally arid climate. The process is one of alternately repeated solution and recrystallization.

Other materials precipitated from surface waters—notably silica and hydrated oxides of iron, manganese, and aluminum—have the reverse effect. Once formed they do not redissolve. They tend to cement the surface material, which thereby becomes *case-hardened* and more resistant than before to disintegration.

Quantitatively insignificant are the prying effects of roots, lichens, and other forms of vegetation. Burrowing animals are somewhat more effective; but in this respect, and especially during the past century, the most effective living agent of mechanical weathering is man.

CHEMICAL ASPECTS

WEATHERING OF SILICATES   Rainwater, because of its dissolved carbon dioxide and oxygen, has a mildly acid oxidizing character ($pH = 6$–7; $Eh = +0.3$ to $+0.4$, see Chapter 8). In temperate, moist climates its acidity is likely to be increased by solution of "humic acids" as it percolates downward through rotting vegetation detritus—for example, the floor carpet of a conifer forest. This is not the case in equatorial forests, where bacterial activity outstrips plant growth and vegetable remains are eliminated from the soil surface. Soil waters here tend to be neutral.

Chemical reaction between surface water and mineral grains involves hydrolysis and oxidation, with simple solution (as in salt beds) and carbonation reactions locally significant. What concerns us most, of course, is reaction of silicates to waters in the compositional range stated above. At the surface of any grain, where electric charges are unbalanced, cations go in the first instance into ionic solution. Some ions, such as K^+, Na^+, Ca^{2+}, and Mg^{2+} released from common silicates tend to remain in solution, and as the percolating waters move downward toward the water table and outward to drainage channels, these elements are progressively removed from the weathering zone. Ultimately they find their way to the sea or to inland bodies of water.

The fate of the other principal rock-forming elements—iron, aluminum, and silicon—is more variable and depends on the chemical properties and mobility of the solvent water:

1. Ferrous iron Fe^{2+} is relatively soluble in slightly acid soil waters. If these are in a state of continuous circulation, iron is thus removed along with other cations. In a neutral or slightly alkaline environment, however, ferrous iron is

rapidly oxidized and precipitated as the hydroxide $Fe(OH)_3$ that tinges so many soils with a yellowish-brown color.

2. Silica is slightly but significantly soluble (2–4 millimoles/liter) in water over a wide pH range (4–9). It enters solution as the silicic acid anion $[SiO_4]^{4-}$ and is also present as colloidal silicate detritus—fragments of linked $[SiO_4]^{4-}$ and $[AlO_4]^{5-}$ networks from which "cementing" cations have been removed in solution. An important element in weathering is repreciptation of colloidal silica in the soil itself as chemical properties (such as pH) of the moving solvent change with environment.

3. Alumina is soluble in acid waters with $pH < 4$, almost insoluble in the pH range of most surface waters (5 to 9). Concentration of aluminum is thus highly characteristic of the residues of chemical weathering. Normally it is precipitated as a clay mineral. Particles of colloidal size commonly coat the surfaces or penetrate cleavage cracks of feldspar grains that in the course of weathering continuously supply the necessary Al and Si atoms. The nature of the clay precipitate depends upon conditions in the weathering system. Where water circulates freely, soluble cations are steadily removed, and the residual products are clays of the kaolinite family. If circulation is slow, on the other hand, the less-soluble cations such as Mg^{2+} enter into combination with the silica–alumina complex and the product is a montmorillorite clay. Montmorillonites also form where there is an abundant supply of Mg^{2+} and Fe^{2+} ions from unstable volcanic materials such as pyroxenes, olivine, and basaltic glass. There is yet another possibility. Alumina is so much less soluble than silica in alkaline waters that it may precipitate freely as a simple hydroxide $Al(OH)_3$, as it does in special soil types of tropical regions (*bauxites and laterites*).

OTHER REACTIONS   Carbonates dissolve in water containing appreciable carbon dioxide. A familiar instance of regional significance in limestone terranes is solution of calcite to give Ca^{2+} cations and bicarbonate anions $[HCO_3]^-$:

$$CaCO_3 + H_2O + CO_2 \rightarrow Ca^{2+} + 2[HCO_3]^-$$

Pyrite becomes oxidized and hydrated to $Fe(OH)_3$ and sulfuric acid, strongly affecting the course of weathering of associated silicates by lowering the pH value of soil waters:

$$4FeS_2 + 14H_2O + 15O_2 \rightarrow 4Fe(OH)_3 + 8H_2SO_4$$

Magnetite likewise undergoes combined hydration and oxidation, with $Fe(OH)_3$ again the insoluble residual product. Water removes some minerals in solution from evaporite beds (halite NaCl, sylvite KCl), and hydrates others; for example,

$$\underset{\text{anhydrite}}{CaSO_4} + 2H_2O \rightarrow \underset{\text{gypsum}}{CaSO_4 \cdot 2H_2O}$$

RESISTANCE OF MINERALS   In spite of the sensitivity of weathering reactions to differences in commonly encountered surface conditions, it is possible to generalize in an empirical fashion as to the relative resistance and vulnerability of minerals to the weathering process. Subject to many exceptions they can be listed as follows in order of increasing resistance:

1. Minerals significantly soluble in surface waters: halite NaCl, calcite $CaCO_3$, and others.
2. Iron oxides and sulfides: magnetite, pyrite. High-temperature ferromagnesian silicates of the orthosilicate and inosilicate family: olivines, pyroxenes, amphiboles.
3. Feldspathoids and feldspars.
4. Muscovite and quartz, tourmaline, garnet, zircon.

SOILS

The residual end product at the site of weathering is the *soil*—a layered system in process of internal change (*immature*) or in a more or less steady state, the *mature* soil. The nature of the soil in any locality reflects the combined influence of many factors, some of which are interdependent: parent rock, topography, climate, vegetation, fauna, and time. Immature soils in regions of high relief tend to reflect most strongly the character of the parent rock. Their principal components may be scarcely altered rock fragments and mineral grains. The situation is completely otherwise in stable continental areas of low relief where the soil mantles rocks long exposed to continuous weathering. This is the case over large areas of the dry interior of Australia.

The entity in soil science is the *soil profile*, a compound layered system consisting of the following generalized downward sequence:

A horizons:

A_0, leaf mold.

A_1, layer stained dark with humus; organic materials are an essential though in many cases subordinate part of the soil.

A_2, bleached layer.

Soil in the A horizons suffers continuous removal (*eluviation*) of dissolved and colloidal weathering products by downward-moving water.

B horizons:

Between the A horizons and relatively unweathered rock below are one or more horizons of *illuviation*, where material brought from above is precipitated or flocculated. The principal constituents, depending upon factors such as climate and acidity of soil waters, may be silica, kaolin clays, montmorillonite clays, or even iron and aluminum hydroxides.

C horizon:

The zone of partially weathered rock.

SOIL TYPES   Elsewhere we have stressed the uniqueness of all geological events and of their products. This is nowhere more obvious than in soil profiles. Classifications of soil types therefore are elaborate and varied. Even within a single geographic province such as the Central Valley of California or the inland plateau of the state of São Paulo, Brazil, soils are highly diversified. This aspect of geology, of fundamental importance in agriculture and conservation, is covered in standard texts on soil science. Here we illustrate diversity of soil type in relation to one principal variable, climate, by brief reference to three of many widely developed general types of profile.

PODSOL SOILS   The podsol soils[2] are characteristic of forest-covered landscapes of moist, cool, temperate climates. Soil water, rendered acid by percolation through abundant leaf litter (especially on the floors of forests dominated by oak or conifers in the Northern, *Nothofagus* in the Southern Hemisphere), completely removes alumina from the A horizon. This is a conspicuous white layer of almost pure silica. The B horizon consists of clay minerals—mainly kaolinite and illite—stained brown with hydrated iron oxide.

LATERITE SOILS   The laterite soils are widely distributed in tropical regions of plentiful seasonal rainfall. Very high bacterial activity prevents accumulation of rotting vegetable debris at the A_0 horizon. Soil waters are neutral or slightly alkaline and remove silica in preference to alumina; iron is readily oxidized. The mature soil profile that develops is usually thick—10 to 30 meters—and is composed principally of iron and aluminum hydrates. Iron-rich types develop from rocks such as basalt; these are the typical laterites. If the parent rock is aluminous, for example, rich in feldspars and/or feldspathoids, the resulting soils are rich in aluminum hydrates. These include *bauxites*, the main commercial source of aluminum.

PEDOCALS   The pedocals are the characteristic soils of arid or semiarid regions with limited summer rainfall. Water moving toward the surface during the dry season precipitates calcite, which may form a strongly cemented C horizon (*caliche*) not far below the surface.

SOILS AND STRATIGRAPHY   Distribution and degree of maturity of soil types in any area can give valuable information regarding its later geological history. Stable surfaces can be distinguished from younger and less stable surfaces by maturity of the soil profile. Since soil develop-

---

[2] The soils are described here in terms of the classic classification. For a brief description of the soil classification now used by the U.S. Department of Agriculture, see U.S. National Atlas Map Sheet 86, "Soils," published by the U.S. Geological Survey, 1:7,500,000, 1969.

ment is so sensitive to climate and vegetation cover, climatic fluctuations during Pleistocene and early historic times have left their imprint on soil profiles in lands of the temperate zone.

The soil profile, of course, does not conform to the fundamental stratigraphic law of super-position. The upward succession of the C, B, and A horizons records a single geological event. Nevertheless soil scientists can distinguish super-posed events of shorter duration that have interrupted development of the soil and so are recorded in the profile. Soil profiles developed on Tertiary volcanic rocks in southeastern New Zealand contain finely divided windblown glacial silt, a relic of the dying stages of Pleistocene glaciation several hundred kilometers to the west. At the far north of New Zealand the only relic of the full extent of volcanic ash showers from major eruptions far to the south a few thousand years ago is in the contaminated profiles of thick podsol soils.

Soils are transient surface deposits, especially vulnerable to erosion. So fossil upland soil profiles of pre-Tertiary age are relatively rare. It must be remembered, moreover, that soils as we know them today, are products of only the latest part of geological time. There were no oak or *Notho-phagus* forests, no prairie grasslands in pre-Cretaceous times. There is no record of any substantial land flora until well into Paleozoic times. Present-day patterns of weathering cannot be extrapolated backward into the Precambrian, nor can the uniformitarian principle in its strictest form be applied to the development of soil through most of geologic time.

WEATHERING AND CRUSTAL EVOLUTION   Although weathering is a surface phenomenon, the surface of weathering is perpetually in process of destruction and renewal. Weathering therefore has had and continues to have a significant role in the differentiation and redistribution of elements in the outer skin of the crust. Some elements such as sodium, chlorine, and boron have been steadily removed from crustal rocks and stored progressively in ocean waters. Others that have been similarly removed have been reprecipitated and concentrated in marine sedi-ments—calcium in limestone; manganese as deep ocean precipitates; potassium, barium, and others as ions adsorbed by finely divided marine clays. What is left mantling the land surface is a puri-fied residue enriched in silicon aluminum and iron, and depleted in most other elements including the large number that are minor or trace components of common crustal rocks.

Slope Processes

Slope processes, also but less accurately called "mass wasting," include all the processes that take place on a slope and result in downslope transfer of loose material, called colluvium, to the streams that carry it away. In hilly and mountainous regions, slope processes dominate over a large fraction of the area. Not only are they agents of transport, they also mold the slope. Characteristic features of the slope—such as shape (in plan and profile), angle of slope, smoothness—are formed by, and indicative of, the several processes that occur.

A variety of agents can be active: water as drops, sheets, streams, interstitial films, or ice; plants and animals. Gravity is the dominant force. These various agents and processes may operate in succession or simultaneously. They may act cooperatively or competitively, aiding or inhibiting each other; for example, in a certain climate, alternative processes may produce gullying or creep. Creep may require a high moisture content, which may in turn depend on a dense vegetation and high water table; if so, gullying will tend to inhibit creep by destroying vegetation and lowering the water table. On the other hand, if creep is rapid enough, it can keep incipient gullies filled, preventing them from dominating the landscape. Which process will come to dominate will depend on a complex interplay of factors and events; the triggering event may be as trivial as the decision of a ground squirrel on the site of his burrow.

Some slope processes are slow and steady; the net motion is the sum total of minute increments of motion continued year after year. Although it is possible for some kinds of slope motion, such as creep or slow flow, to be uniform, it is likely that in all slope processes the motion is periodic or cyclic; that is, it is greater in some seasons of the year than in others, and during part of the year there may be no motion at all. Other slope processes are spasmodic or catastrophic. There may be no activity at all for periods up to centuries in length, while the ground is prepared—perhaps by weathering, perhaps by undermining—for another spurt of activity, and then the net erosion of centuries may take place in days, minutes, even seconds. Landslides, rockfalls, and avalanches are examples, but some kinds of waterborne erosion also have this pattern of activity.

CREEP

Creep is the imperceptibly slow downslope movement of colluvium, whose effect can be measured only by observations extending over a period of years. It is the sum of a very large number of minute displacements of individual grains and particles, which do not necessarily all move at the same rate. In some instances, at any one time only a small fraction of the surface is being displaced; some creep of this kind is of biological origin: earthworms, burrowing of rodents. A common form of creep is due to expansion followed by contraction of the surface layer. Outward movement in expansion will be normal to the slope, but will have a slight downslope component due to gravity; contraction will similarly have a downslope component of gravitational origin. Expansion and contraction may be due to cycles of freezing and thawing, or to swelling of certain clays or of humus-rich soil after seasonal rainfalls (Figure 7–2). Uniform creep may occur if, because of changes in moisture content or for some other reason, the delicate balance between the downslope component of weight and the shear resistance (mainly by friction) along some plane parallel to the slope is disturbed; such creep, however, is likely to pass abruptly into a landslide.

Many slope processes involve water directly as the transporting medium. Water may be in the form of raindrops, as sheets that cover the

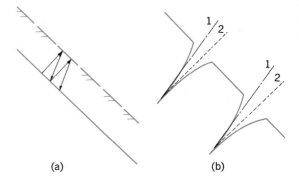

FIG. 7–2 Two mechanisms of creep. (a) Creep by outward expansion of soil. Arrows are displacement vectors of particles at the soil surface. (b) Creep by opening and closing of shrinkage cracks. 1. Position of crack at beginning of dry season. 2. Position of same crack after closing at beginning of wet season. (Widths and displacements are exaggerated.)

ground whenever rainfall intensity exceeds the infiltration capacity of the soil; or it may form rills and gullies. These processes are effective only on barren slopes (as in arid regions during infrequent storms), on plowed lands, or in badlands. Elsewhere the cover of sod, leaf litter, or roots impedes erosion by running water. In regions of dense sod, water flowing through rodent burrows and cracks in the soil (piping) erodes the walls of its conduits and contributes the major part of slope transport.

A slope process intermediate in character between creep and water transport is *solifluction* (Figure 7–3), the slow downslope sludging over a frozen substratum of the surface soil of arctic and alpine regions, rendered liquid during the annual thaw by its high water content and disaggregated clay particles. The annual movement by solifluction may amount to a few centimeters or to a meter or more, and its aggregate effect is to produce sheets and streamlike bodies of colluvium of great extent.

LANDSLIDES

Landslides, because of their adverse effects, are slope phenomena of vital human concern. Their velocity may range from a few centimeters per year to as much as 100 meters per second.

FIG. 7–3 *Tongue of solifluction debris. Head of Totatlanika River, Alaska Range. Bedrock is chiefly quartz–sericite schist.*

Landslides include falls, rock and soil avalanches, block glides, slumps (or rotational slides), and slow flows (Figure 7–4). They are marked by a surface of shear failure at the base of the moving mass. Landslides occur when the frictional resistance or cohesion of the material beneath the slope is exceeded by the component of weight, (aided at times by seepage pressures) along a surface, which becomes the surface of shear failure. The buoyant effect of pore water counteracts the component of weight producing frictional resistance, and at the same time the water in-

creases the total weight of the sliding mass; hence most landslides are triggered by accumulation of soil water during periods of heavy rain. Landslides can also be triggered by earthquakes, in which case the horizontal acceleration of the earthquake vibrations augments the downslope component of gravity sufficiently to overcome the resisting force.

Conditions conducive to landsliding are steepness of slope; presence of surfaces of weakness, such as bedding planes, joints, or foliation, parallel to the slope; presence of unconsolidated,

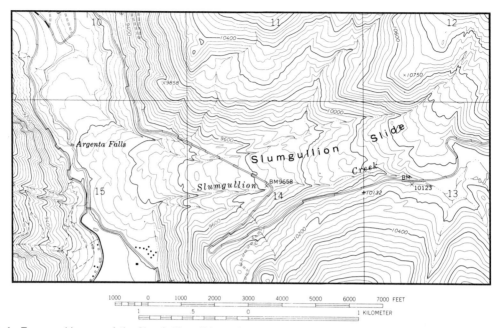

FIG. 7–4 *Topographic map of the Slumgullion slide, a classic earthflow in the San Juan Mountains of Colorado, which dammed Lake San Cristobal (the lower end of which is in the lower left corner of the map). (From U.S. Geological Survey topographic map of Lake San Cristobal, 7½-minute quadrangle, 1964 edition. Contour interval 40 feet.)*

impermeable clay underlying permeable rock; and accumulations of water close to the surface. Terranes of poorly consolidated or tectonically crushed rock, rich in montmorillonite and similar clays, are particularly subject to landsliding on a large scale. Landslides have a characteristic topography. A small landslide may be marked by a hollow with steep headwall scar on a hillside, with a bulge immediately below the hollow. Large landslides have hummocky surfaces, with many low ridges commonly aligned parallel to the contours and many ponds and undrained depressions.

In some regions soil avalanches are an integral part of the process of slope retreat. These occur at a given site once every few centuries or longer, when the layer of weathered rock beneath the vegetation cover has reached sufficient thickness to be unstable.

SHAPE OF SLOPES

The shape and slope angle of valley sides reflect the particular process that is most active on the slopes. For simplicity the discussion will be confined to the side of a long straight ridge. If creep or solifluction is the process transporting colluvium on the slope, then every element of the surface is occupied in succession by all elements of colluvial mantle upslope from it. Hence, (1) if the rate of creep is uniform over the entire slope, only the ridge crest would lose elevation, and most of the slope would lose elevation slowly or not at all. On the other hand, (2) in order for the entire slope to be reduced by a uniform amount, the volume of material passing any point in unit time must be proportional to the distance from that point to the crest of the ridge. This could happen in one of two ways: either the thickness of the moving mantle or the rate at which it moves increases with distance down the slope (linearly for the long straight ridge; in some different manner for an isolated circular hill or the hollow at the head of a ravine). If creep is externally controlled (such as by wetting and drying, freezing, and thawing), the first alternative is unlikely; the depth of penetration of the zero isotherm or of deep drying of the soil is likely to be the same everywhere—greater near the hilltops, if anything. Thus in general the velocity must increase downslope. Again, this can come about in one of two ways (or their combination): (1) the creeping layer is progressively more mobile downslope, through increased water content or progressive weathering; or (2) the driving force that is the downslope component of gravity increases with distance down the slope or, in other words, the slope angle increases downslope and the shape of the hillside is convex upward. Convex hilltops and a rolling, smooth topography are usually indications of creep or similar processes as the dominant slope process.

On the other hand, where transportation by running water (or by soil avalanches) is dominant, slopes tend to be straight and hillslopes are intricately dissected. This is because any process enhanced by slope irregularity tends to increase the rate of erosion on the gully floor but reduce it elsewhere, thus accentuating the gully itself.

Where the rate of slope retreat is discontinuous, abrupt changes in slope must occur. The necessary and sufficient condition for the formation of a cliff is that the lower part of a slope be lowered more rapidly than the upper part. A landslide headwall is a cliff for this reason. Differential erosion can occur in many ways, only some of which may be related specifically to changes in bedrock character. Bedrock character does affect slope mechanism and slope shape, as by controlling the rate of infiltration of water, for instance; it also determines the kind of debris formed by weathering. Similar topography, may, however, develop on dissimilar bedrock.

Climate has an important influence on the slope processes, and hence on landform. In frost climates, creep and solifluction predominate; in consequence mature slopes are broadly convex and ridge crests are rounded (Figure 7–5). A special character of the colluvium in climates where the average annual temperature is close to or below freezing, is the patterning of the ground that results from intense frost action. On gentle slopes, this pattern consists of a polygonal network of boulders and cobbles about centers of fine soil; on steeper slopes it may consist of alter-

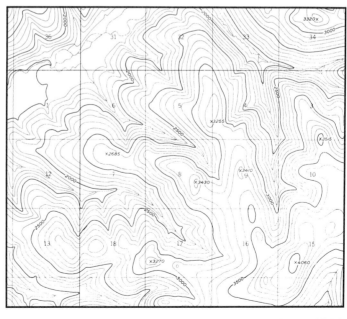

FIG. 7–5 Rounded ridge crests and convex slopes in the Yukon-Tanana Upland, east-central Alaska, a region dominated by frost creep and solifluction. (From U.S. Geological Survey topographic map of Big Delta, A-1 quadrangle, Alaska, 1955 edition. Contour interval 100 feet.)

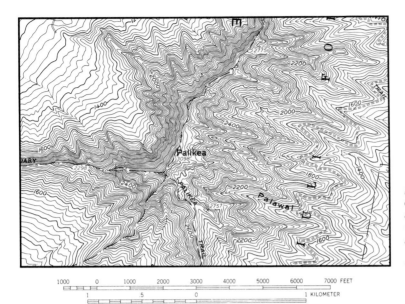

FIG. 7–6 Topographic map of sharp-crested ridges and straight slopes of a region dominated by soil avalanches. (From U.S. Geological Survey topographic map of Schofield Barracks. 7½-minute quadrangle, Hawaii, 1967 edition. Contour interval 40 feet.)

nate stripes of boulders and fine soil extending downslope, or of small steps on the slope. In regions where sudden cold snaps down to −40°C are common, causing tensional stress from the contraction of ice at low temperatures, a polygonal network over vertical ice wedges and veinlets forms from repeated cracking of the frozen soil under tension.

In humid temperate and tropical climates, many processes cooperate to model the slopes, and slopes range from smooth and convex, where creep predominates, as in grasslands, to straight, narrow ridge crests, where periodic gullying or soil avalanches are an integral part of the slope process (Figure 7–6).

In arid climates vegetation is lacking, and slopes tend to be straight and intricately gullied (Figure 7–7). Rock outcrops are numerous, and the influence of rock type on land sculpture is at a maximum.

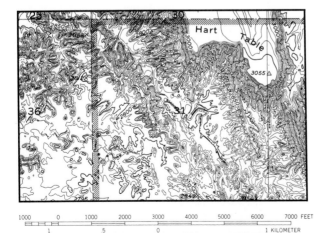

FIG. 7–7 Topographic map of intricately gullied slopes of a semi-arid region. Area is in Badlands National Monument. (From U.S. Geological Survey topographic map of Sheep Mountain table, 7½-minute quadrangle, South Dakota, 1950 edition. Contour interval 10 feet.)

Stream Processes

DRAINAGE BASINS AND STREAM SYSTEMS

Meteoric water flowing in surface-stream channels plays an essential, indeed the most conspicuous, role in denudation of the land surface and in transport of rock debris from higher to lower levels. To gain some understanding of these activities we must consider them, so far as this is possible, in isolation from simultaneous and preceding weathering and slope processes with which they are in fact closely interdependent. It is convenient, moreover, to consider stream processes as they occur within some arbitrarily selected system in which all such operations, however much they may vary from place to place and in time, are themselves interdependent and so achieve a recognizable unity. The major geomorphic unit from this viewpoint is a drainage basin. This is any area from which stream waters are ultimately conducted via a single outlet channel to a body of still water—lake or sea—or into some still larger river. In the headwaters areas of a drainage basin, stream channels are numerous. At lower levels they unite, increase in size and diminish in number, until they enter the master channel that leads to the outlet.

Any drainage basin is endowed with certain externally imposed features and potentialities for development, related, for example, to tectonic activity (which controls elevation), precipitation and other climatic factors, composition and structure of surface rocks. These strongly influence its evolution under the combined operation of weathering, slope and stream processes. What the geologist observes in any particular basin is a transient stage in a continuous course of geomorphic evolution. This applies also to the integrated system of stream channels that has developed and to the hydraulic system comprising the connected streams of water continuously flowing in these channels toward the outlet. Because controlling factors are so diverse, every stream system is unique. But to the modern hydrologist[3] "the subtle but pervasive unity that

exists, despite the tremendous diversity, is probably the most important characteristic of river systems." This, and "an amazing organization of river systems" in general is seen as the expression of "a delicate balance between the forces of erosion and the forces of resistance." Were this not so, it would be impossible to discuss stream processes in general terms.

Characteristics of a drainage basin and its associated stream system that can be measured readily and are useful for comparative purposes are topographic relief, drainage density, and hydraulic discharge.

Total relief, H, is the difference between the elevation of high points at the headwaters and that of the outlet channel.

Drainage density is the sum of stream lengths divided by the area of the drainage basin. Density is highest where the bedrock is easily eroded and relatively impermeable and the surface bare of protective vegetation—for example, badland topography developed in shale and mudstone of semiarid regions (see Figure 7–7). Lower values are typical of forested country even where surface runoff is high. Drainage density is minimal in dune lands and some limestone terranes where runoff also is low, and in arctic regions where soil creep inhibits development of minor drainage channels (see Figure 7–5).

Discharge, Q, is the volume of water passing any point in unit time

$$Q = wdv$$

where w and d are width and depth of the outlet channel and v the mean velocity of the outlet stream. Discharge depends on many factors: climate, total rainfall, rock permeability, and interdependent secondary characteristics such as soil, vegetation, and drainage density. Temperature alone, as a principal factor controlling evaporation on slopes and in stream channels, has a very strong influence on discharge. Given the measured annual discharge Q cm³ and the total map area of the drainage basin A cm², the annual *runoff*, measured (like precipitation) in centimeters per year, is Q/A. Hydrological data of this kind are available for large areas of the world. In the United States, for example, the an-

[3] L. B. Leopold: Rivers, *Am. Sci.,* vol. 50, no. 4, p. 516, 1962.

nual runoff in those regions where the annual precipitation is 75 cm ranges from 20 cm where the mean temperature is 50°F (10°C) to only 5 cm where the mean temperature is 70°F (21°C). The annual runoff from the Mississippi, 17 cm, is only one third that of the Amazon basin (about 51 cm).

THE STREAM AS A HYDRAULIC SYSTEM

Certain aspects of stream erosion stem directly from the physical and chemical properties of water itself. Stream water is an incompressible fluid whose density is about one third that of the sediment that it must transport. Its very low viscosity (one centipoise) implies high mobility and low internal friction in the course of flow. Its chemical activity as a solvent contributes to its efficiency as a transporting agent (of dissolved material). Moreover, water is volatile to a degree that varies widely over the normal range of surface conditions (temperature and humidity), with important consequences with respect to runoff and discharge.

Behavior of a stream as a geological agent depends also on the unique geometry and dynamic character of the stream itself. The factors concerned are volume, velocity, and flow regime (for example, turbulence) of water; slope, shape, cross-sectional area, depth, and wall properties (for example, roughness and cohesion) of the channel; and nature and availability of transportable debris. Ideal systems have been investigated experimentally in the laboratory, where it is possible to vary one or more factors while the others are held constant. Such information is of greatest use to engineers. Its applicability to natural stream systems is more qualitative. This is because of the diversity of hydraulic conditions that prevails in any drainage basin and the wide amplitude in seasonal and other climatically controlled fluctuations affecting runoff and local discharge. Some of the most useful hydrological concepts have been developed empirically, following the uniformitarian approach, from observations on the behavior of natural stream waters under varied conditions.

ENERGY CONSIDERATIONS Water and sediment flowing downward in a stream channel lose potential energy. This is first converted into kinetic energy. In a stream of constant composition flowing at constant velocity, acceleration of water and load falling under gravity is balanced by frictional forces that convert kinetic energy to heat. This heat is removed from the system by conduction, radiation, and evaporation. The final state in a stream system—regardless of local variations and fluctuations in stream velocity, discharge, and load throughout the system—is a still body of water and motionless masses of sediment at lower levels than the sites of origin. The kinetic energy of water and sediment is now zero. The total potential energy has been reduced by an amount depending solely on reduction of the elevation and the total mass of transported material (water plus sediment). This energy has been utilized as work done in overcoming frictional resistance en route.

FLOW REGIMES: TURBULENCE The flow regime, as exemplified by turbulent versus laminar flow, is related to the properties of the flowing medium (in this case water variously charged with sediment) and the character of the channel, through the dimensionless Reynolds number R_e which, as we recall (Chapter 4), measures the ratio of inertial to viscous forces. It is defined as

$$R_e = \frac{Rv\rho}{\eta}$$

where v, ρ, and η are velocity, density, and viscosity, respectively, of the flowing medium, and R is some characteristic length—for instance, the hydraulic radius of the channel [(cross section)/ (wetted perimeter) $= wd/(w + 2d)$; for normal streams that are wide in comparison with depth $R = d$].

Laminar flow can occur only if R_e, as defined above, is less than about 800–2000 (a condition implying very low velocity, since for water the value of η is also low). At higher values of R_e the flow regime becomes turbulent. This is the usual condition across almost the whole section of most natural streams. Laminar flow, if such occurs, is restricted to films a few millimeters thick moving at velocities of only a few centimeters per second along the bottom and walls of smooth channels. The velocity of flow decreases downward within the laminar film.

Another aspect of flow regime concerns the relative tranquillity of water in turbulent flow. The violent perturbations in velocity of water flowing over rapids are characteristic of a flow regime called *shooting* (supercritical) flow. The massive movement of eddying water in swift deep rivers by contrast is designated *tranquil* (subcritical) flow. Deep water and relatively low velocity characterize the tranquil regime, as indicated by low values of another dimensionless quantity, the Froude number F_r, given by

$$F_r = \frac{v^2}{gL}$$

where L is a length dimension related to depth. The Froude number measures essentially the ratio of inertial to gravitational forces.

STEADY-STATE VELOCITY   Consider a stream of water moving at constant velocity V down a uniform slope S in a channel whose hydraulic radius is R ($\approx d$ in most natural streams). Release of potential energy, proportional to S, is exactly counterbalanced by expenditure of energy in overcoming friction. The viscosity of water is so low that internal friction in a stream almost devoid of sediment is minimal. The principal factors determining frictional loss of energy will be the area of contact between water and channel walls (proportional to $R \times d$) and the roughness of the wall material. This latter is designated by an empirically determined roughness factor n (Manning roughness).[4] All these quantities are related empirically by the Chezy-Manning equation

$$V = \frac{R^{2/3} \, S^{1/2}}{n}$$

_____

[4] 0.025 to 0.075 for most natural streams; greater than 0.1 for water moving through vegetation.

where V is expressed in meters per second and R in meters. Note that, other conditions being the same, stream velocities are more sensitive to changes in depth than to change of slope. Herein is an explanation of the apparently paradoxical observation that the rate of flow in the gently sloping downstream reaches of a stream is generally the same as or somewhat higher than that in the steeper headwater reaches. Downstream, depth (hence R) increases, while the bed is generally smoother, and n correspondingly smaller.

TRANSPORT AND DEPOSITION OF ROCK DEBRIS

The capacity of a stream to mold the landscape depends on its power to transport mineral matter in solution, in suspension as wash load and in intermittent motion as bed load.

TRANSPORT IN SOLUTION   The mean composition of dissolved matter in river waters as computed by Livingstone is given in Table 7–1. Allowing for the high contribution of atmospheric carbon dioxide and windblown sea salt, we may estimate the dissolved load of mineral material as perhaps only 50 to 70 percent of these figures.

TRANSPORT IN SUSPENSION   The settling velocity v_s of mineral particles sinking in water is essentially a function of size (as given by Stokes' law,

TABLE 7–1 Dissolved matter (ppm) in river waters (after Livingstone 1963).

	World	North America
$[HCO_3]^-$	58.4	68
$[SO_4]^{2-}$	11.2	20
Cl^-	7.8	8
$[NO_3]^-$	1	1
Ca^{2+}	15	21
Mg^{2+}	4.1	5
Na^+	6.3	9
K^+	2.3	1.4
Fe	0.67	0.16
SiO_2	13.1	9
Total	120	142

Chapter 4) and of shape. Values are lower for tabular flakes of clay minerals than for equant quartz grains of the same size-fraction. If v_s is much less than the mean velocity of streamflow, the particle will travel a large distance before it reaches the stream bed. Coarser material, for which v_s is larger, travels a shorter distance before reaching the stream bed. Here it forms part of the bed load whose patterns of downstream motion we shall consider later. In natural streams flowing at normal rates of a meter or two per second, particles of clay and silt smaller than 0.062 mm in diameter move in continued suspension as wash load. In most large rivers, even where water is visibly muddy, the wash load is not more than one or two percent by weight. The limiting factor is not velocity or "power" of the stream, but availability of fine-grained debris. During times of flood when water moves freely down hillside slopes in the headwaters, and cave-ins occur along the channel banks, the wash load may increase enormously. Concentrations of over 50 percent have been measured. During low-water periods most streams run clear.

Most of the wash load of major rivers reaches the sea. The great deltas of the Nile, the Mississippi and the Amazon are striking evidence of the efficiency of this mode of transport. But silt carried in suspension also finds at least a temporary resting place on river flood plains where it is deposited from receding or stagnant flood waters.

MOVEMENT OF BED LOADS   A sedimentary particle—sand grain or pebble—on the bed of a running stream is continuously subject to a complex system of forces. Factors involved are gravity, the frictional drag of water on the surface of contact, impact of other solid particles in motion, and resistance of friction on the interface between the particle and solid bed material. Obviously such a system of forces is subject to continuous fluctuations—major changes of a long-term nature, as between periods of low water and flood, and continuous minor oscillations related to turbulent flow. In this situation bed material is in a state of intermittent motion, and constitutes the bed load of the stream.

We shall not attempt to review quantitative treatments of bed-load motion and of the "competence" of a stream to carry particles of a critical maximum diameter. Some of the variables concerned are obvious from Stokes' law:

$$v_s = \frac{2}{9} g \frac{(\rho_s - \rho_f)}{\eta} r^2$$

and from the equation relating turbulent flow to a Reynolds number R_e:

$$R_e = \frac{dv\rho_f}{\eta} \approx 800 \text{ to } 2000$$

In these expressions v_s is the settling velocity of a spherical particle of radius r and density ρ_s; v is the mean flow velocity, ρ_f the density, and η the viscosity of the flowing medium; d is the depth of the channel; and g the acceleration of gravity.

A particle on the stream bed can be set in motion if it projects substantially into the main zone of turbulent flow above the thin basal layer in which laminar flow is theoretically possible. In most streams this is the case for particles coarser than medium-grade sand (diameter 0.2 to 0.5 mm). Turbulence and frictional drag on the grain both increase with mean rate of flow. So the maximum grain diameter of sand or gravel that can be set in motion—a measure of the *competence* of the stream for transport—is essentially a function of mean velocity. Silt- and clay-size grains on the other hand are progressively more difficult to move as the grain size decreases; for below some critical value of v_s any such grain is completely immersed in the film of laminar flow. In addition, clays tend to be cohesive. These general relations are illustrated in Figure 7–8. Silt-laden floodwater has significantly higher density and viscosity than pure water. These properties lower the settling velocity of larger bodies and thus increase the competence of the stream to transport coarser material as bed load.

There is a close and sensitive interrelationship between the rate of flow of water, the coarseness (grade) of sand and gravel carried as bed load, its pattern of motion, and the geometric pattern that develops in the bed itself. Along any more or less uniform segment of a stream channel these fea-

FIG. 7–8 *Approximate curves for erosion and deposition of uniform sediment (From Hjulström, in Trask, Recent Marine Sediments, p. 10, Dover, New York). Curve A gives the minimum cross-section velocity necessary to erode sediment of a given size (the curve is represented by a band to emphasize the uncertainty of the data). Curve B gives the cross-section velocity at which sediment of a given size is deposited. The vertical width of the zone between the two curves gives the range of velocity over which material once eroded continues to be transported. The graph shows that coarse material in transport is likely to be deposited with a slight diminution in velocity, whereas fine material (less than 0.05 mm) stays in suspension almost indefinitely. Note also that it takes a stronger current to erode silt and clay than sand.*

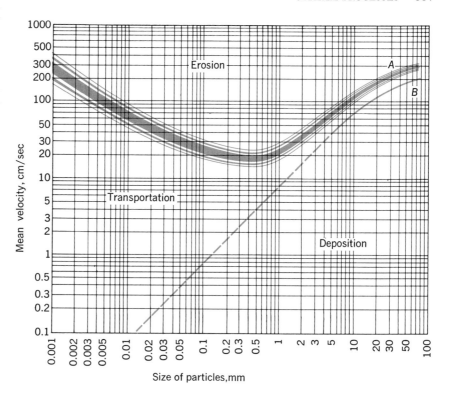

tures tend to become mutually adjusted to a steady state. The moving bed load assumes some regular pattern of bed form, typical of which are systems of symmetrically repeated migrating ripples or dunes and more stationary transverse gravel bars. Their form and size change as the stream velocity fluctuates in response to externally imposed fluctuations in discharge. Since the frictional resistance of the stream bed as indicated by the Manning resistance factor itself directly influences the mean velocity and the turbulence regime of the flowing water, all these factors tend to adjust mutually to a steady state if the discharge remains approximately constant.

SEDIMENT DISCHARGE The quantity of sediment discharged through the outlet of a drainage basin in unit time increases, as might be expected, with increasing hydraulic discharge. It is exceptionally great, and the size of the transported pebbles or boulders is exceptionally large, in those rare floods of great magnitude that recur

at long intervals—perhaps 20 to 100 or even 500 years. It is not these catastrophic events that contribute most to the molding of the landscape and the cumulative transport of sediment towards the sea. The greatest contribution is achieved during the more frequent, but still-limited, number of occasions in which the discharge is notably higher than normal but still far short of the level that characterizes the rare catastrophic flood.

CHANNEL CHARACTERISTICS

In any longitudinal traverse along a stream channel from the headwaters to its outlet, the character of the channel changes according to a recognizable general pattern, always with variations that are unique to the individual stream.

1. In the headwaters segment, the longitudinal profile (slope) of the channel is steep. The channel walls are sharply defined, for the channel itself is simply the line of intersection of opposite

steep valley slopes. Any sediment on the stream bed consists of coarse gravel or boulders. The bed of the channel is subject to continuous downward erosion.

2. Farther downstream, the course of the stream channel becomes sinuous. Any initial slight bend in the course tends to become exaggerated with time, since inertia throws the thread of maximum flow velocity against the outer bank. Here shear stresses and turbulence are locally heightened and the convex bank becomes eroded, so sinuosity of the course likewise increases. As the stream erodes the convex bend, its channel grows wider than necessary to handle the discharge, and a zone of still water and, eventually, an eddy develop on the concave side of the bend. In this eddy, or more commonly along its outer margin, sediment is deposited in a long bank, known as a *point bar*. In a sinuous channel the slope of the valley wall on the inside of a bend is usually much gentler than the opposite slope. It is called a slip-off slope and it is a measure of the relative rates of vertical and lateral stream-bed erosion. Where the river, in migrating against a bend, leaves behind a flat sediment-covered valley floor, downcutting proceeds at an infinitesimal rate compared to lateral erosion, and the stream has reached "grade." Farther downstream the valley flats are wider and longer. Eventually the stream impinges upon its valley walls only at widely separated points. For most of the distance it is bordered by a broad valley flat, and confined by banks of its own making.

3. Most large rivers finally enter and cross a basin of fluviatile deposition. This may be a tectonic depression like the valleys of the Rhine and Po in Europe, the Indo-Gangetic plain of northern India, or the great longitudinal valleys that separate the coastal ranges from the Pacific watershed (Sierra Nevada in California and Andes in Chile). Other such basins are deltas built outward in estuaries—for example, the deltas of the Mississippi and the Nile. The channel pattern as it appears on the map is typically either *meandering* or *braided*. The meandering stream flows in a single channel whose course is a rhythmically repeated series of curves having a radius of curvature two or three times the width of the stream (Figure 7–9). The braided pattern (Figure 7–10) results from repeated splitting of the channel, the resulting branches of which repeatedly rejoin and split again downstream. It tends to develop in coarse, noncohesive sediment such as gravel; for with slight transverse fluctuations in stream velocity sediment can accumulate locally in the middle of a channel and thereby split the thread of maximum velocity.

Both the course and the cross-sectional dimensions of a stream channel change downstream according to a regular general pattern. Width and depth both increase downstream. However, since the increase in width is the more marked effect, the width/depth ratio also increases conspicuously.

DEVELOPMENT OF THE LONGITUDINAL PROFILE

In the longitudinal profile of a major stream we see the temporary product of a long process of evolution in time. Everywhere, by the combined processes of downward or lateral erosion, and locally fluctuating deposition and movement of sediment of all grades, the profile is developing continuously toward a kind of equilibrium. This is controlled from the first by a limiting level—the *base level* of erosion—below which no part of the channel may be eroded. For a large river the base level may be that of the sea or a body of inland water. For a tributary stream it is the level of the outlet into the main river channel. Base level, of course, is subject to slow change in time.

THE GRADED STREAM   It had been assumed in the past that the stream by eroding its bed or locally building it up with a sedimentary deposit tends to achieve the profile that will give it the slope at every point just sufficient to transport the sediment that reaches that point. Were the slope too steep, the stream would erode its bed, increasing its load and reducing its slope and transporting ability immediately downstream; were the slope too flat, it would deposit part of the sediment, decreasing its load and increasing the slope immediately downstream. Such a

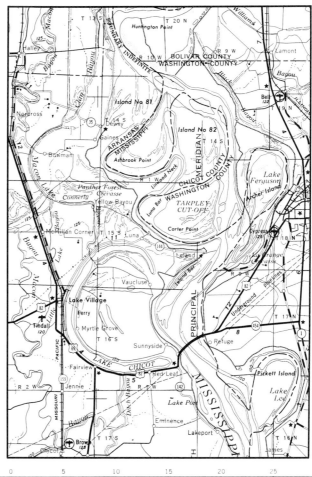

FIG. 7–9 *Meandering channel of the Mississippi River. The boundary between Arkansas and Mississippi follows a 19th-century course of the river. (From Army Map Service topographic map of Greenville, Miss., 1° × 2° quadrangle.)*

stream is called a *graded* stream and is best defined in the words of Mackin (1948):

> A graded stream is one in which, over a period of years, slope is delicately adjusted to provide, with available discharge, and with prevailing channel characteristics, just the velocity required for the transportation of the load supplied from the drainage basin. The graded stream is a system in equilibrium; its diagnostic characteristic is that any change in any of the controlling factors will cause a displacement of the equilibrium in a direction that will tend to absorb the effect of the change.

Leopold and Maddock (1953) emphasize, however, that not only slope, but also the channel characteristics, such as ratio of width to depth and shape of the bed and the banks, can be adjusted by the stream to achieve the equilibrium.

ANCESTRAL AND PRESENT GRADED PROFILES   In many uplands discontinuous flat terraces mantled with stream gravels appear along the valley walls at elevations of perhaps 10 to 100 meters above the present valley floor. These are interpreted as remnants of the beds of ancestral graded streams. In some cases their relative ages can be established from fossil evidence (human or other mammalian remains) and the youngest by radiocarbon

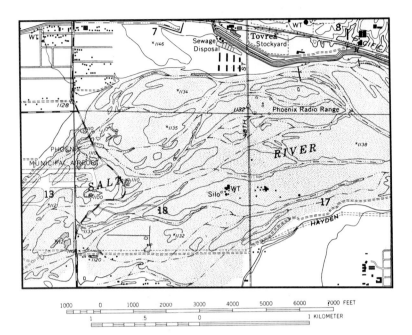

FIG. 7–10 *Braided channel of the Salt River, Arizona. (From U.S. Geological Survey topographic map of Tempe, 7½-minute quadrangle, 1952 edition. Contour interval 10 feet.)*

dating of buried wood. By tracing a series of terrace remnants upstream it is possible to reconstruct a corresponding ancestral stream profile; and this commonly differs markedly from that of the present stream. Some geologists, following a strictly uniformitarian line of reasoning, have argued that the ancestral profile was originally identical with that of the present graded stream. On this basis it is a simple matter to estimate the amount and rate of differential uplift responsible for present divergence of the two profiles. To others this argument seems overrigid. Some external controlling conditions related to climate and dependent characteristics such as runoff and discharge have certainly varied notably in the latest part of geological time. Moreover, the development of a flood plain—the stage in evolution that first makes it possible to recognize fragments of a former profile—ushers in a period in which the possibilities of variation in the sedimentation and flow regime are broadened. Each graded profile developed at some unique point in time will itself have a certain uniqueness. Does this in fact overshadow the tendency toward similarity of profiles that accompanies achievement of the graded condition?

Waves; Coastal and Marine Processes

Marine sedimentary rocks and the sediments of the ocean floor are in the form of relatively thin layers of wide extent. Processes therefore exist that spread the sediment delivered by rivers, and distribute it as a relatively uniform blanket on the sea floor. The chief mechanisms of spreading are waves, tides, and currents.

WAVES

Waves are periodic variations in the height of the water surface about its equilibrium position. A wave is characterized by three fundamental quantities: its *height*, H, the vertical distance between trough and crest; its *length* or *wavelength*, L, the horizontal distance, in the direction of propagation or normal to the crest, between adjacent crests; and its *velocity*, c. The period of a wave, T, which is the interval between passage of adjacent crests, is equal to the wavelength divided by the velocity.

Most waves in standing water bodies are generated by wind (some are generated by landslides and earthquakes). The formation of wind-generated waves is complex and not clearly under-stood. The most promising recent theory involves random fluctuations of air pressure on the water surface from wind-induced turbulence, probably aided at later stages of growth by wind shear. As random pressure fluctuations cause the sea sur-face to rise or fall, they bring into play forces tending to restore the surface to its original level. The restoring forces are surface tension and grav-ity. Surface tension is effective only on very small waves, whose dimensions are measured in centi-meters. Most ocean waves are gravity waves.

In the presence of the generating wind, waves have steep, sharp, asymmetric crests, and broad troughs, and the whole water surface is irregu-larly choppy. This condition is known as *sea*. As waves move away from the area of generating winds, their crests become rounded and they ap-proach a sine-wave form; they are then known as *swell*.

The length, height, and velocity of surface waves are dependent on the duration and veloc-ity of the generating wind. For example, wind blowing at 50 km/hr ultimately produces char-acteristic waves about 6.7 meters high, 76 meters in wavelength, traveling at 40 km/hr; wind blow-ing at 110 km/hr produces waves 14.5 meters high and 376 meters long, traveling 87.5 km/hr. The energy of the waves appears to vary as the fourth or fifth power of the velocity of the gen-erating wind. Much larger waves are generated where the wind can blow over an extensive water surface than where the distance of contact with water is limited. The distance of possible contact between wind and water is known as the *fetch*, and coastlines with large fetch, in the direction of prevailing winds, such as the coast of California, will have much larger waves and more impressive coastal features than those with limited fetch, such as the shores of the Adriatic. Whether a shore is to the lee or windward of a body of water is of great importance in determining its coastal features. In Nevada the shoreline features of the east shore of Pleistocene Lake Lahontan, on the east side of the Carson Desert with a 50-km fetch to the west, include huge boulder banks that could have been built only by large waves; whereas the shoreline features on the west shore,

in the lee of the Sierra Nevada, are barely per-ceptible wave-cut benches.

The wave velocity c is, of course, the velocity of the waveform, not that of the water itself. A particle on the surface of the water moves in a vertical plane and describes in time T a circle with diameter equal to the wave height H; this diameter decreases exponentially with depth so that particle velocity at a depth equal to half the wavelength is less than five percent of the veloc-ity at the surface. The wave velocity is related to depth of water d, and wavelength L as

$$c^2 = \frac{gL}{2\pi} \tanh (2\pi d/L)$$

where g is the acceleration of gravity. In shallow water ($d < L/20$, say), the formula reduces to $c^2 = gd$, whereas for deep water ($d > L/2$, say), it reduces to $c^2 = gL/2\pi$. As waves enter shal-low water, they slow down and shorten, but the period remains constant. As a result, they are refracted so as to travel more nearly normal to the shoreline; that is, they are refracted toward a headland or a stretch of coast with an offshore shoal and away from a coastal indentation or off-shore deep, such as the head of a submarine can-yon. Wave energy travels perpendicular to wave crests; hence it is concentrated in areas toward which the waves are refracted, such as head-lands; in bay heads and similar reaches wave energy is low (Figure 7–11).

As the waves approach the shore, they steepen, because the height increases while the wavelength decreases. Eventually the water in the waves moves forward faster than the wave-form itself, and the wave breaks. The wave then moves forward to the shore as surf. The forward motion of the surf is swash, and the return mo-tion the backwash. Much of the observed sorting on the beach comes about because the swash is much stronger than the backwash, since much of the latter is absorbed in the permeable sand or shingle.

TIDES

The tide is a periodic rise and fall in sea level caused by the gravitational attraction of the

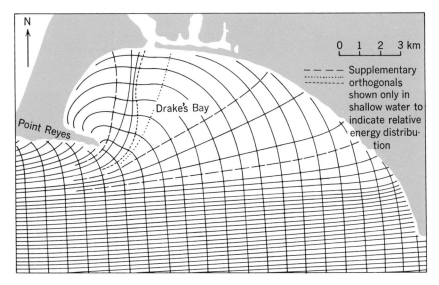

N

Point Reyes

Drake's Bay

0 1 2 3 km

– – – – Supplementary
·········· orthogonals
shown only in
shallow water to
indicate relative
energy distribu-
tion

FIG. 7-11 *Wave refraction diagram showing energy distribution along the beach at Drake's Bay, Calif. Wavefronts trend about due north and the orthogonals at the bottom of the map trend due east. The energy of the wavefront between any two orthogonals remains the same. Wave refraction diagram calculated for a 9-second swell from due west. (From John Cherry, Sand movement along a portion of the northern California coast, Rep. HEL-4-3, Univ. Calif., Berkeley, Hydraulic Engineering Laboratory.)*

moon and sun, which changes with the position of these bodies in the sky. The effect of the sun is about one half that of the moon; it is added to that of the moon when ("spring tides") the sun, moon, and earth are approximately on the same line (full moon or new moon); when lines from the earth to the sun and moon make approximately a right angle (first and third quarter) the effect of the sun is opposed to that of the moon and the tides have a small range ("neap tides"). The period of the tides is governed by the rate of rotation of the earth and the rate of orbital motion of the moon. In general, the tide has several components, the relative amplitude of which depends on latitude. There is, for instance, a semi-diurnal tide (theoretical period 12 hours for the sun, $12^h 25^m$ for the moon) which is maximum at the equator, and a diurnal tide which is maximum at 45° latitude and not felt at the equator. The only tide at the poles is a weak, long period tide. We recall (see chapter 4) that the surface of the solid earth is itself distorted by the gravitational attraction of the sun and moon; it rises and falls with an amplitude of about 30 cm or less.

The calculation of the tides for an imaginary undeformable earth covered with an ocean of uniform depth is a relatively straightforward mathematical problem; the actual prediction of the tides, on the contrary, is an extraordinarily difficult problem, because of the disturbing effects of coastlines, variable depth of water, and the Coriolis force, which deflects tidal currents. (Tide tables are prepared on empirical grounds of past observations.) The tidal range, which should theoretically have a maximum amplitude of about 50 cm, varies enormously, up to 10 meters or more. Some bodies of water (for example, the Bay of Fundy) have natural periods of oscillation (determined by their shape and dimensions) approximately equal to one of the tidal periods, and in them the tidal range can build up by resonance to extremely large values (16–17 meters).

The mouths of estuaries and straits between bodies of water whose tidal maxima are out of phase experience strong tidal currents, which can effectively scour the estuary floor and contribute to its physiography. For example, the average daily tidal flow through the Golden Gate is 6.5×10^4 m³/sec, or 3½ times the discharge of the Mississippi River.

OCEAN CURRENTS

Circulation in the oceans, as explained earlier, is caused mostly by the winds and by differences in water density arising from differences in temperature and salinity; it is also controlled by the

Coriolis force. In the north Pacific Ocean, for instance, currents form a huge clockwise gyre with warm water (Kuroshio) flowing north and northeast in the western Pacific, and cold water (California current) flowing southwest along the west coast of North America; a second gyre circulates counterclockwise around the Gulf of Alaska, north of the Kuroshio. On the horizontal motion described by these gyres is superposed a vertical motion, with cold, dense water generally sinking in high latitudes. Along the west coast of North America, the Coriolis acceleration that deflects the southward flowing current towards the southwest, causes an upwelling of cold bottom water which, in turn, causes the summer sea fogs. The rising water, which is rich in dissolved silica and other nutrients, may be responsible for the abundance of diatoms in Californian coastal sediments in which thick diatomaceous shales dating back to Upper Cretaceous times may imply an oceanic circulation somewhat like the present one for the past 80 million years.

A quite different kind of density current ("turbidity current") arises where water carries a heavy load of suspended sediments and acquires thereby a notably higher density. This condition may be created by storm waves, or by earthquakes stirring a muddy bottom, or where a river with a high load of suspended matter discharges into a clear lake or sea. Currents of dense and muddy Colorado River water have been observed to travel along the bottom of Lake Mead to deposit their sediments against Hoover Dam. Such density currents can indeed transport large quantities of suspended sediment over long distances to very deep water. The huge submarine fans at the mouths of submarine canyons carved into the continental shelf and slope are believed to have such an origin, as are also the great thicknesses of marine sandstone and shale sequences of the "flysch" facies found in many orogenic zones.

COASTAL EROSION

The bulk of marine coastal erosion is accomplished by waves. Their power is indicated by the height of sea cliffs on rocky coasts and the extent of barrier beaches on flat coasts, where the shore has been near its present position and the sea near its present level only within the past 5000 years. The chief mechanisms of wave erosion on hard-rock coastlines are *corrasion*, or the abrasive action of pebbles, cobbles, and sand, hurled against the coast by waves; *hydraulic* action, which is the effect of pressure changes in air forced into cracks in the rock by wave action; and *attrition*, which is the grinding of blocks loosened by hydraulic action. The pressure of trapped air is sufficient to enlarge cracks and force blocks loose from a cliff. In coasts of unconsolidated materials, such as glacial drift, the backwash of storm waves accomplishes much erosion through fluid drag, similar to that on river banks and bottoms.

The rate of wave erosion depends on the hardness and strength of the rock, on the abundance of joints and cracks, and on the wave energy expended on the coast. Hard-rock coastlines are notably irregular or crenulate, as wave action etches out shear zones, joints, and belts of soft rock to form coves and bays, and leaves harder and more massive bodies to be headlands, points, stacks, or islets. Coasts backed by soft rock or unconsolidated materials are generally quite straight. The rate of cliff retreat in coasts of soft rock can be surprisingly rapid. Coasts in Miocene and Pliocene mudstone, shale, and diatomite in California are retreating at rates in excess of $\frac{1}{3}$ meter per year. On the east coast of England, cliffs in glacial drift have retreated at average rates of 1 to 2 meters per year, and at one place the coast retreated 12 to 30 meters overnight during the storm of February 1, 1953! On the other hand, cliffs in granite in Cornwall show evidence of minimal erosion since the sea has stood at its present level.

As they drive the coast back, the waves cut a shallow platform, which is steepest near the shore. The submarine platform at Santa Cruz in California, for example, slopes about 20–40 m/km seaward for 300–600 meters, to a depth of 7.5–12 meters, and beyond that slopes 5.5–16 m/km seaward to depths of about 100 meters (Figure 7–12).

In many parts of the world, former high stands

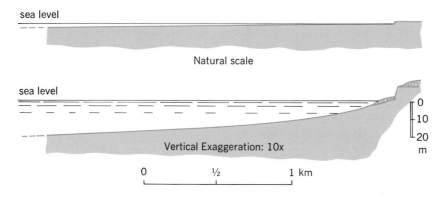

sea level

Natural scale

sea level

Vertical Exaggeration: 10x

0   10   20 m

0   ½   1 km

FIG. 7–12 Profile of sub-marine wave-cut platform at Santa Cruz, California. (From W. C. Bradley, Sub-marine abrasion and wave-cut platforms; Geol. Soc. Am. Bull., vol. 69, pp. 967–974, 1958.)

of the sea are marked by wave-cut benches, studded with sea stacks and backed by fossil cliffs, which extend to altitudes a few meters to a few hundred meters above present sea level (Figure 7–13). The best-preserved of these marine terraces have a mantle of well-sorted, and commonly well-bedded marine sands, which may be fossiliferous. The marine sands are usually buried, at least at the back edge of the terrace, by a deposit of alluvium or colluvium derived from the slopes behind, so that determination of the shoreline angle (the angle between the wave-cut platform and the sea cliff) may be difficult.

According to Bradley, the bedrock platform is cut during a rise in sea level relative to the land, and the mantle of marine sand laid down while sea level was falling. The flights of marine terraces may therefore be due to fluctuations in the level of the sea, probably caused by changes in the volume of the oceans during the glacial episodes of the Quaternary, while parts of the continents were being uplifted or parts of the sea floor being depressed.

The only feature of the ancient terraces that can be used to establish the original sea level, and hence the uplift or deformation of the land, is the shoreline angle. At the back of the modern wave-cut platform the modern shoreline angle ranges in altitude from just above mean sea level at cove heads, to one to two meters below sea level at promontories, so that ancient sea levels can be determined with a precision of a few meters at best.

LONG-SHORE CURRENTS

Where waves approach the shore diagonally, they set up long-shore currents, and more importantly, a long-shore drift of sediment. This pattern of sediment transport is extremely important in the stability of the beach. Long-shore drift is mainly in the breaker zone, and reaches a maximum when the waves approach the shore at an angle of 30°. It carries sediment laterally away from the mouth of rivers, dropping it where the velocity decreases, as on the downdrift side of points where spits and forelands are built in this way. In general, the tendency of long-shore drift is to extend the beach in such a way that it becomes normal to the direction of wave approach. This tendency results in the closing of many bay mouths by curving bars, and a general straightening of a crenulate coast by beaches and offshore barriers. The geometry of the coastline may make this condition impossible of achievement, but the tendency is apparently responsible for the development of cuspate forelands, such as at Dungeness in England and Cape Kennedy in Florida.

DEPOSITIONAL FEATURES

A common depositional feature of gently shelving modern coasts, is a barrier beach or barrier island—a line of beaches and dune-covered islands, a few hundred meters to a few tens of kilometers offshore, enclosing lagoons,

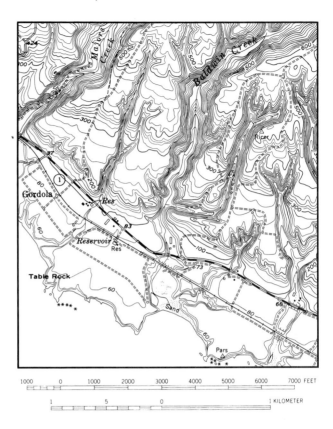

FIG. 7–13 *Topographic map of marine terraces west of Santa Cruz, California. The low well-preserved terrace has a shoreline angle of about 30 meters; a second terrace, with a shoreline angle of about 90 meters is moderately well-preserved; and a poorly preserved remnant with a shoreline angle of about 130 meters can be seen just south of Ricer triangulation station. The higher, flat summits may be stripped bedding planes. (From U.S. Geological Survey, 1:24,000 scale topographic map of Santa Cruz, Calif., quadrangle, contour interval 20 feet.)*

estuaries, or shallow bays. The barrier islands are generally straight or gently curved, concave to the open sea, but may join in cuspate forelands such as Cape Hatteras. Barrier islands border almost the entire east coast of the United States from Long Island to the Rio Grande, and are found in many other parts of the world, such as the southeastern Baltic and the coast of Holland. They are thought to have been built upward from beaches and dune ridges formed during the period of slackening of the postglacial sea-level rise of the past 10,000–12,000 years. For the past 3000–5000 years, sea level has been within a meter or two of its present position, and the barrier islands in this time have been able to reach their present state of perfection. The lagoonal muds behind the barriers rest on eroded Pleistocene sediments and contain no open beach deposits, suggesting that the barrier has existed ever since the sea level rose to its present position. The broad curves of the barrier islands must have been formed within the past 3000 years in adjustment to the patterns of waves and currents.

Many beaches protect the land behind them from coastal erosion; and the best defense against wave attack on the coast appears to be a program designed to induce the growth of a beach. A beach may consist of sand or shingle (pebbles). Beach pebbles are more disk-shaped than those of streams. The various parts of a beach, and elements of the beach profile, are shown in Figure 7–14. The coarsest material in a sand beach is near the crest of the berm, and in a gravel beach near the top of the beach ridge. In a typical gravel beach, the disk-shaped pebbles are concentrated on the ridge, and the spherical pebbles in the foreshore. Many beaches grade sharply into mud flats in the offshore zone.

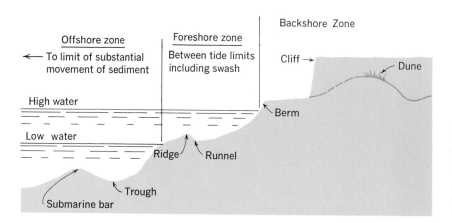

Offshore zone
⟵ To limit of substantial movement of sediment

Foreshore zone
Between tide limits including swash

Backshore Zone

Cliff →   Dune

High water

Low water

Berm

Ridge   Runnel

Trough

Submarine bar

FIG. 7–14 *Composite sand-beach profile. Some sand beaches may be backed by a cliff, others by dunes. (Modified from C. A. M. King,* Beaches and Coasts, *Edward Arnold Publishers, Ltd., 1954, p. 49.)*

Along the beach the coarsest particles are concentrated where the wave energy is greatest. The steepness of the beach varies directly as the coarseness of the beach material. Studies of the change in beach profiles with season show that summer beaches are flat, with a well-developed berm. The summer beach—built by low, flat waves—is destroyed by the steep, high-energy storm waves of winter, and the beach material moved to a breakpoint bar.

The balance between deposition and progradation of the coast at the expense of the sea, and erosion, or retreat of the coast, depends largely on the supply of material available to the waves. This material can come from rivers and be distributed by long-shore drift—for example, much of the coastal sediment of Israel came originally down the Nile—or it can be supplied by coastal erosion elsewhere. In some shallow seas, such as the North Sea, the sediment that builds the coast outward comes from banks on the sea floor that lie within reach of the waves. Thus, in spite of spectacular examples of coastal erosion along the east coast of England, on the whole the coast is growing at the expense of the North Sea.

Transport and Deposition of Sediment by Wind

Erosion of coherent rock by wind is limited to minor etching and polishing of exposed surfaces by sand blast. But given a continuous supply of loose grains of sand and silt grade (mostly 0.3 mm in diameter) wind is a most effective agent of transport, sorting, and deposition of such material. A necessary condition is absence of a protective cover of vegetation. This is met to some degree in coastal strips and river beds wherever the rate at which sediment is supplied (by waves or by flood waters) exceeds that at which a significant plant cover can become established. Wind action is much more spectacular, however, in continental interiors, where the rainfall is so low or irregular that vegetation is sparse or even entirely absent. Examples are great areas of the dry interior of Australia, and especially the extensive and completely barren deserts of North Africa and Arabia. It was in the North African deserts that Bagnold made his classic observations on sand movement which, supplemented by wind-tunnel experiments, form the substance of the most interesting and lucid existing book in the field of sedimentation.[5] What follows is taken largely from Bagnold's work.

SURFACE WINDS

The physical principles underlying transport and deposition of sediment are the same for wind as for flowing water. Differences in behavior of the two media and in their respective effects on

[5] R. A. Bagnold, *The Physics of Blown Sand and Desert Dunes* (Methuen, London, 1941, reprinted 1954).

sediment stem from the lower density and viscosity of air, and the high velocities of normal winds. A grain of quartz is 2000 times denser than the air by which it is transported (instead of 2.7 times in the case of water). Under atmospheric conditions the viscosity of air, η, is 1.78×10^{-4} g cm^{-1} sec^{-1}. The corresponding value for water is 1×10^{-2} at 20°C. The ratio η/ρ, or the kinematic viscosity ν, is about 0.14 for air, and 0.01 for water. The Reynolds number R_e, critical values of which separate different flow regimes, is, as we recall,

$$R_e = \frac{Vl}{\nu}$$

where V is velocity, and l is a dimension of size—the diameter of a pipe or the thickness of a layer of air having a given flow regime. The condition for turbulence is $R_e >$ approximately 10^3.

In a sand cloud driven by a steady desert wind, the great bulk of the grains are transported

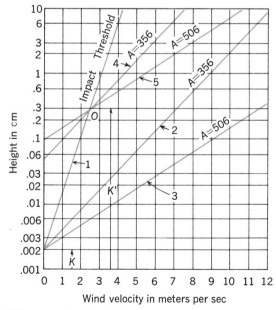

FIG. 7–15 Semilogarithmic graphs showing variations of wind velocity with height above the surface for different velocity gradients. Curves 1 (below 0), 2, and 3, velocity profile without sand movement; curves 4 and 5, velocity profile with sand movement over a loose sand bed. (After Bagnold, op. cit., p. 60.)

within 2 cm of ground level. If therefore we put $l = 2$ cm, and $\nu = 0.14$, turbulence occurs within this thin surface layer wherever the mean velocity exceeds roughly 1 m/sec. In a 50-km-per-hour wind as measured at a height of 1 meter, a velocity of 1 m/sec is exceeded within a millimeter of the ground surface. So in considering the mechanics of sand transport by wind we are invariably dealing with a turbulent flow regime.

The turbulent flow of air has an upward gradient of velocity. In a steady wind it is observed that the velocity V increases upward proportionally to the logarithm of height z (Figure 7–15, curves 1, 2, 3). Thus

$$V = A \log (z/k)$$

where k is the level at which $V = 0$. This level is usually about one thirtieth of the mean diameter of grains covering the surface, and is therefore a measure of surface roughness. For a normal sand floor, $k = 0.01$ millimeter; for gravel averaging 1 cm in diameter, it is 0.3 mm. The coefficient A is related to the tangential stress or drag τ exerted by the wind on the ground surface and to density ρ as

$$A = c\sqrt{\frac{\tau}{\rho}}$$

where c is an empirical constant.

MOTION OF GRAINS

There are three ways in which wind can transport sediment.

1. *Suspension.* Dust and silt particles caught by eddies in a strong turbulent wind are carried rapidly upward to heights of a few hundred or even a thousand meters, and thus can be transported in suspension for many kilometers. The disastrous consequences of wind erosion of this kind in areas where drought and overgrazing have temporarily reduced the ground cover have been demonstrated repeatedly in "dust-bowl" regions of North America. In the typical sand desert, material of dust grade is scanty. It forms by chipping of sand grains under mutual impact. At the onset of a wind storm this dust is whirled

aloft as a misty haze, which eventually clears as the dust particles move on in suspension. Once every decade or so red snow falls along the Southern Alps of New Zealand—the coloring matter being fine red dust blown eastward across the Tasman Sea from Australian deserts 3000 to 4000 km distant.

2. *Saltation.* When a high wind is maintained in the desert, long after dust has vanished, sand is steadily driven in a streaming layer a meter or several meters deep. At any moment the bulk of the flying sand grains are traveling within a few centimeters of ground level. The individual grain jumps upward under impact from other moving particles (Figure 7–16). It acquires a forward motion from the wind and returns to the ground on a low-angle trajectory (10°–16°). The kinetic energy of the descending grain is usually expended in setting another particle in motion (a grain can impart a sliding motion to a stationary grain six times its own diameter). Some descending grains bounce into another saltation. The length of each

saltation increases with wind velocity and depends also on sand grade. For values of A between 115 and 520 cm/sec the calculated jump ranges from 2.5 cm to 27 cm; and there is remarkably close correspondence between these values and the wave lengths of sand ripples developed by winds of the same range of velocity. The great difference between saltation in air and in water reflects marked differences in viscosity. In water a grain can move upward through several diameters, in air through thousands of diameters. About three quarters of the sand moving past a given point in unit time is carried in saltation.

3. *Creep.* Under the saltation layer coarser sand grains move across the desert floor in spasmodic jerks under impact of grains descending from saltation. In a moderate wind the grain moves a few millimeters at a time. In a gale the whole surface seems to be in continuous motion. Kinetic energy is continuously supplied from wind to grains in saltation, and thence passed on to creeping grains. Ultimately, of course, all energy so acquired from wind is dissipated as frictional heat. Thus the general effect of saltation and creep is to slow down the velocity of wind by frictional drag. This is much more effective than the drag of a rough but motionless floor.

The surface over which the sand is moving has a profound effect on the rate of transport of the sand. If saltating sand grains strike hard, elastic surfaces, they rebound into high trajectories with little loss of kinetic energy (Figure 7–16A); such surfaces are provided by outcrops of solid rock and by layers of pebbles. Saltating sand grains striking surfaces of sand of their own size range tend to "crater"; that is, on impact they bury themselves in small pits, forcing aside other grains which move downwind by creep. Trajectories over sand surfaces are low (Figure 7–16B). The kinetic energy of the saltating grain is dissipated in frictional heat. This loss of kinetic energy through cratering is a drain on the capacity of the wind to transport sediment, and consequently a wind of a given speed and given velocity gradient can transport sand at a greater rate over a surface armored with pebbles than over a surface consisting of soft sand.

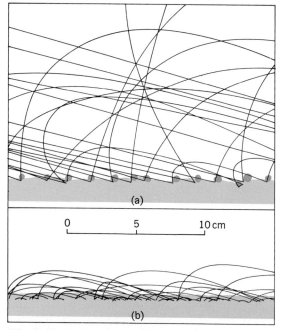

FIG. 7–16 *Paths of sand grains in saltation over two types of surface: (a) over a pebbly surface; (b) over a loose sand surface. (After Bagnold, op. cit., p. 36.)*

THE WIND-SEDIMENT SYSTEM

As the wind strength increases aloft, the value of the coefficient A increases. At a value which depends on the size of the sand, it begins to move by creep induced by frictional drag of the wind. Once the grains begin to move, saltation begins and intensifies to a steady state. The value of the coefficient A drops appreciably, as a result of the load of sand grains, to a minimum value necessary to transport sand in steady saltation. If wind strength is increased to higher values of the coefficient A, the new velocity profiles for the sand-laden wind intersect at a common point 0 (curves 4 and 5, Figure 7–15). The corresponding height k' shows the effect of the increased frictional resistance imparted by the moving sand. No matter how the wind strength increases, its velocity at the height k' above the ground is constant.

The quantity of sand transported varies as the third power of the velocity coefficient A. An empirical equation that describes experimental results for sand transport is

$$q = \frac{C\rho A^3 \sqrt{d/D}}{g}$$

where C is an empirical coefficient that varies with the size and grading of the sediment on the bed, and d/D is the ratio between the average grain size of the sand being transported and a reference sand size. C is approximately twice as large for a pebble-covered surface as it is for a surface of sand. This variation of the value of the coefficient C with the character of the surface is an expression of the loss of carrying power of the wind caused by the cratering effect described in the previous paragraphs.

The threshold value of the coefficient A, at which grains are just put into motion, decreases as the grain size of the sediment decreases. As is the case with water, air within a fraction of a millimeter of the surface moves by laminar flow, and particles within the laminar layer are not lifted into the moving air. Thus there is a particular grain size for which the threshold coefficient A (and therefore the wind velocity at any given level) is a minimum, and particles smaller or larger than this size require stronger winds and

larger values of A to be put into motion. This optimum grain diameter is about 0.08 mm for air, (with a comparable value of A of 86.25 cm/sec), whereas the corresponding grain size for water is 0.2–0.4 mm. Fine dust is entirely within the laminar layer and remains undisturbed even by very strong winds, unless it is stirred by movement of animals or vehicles.

SOURCES OF WINDBLOWN SEDIMENT

Windblown sands do not originate by wind erosion of coarser material. They come from sediments of marine or fluviatile origin; and before sand becomes concentrated in a beach or desert dune as we now see it, it may well have passed through several cycles of erosion, attrition, and sorting by water. Much of the sand of the Sahara desert must have come from marine sandstones in peripheral regions of weathering, or from the fringing Mediterranean beaches.

Windblown silts are of diverse origin. Glacial silts, a major component of sediment deposited freshly in glacial outwash, is certainly a source of much Pleistocene loess in Russia, Europe, and North America (page 356). Loess of the Argentinian Pampa is an accumulation of dust, much of it fine debris of Andean volcanoes far to the west. This material, reworked and transported eastward by river waters, has finally been picked up from arid stretches in the lee of the Andes and thence has been transported to its present site of deposition in moister grasslands areas that stretch westward from the vicinity of Buenos Aires.

DESERT-SAND BODIES

Great stretches of desert are sand-covered. But there are also extensive regions that, though barren of vegetation, are essentially stony desert with little or no sand cover. Accumulation of sand, whether locally as a dune, or regionally as in the Sand Sea of the Egyptian desert, implies long-continued operation in recent times of two conditions. First, prevailing winds from a source area must have maintained velocities above the threshold value necessary to pick up and transport desert sand. In the second place, the ground surface in the area of accumulation must have been such as to trap sand blown in from the source area. A gravel-covered floor efficiently traps sand when the wind velocity drops, as it commonly does at night. Sand then becomes lodged between the pebbles until these project just above the sand surface. The product is a sand reservoir ready to be exploited by the action of strong winds during intermittent storm periods.

Sand in a pebble-strewn reservoir from the first is unevenly distributed. It has been found that a wind of given strength can transport 50 to 75 percent more sand, in a given time, across a pebble surface than across smooth sand. When a strong wind blows across the gravel–sand reservoir it therefore rapidly denudes those patches in which gravel predominates, and dumps some of its sand load downwind on other patches that in the first place were essentially sandy. These grow into mounds. On the upstream face of such a mound, wind speed close to the ground increases and the velocity gradient steepens; on the downstream face, wind speed and velocity gradient decrease.

The net effect of these variations in velocity gradient is that in strong winds the upstream face of a mound is eroded, and sand is deposited on the downstream face. The downstream face steepens until it reaches the angle of repose for dry sand (about 34°), whereupon it avalanches forward to form the mound slip-face. The air current separates from the mound surface at the sharp angle at the top of the slip face, leaving a volume of relatively calm air in the lee of the mound. Thereafter sand grains in saltation over the lip of the slip face fall through the calm air to accumulate on the slip face which periodically avalanches forward as its slope exceeds the angle of repose. Erosion on the upstream face and deposition on the downstream face result in the downwind migration of the mound. Such a migrating asymmetric mound of windblown sand is called a *dune*.

For given conditions of wind speed and sand supply, the rate of migration is inversely related to the height of the slip face. Thus moving sand

mounds and small dunes overtake larger dunes, adding to their size. Furthermore, the lower parts of a transverse sand ridge advance more rapidly than the higher parts.

BARCHANS   The simplest dune form is the *barchan*, an isolated crescentic dune, remarkably regular in form and structure, with perfect monoclinal symmetry (Figure 7–17). The low sides of the dune advance ahead of the high center to form the horns of the dune. Because of converging wind currents on the downwind side of the dune, the slip faces turn inward to face the axis of the dune. The barchan reaches its perfect development in barren areas of constant wind direction and limited sand supply.

SEIF DUNES   Where wind direction in the desert is more variable, longitudinal or *seif* dunes are formed. A seif dune is an orderly chain of dune summits which are repeated along the chain at intervals of 20 to several hundred meters. Seif-dune chains may extend, continuous and straight, for 50 to 100 km along the direction of gentle prevailing winds. The individual dune, which on the Egyptian desert may be 100 meters high, is shaped in part by the spasmodic storm winds that

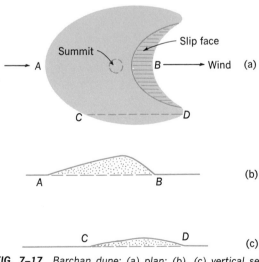

FIG. 7–17 Barchan dune: (a) plan; (b), (c) vertical sections on AB, CD. (After Bagnold, op. cit., p. 209.)

blow obliquely to the prevailing wind direction. The slip face, controlled by the storm winds, is parallel to the trend of the dune, and may alternate from one side to another as the dune-shaping wind alternates from left to right. There are desert regions where arrays of great seif chains alternate with intervening dune-free corridors of coarse or gravel-strewn sand. The regularity of the parallel array may be spectacular. Writing of such a desert terrane, Bagnold says[6]

> . . . for dunes of any given size, the corridors between them may be 10 km or 1 km wide. But the width is approximately the same over a large area, so that the chains, or, on the largest scale the multiple dune systems or parallel chains, all lie parallel to one another and are evenly spaced, thus giving the country an extraordinary aspect of geometric order unseen elsewhere in nature except on a microscopic scale.

WHALEBACKS   The relatively immobile residue left by continuous removal of finer sand during the march of a superincumbent train of seif dunes, may remain as a vast body of relatively coarse sand, sometimes as much as 300 km in length and several kilometers wide. In transverse profile these bodies are gently arched, with summits perhaps 50 meters above ground level. Such bodies of coarse sand, trending parallel to the direction of the prevailing wind, are called *whalebacks*.

TRANSVERSE DUNES   In regions of abundant sand supply and steady prevailing winds, such as the windward coastal areas adjacent to sandy beaches, the wind forms lines of *transverse* dunes. These are asymmetric ridges trending roughly at right angles to the prevailing wind direction, with gentle, essentially erosional, upwind slopes, and steep downwind slopes, whose upper parts are slip faces.

SIGMOID AND LONGITUDINAL DUNES   In humid regions, dune fields may be partially stabilized by vegetation. Renewal of migration starts at

spots, called blowouts, where the vegetation cover has been removed. The resulting dunes, called *sigmoid* dunes, are convex in plan downwind, with a steep outer downwind slope, and a gentle upwind slope. *Longitudinal* dunes, narrow dunes elongated parallel to the wind direction, form by elongation and fragmentation of sigmoid dunes. Both are characteristic of the stabilized dune fields of Pleistocene age, formed from abundant supplies of outwash sand, and accumulating downwind from melt water streams during the Pleistocene glaciations.

THE STRUCTURE OF WINDBLOWN SAND

The internal structure of dunes can be studied by wetting them with water, and removing dry sand from the side of the wetted area. The moist sand, held in place by surface tension of water films, stands in vertical and even overhanging banks. The water penetrates farther in the coarser more permeable layers, which project from the wall of moist sand as low ribs.

Where such studies have been made, dune sand is found to be thinly laminated. Laminae that dip gently upwind accumulate by accretion on the upwind face of a dune. Laminae that dip steeply downwind accumulate by avalanching or by settling individual grains through still air. The former are tightly packed, and are sufficiently firm to support the weight of large vehicles, if sufficiently thick. The latter are loosely packed, and give rise to areas of desert "quicksand."

Glacial Processes and the Quaternary

GLACIERS: FORMATION AND MORPHOLOGY

Recently fallen snow, because of high porosity, has a density of 0.2 g/cm³ or less. Snow falling at high altitudes or in polar regions may survive the year-long weather cycle and accumulate in favored localities year by year. By recrystallization and compaction it becomes more granular and denser with passage of time. The density of last year's snow (*firn or neve*) is 0.5 to 0.6 g/cm³. After 25 to 150 years, now buried to

[6] R. A. Bagnold, *op. cit.*, p. 232.

depths of 30–100 meters, it becomes coarsely re-crystallized ice, with a density of 0.8 to 0.9 g/cm^3.

Under high confining pressures, even at temperatures well below those of melting, crystalline materials tend to yield to long-sustained stress by plastic flow (see Chapter 9). The temperature of natural ice is never far removed from the melting point. At confining pressures of a few bars developed under a thickness of about 30 meters, ice begins to flow outward at an appreciable rate under stress induced by its own weight. A natural mass of ice flowing laterally by this mechanism is called a glacier. Flowing thus to lower altitudes as valley glaciers, or to lower latitudes as continental ice sheets such as that of Greenland, the ice surface reaches a climatic situation where the annual accumulation of snow is exactly balanced by the annual net *ablation* (loss through melting and evaporation). This is the *firn limit*, below which the annual discharge of ice through any cross section diminishes. The glacier may discharge directly into the sea, as in polar regions. Elsewhere, as in valley glaciers, there is a terminal face at which local annual discharge approximately matches local ablation. When ablation exceeds discharge, the terminal face retreats; when discharge exceeds ablation, the front of the glacier advances.

FLOW OF GLACIAL ICE

FLOW REGIMES   In most glaciers the flow of ice follows a recognizable steady regime. Surface velocities, generally less than one meter per day, tend to be highest near the firn limit, where discharge also is high. Although flow rates decrease downstream from about this point, they may still be high even at the terminal face provided the local ablation rate also is high. This is so in the western valley glaciers of southern New Zealand. These descend to elevations of less than 300 meters at latitude 43°S, where torrential, warm summer rains contribute notably to ablation; surface velocities are generally 100 to 200 meters per year within 1000 meters of the terminal faces. Surface velocities decrease in crudely parabolic fashion from the center line to the margins of the

glacier. Flow rates also decrease downward in any vertical section—mostly in the lowest hundred meters. Polar glaciers may be essentially frozen to the valley floor. In glaciers of more temperate regions, which are generally at the pressure melting point, and where a water film develops along the bed, bed velocities may be anywhere between 10 and 90 percent of the surface rate.

For glaciers with a steady flow regime, mean surface rates show a wide range of values: a few centimeters per day in small mountain glaciers; 0.2 to 1 meter per day in valley glaciers of temperate regions; 28 meters per day in some outlet glaciers of the Greenland ice cap. Many glaciers, notably in Alaska, have a much less regular flow regime. Periods of virtual stagnation are broken by sudden surges in which marginal and center-line velocities are almost the same. Surges of this kind occurred simultaneously in 1905 in many glaciers in Yakutat Bay; and the Black Rapids Glacier of the Alaska Range advanced no less than 6500 meters in three months during 1936–37. Even in steadily flowing glaciers long-term oscillations of advance and retreat of the terminal face reflect the influence of climatic fluctuations of similar amplitude. Time lag in response at the terminus makes it difficult to determine either the time or the precise nature of the climatic changes concerned.

MECHANICS OF FLOW   Unlike problems relating to deformation and flow of deep-seated rocks in the solid state, glacial flow is amenable to direct investigation along uniformitarian lines. Measurements on many glaciers have already supplied abundant data on flow rates, flow-induced structures, and the patterns of both in place and in time. A good deal is known, too, regarding the strength and rheologic behavior of ice crystals in response to experimentally controlled stress in the laboratory. In spite of this, and although a number of attempts have been made, there is still no satisfactory flow model that can account for observed patterns of motion and strain or predict glacial behavior under prescribed conditions. This situation is partly the result of the complexity and local variability of the stress system controlling the flow process. Some of the factors concerned are superincumbent load; longitudinal compression under the downhill thrust of upstream ice; friction along wall and bedrock interfaces of varying and, in many cases, indeterminate roughness; and shear related to strain rates and a property of ice analogous to viscosity.

Strain structures that develop within the flowing ice are obvious and tend to follow regular patterns. The significance of some is fairly clear. Crevasses are surface fractures developed by brittle failure of ice at low confining pressure (about 1 bar). Bedding may be obvious. Each bed is the remnant of a season's snowfall, the upper surface delineated by a concentration of dust inherited from snow by melting prior to precipitation of the overlying bed. Glacial bedding commonly shows some regular pattern of folding. The beds must behave as passive markers so that fold patterns (like slip folds in deformed rocks) should provide information regarding the geometry of flow (see Chapter 3). A common secondary structure is a planar foliation, marked by concentration of trapped bubbles in parallel layers a centimeter or less thick. Again, the relation of flow foliation to the geometry of flow is imperfectly understood.

It has long been known that single crystals of ice, suitably stressed, deform readily by translation gliding on the {0001} crystal plane. So this mechanism has been widely invoked in models of glacial flow. Its true significance, however, is dubious. During the course of long-sustained experimentally induced or natural flow, glacial ice completely recrystallizes. The average grain size coarsens greatly with perhaps a fiftyfold increase in mean diameter. The ultimate product in both cases is equigranular, with no indication of the spectacular grain elongation that is characteristic of highly strained metallic aggregates or marble specimens deformed under conditions (cold working) favoring crystal gliding. All that can be said is that the rheologic behavior of glacial ice under shear stress of about 1 bar is broadly comparable with ideal plastic flow. Since flow occurs at temperatures close to those of melting, the flow mechanism is likely to resemble that of hot

working of metals, rather than cold working (involving extensive crystal gliding) and subsequent annealing recrystallization.

GLACIAL EROSION

Glacial ice in contact with bedrock and wall rock is a highly abrasive material. It is armed with angular rock fragments of all sizes from silt to large boulders. Much of this has been supplied by surface avalanche deposits, via deep crevasses in areas of irregular or rapid flow such as ice falls. Some of the larger blocks have been plucked bodily from jointed bedrock as basal melt water has penetrated joints and there refrozen, welding the fragments thus enclosed into the overriding ice. Much of the finer material has been supplied by abrasion of the bed itself. It is not surprising that glacier ice—thus armed for abrasion, endowed with rheologic properties, and moving with a flow regime so different from those of stream water—should mold the landscape into forms that differ strikingly from those produced by stream erosion. The characteristics of the resulting glaciated landscape are easily recognized as such. They are abundantly illustrated by photographs in standard texts. The dynamic significance of some features is fairly obvious; that of others is not obvious.

The glaciated valley is straight and steep-sided, compared with the more sinuous course and sloping sides of the typical stream valley. It heads back into an amphitheater with precipitous walls—a *cirque* (Figure 7–18). Most cirques in recently glaciated terranes are occupied by lakes; for the pattern of flow in existing cirque glaciers —downward along the back wall, upward and forward at the outlet—favors maximum erosion in the middle of the basin. With the passage of time a cirque enlarges headward, while above the level of the ice surface, frost riving and avalanching sharpen the slopes into jagged cliffs. Intervening divides become sharpened to knife-edge ridges with projecting intervening peak remnants, of which the Swiss Matterhorn is a classic example.

The longitudinal profile of a recently glaciated valley is commonly broken at intervals by steps

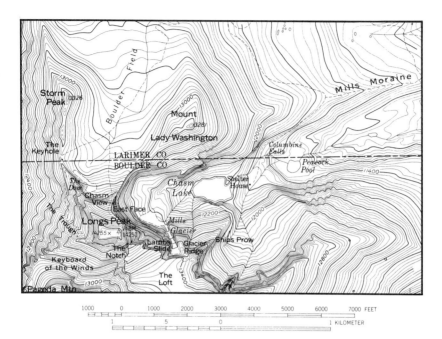

FIG. 7–18 *Topographic map of glacial cirque and lake. (From U.S. Geological Survey topographic map of Longs Peak, 7½-minute quadrangle, Colorado, 1961 edition. Contour interval 40 feet.)*

(Figure 7–19). Tributary valleys enter the main glacial valley at levels high above that of the main valley floor. Evidently the power of a glacier to erode downward is closely related to its cross-sectional discharge.

The eroded surface exposed by glacial retreat is bare rock sculptured in detail that reflects the symmetry of the pattern of ice flow. The glacial pavement becomes polished by the abrasive action of silt-size debris; and superposed on its overall smoothness are scratches, striations, and even deep grooves chiseled out by larger blocks of rock embedded in the overriding ice. Rising above the general level of the valley floor are larger protuberances of rock from a few meters to hundreds of meters high, that have been overridden, but not obliterated, by the glacier. These *roches moutonées* mostly have gently inclined smoothed upstream slopes, and steep irregular downstream faces where joint blocks have been plucked away in the moving ice.

The overall pattern of erosion detail on pavements once covered by continental ice sheets has been used to reconstruct patterns and directions of flow. This approach is legitimate only if cau-

tion is exercised regarding the possible influence of factors other than flow. The symmetry of the erosion pattern reflects the combined influence of the respective symmetries of flow and of bedrock structure. The regular orientation of steep *roche-moutonée* faces over some recently glaciated areas in southern New Zealand is strongly influenced by a corresponding regular trend of highly developed vertical joints in the bedrock (a lineated schist with joints normal to the lineation; Chapter 3).

GLACIAL DEPOSITS

Material deposited directly from a glacier is called *till*. It is a poorly sorted mixture of boulders, sand, and clay-sized particles, mostly of fresh unweathered rock. The larger fragments may possess scratched planar facets formed by abrasion during prolonged moving contact with bedrock. Till may be deposited along the floor of an active glacier; or it may accumulate along the terminal face while this is stationary or in process of slow retreat. Most glacial debris, however, reaches its site of deposition through the agency

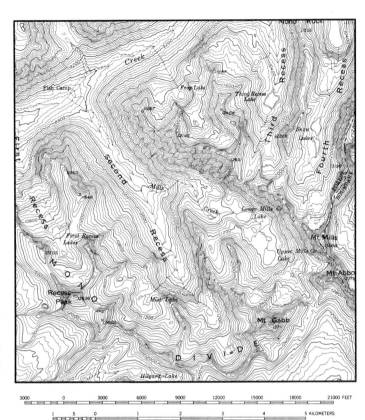

FIG. 7–19 *Topographic map of a glacial valley with steps and hanging tributaries. (From U.S. Geological Survey topographic map of Mt. Abbott, 15-minute quadrangle, California, 1953 edition. Contour interval 80 feet.)*

of streams whose source is glacial melt water. In the course of transport the individual particles become rounded and sorted so that the ultimate deposit may retain in its structure little evidence of its glacial origin.

The form, structure, and composition of glacial deposits reflect in their diversity the possible variety of the transporting and depositional processes. Their study is a highly specialized field beyond the scope of this book. We merely note that the pattern of glacial deposition in formerly glaciated areas permits the expert to reconstruct with some confidence the history and extent of glacial advance and retreat, and corresponding climatic fluctuations that have affected large regions in past geologic time, notably the Pleistocene.

Land forms built of directly deposited till are called moraines. Ground moraines, deposited

beneath retreating ice, form sheets with characteristic hummocky surfaces. They may form effective dams to glacial lakes now occupying the lower portions of formerly glaciated valleys. Morainal ridges are conspicuous along the marginal and terminal surfaces of ablating ice. They build up during periods of protracted standstill, and when the ice finally retreats, are left as linear ridges and as embankments—lateral and end moraines (Figure 7–20).

During periods of glacial stagnation or retreat, melt water pours off as streams flowing beneath, on the surface, or along the shrinking margins of the glacier. This builds moundlike deposits of partly sorted debris with characteristic rounded, flat-topped, or sinuous shapes whose varied forms reflect the relation of glacial to fluvial processes in various kinds of depositional sites (Figure 7–21). From the glacial front and for many kilo-

FIG. 7–20 *Lateral and end moraines of a glacial valley. View of Roaring River Valley in Kings Canyon National Park, California. (U.S. Geological Survey photograph GS-OAL-1-211. See Calif. Div. Mines Geol. Bull., 190, p. 162, photo 20.)*

meters downstream, overloaded rivers of glacial water build fluvioglacial deposits hundreds of meters thick called *outwash plains*. Retreat of glaciers at the close of the Pleistocene sharply reduced the load of rivers previously fed by glacial melt water and debris. In previously glaciated temperate regions such as northeastern United States the now underloaded rivers have removed much of the Pleistocene outwash, the remnants being left as outwash terraces high above the level of today's river floors.

During the waning stages of Pleistocene glaciation much of the finer fractions of fluvioglacial debris was deposited on lake floors. In the transition from glacial to integrated river drainage, lakes were numerous and large, especially ice-marginal lakes with one wall of glacial ice. Char-

acteristic of glacial lake silts is a rhythmic banding, reflecting annual fluctuations in supply of silt-laden water—abundant in summer, little or none during the winter freeze. Each double layer or *varve* consists of a light-colored coarser silt bed (summer deposit) followed by a finer clay bed colored dark with organic matter (the result of slow settling during the winter). Varved silts have considerable significance in reconstructing Pleistocene chronology on an annual basis, much as have annual rings of very old trees. Silt that is temporarily deposited with outwash gravels is easily picked up by the wind. Once wind-borne, it may travel great distances and then be dropped as a blanket of wind-laid silt called *loess*. Glacial loess is widespread in Europe and in the north-central plains of the United States. Not all loess,

FIG. 7–21 *Eskers and crevasse fillings (glaciofluvial debris deposited by running water in tunnels and crevasses in the ice) merging downstream (to the left) with outwash plain. Lakes fill hollows left by blocks of stagnant ice. View north over Matanuska Valley, Alaska. (Photograph by U.S. Air Force.)*

however, is of glacial origin (page 349). The remainder of the fine fraction is carried to the sea where it is flocculated by electrolytes in seawater and is deposited rapidly as glaciomarine clay.

PLEISTOCENE GLACIATION

Glaciers and continental ice sheets today cover 15×10^6 km^2 (some 10 percent of the present land surface); and most of the polar seas are covered with floe ice. But there have been times during the Pleistocene epoch—the past three million years of time—when the total area covered by continental ice was two to three times as great as today. At such times ice sheets such as that covering Greenland today extended over all Canada and much of northeastern and east-central United States. Another ice sheet centered in Scandinavia pushed westward across the site of the North Sea to Scotland, southward into Germany and the Netherlands, and eastward into Poland and the Soviet Union. Valley glaciers in the high mountain ranges of the temperate zones were greatly extended. They have left their unmistakable imprint on the topography of the Alps, the western ranges of North America, the Andes of southern Chile, the southern Alps of New Zealand, and even mountain areas of low relief in western Britain.

So extensive and conclusive is the collective evidence of Pleistocene glaciation—the characteristic landforms and enormous accumulations of morainic debris and outwash—that its import was clearly recognized during the second quarter of the nineteenth century. By the time it had been publicized through the teaching of Louis Agassiz in the 1830's and 1840's, the Pleistocene Ice Age was everywhere recognized as one of the most spectacular events of geological history. Darwin noted its effects along the western coast and southerly tip of South America. But it was not until much later in the century that another aspect of Pleistocene glaciation became appreciated. Man is a creature of the Quaternary. The earliest hominids appeared in eastern Africa far back in Pleistocene time—at least 2 million years ago. Early human development is inextricably interwoven with the violent fluctuations of climate whose imprint is so impressively recorded in glaciated landscapes of the middle latitudes. In Europe the Neolithic emerged from the Paleolithic cultures with the waning of glacial activity. The birth of civilization was postglacial; but its early course in Asia, Africa, and Europe was shaped, and it continues to evolve today, under environmental conditions still strongly influenced by Pleistocene events. That is why glacial processes, which throughout geological time have played on the whole an insignificant part in molding the earth's surface, loom so large in standard treatments of geology.

GLACIAL AND INTERGLACIAL EPISODES

It soon became clear from stratigraphic and geomorphic observations in the European Alps and central United States that climates throughout the Pleistocene were by no means uniformly glacial. Interlayered with extensive till deposits are beds of water-laid sediment and peat with abundant fossil evidence of warm-temperate faunas and floras: Hazel, beech, and oak pollens abound in peat beds instead of the pollens of subarctic conifers; bones of warmth-loving mammals appear instead of remains of the arctic reindeer, musk-ox, and mammoth. At the mouths of glaciated valleys are massive moraines whose weathered state testifies to great age; farther up are less extensive moraines whose component boulders are so little weathered that they seem to have been deposited only yesterday. Remnants of successive floods of glacial outwash are preserved in gravel terraces that flank the valleys of great rivers such as the Rhine whose sources at one time were supplied by the copious melt waters of Pleistocene glaciers. Five major episodes of glaciation came to be recognized in the European Alpine region, four in eastern and central United States. It was realized, too, that in the intervening interglacial periods the climate became even warmer than today. Similar patterns of climatic oscillation have been recognized in northern Europe, the Soviet Union, the Sierra Nevada of California, Alaska, Argentina, and New Zealand. The number of recorded glacial episodes varies from three in some regions to eight in others. Upper sections of deep-sea sediment cores also show regular oscillations between cold- and warm-temperature faunas. And temperature values have been estimated by oxygen-isotope studies of calcium carbonate of fossil skeletal remains.

PLEISTOCENE CHRONOLOGY

The geological approach to chronology meets its severest test when confronted with the problem of identifying, deciphering and relating in time the varied recorded events of Pleistocene and Recent times. Independent chronological systems have been established on the basis of (1) successions of climatic events—glacial and interglacial episodes; (2) successive stages in the development and elaboration of human artifacts, especially stone tools; (3) successions of miscellaneous events such as deposition of varved silt, a volcanic ash fall, outpouring of a lava flow, or a reversal of the earth's magnetic field, that can be assigned absolute dates in years.

Today the student of Pleistocene history attempts to correlate events belonging to these several categories as they are recorded in a single locality or region. Then comes the task of relating the respective chronologies of separate regions—for example, the Alpine region of central Europe and Scandinavia. The ultimate aim is to establish a worldwide chronology of Quaternary climatic variations. Although this aim is far from being accomplished today, and controversy abounds, great progress has been made in the past 60 years.

CLASSIC GLACIAL CHRONOLOGY   By 1909 Penck and Brückner, from a study of glacial outwash preserved in successive gravel terraces that margin the rivers draining northward from the Alps, defined four glacial episodes with three intervening interglacials. The oldest (highest) terrace gravels were later subdivided and a still earlier glacial episode (Donau) was added. Subsequent work has refined the chronology by subdividing each of Penck's glacial episodes, for there is morainal and other evidence that the ice temporarily retreated during each. Penck estimated, on the basis of degree of erosion accomplished, that the penultimate interglacial episode was much longer than the other two. The main divisions of Pleistocene chronology now recognized for the Alpine region of Europe, in order of increasing age, are

    (5) Würm
        interglacial
    (4) Riss
        Great interglacial
    (3) Mindel
        interglacial
    (2) Günz
    (1) Donau

In northeastern United States the classic division is fourfold

    (4) Wisconsin

    (3) Illinoian
    (2) Kansan
    (1) Nebraskan

A number of subdivisions, however, have been recognized. There has been a tendency to overlook these in attempting a transatlantic correlation of the classic divisions.

VARVE CHRONOLOGY OF SWEDEN   The history of the latest part of the last glacial episode in northern Germany and Scandinavia is recorded in a series of end moraines that mark successive stages of standstill or slight advance during the general northerly retreat of the diminishing ice sheet (Figure 7–22). A succession of glacial lakes, many of them extensive, formed in the wake of the retreating ice front. These too have left their record in partially dissected lake sediments, many composed of annually laminated (varved) silts.

In the later part of last century de Geer conceived the idea of compiling a continuous composite sequence of varves covering the southern half of Sweden. Herein would be the material for a year-by-year chronology of events from the time when the ice front uncovered the southern tip of Sweden into historic times. De Geer and his associates counted and measured the thickness of individual varves in numerous sections. Thickness fluctuates from one bed to another in a manner that can be correlated with annual climatic fluctuations. So it is possible to identify corresponding thickness variations in parts of isolated stratigraphic sections, and so to correlate the sections in time.

By such means de Geer was able to show as early as 1926 that 13,000 years have elapsed since the Scandinavian ice front began its retreat across Sweden after the culmination of Würm glaciation. Moreover, the rate of retreat could be accurately established, too, between 120 and 400 meters per annum, over the interval 10,000 to 9000 years ago. The varve chronology of glacial retreat in Sweden has since been tested and substantiated in detail by radiocarbon dating. It stands as a spectacular testimony of the effectiveness of the stratigraphic method—application of Steno's law of superposition in the light of the uniformitarian principle.

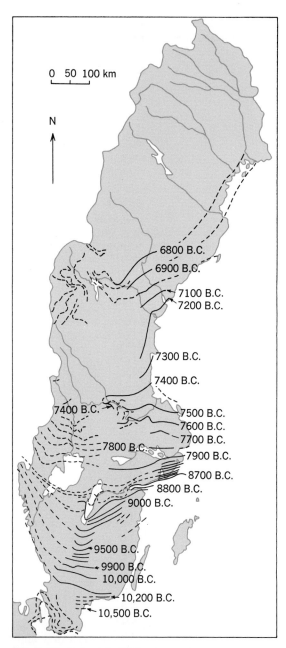

0 50 100 km

N

6800 B.C.
6900 B.C.
7100 B.C.
7200 B.C.
7300 B.C.
7400 B.C.
7400 B.C.
7500 B.C.
7600 B.C.
7700 B.C.
7800 B.C.
7900 B.C.
8700 B.C.
8800 B.C.
9000 B.C.
9500 B.C.
9900 B.C.
10,000 B.C.
10,200 B.C.
10,500 B.C.

FIG. 7–22 *Retreatal ice-fronts and moraines across Sweden with dates determined from varve counting. (From Jan Lundqvist, the Quaternary of Sweden, in K. Rankama, ed., The Quaternary, vol. 1, p. 167, Figure 14.)*

PALEOLITHIC CHRONOLOGY OF WESTERN EUROPE
In Europe the "Old Stone Age"—the period when early man left traces of his existence in the chipped stone tools of Paleolithic cultures—spans much of the period covered by the glacial episodes as defined in central Europe. It begins with the close of the Günz and ends with the final retreat of ice at the end of the Würm stage. Archaeologists have long recognized a sequence in the progressive development of stone and later of bone artifacts. They have used individual stages of artifact development as zone fossils for purposes of correlation, just as paleontologists use stages of organic evolution as shown by fossils. The method as applied in archaeology is unsound for two reasons. First it is highly unlikely that the fundamental assumption made by paleontologists—that identical forms cannot evolve independently—applies to such primitive implements as the rude stone hand ax. In the second place the time scale with which we are now dealing is too refined to permit correlation by indices whose ranges in time may have been half a million years or more. In this connection Zeuner[7] has said

> If we are to obtain a clear idea of the sequence, overlap, alternation, and duration of the industries of the Paleolithic [as recorded by human artifacts], it is absolutely necessary to keep apart the geological (and paleontological) evidence for the climatic chronology from the typological classification of the industries of early man.

The logical approach is to apply a climatic or radiometric time scale to the history of human development as recorded by artifacts, not vice versa. This approach is especially necessary if we attempt to correlate Pleistocene events in distant regions—for example, central Europe and east Africa.

ABSOLUTE CHRONOLOGY It is only by absolute dating that we can hope to establish satisfactory

---

[7] F. E. Zeuner, *Dating the Past*, 3d ed., (Methuen, London, 1952, p. 146).

correlations between Pleistocene events in mutually distant regions. Several methods have been employed. Their results, mutually independent, agree remarkably on a number of critical points in the Pleistocene time scale; and they confirm to an astonishing degree the estimates made from purely geological reasoning by some early workers, notably de Geer and Penck.

1. The radiocarbon method (Chapter 4) has given an accurate chronology of the later part of the Würm stage and subsequent deglaciation, from 40,000 years ago to historic times. Earlier dates are subject to large error, and the method is inapplicable past 85,000 years.

2. By the potassium–argon method (Chapter 4), lavas and tuff beds overlying or underlying moraines, outwash gravels, human remains or artifacts, or fossil faunas and floras, have been dated in many regions over the interval from 4,000,000 to 10,000 years ago.

3. Coral and seashells of marine terraces (recording former high-sea levels) have been dated measuring the degree of recovery to equilibrium ratios (proportional to their half-lives) of members of the uranium and thorium radioactive decay series, from a disequilibrium caused by chemical separation during weathering.

4. Combined geomagnetic and potassium–argon measurements on many volcanic rocks, the world over, have identified and dated a series of magnetic events—reversals of magnetic polarity — of worldwide significance (see Chapter 13). The "magnetic" chronology for the last 4,000,000 years is of crucial importance in Pliocene–Pleistocene stratigraphy.

Mainly from dating by radiocarbon it has been found that the last main glacial stage—the Würm of Europe, the Wisconsin of America—embraces a sequence of climatic events that everywhere was almost contemporaneous:

1. An interglacial period of high sea-level ending about 70,000 years ago.

2. Glaciation from about 70,000 to about 40,000 years ago.

3. Interval of warm climate with great dimi-nution of ice in eastern North America and northwestern Europe 40,000 to 30,000 years ago.

4. Second glaciation (maximum of the Würm stage) 30,000 to 10,000 years ago, with culmination at 18,000 years. As Pleistocene merged into Holocene continental ice finally disappeared from North America about 8000 years ago. The climate became somewhat warmer than today; but 3000 years ago present mountain glaciers began to form as a final cooler period set in, with peaks between 1000 B.C. and 500 A.D. and between 1750 and 1900 A.D.

Further back in time the record is more obscure. But dates of several critical events are becoming firmly established.

1. Some geochronologists today draw the Pliocene–Pleistocene boundary at about 3 m.y. or slightly later. Three worldwide events have been radiometrically dated as 2.5 m.y. to 3 m.y. by the K-A technique.

(a) Onset of glaciation as indicated by volcanic rocks associated with tills in places as far afield as the Sierra Nevada (California) and Iceland and the first appearance of cold-water faunas in New Zealand. Dates range from 2.5 m.y. to nearly 3 m.y.

(b) Magnetic reversal at the boundary between the Gauss (normal) and Matuyama (reversed) epochs, 2.5 m.y. (see Figure 13–13). Some glacial beds lie below, others just above this magnetic boundary.

(c) A short period of magnetic reversal, the Mammoth event, interrupting the Gauss normal epoch at 3 m.y. Debris of glacial origin in a number of deep-sea sediment cores from southern oceans appears shortly after this event —perhaps 2.5 m.y. ago.

(d) A distinctive cold-climate fauna ("cold" or Upper Villafranchian) of western Europe has been dated by K-A analysis at 2.5 m.y.—very much older than was previously suspected on purely stratigraphic evidence.

The collective evidence of global onset of glaciation between 2.5 and 3 m.y. is compelling indeed.

2. The history of early man has been pushed back to 2 m.y. or somewhat earlier by recent work in east Africa. Leakey's discovery of hominid skeletal remains and abundant stone artifacts of "early Paleolithic" type in Tanzania has been supplemented by detailed stratigraphic work at the key Olduvai Gorge localities by Hay and extensive radiometric (K-A) dating of associated volcanic beds by Curtis and Evernden. The result is an unusually well-documented date of 1.9 m.y. for the beginning of the Olduvai human culture; and this continued with little development for perhaps a million years or more.

3. The European mammoth—a highly distinctive Arctic elephant—was a creature of the late Pleistocene, a diagnostic fossil of the Würm epoch and possibly the preceding interglacial. Mammoth remains occur in North America and Asia, too. Their use as a basis for correlation in time has been destroyed by radiometric dating of associated volcanic rocks at several North American localities in the vicinity of 1.4 m.y.

4. German geologists have recently supplied an impressive series of K-A dates for volcanic rocks interbedded with the glacial outwash of terraces on the Rhine Valley. These terraces are correlated with the Günz, Mindel, and Great Interglacial stages of Penck's chronology. The dates range from 570,000 years (pre-Günz), to 420,000 years (Günz), to 140,000 years (Great Interglacial). This is an astonishing vindication of Penck's numerical estimate of Pleistocene time as recorded in the Alpine region. It also confirms, what has long been suspected, that in other parts of Europe (France and Italy) and especially in North America the Pleistocene record goes back far beyond the Günz epoch.

FLUCTUATIONS OF PLEISTOCENE CLIMATE

Obviously the chronology of Pleistocene events is still obscured by some conflicting evidence and by differences of opinion between workers approaching the same problems from different angles. It is clear, however, that the past three million years of time provided one of the most remarkable and certainly the most completely investigated climatic cycles in the history of the world. Most geologists would agree on some significant generalizations that emerge from the complicated record:

1. In Tertiary time there was a worldwide drop in temperature to a point about three million years ago when glaciation became widespread in polar and temperate regions. From that time to the present there have been many climatic oscillations of varying magnitude. In some of the interglacial periods, minor and major, world temperatures were considerably higher than today. Only the final major glacial epoch is completely decipherable; and in this period at least (the past 80,000 years) fluctuations match remarkably in regions as far apart as Scandinavia, central Europe, and North America.

2. During glacial episodes large areas not covered by ice were tundra lands (*periglacial* regions) underlain by permafrost and subject to erosive processes—solifluction and frost action—now typical of subarctic regions in the Northern Hemisphere. The imprint of these processes can still be seen, below the recent soil profile, in warm lands such as southern Germany and New Zealand.

3. Today's warm-temperate lands were subject, in glacial periods, to greater runoff than today. In western North America great lakes developed—Bonneville, covering one third of Utah, and Lahontan, covering most of northwestern Nevada. Only shrunken remnants of these remain today. But the former *pluvial* periods are recorded in ancient terraces that mark successive levels of Pleistocene lakes. The west American pluvials can be correlated directly, by interfingering terrace deposits and moraines, with local glacial episodes. This has not been possible in northern and eastern Africa.

4. Development of continental ice implies transfer of correspondingly very large amounts of water from the oceans. Sea level the world over dropped by 120–145 meters at peaks of glaciation. Most of the harbors that indent the con-

tinental coastlines today are drowned mouths of valleys excavated during the period of low sea level, contemporary with the final major glaciation of the late Pleistocene. There are also marine terraces that record even higher sea levels that those of today, developed during warmer interglacial periods.

ISOSTATIC RECOVERY AND DEGLACIATION

Since the superincumbent ice load was removed during the last retreat from the maximum of Würm (Kansan) glaciation, the continental masses of Scandinavia and northeastern America have risen steadily. Old shorelines rise inland toward the ancient ice centers; and on the oldest shorelines the rise is steepest. Uplift, at first rapid, has gradually decreased. But tide-gage measurements show that it still goes on at a much reduced rate. This history of uplift has great geophysical significance (Chapters 4 and 11); however, it is based on interpretation and correlation of geomorphic features and surface deposits, and relies heavily on identification of pollen assemblages. Geophysical implications, therefore, are open to revision as correlation becomes further refined or modified.

CAUSES OF ICE AGES

Although scattered formations of possible glacial origin occur (infrequently) throughout the stratigraphic record of most continents, widespread deposits of undoubted glacial origin occur only in the Quaternary, in the late Paleozoic of South America, Africa, India, Australia and Antarctica (see Chapter 13), and in the late Precambrian. Of these three occurrences, the Pleistocene ice age is by far the best known. As we have just seen, it consists of a still undefined number of glacial–interglacial oscillations of unequal length spread over the past three million years. What accounts for these oscillations and for the long intervals, of the order of 3×10^8 years or more, between ice ages?

It would seem on the whole that climatic conditions that cause an ice age need not be very different from present ones. Ice begins to ac-cumulate over the years whenever snowfall (mostly in winter) exceeds summer ablation; in many places it seems that a sequence of a few slightly wetter and colder summers could suffice to form, particularly at high altitude, a somewhat enlarged permanent snow cover, which would then automatically tend to grow because of the high albedo of snow. A very large number of climatic factors could, at least in theory, contribute to the onset of glaciation. We enumerate some of these.

1. *Solar radiation.* The temperature of the sea, as recorded in the O^{18}/O^{16} ratio in the shells of some invertebrates, appears to have decreased steadily since late Jurassic times (140 m.y.). This slow and steady decline could perhaps be attributed to a decrease in solar radiation, thus making the sun responsible for the onset of ice ages. This, however, is a purely *ad hoc* hypothesis, for there is no obvious reason why the sun's energy output should fluctuate with a time scale of the order of 10^8 years; nor is there any independent means of testing the hypothesis.

To illustrate the complexity of climatic factors, it has been argued, somewhat paradoxically, that glacial oscillations could be started by an *increase* in solar radiation, which would cause increased evaporation from the oceans and increased cloudiness. Because the albedo of clouds is greater than that of land, increased cloudiness and precipitation would be accompanied by a drop in temperature below the clouds. Thus an ice cover could form locally before the decrease in surface temperature reduced the rate of evaporation.

2. *Orbital motions of the earth.* In Chapter 4 we noted that variations in the orbital motion of the earth and in the inclination of its spin axis cause periodic fluctuations in the average annual amount of solar energy received at fixed points on the earth; we also noted (Figure 4–21) that there seems to be a correlation between the recorded temperature fluctuations in a deep-sea sediment and the predicted fluctuations. The record extends, however, over only a small fraction of the Pleistocene; furthermore, this theory fails to explain why recurring glaciations do not

occur throughout the whole of the geologic record. Motions of the earth may perhaps have modulated climatic fluctuations that clearly must have an additional, more fundamental, cause.

3. *"Continentality of the poles."* It has been remarked that if the poles of the earth happened to be located in open oceans, glaciation would be unlikely because of efficient mixing in the oceans, which would preclude large latitudinal differences in temperature. The present configuration, with a nearly enclosed Arctic Ocean surrounded by large landmasses at one pole, and a large landmass (Antarctica) at the other pole, is thought to be favorable for glaciation. As we shall see in Chapter 13, there is much paleomagnetic evidence that the poles have moved in relation to the continents; and it has been suggested accordingly that polar wandering may be responsible for the onset of glaciation. This, however, is unlikely to be the whole explanation, for the paleomagnetic data unambiguously show that the poles have been within a few degrees of their present position for the last 20 m.y. or so. Why, then, didn't glaciation begin earlier? Furthermore, configurations of poles, land, and ocean resembling the present one have existed over periods with no record of glaciation.

4. *Elevation of land.* As mean annual temperature decreases with increasing altitude, a worldwide orogeny resulting in an unusually high mean elevation of the land could perhaps initiate a glacial episode. Since, however, elevation of the land changes only very slowly, glacial–interglacial oscillations remain unexplained in this hypothesis.

5. *Oceanic circulation.* The general pattern of oceanic circulation and consequent mixing of warm equatorial and cold polar waters is determined in large part by the distribution of land and sea. It has been suggested therefore that changes in configuration and particularly the rather recent emergence of Central America and closing of the Isthmus of Panama, may have affected circulation in the Atlantic Ocean, and particularly the Gulf Stream, in a manner conducive to the development of a north-polar ice cap. Weyl has called attention particularly to the effect of changes in salinity in the North Atlantic. Although the argument may be logical, it remains difficult to see how local changes in geography could induce worldwide glaciation. Our understanding of oceanic circulation is hardly sufficient to predict what would happen under a slightly different configuration of land and sea.

The dependence of circulation on water depth is emphasized in a hypothesis that the extensive Pleistocene ice sheets surrounding the Arctic Ocean require the latter to be ice-free so as to provide the necessary moisture. As water is withdrawn from the ocean to form glaciers, sea level falls, and eventually the shallow sea floor between Iceland and the Faroe islands impedes the flow of warm Atlantic water into the Arctic, which freezes over, reducing snowfall and allowing ablation to exceed nourishment of the glaciers, which disappear. Rising sea level restores circulation and melting of Arctic ice, and the cycle starts again. This hypothesis is open to the objections that (1) if the Arctic Ocean were the source of moisture, mountain ranges around the Arctic should have their largest glaciers on the northern slopes, which they don't; and (2) glaciation on the continents should be contemporaneous with an open, ice-free Arctic Ocean. This does not appear to have been the case.

6. *Changes in composition of the atmosphere.* Atmospheric CO_2 absorbs much of the infrared radiation emitted by the earth and contributes significantly to the warming of the atmosphere (the CO_2 content of the atmosphere is estimated to have increased by 10 percent through the burning of fossil fuels over the past century and may be responsible for the present phase of climatic warming). Active weathering removes from the atmosphere CO_2, which is transferred to the ocean; this cools the earth's surface and may lead, according to this theory, to formation of glaciers. As the glaciers grow, however, they withdraw water from the ocean, which must release CO_2 to the atmosphere; this warms the atmosphere and melts the ice, thus completing a glacial oscillation. Objections to this theory stem from the buffering effect of carbonate precipitation in the oceans, which keeps the CO_2 variation small. It is also difficult to see, on this theory, why

glacial oscillations should not be the rule rather than the exception through geologic time.

Volcanoes contribute H_2O and CO_2 to the atmosphere, and also, in violent explosions, much dust—which may increase the opacity of the upper atmosphere and its albedo. Volcanic action has therefore repeatedly been suggested as a cause of glaciation. This, however, seems unlikely; there is no clear-cut evidence in the meteorological record that the great volcanic explosions of the last two centuries (Tambora 1815, Krakatoa 1883, Katmai 1912, and others) had any effect on weather, nor is there any geological evidence of a correlation between glacial ages and intensity of volcanic action.

In summary, there is at present no single explanation of ice ages. Their rarity in the geologic record suggests that they are cumulative effects of a number of independent factors that happen only rarely to coincide in time. Some of these factors may be external to the earth, as suggested by the slow cooling of the ocean in the 140 m.y. that preceded the Quaternary glaciation. The glacial–interglacial oscillations, with a period of some 10^5 years, will remind the student of mechanics, fluid dynamics, or electrical networks, of the manifold instabilities that characterize systems in which several mutually dependent variables interact. Displacements in space of the earth's spin axis possibly control in some degree the periodicity of these oscillations; other factors, such as displacement of the earth's axis with respect to the earth itself, drifting of continents, changes in the configuration of land and sea, elevation of the land, relief of the sea floor, minor fluctuations in the composition of the atmosphere or of the ocean, may all play a role, if only a minor and indirect one. It is unlikely that we will understand the causes of ice ages before we understand better what makes the weather.

Models of Landscape Evolution

To this point we have been concerned with various processes of weathering, slope erosion, and transport by streams, wind, and glaciers. Act-

ing in concert, they give the landscape its form. We have, however, implicitly assumed throughout this discussion that the landscape already exists: a stream flows down an existing valley, colluvium slides down a hillside, and so on. We now wish to consider in more detail the development of the landscape itself as base-level changes or as a result of tectonic or volcanic uplift. How do the drainage pattern and the slopes develop? Does the landscape preserve any record of the uplift or deformation that initiated the erosional process?

The full development of a landscape takes millions of years and has therefore never been witnessed in its entirety; all we see are bits and pieces of a process in various stages of development. Geologists have attempted to assemble these bits of information into conceptual models describing the successive changes a landscape might undergo. Models developed to date do not exhaust the possibilities, nor do they account successfully for all observed features. Here again, much work remains to be done.

Four models are outlined below. They all apply to the fluvial (stream-controlled) landscape. The first two, which refer to "erosion cycles," assume successive episodes of relatively rapid uplift followed by periods of standstill and erosion. The third model regards the present landscape as representing a steady state and has no cyclic or historical connotations. The fourth model was developed to account for features not explained by the other three.

THE MODEL OF W. M. DAVIS

The first model to be considered is the erosion cycle of William Morris Davis, developed about 1890 from the work of J. W. Powell, G. K. Gilbert, and C. E. Dutton in the basin of the Colorado River during the period 1870–1880. These three men had developed the concepts of grade, base-level, and reduction to a surface of low relief as an end product of erosion. They had also recognized that streams may be classified in terms of their relation to structure as

1. *Consequent.* Those streams whose courses

are a consequence of the structural deformation, such as radial drainage from a dome and the initial streams along synclines.

2. *Antecedent.* Those streams, older than the uplift, that managed to maintain their courses by downcutting as uplifts developed athwart them.

3. *Superimposed.* Those streams whose courses were fixed on an unconformable cover or smooth plain, and which maintained their original courses as they incised themselves into the discordant structure underlying the unconformity or plain.

To these Davis added the notion that the initial form of a landscape cycle may also be a surface of low relief, as well as a fourth class of stream:

4. *Subsequent.* Those streams, commonly tributaries or segments of consequent streams, whose courses are established by erosion along belts of easily weathered or eroded rock, after the uplift that initiated the cycle of erosion.

Davis' cycle was devised to account for two geologic phenomena: (1) Structural relief in deformed regions is many times greater than topographic relief; in spite of wide differences in structural position, the summits and divides of a mountain region are commonly within a few hundred meters of the same altitude. (2) In many regions, drainage is markedly discordant to structure.

In Davis' model, orogenic activity is assumed to occur in spurts, with long intervening periods of quiescence while landscape evolution runs its course; and base level is regarded as fixed for the duration of a cycle. In the ideal model a region of low relief—a sea floor, coastal plain, or surface inherited from a previous cycle—is considered to be rapidly uplifted, probably with a gentle slope toward the sea. Drainage is at first poorly developed, but eventually an integrated stream system is developed, consequent upon the initial slope of the plain. The streams incise their beds; but as they encounter rocks of different degrees of re-

sistance, their long profiles are irregular, with many falls and rapids. As the stream beds are deepened, the adjacent slopes are steepened and lengthened, and slope processes, delivering abundant detritus to the streams, provide them with cutting tools so they incise their beds more rapidly. Both the streams and the landscape are in the stage of *youth.*

The main streams are supposed to reach, by rapid downcutting, a condition in which they can transport just as much material as is delivered to them by tributaries and slope processes. Downcutting ceases, or is slowed to an imperceptible rate. The streams are now graded and regarded as *mature,* although the landscape as a whole is still in the stage of youth. Evidence of a graded condition includes a smoothly concave profile without rapids or falls and the development of an incipient floodplain as the stream begins to migrate laterally much more rapidly than it lowers its bed. The tributaries extend themselves headward, and complex drainage adjustment takes place as tributaries in weak rocks or with low local base levels and steep gradients capture the headwaters of those not so favorably situated. Gradually the remnants of the original surface are consumed, and the landscape is converted into one of steep slopes leading down to the deeply incised streams. When the last remnants of the old landscape are gone, and when relief is at a maximum, the landscape is in the stage of *maturity.*

The rate of weathering and slope modification is supposed to be proportional to the degree of exposure of bedrock and to the steepness of the slope; hence cliffs and rock outcrops are quickly worn back, and the sharp break in slope at the margins of the plateau remnants is rounded, as are the ridge crests and drainage divides when the old landscape has disappeared. All slopes are mantled with a layer of debris, moving downslope at just the rate to keep the rivers supplied with all that they can transport. The whole landscape is now "graded." As the slopes flatten with time, the material contributed is finer, because more deeply weathered, and its rate of supply decreases. The rivers, widening their valleys by lateral planation gradually lower them closer and closer to base level, as both rivers and landscape pass into the stage of *old age*. The ultimate landform, the *peneplain*, is a surface of low, nearly imperceptible relief, in which the rivers meander slowly through broad, flat valleys, separated by slightly rolling uplands along the original divides; here and there an isolated mountain of resistant rock, a *monadnock*, breaks the monotony of the landscape.

The cycle could be interrupted at any stage by renewed uplift. Presumably the streams would quickly adjust their profiles to the renewed uplift, and the slopes would respond less rapidly. The marks of rejuvenation might be breaks in the side slopes of the valleys or terraces and benches on the valley walls. If the region contained rocks of varying resistance to erosion, the old-age stage or partial peneplain might be reached in areas of less-resistant rocks, while the more resistant might still carry patches of a previous peneplain. Renewed uplift in this case would result in a landscape with evidence of two peneplains.

The Davisian cycle offered an explanation for both the accordance of summits and ridge crests and for the discordance of drainage with structure. Its greatest success was an explanation for the landscape of the folded Appalachian Mountains of Pennsylvania. The topographic relief of the Appalachians is only a small fraction of the amplitude of their folds (Figure 7–23). Valleys are developed along belts of limestone and shale, and mountains on quartzite and greenstone; ridge crests and summits are nearly accordant, and define a nearly plane imaginary surface that rises inland from the coastal plain to heights of 600 to 1000 meters near the drainage divide. The main streams such as the Susquehanna, Delaware and Potomac, bear little apparent relation to structure. They rise in the flat-lying Permocarboniferous rocks of the Allegheny Plateau, in what is structurally the lowest part of the Appalachian fold belt, and flow east and southeast across the folds in structurally higher and older rocks, eventually to reach the sea in what was probably structurally the highest part of the orogenic belt— the crystalline rocks of the Piedmont region.

The erosional history of the Appalachians, as interpreted by D. W. Johnson according to the Davisian model, involved peneplanation following the Triassic block faulting which itself followed the late-Paleozoic folding after a period of considerable erosion; partial cover of the peneplain by Cretaceous sediments; and subsequent uparching to create the elongate dome of the Appalachian highlands. Drainage consequent upon the east slope of the dome was superimposed from a Cretaceous cover or from the peneplain onto the folded rocks of the Appalachians, and survives as the main elements of the drainage; headward extension of tributaries in belts of limestone and shale produced a subsequent secondary drainage; the former courses of streams beheaded by capture as the subsequent secondary drainage developed are marked by *wind gaps* across the ridges of quartzite and greenstone. To account for a secondary level of accordant summits of hilltops in the shale and limestone valleys, a second episode of uplift was invoked to initiate a new cycle of downcutting. The ancient peneplain defined by the summits of the quartzite ridges was named the Schooley peneplain, and the partial peneplain of the limestone and shale valleys the Harrisburg peneplain.

The Davis model had an immense impact on American geomorphology and was widely applied. Peneplains, based on accordant summit levels, were recognized in nearly every mountain range and upland. The fashion for finding peneplains reached its extreme with the recognition of 14 partial peneplains in the evolution of the Colorado Front Range.

A SECOND MODEL

The second model of landscape evolution involves a generalization of base level rather than grade. Every point on a stream is considered to be the temporary base level for all points upstream, and every point on a slope to be a base level for the slope above it. The key feature of this model is that slopes do not flatten with time, but wear back in parallel fashion, keeping the slope angle constant, and disappear only when the divides are consumed. As the slope retreats, it leaves at its base a gently sloping bedrock surface of transportation called a *pediment*.

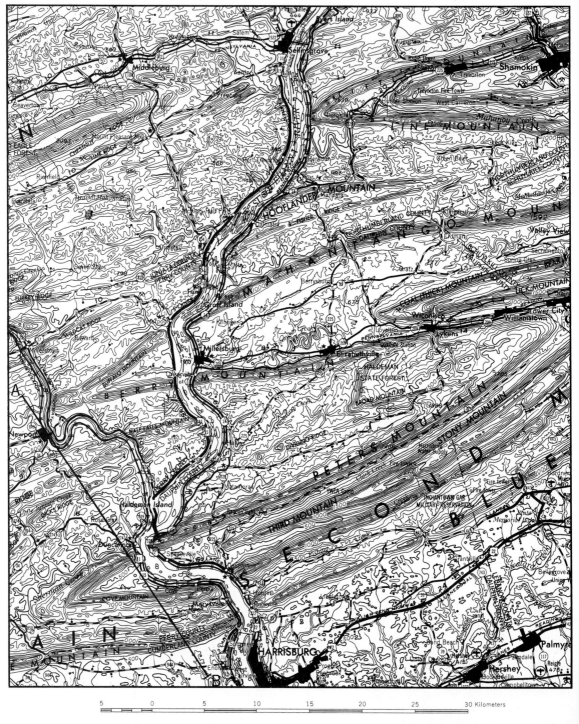

FIG. 7–23a

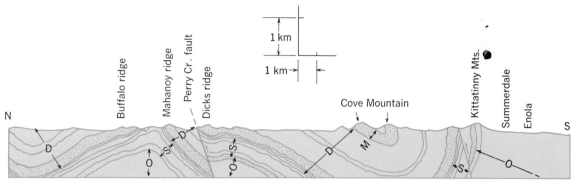

FIG. 7–23 Topographic map and geologic section of a part of the folded Appalachians, showing discordance between drainage and structure and accordant ridge-crests explained by the Davisian geomorphic cycle. (a) Portion of U.S. Army Map Service topographic map of Harrisburg, Pa., 1° × 2° quadrangle, contour interval 100 feet, showing accordant ridge-crests of mountains upheld by resistant Paleozoic quartzite and sandstone formations. (b) Geologic section along the line A–B on the west bank of the Susquehanna River. O, Ordovician rocks; S, Silurian rocks; D, Devonian rocks; M, Mississippian rocks. Resistant formations stippled. Vertical exaggeration approximately 2 times. (Simplified from Bradford Willard and Arthur B. Cleaves, 1938, A Paleozoic Section in South-Central Pennsylvania; Penn. Geol. Survey Bull. G-8).

The pedimentation or parallel retreat cycle evolved from the discovery of pediments bordering the desert ranges of southern Arizona and Sonora, about 1897 (Figure 7–24). The original studies were by W. J. McGee, Sidney Paige, and Kirk Bryan. The explanation of desert pediments has involved much controversy, some holding that lateral corrasion produced the pediment and that backwearing of slopes was incidental to this, and others that parallel slope retreat and pediment formation are spontaneous processes not necessarily linked to lateral corrasion.

The model involving parallel slope retreat was applied to humid regions by W. Penck. Invoking the pervasive influence of base level, Penck argued that a steepened stream gradient caused by an abrupt lowering of base level at the mouth of a stream would not in time be flattened by adjustment throughout the profile, but rather would retreat upstream as a nick point. Above the nickpoint erosion would proceed as though the change in base level had not occurred. Thus a series of rapid uplifts, separated by intervals of quiescence, would be marked on a stream profile by a series of nick points, all migrating upstream.

The application to slopes is somewhat more complicated, and involves Penck's view that rock weathering involves successive stages of com-

minution that follow each other downward from the surface, and that the longer material is weathered the finer and more easily transported it becomes. To him, the typical soil profile would consist of finely comminuted debris at the surface, which grades downward into coarser material that eventually passes into unweathered bedrock. The most rapid weathering, in his view, takes place on bare rock cliffs and ledges, and these are therefore the sites of most rapid erosion. Each stage of reduction of rock would require much more time than the preceding stage of weathering. Furthermore, he regarded the mobility of the weathered mantle (that is, the rate at which it would move down a given slope) to be directly proportional to its fineness. Coarse debris would require a steeper slope for a given rate of creep than fine debris.

Penck assumed that uplift would not be sudden and spasmodic, compared to erosion, but would start slowly, reach a maximum rate, and then gradually decrease to zero. This would be reflected in the landscape by the development, first, of gentle slopes sufficient to transport the thoroughly weathered debris, and then, as the rate of uplift increased, by development of increasingly steeper slopes (Figure 7–25a). Thus convex slope profiles would be evidence of in-

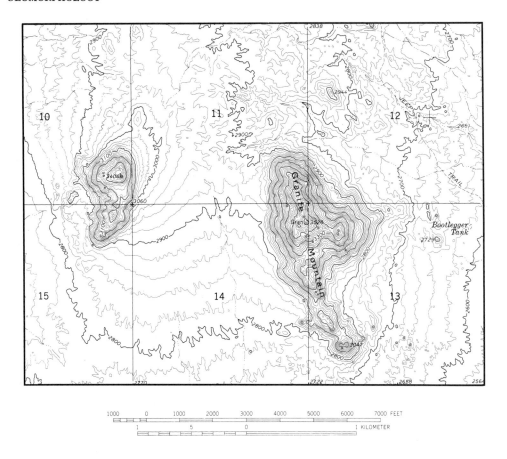

FIG. 7–24 *Topographic map of a pediment and inselbergs (residual hills) on granitic rocks. (From U.S. Geological Survey topographical map of Wildcat Hill 7½-minute quadrangle, Arizona, 1965 edition. Contour interval 20 feet.)*

creasing rate of uplift. The steep slopes would retreat rapidly and consume the gentler slopes above them. At the same time they would leave at their base gentler slopes graded to transport the material delivered to them, and as these in turn retreated, they would be replaced by still gentler slopes that would retreat still more slowly (Figure 7–25b). The ultimate landform would be a multifaceted surface, rising gently from the streams to the divides and slightly concave, in contrast to the gentle convexity of the Davisian peneplain. Here and there would be unconsumed steep-sided remnants of the original landscape, which Penck called *inselbergs* (Figure 7–24).

Penck's interpretation of convex landforms showed lack of understanding of slope processes and is not now taken seriously. The other aspects of his geomorphic model may have application in some environments.

The cycle of parallel slope retreat and pedimentation has been applied by L. C. King to the evolution of entire continental landscapes. King regards the "normal" terrestrial climate and vegetation as that of the semiarid region, and the humid temperate climates of Europe and eastern North America as abnormal. In the semiarid climate, according to King, the sporadic distribution of rainfall results in occasional storms of in-

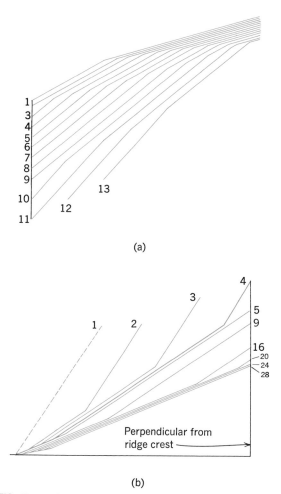

(a)

(b)

FIG. 7–25 *Stages in the retreat of slopes, according to W. Penck. (a) Convex forms due to parallel slope retreat on gradually increasing uplift. Numbers 1–13 mark successive stages in the evolution of the slope profile. (b) Concave forms due to parallel slope retreat after uplift has ceased. Numbers refer to successive profiles assumed by slope after passage of equal increments of time. (From Penck, pp. 137, 158, 1953.)*

tense precipitation (as much as 28 cm in 24 hours), which cover the land with a sheet of water. In such a climate, according to King, slopes tend to retreat parallel to themselves. The completely developed hillslope, in his view, has four elements: a gently convex, or "waxing" slope, at the top; a bedrock escarpment, or "free face" immediately below; a "debris slope" at or near the angle of repose, at the base of the free face; and leading away from the debris slope, the "waning slope" or pediment (Figure 7–26). The angle between the debris slope and the pediment may be sharp or gently concave.

King applied the pediment cycle first to South Africa and later to other parts of the world. According to him, southern Africa is bordered by monoclinal flexures that were deformed originally in the Cretaceous and suffered two subsequent episodes of deformation in the early and late Tertiary. Each episode of deformation formed a coastal escarpment, which retreated inland at a rate of 1 meter every 500–1000 years, or almost as fast as nick points would migrate headward on the African rivers. Thus the topography of South Africa consists of three broad plains, rising stepwise to the interior of the continent, and separated by escarpments a few hundred to 1200 meters high. The rivers plunge over these escarpments in great waterfalls, of which the largest are the Victoria Falls of the Zambeze.

STEADY-STATE MODEL

The steady-state or dynamic equilibrium model treats the landscape as an open system consisting of a set of interdependent elements in which a state of dynamic equilibrium has been achieved. As developed originally by G. K. Gilbert in his classic study of the Henry Mountains

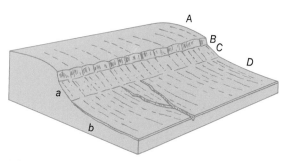

FIG. 7–26 *Elements of a hillside slope, according to King. A, Waxing slope; B, Free face; C, Debris slope; D, Waning slope (pediment); a, talus; b, soil. (From L. C. King, Canons of landscape evolution, Geol. Soc. Am. Bull., vol. 64, p. 728, 1953.)*

of Utah and applied by J. T. Hack to a reinterpretation of the topography of a part of the Appalachians, it is based on four postulates and two "laws" derived from them (paraphrased below from Hack, 1965, p. 5):

1. Other things being equal, erosion is more rapid where the rock offers the least resistance.
2. Other things being equal, steep slopes erode faster than gentle ones.
3. Transportation of eroded material is affected by slope to a degree greater than a simple ratio.
4. Transportation is affected by the quantity of transporting water to a degree greater than a simple ratio.

Law of structure: When the ratio of erosive action as dependent on declivities becomes equal to the ratio of resistance as dependent on rock character, there is an equality of action.

Law of divides: Other things being equal, declivity bears an inverse relation to the quantity of water; that is, a large stream will have a flatter gradient than its tributaries. Therefore, slopes of stream channels are, in general, steeper the nearer they are to divides. The apparent exception to this law in the convexity of hilltops is due to the fact that they are eroded by mass movement.

According to the model, the gradient of a stream is adjusted to the quantity of water and load and to the resistance of its bed and bed load so as to equalize its work in all parts of its course. Hence it generally assumes a smooth, concave-upward longitudinal profile because of the downstream increase in water volume, but the profile may be steeper where it crosses resistant bedrock or has to transport coarse gravel. Similarly, slopes would be more or less steep according to the resistance to erosion of the rocks underlying them, or more precisely, to the coarseness of the products of weathering that have to be transported down the slope. The streams, because of their low gradients, define an imaginary surface that is far gentler than the landscape and closely approximates a plane. In a region of uniform bedrock, vegetation, and climate, the slopes and drainage density will be uniform; therefore ridge crests should rise to approximately the same heights and also define an imaginary surface closely approximating a plane. In a region of diversified lithology, all slopes come to be adjusted to the resistance of the underlying rock. Where lithology changes, the equilibrium slope, drainage density, and local relief change; summits on quartzite, for example, will have a different level of accordance than those on limestone or shale. Once the landscape achieves dynamic equilibrium, most of the traces of its past history have been erased. Uplift can continue indefinitely, and downcutting keep pace with it, and the landscape will not appreciably change. Analysis of landscape in terms of the equilibrium concept is thus independent of time. Relict features that formed under different past conditions are preserved only if complete equilibrium has not been reached.

If uplift slows or ceases, and base level exerts an influence, the rate of erosion on any element of topography must decrease as it approaches base level, and the landscape will flatten. However, if the main streams are able to corrode their beds, base level has no influence; all parts of the landscape degrade at the same rate, and the landscape persists unchanged.

Hack showed that the steady-state model explains many features of the Shenandoah Valley better than the multiple peneplains that were supposed to have explained them; he accounted for the water gaps, wind gaps, and apparently anomalous course of the Potomac by showing that they are all at localities where the resistant formations are unusually thin or have been faulted out. He concluded that whatever may have been the early history of drainage and erosion in the central Appalachians, nothing in the present landscape enables us to reconstruct it.

THE FOURTH MODEL

In the three models so far discussed, weathering per se does not control slope or form; these are controlled primarily by the requirement for transportation of the weathered products. In these models, also, positive and negative feedback dominate at different stages in the evolution of the landscape. Positive feedback is involved in the evolution of the drainage network and the deepening of the stream beds until the streams reach grade or dynamic equilibrium. Thereafter, negative feedback dominates, and any deviation from the equilibrium or graded form accelerates those processes that tend to eliminate the deviation and restore the form.

In his classic paper on the Henry Mountains, G. K. Gilbert noted (on page 103) that "the rapid, but partial removal of weathered rock accelerates weathering; but the complete removal of its products retards weathering." If the implications of this statement are explored, another model of geomorphic evolution is possible, which is non-cycle and non-steady state.

If an impermeable, well-consolidated, or crystalline rock is jointed into blocks 1–3 meters on a side (such as is generally the case with granitic rocks), it must be weathered to sand or clay before it is eroded. It will not usually weather to gravel unless it has a pervasive structure such as cleavage or close jointing. Weathering is most rapid in the zone of vadose water above the water table, where the rock is buried beneath a permeable mantle, and is in contact with a periodically renewed mixture of soil, water, and air, high in organic acids and CO_2. Below the water table, water movement is slow, water and rock reach chemical equilibrium, and weathering is minimal. Outcrops of unweathered rock present an impermeable surface that is in infrequent contact with rainwater that lacks the organic acids and CO_2 of soil water. Exposed rock, therefore, weathers much more slowly than rock that is buried beneath soil. Hence any event that causes the exposure of unweathered bedrock may abruptly reduce the rate of weathering and hence the rate of erosion at the site of exposure, and create a local temporary base level. The area whose debris must pass over the exposure can be lowered to the level of the exposure but not below, whereas the area downslope or downstream may be reduced to a much lower base level. This will take place in stream beds as well as on hillside, provided the bed load of the stream does not contain the gravel necessary for effective corrasion. This is generally the case in tropical regions, where rivers carry mainly silt and

clay, and is also true in most areas of coarsely jointed granitic rock outside the region of frequent frost. In such regions (the foothills of the Sierra Nevada, for example) streams draining granitic rock carry little other than sand.

In such regions an accidental exposure of unweathered rock in a stream bed can grow into a fall or rapid separating graded reaches of gentle declivity, provided the stream elsewhere flows across weathered material and regional base level is lowering. Lines of exposure on a hillside can grow into cliffs, and isolated bedrock exposures into granite domes. Thus many otherwise inexplicable features of the landscape such as rapids on the rivers of northeastern South America, or the cliff-and-bench topography and waterfalls in the foothills of the Sierra Nevada of California (Figure 7–27), can be accounted for by the negative feedback inherent in this model.

A variant of the model separates in time the stages of weathering and erosion. Deep weathering is supposed to occur first during a period of low water table. With uplift, the weathered mantle is stripped, and wherever the depth of weathering was below a graded surface, such a surface, nearly plane, is cut across the easily eroded, weathered mantle. Rocks resistant to weathering (such as quartzite) and randomly distributed bodies of unweathered rock (which may occur in granite) are etched into relief as the hills and mountains of an otherwise nearly flat landscape.

Given enough time, outcrops are weathered and eroded and the irregularities they create erased. However, the rate of weathering of exposed rock may be so slow, and the time needed for its elimination so great, in comparison with the time during which base level is stable, or even the length of geologic periods, that these irregularities may be regarded as having been frozen into the landscape.

Geomorphology and Structure

Erosional topography is influenced by the character and structure of the rocks into which it is cut. To what extent can the geologist read this structure from the shape and pattern of the landforms? And what evidence can he find in the

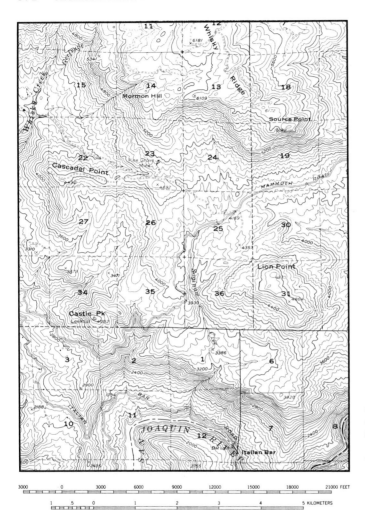

FIG. 7–27 *Topographic map of cliff-and-bench topography developed in massive granodiorite in the Sierra Nevada, California. (From U.S. Geological Survey topographic map of Shaver Lake, 15-minute quadrangle, 1953 edition; contour interval 80 feet.)*

landscape of the latest stages of uplift and deformation?

A simple form of geologic structure that finds topographic expression is a flat-lying sequence of beds of varying resistance to erosion, exemplified by the cliff-and-bench topography of the Grand Canyon of the Colorado. A gently dipping homoclinal sequence, such as underlies the Atlantic and Gulf Coastal Plain of the United States, or borders the Paris Basin, may be expressed as *cuestas*, strongly asymmetric ridges on erosionally resistant rocks, with gentle to imperceptible dip slopes, and much steeper escarpments facing valleys underlain by older yet less resistant rocks. (Resistance may be due as much to higher permeability which reduces runoff as to hardness.) In a steeply dipping homocline, hard rocks may form sharp-crested linear ridges known as *hogbacks* (Figure 7–28).

The topographic influence of domal uplifts may at first be little more than the development of a radial drainage. With continuing uplift and erosion, and exposure of layers of rock of varying erosional resistance, the dome may come to be bordered by circumferential cuesta, or hogbacks, with strike valleys on less-resistant rock; both

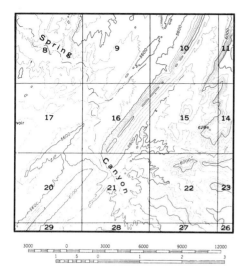

FIG. 7–28 *Topographic map of Hogback in the Emery Sandstone Member of the Mancos Shale. The flat valleys are cut across shale members of the Mancos Shale. The flat-topped hills at the extreme right are mesas capped by flat-lying Mesa Verde sandstone. (From U.S. Geological Survey topographic map of Notom, 15-minute quadrangle, Utah, 1952 edition. Contour interval 80 feet.)*

radial and tangential drainage may be devolped. If the oldest rock exposed is less resistant than those overlying it, the topographic expression of the dome may be a lowland bordered by an inward-facing escarpment. The lowland of the Nashville Basin of Tennessee, located on a broad arch in Paleozoic limestones, is an example.

Fold structures may initially form anticlinal mountains and synclinal valleys; at a later stage, however, topography and drainage are governed mainly by resistance to erosion. Resistant rocks uphold mountains, and valleys are carved in belts of soft or easily weathered rock.

This is well illustrated in two classic areas, the Swiss Jura and the Appalachians of Pennsylvania. In the Jura, folded in the late Tertiary, the structures are so young that many of the anticlines in the Cretaceous limestones are just being breached. In the Appalachians, on the other hand, which were folded in the late Paleozoic, topography bears no relation to structural relief. The even-crested ridges are carved from resistant quartzite and conglomerate, and the valleys are

on belts of limestone and shale. Many of the plunging folds are expressed by zigzag patterns of ridges. One may find here anticlinal mountains and valleys as in the Jura, but these are of purely erosional origin, depending on the hardness of the rock. One finds also synclinal mountains, held up by resistant quartzite or conglomerate, characterized by flat or slightly dished summits and outward-facing escarpments, and anticlinal valleys on shale or limestone, bordered by steep, inward-facing escarpments of quartzite (Figure 7–23). Many of the ridges and valleys are homoclinal, in the sense that beds dip in the same direction on both sides of the topographic feature. Plunging anticlines are marked by long, gently sloping ridges where they are crossed by resistant beds, and synclinal mountains in plunging folds are bordered by abrupt cliffs on their convex sides.

The geomorphology of crystalline terranes is usually less expressive of underlying structure. Schistose and gneissic terranes with a steeply dipping foliation or a nearly horizontal lineation may be reflected by a pronounced grain of minor topography and drainage; but the most pronounced lithologic contrast in most crystalline terrane is that between fresh and weathered rock and, if weathering has been deep, no sign of the underlying structure may appear in the topography. Occasional linear hills on resistant rocks may give a clue to structural trends. Massive crystalline rocks such as granite and granodiorite are frequently expressed topographically by numerous low, irregular rocky hills (Figure 7–29), by a rectilinear drainage following joint patterns, or by numerous low scarps and broad steps that are unrelated to stages of uplift or to bedrock structure.

FAULTS

A major structural geomorphic problem of both theoretical and practical importance is the recognition of faulting from landscape features. With the growing concern with earthquake hazard, the mapping of active faults through their topographic expression is becoming a major part of engineering geologic surveys.

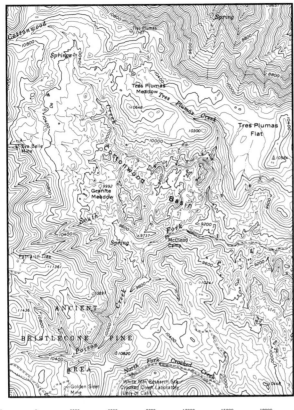

FIG. 7–29 *Map showing topography on quartz–monzonite (center of area), contrasted with smooth slope on dolomite (to left) and original topography on top of faulted basalt flow (at upper right). Several faults trending N 20°E cut the basalt of Tres Plumas Flat, lifting it to the east, and making west-facing scarps (From U.S. Geological Survey topographic map of Mt. Barcroft 15-minute quadrangle, 1962 edition; contour interval 80 feet.)*

Most fault zones are zones of crushed rock; hence the fault surfaces themselves are rarely exposed. Normally, faulting is demonstrated by geologic mapping, which shows a relation between formations on opposite sides of the fault that requires a displacement along the fault surface. If the fault has long been inactive and is not related to the present topography, and if the formations on the two sides are of equal resistance to erosion, the fault trace is likely to be marked by an alluvium- or colluvium-filled trench, and by a notable lack of outcrops.

Many of the great faults of the world, particularly the active ones, were first recognized from topographic expression—either escarpments for which they were thought responsible, or linear valleys, ponds, ridges, and offset streams. Examples are the faults of the East African rift valleys, the range-front faults of the basin-and-range country, and the San Andreas fault of California. Escarpments along faults are of two kinds: *fault scarps* and *fault-line scarps*. The former are escarpments produced directly by offset of the land surface along the fault; the latter are escarpments eroded along faults because of differing resistance of the rocks on the two sides. The distinction is important, for in the first case the fault may still be active and in the second it is probably inactive. What are the criteria for recognizing an escarpment as a fault scarp, and how do we distinguish fault scarps from fault-line scarps?

Both fault scarps and fault-line scarps are

likely to be straight or gently curved for long distances, in contrast to the crenulate pattern of erosional escarpments. (As fault scarps retreat from the fault that produced them, they may also become crenulate.) Most large fault scarps separate areas of erosion on the one side from basins of accumulation on the other. A closed depression on one side of an escarpment, underlain by hundreds to a few thousand meters of young alluvial or lacustrine sediment, reliably indicates a fault scarp. This suitation prevails in the basin-and-range country of North America, and in the African rift valleys. Where rocks on opposite sides of a scarp show no difference in their resistance to erosion, and where a fault can be proved along the base of the scarp by geologic criteria, while other means of forming the scarp can be eliminated, the scarp is probably a fault scarp. Many scarplets cutting alluvial fans in the basin-and-range province can thus be demonstrated to be fault scarps, some of which have come into existence during historic earthquakes.

Probably the most reliable criterion for a fault-line scarp is its location on the downthrown side of the fault, usually indicated by the fact that the rock behind it is older than the rock it faces (Figure 7–30). Even this criterion may fail for transcurrent faults, which may bring a mountain of relatively young rocks opposite a plain cut on old rocks. Other features that may prove the erosional origin of a fault-line scarp include younger sediments and surfaces at the same level on opposite sides of the fault (Figure 7–31), drainage superimposed across the fault—provided the drainage can be demonstrated to be superimposed and not antecedent—and close correlation between topography, internal structure, and resistance of rocks to erosion.

The geomorphic features of transcurrent faults include laterally offset streams, ridges, moraines, and terrace escarpments. Measurements of rate of motion of transcurrent faults in New Zealand have been based on offset terraces and moraines (Figure 7–32). Streams offset by transcurrent faults are lengthened and their gradients thereby reduced. They aggrade their beds on the upstream side of the fault, and if later they are shortened by capture, they incise this valley fill and are bordered by alluvial terraces.

Other features of transcurrent faults are linear ridges and ponds. The ponds may result from grabens along the fault zone or from damming of drainage by lateral displacement of ridges. The ridges are horsts or anticlines, and may be composed of alluvium or lake sediments originally deposited in a fault graben, later squeezed upward during continued movement on the fault.

Whereas active dip-slip faults tend to mark the boundaries of regions of strikingly different relief and altitude, transcurrent faults are characteristically unrelated to physiographic boundaries. The faults of the San Andreas system, for

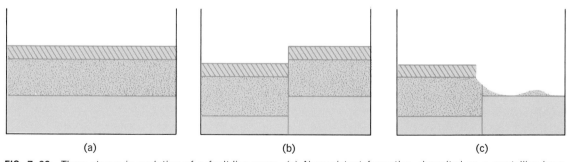

(a)	(b)	(c)

FIG. 7–30 *Three stages in evolution of a fault-line scarp. (a) Nonresistant formation, deposited on a crystalline basement, is overlain by a resistant bed (diagonal lines). (b) Faulting, upthrow on the right. (c) Erosion has removed the rocks on the right, down to the surface of the crystalline basement. Erosion preserves the topography on the left. Stages (b) and (c), although shown here in succession to clarify the concept involved, probably take place concurrently; that is, erosion starts as soon as faulting is initiated.*

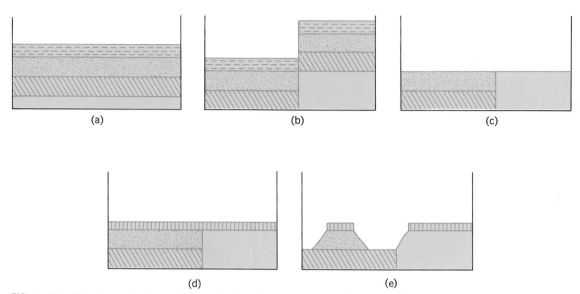

FIG. 7-31 *Five stages in the evolution of a fault-line scarp, scarp facing downthrown block, showing evidence. (a) Deposition of a sedimentary sequence on a crystalline basement. (b) Faulting. (c) Erosion. (d) Extrusion of lava on surface (erosional plain or valley floor) cut across both blocks; (e) Further erosion of left block. Lava mesa on left at same level as lava on right proves that scarp is not a result of displacement on fault. Stages (b) and (c) probably took place concurrently.*

example, in one place cross alluvial plains, a few miles farther may be entirely in mountains, and where they do form physiographic boundaries, they may have the mountain block alternately on one side or the other.

It is difficult to decide whether steep coastlines are fault-controlled or not. For example, the coast ranges of California rise in many places to 500–1500 meters within a few kilometers of the shoreline and face the ocean in imposing cliffs. The sea floor at their base is a nearly flat marine platform, sloping gently seaward to a depth of 100–150 meters, several kilometers offshore. Is the steep coastline a fault scarp, or has the sea, rising and falling during the Quaternary, sawed back the land to form a continental shelf whose boundary fault, if present, lies at the base of the continental slope? Recent surveys suggest that for some segments of the coast a fault explanation may be correct while for other segments an erosional origin is more likely, but there is no certain physiographic criterion for distinguishing between the two.

DEFORMATION AND UPLIFT

Turning to the evidence regarding uplift and deformation that can be read in the landscape, we look first for linear or planar features whose age can be determined within reasonable limits and whose original shape can be reasonably ascertained, such as ancient shorelines, stream terraces, morainal embankments and lines of erratics defining glacier surfaces, alluvial fans, and regional peneplains or pediments defined from accordant summit levels.

Shorelines are perhaps the most reliable of these indicators of deformation. They give, however, only the deformation of a line. Where coasts have numerous bays and islands, deformed shorelines may be found over a large enough area for isobases of uplift to be constructed. However, wave-cut cliffs and other physiographic features are not likely to be developed in protected bays and channels; thus other criteria, such as clays bearing marine fossils, must be used to identify the shoreline. Sea level at the time of the shore-

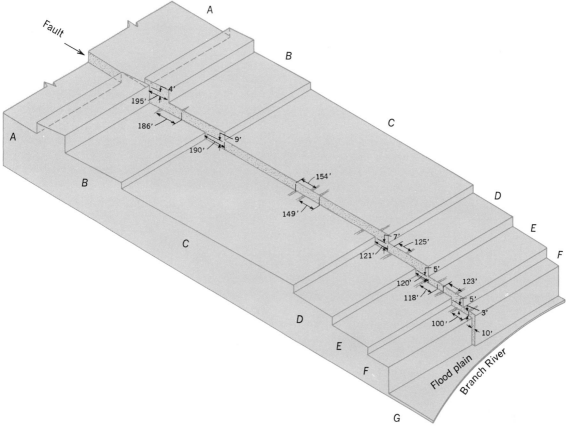

FIG. 7–32 *Sketch of progressively offset terraces of the Branch River, New Zealand, by the Wairau Fault. Numbers give horizontal and vertical displacement in feet of terrace surfaces, terrace scarps, and channels. (After G. Lensen, Geol. Soc. Am. Bull., vol. 79, no. 5, p. 545, 1968.)*

line may be determined with a probable error of a few meters from such features as the shoreline angle, beach ridge, offshore bar, or spit. Lakeshores may possibly be more precisely determined.

The most successful applications of shorelines to studies of deformation have been the investigations of postglacial rebound of areas once covered by continental ice sheets or pluvial lakes. Gilbert's classic study of Lake Bonneville and Crittenden's reinvestigation of its lakeshores are among the best examples (Figure 7–33). The determination of raised shorelines may be difficult, particularly where many shorelines are to be traced and distinguished. The difficulties are

compounded where sea level is rising as the land goes up, as was the case during the retreat of the last ice sheets, for shorelines of different ages may then cross each other in a complicated fashion. In northwest Norway part of the difficulty could be resolved by mapping distinctive deposits of pumice, carried by the Gulf Stream from explosive eruptions in Iceland. In Finland, unraveling of the sequence of shorelines has required interpretation of glacial landforms and deposits, use of varve chronology, pollen stratigraphy, archaeology, and the interpretation of bogs. Some of the evidence on which the reconstruction of the shorelines is based is open to other interpretations. Part of the difficulty in

Finland lies in the fact that the late-glacial seas were diluted with rapidly melting ice and were nearly fresh; in consequence the "marine" deposits have no marine fossils, but are interpreted to be marine on other grounds.

Cut into the bedrock walls of the valleys of many streams are gravel-mantled terraces that are remnants of former stream beds. The profiles reconstructed from these terraces are higher than the modern streams, and have different slopes. It is tempting to use the differences in height and slope as evidence of uplift and deformation since the terraces were carved. Where the profiles slope upstream, as does the ancient profile of the Ventura River in California, one can be confident that deformation has taken place since the terraces were formed; but where the reconstructed profiles slope in the same direction as the modern stream, interpretations of deformation must be made with caution. As indicated in the section on stream process, the profile of a river is controlled not only by base level and total relief, but also by a complex accommodation between depth, width, velocity, and slope. Thus, differences in slope between ancient and modern stream profiles, though possibly caused by deformation, may also simply be due to adjustment of the stream to changing conditions of discharge and bed load as the entire landscape is eroded to a lower level. Each analysis of terrace profiles must be made with this second possibility in mind.

Alluvial fan surfaces have been used as a measure of deformation, on the reasonable assumption that all drainage lines leading down the fan surface from the canyon mouth should initially have the same slope, and that contours on an undeformed fan should therefore be arcs of circles centered at the fan head. If a fan is tilted the contours will be elliptical, and the

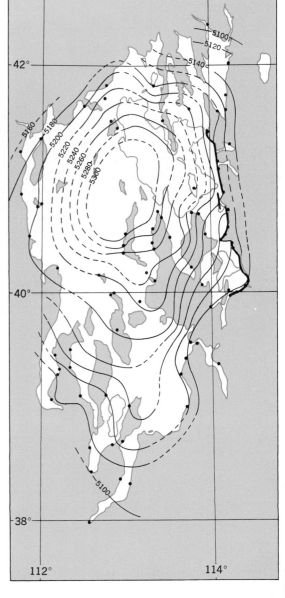

FIG. 7–33 (a) Map showing deformation of the Bonneville (highest) shoreline of Pleistocene Lake Bonneville. Altitudes in feet. The unshaded area shows maximum extent of Lake Bonneville. Within this area, Great Salt Lake, Utah Lake, and Siever Lake are shown. Contours are on the present altitude of the Bonneville shoreline in feet above sea level. The altitude of the lake was originally about 5100 feet. Contours are dashed where uncertain. Heavy black dots are locations of data points on which contours are based. The heavy black line along the east shore of Lake Bonneville is the Wasatch Front fault, which has been active since the lake existed. (After Max D. Crittenden, Jr., New Data on the Isostatic Deformation of Lake Bonneville, U.S. Geol. Survey Prof. Paper 454-F.)

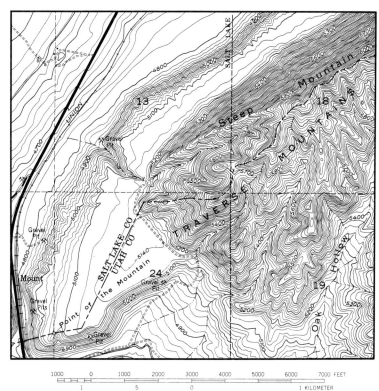

FIG. 7-33 *(b) Topographic map of lake terraces on which the map of Fig. 7-33a is based. (From U.S. Geological Survey topographic map of Jordan Narrows 7½-minute quadrangle, 1951 edition. Contour interval 20 feet.)*

rotation of the fan surface necessary to give circular contours is a measure of the deformation.

Use of accordant summits of mountain ranges as a measure of vertical uplift depends on the assumptions of the existence of a former peneplain and of its slope before deformation. The assumption that the Rocky Mountains were reduced to a peneplain after the Laramide folding, for example, would imply that altitudes in the central part of the range may have been no more than 1000 meters in the early Tertiary, and that 2000 meters or more of uplift has taken place since then. If the surfaces of erosion that extended across the mountains were pediments

rather than peneplains—as was postulated for the Uinta Mountains by W. H. Bradley, and for other ranges of the Rockies by A. D. Howard and J. H. Mackin—the amount of uplift suggested by the accordant summits would be far less, for the slopes of the pediments could have been such as to bring the pediment surfaces to altitudes approaching those of the present ranges. And if the dynamic equilibrium model developed by Hack (see page 372) is applied to the Rocky Mountains, there is no need to postulate any former erosion surface to account for present accordance of summit levels. We have then no way of measuring from the topography, the amount or rate of uplift in late-Cenozoic time.

REFERENCES

GENERAL

King, C. A. M.: *Techniques in Geomorphology,* St. Martin's Press, New York, 1966.

Leopold, L. B., M. G. Wolman, and J. P. Miller: *Fluvial Processes in Geomorphology,* W. H. Freeman and Co., San Francisco, 1964.

Thornbury, W. D.: *Principles of Geomorphology,* Wiley, New York, 1969.

ATMOSPHERE, WEATHER, AND CLIMATE

Haurwitz, B.: *Dynamic Meteorology,* McGraw-Hill, New York, 1941.

Mitchell, J. M.: Theoretical paleoclimatology, in *The Quaternary of the United States* (ed. by H. E. Wright and D. G. Frey), Princeton University Press, Princeton, N.J., 1965.

Sellers, W. D.: *Physical Climatology,* University of Chicago Press, Chicago, 1965.

WEATHERING

Barton, D. C.: Note on the disintegration of granite in Egypt, *J. Geol.,* vol. 24, pp. 382–393, 1916.

Jahns, R. H.: Sheet structure in granites: its origin and use as a measure of glacial erosion in New England, *J. Geol.,* vol. 51, pp. 71–86, 1943.

Keller, W. D.: *The Principles of Chemical Weathering,* Lucas Bros. Publishers, Columbia, Mo., 1962.

Krauskopf, K. B.: *Introduction to Geochemistry,* McGraw-Hill, New York, 1967; Chap. 4, pp. 99–121; Chap. 7, pp. 117–203.

> Chemical weathering and clay minerals and soils.

Richmond, G. M.: Quaternary stratigraphy of the La Sal Mountains, Utah, *U.S. Geol. Survey Prof. Paper 324,* 1962.

> Especially pages 17–25, on the use of soils.

SLOPE PROCESSES

Eckel, E. B. (editor): *Landslides and Engineering Practice,* National Academy of Sciences, National Research Council. Washington, D.C., Highway Research Board Special Report 29 (NAC-NRS Publ. 544).

Especially landslide types and processes by **D. J. Varnes,** pp. 20–47, and stability analysis and design of control methods by **R. F. Baker and E. J. Yoder,** pp. 189–216.

Embleton, C., and C. A. M. King: *Glacial and Periglacial Geomorphology,* St. Martin's Press, New York, 1968.

Kirkby, M. J.: Measurement and theory of soil creep, *J. Geol.,* vol. 75, no. 4, pp. 359–378, 1967.

Wentworth, C. K.: Soil avalanches on Oahu, Hawaii, *Geol. Soc. Am. Bull.,* vol. 54, pp. 53–64, 1943.

Washburn, A. L.: Classification of patterned ground and review of suggested origins, *Geol. Soc. Am. Bull.,* vol. 67, pp. 828–866, 1956.

STREAM PROCESSES

Bagnold, R. A.: An approach to the sediment transport problem from general physics, *U.S. Geol. Survey Prof. Paper 422-I,* 1966.

Henderson, F. M.: *Open Channel Flow,* Macmillan, New York, 1966.

Leopold, L. B., and T. Maddock, Jr.: The hydraulic geometry of stream channels and some physiographic implications, *U.S. Geol. Survey Prof. Paper 252,* 1953.

Malde, H. E.: The catastrophic late Pleistocene Bonneville flood in the Snake River Plain, Idaho, *U.S. Geol. Survey Prof. Paper 586,* 1968.

Rubey, W. W.: The force required to move particles on a stream bed, *U.S. Geol. Survey Prof. Paper 189-E,* pp. 120–141, 1938.

Sundborg, Åke: The River Klaralven, a study of fluvial processes, *Geograf. Ann.,* vol. 38, nos. 2–3, pp. 127–316, 1956.

GLACIERS

Cox, A.: Polar wandering, continental drift and the onset of quaternary glaciation, *Meteorol. Monographs,* vol. 8, no. 30, pp. 112–125, 1968.

Embleton, C., and C. A. M. King: *Glacial and Periglacial Geomorphology,* St. Martin's Press, New York, and Edward Arnold (Publishers) Ltd., London, 1968.

Flint, R. F.: *Glacial and Pleistocene Geology,* Wiley, New York, 1957.

Good discussion of glacial erosion and deposition.

Meier, M. F.: Mode of flow of Saskatchawan glacier, Alberta, Canada; *U.S. Geol. Survey Prof. Paper 351,* 1960.

Nye, J. F.: The mechanics of glacier flow, *J. Glaciol.,* vol. 256, pp. 559–584, 1952.

Rankama, K. (editor): *The Quaternary, vol. 1, 1965: Denmark, Norway, Sweden and Finland; vol. 2, 1967, British Isles, France, Germany, Netherland;* Interscience, New York.

Sharp, R. P.: Glaciers, *Condon Lectures,* Oregon State System of Higher Education, Eugene, Ore., 78 pp. 1960.

Weyl, P. K.: The role of the oceans in climatic change: a theory of the ice ages, *Meteorol. Monographs,* vol. 8, no. 30, pp. 37–62, 1968.

Wright, H. E., Jr., and D. G. Frey (editors): *The Quaternary of the United States* (a review volume for the VII Congress of the International Association for Quaternary Research), Princeton University Press, Princeton, N.J., 1965.

WIND AND DUNES

Bagnold, R. A.: *The Physics of Blown Sand and Desert Dunes,* Methuen, London, 1941, reprinted 1954.

Cooper, W. S.: Coastal sand dunes of Oregon and Washington, *Geol. Soc. Am.* Memoir 72, 1958.

WAVES AND COASTAL PROCESSES

Bagnold, R. A.: Beach and nearshore processes—Part I: Mechanics of marine sedimentation, in *The Sea,* M. N. Hill, editor, vol. 3, Interscience, New York, 1966.

Inman, D. L., and R. A. Bagnold: Beach and nearshore processes—Part II: Littoral processes, in *The Sea,* M. N. Hill, editor, vol. 3, Interscience, New York, 1966, pp. 529–553.

King, C. A. M.: *Beaches and Coasts,* Edward Arnold (Publishers) Ltd., London, 1959.

MODELS OF LANDSCAPE EVOLUTION

Davis, W. M.: *Geographical Essays* (ed. by D. W. Johnson), Dover, New York, 1954 (reprint of a 1909 collection of essays); see especially pp. 249–513.

Gilbert, G. K.: Report on the Geology of the Henry Mountains, U.S. Geographical and Geological Survey of the Rocky Mountain Region, U.S. Govt. Printing Office, Washington, D.C., 1877; see in particular, Chap. 5, Land sculpture, pp. 99–150.

Hack, J. T.: Geomorphology of the Shenandoah Valley, Virginia and West Virginia, and origin of the residual ore deposits, *U.S. Geol. Survey Prof. Paper 484.*

King, L. C.: Canons of landscape evolution, *Geol. Soc. Am. Bull.,* vol. 64, pp. 721–752, 1953.

Mabbutt, J. A.: The weathered land surface in central Australia, *Zeitschrift f. Geomorphologie, n.f.,* vol. 9, n. 1, pp. 82–114, 1965.

Penck, W.: *Morphological Analysis of Land Forms, a Contribution to Physical Geography* (translated by Helle Czech and K. C. Boswell), Macmillan, New York, 1953 (translation of a German work published in 1924).

Thomas, M. F.: Some aspects of the Geomorphology of domes and tors in Nigeria, *Z. Geomorphol.,* pp. 63–81, 1965.

Wahrhaftig, C.: Stepped topography of the southern Sierra Nevada, California, *Geol. Soc. Am. Bull.,* vol. 76, pp. 1165–1190, 1965.

8
SEDIMENTATION
AND SEDIMENTARY ROCKS

THE PRECEDING CHAPTER dealt with the erosion of rocks and the evolution of landscape. This one treats the fate of the eroded material. Most of it, transported by streams, glaciers, wind, and ocean currents, is eventually deposited in thin layers either in the lowest available continental or marine basins, the ocean-floor trenches, or at sites within a few hundred meters of sea level. The sum total of the processes of transportation and deposition we call *sedimentation,* and the unconsolidated materials *sedimentary deposits.* Those of past geological ages, now consolidated (or lithified) into sedimentary rocks, preserve, to a greater or lesser degree, some record of their mode of transportation and deposition. Sedimentary rocks of all ages exist. Indeed the oldest known rocks are sedimentary, showing that processes of erosion and sedimentation have been going on for at least 3.5 billion years.

Stratigraphic interpretation of sedimentary rocks (Chapter 4) has been largely by analogy with present-day sedimentary processes, either observed or inferred; and our understanding of these rocks and of the history they represent has progressed only as rapidly as our knowledge of modern processes of sedimentation on land and beneath the sea. Nevertheless we must keep in mind that the analogy between past and present can never be exact. A complicating factor is the peculiar character of Quaternary environments of sedimentation. The continents stand higher with respect to sea level now than during most of the last 600 million years; and the broad shallow "continental" seas, in which a large part of the sedimentary rocks accumulated, are less extensive now than at most times in the past. There is no existing exact analog, for example, of the broad shallow seas that covered large parts of the interior of North America during much of the Paleozoic era and again in Cretaceous times, although the Persian Gulf and Hudson Bay may be small-scale analogs. Furthermore, the growth and ablation of the continental ice sheets have caused sea level to rise and fall in concert over the entire earth; thus every continental shelf, with the exception of those that were covered with glacial ice, has experienced the same history of sea-level fluctuations in the past few hundred thousand years. Beginning 16,000 or 18,000 years ago, the world ocean experienced a rise of sea level of about 120 meters, followed by a near-standstill 5000–6000 years long; and most coastlines of the world will record exactly the same history of marine transgression followed by standstill. Hence our opportunities for finding analogies with the past are limited. Sedimentary rocks in some respects are ideally suited to interpretation along uniformitarian lines; but paradoxically this approach is limited by worldwide prevalence of conditions imposed by the peculiarities of Quaternary climates.

Here we extend the uniformitarian approach to sedimentation by first reviewing experimental data and theory relevant to chemical evolution of sediments.

Chemistry of Aqueous Sedimentation

Most sedimentary rocks are composed of mineral grains that have been mechanically deposited or chemically precipitated from surface waters. A complete sedimentary cycle of aqueous transport and deposition may cover thousands of years. During this time, and for long periods after deposition, sedimentary grains are continuously exposed to reaction with dilute aqueous solutions whose composition and critical related chemical properties such as pH and Eh also change significantly from one surface environment to another. We have already noted something of the chemistry of rock weathering. Here we concentrate on the same and additional processes particularly as they affect sedimentation and its ultimate products, the sedimentary rocks; but much of the discussion also has implications with regard to the processes of weathering (see Chapter 7).

EXPERIMENTAL APPROACH

The chemical and mineralogical reactions of the surface environment involve the solution and precipitation of mineral phases from aqueous solutions with wide ranges of salt concentration. Relative to the tenth-molal solution so common in the inorganic chemical laboratory, fresh river and lake waters are quite dilute, the oceans are rather concentrated, and many underground brines and waters of saline lakes in arid regions are highly concentrated solutions. All such solutions may be in equilibrium with atmospheric oxygen and carbon dioxide; or, where water motion is restricted, and particularly in the upper layers of a sediment, the concentration of these important constituents may be extremely variable. A controlling influence on such variation may be exerted by activity of organisms.

The surface environment is rather easily duplicated in the laboratory; and we can also make direct field measurements of controlling chemical parameters—composition, pH, oxidation–reduction potentials. Moreover, the very common laboratory standard conditions of 25°C and one atmosphere pressure are close to natural surface conditions, and hence the cumulative data of inorganic chemistry may be applied to the environment of the earth's surface. Classic collections of relevant data of this kind for aqueous systems, such as Latimer's *The Oxidation States of the Elements and Their Potentials in Aqueous Solutions* (see references) are readily available. In recent years they have been extended to systems of special geochemical interest, particularly by Garrels and his colleagues.

As with all geochemical systems we are concerned with knowing to what extent reactions in the air–water–rock system represent a close approach to equilibrium or alternatively are rate-controlled. As we shall see subsequently, many constituents of the oceans are in approximate equilibrium with solid phases in marine sediments. But there is also convincing evidence for extensive disequilibrium; furthermore, many cases of such "inorganic" disequilibrium are related to biological activity. Although seawater is significantly undersaturated in SiO_2, silica precipitation by organisms forms massive chert deposits, which would totally dissolve if equilibrium prevailed. Organisms can precipitate a phase from a solution undersaturated with respect to that phase. Under surface conditions, calcite is the stable form of $CaCO_3$. Aragonite, a polymorph, requires pressures of more than 3 kb to be stable relative to calcite at surface temperatures. Yet marine organisms readily precipitate aragonite, calcite, or both forms in their skeletons. We now understand a little of this process. In the oceans, rates of nucleation and growth of aragonite are favored relative to the same processes for calcite. The main factor influencing this preference is the magnesium-ion concentration. This ion is absorbed on potential growth sites of calcite nucleii and so prevents further growth.

When the concentrations of Mg^{2+}, Ca^{2+} and CO_3^{2-} in the oceans are compared with the solubility of dolomite $[CaMg(CO_3)_2]$ it is apparent that the oceans are oversaturated with respect to this phase. It does not precipitate in the modern oceans and again it seems that formation of dolomite is slow because of adsorption of Mg^{2+} on growth sites. Most dolomite of sedimentary rocks forms at some later stage during diagenesis.

It is perhaps only in recent years that we have begun to appreciate the large influence of the "biomass" in mineral precipitation. But this influence is apparent when one recognizes that many enormous calcareous deposits, for example those that make up whole mountain ranges in European calcareous Alps, were formed largely from materials generated inside living cells.

In large part, experimental sedimentary geochemistry is concerned with accumulating thermodynamic data on the species in natural aqueous solutions and the crystalline phases of sediments. The reactions that occur can then be considered in relation to local environmental variations of factors that control solubilities, oxidation states, and rate processes. The salient problems in aqueous geochemistry involve exact expression of the chemical potential of dissolved ions over a wide range of concentrations, and exact knowledge of the type of chemical entities —ions and ionic complexes—present in these complex solutions. Although theories of such solutions are advanced, they are still inadequate for many of our purposes. We must still make direct measurements, particularly in concentrated solutions. Further, we are only beginning to understand the factors that control mineral formation in living organisms. Before we can fully use minerals to interpret the sedimentary environment we must understand the interplay of equilibrium rates and biological processes. Because the relative significance of these factors is still imperfectly understood, it is still difficult to evaluate rival hypotheses that have been proposed to account for such global phenomena as the accumulation of vast deposits of ferric oxide in sediments laid down in Precambrian seas.

THE ROCK–WATER–AIR–LIFE SYSTEM

On the earth's surface we directly observe a vast array of processes involving the interaction of rocks with water and air. Some of those are essentially processes of transport driven by gravitational and solar energy. But at almost all times, chemical interaction between rock, water, and air is either dominant or essential. Even when a grain of feldspar is transported by wind or water, the first step may have been solution along a grain boundary which separated the grain from its host rock; and the reactivity of that solution may have been increased by organic matter from plants growing on the rock.

Some mineral-forming processes in the surface aqueous environment are obviously inorganic in nature—for instance, the formation of a salt deposit by solar evaporation of an isolated body of seawater. In other cases minerals form within the organic matrix of an organism, and the influence of what Lowenstam calls the biomass is today recognized as having a very large part in mineral synthesis. The energy and membrane systems of the organism may provide local conditions for crystal growth by concentrating and changing the chemistry of solutions exterior to the organism. Thus organisms play a vital part in the formation of many sedimentary products, such as soils, limestones, and coal, and of petroleum and gaseous hydrocarbons impregnating some porous rocks.

Since surface processes involve an environment we can observe directly, (even the deep ocean is becoming increasingly accessible), and since this environment is similar to that of the standard chemical laboratory, our understanding or description of sedimentary processes is, or can be in some respects, exact. We note, however, that since the rate of a chemical reaction normally increases with rising temperature, processes in the cool sedimentary environment may be slow. We need not be surprised, therefore, to find that chemical equilibrium is not always attained and that the end products from the system are in many instances controlled by reaction rates. Almost all igneous and metamorphic rocks on the earth's surface contain iron in the form of magnetite and ferrous silicates. Most of these minerals are unstable on the surface because of the high partial pressure of oxygen in the atmosphere; magnetite should form hematite. This process does occur to some extent in nature, but the rate at which oxygen is produced biologically is more rapid than the rate of subtraction during oxidation of almost infinite existing quantities of ferrous iron. If hydration reactions were rapid, most minerals of igneous and metamorphic rocks would not survive in sediments but would be replaced by highly hydrated minerals such as clays, chlorites, and zeolites. In the massive graywacke deposits of marginal geosynclines, rather unaltered volcanic debris is the dominant material making up the sediments. The sea is not saturated with silica. In seawater in equilibrium with quartz, the silica concentration would be about five times that observed. Yet organisms (diatoms and radiolaria) are able to precipitate almost amorphous, and hence highly soluble, forms of silica from seawater. Some organisms precipitate magnetite instead of the stable oxidized form of iron oxide at surface conditions, but this Fe_3O_4 is precipitated internally within the organism. We could extend this list almost infinitely; but these examples suffice to show that the sedimentary environment is one where rate processes, biologically controlled or otherwise, play a significant role.

CHEMICAL POTENTIALS IN AQUEOUS SOLUTIONS

The nature of the chemical species present in low-temperature aqueous solutions is well understood. Ions, both simple and complex, dominate inorganic mineral solutions. Gases such as CO_2 and O_2 are present as simple or hydrated molecules.

In general, the chemical potential of a species i is described by the equation

$$\mu_i = \mu_i^0 + RT \ln a_i$$

where a_i is the "activity of i." The form of this equation is similar to that for solid solutions (Chapter 5). The activity a is normally related to the molal concentration m_i (moles per thousand grams of water) by the relation

$$a_i = \gamma_i m_i$$

where γ_i is the "activity coefficient." The activity coefficient is defined operationally by the convention:

$$\gamma_i \to 1 \quad \text{as} \quad m_i \to 0$$

Thus in very dilute solutions $a_i \simeq m_i$ and in some geological systems such as most rivers this approximation is adequate. This is not true for ionic species in the oceans and other more concentrated solutions. In these, γ_i must be either measured directly or estimated theoretically. One relation, derived by Debye and Hückel, frequently used to calculate the activity coefficients of ions is:

$$-\log \gamma_i = \frac{Az_i^2 \sqrt{I}}{1 + a_i^0 B \sqrt{I}}$$

where A and B are constants dependent only on the solvent, a_i^0 is a parameter dependent on the size of the ion, z_i is its charge, and I is the ionic strength of the solution, defined as

$$I = \frac{1}{2} \sum^i m_i z_i^2$$

In dilute solutions the equation reduces to

$$-\log \gamma_i = Az_i^2 \sqrt{I}$$

As I approaches zero, γ approaches unity. At larger values of I, γ is less than unity by an amount that increases with increasing charge. When the activity coefficients of simple salts like NaCl are measured in solution, the mean values for cation and anion are obtained. Some values are given in Table 8–1, which indicates the limitations of the common assumption that $a_i \simeq m_i$.

Activity coefficients of neutral entities in solution normally are close to unity. The chemical potential of a simple gaseous component such as O_2 or CO_2, at sufficiently low pressure, can be expressed as

$$\mu_i = \mu_i^0 + RT \ln P_i$$

where P_i is the partial pressure of i in the gas.

TABLE 8–1 *Mean activity coefficients* of some strong electolytes for different molal concentrations m_1 in aqueous solution (25°C)*

m_1:	0.001	0.002	0.005	0.01	0.02	0.05	0.1	0.2	0.5	1.0
HCl	0.966	0.952	0.928	0.904	0.875	0.830	0.796	0.767	0.758	0.809
NaOH	—	—	—	—	—	0.82	—	0.73	0.69	0.68
$CaCl_2$	0.89	0.85	0.785	0.725	0.66	0.57	0.515	0.48	0.52	0.71
KCl	0.965	0.952	0.927	0.901	—	0.815	0.769	0.719	0.651	0.606
$MgSO_4$	—	—	—	0.40	0.32	0.22	0.18	0.13	0.088	0.064
NaCl	0.966	0.953	0.929	0.904	0.875	0.823	0.780	0.730	0.68	0.66
$ZnCl_2$	0.88	0.84	0.77	0.71	0.64	0.56	0.50	0.45	0.38	0.33

* The mean activity coefficient of an electrolyte, often noted $\gamma^{\pm}$, is defined as

$$\gamma^{\pm} = (\gamma_+ \gamma_-)^{1/2}$$

where γ_+ and γ_- are the activity coefficients of the univalent cation and anion, respectively.

SOLUBILITY

All minerals have a definite solubility in water; and on this depend the complementary processes of solution (in weathering) and precipitation in sediments or soils. Solubility, or equilibrium between a solid and a solution, can be described by an equilibrium constant K, called a "solubility product." Thus if calcite dissolves in water,

$$CaCO_3 = \underset{\text{aqueous}}{Ca^{2+}} + \underset{\text{aqueous}}{CO_3^{2-}}$$

equilibrium requires that

$$\mu_{CaCO_3}^0 = \mu_{Ca^{2+}} + \mu_{CO_3^{2-}}$$
$$= \mu_{Ca^{2+}}^0 + RT \ln a_{Ca^{2+}} + \mu_{CO_3^{2-}}^0 + RT \ln a_{CO_3^{2-}}$$

Hence, if

$$\Delta\mu^0 = \mu_{Ca^{2+}}^0 + \mu_{CO_3^{2-}}^0 - \mu_{CaCO_3}^0$$
$$-\Delta\mu^0 = RT \ln (a_{Ca^{2+}})(a_{CO_3^{2-}})$$

The solubility product K is defined as

$$K = [Ca^{2+}][CO_3^{2-}]$$

where brackets represent activity. Hence

$$-\Delta\mu^0 = RT \ln K$$

and since $\Delta\mu^0$ is constant at constant T and P, so is K.

Solution is either congruent, as with NaCl, $CaCO_3$, SiO_2, or incongruent, as with almost all metal silicates. Solution is said to be congruent when the mineral dissolves as an entity; with incongruent solution a new solid phase forms simultaneously and the ratio of atoms in the solution is not that of the parent solid. Thus a mineral such as $KAlSi_3O_8$ (orthoclase) dissolves to form a solution enriched in K and Si and a solid phase—a clay mineral—forms. The reaction can be written

$$4KAlSi_3O_8 + 22H_2O \rightarrow 4K^+ + 4OH^-$$
$$+ \underset{\text{solution}}{8Si(OH)_4} + \underset{\text{solid}}{Al_4Si_4O_{10}(OH)_8}$$

Reesman and Keller dissolved an Na-K feldspar in water at room temperature and found K = 0.000993, Na = 0.000757, Al = 0.0000319, Si = 0.000264, and $OH^- = 10^{-6}$ moles liter^{-1}. The imbalance in constituents will be noted; and, because the solution is in equilibrium with the CO_2 of the air, the dominant species in solution will be Na-K bicarbonates. Because silicates are salts of a weak acid and stronger bases, the solubility of most silicates will be a function of pH and hence will be affected by the local CO_2 concentration. They will also tend to be pH buffers.

Incongruent solution leads to a process of great importance in weathering and in some aspects of ore formation. If water flows slowly over a feldspar, eventually some form of clay mineral will form. Under favorable conditions of high pH the clay itself dissolves incongruently via a process such as:

$$Al_4Si_4O_{10}(OH)_8 \rightarrow \underset{\text{solid}}{Al(OH)_3} + \underset{\text{solution}}{Si(OH)_4}$$

and solid $Al(OH)_3$ (gibbsite) may be formed. This type of reaction controls the formation of a lateritic soil in which hydrated oxides of aluminum and iron are concentrated rather than clay silicates (Chapter 7). During weathering, soluble constituents become leached out and transported far from the parent material. The formation of an aluminum deposit of bauxite (a rather indefinite mixture of hydrated Al oxides) by the above processes is a spectacular example of natural purification, in the course of which aluminum of rock-forming silicates becomes concentrated into an economically workable ore.

The range of possible clay minerals and oxide phases that may result from the incongruent leaching of the silicate minerals of igneous and metamorphic rocks is formidable. Most minerals rich in iron (pyroxenes, amphiboles, olivines) will tend to produce amorphous or crystalline oxides of Ti-Fe-Al and silica, which may later be incorporated into clay minerals. Micas react to produce an array of complex layer silicates intermediate between simple clays and the micas themselves. Feldspars produce clays in a variety of partially crystalline forms.

CONTROLLING FACTORS   Most minerals such as silicates, carbonates, and sulfides are compounds of weak acids. Their solutions will be alkaline. For example, solution of calcium carbonate in water may be considered to proceed via the steps:

$$CaCO_3 \rightarrow Ca^{2+} + CO_3^{2-}$$
$$CO_3^{2-} + H_2O \rightarrow HCO_3^- + OH^-$$
$$HCO_3^- + H_2O \rightarrow H_2CO_3 + OH^-$$

Sulfides will follow a strictly analogous pattern. Obviously, the solubility depends on pH and P_{CO_2} (P_{H_2S} with sulfides). The required constancy of the solubility product,

$$(a_{Ca^{2+}})(a_{CO_3^{2-}}) \text{ or } (m_{Ca^{2+}})(m_{CO_3^{2-}})(\gamma_{Ca^{2+}})(\gamma_{CO_3^{2-}})$$

indicates that any species in solution that decrease the γ terms will increase the m terms or the solubility. All salts increase the ionic strength

and diminish the γ values, and hence $CaCO_3$ will be more soluble in an NaCl solution than in pure water. If no ions are formed, as with quartz solution, presence of electrolytes will cause a small decrease in solubility by locking up some of the solvent on the hydrated ions.

The activity of many ions in solution may be decreased (and hence solubility increased) by formation of complex ions. Typical complex ions include

$$Ag^+ + 2Cl^- \rightarrow AgCl_2^-$$
$$Pb^{2+} + HS^- \rightarrow PbHS^+$$
$$Ag^+ + 2NH_3 \rightarrow Ag(NH_3)_2^+$$
$$Ca^{2+} + CO_3^{2-} \rightarrow \underset{\text{solution}}{CaCO_3}$$

It is becoming increasingly recognized that such complexes play a very large part in determining the levels of concentration of elements in the oceans. Thus, in seawater, about 50 percent of the sulfate ions are tied up in metal complexes; and this is true also for about 90 percent of the carbonate ions, aqueous $MgCO_3$ being the dominant complex. In some natural brines, even ions like Na^+ are present to a large extent as complexes with CO_3^{2-} and HCO_3^-. Any exact study of solubility must thus take account of such possible complexing and ionic strength influences.

PRECIPITATION   Precipitation may occur when concentration is such that the solubility product is exceeded. The nucleation and growth of a solid from solution is often a difficult and slow process (Chapter 5), and so crystals may be reluctant to form even from supersaturated solutions. Nucleation tends to occur preferentially on some existing surface; for example, clay particles commonly form on a feldspar crystal, and in general such surface phases have a characteristic orientation with respect to the structure of the parent crystal. Structurally complex compounds, such as clay minerals, may at first be poorly crystalline or semiamorphous. During later diagenesis or heating, a more perfect crystalline structure may develop.

One of the most remarkable findings of recent years is the number of minerals present in the skeletons of animals. The subject has been summarized by Lowenstam (Table 8–2). Again it should be noted that some of the listed minerals are metastable with respect to the environment exterior to the animal; but it is not certain whether or not this is true with respect to the fluids inside the cell membrane.

Many fine-scale features of sedimentary minerals can provide useful data on the nature of the environment. In general when a given mineral forms from solution, its composition depends on that of the fluid and on the temperature. (Pre-

cipitation within an organism may be directly influenced by the specific biochemistry of the organism itself.) For example, the oxygen isotope composition of carbonates depends on the O^{18}/O^{16} ratio of the water and on the temperature. Thus in favorable cases it is possible to compute ancient temperatures and temperature fluctuations from the isotopic composition of oxygen in carbonates of fossil skeletons and shells. Some difficulties arise however from differences in isotope ratios between water in various environ-

TABLE 8–2   Distribution of mineral species in organisms (after Lowenstam)

	Algae	Protozoa	Porifera	Coelenterata	Bryozoa	Brachiopoda	Annelida	Mollusca	Arthropoda	Echinodermata	Hemichordata	Chordata
Carbonates												
Aragonite (Ca)	+	+		+	+		+	+	+		+	+
Calcite (Ca)	+	+	+	+	+	+	+	+	+	+		
Aragonite and calcite			?	+	+		+	+	+			
"Amorphous"					+		+	+				
Silicates												
"Opaline"	+	+	+					?				
Phosphates												
Hydroxyapatite (Ca)						+						+
Undefined								+	+			
+ Calcite									+			
Oxides of iron												
Magnetite								+				
Goethite								+				
Magnetite and goethite								+				
Amorphous			+					+				
+ Aragonite								+				
Sulfates												
Celestite (Sr)		+										
Barite (Ba)		?										

ments. Relative to normal ocean water, fresh waters have more O^{16} and very saline waters more O^{18}. Clearly this factor must be taken into account in any such computation of ancient temperature.

The magnesium content of the $CaCO_3$ precipitated by organisms is affected by the nature of the living species, and by the temperature and salinity of the water. The same is true for strontium content. The calcite/aragonite ratio in skeletons of some species depends on temperature and salinity; and this may be true for the nature of iron oxide phases. Any study of such factors must be considered in relation to possible postdepositional changes. But while admitting that the subject is still in its infancy, geochemists believe that reasonable deductions regarding paleotemperatures and paleosalinities are possible provided the influence of complicating factors is screened out. Perhaps the major conclusion from such studies is that over the last few hundred million years the oceanic environment has not changed much.

OXIDATION–REDUCTION

Changes in the oxidation states of elements during surface processes is another significant factor in sedimentation, as well as in weathering. The deeper portions of the earth tend to be in a reduced state. The surface, because it is in contact with atmospheric oxygen, is relatively oxidized. Oxidizing processes at the surface are of several types, for example:

$$2Fe_3O_4 + \tfrac{1}{2}O_2 \rightarrow 3Fe_2O_3$$
$$\text{solid} \qquad\qquad\qquad \text{solid}$$
$$Fe_2SiO_4 + \tfrac{1}{2}O_2 \rightarrow Fe_2O_3 + SiO_2$$
$$\text{solid} \quad\; \text{aq} \qquad\quad \text{solid} \quad \text{solution}$$
$$4Fe^{2+} + O_2 + 4H^+ \rightarrow 4Fe^{3+} + 2H_2O$$
$$\text{aq} \qquad\; \text{aq} \qquad\quad \text{aq}$$
$$4Fe^{2+} + O_2 + 10H_2O \rightarrow 4Fe(OH)_3 + 8H^+$$
$$\text{solid}$$

The state of equilibrium of any such reaction can be found in the usual manner if free-energy values are available for all chemical species. It will be noted that equilibrium depends on P_{O_2}, a_{cations} and pH_{solution}.

Let us consider a specific problem. It is well known that manganese hydrates and oxides $MnOOH$ and MnO_2 are precipitated on the ocean floor. Most of the manganese in igneous and metamorphic rocks is in lower oxidation states (Mn^{2+} and Mn^{3+}), and the ocean is known to contain Mn^{2+} at a concentration of about 4×10^{-8} molal. Would we expect precipitation of an oxide with trivalent or tetravalent manganese such as actually occurs?

We can write the reaction

$$4Mn^{2+} + O_2 + 6H_2O \rightarrow 4MnOOH + 8H^+$$
$$\text{aq} \qquad \text{gas} \qquad\qquad\qquad \text{solid}$$

Thermodynamically, at equilibrium

$$4\mu^0_{Mn^{2+}} + 4RT \ln m_{Mn^{2+}} + \mu^0_{O_2} + RT \ln P_{O_2}$$
$$+ 6\mu^0_{H_2O} = 4\mu^0_{MnOOH} + 8\mu^0_{H^+} + 8RT \ln m_{H^+}$$

If we assume that the pH value for ocean water is about 8, P_{O_2} is one bar, and the activity of water is one, we calculate from known standard chemical potentials a Mn^{2+} molality of near 3×10^{-12}, much less than measured in the ocean. It is thus no surprise that an oxide precipitates; but when such low concentrations are involved, there could be problems connected with attainment of equilibrium. It should be noted that changing P_{O_2} to its atmospheric value of about 0.2 bars will hardly affect this result.

While all equilibrium oxidation–reduction problems can be approached in the foregoing direct manner, there is another commonly used method based on standard methods of electrochemical measurement in ionic systems. If a copper electrode is placed in a solution containing cupric ions, Cu^{2+}, it will develop a potential given by the equation

$$E = E^0 + \frac{RT}{nF} \ln a_{Cu^{2+}}$$

where F is the Faraday constant (23.1 kcal/volt) and n the number of electrons involved in the reaction. This equation refers to the potential of the half-cell reaction

$$Cu^{2+} + 2e \rightarrow Cu$$

E^0 obviously refers to a standard potential when

$a_{Cu^{2+}}$ = unity. All such potentials are arbitrarily referred to the hydrogen electrode reaction

$$2H^+ + 2e \rightarrow H_2 \qquad E^0 = 0$$

This convention is necessary because a single electrode potential cannot be measured. An electrode sensitive to hydrogen ions (commonly the glass electrode) measures a_{H^+} or pH. The standard electrode potential of a reaction is related to the standard free energy change by the following relation[1]

$$\Delta G^0 = nFE^0$$

There are some electrodes that measure so-called oxidation potentials. Thus if a strip of smooth platinum is placed in a solution of ferrous (Fe^{2+}) and ferric (Fe^{3+}) ions, it develops a potential described by the equation

$$E = E^0 + \frac{RT}{F} \ln \frac{[Fe^{3+}]}{[Fe^{2+}]}$$

or, in general,

$$E = E^0 + \frac{RT}{nF} \ln \frac{[x]^a}{[y]^b}$$

where x and y stand for the oxidized and reduced species, respectively, a and b are stoichiometric coefficients, and n is the number of transferred electrons. It has become conventional in recent years to refer to this potential E by the symbol Eh.

Since E and ΔG are simply related, instead of discussing ΔG values one can directly use values of Eh. Consider the following type of question. Will ferrous ions at unit activity in a solution of $pH = 1$ be oxidized to ferric ions by atmospheric oxygen? The reaction is

$$4Fe^{2+} + O_2 + 4H^+ \rightarrow 4Fe^{3+} + 2H_2O$$

and can be broken into the parts

$$Fe^{2+} \rightarrow Fe^{3+} + e \qquad E^0 = +0.771$$

and

---

[1]Most texts of physical chemistry follow the convention $\Delta G^0 = -nFE^0$ and all E^0's are reversed in sign. We shall here adopt the convention of Garrels and Christ.

$$2H_2O = O_2 + 4H^+ + 4e \qquad E^0 = +1.229$$

Noting the relation $\Delta G^0 = nFE^0$, we have for the overall reaction

$$\Delta G^0 = +4 \times 0.771 - 4 \times 1.229 < 0$$

The reaction can proceed spontaneously from left to right. Clearly by examining half-cell potentials, it is possible to see whether oxidation or reduction can occur.

Given a value of E^0, it is a simple matter to calculate Eh values for any chemical situation and in particular variation with pH. Consider, for example, the half-reaction

$$2H_2O = O_2 + 4H^+ + 4e \qquad E^0 = 1.229$$

This E^0 refers to water and hydrogen ions at unit activity and a partial pressure of oxygen $P_{O_2} = 1$ bar. In general

$$Eh = E^0 + \frac{RT}{4F} \ln P_{O_2} [H^+]^4$$

Thus, if $pH = 7$ and $P_{O_2} = 1$,

$$Eh = 1.229 + \frac{0.05916}{4} \log (10^{-28})$$

$$= 1.229 - 0.414 = 0.815$$

It may be noted that small changes in P_{O_2} have little influence on the Eh value. For example, if we substitute $P_{O_2} = 10^{-2}$ bar, this will change Eh by only $-(0.05916/4) \log 10^{-2}$, or 0.03 volt. The stability of ions in any redox system such as Fe^{2+}–Fe^{3+} depends on solvent chemistry, P_{O_2}, the nature of solid phases and in some cases the possible formation of complex ions. In natural systems, as opposed to many in the chemical laboratory, few complexing reagents are present in high enough concentrations to affect the situation drastically.

Stability of mineral phases in redox system can be represented graphically in what are called Eh-pH stability diagrams. These show Eh values for various reactions as a function of pH; and to construct them we need fundamental E^0 data and free energies of all solid phases. Separate diagrams may be constructed for various specified concentrations and chemistry (for example, presence of carbonates, sulfide, and so forth).

The diagram for the iron system as computed by Garrels and Christ is shown in Figure 8–1.

The range of Eh-pH conditions measured in natural surface environments is summarized in Figure 8–2. Very acid and highly reducing conditions (low Eh) are generally associated with organic activity. Bacteria may cause reduction of sulfates and may even liberate hydrogen. Another useful diagram, Figure 8–3, summarizes Eh-pH conditions related to the formation of common sedimentary minerals and to preservation of organic matter. When natural systems are considered it must be constantly borne in mind that many reactions involved are very slow.

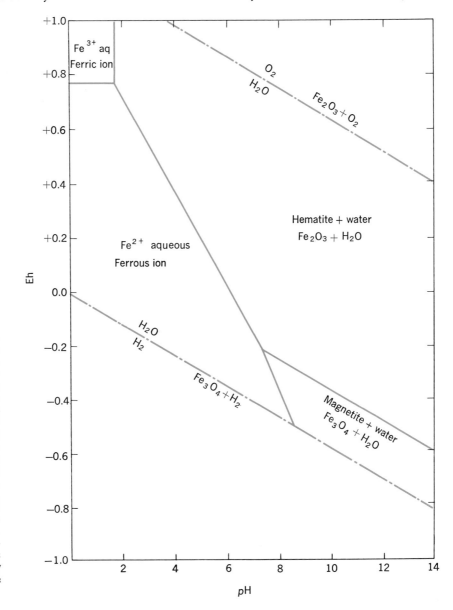

FIG. 8–1 An Eh-pH diagram for the iron system showing fields of stability of major species. For aqueous ions, boundaries are drawn for concentrations $> 10^{-6}$ molar. The upper and lower lines of the diagram represent regions where H_2O is unstable with respect to breakdown to oxygen and hydrogen. (Figure 7–6, modified, from p. 195, Solutions, Minerals and Equilibria by R. M. Garrels and C. L. Christ. Copyright © 1965 by Robert M. Garrels and Charles L. Christ. Reproduced by permission of Harper & Row, Publishers, Inc.)

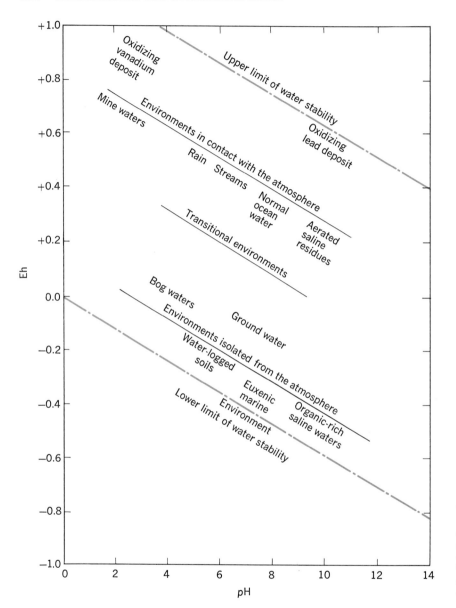

FIG. 8–2 *Eh-pH values of various natural environments. (Figure 11–2, redrawn, from p. 381, Solutions, Minerals and Equilibria by R. M. Garrels and C. L. Christ. Copyright © 1965 by Robert M. Garrels and Charles L. Christ. Reproduced by permission of Harper & Row, Publishers, Inc.)*

If on the contrary they were rapid enough to proceed to equilibrium, we would never find magnetite grains on a beach; yet beach concentrates of magnetite have survived in such quantity as to constitute valuable ores of iron. Nevertheless, in a general way, there is very good agreement between thermodynamic prediction and observation regarding oxidation states in environments of weathering and sedimentation.

ION EXCHANGE, COLLOIDS, AND ADSORPTION

Although the processes of incongruent solution, precipitation, and oxidation–reduction may

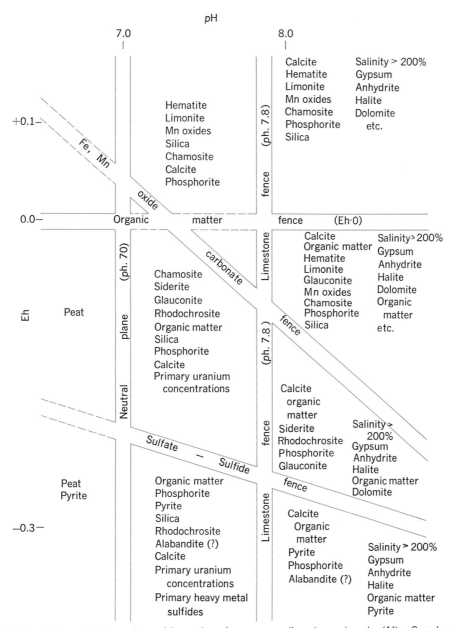

pH

7.0   8.0

+0.1—

Fe, Mn

oxide

0.0—   Organic   matter

carbonate

Eh   Peat

Neutral plane   (ph. 70)

Sulfate — Sulfide

(ph. 7.8)

fence

Limestone   fence   (Eh·0)

(ph. 7.8)

fence

Limestone

fence

−0.3—

Hematite
Limonite
Mn oxides
Silica
Chamosite
Calcite
Phosphorite

Calcite   Salinity > 200%
Hematite   Gypsum
Limonite   Anhydrite
Mn oxides   Halite
Chamosite   Dolomite
Phosphorite   etc.
Silica

Chamosite
Siderite
Glauconite
Rhodochrosite
Organic matter
Silica
Phosphorite
Calcite
Primary uranium
    concentrations

Calcite   Salinity> 200%
Organic matter Gypsum
Hematite   Anhydrite
Limonite   Halite
Glauconite   Dolomite
Mn oxides   Organic
Chamosite   matter
Phosphorite   etc.
Silica

Calcite
organic
matter
Siderite   Salinity >
Rhodochrosite   200%
Phosphorite   Gypsum
Glauconite   Anhydrite
                Halite
                Organic matter
                Dolomite

Peat   Organic matter
Pyrite   Phosphorite
          Pyrite
          Silica
          Rhodochrosite
          Alabandite (?)
          Calcite
          Primary uranium
             concentrations
          Primary heavy metal
             sulfides

Calcite
Organic
matter
Pyrite
Phosphorite
Alabandite (?)

Salinity > 200%
Gypsum
Anhydrite
Halite
Organic matter
Pyrite

FIG. 8–3 *Relation of Eh and pH to regions of formation of common sedimentary minerals. (After Garrels and Christ.)*

dominate chemical reactions in environments of sedimentation and weathering, important roles are also played by other more subtle reactions.

Atoms on the surface of a crystal cannot have their valence forces satisfied as neatly as do the same ions in the crystal interior. Thus in a crystal of halite, $NaCl$ (Figure 2–56) in which both Na^+ and Cl^- are in sixfold coordination, ions located on a planar external surface are in five-coordination, while those located on an external edge are in four-coordination. These surface and edge ions can thus interact strongly with atoms in the surrounding solution. Therefore on a crystal surface there are forces that tend to bind or adsorb a layer of polar molecules or ions if such are present in a surrounding solution, and obviously the capacity for adsorption must be roughly proportional to surface area—that is, inversely proportional to grain size.

Consider a crystal M^+X^- in contact with a solution of other cations and anions, so that there is a chance for ionic exchange in which ions drawn from the solution replace some ions on the crystal surface. If the crystal has a very open structure, and if ions can diffuse easily through the entire crystal, the exchange may become extensive. This is the case for many open zeolite structures, and for many clay minerals (Chapter 2). The compositions of such minerals may thus become strongly modified when placed in a solution of different chemical composition.

Adsorption and ion exchange may merge when particles are very small; both processes become most effective when the sediment contains a mineral in a very finely divided state. Fine-grained material, in accordance with Stokes' law, may resist precipitation. Very fine particles (10^{-5}–10^{-7}cm) of "colloidal" size may even show Brownian motion and behave almost like large molecules. Small particles, because the ratio of surface or distorted sites to normal crystal sites is large, may be abnormally chemically reactive, and significantly unstable with respect to larger crystals of the same compound.

Two problems arise: How do colloidal particles form in nature and how stable are such particles? It is relatively easy to produce colloids in a laboratory by suitable grinding or by precipitation from highly supersaturated media. How much colloidal material can be produced in nature by grinding is uncertain; but in the environment of rock weathering, high supersaturations conducive to separation of colloids are common. For example, consider weathering of a ferrous silicate from an igneous rock, in the oxidizing surface aqueous environment:

$$Fe_2SiO_4 + \tfrac{1}{2}O_2 + 2H_2O \rightarrow \underset{\text{solid}}{Fe_2O_3} + \underset{\text{solution}}{Si(OH)_4}$$

$$\Delta G^0 = -44 \, \text{kcal}$$

The negative free energy of reaction is very high. It implies the possibility of related reactions of somewhat lower but still high $-\Delta G$, leading to metastable products. Such would be colloidal Fe_2O_3 or some hydrated form of this oxide in equilibrium (metastable) with a solution supersaturated with respect to crystalline Fe_2O_3. The same is true for formation of clay minerals from feldspar. In general we conclude that where rates of crystallization and crystal growth of phases formed by weathering are slow, there is a possibility that these may separate as very fine-grained particles. It is not surprising therefore that the silica content of stream waters is higher than that for equilibrium with crystalline quartz, or that these waters may contain appreciable colloidal $Fe(OH)_3$.

Colloidal particles normally are electrically charged because of surface ionization. Thus ferric hydroxide colloids are normally positive and silica colloids are negatively charged. The stability of the particle depends on a number of factors—organic protection, salinity, temperature, and so on—but the exact operation of these factors with natural colloids is still but little understood.

Adsorption phenomena play important roles in geochemical separation of initially associated elements. Sodium and potassium are present in roughly equal quantity in crustal rocks and they tend to be mutually associated. Both are leached in solution as cations (Na^+ and K^+) during weathering and so are transported via streams to the sea. The Na^+ content of seawater is 10 grams per liter; that of K^+ is less than 0.4 g/l. The explanation of this seeming anomaly is simple: The large K^+ ion is much more readily adsorbed on fine-grained marine clays than are Na^+ ions. If a metal forms colloidal oxides it may become separated from a closely associated element that does not. Iron and silicon initially combined in a silicate mineral may become separated because the one is transported by stream waters as colloidal $Fe(OH)_3$, the other as silicate ions in true solution. Clear distinction cannot always be made between adsorption processes and formation of compounds, particularly if the latter are fine-grained or semi-amorphous.

CHEMISTRY OF NATURAL WATERS

The oceans dominate the hydrosphere; but the salts of the oceans or the constituents continuously added to the oceans come from streams, ground waters, and phenomena associated with volcanism and the degassing of the earth (Chapter 6). Either ocean or fresh water may become concentrated by solar evaporation to give highly saline waters and eventually salt deposits. Some idea of the importance of solution processes may be gained from Krauskopf's estimate that the land surface is lowered on the average by one centimeter per 1000 years by solution processes alone.

RIVER (STREAM) WATERS   River waters, though variable, have an average composition in which the major cations are Ca^{2+}, Na^+, Mg^{2+}, K^+ and anions HCO_3^-, SO_4^{2-}, Cl^- (Table 7–1). Contrast this with the totally different composition of ocean waters (Table 8–3). The silica concentration in river waters is a little higher than that in equilibrium with quartz (about 10 ppm). Much of the chloride in these waters may be derived via wind and rain from the sea. This may be partly true also for sulfate which otherwise could be derived from sulfides by oxidation.

Garrels has shown that the composition of ground waters in contact with various types of igneous rocks closely approaches equilibrium corresponding to reactions between the plagioclase feldspars and CO_2-rich waters. Because of organic activity the bicarbonate concentration of many ground and soil waters is much enriched relative to atmospheric partial pressure of CO_2. Thus effective values of P_{CO_2} may be as high as 1 bar. The chemistry of the waters can be understood in terms of reactions such as:

$$2NaAlSi_3O_8 + 2CO_2 + 3H_2O \rightarrow Al_2Si_2O_5(OH)_4$$
$$\text{albite} \qquad\qquad\qquad\qquad \text{clay}$$
$$+ 2Na^+ + 2HCO_3^- + 4SiO_2$$

The Na:Ca ratio of ground water depends on the type of plagioclase with which it is in contact. Garrels concludes that plagioclase and minerals such as biotite, pyroxene, and hornblende provide most of the dissolved ions. Potassium feldspars and silica are more slowly attacked. Typical ground waters from igneous rocks have SiO_2 in the range 20–60 ppm; waters from basic rocks have $Ca^{2+} > Na^+$ and high Mg^{2+} concentrations. These values agree with what would be expected from dominant weathering of plagioclase and ferromagnesian minerals.

OCEAN WATER   *General composition*   The total concentration of dissolved solids in seawater is subject to some variation, especially among surface samples. It has a mean value close to 3.5 percent, but reaches as much as 4 percent in partially enclosed seas in areas of high evaporation, such as the Red Sea. Regardless of the location of water samples, the major elements in sea salt maintain a remarkably constant ratio, the order of abundance being Cl, Na, Mg, S, Ca, K, Br, and C (Table 8–3). Most elements have been detected in seawater; in Table 8–3 we list only a few of the minor constituents to which reference is made in the text.

Most of the dissolved material is in the form of simple ions or cation–anion complexes. The principal cations, in order of abundance are Na^+, Mg^{2+}, Ca^{2+}, K^+; the principal anions Cl^-, SO_4^{2-}, HCO_3^-. Virtually all the sodium, potassium and chlorine are in the form of simple ions. However undissociated complexes such as $MgSO_4$ (11 percent of total Mg) and $CaSO_4$ (8 percent of total Ca) account for much of the sulfate ion. About 90 percent of the bicarbonate ion is tied into metallic complexes, $CaHCO_3^+$, $MgHCO_3$ and $NaHCO_3$; and there is some carbonate, most of it similarly combined as $CaCO_3$, $MgCO_3$ and Na_2CO_3.

Residence times   The computed mass of the ocean waters is 1.417×10^{21} kg; and runoff from the continents as river water contributes 3.333×10^{16} kg annually. At the present rate of influx, assuming no withdrawal by evaporation or other means, this would fill the ocean basins to their

TABLE 8–3 *Concentrations and related figures for major and a few minor elements in ocean waters* as compared with river waters†*

Element	Concentration in Ocean Water, 10^{-6} g/g	Concentration in River Water, 10^{-6} g/g	Residence Time, 10^6 years	Number of Renewal Cycles in 100×10^6 Years
Li	0.17			
B	4.6	0.013	15	7
C	28	11.5	0.1	1,000
N	0.5			
F	1.3			
Na	10,500	6.3	71	1.4
Mg	1,350	4.1	14	7
Al	0.01			
Si	3.0	6.1	0.02	5,000
P	0.07			
S	885	3.7	10	10
Cl	19,000	7.8	104	1
K	380	2.3	7	15
Ca	400	15	1.15	87
Mn	0.002	.02	0.004	25,000
Fe	0.01	0.7	0.006	20,000
Ni	0.002	0.01	0.008	10,000
Br	65	0.006–0.019	450–150	0.2–0.6
Rb	0.12			
Sr	8.0	0.09	3.8	25
Ag	0.00004	0.001	0.02	5,000
I	0.06			
Ba	0.03	0.054	0.02	5,000
Pb	0.00003	0.005	0.0003	300,000
Th	0.00005			
U	0.003	0.001	0.14	700

* B. Mason, *Principles of Geochemistry* (Wiley, 1966, p. 195).
† D. A. Livingstone (*U.S. Geol. Survey Prof. Paper 440-G*, 1963).

present volume in 4.45×10^4 years—a period called the *residence time* of ocean water. If, on the other hand, we make the assumption that the volume of ocean waters has remained constant for the past 100 million years, then ocean water has been completely recycled, via the atmosphere, to the continents and back many times during this period—that is, $10^8/(4.45 \times 10^4) = 2270$ times. This is the number of *renewal cycles* of oceanic water.

The concepts of residence time and renewal cycle have an artificial flavor. But, as we shall now see, they are useful parameters for visualizing the contrasted roles of many elements in weathering

and marine sedimentation. The composition of the dissolved load of river waters (Table 7–1), which reflects the chemistry of weathering, is markedly different from that of salts dissolved in ocean waters. These represent the residue that is left over from chemical sedimentation in the marine environment. Given the respective concentrations of an element in river water X_r and in the ocean X_o, a residence time t_o and a corresponding number of renewal cycles C_o for 100×10^6 years can be computed thus

$$t_o = \frac{X_o}{X_r} \times 0.0445 \times 10^6 \text{ years}$$

$$C_o = \frac{100}{t_o} \times 10^6 \text{ years}$$

The dissolved-salt content of seawater is some 300 times that of river water; so the mean residence time of sea salts is 12.75×10^6 years. Some computed values for various constituents (elements) of sea salts are listed in Table 8–3. Values for minor constituents, because corresponding data for river water are to varying degrees inadequate, are subject to considerable uncertainty. It is obvious, however, that the patterns of behavior of different elements in the weathering–sedimentation cycle cover a broad spectrum between two extremes:

1. The two most abundant elements, Cl and Na, have long residence times. They are continuously stored in the ocean, and their main contribution to marine sediments is as trapped water. Indeed, it was by reasoning along these lines, with the additional completely unrealistic assumption that rivers have supplied salts to the sea at the same rate as today throughout geologic time, that Joly in 1899 made his famous estimate of the age of the oceans as 90 million years. Today it is thought that most chloride and much sulfate of river waters has been derived from marine salt trapped in sedimentary rocks and is being recycled back to the ocean. Of the minor elements, Br is the outstanding example of ocean storing and correspondingly long residence time.

2. At the other extreme, among major elements, are C and Si. These are secreted as carbonates and silica in the skeletons of marine organisms and so are constantly being withdrawn from ocean water. Their residence times are low. So also are values for a number of minor elements that are very insoluble in brines rich in chloride and sulfate ions (among them, Pb and Ag) or are readily adsorbed on marine clays (Ba). Others again are subject to oxidation in seawater and in this state are simply precipitated (Mn) or adsorbed on clay (Fe).

Between the two extremes are elements whose behavior combines features of both, for instance, Ca and Mg. They are more or less in equilibrium with fairly soluble solid phases. Storage of K and B is limited by their capacity for adsorption on clays; storage of Sr by its capacity for substitution for Ca in carbonates.

Water and salts added to the ocean gradually become mixed at a rate that can now be estimated by radiocarbon measurements. It will be remembered that the half-life of C^{14}, produced in the upper atmosphere by cosmic-ray bombardment of N^{14}, is 5.6×10^3 years. The content of C^{14} in atmospheric carbon dioxide moving down and ultimately entering surface waters progressively diminishes. Thus it is possible to measure the time since a given portion of ocean was last in contact with the atmosphere. By such a method, mixing times of oceanic waters are found to be of the order of 10^3–10^4 years. If the residence time of an element is much longer than this mixing time, its concentration in ocean waters should be rather uniform. In a general way this is true for the major constituents of ocean water, but is not always true for minor elements. Thus Schutz and Turekian have found large variations (up to tenfold or more) in the concentrations of Co, Ni, and Ag in various parts of the oceans. Co and Ni have rather short residence times, but Ag does not. Problems of this type abound in chemical oceanography.

Incorporation of dissolved elements in sediments It is obvious that if most salts were not steadily removed from the oceans, enormous salt concentrations would soon be achieved. One of the major problems of ocean chemistry is to determine in what form a given element becomes incorporated in sediments. New phases crystallize (for example, zeolites, carbonates, sulfates, and Mn oxides with large amounts of Co and Ni), ions are adsorbed and exchanged with detrital clay minerals and micas; in many cases organisms induce the precipitation.

If a solution is in equilibrium with a given phase, then from solubility data we can set some limits on concentrations. For example, the concentration of the free sulfate ion in ocean water is about 0.015 molal and its activity coefficient is about 0.12. The solubility product of $BaSO_4$ is approximately 10^{-10}. We might thus expect the barium ion activity at equilibrium to be about 55×10^{-8} molal; the concentration would be significantly greater since in strongly ionic solutions such as seawater $\gamma_{Ba^{2+}}$ must be about 0.3. The measured concentration of Ba^{2+} in the oceans is about 2×10^{-7} molal. The agreement is reasonable, and we conclude that ocean water is approximately in equilibrium with barium sulfate (barite). Barite indeed is present as concretions on ocean floors.

Kramer has considered the concentrations of K, Na, Ca, Mg, P, F, S, H, C, and Cl on the basis of a model in which approximate equilibrium is obtained with the solid phases, clays, zeolites, carbonates of calcium and magnesium, phosphates as apatite, sulfides and sulfates, and ferric oxide. The resulting calculated seawater concentrations are close enough to measured ones to indicate that the major constituents are in approximate equilibrium with some solid phase in the sediment. This implies that the ocean waters have reached a steady state with respect to these elements, additions via solution being balanced by precipitation of solid phases by diverse possible mechanisms.

Although the equilibrium concept may be applied to many elements in the oceans, it is certainly not applicable to all. The silica content of fresh waters is around 13 ppm, that of ocean water only about 3 ppm. The concentration in equilibrium with quartz is about 10 ppm and that for equilibrium with amorphous silica is about 100 ppm. Marine organisms precipitate a nearly amorphous silica and their activity must strongly influence the level of silica in the oceans. When a silica-secreting organism dies, its skeleton will tend to redissolve in seawater. It may survive only under favorable conditions such as local, high silica concentration or preservation of enclosing organic matter. That such situations do exist is shown by repeated occurrence of massive chert beds composed of organically secreted amorphous silica (see below).

Submarine volcanism and the oceans   Studies of the ocean floor have increasingly revealed the enormous extent of submarine volcanism. Volcanic gas must add a significant contribution to ocean water and, as well, spreads huge quantities of reactive glassy materials over the sea floor. Such phenomena must surely play a significant part in ocean sedimentation and complicate the simple, balanced model that we have just described.

Submarine eruptions, much as those from terrestrial volcanoes, may be tranquil or explosive and can occur over a wide range of ocean depths. A common product peculiar to subaqueous eruption is pillow lava, usually of basaltic composition (Figure 8–4, photographed at a depth of about 3000 meters). Submarine lava cools rapidly, and glass is a major or dominant constituent of the quenched product. This glass is easily hydrated to a product (palagonite) that is readily transformed to clay minerals and zeolites. Commonly associated with these products are manganese and iron oxides, either as crusts on the lava or as nodules, as well as chemically precipitated calcite and amorphous silica (chert).

A highly typical rock association in filled geosynclines consists of basaltic pillow lavas and bedded cherts containing large concentrations of Mn-Fe oxides. It has long been debated whether the cherts are inorganic precipitates directly related to volcanism, or whether organic activity plays some intermediate role. The data on silica solubility (Chapter 5) certainly indicates that steam at high pressures could introduce large quantities of silica into the marine environment. This effect could be enhanced if seawater, circulating through a cooling lava pile leached out silica and other constituents. Our knowledge of such phenomena is still meager. The mechanism of silica precipitation is becoming less ambiguous. Under an electron microscope most cherts are seen to contain large quantities of skeletal debris from radiolaria; and it seems that introduction of volcanic silica promotes growth of silica-secreting organisms in unusual abundance. Their skeletons would normally be subject to dissolution in ocean water, but where there is copious volcanic glass and silica concentration is augmented, they are preserved. Thus the source of the silica may indeed be volcanic, but the precipitating agents are living organisms

Many intriguing and little-understood prob-

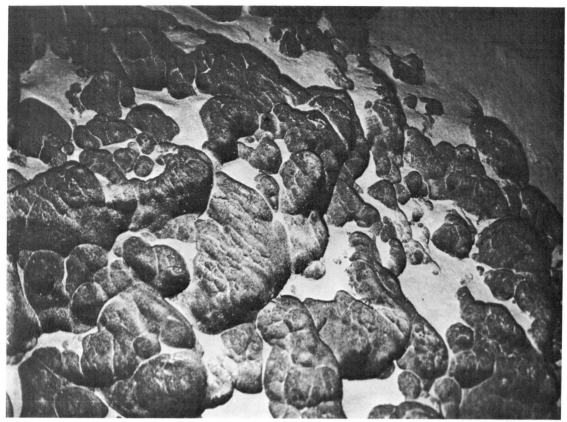

FIG. 8-4 *Surface of submarine lava flow photographed at about 3000 meters. (After Bonatti in P. Abelson, Ed., Researches in Geochemistry, vol. II, 1967.)*

lems remain. For example, what reactions are induced by introduction of volcanic sulfur? Does all such sulfur oxidize rapidly to sulfate, or is the local environment rendered more reducing? If the latter were true, sulfides could precipitate and ocean water would thereby become locally depleted in elements such as silver and mercury. Much remains to be discovered regarding the effects of submarine volcanism on the chemistry of seawater.

Carbonate precipitation   The work of Garrels and his co-workers on activity coefficients and complex ions present in seawater has shown that, at least in the surface layers, ocean water is

close to saturation with respect to the minerals calcite, aragonite, and dolomite. Calcite and aragonite are precipitated mostly by organisms, although direct precipitation does occur locally (for example, the Bahama Bank). Dolomite is directly precipitated only from the waters of some highly saline lagoons, as in South Australia. Most dolomite is formed by later diagenesis. Precipitation of these carbonates must be rate-controlled, and the reluctance of calcite and dolomite to precipitate is attributed to inhibition of growth by surface concentration of magnesium ions on incipient nuclei (p. 385). The exact mechanism by which calcite and aragonite become replaced by dolomite is still poorly understood;

but the process is geologically important and seems to be favored by high salinity.

In the surface environment, carbonate equilibria are related to the following reactions:

$$\underset{\text{solid}}{CaCO_3} \rightarrow \underset{\text{aq}}{Ca^{2+}} + \underset{\text{aq}}{CO_3^{2-}}$$

$$\underset{\text{aq}}{CO_3^{2-}} + H_2O \rightarrow \underset{\text{aq}}{HCO_3^-} + \underset{\text{aq}}{OH^-}$$

$$\underset{\text{aq}}{HCO_3^-} + H_2O \rightarrow \underset{\text{aq}}{H_2CO_3} + \underset{\text{aq}}{OH^-}$$

$$\underset{\text{gas}}{CO_2} + H_2O \rightarrow \underset{\text{aq}}{H_2CO_3}$$

$$\underset{\text{aq}}{Ca^{2+}} + \underset{\text{aq}}{CO_3^{2-}} \rightarrow \underset{\text{aq}}{CaCO_3}$$

$$\underset{\text{aq}}{Ca^{2+}} + \underset{\text{aq}}{HCO_3^{2-}} \rightarrow \underset{\text{aq}}{CaHCO_3^+}$$

$$\underset{\text{aq}}{Ca^{2+}} + \underset{\text{aq}}{SO_4^{2-}} \rightarrow \underset{\text{aq}}{CaSO_4}$$

$$H_2O \rightarrow \underset{\text{aq}}{H^+} + \underset{\text{aq}}{OH^-}$$

A similar set of relations may be written for Mg^{2+} carbonates and complexes. Equilibrium constants for all these reactions are now established with reasonable accuracy and have been used by Garrels and Christ to calculate carbonate solubilities in most environments. In the common natural pH range of 6–8, the bicarbonate ion is the dominant carbonate entity in solution. Equilibrium with calcite or aragonite to a first approximation involves the reaction:

$$\underset{\text{solid}}{CaCO_3} + \underset{\text{aq}}{H_2CO_3} \rightarrow \underset{\text{aq}}{Ca^{2+}} + \underset{\text{aq}}{2HCO_3^-}$$

This carbonate system is a rather efficient buffer with respect to changes in pH and P_{CO_2}. If P_{CO_2}, and hence H_2CO_3 is increased, calcite dissolves; if aqueous H^+ is added, carbonate is decreased and calcite dissolves; if aqueous OH^- is added, calcite will precipitate. The effect of any such addition is damped out or buffered by changes in the ratio of solid and dissolved components.

Precipitation of calcium carbonate is favored by warm, shallow environments, where CO_2 is less soluble in water and is continuously used up in photosynthesis. Because the solubility of calcite in water increases with falling temperature, solution is favored by cold, dark environments, where CO_2 may be more abundant. In fact, cal-

cite dissolves rather rapidly at depths below 4 km—the so-called carbonate "snow line," below which calcium carbonate is a rare mineral.

Phosphates It appears again that the phosphate concentration in the oceans is approximately in equilibrium with the mineral apatite, whose composition ranges between $Ca_5(PO_4)_3OH$ and $Ca_5(PO_4)_3F$. It is secreted by many types of organisms (Table 8–2). Phosphoric acid, like carbonic acid, is weak; and phosphate and carbonate equilibria are controlled by similar factors. Thus one would expect phosphate deposition at sites where precipitation of calcite also is rapid. In general, this expectation is borne out by observation. But in some sedimentary rocks (for example, the Permian Phosphoria formation of Idaho) phosphates are concentrated relative to carbonates in a proportion far exceeding the phosphate/carbonate ratios of seawater. In some cases such enrichment may be a secondary phenomenon; replacement of calcite by apatite is not uncommon. But this is not always so. If the primary precipitation is by organisms, then it is perhaps possible that rather subtle factors in special biological situations may lead to enhanced deposition and concentration of phosphate.

EVAPORITES

Massive salt beds (evaporites) are common in the sedimentary record. They form today by evaporation of lake waters in arid regions, or from marine waters in largely enclosed lagoons where evaporation keeps pace with input of water from the open sea. Occurrence of evaporites in a stratigraphic formation is good evidence of deposition in a semiarid continental environment.

Evaporites formed in land-locked basins have local characteristics related to local geochemistry and so are more varied than salt beds deposited from trapped bodies of well-mixed ocean water. Waters draining basins where volcanoes are active may be exceptionally acid ($pH = 1$). Stream waters in limestone terranes obviously must differ from those draining granite ranges. Terrestrial evaporites, like those deposited from marine waters, may be dominated by halite (NaCl), gypsum ($CaSO_4 \cdot 2H_2O$), or anhydrite ($CaSO_4$). But in some the dominant salts are sodium and magnesium sulfates, sodium carbonate and bicarbonate, borax ($Na_2B_4O_7$), or even soda niter ($NaNO_3$). Concentrations of the less usual salts—for example, the borax beds of California and the soda niter of Chile present problems of source and supply that have not as yet been satisfactorily solved. We note that volcanic processes may concentrate boron and that, under special climatic conditions involving frequent thunderstorms, the atmospheric concentration of nitrogen oxides may be abnormally high. To postulate such processes as an explanation for the origin of beds of pure borates or nitrates, however, is to enter the realm of speculation.

The overall composition of salts dissolved in seawater approximates that of a mixture NaCl 76.8, $MgCl_2$ 10.5, Mg_2SO_4 6.1, $CaSO_4$ 3.7, KCl 2, $CaHCO_3$ 0.7, and KBr 0.2 percent by weight. The experimentally determined order in which salts are precipitated during progressive evaporation of seawater is

Calcium carbonate (calcite)
Calcium sulfate (gypsum or anhydrite)
Sodium chloride (halite)
Magnesium sulfates and chlorides
Sodium bromide and potassium chloride

Evaporation of a column of seawater 100 meters deep to complete dryness would yield a salt bed 150 cm thick of which 116 cm would be halite and 4 cm would be gypsum and anhydrite. The remaining 30 cm would consist of mixed sulfates and chlorides of magnesium and a little potassium chloride (sylvite); calcium carbonate, the first salt to precipitate would be a negligible constituent of the salt bed. Natural salt beds do have such a composition; and they are of great economic value as sources of common salt, gypsum, and (where complete evaporation has been repeated in cycles) potassic salts. Partially solved or unsolved problems still remain. Obviously any assemblage of mixed anhydrous and hydrated soluble salts will be extremely sensitive to diagenetic changes associated with burial. If such deposits become deeply buried and move into metamor-

phic environments they can supply halogens and sulfates for metasomatic processes. Their importance in processes leading to ore formation may be of enormous significance and requires careful study (see Chapter 5). It is significant that minerals such as halite never survive to high grades of metamorphism; either they are leached out in solution or destroyed by reactions of high-temperature hydrolysis.

THE OCEAN BUFFER SYSTEM

The oceans with their complicated chemistry and biology form a highly effective chemical buffer system that influences all surface processes; and since sedimentary rocks may in turn become metamorphic and even fused to give magma, this influence may be reflected indirectly in processes at much greater depths. If a buffer is to work, there must be an approach to equilibrium either chemical or biological. Thus, increase in Ba^{2+} in the ocean must lead to precipitation of more $BaSO_4$; if pH increases, more calcite must be precipitated; if SiO_2 is introduced by volcanic activity, radiolaria flourish and silica is secreted in their skeletons and so removed to maintain the preexisting balance.

Garrels and MacKenzie have stressed the important buffer action of clay minerals, detrital and primary. Thus Na^+/Ca^{2+} may be maintained at a balanced value by cation exchange in marine montmorillonite clays.

$$Ca \text{ clay} + 2Na^+_{\text{aq}} \rightarrow Na_2 \text{ clay} + Ca^{2+}_{\text{aq}}$$

As long as the clay is present, the Na/Ca ratio should be constant. Other aluminum silicates may participate in buffer reactions, such as

$$\text{clay} + Na^+_{\text{aq}} + HCO_3^-{}_{\text{aq}} \rightarrow Na \text{ clay} + CO_2$$

Such reactions may buffer the CO_2 content of both oceans and atmosphere. In the final analysis, equilibrium with common minerals, phosphates, silicates, carbonates and others, and the requirement that an electrolyte solution be neutral, lead to unique and constant chemistry of both the ocean and the atmosphere. Serious search for indications of past oceans with significantly different chemistry have produced negative results. One might suspect that once life approached a biochemical state similar to that of the present, the ocean–atmosphere system would approach constancy. As the age of life biochemically similar to present life now approaches the age of the crust itself, one might guess that ocean chemistry has been similar to that of today for a comparably vast time. Eventually, detailed studies of organic debris, clay minerals, fluid inclusions, and so forth from Precambrian sediments may increase our understanding of ocean–atmosphere evolution.

Nature of Sedimentary Rocks

COMPOSITION AND CLASSIFICATION

It is customary to consider the materials that make up sediments and sedimentary rocks in two categories: *clastic* and *chemical*. Transported fragmental debris of all kinds—sand, gravel, shell fragments—make up the clastic component of the rock. Inorganic precipitates from water (for example, calcite, gypsum, and silica) obviously belong to the chemical category. But the chemical component also includes *biogenic* material extracted from marine and terrestrial waters or partly from the air, and secreted as skeletons of living organisms. Examples include the calcium carbonate skeletons of corals, mollusks and foraminifera, siliceous skeletons of sponges and various microorganisms (diatoms, radiolarians), carbonaceous vegetable remains in peat and coal, liquid and gaseous hydrocarbons distilled from buried organic matter, and phosphatic skeletons and fecal pellets of fishes and other vertebrates. Distinction between the clastic and chemical components of a sandstone, or between the essentially clastic nature of sandstones and the chemical character of limestones is both simple and useful. But there is no need to draw a sharp line between what should be considered clastic and what chemical in the whole class of sedimentary rocks. The microscopic foraminiferal shells that make up so much of limestones—for exam-

ple, the Cretaceous Chalk of Britain—accumulated on the sea floor at some distance from the surface environment of the living organisms. To that degree they are transported material. Then there are limestones composed largely of transported shell fragments. Similar material may be seen in modern shell beaches and shell banks. It is sometimes referred to as *bioclastic*.

Classification of sedimentary rocks is based on easily recognizable characteristics that reflect something of the mode of transport and the environment of deposition. In consequence, classes so defined tend to be mutually gradational. We start by distinguishing essentially clastic from essentially chemical sediments. But the bioclastic limestones belong equally to either category; and there are sandy limestones (calcareous sandstones) that lie squarely in between, just as in the field they may be found to grade laterally or upward into limestone on the one hand, sandstone on the other.

Clastic rocks are classified according to the size, and variation in size, of the component fragments. To standardize what was once an over-loose usage, geologists have adopted a uniform terminology based on size classes, in each of which the grain diameter doubles. Standard usage is shown in Table 8–4. Most terms cover several size classes, so that it is appropriate to qualify them with adjectives such as "fine," "medium," and "coarse." In nature there is complete gradation from one size class to the next; and in many rocks sediment of several sizes is present in significant quantity.

Clastic sediments and rocks are further characterized by their sorting, or the distribution of particles in size classes; for this reflects something of the mode of transport and deposition in different environments. When a disaggregated sediment is analyzed mechanically for size, the weight percent of each size is plotted on a graph as a cumulative-frequency curve (Figure 8–5). In a well-sorted sediment most of the grains fall into two or three size classes. A poorly-sorted sediment is one in which a wide range of size classes is well represented. Commonly a sediment shows only one modal size class, and the percentage of other classes falls away from the

TABLE 8-4   *Size classification of sedimentary particles and of clastic sedimentary rocks*

Diameter, mm	Particle	Sediment	Rock
< 1/256	clay ⎫	mud, ooze	claystone (mudstone)
1/256 – 1/16	silt ⎬		
1/16 – 2	sand	sand	sandstone
2 – 4	granule ⎫		
4 – 64	pebble		conglomerate (rounded)
64 – 256	cobble	gravel	breccia (angular)
> 256	boulder ⎭		

modal class, as in curves *a, b, d-f, i,* in Figure 8–5. Some poorly sorted sedimentary deposits and rocks, such as glacial tills, have two or more modal size classes (curves *c* and *g*).

Most conglomerates have sand in the interstices between the pebbles or cobbles, and therefore are rather poorly sorted (curve *h*). Sand, on the other hand, can be deposited with remarkably good sorting in some environments, and can be mixed with silt and clay in others. Well-sorted sandstones are *arenites;* poorly sorted sandstones, with a matrix of silt and clay, are called *wackes.* Most sandstones consist predominantly of quartz, the most resistant of common rock-forming minerals. A sandstone with more than 25 percent feldspar is called *arkose. Graywackes* contain

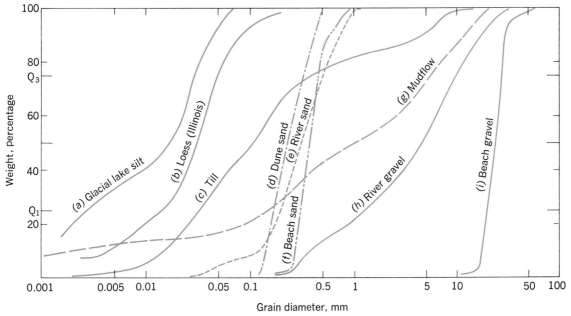

FIG. 8–5   *Logarithmic plots of cumulative grain-size distribution of representative samples of several types of sediments. The steeper the slope of the curve, the better sorted the sediment. The modal size class (class with the greatest weight-percentage) contains the inflection point on the curve. A sediment with more than one modal size class has more than one inflection point, e.g., till in curve (c). (Lake Silt from U.S. Geol. Survey Prof. Paper 293-B, p. 84, 1958; mudflow from W. B. Bull, U.S. Geol. Survey Prof. Paper 437-A, p. A-24, 1964; Loess, from T. L. Pewe, J. Geol., vol. 59, p. 400, 1951; all others recomputed and replotted from W. H. Twenhofel, Treatise on Sedimentation, Dover reprint, 1961.)*

lithic fragments or fragments of ferromagnesian minerals and feldspar grains as well as quartz sand and silt.

Chemical sediments and rocks are classified according to chemical composition:

> *Limestones:* mainly calcite $CaCO_3$.
> *Dolomites:* mainly dolomite $CaMg(CO_3)_2$.
> *Evaporites:* gypsum, $CaSO_4 \cdot 2H_2O$; anhydrite, $CaSO_4$; rock salt, $NaCl$ (halite); various other carbonates, sulfates, and borates.
> *Phosphate rock:* apatite.
> *Ironstones:* hydrated iron oxides (limonite), carbonate (siderite), and silicates of the chlorite family.
> *Coal*

Many of these rocks, especially limestone, coal and phosphate rock, are largely or in part biogenic.

Some Genetic Implications of Rock Composition and Structure

Any sedimentary rock is the ultimate product of a chain of geologic processes: weathering and erosion of rocks in a source region; transport, commonly in several stages, by one or more flowing media; deposition, compaction, and lithification of sediment at the site where it finally comes to rest. Each may leave its imprint on some aspect of the composition and texture of the rock. Also retained are characteristics inherited directly from rocks that supplied the raw waste material in the source area. All that can be inferred regarding the source rocks constitutes what is called the *provenance* of a sedimentary rock or formation.

PROVENANCE

The geology of the source region places definite limits upon the nature of derived sediments. A basaltic terrane cannot supply quartz sand, but can furnish grains of feldspar and pyroxene and tiny fragments of dark-colored lava that are plentiful constituents of many graywackes. To account for odd grains of staurolite, kyanite, or glaucophane that appear in some sandstones we must appeal to metamorphic rocks at the source; for the minerals are unknown in igneous rocks. Abundance of coarse debris in sandstone and conglomerate rules out possible source areas composed of fine-grained friable rocks such as mudstones.

Inferences as to provenance are drawn especially from the mineralogy and lithology of sand and pebbles; for these have generally been transported from the source region by rather direct routes (Figure 8–6). It may even be possible to locate the source area within rather narrow limits. Interpretation of finer-grained sediments is less satisfactory. Silts composed of clay minerals and finely divided quartz–feldspar waste can be derived, under suitable weathering conditions, from many kinds of rocks. Such material, moreover, can be transported great distances in suspension.

Distances and even rates of displacement along transcurrent faults have been estimated by matching coarse angular debris in sedimentary breccias with lithologically identical source rocks on the opposite side. Thus in southern California a conglomerate of middle Miocene age on the southwest side of the San Gabriel fault, a branch or the San Andreas fault system, contains large boulders of anorthosite, gabbro, and distinctive coarse-grained metamorphic rocks (gneiss) that perfectly match source rocks in the Precambrian basement about 35 km to the southeast on the opposite side of the fault. The displacement so demonstrated must have been accomplished within the past 20 million years.

The principal constituents of sands and silts—quartz and feldspars—are so widely distributed among igneous and metamorphic rocks that their value as indices of provenance is correspondingly limited. It is common practice to separate these (and any white mica that may be present) from the minor heavy constituents of a disaggregated rock by floating in a heavy liquid such as bromoform (density 2.8–2.9) and filtering. The heavy fraction commonly contains many varieties of minerals, some of which give invaluable information regarding provenance (Figure 8–7). A horn-

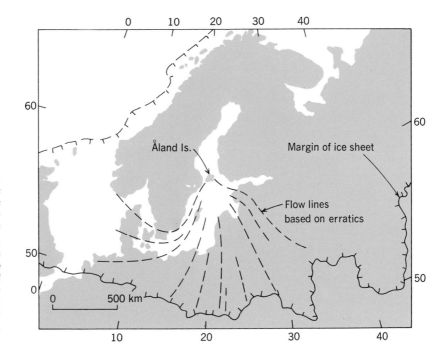

FIG. 8–6 *Distribution of glacial erratics from the rocks of the Åland Islands in the Gulf of Bothnia, one example of closely identified provenance of a component of a till sheet. The till sheets on the south and east margins of the Baltic contain much material derived from the Fennoscandian Shield. (Modified from R. F. Flint, Glacial and Pleistocene Geology, Wiley, p. 125, 1957.)*

blende–biotite–sphene assemblage suggests a granite–granodiorite source; augite–hypersthene–ilmenite, a source including basic igneous rocks; glaucophane–lawsonite–pumpellyite–garnet and kyanite–garnet–staurolite, two very different and highly characteristic kinds of metamorphic terrane (Chapter 10).

WEATHERING AND EROSION AT THE SOURCE

To illustrate the role of weathering and erosion in the source region, consider first the diversified materials that may be supplied under different conditions from a granitic terrane. In every situation there will be abundant quartz sand; and there will always be a few grains of highly resistant minerals, such as tourmaline and zircon, that habitually appear as accessory constituents of granite-derived sediments. Diversity in the sedimentary products stems largely from variation in the respective roles of chemical destruction and mechanical disintegration of feldspar, and these are determined largely by climate, topographic relief, and rock structure:

1. Under humid tropical conditions, all major mineral constituents except quartz are reduced to kaolinite clays, iron and aluminum hydroxides, and dissolved ions, K^+, Na^+, Ca^{2+}, Mg^{2+}. Clastic material supplied to stream waters is essentially quartz sand and high-alumina clay. So today the sediment accumulating offshore along the north coast of Venezuela, though derived from a mountainous terrane (elevation 3000 meters) of crystalline rocks, is largely clay.

2. In temperate to semiarid climates with enough water to cause hydration and swelling of biotite, granitic rocks in areas of high relief disintegrate mechanically without significant destruction of feldspar. The bed load of outward-draining streams is largely feldspar-rich sand. The clay fraction, if significant, will contain montmorillonite and illite. Alluvium beneath the San Joaquin Valley and beach sands near San Francisco in California, both largely derived from the Sierra Nevada, are arkosic sands of this kind.

3. Under arctic conditions, chemical weathering is minimal and frost weathering reduces

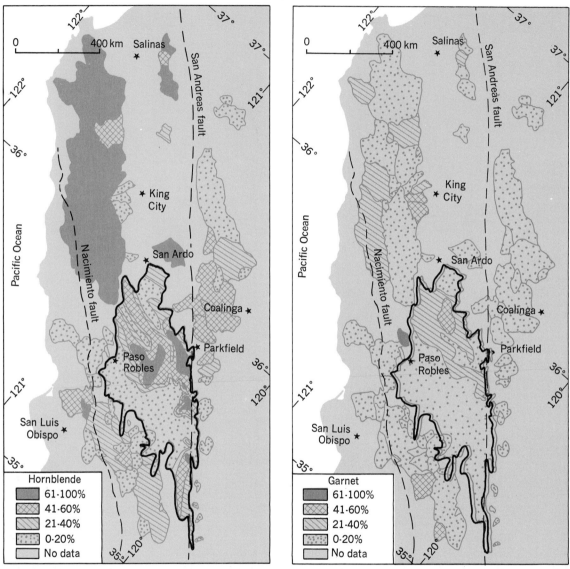

FIG. 8–7 *The distribution of hornblende and garnet in the late-Cenozoic Paso Robles formation of central coastal California, compared with their distribution in stream sands from drainage basins in the surrounding mountains. The Paso Robles formation is outlined by the heavy black line. The areas outlined by light lines in the surrounding area are drainage basins that were sampled for heavy minerals. Percentages are of the heavy-mineral concentrate from the sand. The maps show that the areas of older rock with the greatest concentration of hornblende and garnet are to the northwest of the Paso Robles formation, and the concentration of these two minerals decreases southeasterly across the formation. This indicates that much of the Paso Robles Formation was derived from mountains to the northwest. (From J. S. Galehouse, Provenance and paleocurrents of the Paso Robles Formation, California, Geol. Soc. Am. Bull., vol. 78, pp. 951–978, 1967.)*

granitic rocks to coarse angular fragments. The bed load of streams is largely gravel, and in sediments derived from such sources there are predominant conglomerates. Material of gravel grade may also be copiously supplied by weathering of tectonically shattered granite under completely different climatic conditions. Thus in the San Gabriel and Santa Lucia Ranges in California, where the climate is like that of the nearby Sierra Nevada, the bed load of streams is coarse gravel. Gravel likewise predominates in alluvium of the Los Angeles Basin and central Californian beaches derived from the same source.

It is unsafe to correlate coarseness of a sediment with any single factor. Conglomerates carry a general implication of proximity to a source region where, by reasons of high relief or climatic conditions unfavorable to chemical weathering, the soil profile is perpetually immature and slope debris is mainly of gravel grade. The implication is especially strong where the component pebbles are of soft, rather soluble material, such as limestone. Yet limestone conglomerates are not unknown. One such is in the Cantwell formation in the western part of Mt. McKinley National Park, Alaska; enclosed plant fossils indicate a humid climate, and it is safe to assume a nearby source of high relief, with limestone crags continuously shedding talus into outward-draining streams. Under special conditions debris of gravel grade may be supplied from sources in which prolonged weathering has developed thick profiles of mature soil. All that is necessary is that the soil profile contain a chemically cemented horizon as in the siliceous "duricrust" of central Australia, the iron oxide layers of lateritic soils, and the calcite-cemented "caliche" of semiarid and desert soils. All these may provide material for surface gravels and transported conglomerates.

Some minerals, such as quartz, tourmaline, and zircon, are extremely resistant to weathering and abrasion and persist indefinitely through several cycles of erosion and redeposition. Other minerals, such as olivine, the pyroxenes, and amphiboles, weather readily, and their presence indicates incomplete weathering in the source

area and probable derivation from an igneous or metamorphic source. Abundance of feldspar likewise reflects derivation from an igneous source and incomplete weathering (or possibly recycling from an older arkose). On the other hand, a sandstone composed entirely of quartz, with tourmaline and zircon as the only heavy minerals, must be the residue washed away from mature soils of a thoroughly weathered terrane of crystalline rocks such as cover much of the surface of western Australia and large areas of Ceylon. Finally we note at the other extreme silts consisting exclusively of unweathered minerals, such as hornblende, calcic feldspar, and olivine, which normally are eliminated in the weathering cycle. Silts of this kind are normally derived from glaciers and so suggest corresponding climatic conditions at the source.

Minute surface markings of fine sedimentary particles disclosed by electron microscopy, may provide valuable clues as to their origin. Distinctive patterns are left by the grinding action of glaciers, by the percussion of fine particles against the sand grains in the eolian environment, and by wave action in a littoral environment. Such studies have recently demonstrated the appearance of glaciomarine silts in the deep-sea sediments of the South Pacific at about the Gauss–Matuyama paleomagnetic boundary (Chapter 13)—an important link in the chain of evidence used to date the onset of Pleistocene glaciation (Chapter 7).

Not much can be said regarding provenance of marine chemical sediments, for their composition is determined largely by conditions prevailing at the site of deposition. Chemical sediments of continental basins on the other hand tell us something of the chemical character of surrounding rocks. Salt deposits formed on the bed of the shrinking Lake Bonneville (Chapter 7) consist principally of halite, NaCl derived from sedimentary rocks of the surrounding Great Basin. On the other hand, salts encrusting the playa borders in desert basins of western Nevada are mainly carbonates. The surrounding rocks are mainly volcanic and are low in chlorine. To the southeast in the vicinity of Death Valley and the Mojave Desert of eastern California, desert evaporites are rich in borates—possibly supplied by postvolcanic hot-spring waters, but possibly drawn from weathering products of nearby boron-rich granitic rocks (tourmaline pegmatites).

TRANSPORTATION

The distance of transport can range from a few meters (for example, the angular beach gravel at a cliff base) to thousands of kilometers (for example, the sands and silts that build the Nile and Mississippi deltas). Wind-borne dust may circle the globe before settling on the ocean surface, ultimately to sink and accumulate as the inorganic fraction of deep-sea ooze. Many sedimentary rocks contain clastic material that has been through several cycles of transport and deposition. This does not necessarily imply great lapse of time. Material brought from the Canadian shield by Pleistocene ice sheets and dumped for a time as till in Wisconsin, has since been weathered, eroded, and transported down the Mississippi to the Gulf of Mexico, with halts along the way following periodic floods. Any halt of long duration has provided the opportunity for further weathering. Some beach sands along the Gulf shore far from the outlets of the river have had just such a broken history of transport—the final episode, still in progress, being coastal transport by long-shore drift. The histories of many beach sands include a preliminary phase of stream transport, with later intermittent episodes in dune areas, where sand is carried and sorted by the wind.

MODIFICATION OF PARTICLES IN TRANSPORT Transport progressively modifies the shape and reduces the size of individual particles by mutual attrition and impact, aided in some situations (for example, limestone debris) by the solvent action of running water. The precise effects depend on many variables, including composition, grain size and sorting of transported material, and velocity and viscosity of the medium of transport. As the Reynolds number changes with shifts in these variables, so too does the abrasion or impact effect. The most obvious effect in the poorly sorted bed load of a stream is progressive rounding of the coarser material. Indeed angular joint blocks of a resistant rock such as basalt may be converted to well-rounded cobbles and pebbles during a few kilometers or less of transport in a rapidly flowing stream. Associated smaller particles of fine-gravel grade on the other hand become shattered into angular fragments under impact of pebbles many times their own diameter.

Angular sand is common enough. But there are sands and sandstones, including some beach and desert sands, consisting in large part of smooth, nearly spherical grains of quartz. The ultimate source of these must be the sharply angular quartz grains of granitic and metamorphic rocks. How they acquired their spherical shape remains something of a mystery. Presumably the process was slow, possibly requiring several lengthy cycles of transport. Paradoxical, too, is the common association of two kinds of quartz grain in desert sands—the one rounded and polished, the other frosted by pitting on a microscopic scale. The frosting effect has been traced to repeated impact of wind-blown grains in process of saltation. Perhaps rounding and polishing of quartz grains have been accomplished in some other, presumably aqueous, environment. If so, how have rounded grains become concentrated in wind-borne sands?

SORTING OF SEDIMENTS   Transport is the most efficient means of sorting the clastic component of sediments. Least effective in this respect are glaciers and mudflows, and only slightly more so are turbidity currents. Sorting is effected especially during transport by rivers, by combined wave action and long-shore drift on beaches, and by wind.

Grain size and sorting are a function of the velocity and competence the transporting medium at the site of deposition, and the degree of reworking (winnowing or washing) of the freshly deposited sediment. Large blocks and boulders can be transported only as rockfalls or slides, by glaciers, mudflows, turbidity currents, or by giant floods such as those that occurred on the Columbia and Snake Rivers during Pleistocene time. The maximum size of material that can be trans-

TABLE 8-5 *Current velocity necessary to transport sediment of a given size**

Particle size, cm	Velocity, m/sec
0.03	0.15
0.1	0.20
1	1
10	1.4
55	2.1
100–150	4.5
300	7.3

* Data up to 10 cm from Hjulström, 1939; for larger sizes, from Malde, 1968 (see References).

ported by water currents of given bed velocities is shown in Table 8-5.

Well-sorted materials include glacial-outwash gravels, beach sands, fluviatile sands and gravels, and dune sands. These sediments are deposited in environments characterized by fluctuations in current velocity, so that finer material is carried onward (winnowed or washed out) leaving the material transportable by the most competent currents at the depositional site. The deposits of turbidity currents are less well-sorted because the material is transported en masse and there is generally no opportunity for subsequent reworking. Turbidity currents caused by the dumping of beach sands into the heads of submarine canyons, as seen today off the coast of southern California, may deposit well-sorted sediment—but the sorting is inherited from the parent beach sand.

Where competence of streams, currents, or long-shore drift (usually proportional to their kinetic energy per unit volume) decreases systematically in the direction of transport, the sediment is sorted essentially by washing or winnowing. Thus gravel and conglomerate may be deposited at the heads of alluvial fans and along the margins of a continental basin, and sand or silt toward the basin interior, where the streams are sluggish because of low gradient (Figure 8-8). Beach sands tend to decrease in size in the direction in which wave energy decreases. According to Stokes' law, a fine sediment (silt or clay) should tend to show progressive decrease in grain size

away from the source. This indeed seems generally to be the case. The loess sheets of Illinois, which are wind-borne glacial silt derived from the Pleistocene Mississippi and Illinois Rivers, decrease in grain size eastward from the rivers. Similar decrease in grain size of silt is shown in Figure 8-9.

In an aqueous environment, as Hjulström's curve shows, sorting at the site of deposition of material less than 0.5 mm in diameter results in the selective removal of coarser grains and retention of the finest-size fraction. Sediments deposited from still water tend to be fine-grained and poorly sorted. In general, the currents that brought them to the site of deposition are unable to move them once they are deposited. Poor sorting therefore characterizes the fine-grained overbank silts of river floodplains, the sediment of lagoons and tidal estuaries, and the fine sediment that settles out of suspension on sea floors.

Sediments become sorted with respect to density and shape, as well as grain size. Placer sands are natural concentrates of heavy minerals— magnetite, garnet, zircon, and even gold—from which the much more abundant grains of lighter minerals such as quartz and feldspar have been winnowed away by stream waters or wave action. Spherical, polished quartz grains roll and bounce more easily than angular grains of the same size. Herein may be the reason for their high concentration in far-traveled desert and beach sands.

DEPOSITION

The major control on the character of a sediment is exercised by the environment of deposition. Consider what happens to the finer fraction of sediment brought to the seacoast by a flooded stream. Part will be drifted through tidal creeks onto mud flats, where it will be deposited among blades of eelgrass or salt grass, and may be ingested and excreted by burrowing animals. The resulting deposit, with its sedimentary layering destroyed by organisms, may be a massive mudstone with abundant root markings and worm burrows. The remainder of the suspended load may drift to sea, eventually to settle to the sea

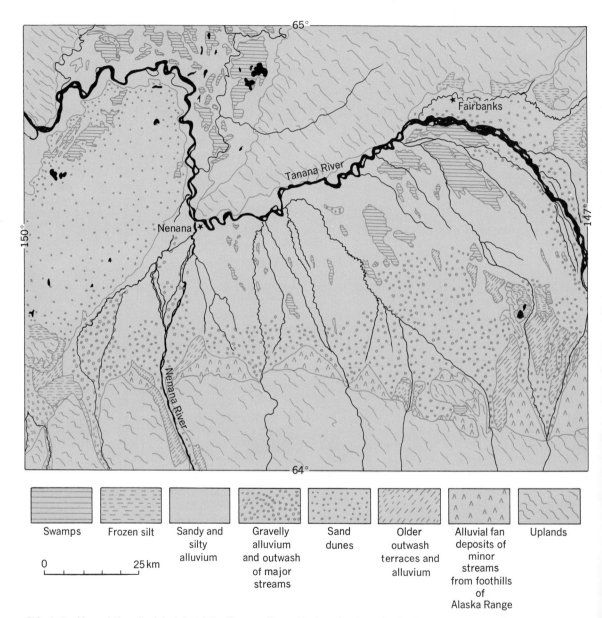

FIG. 8–8 *Map of the alluvial plain of the Tanana Flats, Alaska, showing distribution of coarse and fine fluviatile sediments, swamp deposits, and dune sand. Coarse gravels occur at the heads of alluvial and outwash fans from the Alaska range to the south, and along the upper reaches of the Tanana River. Fine sediments and swamp deposits (mainly peat) lie in the alluvial embayment in the northwest corner of the map, which has been dammed by sediment of the Tanana River. Abundant sand on the Pleistocene river-bed of the Tanana River west of Nenana was driven by northeast winds to form an extensive dune field in the west part of the lowland. (After T. L. Pewe and others, U.S. Geol. Survey Map I-455, 1966.)*

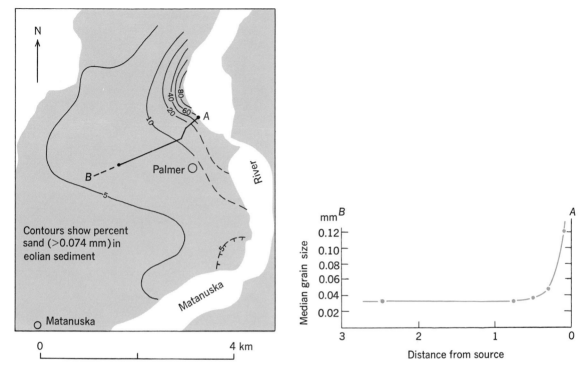

FIG. 8–9 *Map showing decrease in percent of sand particles in wind–borne sediment away from the source area in the flood plain of the Matanuska River, in the Matanuska Valley, Alaska. The graph shows decrease in median grain-size of sediment samples along the line AB. (From F. W. Trainer, U.S. Geol. Survey Bull., no. 1121-C, 1961.)*

floor as a fine lamina. If the bottom waters are stagnant and free of oxygen, there will be no organisms to destroy the lamination, and the fine layering will be preserved. The sand bed load, on the other hand, may be moved down the floor of the estuary by tidal currents, and once beyond the estuary mouth, may be transported by long-shore currents to form a beach. Subsidence and burial may preserve the beach as a linear body of permeable sand. At some point along the beach, part of the sand may be diverted into the head of a submarine canyon, and later may flow down the canyon to the deep sea floor as a turbidity current, there to be deposited as a graded layer intercalated with the laminae of fine mud settling from the surface waters.

COLOR   The color of sediments and sedimentary rocks is related entirely to the content and oxida-

tion state of iron and amount of organic matter. The ferric ion imparts a yellow, brown, or red color to the rock, and the ferrous ion yields blue, green, gray, or black. Organic matter darkens the rock, producing brown to black colors. The various shades from yellow through red appear to depend on the hydration of the ferric oxides. Sediments in which the iron is in some form of $Fe(OH)_3$—limonite or goethite—are brown or yellow; as water is driven off, the color changes toward red, and the anhydrous ferric oxide, hematite, is bright red in a finely divided state. Thus the brilliant red colors of red beds and some lateritic soils are due to the abundance of hematite. Only a few percent of iron disseminated through the rock is sufficient to give this color.

The formation of hematite in soils has apparently some temperature limitations, because it is found only in warm temperate and tropical climates. It may form in the soil of the provenance area, and be washed into the depositional basin; or, as recent studies in Baja California have shown, it may form directly in the basin deposits themselves. Since a dry, oxidizing environment seems to be a prerequisite for red-bed formation, red beds are usually taken to mark a continental environment.

Most marine sediments and sediments of fresh-water bodies and coal swamps were probably deposited in reducing or at most very slightly oxidizing environments, and their colors accordingly tend toward gray or greenish gray. With increase in content of organic matter the color of the sediment darkens, the extreme rocks being black shales and coal beds.

DIAGENESIS AND LITHIFICATION

The sediment once deposited continues to alter in response to its history after deposition, and is gradually *lithified* into a sedimentary rock by processes collectively called *diagenesis*. These may begin immediately after deposition and may continue through the subsequent history of the rock; there is no sharp division to be drawn between diagenesis and burial metamorphism.

Most newly deposited sediments have high porosity. The pore spaces are filled by the depositing fluid, commonly seawater, and fluid can move through the sediment at a rate controlled by the size of the interstitial openings, the viscosity of the fluid, and the differential pressure causing fluid flow. Chemical reactions can take place between the sedimentary grains and the pore water, and the grains may be replaced by secondary minerals or may be dissolved. A major effect of early diagenesis, for example, is reaction of K^+ ion in seawater with montmorillonite and kaolinite, to form illite, a clay mineral with muscovite structure. Minor elements that may become significantly concentrated in marine clays are boron and barium. Many, perhaps most, dolomitic rocks are formed by early diagenetic replacement of calcite (of limestone) by dolomite by exchange of Ca^{2+} for Mg^{2+} held in solution in seawater. The exchange appears to be favored

by warm temperatures and high salinity. The necessary salinity may be caused by evaporation of interstitial brines in limey muds and reef rock at high-tide levels.

Another aspect of diagenesis is precipitation of minerals such as quartz, calcite, dolomite, or zeolites from pore waters within the pores themselves. Quartz grains of sandstone may thereby become enlarged; the pore volume is reduced, and both porosity and permeability of the rock diminish to a point where cementation of grains is complete.

After deposition, most sediment becomes buried by younger sediments whose steadily increasing weight presses the sedimentary particles together, forcing out the interstitial water and decreasing the porosity. The clay particles forced together adhere, and an important role in lithification of the rock is thus played by compaction.

Studies of recently deposited marine sediments show them to be heavily populated by bacteria. The vital processes of these bacteria produce important postdepositional changes in sediments, and are apparently responsible for considerable diagenesis. In an oxidizing environment, aerobic bacteria oxidize organic matter to CO_2, nitrates, and sulfates, and release phosphate. In a reducing environment, anaerobic bacteria reduce some organic materials in order to obtain oxygen for energy by oxidation. Ammonia, sulfides of iron and hydrogen, organic matter, and insoluble phosphate are left in the sediment. The effect of bacterial action in diagenesis and lithification is still not fully understood, but clearly it must be significant.

Depositional Environments and Paleogeography

SEDIMENTARY FACIES

Most clearly legible in the genetic record embodied in a sediment is the imprint of the environment of deposition. Characteristics related to environment collectively define the *facies* of a sedimentary bed, member, or formation. Facies has a dual character: it includes faunal and lithological aspects, customarily distinguished respectively as *biofacies* and *lithofacies*. Since both are determined by depositional environment, the two are intimately related.

Regional mapping of facies variation in sedimentary rocks of the same age gives a picture of geographic conditions at a corresponding period in time—a *paleogeography*. To reconstruct a succession of paleogeographies (for example, through Jurassic and Cretaceous time) in any region is to provide a picture of broad crustal movements and rise and fall of sea level over a corresponding period of time. This is a most important side of stratigraphy. The validity of such reconstructions depends of course on the validity of interpretation of individual sedimentary facies along uniformitarian lines. As we go far back in time, the strictly uniformitarian approach becomes less certain—especially with respect to biofacies. Admittedly, absence of a land flora and possible differences in compositions of atmosphere and oceans in Precambrian times may have led to peculiarities in some depositional environments having no parallel today. For example, throughout a large section of Precambrian time, iron was being precipitated as carbonate and hydrous silicates from seawater over large segments of the shields. However, at least from Cambrian times onward, the processes of weathering, transport, and deposition have operated much as they do today; whereas over the same period organic evolution along diversified lines has been so far-reaching that great caution is necessary if we are to interpret biofacies of Paleozoic sediments in terms of today's ecology.

Environments are broadly classified in relation to sea level, for this is the base level of subaerial erosion and deposition and of wind-induced waves and currents, and represents a universal transition between markedly different faunas and floras. *Continental* environments belong exclusively to the land surface, unaffected by tidal waters. *Marine* environments are exclusively beneath sea level and are unaffected by waves and tides. Between the two are *transitional* environments of shallow marine waters, the upper limit of which is high-tide level.

CONTINENTAL ENVIRONMENTS

The environment of deposition of a continental sediment is determined primarily by the depositing agency and the climate, and secondarily by the vegetation cover. Continental environments include alluvial and fluviatile (the surface of alluvial fans and river floodplains), lacustrine (the shores and floors of lakes), and glacial and eolian environments.

THE ALLUVIAL-FAN ENVIRONMENT   Alluvial fans are found in all climates, from the most arid to the most humid, and from the tropics to the arctic. Where alluvial-fan deposits were preserved in the stratigraphic record, they were built along the margins of a subsiding basin by streams or mudflows from an adjacent highland. In size, alluvial fans range from miniature features, a few meters across, and essentially ephemeral, on the borders of stream valleys and at the base of bluffs, to the immense features of such depositional basins as the Indo-Gangetic plain, which may extend outward for hundreds of kilometers. The primary control is climate, for on this depend the character of the depositing medium and the nature of the vegetation. Where both the source area and the depositional area are arid, deposition is likely to be by flash floods and mudflows, and there is little opportunity for reworking the material once deposited. Where the source area is humid and the depositional basin arid, mudflows may still be the prevailing mechanism for primary deposition; but the deposits may be worked over by streams. Where both are humid, deposition by streams predominates, and there is gradation into a typical fluviatile environment.

Mudflow are mixtures of sediment and water, in extreme cases containing 60 or 70 percent sediment. Deposits are characteristically unsorted. Individually they may be a few centimeters to a few meters thick, and if originally fluid enough, may exhibit graded bedding. Blocks of rock floated or transported by mudflows range up to 3 meters on a side.

From the Chezy formula, mudflow velocity is appreciable only if the depth is kept above some critical value. Depth, in turn, is maintained by a confining channel. Some mudflows construct sharp, steep-sided, natural levees, as a result of drainage of water away from the margins of the flow, and these levees confine the flow. Depth of other mudflows is maintained by a fan-head trench. Once beyond the trench, the flow spreads, thins, and comes to rest within a distance of one km or less. Since no mechanism is available to carry sediment farther, accumulation of successive mudflows fills the fan-head trench, and eventually aggrades the canyon at the head of the fan. Canyon walls may be stabilized, and the rate of erosion decreases markedly. A new phase of erosion begins with the cutting of a new fan-head trench on some other radius of the fan, and its extension headward into the canyon and down the fan surface. The resulting deposit will consist of overlapping layers of mudflow layers, interbedded with some stream-laid sediment, with numerous channels and local unconformities. Channels are more abundant toward the head of the fan. Their frequency at any site depends on the relative rate of uplift in source area and subsidence in depositional area, as compared to the frequency of mudflows.

With increase in precipitation, particularly in the source area, the character of the drainage changes from the ephemeral mudflows, through intermittent streams on many semiarid alluvial fans, to permanent streams. Earlier mudflow deposits become reworked by the streams; the fine sediment is flushed out, and only coarse bed load remains. Sorting is greatly increased. Intermittent streamflow commonly does not provide water for permanent streamside vegetation, and where bed load is coarse (coarse sand and gravel) the stream spreads laterally and is typically braided. Stream banks are low, are rapidly eroded as the stream shifts course, and the resulting sediment is predominantly well-sorted and reasonably well-bedded gravel or coarse sand. Permanent streams, or a high groundwater table permit growth of streamside

vegetation, which increases bank resistance. During flood, the overflow currents are quickly checked in the vegetation, and natural levees are built as the sediment is dropped. The channel is deepened and narrowed by building of the banks. Eventually, only silt and fine sand of the suspended load is deposited on the fan surface by flood waters, whereas the bed load consists of coarse sand and gravel. The stream changes course by overtopping and cutting through its levees, removes the fine silt layer of a newly occupied sector of the fan, and gradually builds up a new confined channel as vegetation develops on its banks. The abandoned channel is silted up.

With a slow rate of subsidence and sediment accumulation, the stream over the years may come to occupy all parts of its fan before a layer equal to the depth of the average mature channel accumulates. In such case the bulk of the sediment in the resulting deposit is bed material: coarse sand or gravel. If the rate of subsidence and sediment accumulation is rapid, the stream may occupy only a small part of the fan area during the deposition of a layer equal to the depth of the average mature channel. In this case much of the overbank silt will be preserved. Such a deposit will be finer-grained overall than the deposit of slow subsidence. Soil zones and vegetation layers may be preserved. The distinction between a fairly rapid accumulation of coarse gravel in a semiarid environment and a fairly slow accumulation in a more humid environment cannot be based on the character of the sediment itself, but must rely on other indications of the climate, such as fossil plant remains and preserved soil zones.

This rather extended exposition of the alluvial environment is given to indicate the various ways in which a single kind of sediment—coarse gravel, for example—may accumulate, depending on the interplay between climatic factors and rate of subsidence.

FLUVIATILE ENVIRONMENT   The fluviatile environment is that of the river bed and its floodplain. We have already seen (Chapter 7) that streams have essentially two patterns: meandering and braided, depending (in part) on the character of the sediment load. Streams carrying predominantly bed-size material (coarse sand and gravel), such that their banks as well as their beds consist of uncohesive materials, tend to have broad, shallow, braided channels; streams whose banks consist predominantly of fine, cohesive materials (silt and clay) or are otherwise resistant to erosion (densely vegetated or bedrock) tend to have deep, narrow, meandering channels.

The deposits of the braided river closely resemble fan gravels, and need not be considered further. Those of meandering rivers are more complicated. The meandering river shifts course in two ways: (1) by lateral erosion on the outside of a meander, and deposition of pointbars on the inner side; and (2) by levee breaks, producing either cutoffs of meanders or complete shifts of the stream to another part of the depositional plain. In the first case, the river removes the fine suspended sediment of its floodplain and levees, and replaces it with relatively coarse point-bar deposits; in the second case, abandoned meanders and river courses become ox-bow lakes, and these being the sumps of floodwaters, accumulate the finest sediment, including highly cohesive clays. These clay plugs and associated peaty swamp deposits, are extremely resistant to lateral erosion, and may be preserved extensively in the ultimate deposit. Accumulation of point-bar deposits as the river shifts laterally is by lateral accretion, whereas accumulation of overbank silts and abandoned-channel filling is vertical accretion.

Wolman and Leopold observed that most streams overtop their banks and flood their plains about once every 1 to 3 years. If accumulation on the floodplain were mainly by vertical accretion, one would expect that the frequency of overbank floods would decrease with time. Some rivers with recently graded floodplains should flood once a year or more often, and others, with floodplains of much greater age, should flood much less frequently. Since this does not seem to be the case, they concluded that rivers migrate sufficiently rapidly to regrade their floodplains, and that fluviatile deposits are predominantly point-bar deposits. The extent to which this has been true throughout the geologic

past, and may be used as a model for fluviatile deposition, is uncertain. All modern streams have been influenced by the same episode of rapid sea-level rise followed by 5000 to 6000 years of standstill. Their present behavior reflects adjustment to the period of standstill, influenced somewhat by artificial controls on flooding. To what extent the sediment of the period of rapid sea-level rise would also be predominantly point-bar deposits is uncertain. The only rivers for which there are abundant data—the Mississippi, the Rhine, and the Rhone—were glacial streams during the period of sea-level rise, and laid down coarse gravels. The sedimentary record of the early Cretaceous Morrison formation of the western United States, a typical fluviatile sedimentary rock, suggests that vertical accretion has accounted for a large proportion of fluviatile sediments in times past.

THE LACUSTRINE ENVIRONMENT   Lacustrine environments are similarly varied, from the shoreline with wave and current action, to the still water of a deep lake basin. In a sense they are a microcosm of the marine environment, but with an important difference. The lack of electrolytes in fresh lake waters means that suspended sediment does not flocculate. The fine particles settle slowly, in accordance with Stokes' law. Hence alternations of periods when the lake is turbid and clear are reflected by alternating coarser and finer lamina on the lake floor, or by laminae alternately rich and poor in organic matter. Lakes saturated with salts, such as calcium sulfate, may, if seasonally inundated, deposit thin layers of gypsum on their floors during the dry season. The thickness of the annual gypsum lamina is not more than a few millimeters (5 mm at most), since this is the amount of calcium sulfate that can be held by 4 meters of saturated water (the maximum likely to be evaporated in any year). Thus lacustrine deposits are more likely than any other to be varved. The Eocene Green River formation of Utah and Wyoming is a classic example of a nonglacial varved sediment.

THE EOLIAN ENVIRONMENT   Eolian sediment accumulates in two strikingly different environments. Eolian sand accumulates in dune fields dominated by moving mounds of sand, and essentially free of vegetation; eolian silt (loess) accumulates as a blanket, which settles out of stagnant air trapped in forest or grass cover.

Most eolian sandstones of past geologic time seem to have accumulated under arid conditions. The most notable are those of Permian to Cretaceous age of the Colorado Plateau, Permo-Triassic sandstones of northwest Europe (New Red Sandstone), and the Tertiary Nubian sandstone of northeast Africa. Modern dunes are found in three widely different environments.

1. The largest dune fields, comparable in extent to the great eolian sandstones of the past, are in the tropical deserts of the world: the Sahara, Arabian, and Australian deserts. In these fields the characteristic dunes are either barchans or seif dunes, with the seif dunes covering the greatest area. Transverse dune ridges are rare.

2. Extensive dune fields were formed in the periglacial regions from sand derived from the floodplains of the glacial melt-water streams.

3. Bare dune fields up to 25 km wide border many windward coasts, where the dunes are fed with fine uniform sand from adjacent beaches. Transverse and barchan dunes are the most common.

Dune sand preserves to an unusual degree the record of transport direction in its cross-bedding. As the dunes march across the country, during a period of aggradation, the lower part of the dune may be added to the sedimentary accumulation; the remainder is eroded by the wind and swept onward to contribute to the sedimentary deposit downwind. The lower parts of the slip-face structures are preserved, as spectacular cross-bedded layers up to 20–30 meters thick, the cross-bedding generally concave upward, and tangential to the bedding at its base (Figure 8–10). Studies of cross-bedding in the sandstones of the Colorado Plateau show uniform dips in a southerly or easterly direction—presumably the direction toward which the wind was blowing.

According to Bagnold, seif dunes accumulate alternately from one side or the other, by winds whose direction varies during the year. Such dunes should, in cross section, show cross-bedding with opposed dips. The lack of opposed dips in the cross-bedded sandstones of the past suggests that they accumulated mainly as transverse dune ridges.

The best known loess deposits are those of the Pleistocene, derived mainly from glacial rock flour, spread on the outwash plains by flooded melt-water streams. Loess blankets much of the U.S. Midwest, south of the margin of the last icesheet, and an extensive area across central and eastern Europe, where it provides the richest agricultural soils. It makes the soils in parts of southeast New Zealand and in Patagonia. Loess derived mainly from the Gobi Desert covers large parts of northeast China.

In northwest Canada and Alaska, where strong south winds create dense dust storms from glacial silt on gravel outwash plains, loess is accumulating today on Pleistocene terraces and on the lower slopes of adjacent hills, where it becomes trapped in the cover of forest or dense brush. The upper limit of loess accumulation appears to be the upper limit of brush on the hills, and no loess is now forming in the low tundra of the hilltops, nor does it appear to have accumulated there during the Pleistocene. By analogy, we may assume that loess accumulation of the Pleistocene in other parts of the world formed on land similarly well vegetated, either as forest or grassland.

Unlike transport by water currents, which is always in a downslope direction,[2] eolian transport is independent of direction of slope. Dune fields derived from the adjacent beach have migrated to altitudes of 1000 meters in the coastal mountains of Chile and Peru. Since both dune sand and loess can be deposited at altitudes higher than their source, neither can be used to give the direction of slope of the ancient environment.

TRANSITIONAL ENVIRONMENTS

The sediments that accumulated in the transitional environments are our record of past sea

---

[2] Except in tidal currents

FIG. 8–10 *Eolian cross-bedding in the Navajo sandstone; Zion National Park, Utah.*

levels, and reflect the complex interplay of marine and subaerial processes along the shore. They include the environments of deltas, tidal swamps, marshes and estuaries, beaches, barriers and offshore bars, lagoons, and coral reefs. Local environments today are of limited lateral extent. The typical coast shows a complex mosaic of environmental patterns, reflecting the interplay of currents and waves, as they move sediment from place to place along the shore. Such is the case in modern depositional coastlines, such as that of the northwest coast of the Gulf of Mexico (Figure 8–11). In stratigraphic sections, comparable intricacy of pattern can be seen in a complex interfingering of the deposits of the various environments, as delta distributaries, ocean currents, and wind shift from time to time. These environmental shifts are superposed in turn on much larger changes in facies due to variations in the rate of subsidence or sea-level rise, as compared with the overall rate of sedimentation.

DELTAS   The sites of most rapid accumulation in the transitional zone today are deltas. Those of the Mississippi, the Rhone, and the Fraser advance at rates measurable in meters or even kilometers per decade—orders of magnitude greater than changes in other parts of the coast. Presumably, therefore, deltaic deposits should be widely distributed in the stratigraphic record. If this is so, the fact has not yet been recognized, perhaps because we know too little of the structure of modern deltas in three dimensions.

The Mississippi delta, the most thoroughly studied, is probably atypical, for its unusual "bird-foot" pattern with delta distributaries and bordering levees extended seaward between shallow bays is almost unique. More commonly, the delta front in plan is smoothly convex outward and is bordered by barrier beaches and bars, as are the deltas of the Nile, Rhone, and Niger.

Physiographically, the typical delta is a plain extending partly above and partly below sea level, fronted by a gentle seaward slope to the sea floor over which the delta is advancing. In cross section (Figure 8–12c) it consists of (1) the topset beds, a nearly flat-lying complex of sediments deposited on the delta plain, resting on (2) the seaward dipping foreset beds of the delta front, which rest in turn on (3) the bottomset beds formed of the fine sediment swept beyond the delta front by currents, and settling on the sea floor. Whereas the foreset beds of small streams in quiet lakes may be as steep as the angle of repose, those of large rivers seldom have a dip of more than 1°. Those of the Mississippi delta dip ½°, giving a discordance between foresets, bottomsets, and topsets that could hardly be recognized without careful geologic mapping.

The foreset and bottomset beds of a typical marine delta are marine sediments, usually silt and clay, or fine sand. The fine silt and clay of the foresets and bottomsets are deposited in deep water, out of reach of waves, and are typically poorly sorted and structureless. Bottomset beds may have a mottled structure caused by burrowing organisms. Topset beds are more complicated. The first-deposited topsets at the front of the advancing delta are marine silts and sands. Being within reach of wave action they are win-

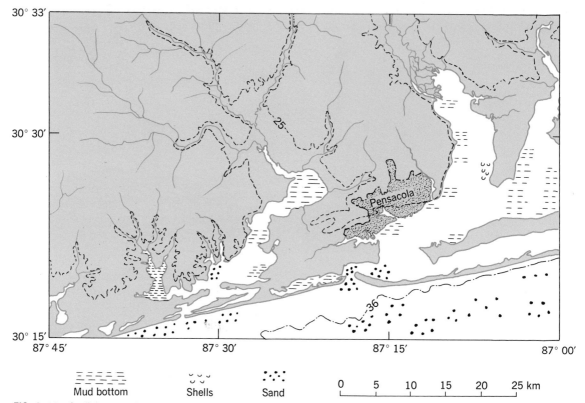

FIG. 8–11 Outline map of a part of the coast of the Gulf of Mexico, showing offshore bars, passages, and bays. [From Pensacola (1:250,000) sheet, U.S. Army Map Service 1957 ed., rev. 1966.]

nowed and sorted by waves, and as a result are thinly laminated. The marine topsets are overlain, in turn, by continental sediments as the delta plain grows above sea level. The continental sediments are a geographically complex assemblage of marsh deposits, sediments of natural levees, and channel sands. According to Fisk (1961) prominent features of the bird-foot delta are barfinger sands, linear accumulations of bed-load sand built as bars before the advancing distributary mouths. Shepard and Scruton (in Shepard *et al.*, 1960) were unable to find any evidence of such sands.

As the delta extends seaward the alluvial plain upstream from the delta front slowly aggrades; eventually, shorter, steeper courses to the sea are available on one side or the other of the delta. A breach in the natural levees during flood may result in a complete change in course and abandonment of the delta. A new delta starts its growth and eventually overlaps the side of the abandoned delta. The abandoned delta, meanwhile, subsides in part below sea level due to compaction of the deltaic sediments, and is moreover now subject to unopposed wave attack. Removal of fine sediment from the upper foresets and topsets through wave and current action may leave a residual mantle of clean sand. Along the delta front the waves may heap this sand into a barrier island, which encloses a broad, shallow sound in which marine sediments may accumulate on top of the marsh and levee deposits.

Seven such deltas have been discovered at the mouth of the Mississippi Valley, all formed within the last 5000 years (Figure 8–12d) and at least three have been recognized for the Rhone.

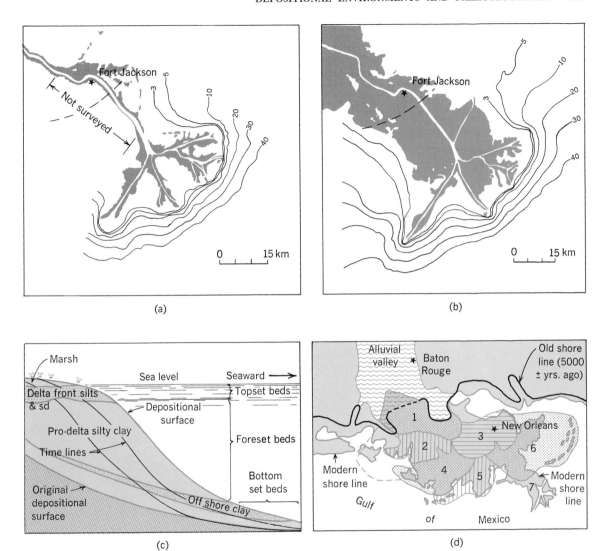

FIG. 8–12 *Aspects of the Mississippi Delta. (a) The Mississippi Delta in 1874. (b) The Mississippi Delta in 1940. (c) Cross-section of a typical deltaic sequence. (d) The overlapping deltas of the Mississippi River, all younger than 5000 years. Deltas are numbered in order of their development. Contours in fathoms; 1 fathom = 1.83 meters. (Modified from P.C. Scruton in F. P. Shepard, et al., eds., Recent Sediments, NW Gulf of Mexico, American Association of Petroleum Geologists, figs. 2, 1, 9, 15, 1960.)*

BARRIER ISLAND–TIDAL MARSH COMPLEX   Much of the eastern coastline of the United States from New Jersey to the Rio Grande is bordered by a series of barrier islands, behind which are tidal marshes, estuaries, and lagoons. This coast shelves broadly, and the submerged coastal plain extends seaward for 50–200 km as the gently sloping continental shelf. The latest event on this shelf was a sea level rise of 140 meters between about 6000 and 18,000 years ago, decreasing gradually to a state of near standstill which has prevailed for the last 5000 to 6000 years. The barrier islands appear to have built up to their present height as the sea rose, for there are no open sea-floor sediments among the Holocene deposits that mantle the floors of lagoons immediately landward.

The barrier islands are broken at intervals by tidal inlets, through which currents flow with velocities as high as 2 m/sec. The barrier islands are wave-built sand beaches, composed of sand supplied from rivers by long-shore drift and currents, and topped by dunes. In the marshes and lagoons behind the barrier islands there is a diversity of environment, depending on climate, depth of water, and animal and plant ecology. Near the Rio Grande high rates of evaporation in the tidal lagoons lead to precipitation of evaporite carbonates and sulfates. To the east, increasing supplies of fresh water lead to successively less brackish environments, with accordant changes in biota. When sea level first rose at the close of the Pleistocene period, the lagoons and estuaries were relatively deep, and fine sediment accumulated as thin laminae on the floors. With gradual shoaling by sediment accumulation, they became converted to tidal marshes, in which the sediment is trapped in thick growths of salt grass. The tide circulates onto the marsh via meandering tidal creeks. Tidal currents keep the inlets scoured.

Studies in Georgia show that over long intervals of time the barrier islands and tidal inlets tend to migrate southward as a result of long-shore drift. The main accumulation of sand in the barrier is deposited as steeply dipping beds on the upcurrent side of the inlet, while the inlet erodes the barrier on its downcurrent side. The sand is deposited into the deep inlet channel, and the foresets, dipping parallel to the direction of the coast, are the most likely to be preserved of all the barrier deposits. Elsewhere, the barrier sands dip very gently seaward.

On the seaward side of the barrier, waves spread the sand to a depth of about 10 meters. Below that depth, waves are unable to transport anything coarser than silt, and the modern shallow *neritic* sediments seaward of that depth are fine silt and clay, which would show up in the stratigraphic record as shale. A cross section of a typical barrier island is shown in Figure 8–13.

Ancient analogs of the modern barrier beaches have been recognized in the Cretaceous deposits of New Mexico, Colorado, Wyoming, and Montana. During the Cretaceous period a great seaway extended north over the site of the present Rocky Mountains and Great Plains, connecting the Arctic Ocean with the Gulf of Mexico. Sediment was supplied from a landmass on the west and now forms a sequence of sedimentary rocks, which on the western border are mainly continental deposits—fluviatile sandstone and siltstone, with coal beds—interfingering eastward with marine shales. The coal-bearing continental sequence is known as the Mesa Verde group, and the marine shale is the Mancos shale. Each covers the same broad interval of Cretaceous time. At any particular time horizon, the zone of contact between the continental sediments and the shallow marine shales to the east is marked by lenses of clean sand, thinning eastward, and in rather

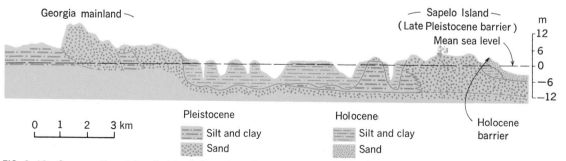

FIG. 8–13 Cross-section of Sapelo Island, Georgia, a Pleistocene and Holocene barrier island. (From Hoyt et al. *in* Deltaic and Shallow Marine Deposits, *edited by L.M.J.U. Van Straaten, Elsevier, New York, p. 172, 1964.*)

abrupt contact westward with interbedded silts and coal deposits. These lenses of clean sand apparently are the ancient barrier beaches. They are well-sorted and are of considerable economic importance, because their high porosity makes them valuable oil and gas reservoirs. Figure 8–14 is a diagrammatic cross section of these sand lenses, deposited in overlapping relation as rapid sedimentation from the west built out the coast eastward into the Cretaceous sea.

REEF ENVIRONMENT   A third transitional environment is the organic reef, which consists largely of calcium carbonate, secreted in skeletons of fixed (sessile) marine organisms—mostly corals, algae, and bryozoa. Barrier reefs, atolls (or reefs enclosing circular lagoons), and shallow carbonate platforms of this kind are common today in tropical seas. Reefs border the southern coast of Florida, the coast of Yucatan, and many of the Caribbean islands; they are found in the Red Sea, the Indian Ocean, and are widespread along the northern coasts of Australia—especially the Great Barrier Reef along the Queensland coast. Atolls and fringing reefs are found throughout the Pacific Ocean, between the latitudes of 30° N and 30° S.

The typical reef consists of a wall of colonial corals, dropping steeply on its seaward side. Blocks of coral broken by the waves from the seaward face accumulate as a talus breccia, and as the talus reaches the level of coral growth, new colonies are established on it. Surge channels are cut through the wall, which may be separated from land by a shallow lagoon in which silt and clay from the land (or, more likely, calcareous sediment) accumulates. Atolls enclose lagoons in which only carbonate sedimentation takes place.

The coral atolls of the western Pacific (Figure 8–15) were established on the wave-planed tops of ancient volcanoes, beginning in late-Cretaceous or early-Tertiary time. Gradual sinking of the volcanic foundation from that time onward has permitted continuous complementary upward growth of reef material to a present thickness of 700–1300 meters.

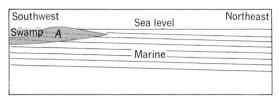

Stage 1

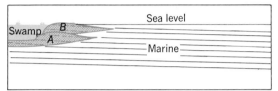

Stage 2

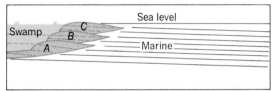

Stage 3

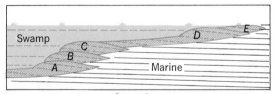

Stage 4

FIG. 8–14 *Diagrammatic cross-sections showing development of barrier island sands along the Mesa Verde-Mancos Shale contact in the San Juan Basin, New Mexico. (Stage 1) Strandline stabilized at A because subsidence is in equilibrium with sedimentation, resulting in deposition of sand bench A. (Stage 2) Slight decrease in rate of subsidence relative to sedimentation, causing strandline to shift seaward to B and stabilize once again, resulting in deposition of strand line B. (Stage 3) Slight decrease in rate of subsidence relative to sedimentation, causing further seaward shift of strandline and deposition of sand bench C. (Stage 4) Large decrease in rate of subsidence relative to sedimentation, causing strandline to shift rapidly to D, leaving relatively thin sand section in its wake. Strandline stabilized at D resulting in deposition of sand bench D, then regressed rapidly to E. (From C. T. Hollenshead and R. L. Pritchard in* Geometry of Sandstone Bodies, *edited by J. A. Peterson and J. C. Osmond, American Association of Petroleum Geologists, p. 103, 1961.*

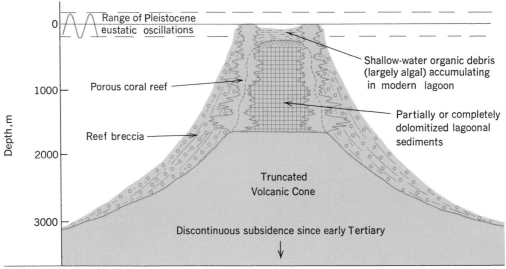

FIG. 8–15 *Diagrammatic cross-section of a typical coral reef. (From R. W. Fairbridge, The dolomite question, in R. J. Leblanc and J. G. Breeding, eds., Regional aspects of carbonate sedimentation (a symposium), Soc. Econ. Paleontol. Mineral. Spec. Publ. 5, pp. 125–128, 1957.)*

MARINE ENVIRONMENTS

The environment of a marine sediment is determined primarily by the depth of water, distance from shore or accessibility of terrigenous sediment, the configuration of the basin of sedimentation, and circulation within the basin, which controls oxygen content and abundance of organic nutrients. Environments include the shallow seas of the continental shelves (generally less than 200 meters deep), the continental slope, the floors of deep troughs and basins, and at least three recognizably different topographies of the ocean floor: abyssal plains, the normal ocean floor of rounded abyssal hills 50 to 500 meters high, and the tips and sides of submerged eminences, called *seamounts.*

OCEAN-FLOOR ENVIRONMENT   Sediment accumulates on the sea floor by several mechanisms, but there are two general categories: *pelagic,* which includes many *biogenic* sediments, and *turbidities.*

Pelagic sediments   A rain of fine particles is constantly descending from the surface to deep water. Much of these consist of the calcium carbonate shells of foraminifera and tiny carbonate plates (coccoliths) of one-celled lime-secreting algae, as well as siliceous tests of diatoms and radiolaria. As the descending carbonate grains eventually encounter deep cold water with higher dissolved CO_2, they begin to dissolve, so that calcite is an insignificant component of sediments laid down in the abyssal environment below 4000 meters. Carbonate sedimentation now takes place only along a narrow band of about 10° north and south of the equator. Where upwelling waters bring nutrients to the surface, as along the west coast of the Americas, diatoms and other organisms flourish in near-surface waters, and their siliceous remains accumulate on the floor beneath (Chapter 7).

Another component of the particle rain is wind-borne dust, derived from the continents. Some of this is the finest fraction of volcanic ash from great eruptions, distributed around the globe by upper-atmosphere winds; the remainder is derived by wind erosion from deserts and other continental regions. The concentration is greatest in the Northern Hemisphere, where the continents are most extensive. Still another component is fine sediment in suspension that is transported seaward by offshore currents. Most fine sediment is flocculated into larger grains when it comes in contact with seawater; consequently, the contribution of land-derived clay is significant only within a few hundred kilometers of the coast.

Sediment may precipitate chemically on the sea floor. Minerals such as the zeolite phillipsite, glauconite, and even orthoclase, have been found as precipitated crystals in deep-sea sediments; and nodules and crusts of manganese oxides, rich in iron and a number of rare elements such as cobalt, nickel, and copper, are found widely distributed on the sea floor. Phosphatic nodules are also found. Life may flourish in even the deepest troughs of the sea; and areas such as the Blake Plateau off the coast of Florida and Georgia have a rich fauna of corals, living at a depth of 600 to 1000 meters.

Turbidites   Turbidity currents are rather infrequent, catastrophic phenomena, which can rapidly transport great quantities of sediment to the deepest sea floor. A typical turbidity current deposit or *turbidite* is a thin layer (1–100 cm) of fine sand and silt, which may be graded from coarse at base to finer at the top (or may be uniform in grain size throughout), and may be laminated at the top. Where these occur, they are interbedded with thin layers of pelagic sediment. The flat abyssal plains apparently owe their flatness to burial of the normal hilly relief by turbidity-current deposits; and on the floors of troughs and basins bordering the continents these apparently form thick accumulations. Huge fans have been built by turbidity currents on the deep sea floor off the mouths of submarine canyons along the west coast of North America; and some basins, such as the Los Angeles and Ventura Basins, once more than 4000 meters deep, have been completely filled with material of this kind. A clue to a turbidite origin is the presence of shallow-water foraminifera and terrigenous plant remains in the coarse layers (turbidites) interbedded with deep-water foraminifera and radiolarians in the fine, interbedded pelagic sediment. The thin, sandstone beds of many great sedimentary deposits of alternating sandstone and shale, common in the fold belts of the world, and once thought to be of shallow-water origin, are now interpreted as deep-sea turbidites.

SHELF SEAS (NERITIC ENVIRONMENT)   Shallow seas of the continental shelves today border most of the land areas of the world, and extend to the interiors of the continents in such gulfs as Hudson Bay, the North and Baltic Seas, the Persian Gulf, and the Gulf of Carpenteria.

Sediments in process of deposition on these shelves today lie unconformably on a surface of erosion cut by ice sheets and rivers during the last glacial episode of the Pleistocene period, prior to the general rise of sea level that began 18,000 years ago.

Much of the continental cratons are mantled with ancient sediments deposited from shelf seas. Examples are the Paleozoic cover of the Russian Platform, the Permian and Mesozoic rocks of the ancient North Sea Basin (that included western Germany, northern France and southeast England) and the Paleozoic marine strata of North America around the margins of the Canadian shield.

The character of sediments deposited in shelf seas depends on the supply of terrigenous debris from land, the climate, and the circulation of water. Where land-derived sediment is abundant, silt or clay accumulates, ultimately, to form mudstones. During a phase of advancing sea, these are deposited over a thin sheet of sand reworked by the waves from previously built barrier beaches as these retreat landward. Where terrigenous sediment is not abundant, accumulations on the shelf may be largely chemical or biogenic. A classic accumulation of chemically or biochemically precipitated limestone is taking place today on the Great Bahama Bank, southeast of Florida. Cold bottom waters, rising, and spreading over the shallow Bahama Bank, are warmed and lose some dissolved carbon dioxide causing supersaturation in $CaCO_3$. This precipitates, probably through algal decay, in the form of fine needles of metastable aragonite. Under the gentle rolling action of waves and bottom currents, precipitated microconcretions of $CaCO_3$

have built great banks or submarine dunes of calcareous sand.

Inlets of shelf seas in arid climates are possible sites for precipitation of marine evaporites. Some of these evaporite deposits are rhythmically layered on a very fine scale, each layer consisting of alternations of calcite, anhydrite, or halite with magnesite, gypsum, or chlorides. These rhythms may record annual cycles of evaporation.

CONTINENTAL SLOPE AND SEA FLOOR   Sediments accumulating on the continental slopes and the deep-sea floor are mainly pelagic ooze. The normal rate of accumulation (excluding the abyssal plains) is exceedingly slow. It has been estimated to be about 1 mm per thousand years in the north Pacific, where wind-borne dust is a major component of the sediment, to ½ mm or less per thousand years in the south Pacific, where most of the sediment may be authigenic or organic.

BASINS   The variety of basin-floor environments depends on the influence of circulation on the oxygen content of the basin waters. Several types of basins are recognized, with circulation controlled by a single shallow entrance (Figure 8–16). (1) If evaporation from the basin exceeds inflow from the adjacent land, the basin water becomes denser as salts become concentrated,

and sinks (Figure 8–16a). Inflow takes place along the surface, and a countercurrent of heavy basin water pours out at depth. The sinking basin water has a high concentration of oxygen, and environment of the basin floor is one of oxidation. No organic matter is preserved in the floor sediments. The Mediterranean is such a basin. A similar condition prevails in polar regions, where residual concentration of salts in the surface water is by freezing of sea ice (Figure 8–16b). (2) On the other hand, if inflow to the basin exceeds evaporation, a surface layer of light fresh water moves outward from the basin to the open sea (Figure 8–16c). The deep water circulation, if it exists, is by deeper ocean waters moving into the basin. Circulation in the basin is sluggish, the oxygen is consumed, and the environment of the deep basin floor is one of reduction, favoring retention of organic matter and precipitation of sulfides. The floors of the Black Sea and of many Norwegian fjords are of this type. (3) The third type is more widely connected to the sea. Its basin waters are determined by the lowest level of the basin rim, through which the ocean water of that level pours (Figure 8–16d). The oxygen content of the ocean water is kept at saturation at the surface by mixing with the air and by photosynthesis. Food production by plants can take place only in the upper 100 meters, where sun-

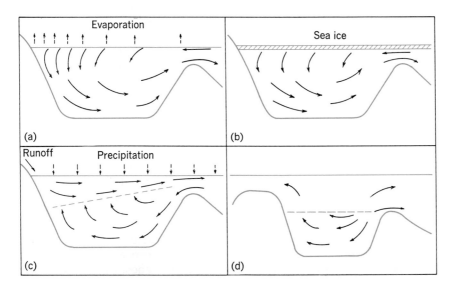

FIG. 8–16 *Four types of marine basins, showing circulation of seawater. (From K. O. Emery, The Sea Off Southern California, Wiley, 1960.)*

light penetrates; as dead organic matter sinks to deeper levels, it is consumed by other organisms, which utilize dissolved oxygen to obtain energy by oxidation of this food. The oxygen content of the water therefore falls to a minimum of about $\frac{1}{10}$ its surface value, at a depth of 500 to 700 meters. Below that depth oxygen content slowly increases to a value about $\frac{2}{3}$ that at the surface at 2000 meters. This value is maintained at greater depths. The oxygen contents of waters of basins whose thresholds are at the oxygen minimum (between 500 and 700 meters) will be low and they are conducive to a reducing environment. Basins whose thresholds are at much higher or lower levels will have oxidizing environments.

Basin-floor environments also are influenced by proximity to land. Where a rapid influx of sediment exists, such as in the Mediterranean Basin near the mouth of the Rhone, or in the basins immediately adjacent to the coast of southern California, sedimentation by fallout from surface waters is rapid, and numerous turbidity currents sweep to the basin floor from the adjacent shore, rapidly filling it. Basins separated from land by submarine ridges, such as those farther offshore to southern California, have no turbidity current deposits and accumulate sediment much more slowly.

ABYSSAL PLAINS   Parts of the ocean floors, adjacent to land areas, are characterized by extreme smoothness and an unusual thickness of the low-velocity surface layer, which is interpreted as young sediment. These are thought to have been filled largely by turbidity currents from the adjacent landmass or from the continental shelf. Several instances of turbidity-current movement have been recognized in the past few years from sudden simultaneous rupture of submarine cables; and the huge turbidity current triggered by an earthquake off the Grand Banks of Newfoundland in 1929 probably deposited a thin sheet of sediment over most of the abyssal plain of the western part of the North Atlantic. The sediment of an abyssal plain consists therefore of turbidity-current layers interbedded with fine pelagic ooze; this, in a stratigraphic section, would appear as a sequence of thinly interbedded sandstone, or graywacke and dark shale. Turbidity-current deposits are thought also to account for the flat floors and thick wedges of sediment in the deep trenches that lie adjacent to landmasses, notably the Peru–Chile trench and the Aleutian trench.

Paleogeographic Synthesis

The accumulated data of stratigraphy, lithology, sedimentary structures, and biofacies constitute material for paleogeographic synthesis. This usually relates to some rather large area and the conditions prevailing there over some selected interval of time, for example, southeastern England and northern France during the latter half of Cretaceous time. We have just seen how much may be inferred from environmental implications of the sedimentary record at representative points throughout the region in question. In this respect we can make good use, too, of sedimentary structures, as described in Chapter 3, and chronological aspects of stratigraphy, as outlined in Chapter 4. Structures such as bedding give useful information regarding depositional environment (for example, the cross-bedding of ancient dune sands, varves of glacial lakes, and graded bedding of turbidites). Cross-bedding of eolian sands, and the symmetry and parallel orientation of flute markings, are indicators of direction and sense of transport as well (Figure 8–17). Paleogeographic synthesis is a complex but geologically rewarding task. It cannot be emphasized enough that the geometric picture that emerges is complete only if seen in three dimensions, one of which (vertical) has a time significance. Above all, studies of this kind are concerned with measurements made in the field and visualized *in toto* through construction of maps and cross sections. It is only through this means that the chemical, physical, mineralogical, and paleontological evidence accumulated in the laboratory become mutually relevant and contribute to a picture of geological events and conditions on a geographic scale.

When correlations between stratigraphic columns have been established, units are selected

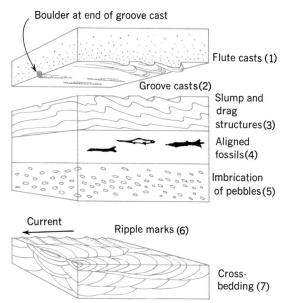

Boulder at end of groove cast

Flute casts (1)

Groove casts (2)

Slump and drag structures (3)

Aligned fossils (4)

Imbrication of pebbles (5)

Current

Ripple marks (6)

Cross-bedding (7)

FIG. 8–17 *Seven indicators of current direction. Numbers (1) through (3) are commonly found in turbidite sequences; (5) through (7) are commonly found in fluviatile sedimentary rocks.*

between surfaces of contemporaneity (as nearly as can be ascertained). For each unit so selected, a series of maps can be prepared showing the variation of significant parameters. One map will show the variation in thickness with lines of equal thickness, called *isopachs* (see, for example, Figures 8–19 and 8–24). Maps can also show the variation in average or maximum grain size in sandstone or conglomerate (Figure 8–18), and the distribution of characteristic minerals or rock types in the conglomerate. A series of maps, called *lithofacies* maps (for example, Figures 8–24 and 8–28), will show the percentage of conglomerate, sandstone, or shale, or the ratio of conglomerate plus sandstone to shale, again the ratio of clastic to chemical sediments. Other lithofacies maps may show simply the area in which each lithologic type predominates. Maps are also prepared to summarize the data on current directions, as indicated by cross-bedding, imbrication, and other current indicators.

Once the various objective maps are constructed, the interpretive model of the sedimen-

tary basin can be made. This is essentially a paleogeographic map of the region, in which shorelines, mountain and upland source areas, areas of continental and marine sedimentation, and sea-floor depths are indicated as completely as data allow; and the disposition of currents, stream patterns, and wind directions is shown. With the geography reconstructed, the tectonic history can be evaluated. The three examples cited later in this chapter are based on environmental reconstructions of this sort.

Diastrophic Implications of Sedimentary Facies

DIASTROPHIC VERSUS EUSTATIC EFFECTS

In any stratigraphic section, vertical changes in lithology from bed to bed or from one formation to the next reflect the total influence of changing provenance, conditions of transport, and depositional environment over some corresponding interval of time. Most clearly legible in the record are environmental effects—that is, changes in sedimentary facies. There is one controlling factor that is especially significant: the relative depth or elevation of the depositional site in relation to sea level. This, in turn, is the expression of two compounded effects—*diastrophic* and *eustatic*. Changes in depth that are directly brought about by crustal deformation in the area of deposition are termed diastrophic. They may extend over large segments of the crust and collectively may span long intervals of time—for example, the sequence of diastrophic events covering at least the whole of Ordovician and Silurian time that culminated in the Caledonian orogeny of northern Scotland and Scandinavia (Chapter 13). Eustatic changes of sea level on the other hand are worldwide, so they simultaneously affect to the same degree all sites of deposition.

Eustatic changes in sea level are due either to major changes in the mean depth of the oceans or to changes in the total volume of oceanic waters. Such events are difficult, if not impossible, to detect in the older part of the strati-

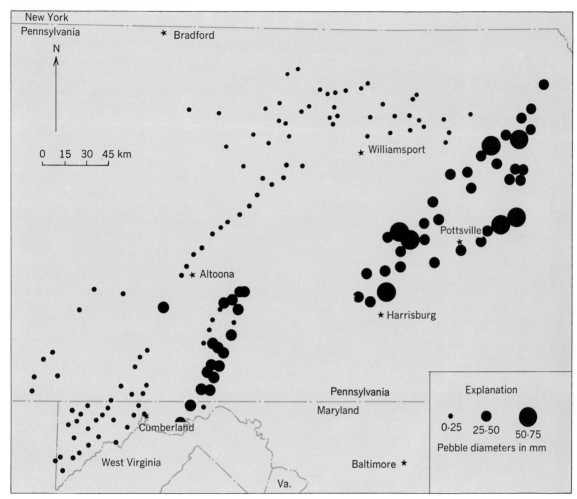

FIG. 8–18 *Distribution of pebble size in the Pocono formation in Pennsylvania and Maryland, showing decrease in size away from a source area to the southeast. The direction of dip of cross-bedding in the sandstones shows also that streams that deposited the Pocono formation flowed northwesterly. (From B. R. Pelletier,* Geol. Soc. Am. Bull., *vol. 69, no. 8, pp. 1033–1064, 1958.)*

graphic record. The most massive oceanic subsidence that has been detected is the sinking of the Darwin rise, a vast area in the western Pacific, through 1500 meters during the last 100 million years. This large-scale diastrophic movement, provided it was not compensated by uplift of the ocean floor elsewhere, must have dropped the worldwide sea level by some 150 meters—a eustatic change. The buildup of continental ice sheets during the last episode of Pleistocene glaciation was responsible for steady withdrawal of water, via the atmosphere from the oceans. The result was a eustatic drop of 130 meters in sea level with reference to today's datum. This event has long been recognized, for the drowned valleys that constitute many of today's harbors were eroded subaerially before the ocean waters were replenished to their present level by postglacial melting of the receding ice sheets. If melting were to continue, with ultimate elimination of the Antarctic and Greenland icecaps, world sea level would rise an additional 45 meters.

SEDIMENTATION IN RELATION TO DIASTROPHISM

In general, changes in the local environment of deposition, as recorded by facies changes in any thick vertical sedimentary sequence, reflect the shift between sedimentation and crustal deformation with the passage of time. If sedimentation proceeds more rapidly than subsidence of the floor of the basin of deposition, environment and facies may shift from deeper to shallower marine, through transitional, to continental sediments. The extreme case is the filling of a stable basin whose floor maintains a constant level throughout the cycle of deposition. If, on the other hand, the rate of subsidence exceeds that of deposition, the upward stratigraphic sequence is from shallower- to deeper-water facies—for example, conglomerate to sandstone to shale. Typical of some geosynclines is a general balance between deposition and synchronous subsidence. This is the case in the Mesozoic filling of the Andean geosyncline of Chile; volcanic flows and pyroclastic sheets with interbedded shallow-water marine and continental sediments whose total thickness aggregates at least 30 km.

The changing lithology of a sedimentary sequence also provides information regarding diastrophic events in the source area. For example, the presence of conglomerate beds containing boulders of nonresistant rock, such as limestone, indicates continuously maintained rapid transport, and hence rugged relief in the source area. We may infer rapid uplift and erosion at the source. Similar conditions are implied by the presence of easily weathered minerals, such as feldspars and pyroxenes, in sandstones. Absence of such materials in no way implies a source region of low relief. Rapid weathering under humid tropical conditions may compensate the effect of high relief and rapid uplift, and the resulting sediment may in consequence be uniformly fine-grained and composed predominantly of quartz and clay.

The margin of a deep ocean basin may be steepened because of warping or faulting. Sediment deposited on the steep slope may move onto the basin floor as great slides. The slide deposits, buried in the stratigraphic sequence, may have a completely chaotic inner structure, in which blocks of sandstone are embedded in shale and clay, and layers of sand and clay are intricately faulted and folded. The *Wildflysch* deposits of the Alps and Carpathian Mountains, the *Argile scagliose* of the Appenines, and contorted deposits containing huge exotic blocks in the Mesozoic and Tertiary rocks of the coast ranges of California seem to have this origin.

Another line of approach is to compute the total volume, or at least a lower limit, of the total sedimentary fill of a major basin. Here seismographically determined basin profiles are of great assistance, as also are well logs in basins that have been extensively drilled for petroleum. The next step is to locate the source area through provenance studies. In this way we can place limits upon the thickness of cover rock that has been stripped from a source of known extent over a limited span of time—the period of basin filling. Since erosion of the source rock can take place only above sea level, it is now possible to arrive at a minimum rate of uplift in the source area that can account for the observed volume of sedimentary fill in the complementary basin of deposition.

THE CRETACEOUS ROCKS OF WESTERN NORTH AMERICA

A classic example of the diastrophic influence on sedimentary rocks is to be seen in the Cretaceous rocks of western North America. These are a huge wedge of mainly clastic sedimentary rocks 1500 km wide and originally extending from the Mexican border to the Arctic Ocean in northern Alaska. They thicken westward from a feather edge in Kansas and Iowa to as much as 6000 meters in western Wyoming and Utah (Figure 8–19). To the west, where the rocks are thickest, they are mainly continental—coarse on the west and finer-grained on the east. If a given time horizon is traced eastward, the floodplain deposits are found to merge eastward into a belt

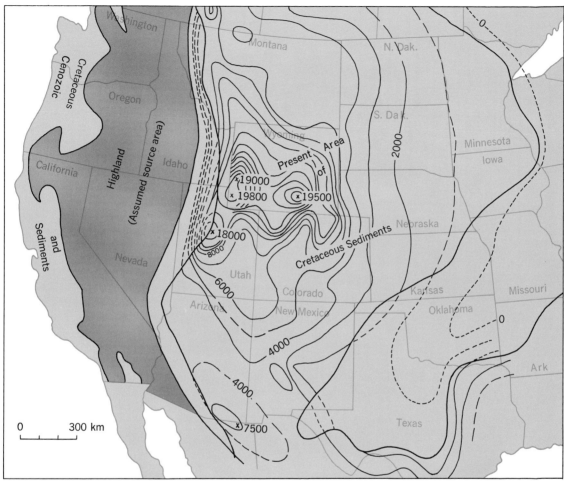

FIG. 8–19 *Isopachs on the thickness of Cretaceous rocks in the western United States, after Gilluly, 1963. Thicknesses are in feet. Dashed contour lines are inferred isopachs. (From P. C. Bateman and C. Wahrhaftig, in Calif. Div. Mines and Geology Bull. 190, p. 126, 1966.)*

in which thick coal beds abound; this in turn passes into a belt of coarse, clean sand, and still farther east, into shale.

When the information from many local sections is organized into correlated stratigraphic columns, the entire succession is seen to be continental to the west, interfingering in a series of great wedges with marine shale on the east. Each eastward-extending wedge of fluviatile sand and shale is sheathed by an assemblage containing abundant coal beds, which in turn is sheathed

by the clean permeable sand. The entire sequence is shown in Figure 8–20, and a detail in northern New Mexico in Figure 8–21 (see also Figure 8–14). The various contemporaneous lithologic assemblages in a west–east section give a picture of mutually gradational depositional environments. On the west was a fluviatile environment—essentially broad, flat alluvial fans with the coalescing floodplains of many rivers. This passed eastward into a belt of coastal swamps, where dense vegetation growing in shallow la-

Utah

Colorado and Wyoming

Site of Wasatch
mountains and western
edge of Colorado plateau

Site of Cordilleran
front range

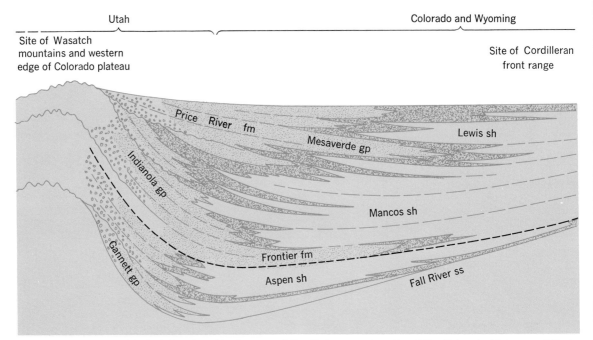

FIG. 8–20 (Above and facing) *Stratigraphic diagram of the Cretaceous deposits of the Colorado Plateau and Rocky Mountains, showing the interfingering of continental and marine sediments in western Colorado. (From P. B. King,* Evolution of North America, *Princeton Univ. Press, 1959. Copyright © 1959 by Princeton University Press. Reproduced by permission.)*

goons filtered out clastic sediment and accumulated as layers of peat, which were later compacted to coal. The eastern limit of the coastal swamps was a line of offshore barrier islands, with sandy beaches on their seaward sides. Seaward of the barriers was a shallow continental sea through which settled the silt and clay today represented by thick shales.

The interfingering relations of continental and marine facies are the result of variations in relative rates of subsidence of the basin and of influx of sediment from the source area to the west. When sedimentation exceeded subsidence, the sea shoaled, the alluvial plain was extended seaward, and the barrier-island and coal-swamp environments migrated eastward. When subsidence exceeded sedimentation, the sea advanced westward over the coal swamps, driving a sequence of barrier islands ahead of it (or at times of rapid subsidence, flooding the coal swamp before barrier islands could be built). Thus the interfingering marine and continental wedges were formed.

Whether the controlling factor was variation in rate of subsidence in the basin or of uplift and erosion in the source area, or whether both played a part, cannot be determined definitely. It is significant, however, that angular unconformities, suggesting renewed mountain building, occur at the extreme west in rocks corresponding in age to the base of each of the continental tongues. This suggests that variations in rate of uplift, erosion, and sediment production from the western source area had a lot to do with the intertonguing relations.

Throughout the Cretaceous period the shoreline gradually shifted eastward until, near the close of the period, the sea had disappeared entirely from the area of the Great Plains and continental sediments were being deposited in that area. Since then the entire region has been uplifted 500–20,000 meters and the sedimentary cover has been largely removed. The record of this infilling of the Cretaceous marine basin is now preserved in and around the margins of nu-

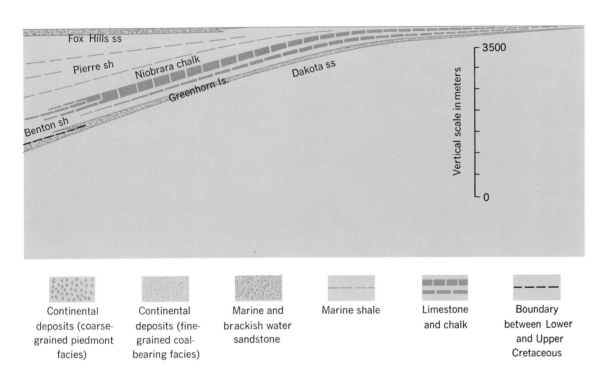

Kansas and Nebraska

Iowa

Site of Great Plains

Fox Hills ss

Pierre sh

Niobrara chalk

Greenhorn ls.

Dakota ss

Benton sh

3500

Vertical scale in meters

0

| Continental deposits (coarse-grained piedmont facies) | Continental deposits (fine-grained coal-bearing facies) | Marine and brackish water sandstone | Marine shale | Limestone and chalk | Boundary between Lower and Upper Cretaceous |

merous basins throughout northern New Mexico, Utah, Colorado, Wyoming, and Montana, and in the sedimentary rocks beneath the Great Plains. It is not only a record of sedimentation, but also of regional diastrophism, in which a large segment of western North America sank nearly 6000 meters, and an adjacent landmass still further west was comparably uplifted.

In 1949 James Gilluly showed that the source for the sediment had to be a belt of land less than 600 km wide, in Nevada, eastern California, Idaho, and Oregon (see Figure 8–19); for beyond this, marine sedimentary rocks were accumulating during Cretaceous time along the western margin of North America to thicknesses in places as great as 9500 meters. In a revised calculation, published in 1963, Gilluly showed that at least

8 km had to have been eroded from this belt to provide the Cretaceous sedimentary wedge of the Rocky Mountains and Great Plains. Since this source region has marine sedimentary rocks of early Mesozoic age, and is still standing today at an average altitude in excess of 2 km, uplift since early Mesozoic times may have been at least 10 km.

THE BASINS OF SOUTHERN CALIFORNIA

NATURE OF THE BASEMENT In striking contrast to the shallow seas in which the Cretaceous rocks of the Rocky Mountains accumulated are the deep basins of southern California, whose geology has become exceptionally well-known because of exploration for oil. They represent a type of basin

SW. (Landward)   (Seaward) NE.

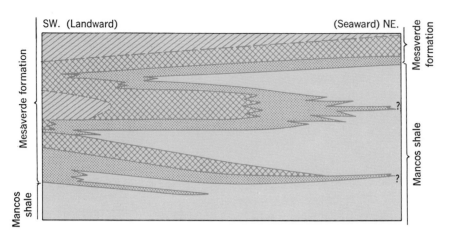

FIG. 8–21 *Diagram of interfingering continental–marine relations in the well-exposed Cretaceous rocks of northwestern New Mexico. Blank area, marine shale; dotted, near-shore and beach sandstone; cross-hatched, lagoonal deposits (interbedded coal, clay, and sandstone); lined, continental flood-plain deposits. (From J. D. Sears, C. B. Hunt, and T. A. Hendricks, U.S. Geol. Survey Prof. Paper 193-F, p. 108, 1941.)*

environment that may have been common in the mobile belts of the world; and are perhaps exemplified today by the modern basins in the continental borderland off the coast of southern California.

Southern California (Figure 8–22) is a region of rugged mountains with interspersed flat alluvial valleys of structural origin. The ranges reach altitudes of 3500 meters and are separated from the valleys by steep active faults—some normal, others reverse—many with considerable strike-slip displacement. The sedimentary rocks in the ranges are generally folded. Folds have also been traced beneath the flat valley floors and may be expressed on the surface as lines of low hills. This pattern of relief continues offshore, where the peaks of some of the ranges project above the surface of the sea as islands, such as Santa Cruz and Santa Catalina. Most of the submarine ranges, however, form submerged shallow banks. The basins are 1000 to 2000 meters below the bank tops and islands.

The basement rocks of the basin floors and the mountain ranges are a metamorphic-plutonic complex with a long and varied history. Some of these rocks bear the imprint of Precambrian plutonism and metamorphism. The latest events recorded in the basement were the late-Jurassic and mid-Cretaceous orogenies, during which were emplaced the composite granodioritic batholiths of the Sierra Nevada and southern California. Today we recognize three contrasting provinces of basement rock (Figure 8–22):

Province A. Granodioritic and dioritic plutons, intruding slates and metavolcanic rocks.

Province B. Distinctive Precambrian schists, large bodies of anorthosite (a feldspathic extreme of the gabbro family composed mainly of plagioclase), gabbro, and pink granite.

Province C. Metamorphosed sedimentary and volcanic rocks containing glaucophane, lawsonite; intrusive bodies of serpentinite.

These provinces are so distinctive and well-defined that provenance studies in younger sediments of the basin fills are especially revealing.

Following the mid-Cretaceous orogeny, a surface of relatively low relief was carved across the basement of southern California in the space of perhaps 10 million years. Subsequent sedimentation was localized in well-defined basins of deposition, which we shall consider in two distinct age categories.

LOS ANGELES AND VENTURA BASINS   The first sediments to be deposited on the eroded basement surface in this sector of southern California were continental sand, clay, and gravel, interbedded with shallow marine conglomerate and sandstone. From late-Cretaceous to early-Miocene time the sequence of formations in the continental area, where they are exposed today, is an alternation of (a) marine shallow-water sandstone and shale, and (b) continental red beds (clay, sandstone and conglomerate, colored red by iron oxides and containing fossil land-mammal

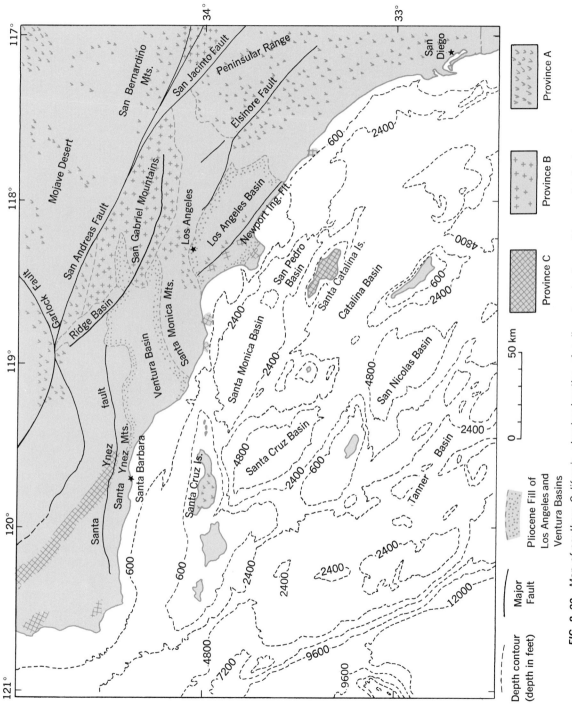

FIG. 8–22 Map of southern California, showing location of sedimentary basins and known distribution of metamorphic and plutonic basement rocks. (Data compiled from R. F. Yerkes et al., U.S. Geol. Survey Prof. Paper 420-A, 1965, and other sources.)

435

remains, indicating a semiarid climate). The crust was not quiet during this period, for as much as 5000 meters of these near-sea-level sediments accumulated in the Los Angeles Basin, which means that the basin floor subsided continuously by a like amount. A similar thickness accumulated in the Ventura Basin—mostly shallow-water or continental rocks, except along the northern margin of the basin, where the Santa Ynez Mountains are today. Here the lithological facies and fossils both indicate deep water. To supply this vast volume of sediment, the mountain area—the Peninsular Range, and the San Gabriel and San Bernardino Mountains—must have risen considerably during the interval of deposition (50 million years). How much they rose we are not sure, for the eastern limit of the source area has not been established. Some of the sediment could have come from as far away as southern Arizona, or northern Mexico, for the lower Colorado River was probably not in existence at that time.

In the middle of the Miocene period, the crust of southern California appears to have been affected once more by strong deformation. At the onset of crustal movement, andesitic lavas were extensively erupted from some source unknown, over much of the southern California region. The existence of former highlands along the southwest side of the Los Angeles Basin, where the Santa Monica and San Pedro Basins are today, is inferred from coarse breccia of Mid-Miocene age containing abundant blocks of glaucophane-bearing schist that today is found in many places along the southwest margin of the basin. This breccia interfingers eastward with light to white siliceous shales consisting almost entirely of the shells of diatoms (one-celled siliceous aquatic plants). Both the Los Angeles and the Ventura Basins rapidly deepened at a rate that greatly exceeded the influx of sediment; for paleontologists have identified in the overlying Upper Miocene and Pliocene deposits foraminifera (one-celled marine animals) closely related or identical to species that now live only at depths of 700–2000 meters.

The deep-water Upper Miocene and Pliocene sedimentary fill of both basins consists of two alternating lithofacies respectively dominated by shale and sandstone. The shale beds clearly were laid down in relatively deep water, for they contain deep-water fossil foraminifera. The sandstone beds, individually from a few centimeters to a few meters thick, commonly are graded; and in some graded beds cobbles and boulders at the base grade through coarse sand to silt at the top. Other beds contain irregular and contorted blocks of shale (Figure 8–23a). Their contacts with underlying beds are irregular; linear ridges and other projections into the underlying beds are interpreted as casts of erosional marks on the sea floor, due to the passage of turbidity currents (Figures 8–17 and 8–23b and c). The enclosed foraminiferal fossils are mostly shallow-water species, but some deep-water types are also included. These sandstone beds are interpreted as deposits from turbidity currents—sudden flows of sediment-charged water triggered by exceptional floods in rivers discharging into the basins, or by earthquake shock acting on unstable accumulations of shallow-water sediments on submarine slopes or at the heads of submarine canyons. A lithofacies and isopach map of the Lower Pliocene fill of the Los Angeles Basin is shown on Figure 8–24, and a paleogeographic interpretation of Figure 8–24, on which this history is based, is shown on Figure 8–25.

Eventually both basins were filled. The Ventura Basin in addition was strongly compressed, uplifted and overthrust from the north and south (Figure 8–26). The Los Angeles Basin, except for growth of some anticlines, and faulting and folding around its margins, is still relatively undeformed. In the center of the basin 8000 to 9000 meters of flat-lying beds, from late Cretaceous to Pleistocene in age, rest on the basement (Figure 8–27). This implies what geologists consider a high rate of sedimentation—a mean value, maintained over 80 million years, of at least 1 cm per 100 years.

SANTA MONICA AND SAN PEDRO BASINS   Some time after the middle Miocene, the highland west of the Los Angeles Basin collapsed to form the Santa Monica and San Pedro Basins. These are now filling with sediment. Sand moves southward along the beaches from the Santa Clara River and along the shore of Santa Monica Bay and is apparently diverted into the heads of two great submarine canyons: the Hueneme Canyon at the north end of Santa Monica Basin and the Redondo Canyon at the south end. The record of this diversion is clear because sand movement along the coast has been measured and there is a great deficit in the sand to the southeast of each of these canyons. Study of the sediment on the floor of Santa Monica Basin shows the greatest proportion of coarse sediment to be at the mouths of these canyons and the proportion to decrease away from them (Figure 8–28). Thus Santa Monica Basin is now filling in the way the Los Angeles Basin did in the Pliocene. Once Santa Monica Basin is filled, we may expect that the basins farther seaward, which now only receive a slow rain of pelagic sediment, will in turn be filled by turbidity currents.

FLYSCH SEDIMENTATION   The assemblage of monotonously interbedded sand and shale comparable with those of the Californian basins, and thought to have been deposited by turbidity currents, is unusually common in the mobile belts of the world. It is widespread in the Alps, Carpathians, Appenines and other ranges of the great Alpine–Himalayan chain, where the sediments in question are of late-Mesozoic and early-Tertiary age. The Alpine geologists call this assemblage the *flysch;* and comparable thick sequences of interbedded marine sands and shales elsewhere are called flysch facies. The flysch facies has been

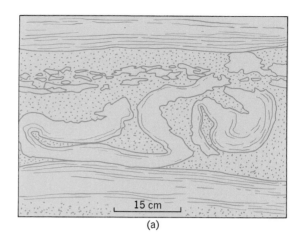
(a)

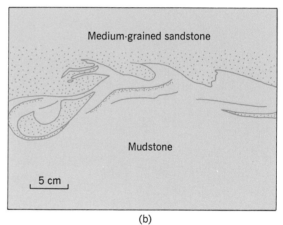
(b)

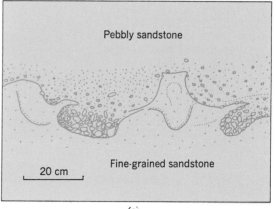
(c)

FIG. 8–23 *Sketches of features of turbidity-current deposits in the Ventura Basin. (a) Contorted mudstone layer in graded sandstone turbidite, probably resulting from detachment and transport by a turbidity current. (b) Flame structures: tongues of mudstone squeezed into the base of a massive sandstone, possibly from the weight of the overlying sand when it was deposited as a turbidite, and dragged from right to left during the final stages of motion of the turbidite. (c) Load pockets: accumulations of coarse pebbles in hollows scoured at the base of a turbidite, and subsequently deepened as the adjacent older sand is squeezed upward. Part (a) sketched from a photograph; (b) and (c) reproduced from sketches. (All in J. C. Crowell et al., Calif. Div. Mines and Geology Spec. Rept., 1966.)*

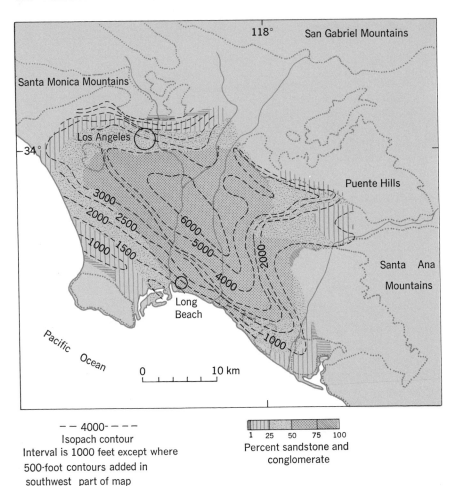

- − − 4000- − − −
Isopach contour
Interval is 1000 feet except where
500-foot contours added in
southwest part of map

1   25   50   75   100
Percent sandstone and
conglomerate

FIG. 8–24 *Isopach and lithofacies map of the lower Pliocene rocks of the Los Angeles Basin, showing that coarse sediment entered the basin from two or three points on its margin. (From R. F. Yerkes, et al., U.S. Geol. Survey Prof. Paper 420-A, 1965.)*

recognized in the early-Paleozoic rocks of Wales and Scotland and of the Appalachian system, and even in Precambrian sediments of the Canadian shield. Interpretation of all these as deposits from turbidity currents poured at intervals into deep basins and troughs is well-founded. Turbidity currents have been produced in the laboratory; their effectiveness in transport of mixed coarse and fine sediment on very gentle slopes has been demonstrated, and the resulting artificial deposit has the same structural character as that just described for natural sediments. In the case of the southern Californian flysch we can apply with confidence the uniformitarian principle. Among the Pliocene fossil foraminifera of the upper members it is easy to distinguish beyond doubt species that are respectively almost identical with living shallow-water and with deeper-water species in immediately adjacent seas. Here, it is the biofacies that establish the deep-water origin of shales and the shallow-water immediate source of the flysch sandstones.

THE PENNSYLVANIAN OF THE NORTH-CENTRAL UNITED STATES

OUTLINE OF GEOLOGICAL HISTORY   Our third example, in striking contrast to the others, records sedimentation on a stable platform. The Pennsylvanian system contains most of the coal re-

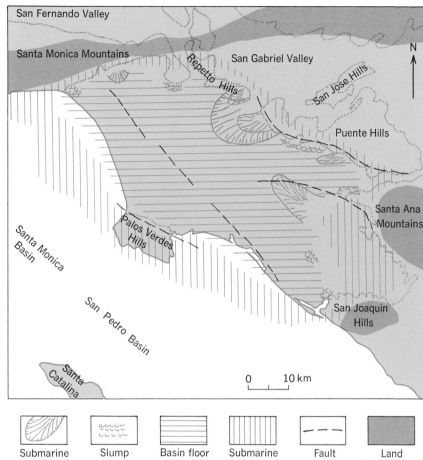

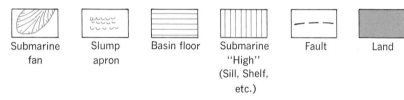

FIG. 8–25 Reconstruction of the geography of the Los Angeles Basin in early Pliocene time. (From B. L. Conrey, Calif. Div. Mines Geol. Spec. Rept. 93, 1967.)

sources of the eastern United States, and great reservoirs of oil and gas. In our area of interest it is preserved in four basins (Figure 8–29). The Michigan, Illinois, and Midcontinent Basins are on the continental platform; the Appalachian Basin includes the northwestern part of the Appalachian geosyncline.

The great crystalline Precambrian core of North America, whose exposed part is the Canadian shield, slopes southward in the central United States beneath a cover of Paleozoic rocks generally less than 2000 meters thick. These accumulated during those intervals of Paleozoic time when the platform was flooded by shallow seas, and today they outcrop as extensive thin sheets of limestone, shale, and generally pure quartz sandstone. During intervening periods the platform was slightly above sea level, as it is today, and was subject to subaerial erosion.

Along the southeastern side of the continental platform was the Appalachian geosyncline, a rather rapidly subsiding belt that during early- and middle-Paleozoic times became filled with great thicknesses of limestone, shale, sandstone, and conglomerate.

At the close of the Mississippian period east-

South

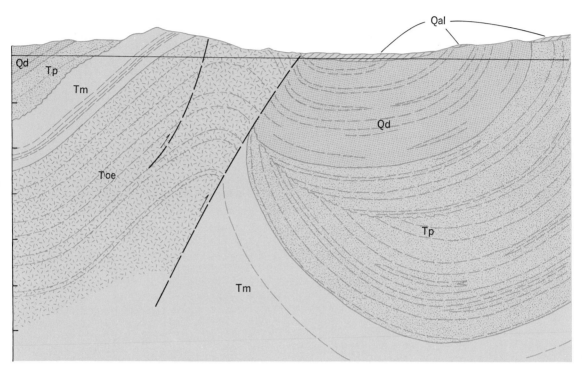

FIG. 8–26 (Above and facing) *Cross-section of the Ventura Basin, showing the remarkable thickness of Pliocene sediments and the subsequent deformation. Qal, relatively undeformed late Quaternary alluvium and terrace gravel; Qd, folded early Quaternary sediments; Tp, Pliocene sedimentary rocks; Tm, Miocene sedimentary rocks; Toe, Oligocene and Eocene rocks. Horizontal and vertical scale the same. (Simplified from T. L. Bailey and R. H. Jahns, in Geology of the Transverse Range Province, Southern California, Calif. Div. Mines Bull. 190, 1954.)*

ern North America was uplifted and subjected to erosion. In Pennsylvanian time the Illinois Basin, the chief focus of this discussion, was formed. It behaved differently in the north and the south; the southern part of the basin subsided fairly rapidly, and nearly 1000 meters of sedimentary rocks accumulated there; the northern part remained a shallow stable platform and received less than 200 meters of sediments over the same interval of time. Pennsylvanian sedimentation began first in the deep southern part of the basin, which was the first area to be depressed and inundated by the sea after the post-Mississippian period of erosion, and eventually spread over the entire platform area of the northeastern United States. The shallow continental Pennsylvanian sea connected with the world ocean through New Mexico and Arizona, for to the southeast and east lay the mountainous areas that were providing the terrigenous sediment of Pennsylvanian times.

LATE-PALEOZOIC CYCLOTHEMS The sedimentary rocks of Carboniferous and Permian age in many parts of the Northern Hemisphere exhibit to a marked degree a cyclic repetition of lithology. These repeating units, called *cyclothems*, are taken by some geologists as evidence of world-wide fluctuations in sea level, whereas other geologists attribute them to local variations in tectonic activity or climate, and still others attempt

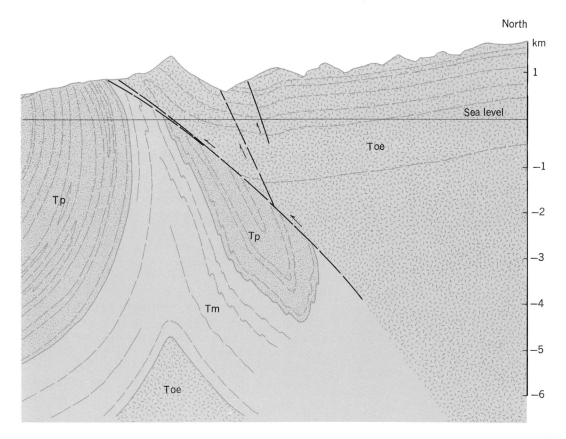

to explain them without invoking a cyclic cause. Theories for their origin are summarized below.

A typical cyclothem in Illinois (see Figure 8–30) has sandstone and shale at the base, overlain by discontinuous layers of fresh-water limestone, which is overlain in turn by a coal bed. A meter or less of hard flinty clay beneath the coal, called underclay, is interpreted to be the soil beneath the coal-swamp vegetation. The coal is overlain by gray shale with a marine invertebrate fauna and scattered plant fossils (apparently floating vegetation), which grades upward into a variable alternating sequence of marine limestone, black marine shale, and gray marine shale. This marine sequence is overlain in turn by the basal sandstone and shale of the next cyclothem. Figure 8–30 represents an ideal cyclothem from which cyclothems of Illinois may depart individually to some degree by omission of one

or more units. The lower half of a typical cyclothem is generally thought to have been deposited in a continental environment, and the upper half (or part) to have been deposited in marine waters.

Eastward, in eastern Ohio and Pennsylvania, the marine part of any cyclothem thins and eventually pinches out. On the east the clastic units at the base are thicker and coarser and the coal beds are generally thicker (Figure 8–31). In the Anthracite Basin of Pennsylvania the equivalent, presumably, of the Illinoisan cyclothems is an alternation of sandstone and coal. To the west, into Kansas and the Midcontinent Basin, the marine part of the cyclothem thickens and becomes predominant, and the sandstone units become less and less important. (It is well to remember that gaps in correlation exist between the basins shown in Figure 8–29.) At any moment in time during the deposition of a cyclothem, a

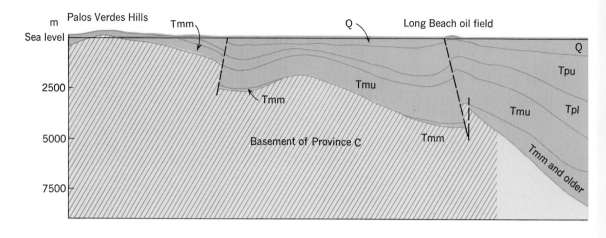

FIG. 8–27 (Above and facing) Cross-section of the Los Angeles Basin, at natural scale, showing thickness of Pliocene rocks. Q, Quaternary deposits; Tpu, Upper Pliocene sedimentary rocks (marine and continental); Tpl, Lower Pliocene marine sedimentary rocks; Tmu, Upper Miocene marine sedimentary rocks; Tmm, Middle Miocene rocks. Location of section is shown on map at lower left. (Modified from R. F. Yerkes U.S. Geol. Survey Prof. Paper 420-A, Plate 4, 1965.)

shallow sea to the west lay in contact with an area of continental deposition to the east. During the progress of the cyclothem (as given in the preceding paragraph) the shoreline gradually migrated eastward.

With the exception of the sandstones, the beds show remarkable continuity, particularly in the Illinois and Midcontinent Basins. Individual coal and limestone beds, only a few centimeters thick, can be traced for distances of over 100 km. Some coal beds a few meters thick have been correlated from Kansas to Pennsylvania. These correlations, if correct, suggest monotonous uniformity throughout much of central North America at this time.

The sandstone, on the other hand, occurs mainly in sinuous lenticular bodies, a few hundred meters to a few kilometers wide, and a few meters to 40 meters thick, although some of the sandstone is in thin sheets. The distribution of sandstone in Illinois has been mapped through study of data from thousands of wells. Typical results of this study are shown in Figure 8–32, which shows the sandstone bodies cutting out underlying beds and draped by an overlying bed. The lenticular sandstone bodies are interpreted as channel fillings—the bed load of streams flowing southwest from sources in eastern Canada, Pennsylvania, and New England, toward the sea in the southwestern United States. This interpretation is in agreement with the cross-bedding, which shows that the currents that transported

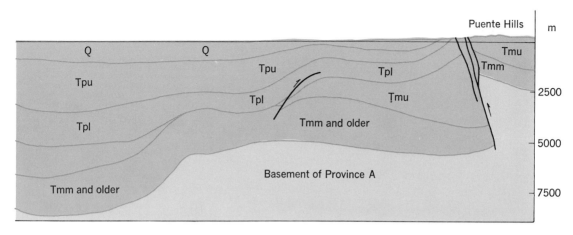

and deposited the sandstone were flowing southwest.

A crucial factor in any explanation of the cyclothems is the interpretation of the linear sand bodies. Many geologists interpret the sandstones as the aggradational bed-load fill of channels cut by streams on the abandoned sea floor of a retreating sea. Other geologists believe that they could have been deposited below sea level, possibly as "bar-finger" sands at deltaic distributary mouths similar to those described by Fisk from the mouths of the Mississippi, or in channels scoured by tidal currents. The pattern of the linear sand bodies and the current directions indicated by cross-bedding within them strongly support an origin as the bed load of streams. One might suppose, in this case, that the channel sands indicate periods of lowered sea level, when the streams cut deep channels in the abandoned sea floor. These periods might have been followed by periods of rising sea level, during which the streams filled the channels. The rising sea level might then have led first to coal swamps and then to open-sea conditions as the shoreline advanced landward. The amount of sea-level change required by this interpretation is open to question. For example, at Natchez, Mississippi, about 325 airline km above the river mouth, the alluvial plain of the Mississippi River is 20 meters above sea level, and the river has scoured its bed to a depth of 17 meters below sea level. If the channel at Natchez were filled with sand, the linear sand body could be more than 40 meters thick without representing any change in base level.

Number of cyclothems   It is difficult to determine the precise number of cyclothems in any one basin, because different authorities group the beds differently. Alternations between limestone and shale, or between coal and sandstone, which one worker regards as the result of minor changes in sediment pattern during a single cyclothem are interpreted by another as truncated cyclothems and are correlated with entire cyclothems elsewhere. In general, however, the cyclothems appear to range from 2 to 70 meters, and to average 7 to 15 meters, in thickness. About 30 cyclothems have been recognized in the Pennsylvanian of Illinois, and at least 40 and possibly 50 or more from Pennsylvania and eastern Ohio, where the section of Pennsylvanian rocks is more complete.

Significance of the cyclothems   If the usual interpretation of the cyclothems is correct (that is, that the lower part of sandstone and shale overlain by coal was deposited in a continental environment and the upper part of limestone and shale in a marine environment), the alternation of thin beds of coal, limestone, and shale over extensive areas indicates widespread stability. Thus slight changes in sea level or other controlling conditions could affect large areas. A vast area must have been tectonically quite stable during many of the cyclothemic marine

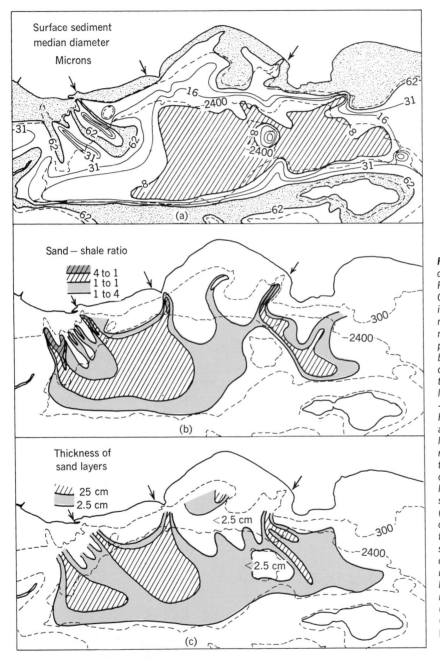

FIG. 8–28 *Maps of the floor of Santa Monica and San Pedro Basins, off southern California, showing variation in three sedimentary parameters, which indicate that modern sediments were deposited in large part by turbidity currents that flowed down large submarine canyons to the basin floors. Dashed lines are the −300 ft and −2400 ft depth contours. Heads of submarine canyons are marked by arrows. Catalina Island is at the lower right corner, Long Beach in the upper right corner, Anacapa Island on the extreme left. (a) Median diameter of surface sediment, in microns (dotted, coarser than 62 microns; diagonal lines, less than 8 microns). (b) Sand shale ratio after eventual compaction (explanation on map). (c) Thickness of sand layers (diagonal lines, thickness greater than 25 cm). (From D. S. Gorsline and K. O. Emery, Geol. Soc. Am. Bull., vol. 70, pp. 279–280, 1959.)*

invasions to allow such lateral uniformity, along with vertical diversity of lithology. Some regions, of course, were subsiding more rapidly than others. In the regions of even the most rapid subsidence, sedimentation seems to have kept the basins filled to the general level; otherwise they

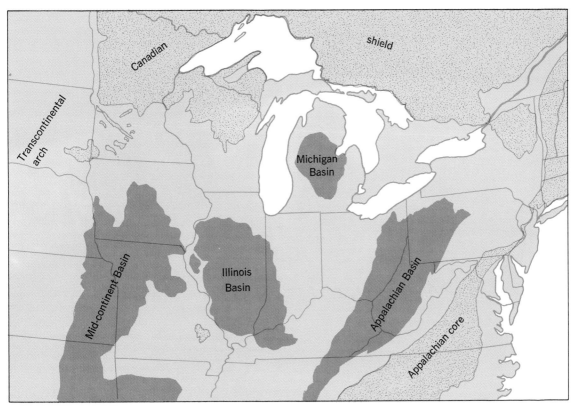

FIG. 8–29 *The geologic setting of Pennsylvania sedimentation in the east-central United States. Stippled pattern, Precambrian rocks and crystalline rocks of the Appalachian region; light color: Cambrian through Mississippian sedimentary rocks (includes Mesozoic and Cenozoic rocks of the Atlantic coastal plain and the Great Plains); dark color, Pennsylvanian sedimentary basins. (From P. E. Potter and H. D. Glass,* Illinois State Geol. Survey Rep. Invest.*, no. 204, 1958.)*

would have had relict lakes during periods of marine withdrawal. The southern Illinois Basin seems to have been such an area.

Any interpretation of the cyclothems must take into account the fact that they occur not only in North America, but also widely throughout northern Europe, in fact wherever late-Paleozoic coal measures occur. This cyclic alternation of continental and marine sediments must, therefore, be due either to worldwide cyclic alternations of conditions of sedimentation peculiar to late-Paleozoic time or to some influence, perhaps of the late-Paleozoic vegetation, that leads to a cyclic accumulation of sediment in the transitional environment. In regard to the latter possibility, it is well to note that cyclic deposition

is a characteristic of coal measures of any age, even those that appear to have been deposited in continental basins far from the sea. For example, the Mid-Tertiary Nenana coal field of central Alaska, which accumulated in such a basin, contains at least thirteen cyclic repetitions of sheets of pebbly sandstone alternating with coal or coal and shale.

Theories of origin of the cyclothems   Many workers see in the cyclothems evidence of a cyclic alternation of controlling external conditions, either climatic or tectonic; others attempt to explain the cyclothems as the result of an inherent cyclic tendency of sedimentation in the transitional environment even though tectonic and

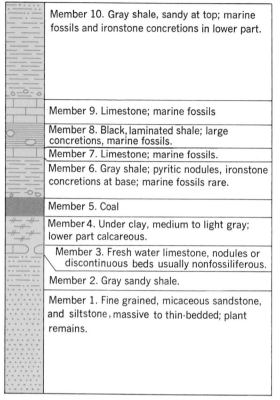

Member 10. Gray shale, sandy at top; marine fossils and ironstone concretions in lower part.

Member 9. Limestone; marine fossils

Member 8. Black, laminated shale; large concretions, marine fossils.

Member 7. Limestone; marine fossils.

Member 6. Gray shale; pyritic nodules, ironstone concretions at base; marine fossils rare.

Member 5. Coal

Member 4. Under clay, medium to light gray; lower part calcareous.

Member 3. Fresh water limestone, nodules or discontinuous beds usually nonfossiliferous.

Member 2. Gray sandy shale.

Member 1. Fine grained, micaceous sandstone, and siltstone, massive to thin-bedded; plant remains.

FIG. 8–30 *Columnar section of an ideal cyclothem. (From W. C. Krumbein and L. L. Sloss,* Stratigraphy and Sedimentation, *Freeman, 1956. Copyright © 1963.)*

climatic conditions may have been constant or altering at a uniform rate.

J. M. Weller, who first recognized the importance of the cyclothems of Illinois, attributed them to tectonic oscillations, centered primarily in the source areas. Each oscillation, in his view, consisted of a long, gradual subsidence followed by a short, sharp uplift. This tectonic control theory was based on the disconformities that he supposed existed at the base of the sandstone units, which he interpreted as requiring withdrawal of the sea.

Other cyclic tectonic hypotheses invoke variations in the rate of subsidence, with constant sedimentation, or variations in the rate of sedimentation (due to uplift in the source areas) with constant subsidence, to explain the alternation between continental and marine sediments. When sedimentation exceeded subsidence, the shoreline would be prograded and continental conditions would prevail. When subsidence exceeded sedimentation, the sea would flood the coal swamps, and marine conditions would prevail. In such theories, the channel sands are not evidence of widespread disconformities.

Another group of cyclic theories calls upon variations in climate to account for the sedimentary cycles. The most appealing of these is the glacial control theory of Shepard and Wanless. They attributed the cyclothems to eustatic shifts in sea level caused by waxing and waning of great continental glaciers in the Southern Hemisphere continent of Gondwanaland, where there is widespread evidence of repeated Permocarboniferous glaciation (Chapter 13). This theory has great appeal, for it explains sedimentary phenomena in one part of the globe as the necessary consequence of conditions existing in another part, a relation we observe in the Quaternary. If it is correct, we have a means for worldwide correlation in the late Paleozoic, for there should be the same number of cyclothems in all regions that show them. The period of cyclic sedimentation, however, seems much longer than that for which we have direct evidence of glaciation, and those who doubt the glacioeustatic theory emphasize a general difficulty in correlating cyclothems even throughout a single continent, let alone from one continent to another.

Other climatic hypotheses have appealed not to the indirect effects of glaciation, but rather to direct climatic effects in the source area. Changes to aridity in the source area, for example, were thought to bring on rapid erosion through destruction of protective vegetation cover. When the resulting sedimentary wedge reached sea level, a coal swamp would grow on it. Later inundation by the sea during the slow subsidence of the basin would drown the swamp and lead to accumulation of marine shale and limestone.

Contrasted with the theories of cyclic control are the theories, favored mainly by European

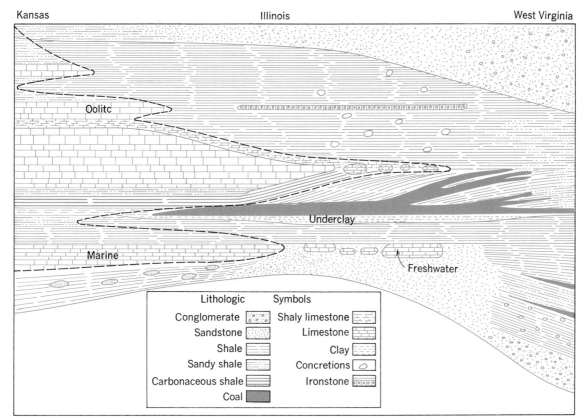

Kansas   Illinois   West Virginia

FIG. 8–31   *Lateral variation of a typical cyclothem across the east-central United States. Vertical distance represented is about 30 meters. Horizontal distance represented is about 1500 km. Dashed black line is boundary between marine and continental facies. (From H. R. Wanless,* Interna. Geol. Congr. Rept. 18th Session, Great Britain, *Part IV, p. 21, 1948.)*

geologists, and summarized by Duff, Hallam, and Walton,[3] that invoke an inherent cyclic habit of the depositional process. These theories emphasize that conditions in the source area could have been constant and that the depositional basin could have been subsiding tectonically at a uniform rate. In effect, they imply that cyclic variation in tectonic or climatic controls is not proved by the cyclic alternation in sediments; neither is it disproved. A modern analogy might be the overlapping deltas of the Mississippi River. Ac-

cording to these theories, cyclothems would not be contemporaneous throughout the entire area of deposition of the Pennsylvania coal measures, but would consist of bodies of sediment overlapping in space and time.

Some theories call upon variations in the rate of compaction of sediments, which lead to marine inundations followed by progradation of the shore. The sedimentary wedge is built upward to sea level, and at that point is covered by a coal swamp. An abrupt increase in the rate of compaction of the sediment would lead to flooding of the swamp by the sea, and the cycle would then be repeated. Rapid compaction is thought to be triggered by a slight increase in superin-

[3] P. McL. D. Duff, A. Hallam, and E. K. Walton, *Cyclic Sedimentation* (Elsevier, New York, 1967, pp. 148–156).

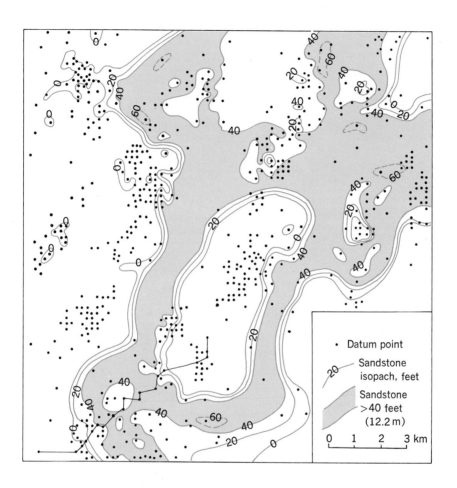

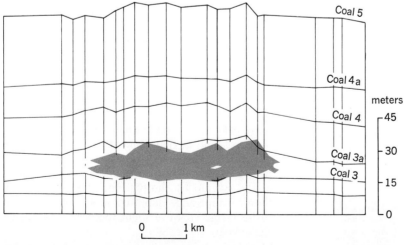

FIG. 8–32 *Isopach map and cross-section of a typical channel sandstone of the Pennsylvanian rocks of the Illinois Basin, showing cutoff of older beds and sinuous pattern of channel. Black dots represent data points, which are measurements of electrical resistivity in wells. The locality is in the southwest corner of Indiana, between 10 and 20 km west of the city of Evansville. (From P. E. Potter, Illinois State Geol. Survey Rept. Invest., no. 217, fig. 35, p. 54, 1963.)*

cumbent load over what the uncompacted sediment, such as peat, could normally support.

Other theories call for changes in the position of rivers to account for the cyclothems. A supply of fresh water from a nearby distributary would prevent a salt-water invasion of a coal swamp at sea level. A shift in the pattern of distributaries cutting off the fresh-water supply would allow seawater to invade the swamp, killing the vegetation. With continued slow subsidence, deposition of shale and limestone would take place on the shallow sea floor, and would be brought to a close only by the advance of deltaic distributaries bringing sand and clay deposition to sea level or above. Coal swamps would accumulate on the delta surface and the cycle would be repeated.

Another theory calls for change in the character of the swamp vegetation through the passage of time. After the sea floor is built to above sea level by incursions of sand and clay, the initial coal swamp consists of dense arboreal vegetation that keeps out seawater. As the peat beneath the coal swamp increases in thickness and the necessary mineral nutrients are rendered unavailable, the vegetation of the coal swamp deteriorates, and eventually is not able to retard the inflow of seawater. A marine inundation kills the swamp vegetation. With continued subsidence and compaction of peat to coal, water depth increases, leading to open-sea conditions and deposition of limestone and marine shale. These conditions would be brought to an end only by the return to this part of the basin of deltaic distributaries, which would carve deep channels through the previously deposited marine and swamp sediments as they prograded forward between natural levees. Overbank silts and floods of silt and sand through crevasses in the levees would raise the sea floor to sea level, and conditions for a coal swamp would be restored.

It is not yet possible to choose definitely among many of these theories on the basis of the evidence available. Possibly several causes are responsible. Glacially induced sea-level fluctuations may be responsible for some of the widespread cyclothems, whereas the more local cyclothems may be the result of the cyclic character of sedimentation.

The environment of accumulation of the thin, persistent, late-Paleozoic coal beds remains something of a mystery. The cyclothems in general lack barrier-island sands of the sort found in the Cretaceous of the Rocky Mountains. Whatever their origin, if the coal-forming environment had been a relatively narrow swampy belt between a sea on one side and an alluvial plain on the other, it is hard to understand what kept the sea from inundating the swamp. On the other hand, if coal-swamp conditions had succeeded fluviatile conditions over the entire region at the same time, and were replaced in turn at an instant in time by marine conditions, the flatness required for such widespread changes would not provide the slope for the late-Paleozoic rivers.

SUMMARY

Although all gradations are possible, major accumulations of sediment now exposed on the continent tend to conform to one or other of two contrasted categories—*platform* and *geosynclinal* accumulations.

To the first belong the relatively thin laterally extensive sheets of sediments that mantle stable platforms. These are exemplified by the Pennsylvanian rocks, including coal measures, of east-central United States. Platform accumulations commonly thicken locally in broad equidimensional basins where slow subsidence may lead to great thicknesses of sediment, as exemplified in the Illinois Basin. In the almost circular Michigan Basin the total thickness of Paleozoic rocks amounts to 4000 meters. Even in the basin areas neither sedimentation nor subsidence is rapid. In the Pennsylvanian rocks of Illinois we see a condition in which fluctuation in sea level—probably more extreme than at any other time in the Phanerozoic except the Quaternary period—may have exercised the major control in the pattern of sedimentation.

Geosynclinal accumulations form thick elongate bodies with abrupt lateral variations. They form in mobile belts. Some geologists recognize two principal classes—miogeosynclinal and eugeosynclinal:

The miogeosynclines, or parts nearer the continental interior, were only mildly affected by crustal activity until late in their history and received mainly carbonate and quartzose sediments (limestone, dolomite, shale, sandstone and quartzite). The eugeosynclines, or parts farther from the continental interior and nearer the ocean basins, were much more affected by crustal activity throughout their history and were the first to feel the effects of orogeny. The eugeosynclines received large volumes of volcanic and volcanic-derived sediments, as well as poorly sorted clastic sediments (argillites and greywackes); carbonate rocks are minor, but beds of siliceous sediment (chert) are common.[4]

Although it is useful, perhaps, to distinguish two contrasted patterns of geosynclinal sediments, it must be admitted that some patterns are intermediate in character, and some fit neither category.

The Cretaceous sediments of the Rocky Mountain region and the later Tertiary basin fillings of southern California occur in mobile

---

[4] P. B. King, Explanation to the tectonic map, *U.S. National Atlas* (sheets 69, 70, 1967), published by U.S. Geological Survey.

belts but hardly are typical of geosynclines. In both cases rapidly subsiding areas received a rapid influx of sediment. In the Rocky Mountain region rapid uplift of land to the west enabled sedimentation to keep pace with subsidence, and the depositional environment remained close to sea level. This was not the case in southern California, where sedimentation was outstripped by subsidence.

We know too little yet about the conditions of accumulation of deep-sea sediments and the tectonic history of the sea floor to attempt a diastrophic classification of their environments of sedimentation. However, new theories of evolution of the sea floor, described in Chapter 13, suggest the possibility of an additional tectonic environment: The flanks of the midoceanic ridges, where a slow accumulation of pelagic sediment is carried toward the continental margin by sea-floor spreading, and first is buried by floods of terrigenous turbidities in the deep trenches and abyssal plains along the continental margin, and finally is deformed and metamorphosed during underthrusting beneath the continents. Possibly some of the puzzling rock successions of the world's deformed belts, such as the Franciscan formation of California, have had this origin.

REFERENCES

GENERAL

Krumbein, W. C., and L. L. Sloss: *Stratigraphy and Sedimentation,* W. H. Freeman and Company, San Francisco, 1956.

Kummel, B.: *History of the Earth,* W. H. Freeman and Company, San Francisco, 1961.

Pettijohn, F. J.: *Sedimentary Rocks* (2d ed.), Harper & Row, New York, 1957.

CHEMISTRY OF AQUEOUS SEDIMENTATION

Arrhenius, G., and E. Bonatti: Neptunism and vulcanism in the ocean, in *Progress in Oceanography* (edited by M. Sears), Pergamon, New York, 1964.

Bonatti, E: Mechanisms of deep-sea volcanism in the

South Pacific, in *Researches in Geochemistry,* vol. 2 (edited by P. H. Abelson), Wiley, New York, 1967.

Degens, E. T.: *Geochemistry of Sediments,* Prentice-Hall, Englewood Cliffs, N.J., 1965.

Garrel, R. M.: Genesis of some ground waters from igneous rocks, in *Researches in Geochemistry,* vol. 2 (edited by P. H. Abelson), Wiley, New York, 1967.

Garrels, R. M., and C. L. Christ: *Solutions, Minerals and Equilibria,* Harper & Row, New York, 1965.

Kramer, J. R.: History of sea water. Constant temperature-pressure equilibrium models compared to liquid inclusion analyses. *Geochim. et Cosmochim. Acta,* vol. 29, pp. 921–945, 1965.

Krauskopf, K. B.: *Introduction to Geochemistry,* McGraw-Hill, New York, 1967.

Latimer, W. M.: *The Oxidation States of the Elements and Their Potentials in Aqueous Solutions* (2d ed.), Prentice-Hall, Englewood Cliffs, N.J., 1952.

Livingstone, D. A.: Chemical composition of rivers and lakes, in *Data of Geochemistry,* 6th ed., *U.S. Geol. Survey Prof. Paper 440-G,* 1963.

Lowenstam, H. A.: Biologic problems relating to the composition and diagenesis of sediments, in *The Earth Sciences* (edited by T. W. Donnelly), University of Chicago Press, Chicago, 1963.

MacKenzie, F. T., and R. M. Garrels: Chemical mass balance between rivers and oceans, *Am. J. Sci.,* vol. 264, pp. 507–525, 1966.

Mason, B.: *Principles of Geochemistry* (3d ed.), Wiley, New York, 1966.

Reesman, A. L., and W. D. Keller: Calculation of apparent standard free energies of formation of six rock-forming silicate minerals from solubility data, *Am. Mineral.,* vol. 50, pp. 1729–1739, 1965.

Schutz, D. F., and K. K. Turekian: The distribution of cobalt, nickel and silver in ocean water profiles around Pacific Antarctica, *J. Geophys. Res.,* vol. 70, pp. 5519–5528, 1965.

Weyl, P. K.: *Oceanography* (preliminary edition), Wiley, New York, 1968.

NATURE OF SEDIMENTARY ROCKS

Compton, R. R.: *Manual of Field Geology,* Wiley, New York, 1962; Chapter 12, Field work with sedimentary rocks, pp. 208–249.

Trask, P. D.: *Recent Marine Sediments,* 2d printing, *Soc. Econ. Paleontol. Mineral. Spec. Publ. 4,* 1955. (Reprinted 1968, Dover, New York.)

Twenhofel, W. H.: *Treatise on Sedimentation,* 1932. (Reprinted 1961, Dover, New York.)

Williams, H., F. J. Turner, and C. M. Gilbert: *Petrography,* W. H. Freeman and Co., San Francisco, 1954, pp. 251–384.

GENETIC IMPLICATIONS OF ROCK COMPOSITION AND STRUCTURE

Galehouse, J. S.: Provenance and paleocurrents of the Paso Robles Formation, California, *Geol. Soc. Amer. Bull.,* vol. 78, no. 8, pp. 951–978, 1967.

Garner, H. F.: Stratigraphic-sedimentary significance of contemporary climate and relief in four regions of the Andes Mountains, *Geol. Soc. Amer. Bull.,* vol. 70, no. 10, pp. 1327–1368, 1959.

Hjulström, F.: Transportation of detritus by moving water, in *Recen Marine Sediments* (edited by P. D. Trask), Dover, New York, 1968.

Krinsley, D. H., and J. Donahue: Environmental interpretation of sand grain surface textures by electron microscopy, *Geol. Soc. Am. Bull.,* vol. 79, no. 6, pp. 743–748, 1968.

Malde, H. E.: The catastrophic late Pleistocene Bonneville flood in the Snake River Plain, Idaho, *U.S. Geol. Survey Prof. Paper 596,* 1968.

Plumley, W. J.: Black Hills terrace gravels: a study in sediment transport, *J. Geol.,* vol. 56, pp. 526–577, 1948.

Sundborg, Åke: The River Klaralven—a study of fluvial processes, *Geograf. Ann. Hafte,* pp. 127–316, 1956.

Trainer, F. W.: Eolian deposits of the Matanuska Valley agricultural area, Alaska, *U.S. Geol. Survey Bull.,* no. 1121-C, 1961.

Van Houten, F. B.: Iron oxides in red beds, *Geol. Soc. Am. Bull.,* vol. 79, no. 4, pp. 399–416, 1968.

Walker, T. R.: Formation of red beds in modern and ancient deserts, *Geol. Soc. Am. Bull.,* vol. 78, no. 3, pp. 353–368, 1967.

DIAGENESIS AND LITHIFICATION

Kaplan, I. R., and S. C. Rittenberg: Basin sedimentation and diagenesis, *The Sea,* vol. 3 (edited by M. N. Hill), Interscience, New York, 1966, pp. 583–619.

DEPOSITIONAL ENVIRONMENTS

The following deal with *continental environments.*

Bagnold, R. A.: *The Physics of Blown Sand and Desert Dunes,* Methuen, London, 1941.

Bull, W. B.: Alluvial fans and near-surface subsidence in western Fresno County, California, *U.S. Geol. Survey Prof. Paper 437-A,* 1964.

Davis, G. H., J. H. Green, F. H. Olmsted, and D. W. Brown: Groundwater conditions and storage capacity in the San Joaquin Valley, California, *U.S. Geol. Survey Water Supply Paper 1469,* pp. 15–36, 56–81, 1959.

Fisk, H. N.: Geological investigation of the Alluvial Valley of the lower Mississippi River, U.S. Army Corps of Engineers, Mississippi River Commission, Vicksburg, Miss., 1944.

———: Fine-grained alluvial deposits and their effects on Mississippi River activity (1947), U.S. Army Engineers Waterways Experiment Station, 1957.

Hooke, R. Le B.: Processes on arid-region alluvial fans, *J. Geol.*, vol. 75, no. 4, pp. 438–460, 1967.

Krinitzky, E. L., and W. J. Turnbull: Loess deposits of Mississippi, *Geol. Soc. Am. Spec. Paper 94*, 1967.

Meckel, L. D: Origin of Pottsville conglomerates (Pennsylvanian) in the central Appalachians, *Geol. Soc. Am. Bull.*, vol. 78, no. 2, pp. 223–257, 1967.

Olmsted, F. H., and G. H. Davis: Geologic features and ground-water storage capacity of the Sacramento Valley, California, *U.S. Geol. Survey Water Supply Paper 1497*, pp. 10–34, 72–117, 1961.

Pelletier, B. R.: Pocono paleocurrents in Pennsylvania and Maryland, *Geol. Soc. Am. Bull.*, vol. 69, no. 8, pp. 1033–1064, 1958.

Pewe, T. L.: Origin of the upland silt near Fairbanks, Alaska, *Geol. Soc. Am. Bull.*, vol. 67, pp. 699–724, 1955.

The following deal with *transitional environments.*

Bernhard, H. A., and R. J. LeBlanc: Resume of the Quaternary geology of the Northwestern Gulf of Mexico Province, in *The Quaternary of the United States*, (edited by H. E. Wright, Jr., and D. G. Frey) Princeton University Press, Princeton, N.J., 1965, pp. 137–185.

Duff, P. McL. D., A. Hallam, and E. K. Walton: *Cyclic Sedimentation*, Elsevier, New York, 1967.

Hill, M. N. (editor): *The Sea*, vol. 3, Interscience, New York, 1966. Especially the following articles:

> **Bagnold, R. A.:** Beach and nearshore processes. Part I—Mechanics of marine sedimentation, pp. 507–528.
>
> **Inman, D. L., and R. A. Bagnold:** Beach and nearshore processes. Part II—Littoral processes, pp. 529–553.
>
> **Ginsberg, R. N., L. R. Michael, K. W. Stockman, and J. S. McCallum:** Shallow-water carbonate sediments, pp. 554–582.
>
> **Guilcher, A.:** Estuaries, deltas, shelf, and slope, pp. 620–654.

Hoffmeister, J. E., K. W. Stockman, and H. G. Multer: Miami limestone of Florida and its recent Bahamian counterpart, *Geol. Soc. Am. Bull.*, vol. 78, no. 2, pp. 175–189, 1967.

Hoyt, J. H.: Barrier island formation, *Geol. Soc. Am. Bull.*, vol. 78, no. 9, pp. 1125–1136, 1967.

Hoyt, J. H., and V. J. Henry, Jr.: Influences of island migration on barrier-island sedimentation, *Geol. Soc. Am. Bull.*, vol. 78, no. 1, pp. 77–86, 1967.

Peterson, J. A., and J. C. Osmond (editors): *Geometry of Sandstone Bodies*, American Association of Petroleum Geologists, Tulsa, Okla., 1961. See, especially, the following articles:

> **Fisk, H. N.:** Bar-finger sands of Mississippi Delta, pp. 29–52.
>
> **Hollenshead, C. T., and R. L. Pritchard:** Geometry of producing Mesa Verde sandstones, pp. 98–118.
>
> **Pryor, W. A.:** Sand trends and paleoslope in Illinois Basin and Mississippi embayment, pp. 119–133.
>
> **Purdy, E. G.:** Bahamian oolite shoals, pp. 53–62.
>
> **Weimer, R. J.:** Spatial dimensions of Upper Cretaceous sandstone, Rocky Mountain area, pp. 82–97.

Shepard, Francis P., Fred B. Phleger, and Tjeerd H. van Andel (editors): *Recent Sediments, Northwest Gulf of Mexico; a Symposium Summarizing the Results of Work Carried on in Project 51 of the American Petroleum Institute, 1951–1958*, American Association of Petroleum Geologists, Tulsa, Okla., 1960. See, especially, the following articles:

> **Rusnak, G. A.:** Sediments of Laguna Madre, Texas, pp. 153–196.
>
> **Shepard, F. P.:** Mississippi Delta; marginal environments, sediments and growth, pp. 56–81.
>
> **Scruton, P. C.:** Delta building and the deltaic sequence, pp. 82–102.

Van Straaten, L. M. J. U. (editor): *Deltaic and Shallow Marine Deposits*, Elsevier, New York, 1964. See, especially, the following articles:

> **Allen, J. R. L.:** Sedimentation in the modern delta of the River Niger, West Africa, pp. 26–34.
>
> **Lagaaij, R., and F. P. H. W. Kopstein:** Typical features of a fluviomarine offlap sequence, pp. 216–226.

The following deal with *marine environments*.

Bouma, A. H., and A. Brouwer (editors): *Turbidites,* Elsevier, New York, 1964. See, especially, the following articles:

Kuenen, P. H.: Deep-sea sands and ancient turbidites, pp. 3–33.

Stanley, D. J., and A. H. Bouma: Methodology and paleogeographic interpretation of flysch formations: a summary of studies in the Maritime Alps, pp. 34–64.

Dzulynski, S., and E. K. Walton: *Sedimentary Features of Flysch and Graywacke,* Elsevier, New York, 1965.

Emery, K. O.: *The Sea off Southern California, a Modern Habitat of Petroleum,* Wiley, New York, 1960.

Hill, M. N. (editor): *The Sea,* vol. 3, Interscience, New York, 1966. See the following articles:

Arrhenius, G.: Pelagic sediments, pp. 655–727.

Heezen, B. C.: Turbidity currents, pp. 742–775.

Heezen, B. C., and H. W. Menard: Topography of the deep-sea floor, pp. 233–280.

Heezen, B. C., and A. S. Laughten: Abyssal plains, pp. 312–364.

Laughton, A. S.: Microtopography, pp. 437–472.

Shepard, F. P.: Submarine canyons, pp. 480–506.

Kuenen, P. H.: *Marine Geology,* Wiley, New York, 1950.

Kuenen, P. H., and C. I. Migliorini: Turbidity currents as a cause of graded bedding, *J. Geol.,* vol. 58, pp. 91–127, 1950.

Menard, H. W.: *Marine Geology of the Pacific,* McGraw-Hill, New York, 1964.

Shepard, F. P.: *Submarine Geology,* 2d ed. (with chapters by D. L. Inman and E. D. Goldberg), Harper & Row, New York, 1963.

PALEOGEOGRAPHIC SYNTHESIS

Potter, P. E., and F. H. Pettijohn: *Paleocurrents and Basin Analysis,* Springer, Berlin, 1963.

ROCKY MOUNTAINS CRETACEOUS

Gilluly, J.: Distribution of mountain-building in geologic time, *Geol. Soc. Am. Bull.,* vol. 60, pp. 561–590, 1949.

———: The tectonic evolution of the Western United States, *Quart. J. Geol. Soc., London,* vol. 119, pp. 133–174, 1963.

Hollenshead, C. T., and R. L. Pritchard: Geometry of producing Mesa Verde Sandstones, San Juan Basin, in *Geometry of Sandstone Bodies* (edited by J. A. Peterson and J. C. Osmond), American Association of Petroleum Geologists, Tulsa, Okla., 1961, pp. 98–118.

King, P. B.: *The Evolution of North America,* Princeton University Press, Princeton, N.J., 1959; see, especially, pp. 108–111.

Sears, J. D., C. B. Hunt, and T. A. Hendricks: Transgressive and regressive Cretaceous deposits in southern San Juan Basin, New Mexico, *U.S. Geol. Survey Prof. Paper 193-F,* 1941.

Weimer, R. J.: Spatial dimensions of upper Cretaceous sandstones, Rocky Mountains, in *Geometry of Sandstone Bodies* (edited by J. A. Peterson and J. C. Osmond), American Association of Petroleum Geologists, Tulsa, Okla., 1961, pp. 82–97.

LOS ANGELES AND VENTURA BASINS

Bailey, T. L., and R. H. Jahns: Geology of the transverse range province, southern California, *Calif. Div. Mines Bull. 170,* Chapter 2, pp. 83–106, 1954.

Conrey, B. L.: Early Pliocene sedimentary history of the Los Angeles Basin, California, *Calif. Div. Mines Geol. Spec. Rep. 93,* 1967.

Crowell, J. C., R. A. Hope, J. E. Kahle, A. T. Ovenshine, and R. H. Sams: Deep-water sedimentary structures, Pliocene Pico Formation, Santa Paula Creek, Ventura Basin, Calif., *Calif. Div. Mines and Geology Spec. Rep. 89,* 1966.

Emery, K. O.: *The Sea off Southern California, a Modern Habitat of Petroleum,* Wiley, New York, 1960.

Natland, M. L., and W. T. Rothwell, Jr.: Fossil foraminifera of the Los Angeles and Ventura Regions, California, *Calif. Div. Mines Bull. 170,* chap. 3, pp. 33–42, 1954.

Winterer, E. L., and D. L. Durham: Geology of southeastern Ventura Basin, Los Angeles County, California, *U.S. Geol. Survey Prof. Paper 334-H,* pp. 275–366, especially pp. 323–334, 1962.

Yerkes, R. F., T. H. McCulloh, J. E. Schoellhamer, and J. G. Vedder: Geology of the Los Angeles Basin, California—an introduction, *U.S. Geol. Survey Prof. Paper 420-A,* 1965.

PENNSYLVANIAN OF EASTERN U.S.

Branson, C. C. (editor): *Pennsylvanian System in the United States, a Symposium.* American Association of Petroleum Geologists, Tulsa, Okla., 1962. See especially the following:

> Wanless, H. R.: Pennsylvanian rocks of eastern Interior Basin, pp. 4–54.

> Branson, C. C.: Pennsylvanian system of central Appalachians, pp. 97–116.

> ———: Pennsylvanian system of the midcontinent, pp. 431–460.

Duff, P. McL. D., A. Hallam, and E. K. Walton: *Cyclic Sedimentation,* Elsevier, New York, 1967, pp. 81–116.

Potter, P. E.: Late Paleozoic sandstones of the Illinois Basin, *Illinois State Geol. Survey Rept. Invest.,* no. 217, 1963. Also Kummel, B.: *History of the Earth,* W. H. Freeman and Company, San Francisco, 1961, pp. 113–127.

Potter, P. E., and H. D. Glass: Petrology and sedimentation of the Pennsylvanian sediments in southern Illinois, a vertical profile, *Illinois State Geol. Survey Rept. Invest.,* no. 204, 1958.

9

DEFORMATION OF ROCKS

DURING MOUNTAIN BUILDING, continental drift, sea-floor spreading, and many other processes that have contributed to the present structure of the earth's crust, rocks and minerals in the crust and mantle have been subjected to distributed mechanical forces (stresses), to which they have responded in a variety of ways. The possible reactions of crystalline solids to stress have been exhaustively investigated by the engineer and materials scientist; and the notions of elasticity, ductility, fracture, and creep are extensively developed and documented in the literature of the mechanics of solids.

Under normal surface conditions ($P = 1$ bar, $T = 25°C$), rocks subjected to short-term loading behave as elastic and brittle solids. A small column of rock, under moderate load in a testing machine, develops an instantaneously recoverable length change directly proportional to the load. When the load exceeds some limiting value, the specimen breaks violently by brittle fracture. This is the familiar reaction of a rock under the sudden impact (load) of the geologist's hammer.

No doubt, crustal rocks also behave as elastic and brittle solids over a wide range of natural conditions. No structural features directly attributable to natural elastic deformations can be observed in rocks because such features disappear when the forces causing them vanish; but

the ability of rocks in the crust and mantle to propagate seismic waves confirms that they are highly elastic in both compression and shear, at least in dynamic situations where forces act for very short periods. Evidence of elastic behavior for stresses of longer duration comes also from the Chandler period of variation of latitude and from earth tides (see Chapter 4). On the other hand, the brittle behavior of rocks in response to natural loading in the upper crust is amply confirmed by the occurrence on all scales of natural surfaces of rupture (fractures, joints, and some types of fault), which resemble structures produced in the laboratory by brittle fracture.

Other evidence suggests, however, that rocks can flow cohesively in the solid state without large-scale rupture and that natural deformations of a nonelastic or permanent kind are common in rocks. The approach to hydrostatic equilibrium embodied in the notion of isostasy indirectly suggests that some upper parts of the earth have properties akin to those of a very viscous fluid. Direct evidence of solid flow in the crust is given, on a small scale, by structures such as foliations, folds, and deformed dimensional markers such as pebbles known to have been "solid" at the time of their incorporation into a rock and, on a large scale, by patterns of orogenesis in an essentially solid continental crust.

455

Concern in the present chapter is with the types of mechanical behavior found in rocks and with the physical and geological interpretations of these phenomena. Our purpose is largely to pose questions many of which have as yet received no convincing answers: What are the physical mechanisms of deformation and flow in solid rocks? How do we interpret the flow structures of rocks in terms of displacements and strains, both local and regional? What are the patterns of distribution and geological significance of natural mechanical forces in the earth?

Answers to these and similar questions emerge only from a combination of several independent lines of approach:

1. The "phenomenological" and empirical theories of deformation developed by the engineer, the physicist, and the rheologist can be used to set up models of rock deformation.

2. Experimental deformation of rock and mineral specimens, over a broad range of temperature, confining pressure, and strain rate, is yielding valuable information on how such materials may be expected to behave under stress of long duration in the crust and in the mantle. Much of this information comes from geological laboratories; for engineers are more concerned with the effects of short-term stresses at lower pressures.

3. Scale-model experiments of a simpler nature can be performed on suitable materials at room temperature and pressure to simulate flow of solid rocks under geological conditions.

4. Field and laboratory studies establish the range of natural deformation structures and provide a basis for their genetic interpretation by direct examination.

In the present chapter we review some of the findings of theory, experiment and observation. Both theory and experiment are fundamentally physical and involve classical notions developed by mathematicians and physicists as a basis for the study of the mechanics of solids, of which "rock mechanics" in its broadest sense is a part. Some of these notions, particularly the theories of stress and infinitesimal strain, are not or-dinarily introduced into elementary courses in physics; and the manner in which they enter elementary teaching in engineering and materials science is not always relevant to the problems of the earth scientist.

Mechanical Properties of Rocks

In Chapter 2 we reviewed some of the elastic properties of crystals and introduced the concept of crystal plasticity. We now examine the part that these and other deformation mechanisms play in the permanent deformation of rocks on a larger scale.

MICROSCOPIC MECHANISM

Under the microscope, rocks and minerals show textural evidence of four main mechanisms of permanent deformation:

1. *Fracture*   Individual mineral grains or groups of grains (especially of quartz and feldspar) are cut by microfractures or have been crushed and granulated. The resulting cataclastic texture suggests that brittle fracture can play an important part in the small-scale deformation of rocks. Fractures occur on all scales—from microfractures, cutting several adjacent grains, to joints and other ruptures, which have propagated for distances measured in kilometers.

2. *Frictional sliding*   Closely associated with brittle fracture is slip along newly generated or preexisting fracture surfaces. When such slip is confined to grain boundaries, as in some poorly cohesive sedimentary rocks, extensive deformation can result with little effect on shape and structure of component grains. More usually, intergranular sliding is accompanied by marginal granulation of the moving grains. Cataclastic flow is the combined process of fracture and frictional sliding, by which the grain size of the flowing rock is progressively reduced by milling and grinding to yield, as the ultimate product, a fine-grained *mylonite*, which can be finely laminated in hand specimens. Some mylonitic rocks are so fine-grained that their crystalline nature can be demonstrated only by use of X rays.

Frictional sliding can be important also in well-bedded or foliated rocks, which can deform by the slip of laminae over one another. This mechanism is important in some types of folding of laminated rocks.

3. *Plastic deformation* It is doubtful whether any cohesive flow of rocks can take place without some pervasive intracrystalline plastic deformation. Common textural evidence includes elongation, flattening and bending of grains, and mechanically induced twinning and kinking.

4. *Recrystallization and grain growth* Post-deformational grain growth by recrystallization or by crystallization of new phases can be viewed as a "healing" mechanism analogous to annealing of cold-worked metals. Such recrystallization is thermally activated and involves diffusion, action of interstitial fluids and migration of grain boundaries. At high temperatures typical of metamorphism, recrystallization can proceed synkinematically, much as in hot-working of metals, and affect drastically the strength and creep resistance of a rock or mineral. End products of such recrystallization are aggregates of crystals free of deformation structures within grains. Such aggregates are typical of many metamorphic rocks and also of glacier ice which should strictly be considered a metamorphic rock deformed close to its melting point.

These four mechanisms act together in various combinations to yield a broad spectrum of mechanical behavior, depending on physical conditions such as pressure, temperature, activity of fluids, and time. Laboratory experiments on deformation of rocks and minerals have been concentrated on evaluating the separate influences of these physical parameters. Some of the findings of these experiments are now briefly reviewed.

EFFECT OF PHYSICAL CONDITIONS ON MECHANICAL PROPERTIES OF ROCKS

CONFINING PRESSURE Rocks deeply buried in the earth tend to support wholly or largely the weight of the overlying column of rock. If we assume that, in the absence of tectonic forces,

over long periods of time pressure at a point in the earth becomes more or less hydrostatic, by relaxation of higher or lower lateral stresses, then the pressure in a rock increases with depth in a manner given by

$$dP = -\rho g\, dr$$

where ρ is density and r is the distance to the center of the earth at a given depth. "Lithostatic" pressure at the base of a 35-km crust of continental rock calculated in such a fashion is about 10 kb. Pressures up to this value can be developed experimentally by immersing a sealed (impermeably jacketed) specimen of rock in a high-pressure medium (gas, liquid, or highly ductile solid) inside a pressure vessel. The pressure so exerted on

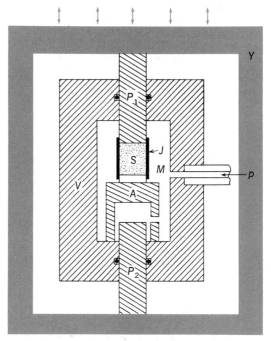

FIG. 9–1 Schematic drawing of triaxial testing machine for deformation of rocks at high pressure. V—pressure vessel; P_1—deforming piston; P_2—balancing piston; Y—yoke that moves both pistons together; A—anvil; J—impermeable jacket; S—specimen; M—fluid medium at pressure p. If pressure across the face of P_1 exceeds p, then yoke moves downward and specimen is compressed. If pressure across the face of P_1 is less than p, then yoke moves upward and specimen is extended.

the specimen by the enclosing medium is called the *confining pressure*. Loads can then be applied to the ends of the specimens by pistons (Figure 9-1). If the load applied by the pistons corresponds to a stress greater than the confining pressure, the specimen tends to shorten ("compression" experiment). If the stress applied by the pistons is less than the confining pressure, the specimen tends to elongate ("extension" experiment). Note that no large-scale tensile stress is present in an extension experiment unless the stress across the face of the piston is negative.

The characteristic effects of confining pressure on coherent rocks has been illustrated by experiments on marble, a rock in which the possible effects are encountered within a relatively restricted range of pressures. Figure 9-2 shows four cylindrical specimens of marble deformed by compression at 25°C.

(a) Confining pressure 1 bar (atmospheric

pressure). Failure was by brittle fracture along surfaces subparallel to the compression axis (axial or extension fractures). The curve relating load per unit area along the axis of compression (axial stress) to shortening in the same direction (axial strain), termed the stress–strain curve, is shown in Figure 9-3. The first response to increasing axial load is elastic shortening; and the corresponding section of the curve is straight and steep. Nonlinear behavior, with shortening of less than one percent, appears momentarily as the curve changes slope, just prior to fracture.

(b) Confining pressure 35 bars. In the stress–strain curve (Figure 9-3) the range of elastic behavior and the amount of nonlinear strain prior to failure by rupture are both slightly increased. Fractures are oblique (at about 30°) to the axis of loading, and are called *faults*.

(c) Confining pressure 300 bars. After preliminary elastic strain as before, the specimen re-

FIG. 9–2 *Specimens of Wombeyan marble after deformation at various confining pressures: (a) 1 bar; (b) 35 bars; (c) 300 bars; (d) 1000 bars. See Figure 9–3 for corresponding stress–strain curves. (Published by permission of M. S. Paterson.)*

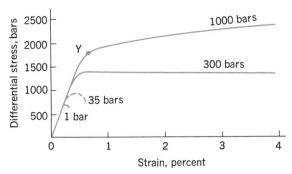

FIG. 9–3 *Stress–strain curves for Wombeyan marble deformed at various confining pressures. (After M. S. Paterson, Experimental deformation and faulting in Wombeyan marble, Geol. Soc. Am. Bull., 1958.)*

mains cohesive, even though deformation tends to be concentrated in discrete zones oblique to the axis of loading. In the corresponding stress–strain curve (Figure 9–3) the initial straight section (elastic strain) is followed by a short section in which the slope changes, and this passes into a third section that is essentially linear and subhorizontal—a record of progressive shortening at almost constant stress.

(d) Confining pressure 1000 bars. Flow following elastic strain is now completely cohesive, is more or less uniformly distributed throughout the specimen and is achieved without appearance of fractures or faults. The corresponding stress–strain curve (Figure 9–3) differs from the preceding curve only in that the linear third section has a positive slope indicating a period of progressive strain under linearly increasing stress.

In all four experiments strain led ultimately to failure by rupture. But the amount of permanent strain prior to rupture (a measure of *ductility*) increases with confining pressure. At 1000 bars, shortening prior to rupture can be 20 to 30 percent.

We can distinguish three main types of behavior in rock deformation:

1. Brittle behavior; the rock breaks along fractures subperpendicular to the least principal stress.

2. Behavior transitional between brittle and ductile; loss of cohesion is less sudden, and failure

is by faulting. Petrographic study of deformed material shows much small-scale fracturing (cataclasis) especially in the vicinity of the faults, together with some plastic deformation of grains.

3. Ductile behavior or cohesive flow; deformation is uniformly distributed throughout the central part of the specimen: the rock, in fact, "flows." In some rocks, such as marble, the fine-scale mechanism is plastic deformation of grains; in others it may be partly or entirely cataclastic.

In all rocks increase in confining pressure favors the transition from brittle to ductile behavior. Absolute values of transition pressures vary greatly from one rock to another. Dry quartzite, for example, remains essentially brittle under confining pressures of 10 kb or more.

Figure 9–4 (after Griggs and Handin) summarizes these notions with some further intermediate types added. In the lowest part of the figure, typical stress–strain curves for the various types of behavior are given. The ruled areas represent the possible variations in these curves for different rock types.

One way of stating these findings is to say that for any rock at a given confining pressure there is a stress at which a throughgoing fracture can develop (a fracture or breaking stress) and a stress at which ductile behavior can begin (a "yield" stress[1]). The experiments suggest that fracture stress is markedly sensitive to pressure and that increased confining pressures cause the fracture stress to approach and finally to exceed the yield stress, so that at high confining pressures ductile flow commences at stresses below the fracture stress.

Ductile flow is taken to begin at the yield stress (point Y in Figure 9–5); but to maintain a state of flow in the specimen the stress must be continuously increased, as shown by the positive slope of the third part of the curve. If the load is

---

[1]Ductile behavior, as can be seen from the upper two curves in Figure 9–3, does not generally commence suddenly at a particular stress value. For this reason an arbitrary value of stress, given by a point in the second part of the curve (such as Y in the curve for a 1000-bar confining pressure) corresponding to a particular small value of permanent strain, is taken as the yield stress.

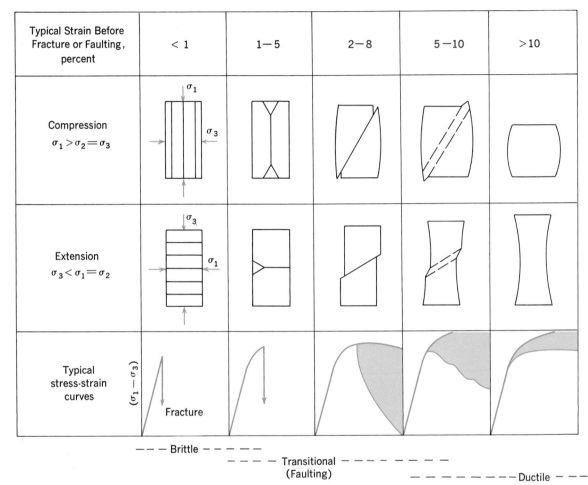

Typical Strain Before Fracture or Faulting, percent	< 1	1—5	2—8	5—10	>10
Compression $\sigma_1 > \sigma_2 = \sigma_3$					
Extension $\sigma_3 < \sigma_1 = \sigma_2$					
Typical stress-strain curves					

— — — Brittle — — — — —

— — — — Transitional — — — — — — — —
(Faulting)

— — — — — — — — Ductile — —

FIG. 9–4 *Schematic representation of the spectrum from brittle fracture to ductile flow, with typical strains before fracture and stress-strain curves for triaxial compression and extension. (After D. T. Griggs and J. Handin, Observations on fracture and a hypothesis of earthquakes, Geol. Soc. Am. Mem. 79, 1960.)*

removed, at point *A* in Figure 9–5, there is an elastic recovery of length along *AB*. If the specimen is now reloaded, ductile deformation recommences only when the stress exceeds *A*. The strained specimen has become stronger than the initial unstrained material. This phenomenon of "strain hardening" or "work-hardening" is observed in most polycrystalline aggregates (it is particularly important in some metals) and in some single crystals where it can be related to high dislocation density following plastic deformation.

High-pressure experiments have confirmed that most rocks can be made ductile by pressure alone. But the term "ductile" is no synonym for "plastic," in a physical sense, and the ductile flow of some rocks is achieved largely by microscopic fracture and frictional slip, and the resulting textures do not resemble those of many naturally deformed rocks that appear to have been "ductile." Also, the pressures required to induce ductile deformation in many rocks exceed those to be expected in the crust of the earth and the shearing stresses that would be required to de-

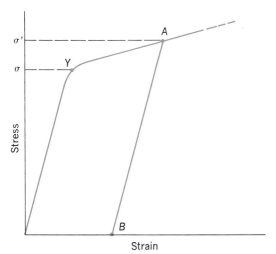

FIG. 9–5 *Loading and unloading curves for a ductile material. σ is initial yield stress; σ' is increased yield stress after unloading.*

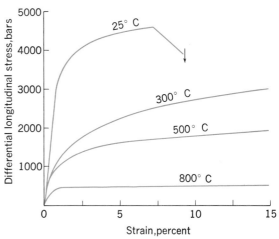

Fig. 9–6 *Stress–strain curves for cylinders of Yule marble cut parallel to foliation and deformed by extension at various temperatures. Confining pressure 5 kb, strain rate 3 percent elongation per minute. (After D. T. Griggs, F. J. Turner, and H. Heard, Deformation of rocks at 500°C to 800°C, Geol. Soc. Am. Mem. 79, 1960.)*

form the rocks at these pressures are impossibly high.

TEMPERATURE   Because of the distribution of heat sources in the crust (see Chapter 12), the temperature at the base of a 30-km crust is likely to be between 400°C and 650°C. Temperature, like pressure, is linked to depth in the crust, and, in a general way, then two quantities are mutually dependent; thus high pressures of the kind employed in the foregoing experiments are likely to be associated in nature with appropriately elevated temperatures. For example, an experiment designed to simulate conditions at a depth of 15 km in the continental crust might combine a pressure of 5 kb with a temperature of 400°C. Many such experiments have been made.

In almost all polycrystalline materials the effect of temperature at any constant high confining pressure is to reduce yield stress, to suppress fracture, and to enhance ductility without markedly altering the general form of the stress–strain curve. For example, the effect of various temperatures on the stress–strain curves for marble deformed in extension at 5 kb confining pressure is shown in Figure 9–6. As temperature increases, the yield stress is lowered, the strain range of ductile behavior is increased, and strain harden-

ing is reduced. At 800°C strain hardening effectively disappears.

In materials in which elevated temperatures cause chemical changes, effects on mechanical behavior are varied. For example, alabaster (a rock that is made of the mineral gypsum, $CaSO_4 \cdot 2H_2O$) compressed at 5 kb confining pressure at a variety of temperatures yielded the stress–strain curves in Figure 9–7. A remarkable feature of these curves is the sudden reduction in yield stress through a narrow temperature range. The experimenters were able to show that this loss of strength occurred through the temperature range at which gypsum dehydrates partly to a hemihydrate or totally to anhydrite ($CaSO_4$). The rock remained ductile at all temperatures.

On the other hand, similar experiments on serpentinite (a rock composed of the hydrous magnesian silicate serpentine), also at a 5-kb confining pressure, yielded the stress–strain curves in Figure 9–8. At temperatures up to 500°C the effects of increased temperature were much as those decribed for marble; ductility was increased and strain hardening reduced. Above 500°C a gradual transition occurred back to-

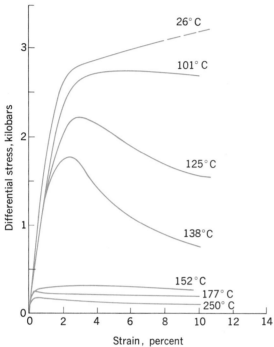

FIG. 9–7 *Stress–strain curves for jacketed Italian alabaster compressed at a 5–kb confining pressure at a strain rate of 3.3 × 10⁻⁴/sec, at different temperatures. (After H. Heard and W. Rubey, Tectonic implications of gypsum dehydration, Geol. Soc. Am. Bull., 1966.)*

ward brittleness. At 650°C and above, some specimens failed by fracture on a single sharp fracture surface. In this rock the temperature-induced dehydration reaction in serpentine (to forsterite and talc) caused embrittlement rather than increased ductility. In both rocks the peculiar behavior reflects the presence of a high-pressure intergranular fluid phase composed of the water released by the dehydration reactions, which, owing to the sealing of the specimens in impermeable jackets, cannot escape. We shall later return to the role of such fluids.

High temperature also plays an important role in accelerating "recovery" of deformed rocks by "healing" the accumulated damage caused by progressive deformation (fractures, plastic deformation structures in crystals, and so on). This damage is certainly the main agent of strain hardening. High temperature eliminates both the deformation structures and associated strain hardening by permitting freer motion of dislocations on the atomic scale (including dislocation "climb"), and by facilitating grain growth, including the appearance of new reaction phases in metamorphic environments. The best-known effect of this kind is "annealing," in which new undistorted grains grow at the expense of highly strained grains with higher free energy. This process commonly takes place in the solid state by migration of grain boundaries. By this process a large intensely deformed crystal becomes replaced by a mosaic of clear unstrained polygonal grains (Figure 9–9). Annealing generally takes place after deformation to reduce the strain energy of deformation left stored in plastically deformed crystals and as the surface energy of fractures. But a similar thermally activated diffusion process proceeds during high-temperature cohesive flow. If the rate of flow is very small, this process may keep pace with or exceed the rate at which imperfections are generated by de-

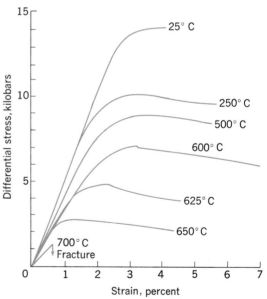

FIG. 9–8 *Stress-strain curves for Tumut Pond serpentinite compressed at a 5–kb confining pressure at various temperatures. (After C. B. Raleigh and M. S. Paterson, Experimental deformation of serpentinite and its tectonic implications, J. Geophys. Res., 1965.)*

FIG. 9–9 *Growth of polygonal grains in strongly strained single crystal of calcite. The specimen was first compressed experimentally at high confining pressure and then annealed. Diameter of specimen about 0.6 cm.*

formation and the flowing rock may consist at any instant of essentially unstrained grains, free of fractures. This seems to be the situation in some types of creep deformation.

PRESENCE OF FLUIDS Most rocks contain a fluid phase (generally aqueous) occupying pores or as a thin film along grain boundaries. Even initially dry rocks can become pervaded at high temperature by water released during dehydration reactions similar to those previously mentioned. Under metamorphic conditions reaction and interchange between the solid and fluid phases can lead to mineralogical reconstructions that materially affect the mechanical properties of a rock in which they occur. Some changes in strength may result from solution of intensely strained parts of grains with corresponding growth of the same mineral elsewhere, or from the growth of new phases stable under the particular metamorphic conditions present.

Recent experimental work has shown that the presence of water can affect the mechanical properties even of single crystals. Quartz, for example, is one of the strongest and least ductile of all the common minerals of the crust. Even at high temperatures and confining pressures, it remains almost perfectly elastic and brittle. In the presence of water, however, quartz and other very strong silicates can become extremely weak and ductile under certain combinations of pressure and temperature. Figure 9–10 shows stress–strain curves for natural quartz crystals at various temperatures, deformed wet and dry at 15 kb confining pressure and a strain rate of 0.8×10^{-5} sec^{-1}. The mechanism proposed by D. T. Griggs to explain this hydrolytic weakening involves increased mobility of dislocations as a result of hydrolyzation of Si-O-Si bonds adjacent to dislocations by migrating water. For metamorphic conditions, this flow mechanism may prove to be the most significant one yet identified in rocks.

Other important effects on the strength of an aggregate are nonchemical and arise merely from the presence of a high-pressure pore fluid. If permeability in an aggregate is sufficiently high, a uniform hydrostatic pressure may exist in the pore fluid. Normally this pressure should not exceed that at the base of a column of fluid (water) of height equivalent to the depth of burial; but deep drilling has shown that pressures of pore fluids, even at relatively small depths, can be greatly in excess of the equilibrium pressure $\rho_{\text{water}} \, gh$ (where h is height of the column of

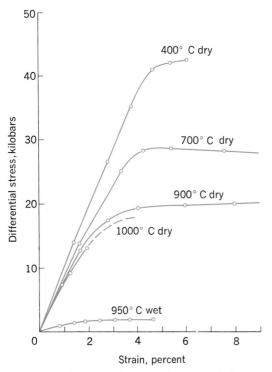

FIG. 9–10 *Stress–strain curves for wet and dry natural quartz crystals deformed at a 15–kb confining pressure and a strain rate of 0.8 × 10⁻⁵/sec. (After D. T. Griggs, Hydrolytic weakening of quartz and other silicates, Geophys. J. Roy. Astron. Soc., 1967.)*

water) and can even approach the lithostatic pressure $\rho_{rock}\, gh$. Factors such as tectonic forces, metamorphism, the action of certain rock layers as semipermeable membranes, dehydration reactions and—perhaps in the mantle and lower crust—partial melting, can increase pore-fluid pressure regionally or locally. In such situations the pressure between solid grains does not correspond to the "lithostatic" pressure described earlier, but is reduced by an amount dependent upon the pore pressure and the geometric properties of the aggregate. Let the lithostatic pressure be P and the pore pressure P_f; then the "effective" pressure between grains P_e is given by

$$P_e = P - \eta P_f$$

where η is a constant depending on such factors as grain size and shape, permeability, viscosity

of the fluid, and so on, which ranges from zero to unity. Most geologists believe that it can be taken as unity.

The mechanical effects on porous aggregates of high pore pressures have been investigated experimentally for a variety of rocks at different temperatures and confining pressures. The outstanding effect is a return to failure by faulting in a rock that, at the same temperature and pressure, would normally be ductile. This effect is observed particularly in rocks in which the ductile flow is cataclastic. Increased pore pressure in these rocks reduces the effective pressure between grains to a value lower than the confining pressure, so that frictional resistance to slip is reduced. If pore pressure is high enough, fracture of grains may be completely suppressed in favor of intergranular slip. Under these conditions, development of faults becomes likely. Note that there is no effect upon the coefficient of friction and that a high pore pressure in no way "lubricates" developing faults.

Even in materials that are ductile as a result of crystal plasticity, increased pore pressure allows the walls of cracks to be held apart and increases the likelihood of the propagation of large-scale fractures.

DURATION OF NONHYDROSTATIC LOADING Deformations other than pure volume dilatations are to be expected only in the presence of nonhydrostatic stress (exceptions are elastic distortions of anisotropic materials, and certain types of solid-state polymorphic phase changes, which include distortions). Most information on the mechanical properties of rocks is obtained from laboratory experiments involving the nonhydrostatic loading of specimens for periods of short duration (seconds or minutes, rarely hours). In geological terms the experiments and the behaviors they examine are effectively instantaneous.

To examine the time-dependent mechanical properties of crystalline solids, experiments of much greater duration have been contrived. These experiments may last for months or years and are of two main types. First are experiments in which a specimen is contrained to deform at a uniform slow rate, the load or stress being adjusted to keep the strain rate constant (controlled or slow–strain experiments). Second are experiments in which load—or, preferably, stress—is kept constant and the variation in strain or strain rate with time is investigated. Both types of experiment have been used on minerals and rocks. The slowest strain rate achieved in slow–strain experiments on rocks is about 10^{-8} per sec (on marble); a geologically realistic strain rate is generally taken to be about 10^{-14} per sec.

The effect of reduced strain rate is to lower yield stress and increase ductility. At room temperature a change in strain rate of marble from 3.3×10^{-4} to 3.3×10^{-7} yields the stress–strain curves in Figure 9–11. At 500°C the same change in strain rate with the same rock yields the curves in Figure 9–12. The reduced strength is much more marked at high temperature and there is an obvious decrease in strain hardening.

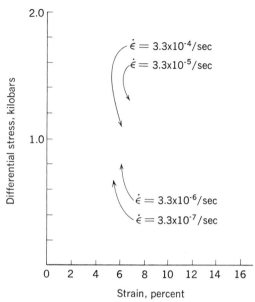

FIG. 9–12 Stress–strain curves for Yule marble extended at a 5–kb confining pressure and a temperature of 500°C at strain rates from 3.3×10^{-4}/sec to 3.3×10^{-7}/sec. (After H. C. Heard, Effect of large changes in strain rate in the experimental deformation of Yule marble, J. Geol., 1963.)

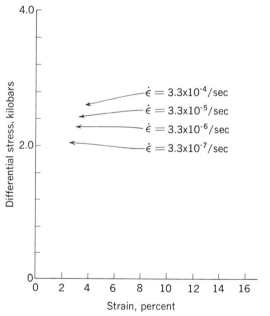

FIG. 9–11 Stress–strain curves for Yule marble extended at a 5–kb confining pressure and room temperature (25°C) at strain rates from 3.3×10^{-4}/sec to 3.3×10^{-7}/sec. (After H. C. Heard, Effect of large changes in strain rate in the experimental deformation of Yule marble, J. Geol., 1963.)

At the slower strain rates in the range of 400°C to 500°C, strain hardening effectively disappears and a state of steady, slow flow at constant stress is achieved. The qualitative effects of increased temperature and decreased strain rate are therefore similar, and the former has been used experimentally to simulate the latter.

These drastic changes in behavior at elevated temperatures seem to reflect an increased role of thermally activated processes leading to synkinematic recrystallization and annealing. If the rate at which these "healing" processes occur matches or exceeds the rate at which "damage" (dislocations, fractures, plastic deformation structures) accumulates, then a steady state of cohesive flow is reached in which, at any particular stage, the aggregate has a minimum amount of internal structural damage. The best empirical representation of such steady–state "pseudo-viscous" flow seems to be the equation of Eyring and others

$$\dot{\varepsilon} = \dot{\varepsilon}_0 e^{-E^*/RT} \sinh \left[\frac{\sigma}{\sigma_0} \right]$$

where $\dot{\varepsilon}$ is the strain rate, $\dot{\varepsilon}_0$ and σ_0 are constants with respectively the dimensions of strain rate and stress, σ is the differential stress, and E^* is the activation energy for self-diffusion.

In a typical creep experiment at constant stress, a strain–time curve of the type shown in Figure 9–13 is obtained. The first nonlinear part of the curve corresponds to a diminishing rate of strain (primary or transient creep) during initial loading. The straight central part represents a phase of uniform creep rate (secondary or steady-state creep) and is followed by a rising part representing an increasing creep rate (tertiary or accelerating creep) prior to rupture of the specimen. An equation of the form

$$\varepsilon = A + B \log t + Ct$$

can be fitted to this result, where ε is strain, t is time, and A, B, and C are material constants of some kind. In nature most or all creep probably occurs in the steady–state field.

SUMMARY OF MECHANICAL BEHAVIOR

In our discussion of the mechanical properties of rocks as deduced from experiments we have

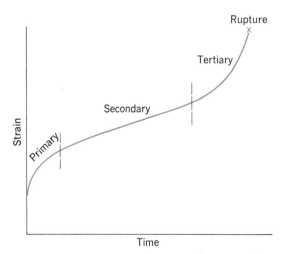

FIG. 9–13 *Typical strain–time curve for creep at constant stress.*

taken no account of structural and mechanical anisotropy arising from the presence of pervasive structures and preferred orientations of grains. We shall look further at these problems later. For the moment we can summarize the mechanical behavior of coherent, isotropic rocks as follows.

Large-scale brittle fracture is restricted to rocks at low confining pressures. In short-term experiments, duplicating the temperature and pressure ranges to be expected throughout most of the crust, rocks are transitional or ductile in their behavior, and the commonest mechanisms of failure or yield are faulting (generally without loss of cohesion on the fault surface), cataclastic flow, and plastic flow. In most common rocks the differential stresses required to initiate these types of deformation are very high—in many instances higher than stresses believed to exist in the crust. These stresses are lowered by the presence of a high-pressure pore fluid and by elevated temperature. The mechanism of deformation also is influenced by these factors. Some rocks become more ductile in such an environment (particularly where hydrolytic weakening occurs); others less.

The most important single physical parameter controlling the cohesive flow of rocks seems to be the duration of loading. It is probable that many of the deformation structures observed in rocks should be interpreted as creep structures, and that the main mechanisms of deformation are thermally activated and involve recrystallization, annealing, and grain growth. This view is supported by many of the textures of metamorphic rocks. But other rocks show evidence of deformation (plastic or cataclastic) with little or no recrystallization; and the existence of earthquakes is a constant reminder that deformation can proceed rapidly, at least locally.

Stress

Before we can explore more fully the significance of deformation structures in the earth, we must understand the notion of stress upon which all theories of deformation depend. In this section we look therefore at the classical theory of stress and examine the possible states of stress that may exist in the earth.

THEORY OF STRESS

STRESS AT A POINT In a continuous body in static (force and moment) equilibrium, an internal surface element ΔA contains a point P. One side of ΔA has an outward unit normal vector $\mathbf{n}$ and is considered positive; the other has an outward unit normal vector $-\mathbf{n}$ and is considered negative (Figure 9–14). Let the surface force exerted by the positive side on the negative side be $\Delta \mathbf{f}$, then the *average stress* across ΔA is given by

$$S_{av} = \frac{\Delta \mathbf{f}}{\Delta A}$$

The stress $\mathbf{S}$ at the point P is then given by

$$\mathbf{S} = \lim_{\Delta A \to 0} \frac{\Delta \mathbf{f}}{\Delta A} = \frac{d\mathbf{f}}{dA}$$

The quantity $\mathbf{S}$ has magnitude and direction referred to the attitude of ΔA at P and is termed the *stress vector* or *surface traction* across ΔA at P. In general, $\mathbf{S}$ is inclined obliquely to ΔA and can be resolved into two components: σ, acting normal to ΔA in the direction of $\mathbf{n}$, and τ, acting in the plane of ΔA (Figure 9–15). The first is called the normal component and the second the shearing component of $\mathbf{S}$.

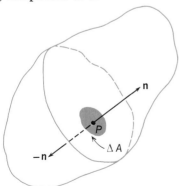

FIG. 9–14 *Body in static equilibrium with internal surface element ΔA (with unit normal vector $\mathbf{n}$) containing a point P.*

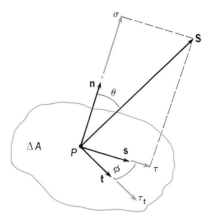

FIG. 9–15 *Stress vector $\mathbf{S}$ resolved into normal component σ and shearing components τ and τ_t.*

The magnitudes of the stress vector and its components are simply related by Pythagoras' theorem

$$S^2 = \sigma^2 + \tau^2 \tag{9-1}$$

and the magnitudes of the two components are given in terms of the magnitude of the stress vector by the following scalar products:

$$\sigma = \mathbf{S} \cdot \mathbf{n} = S \cos \theta \tag{9-2}$$

$$\tau = \mathbf{S} \cdot \mathbf{s} = S \sin \theta \tag{9-3}$$

where θ is the angle between $\mathbf{S}$ and $\mathbf{n}$, and $\mathbf{s}$ is the unit vector in the direction in which τ acts. The shearing component τ_t in any other direction lying in ΔA given by unit vector $\mathbf{t}$ inclined at ϕ to $\mathbf{s}$ is given by

$$\tau_t = \mathbf{S} \cdot \mathbf{t}$$
$$= \tau \cos \phi \tag{9-4}$$
$$= S \sin \theta \cos \phi$$

Note that τ is the maximum shearing component in ΔA.

It is now convenient to introduce a system of right-handed orthogonal Cartesian coordinates axes x, y, and z with origin O different from P and with coordinate planes inclined obliquely to ΔA (Figure 9–16). The unit normal vector $\mathbf{n}$ and the stress vector $\mathbf{S}$ are now written in terms of their components referred to these axes respectively as

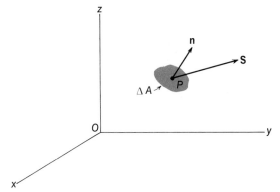

FIG. 9–16 *Right-handed Cartesian coordinate axes x, y, and z.*

n_x, n_y and n_z and S_x, S_y, and S_z.[2] The stress vectors, for three surface elements Δx, Δy, and Δz lying respectively in the three coordinate planes yz, zx, and xy and each containing P can be found in the same way as for ΔA, and each vector can be resolved into three components, one in each of the axial directions. The nine components obtained can be given the following symbols (Figure 9–17):

Components on Δx (yz-plane)

σ_x normal stress in direction x
τ_{xy} shearing stress in direction y
τ_{xz} shearing stress in direction z

Components on Δy (zx-plane)

τ_{yx} shearing stress in direction x
σ_y normal stress in direction y
τ_{yz} shearing stress in direction z

Components in Δz (xy-plane)

τ_{zx} shearing stress in direction x
τ_{zy} shearing stress in direction y
σ_z normal stress in direction z

These are termed the nine *stress components* at the point P. Each component represents the force per unit area that the positive side of a surface element (given by the positive sense of the corresponding axial direction) exerts on the negative side. Where a body is in static equilibrium the opposing forces are equal and opposite.[3]

If the outward normal of a surface element points in the same axial sense (positive or negative) as the normal component, the normal stress on that surface element is considered negative.[4] Shearing components on a surface element are considered positive if they act in an axial direction (positive or negative) with the same sign as the associated normal component.

The relationship between the nine stress components at P and the stress vector across ΔA at P can be established by considering the force

---

[2] Note that the magnitudes of components n_x, n_y, and n_z are numerically equal to the corresponding direction cosines (generally written l, m, and n, respectively) of the normal to ΔA.

[3] The dimensions of stress are force per unit area. Commonly used units are 1 bar = 1.02 kg/cm² = 0.987 atmosphere = 14.5 lb/in.²

[4] This convention identifies compressive stress as positive and tensional stress as negative and is the one used most frequently by geologists. In engineering the reverse convention is generally adopted.

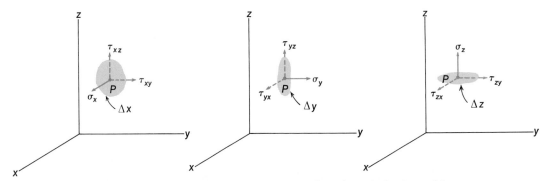

FIG. 9–17 *The nine stress components on surface elements Δx, Δy, and Δz.*

equilibrium of an infinitesimal volume element at P in the shape of a tetrahedron with one face parallel to ΔA and the remaining faces parallel to the three coordinate planes. Summing forces in the three axial directions yields three equations relating components of the stress vector on the surface element to the nine stress components, as follows:

$$\begin{aligned} S_x &= \sigma_x n_x + \tau_{yx} n_y + \tau_{zx} n_z \\ S_y &= \tau_{xy} n_x + \sigma_y n_y + \tau_{zy} n_z \\ S_z &= \tau_{xz} n_x + \tau_{yz} n_y + \sigma_z n_z \end{aligned} \quad (9\text{-}5)$$

These equations show that the nine stress components are necessary and sufficient to define the surface tractions across a surface element of any orientation denoted by the unit normal vector **n** and give a complete statement of stress at a point.

THE STRESS TENSOR In equation (9-5) the nine stress components relate the components of two vectors **S** and **n** and are clearly components of a second-rank tensor (see Chapter 2). Because it relates two polar vectors it is a polar tensor and consideration of the moment equilibrium of a volume element shows also that, in the absence of body torques, the tensor is symmetric. Only six of the stress components are therefore independent and the tensor can be written in matrix form as

$$\begin{pmatrix} \sigma_x & \tau_{xy} & \tau_{xz} \\ \tau_{xy} & \sigma_y & \tau_{yz} \\ \tau_{xz} & \tau_{yz} & \sigma_z \end{pmatrix}$$

In terms of these components and from equation (9-5), equation (9-2) can be written

$$\begin{aligned} \sigma = \sigma_x n_x^2 + \sigma_y n_y^2 + \sigma_z n_z^2 \\ + 2\tau_{xy} n_x n_y + 2\tau_{xz} n_x n_z + 2\tau_{yz} n_y n_z \end{aligned} \quad (9\text{-}6)$$

and equation (9-3) can be written

$$\begin{aligned} \tau = \sigma_x n_x s_x + \sigma_y n_y s_y + \sigma_z n_z s_z \\ + \tau_{xy}(n_x s_y + n_y s_x) + \tau_{yz}(n_y s_z + n_z s_y) \\ + \tau_{zx}(n_z s_x + n_x s_z) \end{aligned} \quad (9\text{-}7)$$

The shearing stress for any direction with unit vector **t** in the plane ΔA can be found by substitution of components of **t** for corresponding components of **s** in equation (9-7).

Because it is a symmetric second-rank tensor, the stress tensor can be put in diagonal form by a suitable coordinate transformation to give

$$\begin{pmatrix} \sigma_1 & 0 & 0 \\ 0 & \sigma_2 & 0 \\ 0 & 0 & \sigma_3 \end{pmatrix}$$

The shearing components vanish on the three orthogonal coordinate planes and the components σ_1, σ_2, and σ_3 (where, conventionally, $\sigma_1 \geq \sigma_2 \geq \sigma_3$) are *principal normal stresses* acting in the direction of the principal axes. For any state of stress at a point, therefore, there are three orthogonal principal planes upon which shearing stresses vanish and on which the stress vectors act in the direction of the corresponding unit normal vectors. For many geologic purposes it is sufficient to specify a stress state in terms of its principal components.

A simple geometric representation of the stress tensor can be obtained from equations (9-5) by expressing these in terms of the principal components as

$$\begin{aligned} S_x &= \sigma_1 n_x \\ S_y &= \sigma_2 n_y \\ S_z &= \sigma_3 n_z \end{aligned} \quad (9\text{-}8)$$

Equations (9-8) can be rewritten as

$$n_x = \frac{S_x}{\sigma_1}$$

$$n_y = \frac{S_y}{\sigma_2} \quad (9\text{-}9)$$

$$n_z = \frac{S_z}{\sigma_3}$$

Using the identity $n_x^2 + n_y^2 + n_z^2 = 1$ we can combine equations (9-9) to give

$$\frac{S_x^2}{\sigma_1^2} + \frac{S_y^2}{\sigma_2^2} + \frac{S_z^2}{\sigma_3^2} = 1 \quad (9\text{-}10)$$

the equation of a real ellipsoid, generally termed Lamé's stress ellipsoid, in the variables S_x, S_y, and S_z, the radius being given by

$$S = \pm\sqrt{S_x^2 + S_y^2 + S_z^2}$$

which is also the expression for the magnitude of

the stress vector at a point on the plane with unit normal vector **n**. The ellipsoid represents, therefore, the locus of the ends of the stress vectors across planes of all orientations through a point and has as its principal radius vectors the principal normal stresses. It is a clear image of the state of stress at a point both in magnitude and symmetry and can be a triaxial ellipsoid ($\sigma_1 > \sigma_2 > \sigma_3$), a prolate or oblate spheroid (respectively $\sigma_1 > \sigma_2 = \sigma_3$ or $\sigma_1 = \sigma_2 > \sigma_3$), or a sphere ($\sigma_1 = \sigma_2 = \sigma_3$).

In terms of principal normal stresses, equations (9-6) and 9-7) reduce respectively to

$$\sigma = \sigma_1 n_x^2 + \sigma_2 n_y^2 + \sigma_3 n_z^2 \qquad (9\text{-}11)$$

$$\tau = \sigma_1 n_x s_x + \sigma_2 n_y s_y + \sigma_3 n_z s_z \qquad (9\text{-}12)$$

PLANE STRESS   Many simple stress problems encountered in geology can be treated adequately in two dimensions (say, in the xy-plane) by setting components acting in the z direction equal to zero to give a tensor of the form

$$\begin{pmatrix} \sigma_x & \tau_{xy} & 0 \\ \tau_{yx} & \sigma_y & 0 \\ 0 & 0 & 0 \end{pmatrix} \quad \text{or} \quad \begin{pmatrix} \sigma_x & \tau_{xy} \\ \tau_{yx} & \sigma_y \end{pmatrix}$$

representing a state of plane stress. Under these conditions the equations for the normal and shearing components of the stress tensor on a surface of given orientation [equations (9-6) and (9-7), respectively] become greatly simplified for planes with unit normal vectors lying in the xy-plane. Let the components of **n** in the x and y directions respectively be expressed as

$$n_x = \cos\theta \quad \text{and} \quad n_y = \cos\left(\frac{\pi}{2} - \theta\right) = \sin\theta$$

where θ is the angle between **n** and the x-axis (Figure 9–18). Then equation (9-6) becomes

$$\sigma = \sigma_x \cos^2\theta + \sigma_y \sin^2\theta + 2\tau_{xy}\sin\theta\cos\theta \qquad (9\text{-}13)$$

and equation (9-7) becomes

$$\tau = (\sigma_x - \sigma_y)\sin\theta\cos\theta + \tau_{xy}(\cos^2\theta - \sin^2\theta) \qquad (9\text{-}14)$$

Using the trigonometric identities

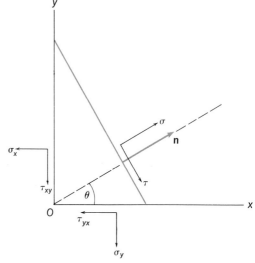

FIG. 9–18   Stresses σ and τ on plane with unit normal vector **n** in the xy-plane.

$$\cos^2\theta = \frac{1}{2} + \frac{1}{2}\cos 2\theta$$

$$\sin^2\theta = \frac{1}{2} - \frac{1}{2}\cos^2\theta$$

$$\sin\theta\cos\theta = \frac{1}{2}\sin 2\theta$$

we can rewrite equations (9-13) and (9-14) respectively in the familiar forms

$$\sigma = \frac{\sigma_x + \sigma_y}{2} + \frac{\sigma_x - \sigma_y}{2}\cos 2\theta + \tau_{xy}\sin 2\theta \qquad (9\text{-}15)$$

and

$$\tau = \frac{-(\sigma_x - \sigma_y)}{2}\sin 2\theta + \tau_{xy}\cos 2\theta \qquad (9\text{-}16)$$

By means of equations (9-15) and (9-16), two-dimensional stress problems can be solved.

Transformation of the plane stress tensor to principal axes yields

$$\begin{pmatrix} \sigma_1 & 0 \\ 0 & \sigma_2 \end{pmatrix}$$

where $\sigma_1 \geq \sigma_2$ are principal normal stresses. In terms of these components equations (9-15) and (9-16) reduce respectively to

$$\sigma = \frac{\sigma_1 + \sigma_2}{2} + \frac{\sigma_1 - \sigma_2}{2} \cos 2\theta \quad (9\text{-}17)$$

and

$$\tau = \frac{-(\sigma_1 - \sigma_2)}{2} \sin 2\theta \quad (9\text{-}18)$$

PRINCIPAL SHEARING STRESSES   For a plane or planes with θ lying between 0 and $\pi/2$ the value of the shearing component must reach a maximum between the two vanishing shearing stresses on the principal planes. For this value of θ

$$\frac{d\tau}{d\theta} = -(\sigma_1 - \sigma_2) \cos 2\theta = 0$$

from which $\theta = \pi/4$ and $3\pi/4$. The corresponding planes are an orthogonal pair inclined at 45° to the principal axes (Figure 9–19), and the magnitude of the maximum shearing stress can be found in terms of the principal normal stresses by substitution of the values of θ in equation (9-18) as

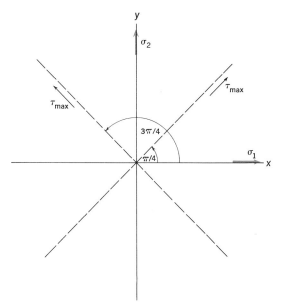

FIG. 9–19 Planes of maximum shearing stress (dashed lines) with unit normal vectors in the xy-plane.

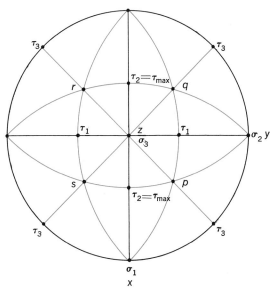

FIG. 9–20 Stereographic projection of principal planes (black lines) and planes of principal shearing stress (colored lines).

$$\tau_{\max} = \frac{\pm(\sigma_1 - \sigma_2)}{2} \quad (9\text{-}19)$$

The shearing stress $\tau_{\max}$ is called the principal shearing stress. A similar argument shows that for a general state of nonplane stress there are three principal shearing stresses, on three pairs of orthogonal planes bisecting the angles between the principal axes, given by

$$\tau_1 = \frac{\pm\sigma_2 - \sigma_3}{2}$$

$$\tau_2 = \frac{\pm\sigma_1 - \sigma_3}{2} \quad (9\text{-}20)$$

$$\tau_3 = \frac{\pm\sigma_1 - \sigma_2}{2}$$

of these the largest is clearly $\tau_2 = \tau_{\max}$. The orientation of the six planes of principal shearing stress (colored lines) are shown in stereographic projection in Figure 9–20 along with the principal planes (black lines).

The maximum shearing stress on an arbitrary plane with unit normal vector **n** can be expressed in terms of the principal shearing stresses as

$$\tau^2 = 4(\tau_1^2 n_y^2 n_z^2 + \tau_2^2 n_z^2 n_x^2 + \tau_3^2 n_x^2 n_y^2) \quad (9\text{-}21)$$

This equation gives only the magnitude of the shearing stress. Equally important is the direction in the plane in which this stress acts [given by the vector **s** in equations (9-7) and (9-12)]. Because **s** is fixed by **n** and the stress vector **S** its components can be found simply by considering force equilibrium along the coordinate axes. For example, force equilibrium along the x-axis requires that

$$\sigma n_x + \tau s_x = S_x$$

from which

$$s_x = \frac{S_x - \sigma n_x}{\tau} \quad (9\text{-}22)$$

Similar expressions can be found for the other components of **s**.

DEVIATORIC STRESS   The directions corresponding to the points p, q, r, and s in Figure 9–20 are equally inclined to the three principal axes and represent the directions of the four long diagonals ($\bar{3}$ rotation axes) of a cube with edges in the three axial directions. The magnitudes of the components of the unit vectors in these four directions are seen to be $\pm 1/\sqrt{3}$, and by substitution of these values into equation (9-11) the normal stresses on all four planes normal to these vectors are found to be

$$\sigma_0 = \frac{\sigma_1 + \sigma_2 + \sigma_3}{3} \quad (9\text{-}23)$$

Because these four planes stand in the same mutual relationship as the faces of a regular octahedron, σ_0 is generally called the "octahedral" normal stress, but it is also termed the mean normal stress.

The magnitude of the shearing stress on the same planes—the octahedral shearing stress—can be found from equation (9-21) as

$$\tau_0 = \pm \frac{2}{3} \sqrt{\tau_1^2 + \tau_2^2 + \tau_3^2} \quad (9\text{-}24)$$

or by substitution of the values of (9-20) into equation (9-24) as

$$\tau_0 = \pm \frac{1}{3} \sqrt{(\sigma_1 - \sigma_2)^2 + (\sigma_2 - \sigma_3)^2 + (\sigma_3 - \sigma_1)^2}$$

$$(9\text{-}25)$$

A convenient decomposition of a stress state is into two parts by subtraction of the tensor corresponding to the mean normal stress, the remainder being termed the "deviatoric part" of the stress state or the stress deviator. The mean normal stress is isotropic and is represented by a spherically symmetric tensor. It corresponds to a hydrostatic pressure p. The deviatoric part is a tensor with the same symmetry as the original stress tensor, and is referred to the same principal axes. Let the principal components of the stress deviator be σ_1', σ_2' and σ_3'; then these are related to the principal normal stresses by

$$\sigma_1' = \sigma_1 - \sigma_0 = \frac{2\sigma_1 - \sigma_2 - \sigma_3}{3}$$

$$\sigma_2' = \sigma_2 - \sigma_0 = \frac{2\sigma_2 - \sigma_1 - \sigma_3}{3} \quad (9\text{-}26)$$

$$\sigma_3' = \sigma_3 - \sigma_0 = \frac{2\sigma_3 - \sigma_1 - \sigma_2}{3}$$

from which

$$\sigma_1' + \sigma_2' + \sigma_3' = 0$$

For any deviator, therefore, the sum of the principal normal stresses vanishes. The principal shearing stresses for the deviatoric part can be defined in the same way as for the complete tensor; for example, from equation (9-20),

$$\tau_1' = \pm \frac{(\sigma_2' - \sigma_3')}{2} = \frac{[(\sigma_2 - \sigma_0) - (\sigma_3 - \sigma_0)]}{2}$$

$$= \pm \frac{\sigma_2 - \sigma_3}{2} = \tau_1$$

Similarly $\tau_2' = \tau_2$ and $\tau_3' = \tau_3$ and the principal shearing stresses of the deviator are identical to those of the complete tensor.

The importance of the decomposition of a stress state into its isotropic and deviatoric components immediately becomes clear. The isotropic part corresponds to a hydrostatic pressure and the deviatoric part to the general notion of nonhydrostatic or "shearing" stress. Experimental evidence suggests that solids, such as rocks, are permanently deformed only in response to the deviatoric part of the stress state. However, the isotropic or "hydrostatic" part controls dilatation (volume change, generally in the elastic range) and also exerts an important influence on the mechanism by which distortional deformations are achieved—for example, by fracture, ductile flow or some other mechanism. For many purposes, and particularly in the mathematical theory of plasticity, only the deviatoric part of the stress is generally considered.

MOHR CONSTRUCTION   A simple two-dimensional representation of a state of stress (or any other quantity represented by a symmetric second-rank tensor) is given by the Mohr diagram, in which values of σ and τ for surface elements of all orientations are represented by points in a $\sigma\tau$ space—the "stress plane." We illustrate the construction for plane stress referred to its principal axes.

For a surface element with unit normal vector inclined at θ to x in the xy-plane the stress components σ and τ are given respectively by equations (9-17) and (9-18). Equation (9-17) can be rearranged as

$$\sigma - \frac{\sigma_1 + \sigma_2}{2} = \frac{\sigma_1 - \sigma_2}{2} \cos 2\theta$$

and squared to give

$$\left(\sigma - \frac{\sigma_1 + \sigma_2}{2}\right)^2 = \left(\frac{\sigma_1 - \sigma_2}{2} \cos 2\theta\right)^2 \quad (9\text{-}27)$$

Equation (9-18) is squared and added to equation (9-27) to give

$$\left(\sigma - \frac{\sigma_1 + \sigma_2}{2}\right)^2 + \tau^2$$
$$= \left(\frac{\sigma_1 - \sigma_2}{2}\right)^2 (\cos^2 2\theta + \sin^2 2\theta)$$

or

$$\left(\sigma - \frac{\sigma_1 + \sigma_2}{2}\right)^2 + \tau^2 = \left(\frac{\sigma_1 - \sigma_2}{2}\right)^2 \quad (9\text{-}28)$$

Equation (9-28) is the equation of a circle (the "stress circle") in variables σ and τ of radius $\pm(\sigma_1 - \sigma_2)/2 = \tau_{\max}$, shown drawn in the stress

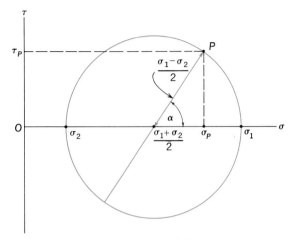

FIG. 9–21   Mohr circle for state of plane stress.

plane in Figure 9–21. Its center lies at $\sigma = (\sigma_1 + \sigma_2)/2$, $\tau = 0$ on the σ-axis (conventionally taken as the abscissa), and it passes through σ_1 and σ_2, as shown. Points on this circle represent all possible combinations of σ and τ for planes of all orientations with unit normal vectors in the xy-plane.

Consider, for example, a point P on the circle such that the diameter of the circle through P is inclined at α to the σ-axis as shown in Figure 9–21. Let the coordinates of this point represent the stress components σ_p and τ_p on a surface element with unit normal vector inclined at θ to the x-axis in the xy-plane. Then, from Figure 9–21,

$$\cos \alpha = \frac{\sigma_p - \frac{1}{2}(\sigma_1 + \sigma_2)}{\frac{1}{2}(\sigma_1 - \sigma_2)} \quad (9\text{-}29)$$

Substituting the value of σ_p from equation (9-17) we obtain

$$\cos \alpha =$$
$$\frac{\frac{1}{2}(\sigma_1 + \sigma_2) + \frac{1}{2}(\sigma_1 - \sigma_2)\cos 2\theta - \frac{1}{2}(\sigma_1 + \sigma_2)}{\frac{1}{2}(\sigma_1 - \sigma_2)}$$

from which

$$\cos \alpha = \cos 2\theta$$

and

$$\alpha = 2\theta \quad (9\text{-}30)$$

Angles measured in the stress plane are thus

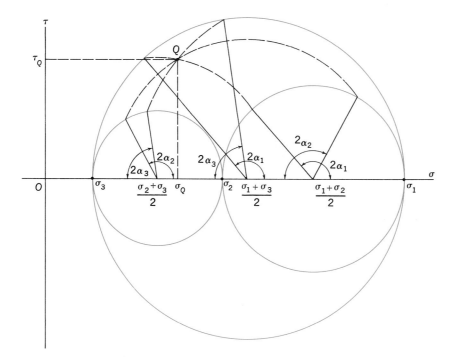

FIG. 9–22 *Mohr circles for a general state of stress $\sigma_1 > \sigma_2 > \sigma_3$. Point 2 corresponds to a plane with unit normal vector inclined at α_1 to the σ_1-axis, α_2 to the σ_2-axis, and α_3 to the σ_3-axis. The normal stress on the plane is given by σ_Q and the shearing stress by τ_Q.*

twice as large as corresponding angles measured in the *xy*-plane. With this information we can find the values of σ and τ by graphical construction for surface elements with any value of θ.

The diagram can be extended simply to three dimensions by constructing a stress circle for each of the principal planes, as shown in Figure 9–22. Because a stress circle can be drawn for *any* plane, the stress components σ_Q and τ_Q on a plane Q with unit normal vector inclined at α_1 to the σ_1-axis, α_2 to the σ_2-axis, and α_3 to the σ_3-axis can be found by constructing the stress circles for three planes intersecting in the unit normal vector and finding the image of their intersection in the stress plane (Figure 9–22).

HOMOGENEOUS AND HETEROGENEOUS STRESS So far, all our remarks have applied strictly to stress at a point. At such a point in a continuous body three orthogonal principal axes are always present. If in a body the stress at every point has the same magnitude and orientation of principal axes the stress is said to be homogeneous. If, on the other hand, the stress varies from place to place it is said to be heterogeneous. Because of the continuity of stress and the established properties of stress at a point, in any stressed continuous body there are three families of orthogonal curvilinear lines which represent the variation in orientation of principal axes throughout a heterogeneously stressed body. At any point three such lines intersect orthogonally to give the directions of σ_1, σ_2, σ_3 at that point. These lines are called "stress trajectories." Similar lines can be drawn for the principal shearing stresses. For some simple two-dimensional situations, stress trajectories are easily constructed.

SUPERPOSITION OF STRESSES If to a body in a state of stress a further stress is applied, then, because stress is a tensor quantity, the resultant state of stress is represented by a tensor whose components are sums of the corresponding components of the superposed stresses.

The notion of superposed stress raises a problem in the definition of a state of stress, as presented above, which until now has been ignored. No account has so far been taken of any changes in shape of a body as a result of stress; that is, the material in which the stresses act has been assumed to be perfectly rigid and no distinction has been made between coordinate systems in the stressed and unstressed states. Where the notion of superposed stresses arises this omission becomes obvious. If a theory of stress applicable to real bodies is desired, these cannot be assumed to be rigid. In such deformable bodies, the orthogonal surface elements defining the components of stress in the initial stress state cannot have the same orientation as those defining the components of the final stress state, and, in fact, each set of stress components is clearly referred to a different coordinate system.

This difficulty can be resolved to a first approximation by placing restrictions upon the allowable shape changes or strains of the body, and the notion of stress becomes thereby linked with the notion of a particular kind of strain. The simplifying assumption made is that the strains are linear and infinitesimal in magnitude, so the rotation and distortion of the surface elements as a result of stress are negligible and volume and surface elements can be considered the same in strained and unstrained bodies. This assumption forms the basis for the theory of linear elasticity. Where deformation in response to stress is permanent and of large magnitude, as in the slow flow of rocks in the crust, this simplification cannot be made. For deformations of this kind there is no simple functional relationship between stress and an observed finite deformation.

STRESS IN THE EARTH

So far, this discussion of stress has been of continuous stresses in a continuous body. No real materials are truly continuous and the states of stress at a point and homogeneous stress introduced earlier are clearly ideal abstractions that cannot be duplicated in real solids. In a rock, for example, there must be abrupt changes in the state of stress across boundaries between grains of different composition and orientation, and in dry porous rocks there must be great stress concentrations in the materials surround-

ing the unsupported pores and across the small areas of actual physical contact between grains. Nevertheless, experiments show that if the scale of structural heterogeneity is relatively small compared to the whole stressed body, the theory of continuous stress, and even in some situations, of homogeneous stress, is an abstraction of practical use. Engineers, for example, base many of their designs upon the theory of stress, as introduced in the preceding section, and most of the experimental studies of rock deformation and theoretical studies of stress in the earth adopt the same theory.

Stresses in the earth's crust and mantle must be predominantly compressive. There is evidence, however, that tensional stresses can arise in near-surface rocks and many of the experimental stress states used in rock mechanical studies involve tensions. We look now at some features of common homogeneous stress states.

EXPERIMENTAL AND NATURAL HOMOGENEOUS STRESS STATES Most of the stress states to be expected in the earth and those used in experimental studies can be found in the following list (illustrated by Mohr diagrams):

1. *Uniaxial (simple) tension* (Figure 9–23) is the stress state of the engineer's "tensile test" with σ_3 negative and $\sigma_1 = \sigma_2 = 0$. The tensor is axially symmetric.

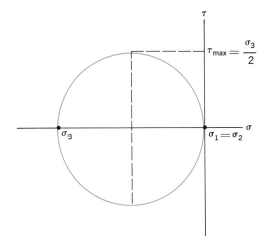

FIG. 9–23 *Uniaxial (simple) tension.*

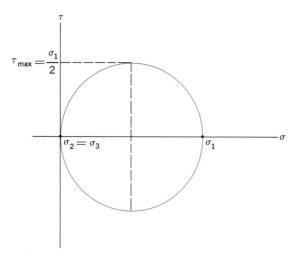

FIG. 9–24   *Uniaxial (simple) compression.*

static pressure. Principal stresses are all positive with $\sigma_1 > \sigma_2 = \sigma_3$, and the tensor is axially symmetric.

4. *Triaxial extension* (Figure 9–26) is the converse of triaxial compression in which the principal stresses are still positive but $\sigma_1 = \sigma_2 > \sigma_3$. No tensional stresses exist in this state and the tensor is axially symmetric. Triaxial compression and extension are the stress states used most commonly in deformation experiments on rocks and they are to be expected, at least locally, in the crust and mantle. Experimentally they are achieved by applying a hydrostatic fluid pressure to the sealed walls of an axially loaded cylindrical specimen. For triaxial compression the fluid pressure is less than the axial stress; for triaxial extension it is greater.

5. *Simple shear* (Figure 9–27) involves the application of shearing stress to a particular plane in a body. Moment equilibrium requires that an equal and opposite shearing stress appear on a plane at right angles to the plane of application with normal in the direction of the first shearing stress. Normal stresses σ_1 and σ_3 appear on the planes bisecting angles between the two planes of shear such that σ_1 is positive, $\sigma_3 = -\sigma_1$, and $\sigma_2 = 0$. Possible combinations of normal and shearing stress fall anywhere in the stippled area of Figure 9–27. An approach to this stress state

2. *Uniaxial (simple) compression* (Figure 9–24) corresponds to the engineering compression test and is used extensively to study the crushing strength of rocks at atmospheric pressure. Principal stresses are σ_1 positive, with $\sigma_2 = \sigma_3 = 0$, and the tensor is axially symmetric. Neither uniaxial compression nor uniaxial tension are to be expected at depth within the earth.

3. *Triaxial compression* (Figure 9–25) represents uniaxial compression combined with hydro-

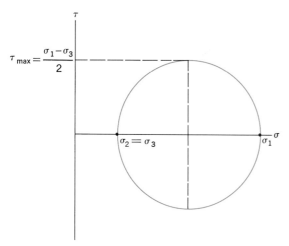

FIG. 9–25   *Triaxial compression.*

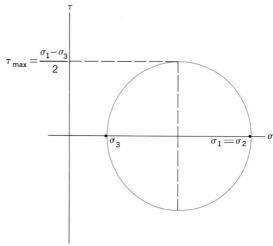

FIG. 9–26   *Triaxial extension.*

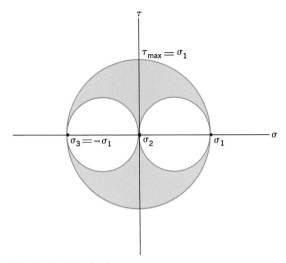

FIG. 9–27 *Simple shear.*

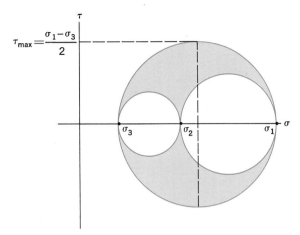

FIG. 9–29 *General state of stress.*

can be achieved experimentally by torsion of a thin-walled hollow cylinder. Symmetry of the tensor is $2/m\,2/m\,2/m$ and the stress is deviatoric ($\sigma_1 + \sigma_2 + \sigma_3 = 0$). In nature a similar stress state may exist in zone of strong tangential shearing (perhaps along faults or thrusts), but it is doubtful if in these situations the stress is ever free of a hydrostatic part.

6. *Plane stress* (Figure 9–28) has been discussed above. Principal stresses are $\sigma_1 > \sigma_2$, $\sigma_3, = 0$, where both σ_1 and σ_2 are positive. If one

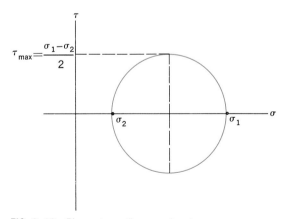

FIG. 9–28 *Plane stress (in $\sigma_1\sigma_2$ plane).*

of the principal stresses is negative, $\sigma_2 = 0$; if two are negative, $\sigma_1 = 0$. A stress state approaching plane stress is used in some model experiments and can probably occur at the surface of the earth. The tensor has symmetry $2/m\,2/m\,2/m$.

7. *General state of stress* (Figure 9–29) has $\sigma_1 > \sigma_2 > \sigma_3$ and is probably the commonest state of stress in geologic bodies in which all three principal stresses are generally positive. The tensor has symmetry $2/m\,2/m\,2/m$ and possible combinations of normal and shearing stresses can fall anywhere in the stippled area of Figure 9–29.

A hydrostatic pressure ($\sigma_1 = \sigma_2 = \sigma_3$) has spherical symmetry and corresponds to a point of the σ-axis. No shearing stresses on any planes exist in such a stress state. The same is true for the hydrostatic part of a general stress state. The deviatoric part of a stress state has the same configuration of stress circles as the total stress but their position on the σ-axis is displaced from those of the total stress by an amount equal to σ_0, the mean normal stress. Thus the Mohr diagram for the deviatoric part of any stress state can be found by shifting the origin of the stress plane to the left an amount equal to σ_0 (assuming this to be positive). During this shift (Figure 9–30) the values of τ on planes of all orientations remain constant as required by their independence of the "hydrostatic" part of the stress tensor.

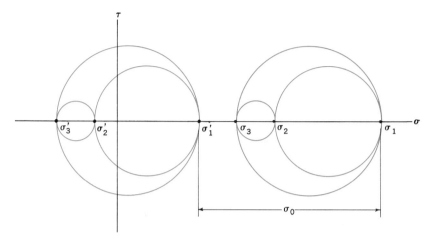

Fig. 9–30 *Deviatoric stress.*

SHEARING STRESS IN THE EARTH   As we saw at the beginning of this chapter, the isotropic part of stress (the pressure) increases with depth in the earth and, with certain assumptions about the mechanical condition of rocks, reasonable estimates of its value can be made, even at great depths. In contrast, little is known about past or present states of shearing stress, even in the crust. Because the surface of the earth is free and unconstrained on planes tangent at the earth's surface all stresses, both normal and shearing, must vanish. We know therefore that stress trajectories from within the earth meet the topographic surface orthogonally or are parallel to it, so at a point on the topographic surface the surface itself is a principal plane.

Near to the surface, in mines and boreholes, attempts are made, mainly by civil and mining engineers, to determine the *in situ* state of stress by direct measurement. Several methods that have been devised yield reasonable results. Some of these, such as "strain relief," measure strains and provide an estimate of stresses only by way of the elastic properties of the rock which must therefore be determined. Other methods, particularly the "flatjack," measure load directly and require no knowledge of elastic properties. In most *in situ* stress measurement, vertical and horizontal stresses are measured on the assumption that stress trajectories at the depths concerned are vertical or horizontal. In anisotropic and heterogeneous folded and faulted rocks or close to geologic boundary surfaces separating rocks with very different properties, it is unlikely that this condition is always met, even close to the earth's surface. Also, the measurements are made generally in mine workings, which are themselves regions of strain relief resulting from removal of material and in which the natural stress field of the region is generally perturbed.

Some estimates of magnitudes of shearing stresses at depth can be made by assuming that stresses arising from elastic deformation due to deep burial remain partly or wholly unrelaxed so that a truly hydrostatic condition is not reached. Consider, for example, a perfectly elastic earth and a volume element at a relatively small depth z. To a first approximation, the vertical normal stress σ_v is given by

$$\sigma_v = \rho g z$$

and the horizontal normal stress, σ_h (assumed to be equal in all directions) is given by

$$\sigma_h = \rho g z \left(\frac{\nu}{1 - \nu} \right)$$

where ν is Poisson's ratio for the rock (page 490). An average value for Poisson's ratio in isotropic rocks in their elastic range is about 0.3, so for a perfectly elastic rock at depth the ratio σ_h/σ_v should be about 0.4. Most *in situ* stress measurements in near-surface rocks yield values of this ratio in the range 0.5 to 1.0, and values as high as 2.0 have been reported. In rocks that are not strictly elastic (or in which Poisson's ratio is unusually high) the ratio approaches unity, which it reaches for a material that cannot maintain shearing stresses indefinitely. For example, in a fluid, Poisson's ratio is 0.5 and $\sigma_h = \sigma_v$ as demanded for hydrostatic equilibrium. Values of the ratio σ_h/σ_v greater than unity indicate the presence of forces other than those caused by the mass of the overlying rock.

Estimates of the nonhydrostatic stress in the mantle have been made from gravity measurements indicating unequal density or mass distributions (undulations of the geoid; see Chapter 11). Such calculations generally yield values of 10 to 100 bars. Direct evidence of the presence of present-day shearing stresses in the crust (and mantle) is given by seismic activity. Earthquakes, whatever their mechanism, most probably result from sudden releases of distortional strain energy, which is most likely accumulated in regions of abnormally high shearing stress in the crust and mantle down to depths of 700 km. The magnitudes of the stresses required to cause earthquakes are surprisingly difficult to estimate. What can be estimated is a quantity called the "stress drop." For an infinitely long vertical fault surface with visible strike slip displacement, for example, the stress drop is given by σ, where

$$\sigma = \frac{1}{2} \frac{U_m \mu}{w}$$

and U_m is the maximum displacement, μ the rigidity, and w the fault "width." Stress drops estimated in this and other ways are generally in the range 10 to 100 bars. This figure is surprisingly low and contrasts greatly with the several-kilobar drops in differential stress measured in typical laboratory experiments on the sudden fracture of rocks. It has been suggested by some seismologists that the stress drops accompanying earthquakes account for most of the shearing stress present in the strain-relieved body prior to the earthquake. If true, this view suggests that large-scale shearing stresses of relatively small magnitude are permitted at depth in the crust and mantle.

PRINCIPAL STRESS DIRECTIONS   Because stresses are difficult to measure directly, the earth scientist is generally forced to measure some aspect of strain and from this infer what he can about the state of stress. Such an analysis is ideally possible only if the state of strain is functionally related to a unique stress state, as in a linearly elastic material. In attempting to reconstruct past patterns of stress in the crust, particularly in orogenic regions, geologists are concerned with orientations of principal stress directions (stress trajectories), because these indicate the distribution of mechanical forces at various periods in the earth's history. But the only strain information available, in favorable circumstances, is given by structures resulting from permanent strains of finite magnitude.

In principle, to determine a state of stress from a finite strain is an impossible task. A given finite strain is the result of the superposition of a sequence of incremental strains, each of which can be treated as infinitesimal in magnitude, as is done in the mathematical theory of plasticity. Each of these strain increments is functionally related by way of a material property to an instantaneous state of stress. Under very special circumstances, this relationship could be the same for each increment. In real materials, on the other hand, the state of stress and the material properties change during the sequence and the final state of finite strain has no relationship to any particular state of stress. We shall see later that study of the symmetry of the fabrics of deformed rocks can be a guide to the symmetry of such a strain sequence, and perhaps even to the symmetry of the successive stress states responsible for the strains.

In recent years, careful study by geologists of certain permanent deformation structures in rocks has shown, however, that "paleo"-principal stress directions can be determined for the very last state of stress that has acted on a rock. Normally, this state of stress corresponds to an elastic strain, long vanished; but if the stresses just exceed the yield or fracture strength of a rock, the elastic strain present may be converted into a permanent strain that, for a given body, is of mean magnitude similar to that of the elastic strain it replaces. This notion is best examined in terms of a hypothetical example.

Consider a marble composed of equant polygonal calcite grains in random orientation homogeneously elastically strained in response to a

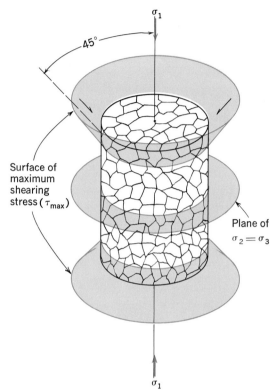

the orientation of the twin lamellae and the direction [0001] as measured microscopically in the thin section of the rock, a number of estimates of the orientation of σ_1 can be made from different grains (as shown diagrammatically in Figure 9–32). The estimated orientation of σ_1 can be plotted in projection as C (for "compression") points. At 90° from each orientation of C in the plane containing the pole of the corresponding $\{01\bar{1}2\}$ lamella can be plotted a point T (for "tension," although no tensional stresses exist in a triaxial test). These points, when plotted in projection, come to lie in a girdle in a plane perpendicular to the maximum concentration of C points (Figure 9–33). The point of maximum concentration of C points, therefore, is the best estimate of the orientation of σ_1 and the plane of preferred orientation of T points is the best estimate of the $\sigma_2 = \sigma_3$ plane. For a triaxial stress ($\sigma_1 > \sigma_2 > \sigma_3$) these lamellae in the orientation of the plane of maximum shear stress bisecting the angles between the directions of σ_1 and σ_3 will form preferentially, and the maximum concentration of C points will indicate the direction of σ_1 and the maximum concentration of T points, the direction of σ_3.

If deformation is allowed to proceed beyond the initial yield, the strong concentrations of C and T points will weaken as grains begin to rotate, twin planes with low shear stress are activated and grains become completely twinned.

This simple technique has been used by geologists to determine principal stress directions corresponding to small permanent strains in natural rocks. The technique has been used mainly on $\{01\bar{1}2\}$ twin lamellae in calcite; but $\{02\bar{2}1\}$ twin lamellae in dolomite and "deformation lamellae" (irrational laminar domains of localized plastic deformation) in quartz have also been used with success. Given a suitable fracture criterion to predict angles between principal stresses and faults, the technique can be used also in the analysis of patterns of fractures with small displacements, both as microfractures in thin sections, and as regional fault patterns. Other structures, such as the planar limbs of incipient kink folds may also prove to be amenable to this kind of analysis.

FIG. 9–31 *Cylindrical specimen of marble elastically strained in triaxial compression ($\sigma_1 > \sigma_2 = \sigma_3$). Maximum shearing stress $\tau_{max} = (\sigma_1 - \sigma_3)/2$ is reached on two conical surfaces with apical angles of 45° about the σ_1-axis.*

uniform axial stress represented by the principal stresses $\sigma_1 > \sigma_2 = \sigma_3$ (Figure 9–31). Let the stress increase until the yield stress for twin gliding of $\{01\bar{1}2\}$ is exceeded in crystals with one of the three possible twin planes oriented so that the maximum shearing stress acts in the right sense for twinning (such planes are inclined at 45° to σ_1). In such grains a few thin twin lamellae appear (Figure 9–32) and much of the elastic strain is relieved. In the lamellae the strain is a relatively large finite shear; but because the lamellae are few in number, thin and randomly distributed, the total mean strain for the aggregate is still of a magnitude that can be considered infinitesimal. If it is assumed that each twin lamella formed on a surface inclined at exactly 45° to σ_1, then, from the sense of twin gliding,

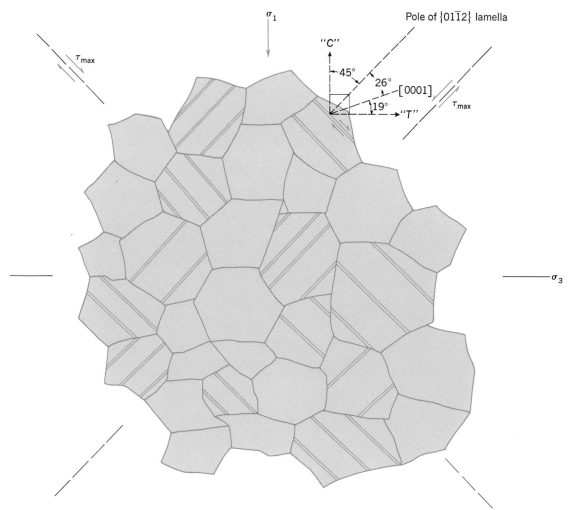

FIG. 9–32 *Section through specimen in Figure 9–31 showing development of thin [01$\bar{1}$2] twin lamellae in grains of suitable orientation. These lamellae have a preferred orientation in the surfaces of maximum shearing stress. For each lamella the most favorable orientation of "C" and "T" directions can be found as shown. Note that "C" and "T" lie in the plane containing [0001] and the pole of the [01$\bar{1}$2] lamella.*

Even rocks in which the grains were in a state of preferred orientation prior to deformation can be analyzed in this way provided that account is taken of the resulting bias on the distribution of C and T points.

EFFECTIVE STRESS On page 464 the notion of "effective pressure" in an aggregate containing a high-pressure pore fluid was introduced. We look now at the effect of such a pore fluid on the state of stress in a porous aggregate under non-hydrostatic loading.

Let a porous and permeable water-saturated rock be placed in an impermeable jacket and loaded in compression triaxially under high confining pressure in a testing machine (Figure 9–34). The stresses acting across the surfaces of the specimen are given by an axially symmetric tensor that, referred to principal axes, has the form

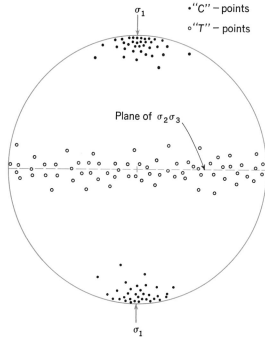

• "C" – points
∘ "T" – points

$σ_1$

Plane of $σ_2σ_3$

$σ_1$

FIG. 9–33 *"C" and "T" points plotted from an axial section of the specimen in Figure 9–31 (diagrammatic). The highest concentration of "C" points is the best estimate of the direction of $σ_1$ and the plane of concentration of "T" points is the best estimate of the $σ_2σ_3$ plane.*

$$\begin{pmatrix} σ_1 & 0 & 0 \\ 0 & σ_2 & 0 \\ 0 & 0 & σ_2 \end{pmatrix} \quad (9\text{-}31)$$

In the static pore fluid, deformation associated with loading causes the appearance of a hydrostatic pressure p which corresponds to the spherically symmetric tensor.

$$\begin{pmatrix} p & 0 & 0 \\ 0 & p & 0 \\ 0 & 0 & p \end{pmatrix} \quad (9\text{-}32)$$

(This value can be increased experimentally to any value by pumping fluid through a hollow piston, as shown in Figure 9–34.) This pressure acts uniformly over the surfaces of the solid grains so that the state of stress represented by the tensor in (9-31) must be the sum of tensor in (9-32) and another tensor, which can be found by subtracting corresponding components as

$$\begin{pmatrix} σ_1 - p & 0 & 0 \\ 0 & σ_2 - p & 0 \\ 0 & 0 & σ_2 - p \end{pmatrix} (9\text{-}33)$$

This state of stress, called the "effective stress," acts in the solid part of the aggregate.

Consider now a plane surface through the specimen oblique to the principal axes with unit normal vector **n**. From equations (9-11) and (9-12), respectively, the effective normal and shearing stresses on this surface in the solid part of the aggregate can be found as

$$σ = (σ_1 - p)n_{\tilde{x}}^2 + (σ_2 - p)(n_{\tilde{y}}^2 + n_{\tilde{z}}^2) \quad (9\text{-}34)$$

and

$$τ = (σ_1 - p)n_x s_x + (σ_2 - p)(n_y s_y + n_z s_z) \quad (9\text{-}35)$$

By means of the identities

$$n_{\tilde{x}}^2 + n_{\tilde{y}}^2 + n_{\tilde{z}}^2 = 1$$
$$n_x s_x + n_y s_y + n_z s_z = 0$$

equations (9-34) and (9-35) reduce respectively to

$$σ = (σ_1 - σ_2)n_x + (σ_2 - p) \quad (9\text{-}36)$$

and

$$τ = (σ_1 - σ_2)n_x s_x \quad (9\text{-}37)$$

From these equations we see that the presence of pore pressure p has no effect upon the shearing stresses on any surface, whereas the normal stress is reduced by the amount p. This fact may have important bearing upon the possibility of fracture at depth in the earth.

Elastic Deformation

An elastic body is one that deforms (generally a small amount) when stressed but recovers its original shape when the stress disappears. Most solids are elastic for stresses of small magnitude; others, like rocks, behave elastically even for large stresses. Elastic behavior of earth materials is of fundamental importance in seismology and other branches of geophysics; and it affects also nonelastic behavior such as fracture, ductile flow, and creep because these occur in elastically strained materials.

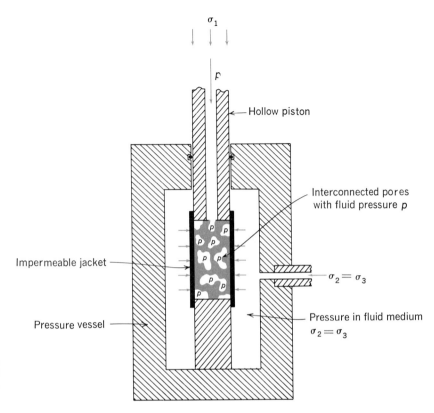

σ_1

P

Hollow piston

Interconnected pores
with fluid pressure p

$\sigma_2 = \sigma_3$

Pressure in fluid medium
$\sigma_2 = \sigma_3$

Impermeable jacket

Pressure vessel

FIG. 9-34 *Effective stress in porous permeable specimen with pore pressure p is given by*

$$\begin{matrix} \sigma_1 - p & 0 & 0 \\ 0 & \sigma_2 - p & 0 \\ 0 & 0 & \sigma_2 - p \end{matrix}$$

where σ_1 is the axial stress applied by the piston and $\sigma_2 = \sigma_3$ is pressure in confining fluid.

The simplest theory of elasticity is based on Hooke's law, the generalized form of which for elastically anisotropic bodies is given on page 103. An ideally elastic body obeying Hooke's law deforms independently of time or its previous history and the path of deformation is a sequence of equilibrium states. Deformation is frictionless, fully reversible, and of very small magnitude, and the work done is stored in the body as elastic strain energy. Quantitative treatment of the small deformations characteristic of elastic bodies has been made relatively simple by the development of the theory of infinitesimal strain, which we now briefly examine.

INFINITESIMAL STRAIN

In response to stresses in the earth, rocks can deform in a manner that for many practical purposes can be considered continuous. On a fine scale, no deformation of real bodies such as rocks can be strictly continuous, especially where it is permanent and involves mechanisms such as plastic flow of crystals, grain boundary slip, small-scale fracture and cataclasis, atomic diffusion, and so on. In an elastic deformation none of these mechanisms contributes under ideal conditions and only distortion of interatomic bonds is involved. No permanent discontinuities appear and the condition of continuity of strain required by the theory of infinitesimal strain is closely approached.

Any theory of strain can be developed, like that of stress, with no reference to material properties. The concepts involved are purely geometric and the only conditions that need be fulfilled for a general theory are those of continuity and compatibility of strains at all stages. Thus, in a body undergoing strain, no gaps must appear and points that were initially neighbors must so remain. Under these conditions, a strain can be described most generally as a change in the configuration of a body, and its simplest representation is by a one-to-one geometric transformation in which the transformed coordinates of points are a function of their initial coordinates. A state of strain is completely specified if displacements of all points are known. These displacements, **u**, form a continuous vector field. For most deformations the values of **u** are a function of position.

In strain theory, attention is focused not upon the displacements themselves, but on *relative* displacements, because we need to know how lengths of material lines and angles between them are changed by deformation. Consider, for example, a continuous body referred to orthogonal Cartesian coordinate axes x, y, and z, homogeneously transformed to a new configuration (Figure 9–35). We can write a general equation for the components (u, v, and w) of the displacement vector of a point (x, y, z) in matrix form as

$$\begin{pmatrix} u \\ v \\ w \end{pmatrix} = \begin{pmatrix} e_x & e_{xy} & e_{xz} \\ e_{yx} & e_y & e_{yz} \\ e_{zx} & e_{zy} & e_z \end{pmatrix} \begin{pmatrix} x \\ y \\ z \end{pmatrix} + \begin{pmatrix} t_x \\ t_y \\ t_z \end{pmatrix} \quad (9\text{-}38)$$

where t_x, t_y, and t_z are components of a uniform translation and the components e are scalar coefficients (because the transformation is homogeneous), forming the components of what is clearly a second-rank tensor relating the vector of displacement **u** to the vector of position **x**.

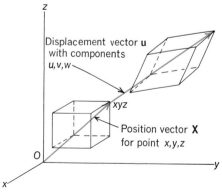

FIG. 9–35 *Homogeneous strain of a body containing point x, y, z, with position vector* **x***. Displacement* **u** *of point x, y, z has components u, v, w.*

The components e in equation (9-38) are complicated for finite displacements; but if the permitted displacements are small, so that the squares and products of their partial derivatives with respect to position can be neglected, then they can be written as

$$\begin{pmatrix} \dfrac{\partial u}{\partial x} & \dfrac{\partial u}{\partial y} & \dfrac{\partial u}{\partial z} \\[2ex] \dfrac{\partial v}{\partial x} & \dfrac{\partial v}{\partial y} & \dfrac{\partial v}{\partial z} \\[2ex] \dfrac{\partial w}{\partial x} & \dfrac{\partial w}{\partial y} & \dfrac{\partial w}{\partial z} \end{pmatrix} \quad (9\text{-}39)$$

Matrix (9-39) represents a second-rank tensor, but it is in general not symmetric because it includes a statement of the curl of the vector field **u**, corresponding to an infinitesimal rigid-body rotation not generally regarded as part of the strain. Removal of this rotational component[5] leaves a symmetric tensor with components

$$\begin{pmatrix} \dfrac{\partial u}{\partial x} & \dfrac{1}{2}\left(\dfrac{\partial u}{\partial y} + \dfrac{\partial v}{\partial x}\right) & \dfrac{1}{2}\left(\dfrac{\partial u}{\partial z} + \dfrac{\partial w}{\partial x}\right) \\[2ex] \dfrac{1}{2}\left(\dfrac{\partial v}{\partial x} + \dfrac{\partial u}{\partial y}\right) & \dfrac{\partial v}{\partial y} & \dfrac{1}{2}\left(\dfrac{\partial v}{\partial z} + \dfrac{\partial w}{\partial y}\right) \\[2ex] \dfrac{1}{2}\left(\dfrac{\partial w}{\partial x} + \dfrac{\partial u}{\partial z}\right) & \dfrac{1}{2}\left(\dfrac{\partial w}{\partial y} + \dfrac{\partial v}{\partial z}\right) & \dfrac{\partial w}{\partial z} \end{pmatrix}$$

which is known as Cauchy's infinitesimal strain tensor. In terms of the components e of equation (9-38) this matrix can be written

---

[5] A general second-rank tensor can always be expressed as the sum of two parts. Let the tensor be represented by the matrix of coefficients t_{ij} (where $i, j = 1, 2$ and 3); then it can be expressed as the sum of two tensors $s_{ij} = \frac{1}{2}(t_{ij} + t_{ji})$ and $u_{ij} = \frac{1}{2}(t_{ij} - t_{ji})$. The tensor s_{ij} is symmetric ($s_{ij} = s_{ji}$) and the tensor u_{ij} is "antisymmetric" ($u_{ij} = -u_{ji}$). In the example given above the rigid-body rotation is therefore represented by an antisymmetric tensor:

$$\begin{pmatrix} 0 & \dfrac{1}{2}\left(\dfrac{\partial u}{\partial y} - \dfrac{\partial v}{\partial x}\right) & \dfrac{1}{2}\left(\dfrac{\partial u}{\partial z} - \dfrac{\partial w}{\partial x}\right) \\[2ex] \dfrac{1}{2}\left(\dfrac{\partial v}{\partial x} - \dfrac{\partial u}{\partial y}\right) & 0 & \dfrac{1}{2}\left(\dfrac{\partial v}{\partial z} - \dfrac{\partial w}{\partial y}\right) \\[2ex] \dfrac{1}{2}\left(\dfrac{\partial w}{\partial x} - \dfrac{\partial u}{\partial z}\right) & \dfrac{1}{2}\left(\dfrac{\partial w}{\partial y} - \dfrac{\partial v}{\partial z}\right) & 0 \end{pmatrix}$$

$$\left(\begin{array}{ccc} e_x & \tfrac{1}{2}(e_{xy} + e_{yx}) & \tfrac{1}{2}(e_{xz} + e_{zx}) \\ \tfrac{1}{2}(e_{xy} + e_{yx}) & e_y & \tfrac{1}{2}(e_{yz} + e_{zy}) \\ \tfrac{1}{2}(e_{xz} + e_{zx}) & \tfrac{1}{2}(e_{zy} + e_{yz}) & e_z \end{array}\right)$$

or a new symbol ε can be introduced to give

$$\left(\begin{array}{ccc} \varepsilon_x & \varepsilon_{xy} & \varepsilon_{xz} \\ \varepsilon_{yx} & \varepsilon_y & \varepsilon_{yz} \\ \varepsilon_{zx} & \varepsilon_{zy} & \varepsilon_z \end{array}\right) \qquad (9\text{-}40)$$

where the matrix of components ε is symmetric. This is the usual form for the strain tensor.

CONVENTIONAL STRAIN COMPONENTS The foregoing development of the components of strain has been included to support the assertion made on page 104 that strain can be represented by a symmetric second-rank tensor. Unfortunately, the six independent components of matrix (9-40) are not the strain components in general used by engineers. Before we examine those that are (the "conventional" or "engineering" strain components), let us look briefly at the geometric meaning of the components of the strain tensor and their relationships to the components e of equation (9-38). Consider the two-dimensional homogeneous transformation shown in Figure 9–36, in which a rectangle with edges in the x- and y-directions is transformed to a parallelogram. Let the displacements **u** be given by the matrix equation (neglecting uniform translation)

$$\mathbf{u} = \mathbf{E}\mathbf{x}$$

where **E** is a matrix

$$\left(\begin{array}{cc} e_x & e_{xy} \\ e_{yx} & e_y \end{array}\right)$$

which is not symmetric. The line PQ of initial length Δx is extended to PQ' and its length resolved onto the x-axis becomes $\Delta x + \Delta u$, where Δu is very small compared to Δx. The length of Δu can be estimated as

$$\Delta u = \frac{\partial u}{\partial x}\Delta x$$

from which

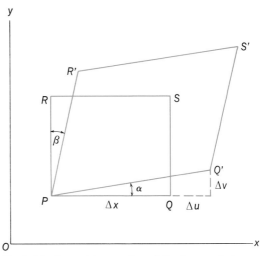

FIG. 9–36 *Geometric meaning of the tensor strain components (two-dimensional).*

$$e_x = \varepsilon_x = \frac{\Delta u}{\Delta x}$$

The component ε_x is thus a measure of the change in length per unit length of the line PQ in the x-direction. Similarly, ε_y is a measure of the change in length per unit length of the line PR in the y-direction. Both quantities, being ratios of lengths, are dimensionless and are very small compared to unity (0.01 or less).

Considering now the small change in direction of the line PQ given by the small angle α, we can write

$$\tan \alpha = \frac{\Delta v}{\Delta x + \Delta u}$$

But Δu is very small in comparison with Δx and, to a first approximation,

$$\tan \alpha = \frac{\partial v}{\partial x} = e_{yx}$$

Similarly, where β is the small angle denoting the change in direction of PR,

$$\tan \beta = e_{xy}$$

Because α and β are very small angles, we can write $\tan \alpha + \tan \beta = \tan (\alpha + \beta)$; thus,

$$\tan(\alpha + \beta) = \frac{\partial u}{\partial y} + \frac{\partial v}{\partial x}$$

from which

$$\varepsilon_{xy} = \varepsilon_{yx} = \tfrac{1}{2}\tan(\alpha + \beta)$$

The off-diagonal components represent, therefore, the change in angle between initially orthogonal lines. Let this change in angle be $\psi = \alpha + \beta$; then

$$\varepsilon_{xy} = \varepsilon_{yx} = \tfrac{1}{2}\psi \quad \text{(in radians)}$$

because ψ is of very small magnitude.

A similar development in three dimensions shows that the diagonal components of matrix (9-40) represent the changes in length of three initially orthogonal lines, and the off-diagonal components represent changes in the angles between them.

The conventional strain components can be defined directly as follows. Consider three initially orthogonal material lines in the directions of the x-, y-, and z-axes (Figure 9–37). Each segment of the line PQ after deformation has changed in length and become curved. Let the initial length of a segment at P be Δx and the final length be Δ_x'. Then the average extensional or normal strain of the segment is defined as

$$\frac{\Delta x' - \Delta x}{\Delta x} = \frac{\Delta u}{\Delta x}$$

where Δu is the change in length of the segment.[6] The normal or extensional strain ε_x of the line at point P is then defined as

$$\varepsilon_x = \lim_{\substack{\Delta x \to 0 \\ \text{at } P}} \frac{\Delta u}{\Delta x} = \frac{\partial u}{\partial x}$$

Similar expressions for the remaining orthogonal lines give respectively ε_y and ε_z.

Three components of *shearing strain* at P are defined by the changes in angles between tangents to the lines at P. Thus, for example, for

---

[6] In engineering literature, extension (increase in length) of a line is considered positive. Because most geologists take compressional stress as positive it is preferable to reverse this convention in geologic discussions and consider shortening of a line a positive normal strain.

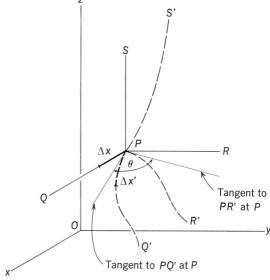

FIG. 9–37 *Geometric meaning of conventional strain components.*

lines PQ and PR (Figure 9–37) the angle between the tangents at P after deformation is θ and the shearing strain γ_{xy} is defined as

$$\gamma_{xy} = \tan\left(\frac{\pi}{2} - \theta\right) = \tan\psi = \psi \quad \text{(in radians)}$$

Two other shearing strains—between PR and PS, and PQ and PS—are similarly defined as γ_{yz} and γ_{xz}, respectively. The engineering strain components are thus related to the tensor strain components as shown in Table 9–1.

PRINCIPAL STRAINS   Because the strain tensor is symmetric it can be referred to its principal axes to give three independent principal components:

$$\begin{pmatrix} \varepsilon_1 & 0 & 0 \\ 0 & \varepsilon_2 & 0 \\ 0 & 0 & \varepsilon_3 \end{pmatrix}$$

In any homogeneously strained body, therefore, or at any *point* in a heterogeneously strained body, there are three orthogonal material lines that undergo pure length changes and remain orthogonal after deformation (the shearing components vanish). The three components $\varepsilon_1 \geq \varepsilon_2 \geq \varepsilon_3$ are called principal strains, and the three

TABLE 9–1   *Components of infinitesimal strain*

Tensor Components	Conventional Components
ε_x	ε_x
ε_y	ε_y
ε_z	ε_z
$\varepsilon_{xy} = \varepsilon_{yx}$	$\frac{1}{2}\gamma_{xy}$
$\varepsilon_{yz} = \varepsilon_{zy}$	$\frac{1}{2}\gamma_{yz}$
$\varepsilon_{xz} = \varepsilon_{zx}$	$\frac{1}{2}\gamma_{xz}$

orthogonal directions are called principal axes or directions of strain. For a general transformation with a nonsymmetric *e*-matrix the orthogonal material lines in the strained and unstrained body do not coincide in direction but are related by an infinitesimal rigid body rotation given by the antisymmetric part of the *e*-matrix. Such a strain is termed *rotational*. If the antisymmetric part of the *e*-matrix vanishes the strain is nonrotational. Any nonrotational strain or nonrotational part of a general strain, as specified by the strain tensor, is termed a *pure strain*.

OTHER FEATURES OF INFINITESIMAL STRAIN   The properties of the strain tensor correspond very closely to those of the stress tensor. For example, a general strain tensor can be divided into isotropic and deviatoric parts. These two parts are particularly important in the elastic theory of isotropic bodies. By Hooke's law the deviatoric stresses are proportional to the deviatoric strains and the isotropic stresses are proportional to the isotropic strains. The isotropic part of the strain tensor is termed the octahedral or mean normal strain and is a pure volume dilatation ε_0 defined as

$$\varepsilon_0 = \frac{\varepsilon_1 + \varepsilon_2 + \varepsilon_3}{3}$$

It is related to the more familiar quality, the "cubical dilatation" ε_v, by

$$\varepsilon_0 = \frac{\varepsilon_v}{3}$$

The deviatoric part is a pure shearing strain with no volume change. It is important in the mathe-

matical theory of plasticity where, since Poisson's ratio is taken as 0.5, no volume changes are generally considered.

Many of the other equations connected with the theory of stress at a point have direct analogies in the theory of strain at a point, with the strain components substituted for the corresponding stress components. Where conventional strain components are used the substitutions can still be made, but care must be taken because of the factor of two that relates the two sets of shearing components. For example, the equation for extension ε_n of a line with unit normal vector **n** is given in terms of the tensor strain components by

$$\varepsilon_n = \varepsilon_x n_x^2 + \varepsilon_y n_y^2 + \varepsilon_z n_z^2 + 2\varepsilon_{xy} n_x n_y \\ + 2\varepsilon_{yz} n_y n_z + 2\varepsilon_{zx} n_z n_x \qquad (9\text{-}41)$$

and in terms of the conventional strain components by

$$\varepsilon_n = \varepsilon_x n_x^2 + \varepsilon_y n_y^2 + \varepsilon_z n_z^2 + \gamma_{xy} n_x n_y \\ + \gamma_{yz} n_y n_z + \gamma_{zx} n_z n_x \qquad (9\text{-}42)$$

Equation (9-41) is seen to be similar to equation (9-6) for normal stress on the same plane. Referred to principal-axes equations, (9-41) and (9-42), both simplify to

$$\varepsilon_n = \varepsilon_1 n_x^2 + \varepsilon_2 n_y^2 + \varepsilon_3 n_z^2$$

Similarly, the tensor shearing strain ε_{nm} of a pair of orthogonal lines with unit vectors **n** and **m** can be expressed in terms of the tensor strain components as

$$\varepsilon_{nm} = \varepsilon_x n_x m_x + \varepsilon_y n_y m_y + \varepsilon_z n_z m_z \\ + \varepsilon_{xy}(n_x m_y + n_y m_x) + \varepsilon_{yz}(n_y m_z + n_z m_y) \\ + \varepsilon_{zx}(n_z m_x + n_x m_z) \qquad (9\text{-}43)$$

an equation similar to (9-7) for the shearing stress on the same plane in direction **s**. In terms of the conventional strain components, equation (9-43) can be modified to give the conventional shearing strain γ_{nm} as follows:

$$\gamma_{nm} = 2\varepsilon_x n_x m_x + 2\varepsilon_y n_y m_y + 2\varepsilon_z n_z m_z \\ + \gamma_{xy}(n_x m_y + n_y m_x) + \gamma_{yz}(n_y m_z + n_z m_y) \\ + \gamma_{zx}(n_z m_x + n_x m_z) \qquad (9\text{-}44)$$

Other equations for strain can be written corresponding to those for stress.

Two-dimensional graphic representation of a state of infinitesimal strain can be made by a Mohr diagram. But the most frequently used representation is the *strain ellipsoid*, given by

$$\frac{x^2}{(1 + \varepsilon_1)^2} + \frac{y^2}{(1 + \varepsilon_2)^2} + \frac{z^2}{(1 + \varepsilon_3)^2} = 1$$

This is the ellipsoid into which a unit sphere in the undeformed body is distorted by the strain; its principal axes coincide with the direction of the principal strains. It is a clear image of the symmetry of pure strain: for axial strains it is a spheroid, either prolate or oblate (symmetry ∞/m $2/m$ $2/m$) and for a pure dilatation (isotropic strain) it is a sphere (symmetry ∞/m ∞/m ∞/m). For a general strain it is a triaxial ellipsoid (symmetry $2/m$ $2/m$ $2/m$). It is convenient to consider also the ellipsoid in the unstrained body which becomes a sphere in the strained body, called the *reciprocal strain ellipsoid*. If the principal axes of the strain and reciprocal strain ellipsoids are in the same directions a deformation is a pure strain and is nonrotational. For a general transformation with a rotational component the two sets of axes are related by an infinitesimal rotation that defines the rotational component and the rotation axis. If the rotational component is included as part of the transformation, symmetries of $2/m$ and $\bar{1}$ are possible. All strains being second-rank tensors, are, however, centrosymmetric.

A state of strain for which one of the principal strains is zero is termed a plane strain. Two types of plane strain are of particular importance in elementary elasticity theory and are significant also in permanent deformations as finite strains. The first of these, termed *pure shear*, is a deviatoric strain (that is, $\varepsilon_1 + \varepsilon_2 + \varepsilon_3 = 0$) and can be expressed two-dimensionally by the tensor

$$\begin{pmatrix} \varepsilon_1 & 0 \\ 0 & -\varepsilon_1 \end{pmatrix}$$

All displacements lie in the plane of ε_1 and ε_2 (the "deformation plane") and a circle in this plane is distorted into a "strain ellipse," which intersects the circle, as shown in Figure 9–38, along two orthogonal lines of no strain symmetrically inclined to the principal axes. A material line in the deformation plane inclined at θ to the direction of ε_1 is infinitesimally changed in length by an amount ε, where

$$\varepsilon = \frac{(\varepsilon_1 + \varepsilon_2)}{2} + \frac{(\varepsilon_1 - \varepsilon_2)}{2} \cos 2\theta \quad (9\text{-}45)$$

If θ is less than 45°, the line is shortened; if θ is greater than 45°, the line is lengthened; and if θ equals 45°, the line is unchanged in length.

The second plane strain, termed a *simple shear*, differs from pure shear only in the presence of a rigid-body rotation (in the deformation plane) of magnitude $\eta = \frac{1}{2}\gamma$, where γ is the conventional shearing strain between lines initially in the x- and y-directions. The effect of this rotation is to maintain one direction of no strain in the same direction (Figure 9–39). This difference between pure and simple shear becomes very important in progressive finite deformations.

For three-dimensional strain the six conventional strain components are derivatives of only three components of displacement and are not

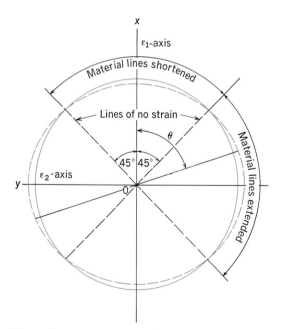

FIG. 9–38 *Infinitesimal pure shear.*

truly independent. They are connected by six relationships called the *compatibility conditions*, as follows:

$$\frac{\partial^2 \varepsilon_x}{\partial y^2} + \frac{\partial^2 \varepsilon_y}{\partial x^2} = \frac{\partial^2 \varepsilon_{xy}}{2\partial x\,\partial y} \qquad (9\text{-}46)$$

(and two similar equations involving y, z and z, x)

$$\frac{\partial^2 \varepsilon_x}{\partial y\,\partial z} = \frac{\partial}{\partial x}\left(-\frac{\partial \varepsilon_{yz}}{\partial x} + \frac{\partial \varepsilon_{zx}}{\partial y} + \frac{\partial \varepsilon_{xy}}{\partial z}\right)$$

(and two similar equations permuting x, y, and z)

These equations must be satisfied by the components of strain in order that uniqueness and continuity of deformation be maintained. Physically these conditions require that no cracks or holes appear in the deformed body. Various methods of arriving at the compatibility equations have been used, mostly based upon the notion that the derivatives of the displacements at a point be finite and continuous.

ELASTIC BEHAVIOR OF ROCKS

Problems in linear elasticity require the determination of 15 unknown quantities—namely, six components of stress, six components of strain, and three displacements. Nine equations in these unknowns can be written immediately, in the absence of body forces, as the three stress equations of equilibrium stating that the sum of all forces per unit volume is zero

$$\frac{\partial \sigma_x}{\partial x} + \frac{\partial \tau_{xy}}{\partial y} + \frac{\partial \tau_{xz}}{\partial z} = 0 \qquad (9\text{-}47)$$

(and two similar equations in y and z)

and the six equations relating strains to displacements

$$\varepsilon_x = \frac{\partial u}{\partial x} \qquad \varepsilon_y = \frac{\partial v}{\partial y} \qquad \varepsilon_z = \frac{\partial w}{\partial z}$$

$$\varepsilon_{xy} = \frac{1}{2}\left(\frac{\partial u}{\partial y} + \frac{\partial v}{\partial x}\right)$$

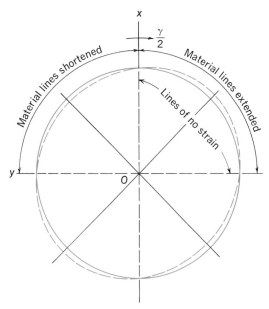

FIG. 9–39 *Infinitesimal simple shear; equivalent to a pure shear plus an infinitesimal rotation $\gamma/2$.*

$$\varepsilon_{yz} = \frac{1}{2}\left(\frac{\partial v}{\partial z} + \frac{\partial w}{\partial y}\right) \qquad \varepsilon_{zz} = \frac{1}{2}\left(\frac{\partial u}{\partial z} + \frac{\partial w}{\partial x}\right)$$

The six remaining equations relate stresses to strains by way of Hooke's law.

The general statement of Hooke's law for anisotropic solids has been given above for crystals, all of which are elastically anisotropic to some degree. In an ideally continuous isotropic solid the number of independent elastic coefficients reduces to two, but in conventional discussions four interrelated quantities are generally introduced, defined as follows:

1. Elastic or Young's modulus E, given by

$$E = \frac{\sigma}{\varepsilon}$$

where σ is normal stress and ε is extensional strain (remember that in an isotropic material the directions of these coincide).

2. Rigidity or shear modulus μ, given by

$$\mu = \frac{\tau}{\gamma}$$

where τ is shearing stress on a plane and γ is the corresponding conventional shearing strain between the line in which the stress acts in the plane and the normal to the plane.

3. Bulk modulus K, given by

$$K = \frac{\sigma_0}{\varepsilon_v} \quad \text{or} \quad \frac{\sigma_0}{3\varepsilon_0}$$

where ε_v is the "cubical dilatation" or volumetric strain $\Delta V/V$ and ε_0 is the octahedral or mean normal strain. Compressibility β is defined as the reciprocal of K (see Chapter 2).

4. Poisson's ratio ν, given by the ratio of lateral contraction to elongation of a cylinder in a simple tensile test. It is a dimensionless number reaching a maximum of 0.5 for an incompressible solid. The dimensions of the other three quantities are those of stress.

Of these four quantities only two are independent, and many simple expressions relating all four quantities can be derived; for example,

$$K = \frac{E\mu}{3(3\mu - E)}$$

$$E = 2\mu(1 + \nu)$$

$$\nu = \frac{3K - E}{6K}$$

$$\mu = \frac{E}{2 + 2\nu}$$

In terms of these quantities six equations relating the components of stress to the components of strain can be written in a number of ways; for example,

$$\varepsilon_x = \frac{1}{E}[\sigma_x - \nu(\sigma_y + \sigma_z)] \qquad (9\text{-}48)$$

(and two similar equations in y and z)

$$\varepsilon_{xy} = \frac{(1 + \nu)}{E}\tau_{xy} \qquad (9\text{-}49)$$

(and two similar equations in yz and zx)

For convenience a fifth quantity, Lamé's constant λ, is often introduced:

$$\lambda = \frac{\nu E}{(1 + \nu)(1 - 2\nu)} = K - \frac{2}{3}\mu$$

By means of this constant, Hooke's law for an isotropic solid can be simply written in terms of components of stress and strain and the volumetric strain as

$$\sigma_x = \lambda\varepsilon_v + 2\mu\varepsilon_x$$

$$\sigma_y = \lambda\varepsilon_v + 2\mu\varepsilon_y$$

$$\sigma_z = \lambda\varepsilon_v + 2\mu\varepsilon_z$$

$$\tau_{xy} = 2\mu\varepsilon_{xy} \qquad (9\text{-}50)$$

$$\tau_{yz} = 2\mu\varepsilon_{yz}$$

$$\tau_{zx} = 2\mu\varepsilon_{zx}$$

The 15 equations given above, together with the compatibility equations and the boundary conditions at the surface of a deformed body, form the necessary and sufficient conditions for solutions to problems of isotropic linear elasticity.

For most engineering purposes the above statement of Hooke's law is adequate. Most metals are aggregates of high-symmetry crystals generally lacking marked preferred orientation, and their elastic behavior is close to that of the ideal isotropic body. But the geologist must be conscious of two important factors that materially affect the elastic properties of rocks in the earth, as follows:

1. Most rocks in the crust and, we believe, the upper mantle are composed of low-symmetry crystals (generally triclinic, monoclinic, or orthorhombic) and in many rocks exposed at the surface these minerals are found to be in a state of preferred orientation. Simple considerations suggest, therefore, as sensitive measurements prove, that most rocks are elastically anisotropic to some degree and that measurement of two independent elastic constants is insufficient to determine fully their elastic behavior.

2. Elastic constants vary with temperature and pressure, and laboratory determinations of these quantities made at atmospheric pressure and room temperature may not apply to rocks deep in the crust and mantle.

ROCKS AS ISOTROPIC ELASTIC SOLIDS   Some rocks, notably many igneous rocks which comprise a significant proportion of the crust, approach isotropy in their structural properties. Where preferred orientations of minerals occur in these rocks, they are generally weak and their effect on elastic properties is small or insignificant. Such rocks can be taken as elastically isotropic without serious error.

The elastic constants of rocks (and minerals) can be determined experimentally under static or dynamic conditions. An example of the former is determination of bulk modulus by measuring volume changes in specimens placed under hydrostatic pressure by immersion in a fluid at high pressure. An example of the latter is determination of the velocities of propagation of elastic body waves, V_p and V_s, and calculation of elastic constants from the equations of isotropic elasticity. From V_s, for example, the shear modulus can be found as $\mu = \rho V_s^2$ (where ρ is the density) and the bulk modulus and hence the compressibility can be found from the relationship

$$K = \rho \left(V_p^2 - \frac{4}{3} V_s^2 \right)$$

Other elastic constants can be found from the connecting relationships. The two methods do not give precisely the same results because static measurements are generally made isothermally, whereas dynamic measurements are inherently adiabatic. Differences between the two sets of measurements do not appear to be great at low temperatures and pressures. Most materials have slightly different constants for compression and tension.

At elevated pressures the elastic properties of most rocks change. At slightly increased pressures (up to about 1 kilobar) these changes can be attributed to the closing of pores and other spaces in rocks, and are not reversible. At greatly increased pressures, measurable changes still occur which may be very large at extreme pressures. By the use of shock waves, very high pressures in the megabar range can be achieved. But the structural condition of a rock during the passage of a shock wave is imperfectly understood, and the equation of state relating pressure and density obtained in this way differs from the normal adiabatic and isothermal equations of state. However, the state of rocks and minerals during and after passage of shock waves is important to the geologist concerned with impact sites of large meteorites on the surface of the earth and moon, and practically everything that can be said about equations of state in the deep mantle and core comes from information obtained in shock-wave experiments.

Although rocks can be effectively isotropic, they are composed of anisotropic minerals and their elastic properties must depend to some degree on the elastic properties of the component grains. Various attempts have been made to obtain relationships between the elastic constants of crystals and the elastic constants of the polycrystalline aggregates they form—none of which has proved wholly successful. The most often cited approximations are those of Voigt and Reuss. For example, in a monomineralic rock with no pores, composed of randomly oriented crystals with elastic moduli c_{ij} ($i, j = 1, 2, 3, 4, 5,$ and 6), Voigt gives the following expressions for the bulk and shear moduli:

$$K = \frac{(A + 2B)}{3} \qquad \mu = \frac{(A - B + 3C)}{5}$$

where

$$3A = (c_{11} + c_{22} + c_{33})$$
$$3B = (c_{23} + c_{31} + c_{12})$$
$$3C = (c_{44} + c_{55} + c_{66})$$

This approximation takes no account of grain shape or the fact that most rocks contain minerals of several different kinds.

ELASTIC ANISOTROPY OF ROCKS   For most purposes seismologists, who are most concerned with the elastic properties of rocks, treat rocks of the crust and mantle as elastically isotropic. The paths of seismic waves through the earth are generally long compared with the scale of variation in composition and structure; thus, particularly in the crust, the mean elastic behavior along a heterogeneous path is observed. But sensitive measurements begin to suggest that the upper mantle might be systematically anisotropic through large domains, a fact that might yield information on patterns of convective or other flow in the mantle.

Many of the rocks exposed at the surface of the earth are anisotropic to a degree that cannot be ignored for certain purposes: The principles governing the relationship between structural and elastic anisotropy in rocks and in minerals are essentially the same except that the symmetry of a rock structure is statistically defined as the symmetry of its fabric. The common point groups of rock fabrics, listed in Table 3–1, define the types of elastic anisotropy to be expected in rocks, but the degree of anisotropy depends also upon the compositions of minerals present and the perfection of their preferred orientations. The most pronounced effects are observed in strongly foliated rocks, such as schists and phyllites, in which highly anisotropic minerals, such as mica and chlorite, are in a state of strong preferred orientation. But even monomineralic rocks composed of equant grains of minerals, such as quartz or olivine, that are not so strongly anisotropic have easily measurable differences in elastic properties in different directions.

Many rocks prove to have triclinic fabrics with symmetry $\bar{1}$. A complete description of the elastic properties of such a rock would require determination of 21 elastic constants—an impossible task. Fortunately, many common rocks have much higher symmetry if only the most prominent features of their fabrics are considered. Uniformly bedded, laminated, or foliated rocks lacking other prominent structures, for example, approach axial symmetry (group $\infty/m\,2/m\,2/m$). If a regular linear structure is present in the structural surfaces the symmetry is more nearly orthorhombic (group $2/m\,2/m\,2/m$). A further simplification is achieved if a quantity such as linear compressibility, rather than elastic moduli or compliances, is determined. Linear compressibility is a less complex quantity than elasticity, since it is represented by a second-rank instead of a fourth-rank tensor. Measurement of only

three principal components (the directions of which can be generally determined from structures visible in hand specimens) permits the degree of anisotropy to be established for rocks of high symmetry.

DEPARTURES FROM LINEAR ELASTICITY   Laboratory experiments show that the theory of linear elasticity is only an approximate model for the behavior of real rocks. The most important failure of Hooke's law, from the point of view of the geologist, is expressed by creep in response to shearing stresses of long duration. Most of the flow structures of deformed rocks—such as, for example, some common types of folds—are probably structures formed by creep.

Other effects occur, however, that indicate a failure of Hooke's law even under conditions of rapid loading. One example is the damping or "attenuation" of seismic waves so that amplitude decreases with distance from the seismic source in a manner more or less independent of frequency. This phenomenon occurs even though loading is rapid and the strains involved are well within the range normally taken as that of linearly elastic behavior. By such attenuation the energy of a wave is somehow dissipated in a non-elastic way as it propagates. The phenomenon is observed also in single crystals, but the effect is much greater in polycrystalline aggregates. The degree of attenuation is expressed by a parameter Q, where

$$\frac{1}{Q} = \frac{\Delta E}{2\pi E}$$

and $\Delta E/E$ is the percent of strain energy lost per cycle. The energy of a wave with wavelength λ will be attenuated with distance x as $e^{-\alpha x}$, where $\alpha = 2\pi/Q\lambda$. The energy, for simple harmonic motion, is proportional to the square of the amplitude.

Probably the most important cause of attenuation of seismic waves in near-surface rocks is movement on structural discontinuities such as fractures, grain boundaries, pores, and so on. In this process some energy is converted to heat by frictional sliding and is dissipated by conduction. Other explanations involve mismatch between stressed elastically anisotropic grains with resultant scattering of waves, and, within single crystals, some plastic deformation and crack propagation.

The low-velocity layer or channel of the upper mantle is a region of particularly strong attenuation. For this region Q is between 100 and 200 which means that a wave having a period of one second and velocity of 6 km/sec is attenuated by about 1 percent in 1 km. This observation fits the role of this layer as a zone of supposedly low shear strength and creep resistance as required by the theory of sea-floor spreading. In this region the presence of interstitial molten material may be one cause of departure from ideally elastic behavior. In contrast, the lower mantle has values of Q of perhaps 2000 or more, and seismic waves, particularly those of long wavelength, are observed to travel several times around the earth without much attenuation.

Fracture and Faulting

Rocks can be made to break or "fail" in a variety of ways in laboratory experiments. Some failure is catastrophic and a specimen separates suddenly into two or more pieces, which can generally be fitted back together again without serious mismatch on the broken surfaces. We have termed such behavior brittle. In a compression experiment the fracture surfaces are either parallel to the compression axis (extension fractures) or oblique to the compression axis (shear fractures or faults). The former behavior is most typical of simple compression and the latter of triaxial compression at low confining pressures. In a simple tensile test the fracture surfaces are subperpendicular to the axis of tensile stress.

Other failures involve maintenance of cohesion on the oblique failure surface. The pieces of the specimen do not suddenly separate but slide slowly on the failure surface which develops a finely granular polished and striated coating (slickenslide). If the axial load on the specimen is momentarily relaxed and then reapplied, slip will begin again on the same failure surface. Such behavior is typical of specimens deformed triaxially at moderate confining pressures and is transitional toward cohesive flow (ductile behavior), into which it grades at high confining pressures.

Natural failure surfaces in rocks are generally classified broadly as joints and faults, but in fact such surfaces exhibit an enormous range in features. Joints, for example, are typically very clean fractures with no sign of displacement on opposite sides. These features suggest that joints are brittle fractures. Faults, on the other hand, range from clean fractures with visible small displacements to complex and diffuse mylonite zones tens or hundreds of meters wide which, geological evidence suggests, have slipped time and time again —in some cases, for distances of hundreds of kilometers. Such structures seem to be more akin to the faults and ductile faults of the experimenters and we must be careful in discussing them to distinguish between the "failure" phenomena which nucleated and propagated the original surface of rupture and the subsequent displacements which have taken place. We can expect intuitively that a close relationship might exist between the initial failure surface and the state of stress or elastic strain immediately preceding it; whereas, once the failure surface is formed, it becomes a surface of low cohesion, and slip may continue on it in response to stresses of a quite different kind.

One reason a geologist studies natural fractures in the crust is in an attempt to learn something about the stress states responsible for their formation, and, in the case of active faults, particularly those with which earthquakes are associated, to establish present distributions of mechanical forces.

We look briefly now at experimental and theoretical evidence bearing on fracture and faulting and attempt to relate it to natural structures.

FRACTURE

If there is a unique type of "brittle" fracture, it is the extension or axial fracture just described. Formation of such fractures subperpendicular to an axis of simple tension is easily pictured as occurring where the tensile normal stress on the surface perpendicular to the tension axis exceeds a value σ_t, the tensile cohesive strength of the material. In simple compression, on the other hand, no tensile stresses should be present if the material is continuous and the stress homogeneous; and it is difficult at first sight to see how extension fractures form.

Another discrepancy in theory appears if we consider the probable values of σ_t. Simple theoretical calculations based on the strength of atomic cohesions suggest that $\sigma_t \cong E/10$, where E is Young's modulus. Experiments show a vast discrepancy between this value of σ_t and that measured in tensile tests. For example, for most compact igneous rocks E has a value of about 1 megabar, so the theoretical tensile strength is about 100 kilobars. Observed tensile strengths of such rocks is of the order of 1 kb or less.

To gain some insight into the reasons for this discrepancy and the origin of extension fractures in compression we must abandon temporarily our view of a rock as a uniform continuous solid medium and must consider the effect upon stress distribution of flaws and cracks present in most rocks on a very small scale. Such imperfections occur along grain boundaries and within grains as cracks opened by plastic flow. At elevated pressures such pores and cracks seem to close irreversibly. At low confining pressures, however, some of them will remain open and, in the absence of a high pressure interstitial fluid, unsupported, and stress concentrations therefore occur in their vicinity. A theory of brittle fracture of solids based upon the presence of microscopic flaws (Griffith theory) was proposed many years ago and has been modified since. We look now at the relevance of this theory to the fracture of rocks.

GRIFFITH THEORY OF BRITTLE FAILURE Griffith departed from continuum mechanical theory by assuming that a solid is filled with minute elliptical cracks. When such a body is placed in simple tension, local stress is increased around the tips of cracks oriented normal to the axis of tension. By examining the conditions under which such cracks would grow, Griffith developed a mathematical model consistent with observed low values of tensile strength. He showed that the velocity of propagation of a crack v_c is given by

$$v_c = Kv\left(1 - \frac{c_0}{c}\right)^{1/2} \qquad (9\cdot51)$$

where v is the velocity of sound in the material, c_0 is the crack half-length required for spontaneous propagation, c is the crack half-length at any stage, and K is a dimensionless constant. From this expression the crack is seen to accelerate as it propagates, reaching a maximum of Kv as the crack grows very large. The constant K is less than unity, so the velocity of crack propagation is limited by the speed of sound. For a fuller treatment, the reader is referred to Chapter 12 in the book by Jaeger and Cook listed in the references.

In a real material, cracks are of many sizes, shapes, and orientations. Under these conditions, even where loading is by simple compression, some of the cracks develop tensile stresses at their tips. Such "induced" tensile stresses enable certain cracks to grow. There is evidence to suggest that, in simple compression, cracks grow along a curved path until they become parallel to the compression axis when growth ceases. If a sufficient number of cracks grow in this direction, they may locally run together to form a large-scale fracture surface, which propagates right through the body. Most rocks, however, are markedly stronger in simple compression than in simple tension, and thus tensile stresses induced by a particular simple compressive stress must be smaller than those resulting from a tensile stress of the same magnitude.

It is likely that typical extension fractures in compression originate as a result of local tensile stresses induced by the presence of preexisting cracks and other flaws. Such fractures appear to begin at a particular region in the specimen where microfractures coalesce and then to propagate outward at high velocity (which, in a very brittle material, may be about half the speed of sound) in a roughly plane surface. In detail the surface along which the fracture propagates is not plane and smooth because of fre-

FIG. 9-40 *Plumose structure on a joint surface. Each black and white division on the scale is 1 cm.*

quent minor changes in direction of the propagating fracture front. The surface is ribbed and ridged in a characteristic pattern which has been called *plumose structure* (Figure 9-40). This behavior seems to be characteristic of materials such as rocks which contain many large-scale discontinuities.

JOINTING IN ROCKS From the discussion in Chapter 3 we see that the term "joint" is applied to a great variety of natural fracture surfaces, the distinguishing feature of which is that no appreciable slip or displacement has occurred along them. This feature, together with the cleanness of the rupture surfaces, has led most geologists to interpret joints as brittle fractures of some kind. Some are characterized by plumose surface features and appear to be extension fractures; still others are in conjugate sets of variable dihedral angle and have been interpreted as shear joints.

A number of theories have been advanced to account for joint development, none of which is wholly acceptable. Some geologists have suggested that they are generated at the time of formation of the rock. This may be true of some joints in sedimentary sequences, which are perpendicular to bedding and may have formed during compaction and lithification, and it is certainly true of the columnar joints in lava flows developed in response to tensional stresses in a cooling sheet. But such a theory does not account for many of the joints of metamorphic rocks that have clearly developed at a late stage after the development of structures such as folds and foliation, or for joint sets that can be shown by the presence of thin films of secondary minerals of different kinds to have developed in several distinct episodes. Other geologists have proposed that joints are essentially fatigue fractures resulting from continued cyclic elastic straining of rocks during the passage of seismic waves or as a result of earth tides.

Perhaps the most widely accepted theory holds that joints are brittle fractures caused by stresses developed in rocks raised from within the crust by uplift and erosion. During such uplift in a spherical earth a body of rock must undergo a lateral expansion which can be established on purely geometric grounds. For a body with horizontal dimension l at depth the expansion can be expressed as the extensional strain $\Delta l/l$ where Δl is the increase in the dimension. If the body is elastic a tensile stress $\sigma_T = E\Delta l/l$ develops as a result of this forced expansion. Consider now a body of rock at depth containing residual stresses of tectonic origin. Let the residual stress be a horizontal compressive stress σ_x' in the x-direction of a coordinate system (z-axis is vertical). This stress is superposed upon a lithostatic stress $\sigma_z = \rho g z$ and the three principal stresses are in the directions of the coordinate axis and are given by

$$\sigma_x = \sigma_1 = \rho g z \left(\frac{\nu}{1 - \nu}\right) + \sigma_x'$$

$$\sigma_y = \sigma_2 = \rho g z \left(\frac{\nu}{1 - \nu}\right) + \nu\sigma_x'$$

$$\sigma_z = \sigma_3 = \rho g z$$

where ν is Poisson's ratio. During progressive uplift the magnitudes of the stresses σ_x, σ_y, and σ_z change in the manner shown qualitatively by the three curves shown in Figure 9-41. At depth D_1 all stresses are compressional and σ_1 and σ_2 are horizontal. We assume that the stress differences are insufficient to induce shear failures. At inter-

mediate depth D_2, σ_2 has become vertical. Above this depth the stress difference between σ_1 and σ_3 may become large enough for vertical conjugate shear joints to develop, releasing much of the stress. At higher levels, such as D_3, the stress σ_y may become tensile and vertical extension fractures may develop.

The foregoing sequence of events is hypothetical and clearly cannot account alone for the great complexity and variety of observed joint patterns. There is little doubt that other factors are important; it has been suggested, for example, that the presence of a high-pressure pore fluid may be a controlling factor in the development of joints, particularly at depth. Also difficult to explain in terms of this theory are the "unloading joints" or "sheeting" structures that conform broadly to the topographic surfaces cut in massive granites.

In summary we must admit that the origin of joints is not well understood.

FAULTING

Most regions of the earth's surface contain an abundance of faults—that is, fractures in the earth's surface across which the rocks have been displaced. In speaking of faults and the displacements that have occurred on them, a geologist must constantly bear in mind the distinction between the development of a fault—that is, the first appearance of a planar failure surface—and

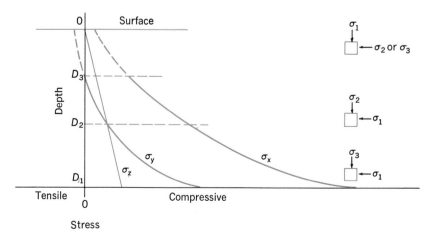

FIG. 9–41 Change in principal stresses during uplift from an initial condition with σ_1 horizontal and σ_3 vertical. (After N. Price, Fault and Joint Development in Brittle and Semi-Brittle Rock, Pergamon Press, 1966, reproduced with permission.)

displacements on a fault, which, seismically active faults prove, can continue for very long periods. Once a fault appears it can become a locus of displacements in response to stress distributions significantly different from the one that caused the initial failure, and the layers of crushed rock, mylonite, or other cataclastic material along a fault may be testimony more to its subsequent history than to the conditions under which the fault was nucleated and initially propagated.

In experimental studies, fracture surfaces termed faults tend to form oblique to a compression axis at low-to-moderate confining pressures in the absence of tensile stresses. In most geologic situations in which faults form, the general stress state is likewise compressional ($\sigma_1 > \sigma_2 > \sigma_3$) and a failure criterion for faulting must be applicable to these conditions. Several such criteria have been proposed based upon factors such as maximum shearing stress, maximum shearing strain, and considerations of strain energy. Of these the most useful have proved to be those theories which predict failure on surfaces oblique to the compression axis as a result of the presence of shearing stresses exceeding some initial value. The simplest such

model would be failure on surfaces of maximum shearing stress

$$\tau_{max} = \pm \frac{\sigma_1 - \sigma_3}{2}$$

This criterion predicts two conjugate surfaces of shear failure inclined at 45° to σ_1 and intersecting in σ_2 for a general state of stress and conical surfaces at 45° to σ_1 for an axial compression. Such failure surfaces are not observed.

A much more realistic general theory of failure (that of Mohr) takes both shearing and normal stresses into account and states that failure occurs where the shearing and normal stresses on a surface are connected by a critical relationship

$$\tau = f(\sigma)$$

characteristic of the material. This function can be plotted in the Mohr stress plane and its form for a particular rock can be determined experimentally in compression experiments under a variety of confining pressures. For example, for each failure a Mohr circle for the state of stress at the instant of failure can be drawn (Figure 9–42). Each of these circles must just touch the curve for the function, which can therefore be

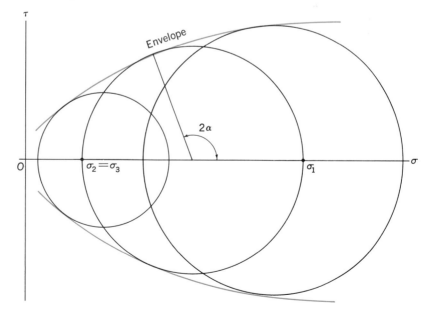

FIG. 9–42 *Mohr envelope for failure. Each circle corresponds to a state of triaxial stress at failure. For the state of stress given by $\sigma_1 > \sigma_2 = \sigma_3$ failure occurs on a plane inclined at α to the σ_1 direction.*

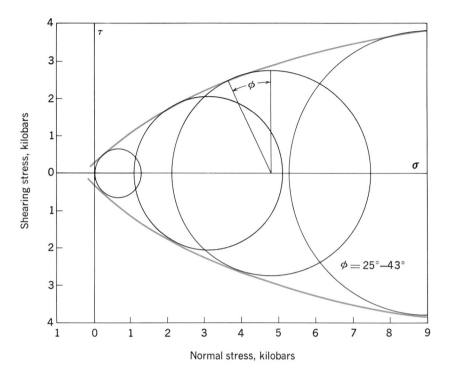

FIG. 9–43 *Mohr envelope for ultimate compressive strength (greatest stress in compression that the material can bear) for Hasmark dolomite at room temperature. (After J. Handin and R. V. Hager, Experimental deformation of sedimentary rocks under confining pressure: tests at room temperature on dry samples, Am. Assoc. Petrol. Geol. Bull., 1957.)*

constructed as the envelope of the successive circles (the Mohr envelope). Any combination of σ and τ corresponding to a point on this curve will induce failure. For a particular stress state, this combination of stress is reached on a surface with the normal inclined to the σ_1 axis at angle α (that is, half the angles 2α in Figure 9–42); this surface should be the failure surface.

In Figure 9–43 is shown a typical Mohr envelope. In some rocks the two branches of the curve are almost straight lines; in others they are concave towards the σ-axis. The fact that, in almost all rocks, the two branches seem to become farther apart for increasing values of σ shows that the shear stress at failure increases with the normal stress. In Figure 9–43 the curves are shown only for compressional normal stress. For cohesive materials the curves extend across the τ-axis into the field of tensile normal stress, where their forms become uncertain.

NAVIER-COULOMB CRITERION   One specialization of the Mohr theory has proved to be especially useful to geologists. The Mohr envelope is assumed to be two straight lines of the form

$$\tau = \tau_0 + \mu_i \sigma \qquad (9\text{-}52)$$

In this expression τ is the shear stress for failure and τ_0 is the cohesive shear strength of the material (in the absence of normal stress). The term $\mu_i \sigma$ arises because it is assumed that resistance to shear failure is overcome only when both the cohesive strength and the resistance to frictional sliding on the failure surface are exceeded. By analogy with sliding friction, the quantity μ_i is called the coefficient of internal friction. Equation (9-52) can be written also as

$$\tau = \tau_0 + \sigma \tan \phi$$

where ϕ is called the angle of internal friction. A Mohr envelope for this criterion is shown

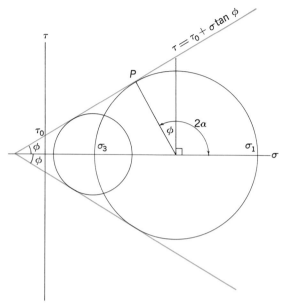

FIG. 9–44 *Mohr envelope for the Navier-Coulomb criterion.*

in Figure 9–44. The two straight-line branches are inclined to the σ-axis at angle ϕ and intersect the τ-axis at τ_0. The state of stress corresponding to the failure condition at point P is reached on a pair of surfaces intersecting in the σ_2 direction with normals inclined at α to the σ_1 direction, where

$$\alpha = \pm\left(\frac{\pi}{4} + \frac{\phi}{2}\right)$$

This relation, due to Navier and Coulomb, predicts failure on a pair of conjugate planar surfaces with the σ_1 direction as their acute bisectrix. In an experiment only one of these two failure surfaces may actually develop. In a quasi-isotropic material the two surfaces have the same probability of developing, but once one of the pair has developed, there is a change in the stress distribution, including generally a fall in the magnitude of the axial compressive stress, and the other surface may fail to develop.

From observed angles between the axis of compression and the failure surface, the coefficient of internal friction for rocks can be esti-

mated. For most isotropic, compact, coherent rocks, measured values lie between about 0.7 and about 1.7. For sedimentary rocks, such as siltstones and limestones, values are in the lower part of this range; for massive igneous rocks, such as granite and gabbros, in the upper part of the range.

MODIFIED GRIFFITH THEORY   Straight-line envelopes are not observed for most rocks. Most envelopes are curved, indicating a nonlinear relationship between τ and σ at failure. A closer theoretical fit to experimentally determined Mohr envelopes has been obtained by McLintock and Walsh, who assumed that under compression the preexisting cracks and flaws in a rock required by the Griffith theory of brittle failure at low pressures become closed as the normal stress across them reaches a critical value σ_c. The normal "effective" stress holding the two sides of a particular crack together is then $\sigma_e = (\sigma - \sigma_c)$, where σ is the total normal stress. For failure to occur the flaw must be propagated, but frictional sliding must also take place between the walls of the crack. The shear stress for friction sliding τ is given by

$$\tau = \mu_s(\sigma - \sigma_c)$$

wher μ_s is the coefficient of sliding friction. If high confining pressures are involved, σ_c can be assumed to be much less than σ and a failure criterion based upon propagation and sliding of a Griffith crack can be found of the form

$$\tau = 2\sigma_t + \mu_s\sigma \qquad (9\text{-}53)$$

where σ_t is the strength of the rock in simple tension. This criterion resembles the Navier-Coulomb relationship in corresponding to a straight-line Mohr envelope. Where σ is tensile, however, the Griffith criterion must be used, which is given by

$$\tau = 2(\sigma_t^2 - \sigma_t\sigma)^{1/2} \qquad (9\text{-}54)$$

For σ = 0, this relation simplifies to

$$\tau = 2\sigma_t$$

which agrees with the modified Griffith criterion

for σ compressive. Both criteria can therefore be represented by a continuous Mohr envelope with two straight branches corresponding to equation (9-53) for σ positive, passing into the parabola corresponding to equation (9-54) for σ negative (Figure 9-45). The tensile strength σ_t (reached at point P on the plane perpendicular to σ_1) is $\tau_0/2$, as given by the Navier-Coulomb equation. The envelope in Figure 9–45 corresponds very closely to the behavior of an ideal isotropic cohesive rock.

In the preceding discussion of failure criteria, no account has been taken of the fact that some rocks are anisotropic. The commonest and most important type of anisotropy, that of the layered and foliated rocks, takes the form of a parallel set of surfaces across which cohesive strength is generally significantly less than that of the material between. Experiments on such anisotropic rocks show that the presence of a foliation or layering has a marked effect both on the stresses required for failure and on the angle of inclination of fault surfaces to the compression direction. Experimental evidence suggests that, in foliated rocks, faults tend to form parallel to the plane of foliation if this is inclined at between 15° and 45° to the compression axis. For other inclinations faults form that transect the foliation, but unless the foliation is perpendicular to the compression axis a single set of faults appears and its inclination to the compression axis is not that predicted by the Navier-Coulomb model.

Another effect that has been ignored in the preceding discussion is the effect of the intermediate principal stress σ_2. In triaxial compression experiments, $\sigma_2 = \sigma_3$; but in triaxial extension experiments, $\sigma_2 = \sigma_1$. Since comparison of results of experiments of the two kinds on the same rock shows that the shear stress for failure in extension is consistently lower than the shear stress for failure in compression, it is suggested that the absolute value of the intermediate principal stress may modify the failure criterion. Until an apparatus can be contrived that can reproduce a general stress state ($\sigma_1 > \sigma_2 > \sigma_3$) the actual effect of the intermediate principal stress cannot be fully investigated.

EFFECT ON FAULTING OF HIGH PORE PRESSURES In porous permeable rocks saturated with an undrained pore fluid at high pressure, the effective stress rather than the total stress controls failure. Under these conditions the Navier-Coulomb criterion can be represented by

$$\tau = \tau_0 + (\sigma - p)\tan\phi$$

where p is the pore pressure. The presence of a high pore pressure, therefore, does not affect the cohesive strength of a rock, but it reduces the magnitude of the frictional term while theoretically leaving the coefficient of internal friction unchanged. The general effect of pore pressure is thus to reduce the total resistance to shear and allow rocks at depth to fail at differential stresses lower than those required for faulting of dry rocks. There is experimental confirmation of this view; and there is some evidence that shallow seismic failure, generally attributed to faulting, is also intensified by the presence of abnormally high pore pressures.

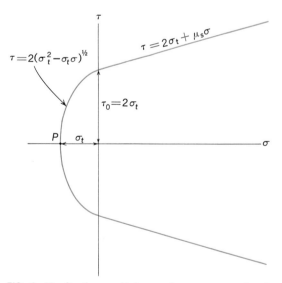

FIG. 9–45 Continuous Mohr envelope corresponding to the Griffith theory for tensile normal stress and the modified Griffith theory for compressive normal stress.

FAULTING AND STRESS DISTRIBUTION   Anderson long ago indicated the probable stress states preceding near-surface faulting in rocks. The

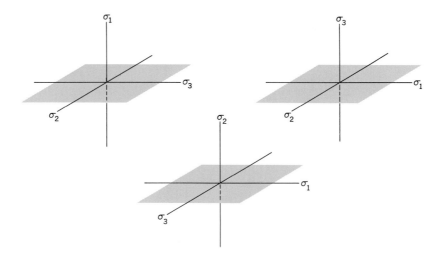

FIG. 9-46 *Possible orientations of principal stresses at the earth's surface (shown by colored plane).*

surface of the earth is everywhere a principal plane of stress, and if this surface is considered to be plane and horizontal for large areas only three general stress states need be considered (Figure 9-46), as follows:

1. σ_1 vertical; σ_2 and σ_3 horizontal.
2. σ_1 horizontal; σ_3 vertical.
3. σ_1 horizontal; σ_2 vertical.

If we adopt the Navier-Coulomb or modified Griffith theories as an adequate model of fault development then case 1 corresponds to normal faulting, case 2 to reverse faulting and case 3 to strike-slip faulting. The angles of dip for the corresponding faults for an average rock with $\mu_i \cong 0.8$ given by the Navier-Coulomb theory are 65° for normal faulting; 25° for reverse faulting and 90° for strike-slip faulting (Figure 9-47). These values conform closely to mean fault attitudes observed in surface rocks.

At depth in the crust this simple notion of stress distribution and associated faulting clearly need not hold. In fact, many faults presently exposed at the surface by erosion must have formed

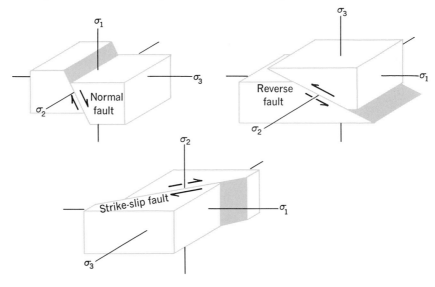

FIG. 9-47 *Normal faulting, reverse faulting, and strike-slip faulting at the earth's surface.*

at depth, and in their attitude they do not fit the simple picture given above. Some normal faults are gently dipping; some reverse faults are steeply dipping; and many faults on which displacement vectors can be determined are oblique slip faults. To examine the possible fault patterns to be expected at depth, geologists have attempted to determine stress distributions in situations that model simple natural conditions of geologic importance. At present, only two-dimensional stress distributions can be modeled. For example, an important stress distribution is that to be expected in a thick horizontal slab of rock with its upper surface free. A thick sedimentary plate filling a basin of deposition is a natural analog of such a slab. At the upper surface of the slab all shearing and normal stresses vanish and the principal stress trajectories must be vertical or horizontal as proposed by Anderson. But at depth, depending upon the boundary conditions of the slab and the effects of gravitational body forces, this simple orientation of stress trajectories is unlikely to be maintained.

The classical method used by engineers to construct stress trajectories for such situations is to assume isotropic elasticity and seek solutions in terms of "stress functions" of which all stress components are second partial derivatives. Because of the requirements of mechanical equilibrium and compatibility of strains [equations (9-46) and (9-47)], stress functions must satisfy certain differential equations which can be solved under proper boundary conditions. For plane stress only one stress function is needed, which can be obtained as follows. From equation (9-47)

$$\frac{\partial \sigma_x}{\partial x} + \frac{\partial \tau_{yx}}{\partial y} = 0$$

$$\frac{\partial \tau_{xy}}{\partial x} + \frac{\partial \sigma_y}{\partial y} = 0 \qquad (9\text{-}55)$$

and the compatibility conditions for plane strain, equation (9-46), are

$$\frac{\partial^2 \varepsilon_x}{\partial y^2} + \frac{\partial^2 \varepsilon_y}{\partial x^2} = \frac{\partial^2 \gamma_{xy}}{\partial x \, \partial y} \qquad (9\text{-}56)$$

By use of equations (9-48) and (9-49) and the

condition $\sigma_z = \nu(\sigma_x + \sigma_y)$ for plane strain, the strains can be expressed in terms of stresses as

$$(1 - \nu)\frac{\partial^2 \sigma_x}{\partial y^2} - \nu \frac{\partial^2 \sigma_x}{\partial x^2} + (1 - \nu)\frac{\partial^2 \sigma_y}{\partial x^2} - \nu \frac{\partial^2 \sigma_y}{\partial y^2} =$$

$$2\frac{\partial^2 \tau_{xy}}{\partial x \, \partial y} \qquad (9\text{-}57)$$

From the equations of equilibrium, equations (9-55), by way of equation (9-57) is obtained the simple result

$$\left(\frac{\partial^2}{\partial x^2} + \frac{\partial^2}{\partial y^2}\right)(\sigma_x + \sigma_y) = 0 \qquad (9\text{-}58)$$

Let there be a "stress function" Φ such that

$$\sigma_x = \frac{\partial^2 \Phi}{\partial y^2} \qquad \sigma_y = \frac{\partial^2 \Phi}{\partial x^2} \qquad \tau_{xy} = -\frac{\partial^2 \Phi}{\partial x \, \partial y} \qquad (9\text{-}59)$$

From equations (9-58) and (9-59) can be obtained the "biharmonic equation"

$$\frac{\partial^4 \Phi}{\partial x^4} + 2\frac{\partial^4 \Phi}{\partial x^2 \, \partial y^2} + \frac{\partial^4 \Phi}{\partial y^4} = 0$$

Any solution of this equation yields stresses, by way of equation (9-59), that satisfy both the compatibility conditions and the equations of equilibrium. For particular boundary conditions the stress trajectories in a body can then be found and, if a failure criterion is adopted, the most likely orientation of the fault surfaces in various parts of the body determined.

The foregoing method is mathematically complex and inflexible. In geologic problems isotropic elasticity cannot always be assumed, body forces must be taken into account, and the lateral and vertical variation in material properties that is generally present must be considered. In recent years the development of high-speed computers has facilitated the parallel development of approximate methods of stress (and strain) analysis that are extremely flexible and allow factors such as variation in material properties to be taken into account. To geologists these methods, particularly the "finite-element method," have opened up the possible exploration of stress distributions in a large variety of complex situations of geologic importance. Such distributions are important not only for problems of faulting, but also for problems of folding and ductile deformations in general.

THE PROBLEM OF OVERTHRUST FAULTS   At many places in the continental crust, such as the Alps, the Himalayas, the Andes and several regions in the western and southwestern United States, great fault surfaces are exposed, along some of which thick plates of rock of great lateral extent have been moved distances of 100 km or more. Characteristically the fault surfaces are gently dipping (10° or less) or subhorizontal. In some the slip is locally down the dip of the fault.

Some of the fault surfaces are clear-cut and free from thick zones of crushed or mylonitized rock, and it is hard to escape the conclusion that the main mechanism of displacement was frictional sliding of some kind. Two possible origins for the mechanical forces that moved the plates come to mind, acting separately or together. First, the plates could be pushed from one end by tangential forces in the crust; and second, the plates could have moved downslope by gravitational gliding under their own body forces.

From theoretical considerations, Hubbert and Rubey have made estimates of the length of a thrust plate that could be moved by either of these forces, assuming that frictional sliding at the base is involved. Using the Navier-Coulomb criterion with values of τ_0 of 200 bars and of ϕ of 30°, and by considering body forces for a uniform density of $\rho = 2.31$ g/cm^3, they find that the maximum length of a thrust plate 5 km thick is about 18.4 km. The pushing of plates of intermediate thicknesses 30 km or more, as is observed, is impossible. Similarly, they find that for gravitational gliding of a block of similar size slopes of about 30° would be required. Such slopes are not observed.

The solution to the problem according to these investigators lies in the presence at depth in the vicinity of the thrust surface of a high-pressure pore fluid. Failure and slip under these conditions is controlled not by the total stress but by the effective stress. For example, let the bulk density of a fluid-filled rock be $\bar{\rho}$; then the combined

overburden pressure $\bar{\sigma}_z$ resulting from body forces at depth z is

$$\bar{\sigma}z = \bar{\rho}gz$$

Let the fluid pressure at depth z be p. The combined pressure $\bar{\sigma}_z$ is the sum of the lithostatic pressure of dry rocks σ_z and the pore pressure, that is

$$\bar{\sigma}_z = \sigma_z + p$$

As p approaches $\bar{\sigma}_z$, σ_z falls to zero and the overlying plate of rock "floats." The normal stresses acting across the base of the block are correspondingly reduced together with the frictional resistance to slip.

Evidence from deep drilling suggests that at present there are regions in the crust where p approaches $\bar{\sigma}_z$. We can assume therefore that the ratio $\lambda = p/\bar{\sigma}_z$ ranges between zero and unity. For $\lambda = 0.8$, for example, a thrust block 1 km thick and 32.9 km long can be moved by pressure from one end. For the same value of λ a block 5 km thick and 57.3 km long can be moved and, if λ is increased to 0.9, the length increases to over 100 km.

The same phenomenon also decreases the angle of the slope down which a plate can glide gravitationally. An increase of λ from zero to 0.8 reduces the angle from 30° to 6.6°. For $\lambda = 0.95$ the angle is reduced to 1.6°. For combined lateral and gravitational forces with $\lambda = 0.95$ a block 6 km thick and 320 km long can glide down a slope of 0.5°.

Under even lower levels of force movement may still be effected by the passage of seismic waves. A block just in static equilibrium on a slope, for example, may undergo a small net slip as a result of the motion of a small dislocation along its interface with the basement during the propagation of seismic waves of large amplitude.

The theory of overthrust faulting based on the presence of high fluid pressures at depth is an attractive one, which goes far toward explaining some of the most enigmatic structures of the crust. Some thrust faults, however, have detailed structural properties that suggest that frictional sliding was not the main mechanism of differential displacement. Notable among such thrust faults are those paralleled by great thickness of mylonite or of plastically deformed rocks. Some such "faults" are not discrete surfaces of rupture but quite thick laminar zones in which deformation has been concentrated. Those structures should more properly be considered along with others resulting from flow.

Flow of Rocks

Many different structural features observed in the continental crust by geologists confirm that one of the most important mechanical behaviors exhibited by rocks, particularly in orogenic regions, is cohesive flow in the solid state. Some of the structures observed compare closely with structures formed in rocks by experimental deformation; others resemble no structures yet so formed, and geologists can only speculate on their origin and significance.

Rocks appear to have the capacity to flow cohesively under almost any combination of physical conditions found in the crust and mantle. Some rocks, with mineral assemblages indicating that they have never been elevated to high temperatures, or deeply buried to incur excessive pressures, are permanently strained, folded, or otherwise deformed without marked changes in their textural properties. But the most dramatic direct evidence of solid flow is found in the metamorphic rocks, and there can be little doubt that metamorphic conditions provide the most suitable environment for cohesive flow at the expense of brittle fracture and faulting.

From the manner in which the earth adjusts to surface loads, and from the drifting of continents and spreading of the ocean floors (see Chapters 3 and 4), we conclude also that the mantle itself is capable of large-scale flow even though seismic observations require it to be solid in the sense that it has a high rigidity. Broadly speaking, flow in the mantle is probably analogous in some way to the flow of solid ice in glaciers (Chapter 7). Rheologic properties of the mantle are just as important as those of crustal rocks, since they determine how, and at what rate, the mantle will respond to the temperature and density perturbations that cause it to flow.

Study of phenomena of solid flow in rocks can proceed in a number of directions, depending upon the aims of the investigator. We have previously reviewed some of the experimental data bearing on the ductile and creep flow of rocks and the effects on flow of factors such as elevated temperature, pressure, and the presence of aqueous fluids. In what follows, we examine the flow theories for solids developed by rheologists (scientists who investigate flow), introduce some of the geometric problems of deformations of large magnitude, and, in the light of these theoretical notions, consider the genesis of some of the common structures formed by flow in solid rocks.

RHEOLOGIC PROPERTIES OF ROCKS

To provide a basis for the discussion of the flow properties of real materials, rheologists have developed a number of phenomenological mathematical models describing ideal types of behavior. Each model is expressed by a set of constitutive or "rheological" equations which relate some aspect of strain to some aspect of stress. For example, the constitutive equation for a linearly elastic material is

$$\boldsymbol{\sigma} = \mathbf{C}\boldsymbol{\varepsilon}$$

which expresses a unique relationship between a state of stress and a state of infinitesimal strain, by way of the scalar constants $\mathbf{C}$, which express a material property.

The types of ideal behavior most relevant to deformation of rocks appear to be three in number:

1. *Linear elasticity* has been explored above for both isotropic and anisotropic solids. It is the only type of behavior obvious in rocks under stresses of small magnitude and short duration, and is particularly important in dynamic loading of the seismic type. But elastic deformation is retained and is recoverable even in rocks undergoing ductile flow and creep in response to continuously maintained stresses, as can be demonstrated by simple laboratory experiments.

2. *Plasticity* is a term used in a phenomenological sense to denote ductile behavior—that is,

permanent deformation beyond the yield stress in short-term experiments. Use of the term in this sense does not necessarily imply that only crystal plasticity is involved, although it commonly is. Two types of plastic behavior can be distinguished by the presence or absence of strain hardening.

3. *Viscosity* applies strictly to the behavior of a fluid and it is a measure of the relationship between either strain rate or velocity gradient and stress. Secondary or steady-state creep (pseudoviscous flow) resembles viscous flow in many respects, in being time-dependent, and it has become customary to view the slow flow of rocks as basically a viscous phenomenon.

Experimental study of rock flow suggests that the observed behaviors can be modeled in terms of these three types of ideal behavior combined in various ways. Some rocks under certain conditions appear to be simultaneously elastic and viscous; under other conditions one type of behavior may predominate to the effective exclusion of all others.

PLASTIC DEFORMATION   The mathematical theories of plasticity have been developed mainly by engineers as models for the ductile behavior of metals. The theories have never reached the levels of utility and acceptance of the theory of linear elasticity for several reasons. The most important of these is that ductile deformation is an irreversible process in which energy is dissipated as heat by permanent strain and not stored elastically. Thus, the total finite strain, although it is related in some fashion to the final stress state, depends upon the path followed by the deformation. This feature contrasts sharply with reversible linear elastic deformation in which the path followed to reach a particular state of strain is immaterial. A finite plastic deformation is thus the integral over a definite path of a sequence of infinitesimal strain increments, each one of which is related in some way to an instantaneous stress state. Theories of plastic behavior are concerned with the relationships between these two quantities or their time derivatives.

Of great interest to engineers and geologists alike are the conditions under which a crystalline solid passes from the elastic to the plastic state during progressive loading, under appropriate conditions. We have already introduced the term "yield" (analogous to "failure" for rupture) to specify this transition. Experimental studies indicate that the yield condition is not always reached suddenly at a particular state of stress or elastic strain, but is commonly entered gradually as shown by the generally rounded form of the part of the stress–strain curve linking elastic deformation to permanent deformation (see Figure 9–3). In theoretical models of plastic deformation it is convenient to view ductile deformation as beginning at a particular state of stress and strain (the yield point) so that ideal stress–strain curves have one of the two forms shown in Figure 9–48. The left-hand curve is for a nonstrain hardening and the right-hand curve for a strain-hardening elastic–plastic material (in the simplest models of ductility the elastic properties are ignored and a material is assumed to be rigid–plastic). Few real solids have curves corresponding to either of these ideal types. Some even have curves that fall sharply at yield.

Attempts have been made to develop stress criteria for yield resembling those for rupture. The problem of yield is more complex than that of fracture because there are no characteristic methods of plastic failure corresponding to the extension fracturing and faulting so commonly a feature of rupture of most solids, and different crystalline and polycrystalline materials behave in very different ways. For example, under triaxial compression some rocks, such as marble, yield fairly uniformly (within limits set by design of apparatus) in that transition to ductile behavior affects most grains to some degree simultaneously, and flow is distributed more or less homogeneously in the rock. In other rocks, such as, for example, phyllites compressed parallel to foliation, plastic yield is first concentrated in narrow zones of large strain, which increase in width and number as deformation proceeds, until the whole specimen has yielded. Such behavior is observed also in certain metals loaded at atmospheric pressure, and thin zones of yielding

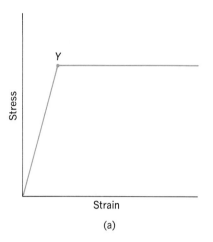

Stress

Strain

(a)

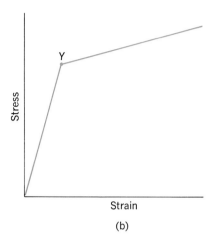

Stress

Strain

(b)

FIG. 9–48 Stress–strain curves for ideal elastic-plastic materials. (a) Non-strain-hardening. (b) Strain-hardening. Yield points Y.

(Lüders bands) can be seen nucleating and propagating on the unconfined surfaces of test specimens. The gradual spread of plastic behavior through a specimen is particularly characteristic of strain-hardening materials. Once yield occurs in a particular domain, stress required to continue strain of the same region is increased by strain hardening. Further loading results in spread of yield to domains that have remained elastic, and the zone of yield is slowly propagated through the material.

In triaxial extension the effects of the presence or absence of strain hardening are still more striking. In a nonstrain-hardening material, yield generally begins in a narrow zone. Reduction of cross-sectional area caused by this localized strain results in an increase in local stress, and deformation "runs away" in this region—resulting in progressive thinning or "necking" and, ultimately, in rupture and separation. Such a process seems to be responsible for the formation of some types of boudin in layered rocks extended in the plane of the layering. If, on the other hand, the material is strongly strain-hardening, the increase in local stress at the incipient neck is balanced by an increase in strength, and the zone of deformation spreads uniformly throughout the loaded body.

The yield criteria used to determine the onset of ductile behavior are expressed in terms of a "yield stress" σ_c, which can be measured experimentally in a state of uniaxial stress (generally simple compression or tension). This stress is assumed to have the same value in compression and extension and to be independent of the isotropic component of the stress tensor. The simplest criterion is the maximum shear stress theory (Tresca and St. Venant) which assumes that yield begins when the maximum shear stress $\tau_{\max} = (\sigma_1 - \sigma_3)/2$ reaches a critical value. From the definition of σ_c as the differential stress in axial compression or tension, we see that $\sigma_c = 2\tau_{\max}$. Another criterion in general use (von Mises) is based upon a critical value of the strain energy of elastic distortion corresponding to a stress given by

$$\sigma_c = \frac{1}{\sqrt{2}}[(\sigma_1 - \sigma_2)^2 + (\sigma_2 - \sigma_3)^2 + (\sigma_3 - \sigma_1)^2]^{1/2}$$

Remembering that the octahedral shear stress τ_0 is given by

$$\tau_0 = \frac{1}{3}[(\sigma_1 - \sigma_2)^2 + (\sigma_2 - \sigma_3)^2 + (\sigma_3 - \sigma_1)^2]^{1/2}$$

we can write this criterion in terms of shear stress as

$$\sigma_c = \frac{3}{\sqrt{2}}\tau_0$$

For both criteria the components of the stress deviator can be substituted for the components of total stress.

In simple experiments on metals, results have

been obtained that conform with either criterion; the von Mises criterion is generally favored.

Once the yield stress is passed a ductile material begins to flow either at constant stress or, if strain hardening occurs, under increasing stress. This behavior is of most interest to geologists because it leads to large strains such as those that have clearly occurred in many rock bodies. The theories developed to express relationships between stress and strains in deformations of this kind are mathematically complex. To illustrate the complications of such theories, we consider the basis for a very simple model of ideal plasticity.

In this theory (an "incremental" or "flow" theory) a material is considered to be elastic–plastic. Total strain ε_T at any instant is thus composed of two parts, an elastic strain ε_E and a plastic strain ε_P. The following assumptions are made:

1. The material is isotropic and is linearly elastic for mean normal stress σ_0 at all times, that is

$$\sigma_0 = 3K\varepsilon_0$$

where K is the bulk modulus and ε_0 the mean normal strain.

2. Below a certain stress σ_c (given, for example, by the von Mises criterion) the material obeys Hooke's law.

3. For plastic deformation, the material is incompressible ($\nu = 0.5$) and only deviatoric stresses and strains need be considered.

4. The principal axes of stress and strain are coincident during plastic deformation.

5. The rate of change of plastic strain[7] at any

---

[7] In a small time interval Δt let the deviatoric infinitesimal strains ε' occur. The strain rate $\dot{\varepsilon}'$ is then a symmetric tensor with components

$$\begin{pmatrix} \dfrac{\partial \varepsilon_x'}{\partial t} & \dfrac{\partial \varepsilon_{xy}'}{\partial t} & \dfrac{\partial \varepsilon_{xz}'}{\partial t} \\[2ex] \dfrac{\partial \varepsilon_{yx}'}{\partial t} & \dfrac{\partial \varepsilon_y'}{\partial t} & \dfrac{\partial \varepsilon_{yz}'}{\partial t} \\[2ex] \dfrac{\partial \varepsilon_{zx}'}{\partial t} & \dfrac{\partial \varepsilon_{zy}'}{\partial t} & \dfrac{\partial \varepsilon_z'}{\partial t} \end{pmatrix}$$

time is proportional to the instantaneous stress state. A proportionality factor with the dimensions of viscosity is so defined. This quantity is not a true material constant in that it varies with stress, strain rate and time. Variations of this kind are to be expected in real materials such as ductile rocks as a result of progressive modification of internal structure during the history of finite strain.

From these and other basic relationships a set of differential equations can be obtained which, theoretically at least, can be integrated over a particular path to obtain a relationship between total (elastic and plastic) finite strain and stress. In practice, even without the presence of plastic anisotropy, solutions of many problems in plasticity are very difficult.

VISCOUS DEFORMATION   There is evidence that, for loading of long duration, rocks behave in many respects like fluids of very high viscosity. When fluids flow there is an internal resistance to deformation. In an ideal or Newtonian fluid the instantaneous stress is proportional to the rate of strain; thus a generalized constitutive equation of the form

$$\boldsymbol{\sigma} = \mathbf{V}\dot{\varepsilon}$$

can be written in which the tensor $\mathbf{V}$ expresses a material property of the fluid. In this generalized form the constitutive equation holds for an anisotropic material. In most theories of fluid flow, as in theories of plastic flow, isotropy is assumed and in terms of conventional normal and shearing strain components two types of equation can be written for shearing and normal stress, respectively, as

$$\tau = \eta\dot{\gamma}$$

where η is a material constant termed the coefficient of viscosity and

$$\sigma = \theta\dot{\varepsilon}$$

where θ is a second material constant known as the "tensile" viscosity or the coefficient of viscous traction. The quantities η and θ conform respectively to the shear modulus μ and Young's modulus E of elastic theory. If a fluid is incompressible (probably the only case of interest to geologists seeking analogies between flowing rocks and fluids), Poisson's ratio ν, is 0.5, and the relationship

$$E = 2\mu(1 + \nu)$$

of elastic theory can be "translated" into an equivalent expression for viscous fluids to yield

$$\theta = 3\eta$$

Some fluids over certain ranges of flow rate are approximately Newtonian; that is, their viscosities are independent of stress and time, and have stress–strain rate curves that are essentially linear (Figure 9–49). Other fluids, particularly those with complex internal structures typical of polymers (silicate melts are an example of such liquids) have viscosities that vary markedly with strain rate, reflecting changes in internal configuration as flow rate changes. The viscosity may increase with flow rate as shown by the lower curve in Figure 9–50, or it may decrease as shown in the upper curve. The last condition is that of "thixotropic" materials such as some sediments and soils which become very fluid when disturbed by, for example, seismic waves. It is likely that most rocks which are "viscous" in their properties of solid flow are also nonlinear. There is, however, one type of flow known as diffusion or vacancy creep for which the viscosity is independent of stress. The mechanism of diffusion

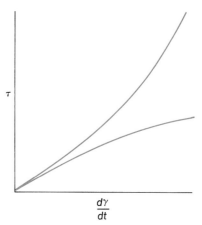

FIG. 9–50   Non-Newtonian viscosity.

creep, as the name implies, is a migration of lattice vacancies from regions where such vacancies may be created (for example, on the face of a crystal across which a tensile stress acts) to regions where vacancies are destroyed (such as a part of the crystal in compressive stress). It would be of great interest to geologists to know if this mechanism can contribute to flow in the mantle, for hydrodynamic equations governing convection become prohibitively complicated ("nonlinear") when viscosity is made to depend on stress or, indeed, on any other variables (such as temperature, pressure, and so on).

In fluids, and perhaps also in solids, viscous flow is an expression of diffusion. A state of stress places a bias on the directions and magnitudes of the components of diffusion, the result of which we call viscous flows in fluids and pseudoviscous flow in solids. Such flow is thus a temperature-dependent rate process involving a Boltzmann factor and an activation energy E_f such that

$$\frac{1}{\eta} = Ae^{-E_f/kT}$$

Strictly speaking, E_f depends on pressure through an activation volume (see Chapter 5).

VISCOELASTICITY   Ideal elastic, plastic, and viscous behavior of the kind introduced above are abstractions of the properties of real materials. But they serve as bases from which to attempt to

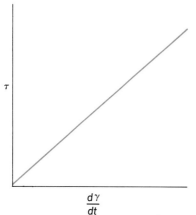

FIG. 9–49   Newtonian viscosity, $\tau = \eta \, \dfrac{d\gamma}{dt}$.

describe the observed behaviors of real materials in experimental and natural flow. Such descriptions generally involve the modeling of a real behavior as a combination of the ideal types occurring either simultaneously or over distinct ranges of physical conditions.

An example of such a material (the Maxwell solid), introduced in Chapter 4, is a crude model of a rock that is elastic for stresses of short duration (seismic waves and earth tides) and viscous for tectonic forces of long duration.

A different type of viscoelastic behavior can be modeled by assuming that the elastic behavior itself is "damped" by a viscous component so that the two types of behavior appear simultaneously. The stress at any instant is written as the sum of two terms

$$\tau_T = \tau_E + \tau_V \qquad (9\text{-}60)$$

where the elastic stress τ_E is related to the strain γ

$$\tau_E = \mu\gamma \qquad (9\text{-}61)$$

and the viscous stress τ_V is related to the strain rate $\dot\gamma$

$$\tau_V = \eta\dot\gamma \qquad (9\text{-}62)$$

Substitution of equations (9-61) and (9-62) into equation (9-60) yields

$$\tau = \mu\gamma + \eta\dot\gamma \qquad (9\text{-}63)$$

Equation 9-63 can be solved to give

$$\gamma = \frac{\tau}{\mu}[1 - e^{-(\mu/\eta)t}]$$

which shows the strain is slowed by the viscous component and approaches its maximum (finite) value only at infinite time. A strain-time curve for such a material is given in Figure 9-51. On unloading, all the strain disappears slowly and the original dimension is reached only at infinite time. This type of behavior resembles primary creep.

A more general type of behavior is obtained by combining the first type of viscoelastic behavior (Maxwell solid) with the second (Kelvin solid) to obtain a material with strain-time properties as illustrated in Figure 9-52. The loading

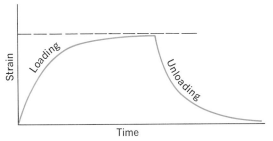

FIG. 9–51   *Strain–time curve for Kelvin solid.*

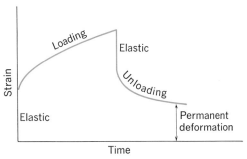

FIG. 9–52   *Strain–time curve for combined Maxwell, Kelvin solid.*

part of this curve corresponds fairly closely to the primary and secondary parts of a typical creep curve (Figure 9–13), but steady-state creep is not truly linear.

A ductile material can be modeled by a combination of Maxwell viscoelasticity with the existence of a definite yield stress below which the deformation is entirely elastic. Such a (Bingham) material has a constitutive equation for shearing stress of the form

$$\tau = \tau_c + \eta\dot\gamma$$

where τ_c is the yield stress in shear.

Although conceptually useful, none of the above is an adequate model for the viscoelastic properties of the mantle. Something is known, however, about these properties from the damping of seismic waves (page 492). Both the Maxwell and the Kelvin models lead to a damping of waves which is dependent on frequency, contrary to observation.

A creep law commonly used for the mantle is

an empirical relationship proposed by Lomnitz for strain rates 10^{-4} to 10^{-5} as

$$\gamma = \frac{\tau}{\mu} \{1 + q \log (1 + at)\}$$

where a and q are constants and t is time, and modified by Jeffreys to

$$\gamma = \frac{\tau}{\mu} \left\{1 + \frac{q}{\alpha} (1 + at)^\alpha - 1\right\}$$

where α is another constant.

COHESIVE FLOW IN ROCKS   The simple phenomenological theories reviewed above are of help in stating simply the flow properties of rocks; but they are developed for isotropic continuous materials and therefore cannot closely approximate the type of behavior to be expected in structurally complex polycrystalline aggregates such as rocks deformed under the great variety of physical conditions existing now or in the past in the earth.

What general conclusions about the rheologic properties of rocks can we draw? Is cohesive flow more akin to ideal plastic or to ideal viscous behavior? How important are the elastic properties of rock in permanent deformations? A few general answers to some of these question can be given.

In response to long-term stresses in the upper parts of the earth, rocks appear to behave as essentially viscous materials; they creep continuously. Estimates of the "viscosity" of this region based on rates of uplift following removal of water or ice loads range from 10^{20} to 10^{22} poises (see page 225). These seems to be little doubt also that many of the complex deformation structures of orogenic regions, such as the great fold nappe of the Alps, should be properly viewed as creep structures rather than structures produced by ductile flow.

Do these conclusions mean, therefore, that rocks are fluids, lacking a yield stress, and incapable of supporting any load without creep? The answer to this question appears to be no. We are all familiar with the essential permanence (ignoring the effects of weathering) of steep slopes in rocks, and of the existence of bodies of rock, such as the Himalayas, that have remained elevated and unsupported laterally for millions of years and yet have not obviously flowed outward under gravity. Under ordinary conditions of temperature and pressure, rocks seem to have a fundamental strength that allows them to resist small loads or loads of relatively small lateral extent. But estimates of the yield strength of the crust and upper mantle as a whole are surprisingly low (see discussion on scaling in Chapter 4)—generally less than 10 bars.

Because of the smallness of this yield strength for creep or viscous flow, geologists are no longer forced to seek tectonic stresses of high magnitude to account for the large amounts of finite deformation demonstrable in orogenic regions. If the strengths of rocks resembled those encountered in short-term triaxial tests involving ductile behavior, it would be necessary to postulate stresses of the order of several kilobars existing locally for long periods of time. Even the most intense and rapid deformations (those occurring at the source of an earthquake) now are believed to involve large-scale stresses only in the range of 10 to 100 bars. This general lowering of our estimates of shearing stresses in the earth which has come with the recognition of the importance of creep and viscous flow has increased the probability that much deformation may be in primary or secondary response to stresses of gravitational origin which, although small, can locally reach values significantly greater than the strength of rocks, particularly at high temperatures. Differences in density at depth, and resulting upward flow of lighter materials, may be an important mode of deformation in a variety of geologic environments, from a shallowly buried sedimentary basin and regions of active metamorphism in the crust to the deep mantle. It is possible that mantle material, becoming less dense by hydration, may rise in this fashion even to the earth's surface. Such may be the origin of serpentinite bodies of the Alpine type (Chapter 6).

Rocks, therefore, are weak, very viscous materials. Does this conclusion mean that their elastic and "plastic" properties are unimportant? The answer is again no. If rocks were not highly elastic for certain loads they could not store the strain energy released as earthquakes; nor could the waves so generated propagate through the mantle and crust. Also, in spite of the importance of gravitational body forces in deformation, tectonic stresses of large magnitude undoubtedly exist; they are required by present theories of global tectonics. Such forces are clearly transmitted laterally in rocks to nucleate folds, faults, and other structures. If the rocks were not elastic, such lateral transmission of force would be very difficult to explain.

Likewise, we can be certain that some rocks are truly ductile under some circumstances. Study of deformed rocks confirms that crystal plasticity and cataclasis are important natural deformation mechanisms, particularly in regions of concentrated strain (and, presumably, stress), such as the vicinity of large thrusts and zones of "shear" that traverse the crust. In regions of rapid strain, strong rocks may be placed under extremely high local stresses, which can be relieved only by failure or yield similiar to that observed in the laboratory.

It appears, therefore, that the whole experimental spectrum of rock behavior under stress is duplicated in nature at some time or place, and we would be wrong to typify rocks with one particular set of rheologic properties, or, in fact, to expect rocks to conform closely to any of the rheologic models so far developed. Of two things, geologists can be reasonably certain: First, the ever-present structural anisotropy of rocks has more effect on permanent than on elastic deformations and must enter any realistic set of constitutive equations; second, the progressive structural reconstruction of flowing solid rocks must make their material properties time-dependent and nonlinear.

FINITE DEFORMATIONS

The permanent strains developed in flowing rocks are of large magnitude, and the powers and products of the derivatives of the displacements cannot be neglected. The theory of infinitesimal strain, which has been introduced for small elastic deformations, does not serve as an adequate description of such deformations, and must be replaced by the mathematically more complex theory of finite strain.

We review briefly some of the geometric problems of finite strains and the sequences of incremental strains of which they are the end products.

FINITE HOMOGENEOUS STRAIN   A theory of finite strain based upon a general nonlinear geometric transformation is too complex to have any simple application to deformed rocks. A great simplification in theory is achieved by considering only finite homogeneous strains in which coordinates of points in the strained state are linear functions of corresponding points in the unstrained state. Such a simplification places no restrictions on the magnitudes of displacements and can be represented by the matrix equation

$$\mathbf{x}' = \mathbf{B}\mathbf{x} + \mathbf{t} \qquad (9\text{-}64)$$

where $\mathbf{B}$ is a matrix of scalar coefficients and $\mathbf{t}$ is a column vector of coefficients, both being independent of $\mathbf{x}$. The vector $\mathbf{t}$ represents a uniform translation and can be neglected in further discussion. Equation (9-64) thereby reduces to

$$\mathbf{x}' = \mathbf{B}\mathbf{x}$$

which corresponds to a transformation with a unique inverse as follows:

$$\mathbf{x} = \mathbf{B}^{-1}\mathbf{x}'$$

where $\mathbf{B}^{-1}$ is the matrix inverse to $\mathbf{B}$.

The transformation matrix $\mathbf{B}$ is in general not symmetric; but it can always be factorized into a symmetric matrix $\mathbf{D}$ and an orthogonal matrix $\mathbf{R}$ (corresponding to an isometric transformation; see page 26), such that

$$\mathbf{B} = \mathbf{R}\mathbf{D} \qquad (9\text{-}65)$$

The matrix $\mathbf{D}$ represents a pure (rotation-free) strain, and the matrix $\mathbf{R}$ a rigid-body rotation. For example, the transformation shown in Figure 9–53, which we have called a "simple shear" for infinitesimal strain, corresponds to the transformation

$$\begin{pmatrix} x' \\ y' \\ z' \end{pmatrix} = \begin{pmatrix} 1 & 0 & 0 \\ 0 & 1 & \tan\psi \\ 0 & 0 & 1 \end{pmatrix} \begin{pmatrix} x \\ y \\ z \end{pmatrix}$$

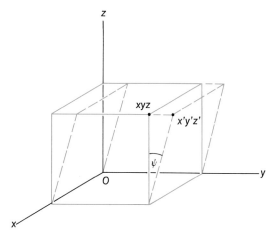

FIG. 9–53 *Finite simple shear.*

or

$$x' = Bx$$

The matrix **B** is clearly nonsymmetric but it can be expressed in terms of a rotation matrix **R** and a pure-strain matrix **D** by way of equation (9-65), from which

$$D = R^{-1}B \qquad (9\text{-}66)$$

The form of matrix **R** is

$$\begin{pmatrix} 1 & 0 & 0 \\ 0 & \cos\theta & \sin\theta \\ 0 & -\sin\theta & \cos\theta \end{pmatrix}$$

where θ is the angle of clockwise rotation about the x-axis. Because **R** is orthogonal, its inverse R^{-1} is identical to its transpose R^T and equation (9-66) can be written

$$D = \begin{pmatrix} 1 & 0 & 0 \\ 0 & \cos\theta & -\sin\theta \\ 0 & \sin\theta & \cos\theta \end{pmatrix} \begin{pmatrix} 1 & 0 & 0 \\ 0 & 1 & \tan\psi \\ 0 & 0 & 1 \end{pmatrix}$$

from which

$$D = \begin{pmatrix} 1 & 0 & 0 \\ 0 & \cos\theta & \cos\theta\tan\psi - \sin\theta \\ 0 & \sin\theta & \sin\theta\tan\psi + \cos\theta \end{pmatrix} \qquad (9\text{-}67)$$

But since **D** is symmetric, the two nonzero off-diagonal components in equation (9-67) are equal; that is,

$$\sin\theta = \cos\theta\tan\psi - \sin\theta$$

from which

$$\tan\psi = 2\tan\theta$$

and matrix (9-67) becomes

$$\begin{pmatrix} 1 & 0 & 0 \\ 0 & \cos\theta & \sin\theta \\ 0 & \sin\theta & 2\sin\theta - \cos\theta \end{pmatrix}$$

which is the transformation matrix for the pure-strain part of **B**.

The splitting of a linear transformation matrix into a symmetric pure-strain matrix and an orthogonal rotation matrix is analogous to the splitting of the e-matrix of equation (9-38) for infinitesimal strain into a symmetric matrix corresponding to Cauchy's infinitesimal strain tensor and an antisymmetric matrix corresponding to an infinitesimal rotation (note, however, that **R** and **D** are multiplied, not added, to yield **B**).

The two transformations corresponding to **D** and **R** for simple shear are shown diagrammatically in two dimensions in Figure 9-54. Multiplication of the corresponding matrices commutes and the order in which the two transformations are performed is immaterial.

The above simple example is perfectly general and we can view any finite homogeneous strain as consisting of two parts, as follows:

1. A pure strain, represented by a symmetric matrix **D**, that changes lengths of and angles between material lines. This matrix clearly relates a vector **x** in the unstrained state to a vector **x'** in the strained state and is a symmetric second-rank tensor. But the components of **D** do not have the same simple geometric meanings as the components of the corresponding tensor ε of infinitesimal pure strain.

This pure-strain part in turn consists of two parts. The first is a distortion, which changes only the shape of a body, and the second is a dilatation, which changes only the volume. If **D** referred to principal axes has the form

$$\begin{pmatrix} d_1 & 0 & 0 \\ 0 & d_2 & 0 \\ 0 & 0 & d_3 \end{pmatrix}$$

then the ratio of the strained to unstrained vol-

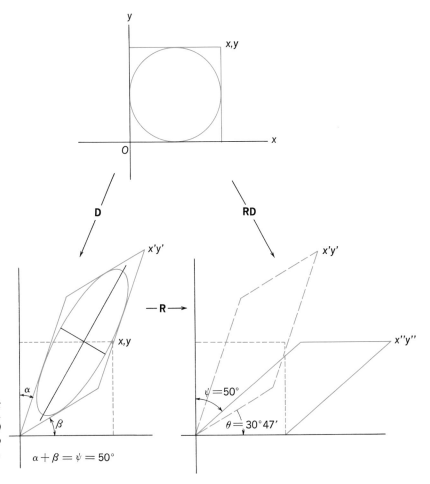

FIG. 9–54 *Simple shear (ψ = 50°) expressed as a product of a pure shear **D** and a rotation **R**. The rotation angle θ is found from the relationship $\tan \theta = \frac{1}{2} \tan \psi$. For $\psi = 50°$, $\theta = 30°47'$.*

ume (the "modulus" of the transformation) is given by the determinant of **D**, that is by

$$|\mathbf{D}| = d_1 d_2 d_3$$

For the case of simple shear given above, this determinant is unity and volume is conserved during deformation. For any homogeneous strain in which volume changes, the dilatation (either positive or negative) can be represented by a matrix **V** of the form

$$\begin{pmatrix} v & 0 & 0 \\ 0 & v & 0 \\ 0 & 0 & v \end{pmatrix}$$

where the components v are given by $|\mathbf{D}|^{1/3}$, and

the remaining distortion by a matrix **S** of the form

$$\begin{pmatrix} \dfrac{d_1}{v} & 0 & 0 \\ 0 & \dfrac{d_2}{v} & 0 \\ 0 & 0 & \dfrac{d_3}{v} \end{pmatrix}$$

2. A rotation, represented by the matrix **R**. As with infinitesimal strains, if a rotational part is present a deformation is termed "rotational"; otherwise it is "nonrotational" and is a pure strain.

The most general type of homogeneous deformation is therefore given by

B = RVS

To the geologist interested in finite strain of geologic bodies, only the part of the transformation corresponding to **S** (the pure distortion) is generally determinate and thus of interest.

COMPONENTS OF FINITE STRAIN   Finite-strain components at a point corresponding to the conventional components of infinitesimal strain can be defined as follows:

1. The finite normal or extensional strain of a material line in the x-direction is given as before by ε_x. This and the two corresponding components in directions y and z are not convenient for computations since their squares and products cannot be neglected. Instead a quantity λ_x is used, where

$$\lambda_x = (1 + \varepsilon_x)^2$$

is called the "quadratic elongation" or "elongation" of the line *initially* in the x-direction. Two similar quantities λ_y and λ_z can be defined.

2. The shearing strain between material lines initially in the x- and y-directions is given, as for infinitesimal strain, by γ_{xy}; but because the angle of shear ψ is finite, $\gamma_{xy} = \tan \psi$.

In this fashion six conventional finite-strain components (λ_x, λ_y, λ_z, γ_{xy}, γ_{yz}, and γ_{zx}) are obtained. Where the finite strain is referred to principal axes the shearing components vanish and only three principal quadratic elongations (λ_1,

λ_2, and λ_3) survive.[8] In terms of these principal components, the ellipsoid of finite strain becomes

$$\frac{x^2}{\lambda_1} + \frac{y^2}{\lambda_2} + \frac{z^2}{\lambda_3} = 1 \qquad (9\text{-}68)$$

and the transformation matrix for a pure strain (**D** or **S**) becomes

$$\begin{pmatrix} \sqrt{\lambda_1} & 0 & 0 \\ 0 & \sqrt{\lambda_2} & 0 \\ 0 & 0 & \sqrt{\lambda_3} \end{pmatrix} \qquad (9\text{-}69)$$

SOME PROPERTIES OF FINITE HOMOGENEOUS STRAINS
The Mohr construction can be used to express the properties of finite homogeneous pure strains,

---

[8] For some treatments of finite strain, such as, for example, in study of problems in the mathematical theory of plasticity, a second set of strain components can be used. These components are based on the notion that any finite strain is the sum of a sequence of infinitesimal increments. For example, for simple elongation of a material line in the x-direction, an increment in extensional strain is given by

$$\frac{\partial u}{\partial x} \cong \frac{\Delta l}{l}$$

where l is the original length and Δl the change in length. A series of such increments result in a natural or logarithmic extensional strain $\bar{\varepsilon}_x$, denoting a change in length from l to l', where

$$\bar{\varepsilon}_x = \int_l^{l'} \frac{dl}{l} = \ln \frac{l'}{l}$$

TABLE 9–2   *Distortional strain ellipsoids*

	Ellipsoid	Shape of Ellipsoid	Radii	Symmetry
	1	prolate spheroid	$a > b = c$	$\infty / m\ 2/m\ 2/m$
	2	oblate spheroid	$a = b > c$	
	3	triaxial ellipsoid	$a > b > c$ $a, b > r$	
	4		$a > b > c$ $b, c < r$	$2/m\ 2/m\ 2/m$
	5		$a > b > c$ $b = r$	

but the simplest image is the strain ellipsoid defined by equation (9-68). The strain "ellipsoid" for a pure dilatation is a sphere and does not change the symmetry of a particular pure distortion with which it is associated. For this reason, and because many large deformations in rocks can be considered volume-constant, we consider only distortional pure stains.

Let the major, intermediate, and minor principal radii of a strain ellipsoid be given by a, b, and c respectively in axial directions x, y, and z. Five types of strain ellipsoid can be distinguished as shown diagrammatically in Figure 9–55. The properties of these ellipsoids are summarized in Table 9–2 (remember that, if r is the radius of a

unit sphere in the undeformed body and there is no dilatation, $abc = r^3$).

It can be shown simply by suitable substitutions in equation (9-64) that the following geometric relationships hold for all homogeneous deformations:

1. Colinear points (material lines) remain colinear and proportionally spaced.
2. Coplanar points (material planes) remain coplanar and proportionally spaced.
3. Parallel material lines remain parallel and proportionally spaced.
4. Parallel material planes remain parallel and proportionally spaced.

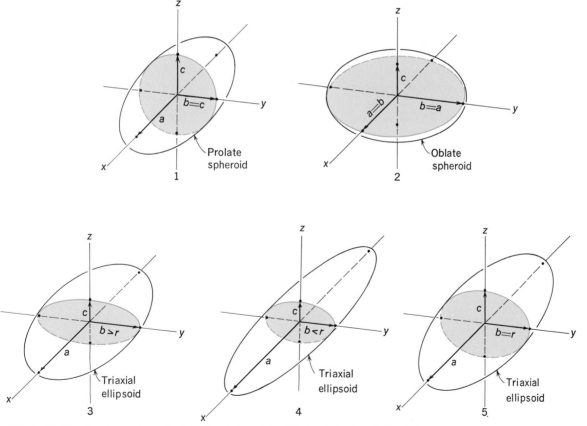

FIG. 9–55 The five types of purely distortional ellipsoids of finite strain (see Table 9–2).

As a result of finite deformations, however, most material lines in a body change their lengths, and most material planes change their areas. But there are always some lines in a volume-constant strain that have the same length in the strained as in the unstrained state. These are called lines of no extensional or normal finite strain. For example, consider the two-dimensional pure distortion (a pure shear) shown in Figure 9–56 by a circle deformed to an ellipse. The lines l and l' joining the points of intersection of the two figures correspond to two material lines in the strained state of length r, the radius of the circle in the unstrained state. Whatever the orientation of these material lines in the unstrained body, they must have been of length r; these are material lines that have the same length in the strained and unstrained states.

In three dimensions, each of the ellipsoids of Figure 9–55 intersects the undeformed sphere along lines any point on which joined to the origin is a line of no finite extensional strain. The orientations of these lines for a particular distortion represented by a matrix S can be simply found. The inverse transformation S^{-1} is given by the matrix, referred to its principal axes

$$\begin{pmatrix} \dfrac{1}{s_1} & 0 & 0 \\[2mm] 0 & \dfrac{1}{s_2} & 0 \\[2mm] 0 & 0 & \dfrac{1}{s_3} \end{pmatrix}$$

Since the strains in the directions of the principal axes are normal strains, S^{-1} can be written also as [see equation (9-69)]

$$\begin{pmatrix} \dfrac{1}{\sqrt{\lambda_1}} & 0 & 0 \\[2mm] 0 & \dfrac{1}{\sqrt{\lambda_2}} & 0 \\[2mm] 0 & 0 & \dfrac{1}{\sqrt{\lambda_3}} \end{pmatrix}$$

where λ_1, λ_2, and λ_3 are principal quadratic extensions. Consider now a radius vector n' of the strain ellipsoid corresponding to a unit radius vector n of the unit sphere in the unstrained

state. In terms of the inverse transformation we can write n in matrix form as

$$n = S^{-1}n'$$

or, expanded, as

$$n_x = \frac{n'_x}{\sqrt{\lambda_1}} \qquad n_y = \frac{n'_y}{\sqrt{\lambda_2}} \qquad n_z = \frac{n'_z}{\sqrt{\lambda_3}} \quad (9\text{-}70)$$

If vector n' has the same length as n, a unit vector, we can write from equation 9-70

$$\frac{n'^2_x}{\lambda_1} + \frac{n'^2_y}{\lambda_2} + \frac{n'^2_z}{\lambda_3} = 1 \qquad (9\text{-}71)$$

By means of the identity $n'^2_x + n'^2_y + n'^2_z = 1$ equation (9-71) can be solved for specific values of one component of n' and the loci of lines of no finite extensional strain in the strained state determined.

These lines are found to lie in the following surfaces for the five ellipsoids in Table 9–2.

Ellipsoid 1. Two circular cones about the x-axis

Ellipsoid 2. Two circular cones about the z-axis

Ellipsoid 3. Two elliptical cones about the z-axis

Ellipsoid 4. Two elliptical cones about the x-axis

Ellipsoid 5. Two planes bisecting the x- and z-axes and containing the y-axis (only for this ellipsoid do the surfaces coincide with circular sections of the triaxial ellipsoid)

All other material lines in the strained states have changed their lengths, growing longer or shorter than they were in the unstrained states. The surfaces thus divide the strain ellipsoid into regions in which lines have extended and regions in which lines have shortened.

DETERMINATION OF HOMOGENEOUS STRAINS IN ROCKS   Many deformed rocks contain structural markers of known approximate initial shape that in the course of a finite deformation have been grossly distorted. If circumstances are favorable,

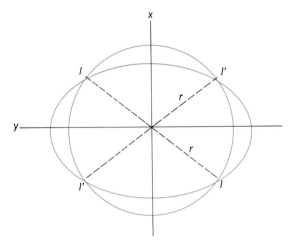

FIG. 9–56 *Lines ll and l'l' are lines of no finite normal strain for the pure shear shown.*

estimates of the magnitudes of components of finite homogeneous strain can occasionally be made. The most favorable initial configuration for a marker is, of course, a sphere. After deformation such a body becomes a finite-strain ellipsoid, and, if it can be extracted from the enclosing matrix or studied on smoothly cut sections of several orientations, the principal strains can be found directly. Oolites, spherulites, pebbles, pisolites, reduction spots in mudstones, and so on, are structures that can possibly be used in this way. Nonspherical bodies such as fossils, worm tubes, sun cracks, cross-bedding and so on, in which lines inclined initially at known angles generally occur can also be used for strain analysis, but they are less satisfactory and commonly lead only to two-dimensional analyses in particular planes, such as, for example, the bedding plane of a sedimentary rock in which the fossils lie.

Most attempts at strain analysis assume that volume is conserved during natural flow in rocks. In flow of metamorphic rocks this condition is probably met fairly closely. But in the deformation of porous sedimentary rocks and in the transition of a sedimentary rock to a metamorphic rock there is evidence to suggest that volume changes of significant magnitude may occur. The techniques of strain analysis are either

mathematical (arbitrary components of strain are measured and attempts made to compute principal strains from these) or graphical (generally involving the Mohr construction for finite strain) and are not discussed here (see Ramsay, 1967). Some difficulties and shortcomings of the technique are as follows:

1. The initial shape of the deformed marker is generally not known exactly. For example, although many deformed pebbles are crudely ellipsoidal, so are many undeformed pebbles. By study of many deformed markers it is sometimes possible to estimate the effect of initial shape variation on the result.

2. The magnitude of strain in a deformed marker many not be the same as that in the commonly homogeneous matrix that encloses it. Under favorable circumstances a marker, such as the delicate imprint of a fossil, can be expected to have the same mechanical properties as the matrix and to be uniformly strained with it. Under less favorable circumstances, another marker, such as a massive quartzite or granite pebble in a mudstone, is unlikely to have the same mechanical properties as the matrix and the deformation may be largely concentrated in one of the two members.

3. For a finite strain the rigid-body rotational part is indeterminate by strain analysis. It is impossible, in addition, to say whether or not a rotation has occurred or to examine the true symmetry of the deformation.

In spite of these difficulties, geologists are actively studying strain information in deformed rock bodies. One aim of such studies is to determine local strains throughout a deformed region in the hope of constructing crude finite-strain trajectories. Another is to establish the relationships between finite strains of various kinds and other associated deformation structures such as foliations, lineations, and folds. The relationships of particular patterns of preferred orientations of grains to associated finite homogeneous strains on a larger scale are also important.

Yet another possible use of data on finite strain presently being explored is in the determination of *relative* rheologic properties of rocks of different kinds deformed homogeneously at the same time. For example, in a conglomerate with a homogeneous matrix, pebbles of several different rock types are deformed to different degrees. If uniform stress is assumed, the differences must reflect differences in flow characteristics of different rocks under one set of physical conditions. If one assumes that the rocks are essentially "viscous," some estimate of the "viscosity ratios" of rocks of different kinds may be obtained by statistical study of pebble shape. In all such studies the influence of mechanical anisotropy must be considered.

PROGRESSIVE DEFORMATION   In the theory of finite strain introduced above only the initial unstrained and final strained state of a body are considered. The "strain" is a geometric relationship between these two states and depends in no way on the path followed from one to the other. Between an unstrained and a strained state there exists an infinite number of possible strain or deformation paths—a particular one of which, in a real given deformation, must have been followed. Any such deformation path can be expressed as the sum of a sequence of infinitesimal strain increments, each one representing the properties of the next small strain at any instant. This is the approach generally adopted in the mathematical theory of plasticity. In this theory a simple path is generally assumed, such as the path of "proportional straining" in which each strain increment $d\varepsilon$ is proportional to the total strain, so that

$$\frac{d\varepsilon_1}{\varepsilon_1} = \frac{d\varepsilon_2}{\varepsilon_2} = \frac{d\varepsilon_3}{\varepsilon_3}$$

A geologist concerned with real progressive deformation in a rock body can make no such simple assumption. Because of the effects of mechanical anisotropy many natural strains must be rotational, and, because of variations in material properties and physical conditions to be expected in a natural deformation, a simple strain path is unlikely.

In a homogeneous istropic continuum the final configuration does not depend on path; in a polycrystalline rock with planar and linear struc-

tures that are developed or modified progressively by deformation, intuition tells us that it might. To illustrate qualitatively what the effects of different paths might be, we consider one simple example of a plane strain that could have followed a pure shear or a simple shear path.

In Figure 9–57 is shown a circular body with a set of marked material lines undergoing a progressive pure shear terminating at the required state of strain. The initial state is T_i, and T_1, T_2, T_3 are states intermediate between this and the final state T_f; an infinite number of other states could be selected. For any given state there is an aggregate strain and an incremental strain that corresponds to the next infinitesimal strain increment. The properties of the first are described by a finite and of the second by an infinitesimal strain. Thus, at T_i, for example, the finite strain is zero, but for the first strain increment all material lines inclined at less than 45° to y begin to shorten and all material lines at more than 45° to y begin to lengthen. The line exactly at 45° is instantaneously unchanged in length. These are the properties of the incremental strains *at any instant*. At T_2, for example, the finite strain shows that some lines (such as L_1) have progressively shortened and others (such as L_3) have progressively lengthened up to this instant. But lines (such as L_2) lying in the shaded portion have rotated across the line of no incremental strain (at 45° to y) and have ceased shortening and begun to extend.

At the final state we find that material lines of different orientations have very different histories, as shown in Figure 9–58. Some have lengthened or shortened progressively; others have first shortened and then extended, even to exceed their initial length. The strain history of material lines for the same strain achieved by a simple shear is shown in Figure 9–59; the inherently lower symmetry of a rotational strain is clearly represented in the pattern. Thus although a finite simple shear is geometrically equivalent to pure shear plus a rigid-body rotation, if the strain histories of material lines are considered the two deformations are symmetrically distinct.

These two simple examples suggest the kind of complexity in the strain histories of material lines and planes to be expected in a three-dimensional body that has followed a deformation path leading to a real, finite homogeneous strain. In a real deformation the incremental strains are likely to vary with finite strain and time rather than to remain constant as in the examples given.

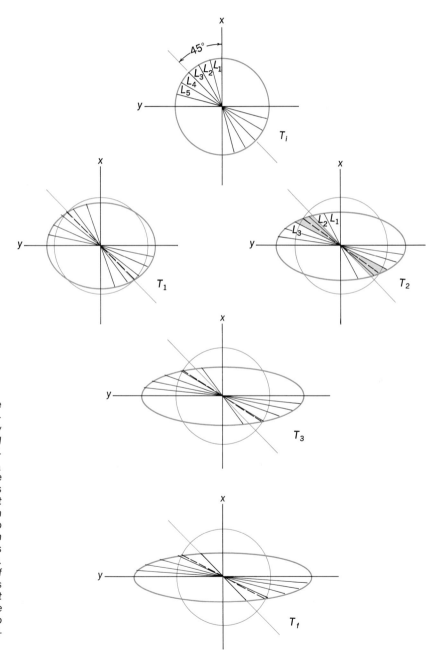

FIG. 9-57 Progressive pure shear (shown in two dimensions) of a circular body containing marked material lines L_1 to L_5. T_i is the initial (unstrained) state; T_1 to T_3 are intermediate strained states and T_f is the final strained state. At each instant the direction of one of the lines of no incremental normal strain (45° to coordinate axes) is shown by a colored line. The corresponding line of no finite normal strain is shown by a dashed line. At state T_2 lines lying in the shaded part have begun to extend after initial shortening.

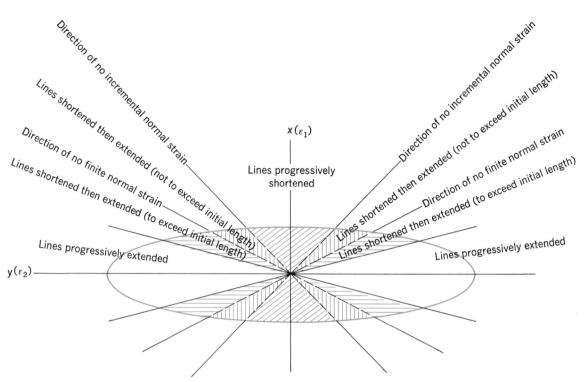

FIG. 9–58   *Normal strain histories of material lines in various directions after a progressive pure shear corresponding to a 50 percent shortening in the y direction. (Modified from J. Ramsay, Folding and Fracturing of Rocks, McGraw-Hill, 1967. Copyright 1967. Used by permission of McGraw-Hill Book Co.)*

Also, in three dimensions, one material line in a surface may be shortening while another material line in a different direction in the same surface is simultaneously extending.

Under certain favorable circumstances a body may be constrained by its surroundings or internal anisotropy to follow a simple deformation path. The most obvious example from a geologist's point of view is progressive simple shear. Plastic deformation of a crystal with a single slip system follows this path, as, less perfectly, does deformation of a well-foliated body by pervasive slip on the foliation surfaces.

FLOW STRUCTURES

The most direct and spectacular evidence of the nature and magnitude of solid flow in rocks comes from studies of structures in crustal rocks, particularly metamorphic rocks. The geometric

properties of some of these structures have been reviewed in Chapter 3. We look now at their genesis. The origins of most flow structures in terms of physical mechanisms and processes are poorly understood. Most experimental work on rocks has concentrated on phenomenological behavior such as ductility and creep, and few experiments have been designed specifically to investigate the genesis of structures such as folds and boudins.

FOLDING AND BOUDINAGE   Folds are the commonest structures formed by flow in solid rocks. They occur on all scales in a large variety of geologic environments and have characteristics that vary widely from place to place and rock body to rock body. In spite of such variation, most folds seem to be the expression of one basic physical fact—namely, that bodies of layered, laminated, or foliated rock are generally mechanically

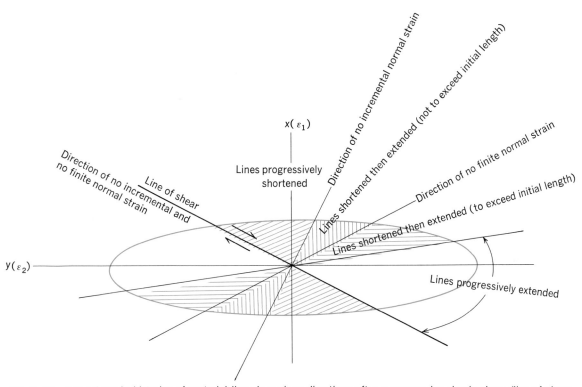

FIG. 9-59 *Normal strain histories of material lines in various directions after a progressive simple shear (line of shear shown by heavy line) corresponding to a 50 percent shortening in the y direction. (Modified from J. Ramsay, Folding and Fracturing of Rocks, McGraw-Hill, 1967. Copyright 1967. Used by permission of McGraw-Hill Book Co.)*

unstable where components of compressive stress act in the plane of structural anisotropy. The nature of such instability has been the subject of much discussion for a hundred years or more, and most geologists now agree that there is no universal explanation of folding. Instead, a number of ideal mechanical models have been proposed to represent folds of different types and these are now generally accepted by most geologists as possible basic fold mechanisms.

1. *Buckling.* A thin elastic rod loaded axially in compression so that its ends are constrained to move only along the compression axis will buckle into a sinusoidal half-wave, as the load F reaches a critical value given by Euler's formula as

$$F = \frac{\pi^2 EI}{l^2}$$

where E is Young's modulus for the material of the rod, I is the moment of inertia of its cross section, and l its length. This formula works equally well for nonelastic materials provided that substitution of appropriate quantities is made. For example, buckling of a ductile (plastic) rod occurs at the critical load F, where

$$F = \frac{\pi^2 E' I}{l^2}$$

and E' is the relationship between instantaneous axial stress $\bar{\sigma}$ and natural strain $\bar{\varepsilon}$; that is,

$$E' = \frac{d\bar{\sigma}}{d\bar{\varepsilon}}$$

Models of buckling more appropriate to geologists involve a plate or layer embedded in an infinite medium. To this system of layer and enclosing medium can be attributed any desired properties—elastic, viscous, or plastic—and mathematical models of buckling behavior under compressive load can be examined. Of most interest is a relatively "stiff" layer in a relatively weak matrix. Geologists have long used the term "competent" for a stiffer member and "incompetent" for a weaker without specifying any particular material property. In early use of these terms, differences in elastic properties, especially rigidity, were probably implied; more recently, differences in viscosity appear to be widely considered dominant in determining relative competence.

Many common rock associations constitute layered systems of this kind. In sedimentary sequences thin sandstone layers in mudstones and, in metamorphic regions, layers of quartzite in schist or marble are common examples. Loading of such layers in compression generally results in an essentially homogeneous shortening of the weaker material, whereas the competent layers tend to buckle into wavelike forms (Figure 9–60). The most relevant theoretical treatment of this problem from the geologist's point of view

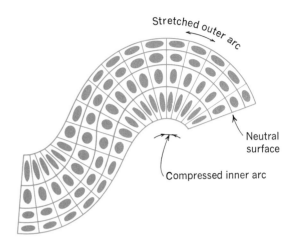

FIG. 9–61 *State of strain in a buckled layer (schematic) showing neutral surface. (After J. Ramsay,* Folding and Fracturing of Rocks, *McGraw-Hill, 1967. Copyright 1967. Used by permission of McGraw-Hill Book Co.)*

is one that treats both layer and enclosing medium as viscous materials. For example, M. A. Biot considered a plate of thickness h and viscosity η embedded in a medium with lower viscosity η_1. Upon compression in the plane of the layers, buckles with a "dominant wavelength" L_d were favored to develop, where

$$L_d = 2\pi h \left(\frac{\eta}{6\eta_1}\right)^{1/3} \qquad (9\text{-}72)$$

independently of the compressive load. The theory predicts also that a pile of n such layers, with perfect lubrication between, will fold with the dominant wavelength

$$L_d = 2\pi h \left(\frac{n\eta}{6\eta_1}\right)^{1/3}$$

In both situations, increase in thickness of the layers should result in an increase in the wavelength of the buckles.

Buckling seems to be an important mechanism in the folding of layered sequences. The forms of folds produced by buckling are extremely variable, but tend to be concentric or parallel rather than similar. The actual strains in a buckled layer depend upon its material properties, but ideally (Figure 9–61) there is extension along the outer arc of the layer, compression

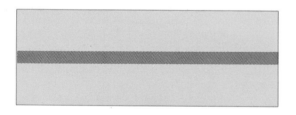

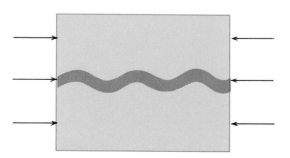

FIG. 9–60 *Buckling of a competent layer in an incompetent material (colored) in response to longitudinal loading (schematic).*

along the inner arc, and, somewhere between, a "neutral surface" along which no extensional strain occurs. On the profile of a series of cylindrical buckle folds, measurement of the length of a neutral surface gives an approximate value for the unfolded length of the layer.

In most theoretical studies, simple compressions are assumed to act in the plane of the buckled layers. In nature, buckling seems to occur so long as a component of compression lies initially in the layer. If a component of extension lies in a competent layer, necking and boudinage replace buckling as the characteristic instability of competent layers. The forms of the boudins are a guide to the relative mechanical properties of the interlayered materials. If there is no difference in properties, boudins do not form.

In general, simple buckle folding and boudinage are most commonly found in layered sequences of rocks containing competent and incompetent members. The competent layers exhibit buckling and boudinage; the incompetent material generally accommodates to the spaces left between the shortening or extending competent layers, and, if the competent layers are thin and few in number, may be homogeneously strained on a large scale. Under these circumstances the presence of buckle folds and boudins can be important indicators of regional strain and strain history.

2. *Bending.* Foldlike forms can appear in layered sequences purely as a result of "bending" during differential uplift. The stresses forming such folds are heterogeneous and no component of compression acts in the folded layers (Figure 9–62). Some geologists, particularly in the Soviet Union, consider many large folds in sedimentary rocks to have formed in this way in response to

FIG. 9–63 *"Flexural-slip" folding of a bedded or foliated sequence of rocks in which the bedding or foliation are surfaces of low cohesion and easy slip.*

the differential upward displacement of "rigid" blocks of basement along steep faults. Folds formed in this way are characteristically monoclinal or box-shaped. But they may in addition show thinning of beds in the dipping limbs as a result of stretching over the faulted basement—a feature not always present in large natural box folds.

3. *Flexural slip.* Folding of uniform sequences of layered or foliated rocks generally involves laminar slip on the folded surfaces, which are generally surfaces of weak cohesion (Figure 9–63). The forms of such "flexural-slip" folds are variable and depend on factors such as spacing of slip surfaces or thickness of layers, depth of cover, internal properties of the layers, and so on. In massively layered sequences they tend to be open folds of large amplitude with concentric or angular hinges. Box and conjugate folds can form in this way. In finely foliated rocks, such as phyllites and schists, flexural-slip folds tend to be chevron-shaped and small in amplitude.

4. *Slip or shear.* In certain rocks, visibly folded structural surfaces do not seem to be surfaces of weak cohesion or boundaries of competent and incompetent layers. The fold forms in such rocks are typically similar and it is difficult to escape the conclusion that the layers have become folded by differential shearing displacements lying in the axial planes of the folds, as shown diagrammatically in Figure 9–64. There is compelling evidence that folding of this kind occurs in response to some kind of instability in very slow laminar flow, not at present understood. Folds so formed are known as slip or shear folds.

5. *Homogeneous deformation.* Homogeneous deformation of perfectly planar layers cannot form folds. But most naturally layered or foliated

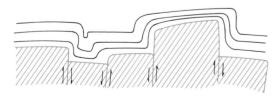

FIG. 9–62 *"Block folding" of a thin sedimentary cover over a faulted basement (schematic).*

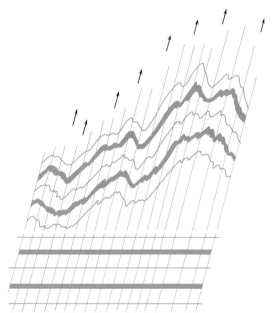

FIG. 9–64 *"Slip" or "shear folding" of a layered body by differential shear (schematic).*

rocks contain irregularities in their planar structures that intense homogeneous deformation can exaggerate into foldlike forms.

Most natural folds can be viewed as being formed by some combination of the above ideal mechanisms acting either together in the same rock, or separately in different members of a layered sequence. It is generally difficult, and commonly impossible, for a geologist to place a fold in one of these categories by inspection of its geometric features, although he generally feels constrained to try. Similar folds, for example, can be formed either by flexural slip or by slip folding. But the shapes of folds as seen in profile are still the clearest guides to the displacements and strains that have accompanied folding, and in the absence of adequate theoretical and experimental data on folding, such geometric studies are likely to remain important for some time to come.

EXPERIMENTAL FOLDING   Many geologists have performed model experiments on the folding of layered materials such as rubber, clay, and paper cards. Most such experiments have been con-

cerned with the behavior of interlayered materials of different properties or competence. The results of some experiments have been fitted to mathematical models and natural observations with some success. For example, folds formed in rubber layers embedded in gelatin have been used to test a theory of sinusoidal buckling based upon an initial elastic instability in a layer constrained in a medium with a lower elastic modulus. The theory predicts folds of initial wavelength L, where

$$L = 2\pi h \left(\frac{E}{6E_0}\right)^{1/3}$$

where h is the thickness of the plate, and E and E_0 are the elastic moduli respectively of the layer and the medium [see equation (9-72) for the case of viscous layers]. Experiments on single layers fitted the predicted values of wavelengths very well for specific values of the modulus ratios. Study of natural folds in layered sedimentary rocks showed the relationship between the thickness of the dominant member (the layer that appears to control fold shape because of its thickness and competence) and fold wavelength to be as shown in Figure 9–65 by a log-log plot. This plot shows the wavelength of the folds to be about 27 times the thickness. This figure corresponds to a modulus ratio E/E_0 of about 500.

Bending experiments have been performed for four types of cohesionless sands to determine the fold and fracture patterns formed during basement uplift. Over a sinusoidal uplift (Figure 9–66) some weak folding was produced followed by faulting, the actual pattern depending upon the type of sand used. An important result was a thinning of the layers at the crest of the fold by about 6 percent. In some experiments (material 2, for example) structures resembling the east-African rift were found.

Few experiments designed to form folds in real rocks have been performed, mainly because of experimental difficulties. Flexural-slip folding of highly foliated rocks has been investigated in recent studies. For example, in one series of experiments small cylinders of fine-grained phyllite enclosed in thick ductile-metal jackets were compressed parallel or oblique to foliation in triaxial

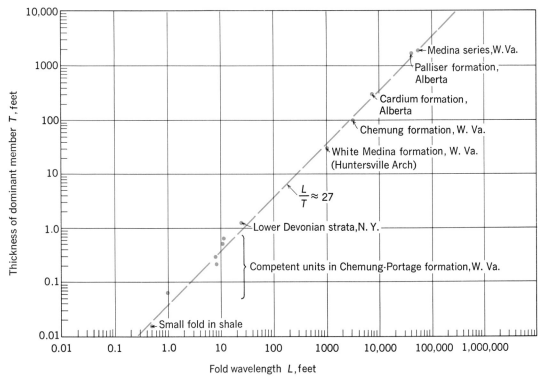

FIG. 9–65 *Log-log plot of the wavelength to dominant member thickness for folds observed at a variety of localities. (After J. B. Currie, H. W. Patnode, and R. P. Trump, Development of folds in sedimentary strata, Geol. Soc. Am. Bull., 1962.)*

apparatus under a confining pressure of 5 kb at room temperature. The specimens became progressively folded by the appearance of successive generations of conjugate kink folds, which crossed one another to form chevron folds with axial planes subperpendicular to the compression direction, much as in the diagrammatic sequence shown in Figure 9–67. Some of the tight folding in the foliations formed in this way (Figure 9–68) resembles closely the chevron folding of metamorphic rocks; but behavior in the experiments was ductile and it has yet to be shown that similar structures can form also under creep conditions.

Kink folding and conjugate kink folding of this kind may prove to be very important mechanisms of flexural-slip folding in natural rocks. Such folds are common in thinly laminated or well-foliated rocks, but they can form also on much larger scales in sequences of coarsely lay-

ered rocks, which have occasional bedding surfaces or formational boundaries of low cohesive strength. The "slip surfaces" in such sequences can be shaly partings between massive isotropic layers of limestone, sandstone, or quartzite, and may be spaced at intervals of 100 meters or more. Kink and conjugate kink folds formed in such sequences can have amplitudes of hundreds or even thousands of meters and may have hinge zones that are not obviously sharp "kink" surfaces; but the common occurrence of box folds (large-scale conjugate kink folds) in such sequences in the early stages of folding is becoming increasingly obvious to geologists, and folds with long straight limbs and narrow hinge regions are perhaps more typical of weakly folded bedded sequences than the gentle concentric or sinusoidal flexures commonly pictured. This common boxy form of folds in many weakly folded sedimentary sequences has led some geologists to

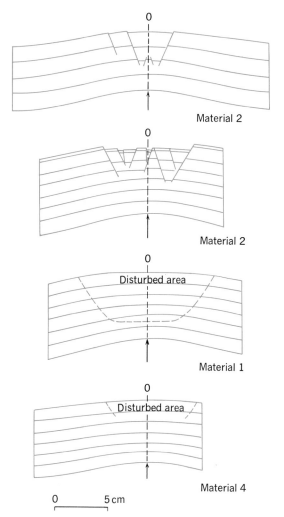

FIG. 9–66 *Fracture and fold patterns produced in cohesionless sands with various properties (materials 1 to 4) over a sinusoidal uplift. (After A. R. Sanford, Analytical and experimental study of simple geologic structures, Geol. Soc. Am. Bull., 1959.)*

interpret them in terms of "bending" of a sedimentary cover in response to differential uplift and subsidence of blocks of underlying basement. If this view is adopted, such folds are not a result of compression in the plane of the layers, and gross shortening of a sedimentary sequence is not necessarily indicated by folding. On the other hand, if the box folds are viewed as conjugate

kink folds of the kind produced experimentally, compression in the plane of the layers and a resultant shortening is required.

PERVASIVE STRUCTURES   The pervasive structures (foliations and lineations) of tectonites vary widely in their detailed properties, but most are direct indicators of flow. The simplest structure of this kind is probably slaty cleavage, about the origins of which geologists have argued for more than 100 years and—in the absence of conclusive experimental evidence—still argue. It seems likely, if not certain, that most slaty cleavage forms (in the manner proposed by some of the earliest investigators) perpendicular to a direction of maximum shortening in a rock body. The most compelling evidence for this view is given by strain analysis of fossils, pisolites, reduction spots, and so on, deformed during the formation of the cleavage. Such analyses show conclusively that deformation is locally homogeneous and that the slaty cleavage forms in the principal plane of the strain containing the two largest principal radii of the ellipsoid of finite strain. Where the strain is not axially symmetric the direction of greatest elongation lying in the slaty cleavage is sometimes marked by a faint lineation.

The physical mechanisms by which slaty cleavage develops are not understood; growth of platy grains in planar preferred orientation and flattening and rotation of preexisting grains may all play a part. It has been suggested that cleavage forms in compressed water-saturated clays, muds, and silts, and that the presence of high pore pressures facilitates the early development of the cleavage.

Slaty cleavage grades with increasing metamorphic reconstruction of a rock into the coarser foliations of the phyllites and schists. These may in part be "mimetic," in that once a planar anisotropy such as slaty cleavage is established, platy and prismatic grains such as mica and amphibole can grow more easily in this plane and tend to emphasize and preserve the early structure. But most coarse foliations of schists and gneisses seem to have formed in response to deformation of some kind, although their relationships to local strain are not easily demonstrated. Some, at least

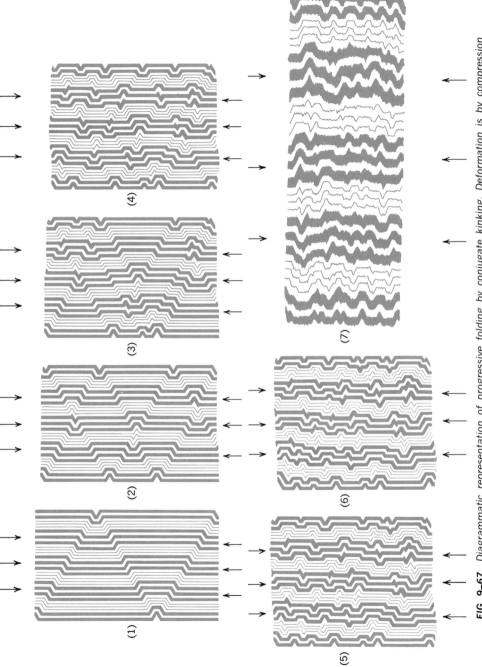

FIG. 9-67 *Diagrammatic representation of progressive folding by conjugate kinking. Deformation is by compression parallel to foliation and increases from (1) to (7). (After L. E. Weiss, Flexural-slip folding of foliated model materials, Geol. Survey Canada, paper 68-52, 1969.)*

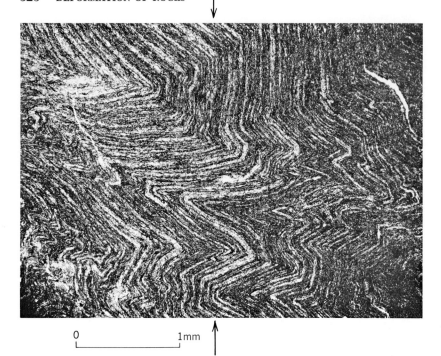

FIG. 9–68 *Experimental chevron folding in phyllite. Compression as shown by the arrows at 5–kb confining pressure 25°C. (After M. S. Paterson and L. E. Weiss, Folding and boudinage of quartz-rich layers in experimental deformed phyllite, Geol. Soc. Am. Bull., 1968.)*

0   1mm

locally, seem to be surfaces of pervasive laminar shear; others seem to be surfaces normal to a direction of regional flattening. Many foliations, particularly the secondary foliations, are intimately associated with folds (as axial-plane foliations), and share a common or similar origin.

It is difficult to make many conclusive statements about foliation, and will remain so until the experimenters succeed in outlining the conditions under which these structures form. The same can be said of lineations. Some of these are found in association with deformed markers, such as pebbles, and appear to indicate the direction of greatest extension in a deformed body. But some lineations, particularly those defined by intersecting planar structures, have less clear mechanical significance in that their orientation is decided partly by the attitude of an older set of surfaces.

In general, then, some of the pervasive structures of deformed rocks can be interpreted in terms of regional strain. To attempt interpretation of them in terms of stress makes little sense.

TRANSPOSITION AND PROGRESSIVE DEFORMATION
In a progressive deformation most preexisting foliations and layerings become transposed into new foliations. To illustrate the relationships between folding, boudinage, and development of foliation, let us consider some ideal examples in two dimensions.

Consider a body containing isolated competent layers compressed along the layers (Figure 9–69). Material lines in the direction of these layers must shorten progressively if the deformation is an increasing pure shear and we can assume that the layers buckle as foliation develops in the matrix perpendicular to compression. The folds formed are symmetric and the enveloping surface does not rotate.

In a second body (Figure 9–70) similar layers are inclined at 30° to the compression axis. From Figure 9–56 we see that material lines in the direction of the layers begin to shorten, and buckle folds appear in the layers. The layers also rotate, as shown by the change in orientation of the enveloping surface. After a certain amount of

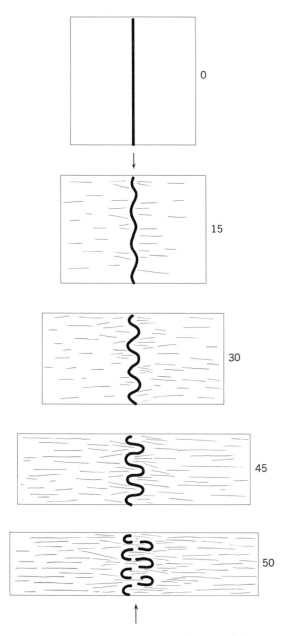

FIG. 9–69 *Behavior of a competent layer parallel to compression axis during progressive pure shear involving development of a secondary foliation (figures refer to percent shortening at each stage). Layer becomes progressively folded with possible separation of hinges for extreme deformation.*

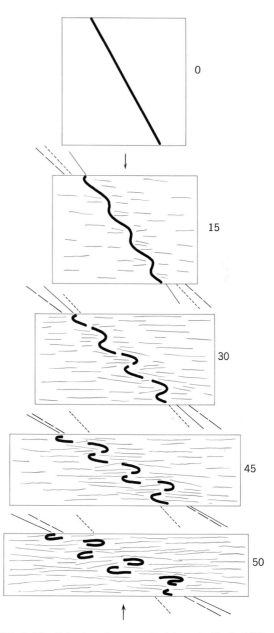

FIG. 9–70 *Behavior of a competent layer inclined at 30° to compression axis during a progressive pure shear involving development of a secondary foliation (figures refer to percent shortening at each stage). Layer is first folded and subsequently boudinaged. Full line is the enveloping surface of the folds; dashed line is the direction of no finite normal strain; dotted line is the direction of no incremented normal strain.*

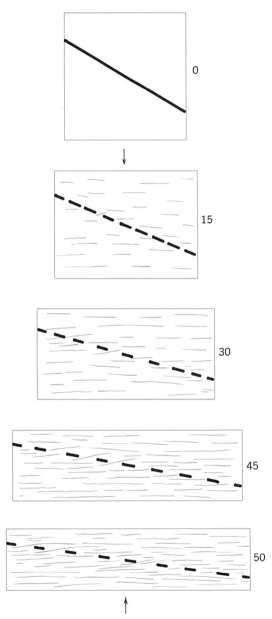

FIG. 9–71 *Behavior of a competent layer inclined at 60° to compression axis during a progressive pure shear involving development of a secondary foliation (figures refer to percent shortening at each stage). Layer becomes progressively boudinaged.*

deformation, the mean attitude of the folded layers, as given by the enveloping surface, rotates through the plane of no incremental normal strain (at 45° to the compression axis) and the folded layers begin to extend. It has been suggested that such layers would first *unfold*; but a more likely effect is the development of boudinage in the already folded layers, as shown diagrammatically in Figure 9–70. After a large deformation corresponding to a progressive pure shear, the initial continuity of the layers is destroyed and the layers become separated in boudins and fold boudins, flattened in the plane of the new foliation, which develops perpendicular to the compression axis.

In a third body with layers inclined at 45° or more to the compression axis (Figure 9–71), progressive pure shear produces only boudinage.

In all three examples, the initial layering becomes "transposed" into the new foliation developing in the matrix, by folding, boudinage, or both. A similar sequence of events occurs during any progressive deformation.

TECTONITE FABRICS   Most rocks deformed cohesively by flow, both in the ductile and creep regimes, acquire characteristic textures and fabrics, particularly patterns of preferred orientation of mineral grains. Many such patterns have been described from naturally deformed rocks or have been formed experimentally in rocks such as marble, dolomite rock, and quartzite. Some of these experimentally formed patterns are developed in response to plastic deformation of grains already present; others have required growth of new grains or annealing recrystallization. Attempts to predict patterns of preferred orientation, stable in particular "stress fields," have been made; however, it seems likely that such factors as magnitude of deformation, energy of grain boundaries, and so on, are more important in the development of fabric than are particular states of stress.

The fabric of a rock is a geometric image of its internal structure and thus of its physical properties. For example, rocks with isotropic fabrics (lacking preferred orientations of grains) tend to be isotropic with respect to physical properties such as thermal conductivity and linear compressibility; conversely, rocks with strong preferred orientations of grains tend to be strongly anisotropic with respect to similar properties. In tectonites (rocks deformed by flow) the fabrics present are generally a result of deformation; and one reason why the geologist studies such fabrics is to obtain information about the deformation history of rocks.

We have seen that strain analysis of deformed markers, as introduced above, yields only the pure strain component of a deformation that always has axial ($\infty/m\ 2/m\ 2/m$) or orthorhombic ($2/m\ 2/m\ 2/m$) symmetry. Many deformations are, however, rotational, and the orientation of the principal axes of incremental strain varies with finite strain. The strain history of rocks deformed in this way is less symmetric than strain analysis suggests and only by examination of their fabrics can the true symmetry of the deformation be established.

These notions are best illustrated by some simple examples drawn from experimental work. Consider, for example, a marble such as Yule marble, which has an axial fabric in which the [0001]-axes of the component calcite grains are in a state of preferred orientation at high angles to a weak foliation (Figure 9–72). The mechanical anisotropy of the rock for plastic deformation has the same symmetry as this initial fabric, and its behavior when placed in a triaxial testing machine depends upon the orientation of the axis of anisotropy with respect to the compression (or extension) axis of the apparatus. Three possibilities and their effect on the strain and resultant fabric are shown in Figure 9–73. If the compression axis coincides with the axis of anisotropy, the cylindrical specimen remains circular in cross section at all stages (symmetry of strain path is axial) and the resultant pattern of preferred orientation of [0001]-axes has the same symmetry (but not form) as the initial pattern. In this example the ∞-fold axis of the load and the ∞-fold axis of the initial fabric coincide, and the final fabric has the same symmetry. If the rock is compressed in the plane of the foliation, the cylindrical specimen becomes ellipsoid in cross section and the resultant pattern of pre-

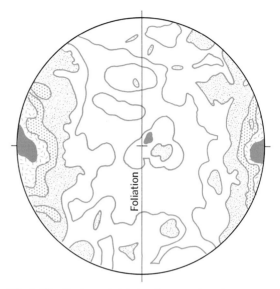

FIG. 9–72 *Contoured fabric diagram (equal area projection) showing the preferred orientation of [0001] in grains of calcite of Yule marble. The density of the stippling shows the intensity of the concentration. The highest concentration is perpendicular to the foliation. (After F. J. Turner, Preferred orientation of calcite in Yule marble, Am. J. Sci., 1949.)*

ferred orientation is orthorhombic. In this situation, the ∞-fold axis of the load parallels a 2-fold axis of the initial fabric (and vice versa) and the symmetry of the strain path and the final fabric become orthorhombic (only the symmetry operations common to both the initial fabric and the load remain as symmetry operations of the strain path and the final fabric). In the last example the rock is compressed oblique to the ∞-fold axis of the initial fabric. The cylindrical specimen becomes elliptical in cross section and the central deformed part rotates with respect to the rest of the specimen. The deformation path is rotational about the 2-fold axis common to the load and the initial fabric and the resultant fabric become monoclinic $2/m$ with its 2-fold axis coinciding with the rotation axis of the strain. Note that the pure strain at any stage still has symmetry $2/m\ 2/m\ 2/m$.

These examples illustrate the operation of Curie's symmetry principle (page 130), which states the possible relationships between the sym-

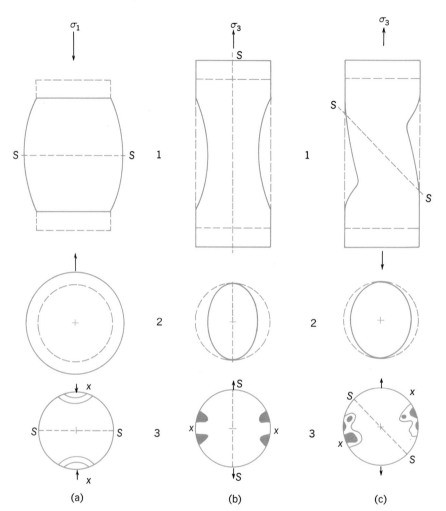

FIG. 9–73 *Diagrammatic representation of symmetry principle governing deformation of Yule marble. Rows 1 and 2 show shapes of initially cylindrical specimens after deformation. Row 1 shows longitudinal sections and row 2 transverse sections. Row 3 shows corresponding fabric diagrams in schematic form prepared from longitudinal sections. The orientation of the initial maximum is given by the foliation SS. (a) Compression normal to foliation. (b) Extension parallel to foliation. (c) Extension at 45° to foliation. (After F. J. Turner and L. E. Weiss, Structural Analysis of Metamorphic Tectonites, McGraw-Hill, 1963. Copyright 1963. Used by permission of McGraw-Hill Book Co.)*

metries of dependent physical phenomena. The symmetry of the strain path and that of the final fabric, as first recognized by Bruno Sander, are the same, and must include the symmetry operations common to the initial fabric and the pattern of loading. (They may include additional symmetry operations, too.) The summation of finite displacements of rock particles (atoms, grains, and so on) during progressive strain is what Sander called the "movement picture" of deformation. It is analogous to and symmetrically identical with the strain path. It is through fabric analysis that the symmetry of the path of progressive strain may be revealed. If a general strain is rotational the resultant fabric is either monoclinic $2/m$ (rotation about one of the principal strain axes, as in simple shear) or triclinic $\bar{1}$ (rotation about an axis or axes inclined to principal strain axes). It is of interest to note that most fabrics of deformed rocks are triclinic; this means either that most natural deformation paths are rotational or that most initial fabrics are of low symmetry. Careful study of natural deformation fabrics sometimes permits a choice to be made between these two possibilities.

Seismic Yielding

Earthquakes remind us constantly that slow flow or creep is not the only type of deformation common in rocks of the earth. During an earthquake, elastically strained rocks "yield" (or "fail") suddenly to release stored elastic strain energy in the form of seismic waves that travel through the earth. The yield in any particular earthquake is not instantaneous and may take from one to ten seconds; but in this period a major earthquake may release an enormous quantity of energy—perhaps, for the largest earthquakes on record, of the order of 10^{25} ergs.

Seismologists have used such natural bursts of energy to investigate the rheologic properties and internal structure of the earth; some of their most important findings are reviewed in Chapter 11. Our present concern is with the region from which the seismic waves radiate (the *focus* or *source* of the earthquake) and the mode of yielding (called the focal or source mechanism) by which a sudden burst of energy is released.

FOCAL MECHANISMS OF EARTHQUAKES

From the known mechanical behavior of rocks at the earth's surface, the most likely focal mechanism appears to be sudden faulting on discrete rupture surfaces followed by frictional sliding. This view is supported by the observation of actual surface displacements on known faults during earthquakes, and the common locations of epicenters (points on the earth's surface directly overlying a seismic focus) close to the traces of known faults or fault zones.

The fault theory of earthquakes which has been the mainstay of seismologists during the last 50 years or so is the "elastic rebound theory" developed by Harry Fielding Reid following the disastrous San Francisco earthquake of 1906. This earthquake was accompanied by surface rupture along the San Andreas fault for more than 300 km. According to this theory, tectonic forces result in the accumulation of elastic strain energy in a body of rock containing a major fault across which frictional forces act to prevent slippage. As the strain accumulates, in some small region of the fault, perhaps where friction is lowest, the stress exceeds the frictional resistance and local slip occurs. The effect of such slip is to increase the stress at the ends of the slipped portion with the result that slip is propagated in one or both directions along the fault (Figure 9–74). This phenomenon resembles the propagation of a dislocation in a crystal except that the magnitude of the slip vector is arbitrary. The sudden propagation of slip along the fault displaces rocks on the two sides and generates seismic waves, which propagate as body and surface waves through the earth, resulting in an earthquake.

For such a model there is no small region of seismic yield, as suggested by the term "focus," but a moving source that can travel from the initial point of rupture (generally taken as the

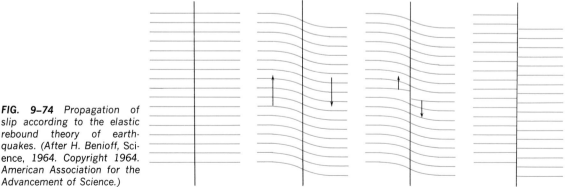

FIG. 9–74 *Propagation of slip according to the elastic rebound theory of earthquakes. (After H. Benioff, Science, 1964. Copyright 1964. American Association for the Advancement of Science.)*

focus) along part or all of the length of an active fault. Estimates of rupture length for the Chilean earthquake of 1960, for example, approach 1000 km, an unusually high figure. A velocity of propagation of rupture of 3 to 4 km/sec has been suggested for strike-slip faults such as the San Andreas.

In spite of the fact that many earthquakes are not associated with strike-slip faulting, or obviously associated with faults of any kind, the elastic rebound theory fits many of the features of earthquakes very well indeed, and some of the later developments of seismology have rested upon an acceptance of the theory. Difficulties have arisen, however, as our knowledge of the mechanical behavior of rocks and minerals at elevated pressures and temperatures has increased. From previous discussions we see that these conditions tend to suppress fracture in favor of ductile flow. Earthquakes occur over a great range of depths in the earth and are classified as shallow (less than 60 km), intermediate (60 to 150 km), and deep (more than 150 km). Some are known to occur at depths as great as 700 km, and any proposed single physical mechanism, such as the elastic rebound theory, must act through the range of temperatures and pressures indicated by these depths.

Compelling evidence suggests that sudden faulting, as observed in the laboratory in conventional short-term triaxial tests, is impossible throughout almost all of this range of depths. Even faulting of a transitional or ductile kind seems unlikely, because frictional forces on the fault must be overcome before the fault can slip, even locally. In dry rocks, for example, with a coefficient of friction of 1.0, the frictional resistance to sliding will be of similar magnitude to the lithostatic pressure. Thus at a depth of 500 km, the frictional resistance to slip would be about 150 kilobars. But extrapolation from the known physical properties of rocks suggest that the shear stress for cohesive flow at this depth is less than 100 bars (this notion is supported by the stress drops during deep earthquakes that are generally estimated between 10 and 100 bars). Thus it would appear that the rocks would deform by cohesive flow and not by slip on a fault surface.

Several ways out of this difficulty have been suggested, some of which we briefly review. The first obvious conclusion to draw is that the focal mechanism for deep focus earthquakes is not faulting, but sudden yield of a different kind. The most commonly cited mechanism of this kind is of a "plastic" nature and involves a sudden change of solid-state phase in a crystalline material. This change could be the transition to a denser phase with associated finite dilatation; or it could be shear displacement of the diffusionless coherent type, with the accompanying finite distortional strain of large magnitude. The first type of phase change is likely to be pressure-sensitive and in a homogeneous mantle would be concentrated at those depths at which pressure reaches the values required for a given transformation. Also, some transformations of this kind require diffusion and proceed too sluggishly to release elastic strain energy in the surrounding material. However, some evidence of volume change during very deep earthquakes has been observed. For an earthquake at a depth of 600 km below Peru, for example, strain seismographs indicated a downward motion of the earth's surface at the epicenter. If the ratio $\Delta V/V$ is assumed to be about 0.03 (a reasonable figure for a change of state), this particular earthquake would correspond to collapse in a spherical source about 0.3 km in diameter.

Coherent transformations are a more likely source mechanism in that they can be induced by shearing stress. One such transformation, known from laboratory experiments to proceed at high presure, is the polymorphic change from enstatite (orthorhombic) to clinoenstatite (monoclinic).

Other proposed mechanisms of sudden yield or locally increasing deformation rate include creep instability and velocity discontinuity in flow, and shear melting during propagation of a flow, perhaps from a preexistent pocket of molten material.

The most attractive theory for earthquakes at most depths so far proposed is that the focal mechanism is, in fact, faulting, made possible at depths by the presence of a high-pressure pore fluid. We have seen that the presence of such a fluid reduces normal stresses and thus frictional resistance to slip while leaving shearing stresses unaffected. Support for this theory comes in part from the experiments on serpentinite discussed on page 461, and in part from observations of an apparent increase in local shallow earthquake activity where high-pressure fluids have been pumped into deep disposal wells. Most rocks in the shallow parts of the crust contain entrapped water and, at depth, water could be released by dehydration reactions. Deeper in the mantle, partial melting of mantle material may yield a pore fluid that behaves in much the same way; and the concentration of deep earthquakes along what, according to the theory of "plate tectonics," are believed to be downgoing slabs of crustal material at certain continental margins suggests also that dehydration reactions may continue even to depths of 700 km.

The problems of earthquakes are far from solved. It seems likely that different mechanisms act at different depths in different places and that no universal explanation will ever be found. But despite their lack of knowledge of the physical

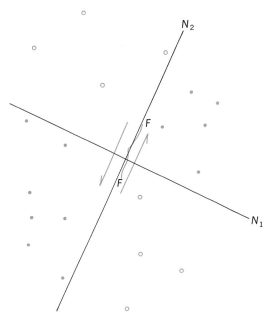

FIG. 9–76 *Hypothetical distribution of first motions associated with strike-slip motion on a vertical fault. A dot indicates a compressional and a circle a dilational first arrival. The nodal planes (vertical) N_1 and N_2 can be drawn through the pattern. Ground breakage along FF confirms that N_2 is along the trace of the fault and that the motion on the fault is as shown by the arrows.*

mechanism that generates seismic waves, seismologists have learned much of value about the patterns of displacement at a focus, as we shall now see.

FIRST-MOTION STUDIES

When an earthquake occurs, the first waves to arrive at any point on the surface of the earth are P-waves. These travel much faster than S and surface waves and are always responsible for the "first motion" observed at any seismographic station. In a P-wave, particle motion is in the direction of propagation, so that at any particular station the arriving wavefront will move a stationary particle either toward the epicenter, corresponding to the arrival of a dilatation, or away from it, corresponding to the arrival of a compression. Study of seismographic records for a

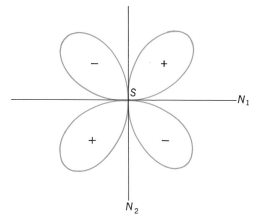

FIG. 9–75 *Two-dimensional radiation pattern for P-waves from a seismic source S. Plus sign indicates compressions and minus sign a dilatational first arrival. The forms of the lobes indicate the amplitudes of the waves. Amplitudes fall to zero along the orthogonal nodal lines N_1 and N_2.*

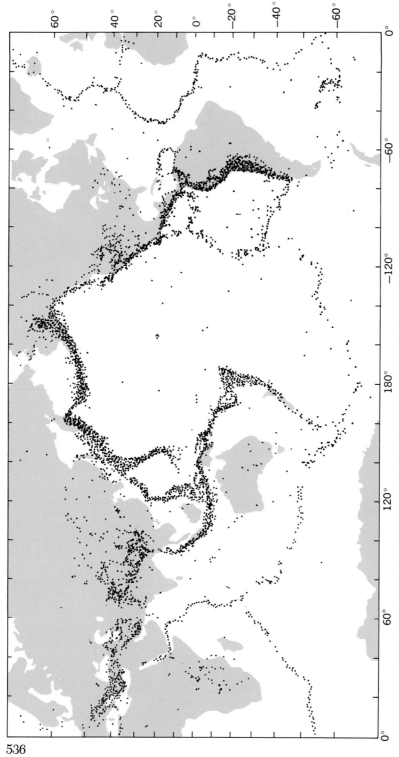

FIG. 9-77 Worldwide distribution of all earthquake epicenters for the period 1961 through 1967 as reported by the U.S. Coast and Geodetic Survey. (After M. Barazangi and J. Dorman, World Seismicity Map of ESSA, Coast and Geodetic Survey Epicenter Data for 1961–1967, Bull. Seismol. Soc. Am., 1969.)

given earthquake generally reveals that such first motions at some stations are compressional and at others are dilatational, and that the distribution of motions of each kind has a definite pattern. Likewise, although they are far less easy to observe, S-wave arrivals have two possible senses of motion, which may be systematically distributed.

In order to understand the reasons for the observed radiation patterns of P-wave first arrivals we must look at the type of displacement most likely to occur at a seismic focus. Seismologists sometimes refer to these kinematic models of an earthquake focus as focal mechanisms; but we must realize that they are not physical mechanisms of the kind described earlier.

DISPLACEMENTS AT A FOCUS   The most commonly used kinematic model of an earthquake focus is based upon the notion of displacement on a fault.[9] The radiation pattern for P-wave first motions calculated from such a displacement is as shown in Figure 9–75, where the "plus" signs indicate compressional first motion and the "minus" signs indicate a dilatational first motion. The pattern is shown in two dimensions (in the plane perpendicular to the fault containing the slip vector) and is quadrantal in form, consisting of two compressional and two dilational lobes

---

[9] A number of sources have been proposed. The one we review here is the "double couple" or "type II" source, which seems to fit most earthquakes.

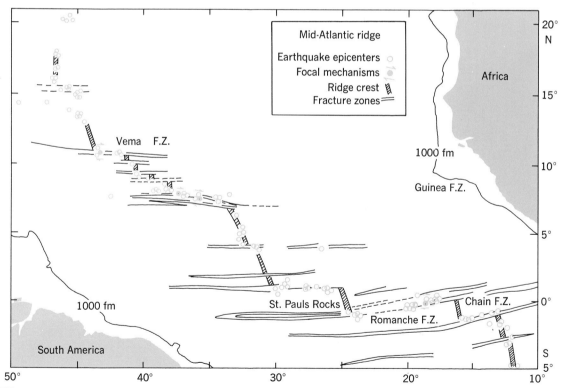

FIG. 9–78 *Location of epicenters (open circles) along the equatorial part of the mid-Atlantic ridge. Focal mechanisms for four earthquakes (solid color dots) on the east–west fracture zones are shown. Strike of inferred fault surface and sense of motion is shown for each by arrows. (After L. R. Sykes, Mechanism of earthquakes and nature of faulting on mid-oceanic ridges, J. Geophys. Res., 1967.)*

separated by orthogonal lines N_1 and N_2. One of these lines lies in the fault plane, the other is perpendicular to it. As the lobes in Figure 9–75 indicate diagrammatically, the amplitude of the first wave is at a maximum along the bisectrices of N_1 and N_2 and falls to zero in the directions of these lines.

In three dimensions the pattern is similar and the lines N_1 and N_2 correspond to two planes (nodal planes), one of which is the fault surface. The line of intersection of these planes (generally called the null direction) lies in the fault perpendicular to the displacement vector.

Let us consider now a very simple hypothetical example of an earthquake on a vertical strike-slip fault. The observed pattern of first motions at stations close enough to the epicenter for the curvature of the earth to be neglected is as shown in Figure 9–76 (a dot corresponds to a station observing a compressional first motion and a circle to a station observing a dilational first motion). By inspection, two lines can be drawn through this pattern, corresponding to the traces of the vertical nodal planes. One of these lines must correspond to the strike of the fault; but because of the high symmetry of the radiation pattern it is impossible to say which. If, as is true of some earthquakes, linear ground breakage is observed along the line FF, as shown diagrammatically in Figure 9–76, then this direction is the most likely strike of the fault. Similarly, even if ground breakage is absent, if geologic mapping reveals the presence of a fault along one of the nodal planes, then it is probable that movement of depth on the fault caused the earthquake.

In practice the technique of "fault-plane solution," as this procedure is called, is much more complex than this simple example suggests. Both the paths of the waves and the shells of the earth through which they travel are curved, and fault planes and slip vectors are not always vertical or horizontal. Corrections can nevertheless be applied for distant stations, and by means of stereographic or similar projections, a three-dimensional picture of the quadrantal distribution of first motions can generally be obtained. This technique, first developed by P. Byerly, has

proved to be a most powerful tool of the seismologist, and, as we shall see below, is now providing compelling evidence in support of the theory of sea-floor spreading.

Although based on a theory of faulting, the kinematic model most generally used in first-motion studies does not apply uniquely to faulting. The same radiation pattern of P-wave first motions, for example, would theoretically be obtained from a sudden distortion corresponding to a pure shearing strain. Thus, sudden permanent yielding other than faulting, or, conceivably, symmetric conjugate faulting of the kind sometimes observed in experiments, would give the same radiation pattern for P as simple faulting. There is theoretical evidence that the S-wave radiation pattern of first motions for simple faulting is distinguishable from that of a more symmetric source. But accurate determination of S-wave first motions is difficult and most seismologists seem content to investigate only the P-wave radiation patterns, interpreting it in terms of the simple fault model, or the pure shear

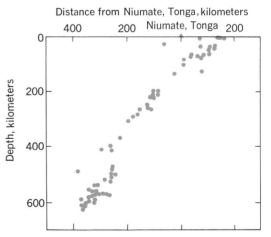

FIG. 9–79 *Vertical section perpendicular to the Tonga arc showing earthquakes in 1965 (from Lamont network) distributed with respect to depth. Some of the epicenters are projected from up to 150 km north and south of the plane of section. (Modified and simplified from B. Isacks, J. Oliver, and L. R. Sykes, Seismology and the new global tectonics, J. Geophys. Res., 1968.)*

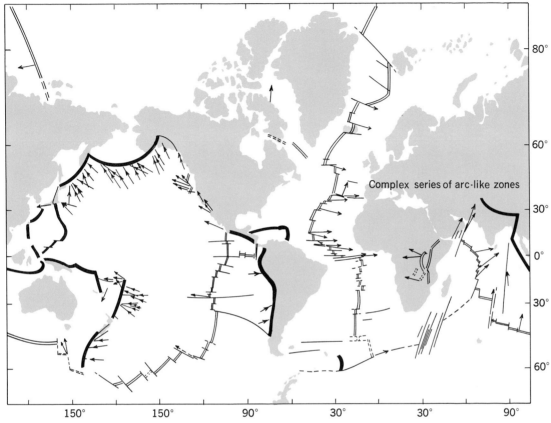

Complex series of arc-like zones

FIG. 9–80 *Map of the major rifts (fine double lines) transform faults (fine single lines) and arcs (thick single lines) of the earth showing the "slip vectors" deduced from focal mechanism studies. The arrows give the direction of motion of the block on which the arrow is drawn relative to the adjoining block. (After B. Isacks, J. Oliver, and L. R. Sykes, Seismology and the new global tectonics, J. Geophys. Res., 1968.)*

model, whichever seems most reasonable. When a more symmetric source is indicated the bisectrices of the nodal planes and the null direction can be taken as principal strain axes or, if isotropy is assumed, principal stress axes.

GLOBAL SEISMICITY

A map of global epicenters (Figure 9–77) reveals that earthquakes are very localized in their distribution. Most occur in a circum-Pacific belt following the west coast of the Americas through the island arcs of the north and west margins in an almost continuous line to New Zealand. A branch extends through the Sunda arc and as a diffuse band through the great Tertiary mountain ranges of Asia and Europe. The remaining frequent earthquakes are extremely localized along the oceanic ridges extending into the great rift system of Africa.

These earthquake belts outline roughly the "rigid" lithospheric plates proposed in the sea-floor-spreading hypothesis (further discussed in Chapter 13), and strong support for the theory has come recently from first-motion studies in different parts of the belts.

Adoping the simple fault model of the focal mechanism and selecting one of the nodal planes as a fault surface, seismologists have determined patterns of displacement along various parts of the worldwide seismic zone. Along the oceanic ridges, earthquakes appear to be of two kinds: along the central "rifts," they correspond to normal faulting; and along the transverse fracture zones, they correspond to strike-slip faulting in the correct sense for the transform-fault theory. For example, Figure 9–78 illustrates part of the mid-Atlantic ridge, showing the location of epicenters and the sense of slip given by first-motion studies of earthquakes on the transverse fractures. All earthquakes on the ridge–fracture systems are shallow-focus, as would be predicted by the spreading theory.

In the most active part of worldwide seismic zone (the circum-Pacific belt) first-motion studies suggest broadly that underthrusting of the continental margins is the main earthquake mechanism. At the margins of the belt of the foci are shallow, but a thin layer of seismic activity (the "Benioff zone") dips down under the continents at about 45° extending locally to 600 or more kilometers (Figure 9–79). The earthquakes in this region are frequent and of large magnitude, and the observed features fit closely the picture of a downgoing slab of lithospheric and crustal material as required by the sea-floor-spreading theory. However, fault-plane solutions suggest that there is a characteristic distribution of mechanism type with depth. Just below the trench, for example, there is evidence of normal faulting. The indicated extension of the upper part of the plate may be connected with the rather sharp bending it must undergo as it turns downward under the continental margin. Below the island arcs the mechanism is consistent with thrusting, and at depth consistent with strong compression in the plane of the slab.

The earthquakes are apparently confined to the upper part of the lithospheric plate. If the seismic activity is in response to either dehydration reactions or plastic yielding of rocks formed at the surface, this is the region in which most seismic activity would be expected.

These data are summarized in Figure 9–80 in terms of the "slip vectors" deduced from fault-plane solutions. The motion of the crust away from the central ridges and towards the island arcs can be clearly seen.

REFERENCES

Few good elementary accounts of the mechanical properties of rocks exist. For a clear introductory account of terminology see *Handbook of Physical Constants,* section II, Strength and Ductility, by **J. Handin** (Geological Society of America, Memoir 97, 1966).

Basic background in theory of stress, strain and general mechanics of solids can be found in such books as *Studies in Large Plastic Flow and Fracture* by **P. W. Bridgman** (Harvard University Press, Cambridge, Mass., 1964); *Theory of Flow and Fracture of Solids,* by **A. Nadai,** vols. I and II (McGraw-Hill, New York, 1950 and 1963); *Elasticity, Fracture and Flow,* by **J. C. Jaeger** (2d ed., Methuen, London, 1962); *Rock Mechanics and the Design of Structures in Rock,* by **L. Obert** and **W. I. Duvall** (Wiley, New York, 1967); *Fundamentals of Rock Mechanics,* by **J. C. Jaeger** and **N. G. W. Cook** (Methuen, London, 1969); and *Mechanics of Incremental Deformations,* by **M. A. Biot** (Wiley, New York, 1965).

Faulting and jointing are considered in the classic *Dynamics of Faulting* by **E. M. Anderson** (2d ed., Oliver & Boyd, London, 1951) and in the more recent *Fault and Joint Development in Brittle and Semi-Brittle Rock,* by **N. J. Price,** (Pergamon, New York, 1966); see also "Stress distribution and faulting," by **W. Hafner** (*Geol. Soc. Am. Bull.,* vol. 62, page 379, 1961). For a discussion of overthrust faulting, see companion papers by **M. K. Hubbert** and **W. W. Rubey,** (*Geol. Soc. Am. Bull.*) vol. 70, p. 115, 1959).

Folding and Fracturing of Rocks by **J. Ramsay** (McGraw-Hill, New York, 1967) is an excellent summary both of classic notions of stress and strain and of the folding of rocks. Some of the same ground and an introduction to the fabrics of tectonites is to be found in *Structural Analysis of Metamorphic Tectonites* by **F. J. Turner** and **L. E. Weiss,** (McGraw-Hill, New York, 1963). A fine collection of papers dealing with problems of rock deformation and seismicity is *Rock Deformation,* **D. Griggs** and **J. Handin,** editors (Geological Society of America, Memoir 79, 1960).

For an elementary introduction to earthquake focal mechanisms see "Earthquake source mechanisms," by **H. Benioff,** (*Science,* vol. 143, page 1399, 1964). Application of first motion studies to worldwide seismicity is treated in "Seismology and the new global tectonics," by **B. Isacks, J. Oliver** and **L. R. Sykes** (*J. Geophys. Res.,* vol. 73, page 5855, 1968).

Recent experimental studies of the important role of gravity in deformation of the earth are described in *Gravity, Deformation and the Earth's Crust* by **H. Ramberg** (Academic Press, New York, 1967).

10
METAMORPHISM

Metamorphic rocks are mineralogically transformed igneous or sedimentary rocks, and the transformation process is called *metamorphism*. As we shall see, there is much evidence that metamorphism is a response to changing physical conditions—and occasionally chemical conditions as well—to which rocks are subjected. The principal physical conditions are temperature and stress, which includes, but is not limited to, hydrostatic pressure.

Broadly speaking, rocks form initially in two clearly defined environments. Sediments are deposited, and most subsequently become lithified, under surface conditions of low pressure and temperature. Igneous rocks crystallize from silicate melts at high temperatures over a much wider range of pressure—low in the volcanic, high in the plutonic, environment. Between these two sets of conditions there exists, within the crust, a broad range of temperature and pressure; and it is to this range that we assign the collective phenomena of metamorphism.

The effects of metamorphism are widespread. A high proportion of all rocks exposed at the earth's surface or known to occur beneath a sedimentary cover only a few kilometers thick, at least throughout the continents, is indeed metamorphic. The bulk of the crust, and some parts of

the mantle[1], may consist of metamorphic rocks. Now most metamorphic rocks, largely as a result of recrystallization and flow in the solid state under nonhydrostatic stress, are mineralogically and structurally anisotropic. This anisotropy in the deep crust and mantle must have significant consequences with respect to heat flow, seismic data, and comparable geophysical phenomena.

Direct Evidence of Metamorphism

Regionally developed in eroded mountain roots and continental shields, or locally bordering igneous intrusions, we see rocks that were once igneous and sedimentary, but whose mineralogical and structural character is now very different from that of the parent material. Without doubt these are metamorphic rocks. On a large scale

---

[1] A problem in semantics is involved here. Any igneous rock that cools slowly enough may be considered metamorphic to the extent that it has been affected by postsolidification processes of unmixing, ordering, and so forth. It is difficult to imagine how the mantle, or parts of it, could have escaped total or partial recrystallization since the time of its formation. The partially metamorphic character of slowly cooled bodies of plutonic rock may partly explain why some geologists have questioned the igneous nature of granite.

542

each metamorphic formation or bed commonly retains its chemical and stratigraphic identity. Thus within a terrane of coarsely crystalline metamorphic rocks in central Ceylon, interlayered with rocks of almost granitic aspect, thick formations of what once were sandstone and limestone preserve their continuity and mutual stratigraphic relation for tens of kilometers. The sandstone has been converted to a coarsely crystalline quartz aggregate (quartzite), the limestone to crystalline calcite rock (marble). Again in the neighborhood of the Boulder batholith, Montana, limestone and dolomite formations have recrystallized and been converted to calcium–magnesium–silicate rocks within a few hundred meters of the contact. But even here the identity of each metamorphic formation has been preserved and each can be mapped as a separate unit.

On a smaller scale, even in completely recrystallized rocks, one can see inherited details of premetamorphic structures. Volcanic structures (filled vesicles, even pillow structures) survive in rocks whose mineralogical character now reflects metamorphic crystallization at relatively low temperatures. Conversely, metamorphosed sediments, still retaining recognizable inherited bedding, may enclose fossils that have become replaced by high-temperature silicates such as wollastonite ($CaSiO_3$).

Collective experience drawn from hundreds of such cases permits the geologist to recognize certain minerals and mineral assemblages as metamorphic, even where direct evidence of the kind we have been discussing is absent. It has become clear that the bulk of metamorphic rocks can be assigned a previous history that is either igneous or sedimentary. And this speaks for the profound mobility of the earth's crust.

Limits and Types of Metamorphism

The range of metamorphism is between the cold sedimentary environment and the hot environment in which magma is generated by rock fusion. There is obviously an overlap with low-temperature processes, sometimes called diagenetic, connected with compaction of buried sediments. At the other extreme, metamorphism overlaps conditions under which the more fusible minerals begin to melt in the presence of water. The ultimate product may be a mixed rock (migmatite), in which a truly metamorphic component is streaked and veined with once molten material of a more or less granitic character. Metamorphism occurs in essentially solid systems, with little or no contribution from silicate-rich liquids (melts). We shall see, however, that a gas phase (H_2O-CO_2) may play an essential role, even though present, at any moment, in no more than trivial volumes.

Most exposed metamorphic rocks are of crustal origin. So, while bearing in mind the extension of metamorphism to depths far below the crust, we shall treat it essentially as a crustal phenomenon. This places limits on the physical conditions of metamorphism responsible for the variety of familiar metamorphic rocks. Thermal gradients in the crust are highly variable; but, on any gradient, rocks begin to melt at 1000°C or somewhat lower temperatures. This then is an approximate upper temperature limit. Locally, the crust is as much as 70 km thick. The upper pressure limit, under such a rock column, can be taken as 20 kb. Relation of pressure to temperature at any particular site of metamorphism depends on the local thermal gradient, or on perturbations caused by local igneous activity. Strain effects are common in metamorphic rocks and express a response to nonhydrostatic stress. But little can be said about the magnitude of such stresses, except that, other things being equal, higher values can probably be sustained for long periods in cold than in hot rocks. Development of a gas phase, as in a dehydration reaction, notably reduces the resistance of the rock to failure by shear and correspondingly lowers the upper limit of sustained nonhydrostatic stress.

Temperature–pressure gradients are related to specific crustal environments. Metamorphic gradients, too, can be recognized where successive mineralogical and structural changes can be traced from a nonmetamorphic to a fully metamorphosed rock. We speak in such cases of increase in degree or *grade* of metamorphism. Corresponding to several general kinds of crustal environment and temperature–pressure situations, it has been found useful to recognize several general types of metamorphism.

Contact metamorphism refers to changes induced in rocks in the vicinity of contacts with intrusive bodies of igneous rocks. With increasing proximity to the contact, metamorphism is increasingly obvious; the grade of metamorphism rises. The zone of metamorphism is termed a *contact aureole*.

Regional metamorphism is effective over large areas (perhaps thousands of square kilometers). The name has no causal implication. The metamorphic terrane may be cut by granitic bodies emplaced as some stage of metamorphic history. But there is no simple relation between metamorphic grade and proximity to contacts. Possible relations between regional metamorphism, regional deformation, and granite intrusion are controversial topics discussed later in this chapter.

Burial metamorphism is a term covering progressive metamorphic responses that can be correlated on geologic evidence with stratigraphic depth in a filled geosyncline. It is the simplest kind of regional metamorphism.

Where regional metamorphism has been accompanied by local emplacement of granitic bodies it may be impossible to draw a sharp line between regional and contact effects. It is even possible that the granites themselves represent the culminating event when metamorphic temperatures have locally transgressed the field of rock fusion. The clearest and best-documented accounts of contact metamorphism, moreover, refer to effects imposed upon regionally metamorphosed rocks in the aureoles of subsequently intruded post-tectonic granitic plutons.

Finally, we note that there are kinds of metamorphism, usually localized, that fall into neither the contact nor the regional category. Spectacular response of rock fragments immersed in hot magmas, especially basaltic lavas, to very high temperature at low pressure has been called *pyrometamorphism*. The term *dislocation metamorphism* may be applied to effects localized in proved zones of intense internal deformation.

Metamorphic Rocks

CHEMISTRY

The character of a metamorphic rock is partly inherited from the parent rock, and partly imprinted in response to an imposed environment. During transformation of shale to mica schist (a metamorphic rock), much of the chemical nature of the shale is still preserved. Any change in bulk composition reflects the extent of chemical exchange between the rock and its surroundings. Involved in the process are diffusion of individual components—especially along grain boundaries and in static aqueous pore fluids—and also diffusion of the fluid phase itself under local pressure gradients. The extent of the exchange depends on chemical potentials, rock permeability, and scale.

On a microscopic scale, chemical changes effected at a given site may be profound. Common in high-grade metamorphic rocks are crystals of almandine garnet, $(Fe, Mg, Mn)_3Al_2Si_3O_{12}$, a centimeter or two in diameter. Each such crystal has replaced a fine-grained crystalline aggregate perhaps muscovite–biotite–chlorite–quartz, formerly occupying the same domain. There must have been extensive reciprocal chemical exchange between the domain of any garnet crystal and its surroundings. On a somewhat larger scale there is a widespread tendency for simple mineral assemblages to become segregated in laminar or lenticular domains a millimeter or more in thickness. These usually follow the trend of preexisting or metamorphically formed planar structures—bedding and foliation. Examples are alternating quartz–albite and epidote–chlorite–muscovite laminae in schists formed from sheared but initially homogeneous graywacke. The precise nature of the segregation process is imperfectly understood. It is generally called *metamorphic differentiation.*

On a still larger scale—for example, in an outcrop or a hand specimen—the gross chemical composition of many metamorphic rocks is essentially unchanged except with respect to more volatile components such as water and carbon dioxide. The laminated mica schist, dotted with large garnets, still retains the overall composition of somewhat dehydrated shale. Amphibolites consisting of hornblende–andesine–epidote–sphene unmistakably are chemically equivalent to hydrated basalt or diabase. There may be detectable differences with respect to minor elements. Thus concentrations of Th and U in regionally metamorphosed rocks may decrease significantly with increasing grade of metamorphism. On the other hand, the minor-element patterns of interbedded metamorphic rocks, derived from graywacke and from basalt, in southern New Zealand have survived metamorphism without significant change. The same situation has been convincingly demonstrated in a study of amphibolites in the Precambrian basement of the Brazilian shield not far from the city of São Paulo. As in New Zealand, the metamorphic rocks have inherited from their basaltic parents a minor-element pattern characterized by such distinctive features as large amounts of chromium, nickel, cobalt, and vanadium. The gross compositions of most of the Brazilian rocks, expressed in terms of standard major oxides, show no appreciable departure from those of approximately saturated tholeiitic basalts.

It is somewhat surprising that metamorphism on this scale so commonly approximates an isochemical model, as if in a system closed to all except volatile components (water, carbon dioxide). Major compositional changes are not uncommon but tend to be local. Well known in this connection is replacement of calcite–dolomite rocks by *skarns* composed of silicates of calcium, magnesium and iron, at immediate contacts with intrusive igneous bodies. Clearly there must have been extensive chemical exchange, in such cases, between magma and limestone. Replacement of one mineral or assemblage by another of different chemical composition, without intervention of melting, is called *metasomatism*. Magmatic gases with unusually high concentrations of elements such as tin, tungsten, copper, or iron may give rise to valuable metasomatic ore bodies in contact aureoles, especially where skarns develop at limestone–granite contacts.

In one subtle respect metamorphism especially on a regional scale, commonly departs from the isochemical model. Notable changes in isotopic composition of oxygen in a whole-rock sample seem to be general and to follow consistent patterns. Such changes imply free exchange between the rock and some external oxygen reservoir such as a continuously replenished supply of water diffusing through the recrystallizing rock from an external source. Oxygen-isotope analysis of metamorphic minerals and rocks clearly has considerable potential for evaluating the sources and systems of circulation of water during a metamorphic cycle, and for estimating temperatures at which metamorphic equilibria were finally attained.

STRUCTURE

The structure of a metamorphic rock reflects a peculiar condition of metamorphism: growth and mutual interference of crystals competing for space in an essentially solid medium. The size of a crystal, the nature of its external surfaces, and the perfection of their development are governed by complex conditions connected with nucleation, diffusion of ions, and surface energy of each of its faces with respect to the adjoining medium. The environment is notably different from that of a crystal growing freely in a yielding, internally disordered, igneous melt where nonhydrostatic stress is essentially absent. So in metamorphic rocks certain minerals tend to exert their own outlines against those of their neighbors; this tendency has no relation to order of growth in time. Many orthosilicates have this property. Typical examples are garnet, staurolite, kyanite, andalusite, and epidote. There is a tendency too, though not universal, for these same minerals to nucleate sparsely and to grow to above-average dimensions as porphyroblasts, perhaps a centimeter or more in diameter. By contrast, silicates with sheet and band structures develop only the simplest crystal faces, notably {001} in micas, {110} in amphiboles. Open-structured framework silicates, notably quartz and feldspars, as well as most carbonates, seldom show rational grain boundaries.

Characteristic of many metamorphic rocks are flow structures resulting from slow yielding to long-sustained tectonic stresses. Old structures, such as bedding, become folded on all scales. New planar structures develop in response to localized shear or more penetrative flow—slaty cleavage, schistosity, and foliation. In such rocks preferred orientation of mineral crystals is widely prevalent.

NOMENCLATURE AND CLASSIFICATION

For description and general discussion of metamorphism the terminology of metamorphic rocks need not be complex. Nomenclature and general classifications in common use employ some combination of readily recognizable structural (textural), mineralogical and chemical criteria.

Structurally defined rock types include the following:

Slate: a fine-grained, mineralogically homogeneous micaceous rock, with a single pervasive slaty cleavage not related to bedding.

Schist: coarser-grained, typically laminated rock, with one or more sets of surfaces (foliation or schistosity); commonly lineated parallel to axes of microfolds in a principal surface. *Phyllite* is intermediate between slate and schist.

Gneiss: coarse-grained rock rich in feldspar, with crude foliation defined by undulating subparallel streaks of mica or hornblende.

Granulite: plane-foliated laminated rock lacking micaceous minerals; quartzofeldspathic and feldspar–pyroxene–garnet assemblages of high metamorphic grade are typical.

Hornfels: fine-grained rock, completely lacking cleavage or schistosity, and consisting of a tight aggregate of random-oriented equant grains; porphyroblasts of some minerals (andalusite, cordierite, biotite) may be present.

These and other rock names may be qualified by adjectives referring to chemical or mineralogical composition. We speak, for example, of *pelitic* hornfels (having an aluminous composition inherited from parent shale) or *magnesian* schists (formed from serpentinite). Pelitic rocks may be further designated by such names as andalusite–cordierite hornfels or almandine–kyanite–mica schist.

Also in general use are a few terms based simply on mineralogy:

Marble: composed principally of recrystallized calcite or dolomite.

Quartzite: composed mainly of recrystallized quartz.

Amphibolite: hornblende-plagioclase rock.

Soapstone: a magnesian rock composed mainly of talc, with tremolite, chlorite or carbonates as possible less abundant ingredients.

Skarn or tactite: Ca-Mg-silicate rock formed at contacts between igneous plutons (especially granites) and limestone or dolomite.

Finally, it is convenient in certain contexts to group metamorphic rocks according to origin. Thus all metamorphosed andesites can be termed *metaandesites*. Names such as *metasediment, metachert, metabasalt* have similar connotations.

Metamorphic Record of Changing Conditions in the Crust

METHODS OF APPROACH

We have seen that locked in the structures of minerals are fragments of information bearing on their crystallization and subsequent history. It is much the same with metamorphic rocks. Here it is the assemblages of associated minerals that record something of the conditions of the metamorphic process. Because so much of the crust consists of metamorphic rocks, to reconstruct the history of large segments and even that of the crust as a whole, we must learn to read the physical record of metamorphic rocks. This involves a multiple approach along several independent lines:

1. Geological mapping gives information as to present distribution of rock types, their structure, and age relations. In favorable situations some limits may be set on depth of burial. From large-scale patterns of strain in general and fold-

ing in particular something may be inferred regarding possible participation of stress-induced flow in metamorphism.

2. Mineralogical studies not only identify the principal metamorphic mineral assemblages, but also reveal successive steps in mineralogical and chemical evolution of rocks as they undergo progressive metamorphism.

3. Chemical analysis of rocks and their component minerals, especially with respect to isotopic composition of certain elements (Sr, Rb, O, and others), gives further information as to chemical evolution and permits us to evaluate the time factor in the succession of events that collectively constitute a metamorphic cycle.

4. The influence of physical variables on metamorphic reactions may be clarified through experimental study of equilibria and reaction rates in systems of appropriate mineral phases. From such data a metamorphic gradient established

from information gathered under 1 and 2 can be translated into a gradient of temperature and pressure in place and in time.

To interpret correctly the possible causes of an observed metamorphic reaction and to reduce the number of necessary experiments, as well as to detect inherent imperfections in the experimental method and underlying assumptions, we must make some general use of simple thermodynamics.

PRELIMINARY THERMODYNAMIC CONSIDERATIONS

Consider progressive metamorphism in response to simultaneously increasing temperature and pressure. This is a common geological situation; for with increase in depth both variables rise. In a particular situation the gradient dT/dP depends on local conditions. Metamorphic transformations fall into a few simple types:

A. Solid $\rightarrow$ Solid + Gas*

$Mg(OH)_2$ brucite	$\rightarrow$	MgO periclase	+	H_2O gas
$MgCO_3$ magnesite	$\rightarrow$	MgO periclase	+	CO_2 gas
$3Fe_2O_3$ hematite	$\rightarrow$	$2Fe_3O_4$ magnetite	+	$\frac{1}{2}O_2$ gas
FeS_2 pyrite	$\rightarrow$	FeS troilite	+	S gas

Both ΔS and ΔV positive, large at low pressures; at high pressures ΔV approaches zero

* At constant pressure, all such reactions will tend to become spontaneous as temperature rises. To understand them we need equilibrium vapor-pressure curves, or curves of univariant equilibrium and information concerning compositions of fluid phases.

B. Solid $\rightarrow$ Solid

(1) Polymorphic transitions:
$$Al_2SiO_5$$
kyanite $\rightarrow$ sillimanite

ΔS and ΔV usually same sign (here positive)

(2) Order $\rightarrow$ disorder transitions:
$$KAlSi_3O_8$$
ordered feldspar $\rightarrow$ disordered feldspar

Both ΔS and ΔV positive; ΔV small

(3) Mixing reactions:
$KAlSi_3O_8$ + $NaAlSi_3O_8$ $\rightarrow$ alkali feldspar
orthoclase   albite   solid solution

Both ΔS and ΔV positive; ΔV small

(4) Reactions between solids:
$NaAlSi_3O_8$ $\rightarrow$ $NaAlSi_2O_6$ + SiO_2
albite   jadeite   quartz

Both ΔS and ΔV large, same sign (here negative)

Most metamorphic reactions in rocks are more complex than these simple illustrations; whatever type they belong to, they usually involve solid or fluid solutions. Nevertheless, enough is known of relative changes in volume and entropy, as illustrated above, to indicate the trend of reaction with respect to variation in temperature and pressure. Since ΔS and ΔV commonly have the same sign, pressure and temperature have opposite effects in displacing equilibrium. For example, the equilibrium

$$\underset{\text{calcite}}{CaCO_3} + \underset{\text{quartz}}{SiO_2} \rightarrow \underset{\text{wollastonite}}{CaSiO_3} + CO_2$$

is displaced from left to right either by increasing temperature at constant pressure, or by decreasing pressure at constant temperature. Most geologists think of the formation of wollastonite during metamorphism of limestone in the first of these contexts. So there is a tendency to equate metamorphic grade with temperature. In discussing metamorphic reactions, it is better to equate increase in grade with entropy increase; for this takes into account the possibility that increasing grade can also be correlated in some situations with a drop in pressure at constant or even decreasing temperature.

Inspection of ΔS and ΔV of a possible metamorphic transformation also brings out its relative sensitivity to changes in the temperature and pressure variables. Clearly transformation of albite to jadeite–quartz will be sensitive to both decrease in temperature and increase in pressure. Disordering of feldspar, on the other hand, is highly sensitive to temperature increase but scarcely affected by pressure. In all cases variation of free energy of the solid phases with pressure and temperature is well understood. Much less is known of the possible influence of nonhydrostatic stress. Departures from the hydrostatic condition are generally assumed to be small and so are ignored in most discussions of metamorphic equilibria. Time and experiment will show whether this attitude is always justified.

Since metamorphic reactions commonly combine all the simple types discussed above, they may be subject to a correspondingly increased number of partially independent variables: P, P_{stress}, T, P_{H_2O}, P_{CO_2}, P_S, P_{O_2}, and others; where P_{H_2O}, P_{CO_2}, $\cdots$ are respective partial pressures of H_2O, CO_2, $\cdots$ in the gas phase. Not all will be critical for every equilibrium. Solid-solid equilibria depend only on the first three variables. However, the rates of such reactions can be greatly accelerated by the presence of a fluid phase, and so by P_{H_2O} as distinct from P. Although the possibility of reaction is described entirely by the controlling variables, what actually happens is determined by reaction rates. These are influenced not only by such variables as P_{H_2O}—which may or may not affect ΔG—but by accelerating factors such as reduction of grain size and renewal of grain contacts during deformation induced by nonhydrostatic stress. All such factors must be considered when we attempt to correlate the observed metamorphic response of a rock with specific conditions of temperature and pressure. These may have been imposed over any interval or intervals of time during a long history of environmental change, starting in the environment of origin and finishing in that of the present outcrop (atmospheric temperature and pressure).

EVIDENCE FROM OXYGEN ISOTOPES

WHOLE-ROCK COMPOSITIONS   The isotopic composition of oxygen seems to be a rather constant and distinctive feature of every major class of rock. In igneous rocks it is determined by the source of the primary magma and by isotopic fractionation during fractional crystallization. The oxygen of sedimentary rocks has a composition that reflects a state of equilibrium between weathering products such as clays or precipitates such as calcite and meteoric or seawater. The composition is expressed, in parts per mil, as

$$\delta_{O^{18}/O^{16}} = \left(\frac{O^{18}/O^{16} \text{ in rock}}{O^{18}/O^{16} \text{ in standard}} - 1 \right) 1000$$

The standard is seawater, for which $\delta_{O^{18}/O^{16}} = 0$.

Some typical ranges of $\delta_{O^{18}/O^{16}}$ for common rocks as determined by Epstein, Taylor, and associates are as follows:

peridotites $+5$ to $+6$
gabbros $+6$ to $+7$
granodiorites and granites $+8$ to $+10$
granite pegmatites $+7$ to $+14$
sandstones $+11$ to $+16$
shales $+14$ to $+19$
limestones $+20$ to $+30$

Meteoric water has a range of -10 to -4; volcanic waters sampled from fumaroles on recently active volcanoes reflect their primary origin ($\delta_{O^{18}/O^{16}} + 6.8$, Paricutin volcano, Mexico).

The isotopic composition of oxygen in metamorphic rocks gives a good indication of the extent to which externally supplied water may have affected the original composition inherited from the parent sedimentary or igneous rock. Amphibolites formed by regional metamorphism of basalt have significantly higher O^{18} ($\delta_{O^{18}/O^{16}} = 7$–$13$) than most basalts ($6$–$7$). Pelitic schists tend to give values (12–18) somewhat lower than shales (14–19). What seems to be implied is isotopic exchange with an external reservoir of water whose composition lies within some intermediate range, perhaps 10–12. This could be water rising from crystallizing granitic magmas in the deep crust. Somewhat surprisingly, values of $\delta_{O^{18}/O^{16}}$ in pelitic hornfels of a number of contact aureoles have been found to remain very much the same as in parent mudstones, except within a meter or so of plutonic contacts.

FRACTIONATION OF ISOTOPES BETWEEN COEXISTING PHASES   The fractionation of O^{18} and O^{16} between two coexisting phases A and B is usually described in terms of the following parameters:

$$R^A = O^{18}/O^{16} \text{ in phase } A$$
α is the fractionation factor R^A/R^B

$$\delta^A = 1000 \left(\frac{R^A}{R^{\text{standard}}} - 1 \right)$$

Partition of isotopes between A and B is usually expressed as $1000 \ln \alpha$, which is approximately equal to $\delta^A - \delta^B$. This varies significantly wih temperature—especially in the range of $100°C$ to $500°C$; but it is virtually insensitive to pressure. Experimental data over the range of metamorphic temperatures are available for quartz–water, muscovite–water and calcite–water. So given δ^{quartz} and $\delta^{\text{muscovite}}$ for any rock we can calculate both the temperature at which isotopic equilibrium was reached and the isotopic composition of coexisting water. Temperatures so calculated are so consistent with increasing grade as indicated by isograds that it is assumed that the isotopic compositions of coexisting phases were "frozen in" when metamorphic crystallization ceased and the system became impervious to water.

Contact Metamorphism

THE CONTACT AUREOLE

The ideal model of a contact aureole is simple enough—a zone of metamorphic rock bordering the contact of an intrusive igneous body and passing outward into unaffected rocks (Figure 10–1). As seen in the field, most aureoles are less regular than the model. Uncertainty attends the subsurface attitude of the contact, so there is likely to be some doubt as to the true width of the aureole. A wide outcrop of metamorphic rock may perhaps reflect a gently dipping, underlying intrusive contact. Moreover, even the true width usually varies from one formation to another.

Most classic accounts of contact metamorphism refer to effects observed where previously folded rocks are cut by forcefully intruded plutons of granodioritic or quartz–dioritic composition. So there is a tendency for individual beds and formations in the surrounding rocks to be

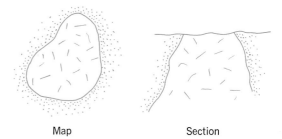

Map   Section

FIG. 10–1 Map and vertical section of an ideal contact aureole (diagrammatic).

drawn out and wrapped round the intrusive contact. A radial outward traverse therefore is likely to cut across the stratigraphic or structural trend of the enclosing rocks and thus encounter abrupt compositional changes from one bed to another. In such a situation the observed sequence of mineralogical changes effected by progressive metamorphism of a given rock type (for example, pelitic sediment) will be incomplete or obscured.

There are complications, too, that are inherent in the large scale of the metamorphic phenomenon. The nature of an aureole related to a large pluton can be appreciated in full only in a region of high topographic relief and continuous rock exposures.

AUREOLE OF INYO BATHOLITH, DEEP SPRING VALLEY, CALIFORNIA

In the White and Inyo Mountains, eastern California, a great thickness of late Precambrian sediments is cut by a composite "granodioritic" batholith whose exposed outcrop is 130 km long and 1500 km² in area. This is the Inyo batholith, much of it radiometrically dated as earlier Jurassic, as also are the easterly plutons of the Sierra

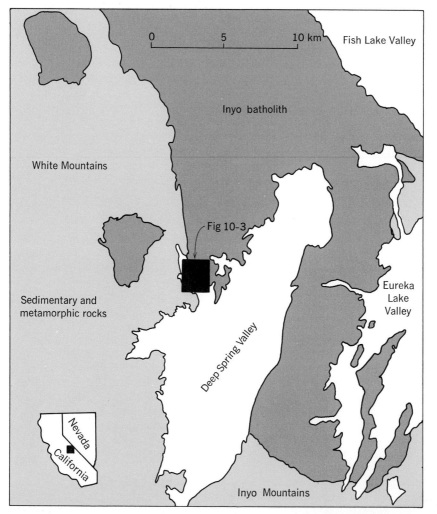

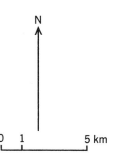

FIG. 10–2 Part of the Inyo batholith, east-central California. (Simplified from E. H. McKee and D. B. Nash, Geol. Soc. Am. Bull., vol. 78, p. 671, 1967.) Deep color, granitic rocks; light color, metasediments.

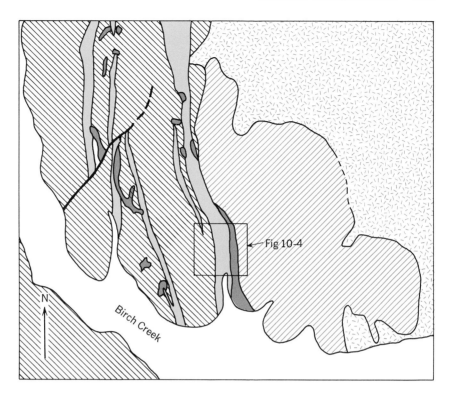

FIG. 10–3 Contact between two granodiorite plutons of the Inyo batholith and Lower Cambrian metasediments, Birch Creek, Deep Spring Valley, California. (After E. H. McKee and D. B. Nash, Geol. Soc. Am. Bull., vol. 78, p. 674, 1967.)

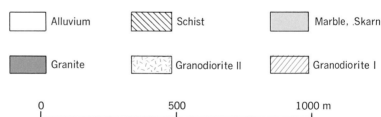

Nevada batholith (page 304) some 50 km to the west. The greater part of the sedimentary pile consists of indurated but unmetamorphosed sandstones, limestones, and dolomites. Within 2 or 3 km of the intrusive contact they show conspicuous evidence of metamorphism. Topographic relief over much of the region is 2 km or more; and the desert climate favors continuous rock exposure over large areas.

Figure 10–2 shows the gross geological features of a part of the western margin of the batholith along the margins of a desert basin known as Deep Spring Valley. In the canyon of Birch Creek on the northwest side of the basin, the aureole is displayed in a series of steeply dipping lower Cambrian limestones and sandstones, now converted to marble, schist, and hornfels (Figures 10–3, 10–4). These are wrapped parallel to the intrusive contact, which also dips outward (westward) at 60°–85°. Within 100 meters of the contact the sedimentary rocks are dominantly calcareous. Otherwise the rocks of the aureole are quartzose and micaceous derivatives of sandstone and less abundant shale.

Within the area of Figure 10–2 the Inyo batholith consists of several independent plutons.

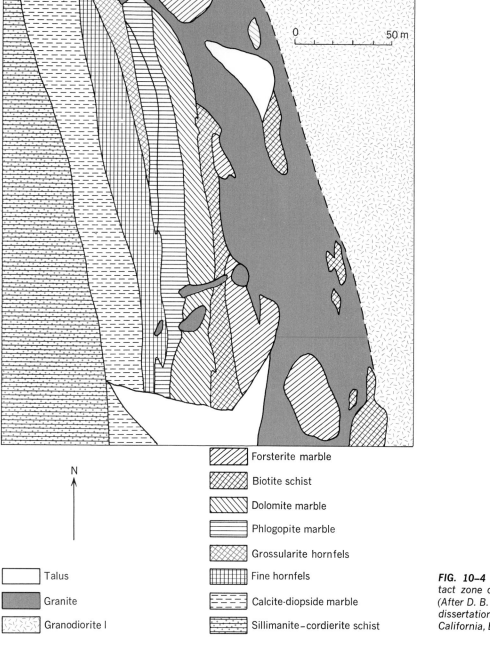

N

Talus

Granite

Granodiorite I

Forsterite marble

Biotite schist

Dolomite marble

Phlogopite marble

Grossularite hornfels

Fine hornfels

Calcite-diopside marble

Sillimanite-cordierite schist

FIG. 10–4 *Detail of contact zone of Figure 10–3. (After D. B. Nash, Master's dissertation, University of California, Berkeley, 1962.)*

The largest of these—the one to which the contact aureole is related—is granodioritic in composition (Granodiorite II, Figure 10–3). But there are smaller plutons, both older (Granodiorite I) and younger (Granite).

EFFECTS OF METAMORPHISM   Metamorphic effects along an inward traverse (eastward from the western edge of Figure 10–2) are as follows:

1. Some 5 or 6 km from the granodiorite contact, pelitic rocks become spotted with vaguely defined, newly crystallized aggregates of chlorite and white mica.

2. In similar rocks at 3 km there are traces of newly formed biotite. At distances of 2 km or less from the contact, brown biotite is conspicuous and is accompanied in more aluminous beds by andalusite.

3. At a little less than a kilometer from the granodiorite outcrop, sedimentary structures, notably bedding, become obscured or obliterated by a planar foliation developed under the deforming influence of the nearby intrusion during its emplacement. Pelitic rocks are biotite–muscovite–andalusite–quartz–feldspar schists (Figure 10–3).

4. Still closer to the contact the mica schists coarsen and become less fissile. From 300 meters inward, sillimanite replaces andalusite. The final high-grade mineral assemblage is now cordierite–sillimanite–biotite–feldspar–quartz, with some undestroyed relics of andalusite. Similar rocks occur as fragments and "islands" 10 or 20 meters long enclosed in the outer part of the intrusion (Figure 10–4).

5. About 50–100 meters from the contact the composition of the invaded rocks abruptly changes. The rocks here are derivatives of limestone and dolomite. There is a wide variety of mineral assemblages reflecting corresponding variation in initial composition:

   (a) Dolomitic limestones with minor siliceous impurity: marbles consisting of calcite-dolomite-forsterite, calcite-diopside, calcite-dolomite, calcite-phlogopite (a magnesian biotite).

   (b) Impure calcareous sediments: calc-silicate hornfelses with diopside–plagio-clase–grossularite, wollastonite–grossularite–diopside.

   (c) More siliceous sediments: hornblende–plagioclase–microcline–epidote–quartz, sometimes with plentiful biotite.

Reaction along the marble–granodiorite contact has produced local zones, some 10 cm wide, of banded Ca-Mg-silicate rock (skarn). A typical inward sequence from dolomitic marble into skarn is calcite–dolomite, calcite–dolomite–forsterite, calcite–serpentine–chlorite, diopside, wollastonite–grossularite–diopside. There has been outward diffusion of (OH), Si, Al, and Mg from the intrusive magma and reciprocal inward transfer of Ca from the marble.

MINERAL ASSEMBLAGES IN RELATION TO ROCK COMPOSITION   Metamorphic rocks of the inner aureole, within 300 meters of the igneous contact at Birch Creek, cover a wide range of chemical composition inherited from their premetamorphic condition. Yet the aureole, whose total exposed bulk in Figure 10–4 is some 10^{10} kg, is composed of only a dozen or so mineral phases:

> quartz, SiO_2
> feldspars   plagioclase, $CaAl_2Si_2O_8$–$NaAlSi_3O_8$
> microcline, $KAlSi_3O_8$
> biotite, $K(Mg, Fe)_3(AlSi_3O_{10})(OH)_2$
> calcite, $CaCO_3$
> dolomite, $CaMg(CO_3)_2$
> wollastonite, $CaSiO_3$
> diopside, $Ca(Mg, Fe)Si_2O_6$
> forsterite, Mg_2SiO_4
> grossularite, $Ca_3(Al, Fe)_2(SiO_4)_3$
> epidote, $Ca_2(Al, Fe)_3Si_3O_{12}(OH)$
> hornblende, $Ca_2(Mg, Fe, Al)_5(Si, Al)_8O_{22}$ $(OH)_2$
> cordierite, $Mg_2Al_4Si_5O_{18}$
> sillimanite, Al_2SiO_5

In a small specimen of any rock the mineral assemblage is simple, consisting of not more than four or five of these phases. Consistent throughout the whole aureole is a predictable relation between the mineral assemblage and the bulk chemical composition of each kind of rock. We shall find that this kind of relation holds good in many other, perhaps in most metamorphic terranes. We shall encounter the same pattern of variation in some other aureoles. But elsewhere again the mineralogical pattern corresponding to the same range of rock composition as at Birch Creek may be entirely different.

This consistent relationship is easy to demonstrate for a group of rocks whose chemical range, as well as individual compositions of all constituent minerals, can be represented by a plot of three chemical variables, such as is shown in Figure 10–5. The variables are molecular percentages of Al_2O_3 (A), CaO (C), and MgO + FeO (F). It is found that quartz and feldspars (plagioclase and/or orthoclase) may occur, although they need not be present, in any mineral assemblage. So Al_2O_3 is corrected in the first place by subtracting an amount equivalent to $(K_2O + Na_2O)$. In phase diagrams such as Figure 10–5, tie lines are drawn between mutually associated minerals. The composition of any rock falls in the triangle that represents its observed mineral composition. Thus a rock with composition X corresponds to the mineral assemblage

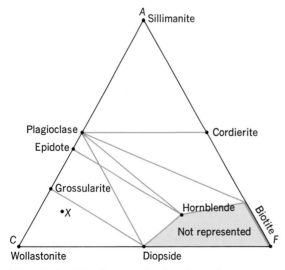

FIG. 10–5 ACF diagram showing three-phase assemblages found in rocks of the Birch Creek contact zone, Inyo aureole, California. Quartz and microline are possible additional members of each assemblage.

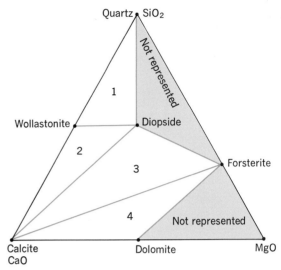

FIG. 10–6 Three-phase assemblages in siliceous dolomitic marbles, Birch Creek contact zone, Inyo aureole, California.

wollastonite–diopside–grossularite found in many calc–silicate hornfelses; some of these contain quartz. It is possible to express composition X in terms of grossularite–wollastonite–hornblende, or alternatively, cordierite–wollastonite–plagioclase. Yet neither assemblage has been found although, individually, hornblende, plagioclase, or cordierite is common enough in other rocks at Birch Creek.

Certain aspects of mineralogical variation in the rocks of Birch Creek cannot be fully nor clearly demonstrated in Figure 10–5 alone. Some ambiguity results from intersection of the diopside–plagioclase and hornblende–epidote tie lines. This is because the additional component Fe_2O_3 plays an essential role in crystallization of epidote. Similarly appearance or absence of biotite depends upon whether K_2O is present or not in excess over the amount that is taken up by feldspar. Again two common phases in the magnesian marbles are dolomite and forsterite; but under conditions governing metamorphism at Birch Creek these are chemically incompatible with silica. They cannot be represented, then, on a phase diagram (Figure 10–5) based on assemblages that may contain free quartz.

Other kinds of phase diagram have been devised to meet these difficulties and to amplify the information conveyed by Figure 10–5. A typical example is Figure 10–6—a simple molecular plot CaO-MgO-SiO₂ for all assemblages derived from dolomitic limestones with silica as the sole additional component. These are (1) wollastonite–diopside–quartz (also represented by the wollastonite–diopside tie in Figure 10–5), (2) calcite-wollastonite–diopside, (3) calcite–diopside–forsterite, and (4) calcite–dolomite–forsterite. It is assumed that all of these could crystallize in the presence of a continuously supplied gas phase, carbon dioxide.

INTRUSION, METAMORPHISM, AND TIME Even in the limited area shown in Figure 10–3, the field evidence indicates three separate episodes of igneous intrusion. These have been confirmed and radiometrically dated by K-A determinations on hornblende and on biotite:

1. Southwest marginal foliated granodiorite (Granodiorite I) along most of the contact, Figure 10–3. Hornblende age, 213 m.y.

2. Granodiorite II (richer in K₂O than the earlier granodiorite), the major intrusive unit in Figure 10–2. Hornblende age, 158 m.y. This is the intrusive episode responsible for the contact aureole. Outside the area of Figure 10–3, biotites from the same pluton have been dated at 162 m.y. and 170 m.y.

3. Minor granite veins cutting both metasediments and granodiorite in the inner aureole. A sheet of this rock 50 meters wide separates the metamorphic rocks from Granodiorite I in Figure 10–4. It pinches out about 300 meters further north. Biotite ages of the granitic dikes are 93–71 m.y. A granitic pluton of the same age is exposed over an area of 5 km², west of Birch Creek in Figure 10–2.

Clearly intrusion of the Inyo batholith was no simple event. The three episodes just mentioned cover a total span of more than 100 million years; and plutons of intermediate age have been mapped nearby, outside Figure 10–2. The aureole and its constituent metamorphic zones trend parallel to the western boundary of the main Granodiorite II pluton along its full extent in Figure 10–2. So metamorphism is correlated with the intrusive event (Granodiorite II) dated at 150–160 m.y. But biotites in contact skarns and in sillimanite schists indicate significantly later dates (143 m.y. and 92 m.y. respectively). The discrepancy has been attributed to loss of argon from biotite reheated during the third intrusive episode.

GENERALIZATIONS

AUREOLE DIMENSIONS Aureoles 2 to 3 km wide are characteristic of granodioritic plutons 10 to 15 km in diameter. There is a rather imperfect correlation between the dimensions of such a pluton and the width of its aureole. Thus the width of the classic Comrie aureole of Scotland, surrounding a diorite pluton 8 km × 1 km in outcrop is only 400 to 500 meters. With certain exceptions the aureoles of basic plutons tend to be narrower than those surrounding intrusions of granodiorite. This may seem paradoxical in view of the relatively high temperatures of basic magmas. In the floor regions of Jurassic diabase sheets —some of them hundreds of meters thick, in Tasmania, in New Jersey, and elsewhere—metamorphic effects in permeable sandstones die out within a few meters from the contact. Finally, the width of a given aureole commonly varies from one rock formation to another. The Comrie aureole is broader in recrystallized volcanic sands than in interbedded slates. Aureoles in calcareous rocks tend to reach their maximum extent in dolomitic members. These variations may well reflect differences in conductivity of wall rocks. The conductivity of most sandstones is 50 to 100 percent higher than that of shale or slate; listed values for dolomite rock are about twice as high as for calcite limestones. Another factor may be relative permeability to outflowing magmatic fluids, for sandstones and dolomites are generally permeable rocks. Again the aureole width may perhaps be reduced where the parent rock (for example, shale) has a high content of combined water.

METAMORPHIC ZONES Contact metamorphism, with respect to its manifestation in space (in the field) has a progressive character. The grade rises from the periphery of the aureole toward the contact. An inward sequence of newly formed mineralogical assemblages, repeatedly seen in pelitic rocks is

> muscovite–chlorite
> biotite–andalusite–muscovite
> biotite–cordierite–sillimanite–microcline
>   (or orthoclase)

Basic volcanic tuffs may show all or part of the sequence

> albite–epidote–chlorite–hornblende
> plagioclase–hornblende
> plagioclase–pyroxenes

Sequences in calcareous members are less regular; but there is a marked preference of tremolite for the outer zones and of wollastonite, diopside, and forsterite for the inner aureole. Within each zone there is a strong correlation between mineralogical and chemical composition of associated rock types.

COMPOSITIONAL CHANGES   Pelitic, quartzose, and basic volcanic rocks tend to retain their initial chemical composition, modified only by change in water content, across the full width of the aureole. Conversion of calcite and dolomite of impure limestones to various silicates involves notable loss of carbon dioxide. At immediate plutonic contacts, calcareous rocks commonly have been locally replaced by Ca-Mg silicates, iron oxides, and even sulfides. Rocks of this kind (skarn or tactite) testify to free exchange of ions between chemically sensitive wall rocks and outward-diffusing late magmatic gases. In the same way boron introduced into pelitic rocks becomes fixed as tourmaline. Late metasomatic effects of this kind show great variety.

Many geologists—the present writers among them—have thought that outward flow of water from crystallizing granitic magma must play a significant role in contact metamorphism. Oxygen-isotope studies on several American aureoles do not support this view—at least with regard to lateral outward flow through pelitic rocks. Pelitic hornfelses and schists, except within a meter or so of the contact, retain an isotopic composition characteristic of shales ($\delta O_{18}/O_{16} = 15$–16 per mil). Compositions typical of granodioritic rocks ($\delta O_{18}/O_{16} < 10$ per mil) prevail throughout most of the plutons examined; but within 50 or 100 meters of the contact the oxygen of granitic minerals may show significant enrichment in O^{18}. This suggests *inward* flow of pore waters from the sedimentary envelope into the magma or hot granite of the border zone. There is, however, evidence of upward flow of water from the intrusive body into overlying rocks.

Marbles in the inner part of the Birch Creek sector of the Inyo aureole (Figure 10–4) show significant isotopic fractionation correlated with expulsion of CO_2: There is distinct depletion of the heavier isotopes—O^{18} relative to O^{16}, and C^{13} relative to C^{12}.

RETROGRESSIVE CHANGES   Progressive metamorphism of pelitic and calcareous sediments involves progressive expulsion of water and carbon dioxide. There is a widespread tendency for reactions in the opposite sense in the final stages of metamorphism. Such effects are termed *retrogressive*. The sense of reaction here is from a high- to a lower-grade mineral assemblage. Andalusite and cordierite crystals of the progressive stage tend to become replaced wholly or in part by aggregates of fine-grained white mica and chlorite. Calcite may be seen crystallizing along cleavage planes of wollastonite prisms; or diopside may become fringed with late tremolite. Here, as also in regional metamorphism, the presence of retrogressive effects raises the familiar question: In a geological event (contact metamorphism) whose imprint is seen in the dimensions of space, what may have been the role of time?

METAMORPHIC GRADIENTS   Successive mineral assemblages seen in rocks of a given composition, along a radial traverse across an aureole imply the previous existence of some gradient in physical conditions. The most obvious possibility is a thermal gradient, with temperature rising toward the contact.

Thermal gradients at intrusive contacts have been explored theoretically by considering simple models based on known thermal properties (conductivity, diffusivity, heat capacity, and so on) of common intrusive and sedimentary rocks. Jaeger has developed a series of models, in one of which a tabular sheet of magma, on the point of crystallization, is injected instantaneously into rocks of uniform thermal properties already at some given initial temperature. Reasonable values are assigned to the temperature range and latent heat of magmatic crystallization. Other models take into account modifying conditions such as multiple intrusion, movement of pore water, thermal effects of metamorphic reactions, and so on. Doubtless even these models are simpler than natural situations. Some geologically significant inferences drawn from Jaeger's models are as follows:

1. Two principal factors determine the dimensions and thermal history of an aureole: the thickness (diameter) of the intrusive pluton, and the maximum temperature developed in the immediate contact zone of the aureole at the moment of igneous intrusion.

2. This maximum contact temperature is significantly lower than that of the magma. It depends on the respective initial temperatures and the thermal properties of both magma and country rock. Some typical values (assuming latent heat of magmatic crystallization = 100 cal/g) are given in Table 10–1. Temperatures of metamorphic crystallization immediately adjacent to granodiorite intrusions have been estimated from the degree of fractionation of oxygen isotopes (O^{18}/O^{16}) between coexisting muscovite and quartz of pelitic rocks (page 549). That for the schist–granite contact of Birch Creek (Figure 10–4) turns out to be 540°C, consistent with a model of magma intruded at 700°C into rocks at 100°C.

3. Other things being equal, the maximum temperature reached at a point at distance X from the contact of a pluton of thickness (diameter) D is a function of X/D. Figure 10–7 shows maximum aureole temperatures calculated for granitic magma at 800°C intruded into a quartzite–shale terrane initially at 100°C (magmatic crystallization range, 800°–600°C; latent heat, 100 cal/g). The same temperature (400°C) is reached at 500 m from a pluton 1 km wide and at 5 km from one 10 km wide. In each case X/D = 0.5. But, as shown below, the two thermal histories are very different.

4. The parameter that controls the time factor in contact metamorphism is D^2. Figure 10–8 illustrates the respective thermal histories of two aureoles developed round plutons of granitic magma intruded at 800°C into sandstone or quartzite initially at 100°C; latent heat of fusion is taken as 80 cal/g. For the same value of X/D = 0.1, the maximum temperature (460°C) is the same for aureoles surrounding plutons respectively 4 km and 10 km in diameter. In the first aureole this temperature is reached 190,000 years after intrusion, and is maintained above 400°C for 250,000 years. In the second it is reached 1,240,000 years after intrusion and maintained above 440°C for a span of a million and a half years.

Returning now to the Inyo aureole we see that several millions of years may have separated igneous crystallization of biotite in the batholith, and metamorphic growth of the same mineral far out in the aureole. The time lag is real, but is insufficient to explain the observed discrepancy between radiometric ages of magmatic and aureole biotites in Deep Spring Valley (page 555).

TABLE 10–1 *Maximum contact temperatures due to instantaneous intrusion of magma (after J. Jaeger)*

Magma and Initial Temperature	Country Rock and Initial Temperature	Maximum Resultant Contact Temperature
Basalt; 1000°C	quartzite; 100°C	560°C
Basalt; 1020°C	quartzite; 20°C	520°C
Granite; 800°C	quartzite; 100°C	560°C
Granite; 800°C	shale; 100°C	685°C

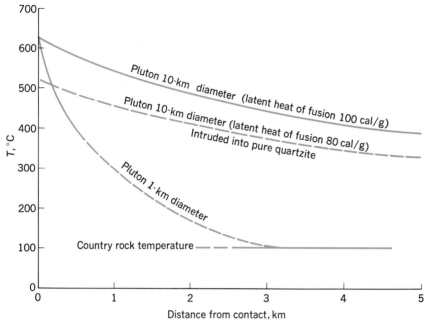

FIG. 10–7 *Gradients of maximum temperature developed in shale-quartzite (initially at 100°C) by intrusion of bodies of granodiorite magma (initially at crystallization temperature, 800° C). (Computed from data of J. Jaeger, Am. J. Sci., vol. 257, pp. 46, 47, Fig. 1, 1959.)*

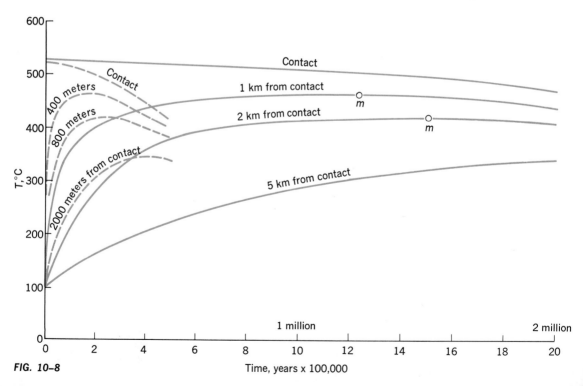

FIG. 10–8

Nor do Jaeger's models completely explain the small dimensions of contact aureoles beneath thick diabase sills. Figure 10–9 illustrates thermal effects following intrusion of a diabase sheet 1 km thick into cold porous sandstone. The crystallization range of the diabase magma is taken as 1000°–800°C; latent heat of crystallization, 100 cal/g. The full curves are based on a model for dry country rock; the broken curve shows how contact temperatures might be reduced and the aureole narrowed by dissipation of heat due to boiling of pore water. The only additional mechanism that might be invoked to explain the insignificant observed contact effects is long-sustained inflow of pore water from water-saturated sediments into the diabase magma itself. Or it may be that natural conditions depart significantly from some that are specified in Jaeger's model (for example, instantaneous intrusion of magma; absence of internal convection).

Regional Metamorphism

DALRADIAN METAMORPHISM, SOUTHEASTERN HIGHLANDS, SCOTLAND

METAMORPHIC PROVINCES OF NORTHERN SCOTLAND AND CALEDONIAN METAMORPHISM   Almost all northern Scotland, an area of several thousand square kilometers, is occupied by metamorphic rocks and intrusive bodies of granodiorite and granite. There are three metamorphic provinces: Lewisian, Moinian, and Dalradian (Figure 10–10). Each has its own metamorphic history. The Lewisian rocks are older Precambrian and bear the imprint of at least two Precambrian cycles of metamorphism. In the Moinian terrane a late Precambrian event has been overprinted and partially obliterated by an early to middle Paleozoic metamorphism correlated with the Caledonian orogeny that affected much of northwest-

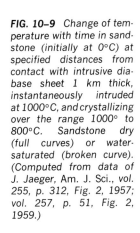

FIG. 10–9 *Change of temperature with time in sandstone (initially at 0°C) at specified distances from contact with intrusive diabase sheet 1 km thick, instantaneously intruded at 1000°C, and crystallizing over the range 1000° to 800°C. Sandstone dry (full curves) or water-saturated (broken curve). (Computed from data of J. Jaeger, Am. J. Sci., vol. 255, p. 312, Fig. 2, 1957; vol. 257, p. 51, Fig. 2, 1959.)*

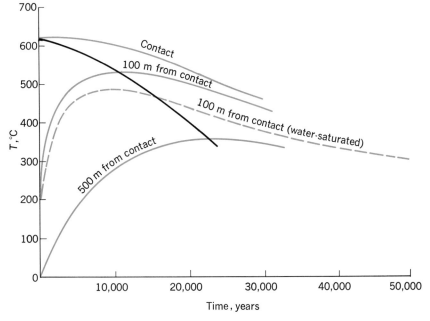

FIG. 10–8 *(Facing) Change of temperature with time in quartzite (initially at 100°C) at specified distances from contacts with granite plutons, instantaneously emplaced at 800°C and crystallizing over the range 800° to 600°C. Diameters of plutons: 10 km (full curves); 4 km (broken curves). Latent heat of crystallization 80 cal/g. (Computed from data of J. Jaeger, Am. J. Sci., vol. 257, p. 311, Fig. 1, 1959.)*

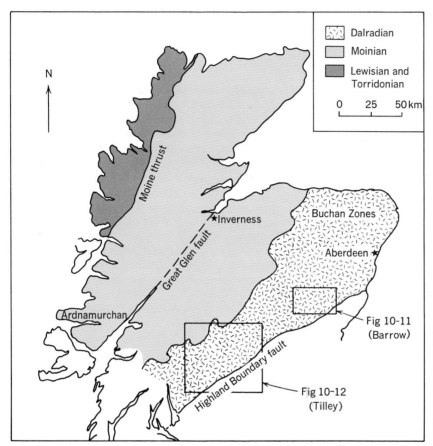

FIG. 10–10 *Map of the Highlands of Scotland showing three provinces of regional metamorphism. (Simplified after M. R. W. Johnson. From F. J. Turner, Metamorphic Petrology, McGraw-Hill, 1968, p. 24. Copyright 1968. Used by permission of McGraw-Hill Book Co.)*

ern Europe. Dalradian rocks in Scotland show the imprint of the Caledonian metamorphism only.

Our discussion here will be confined to the effects of Caledonian metamorphism recorded along the southeastern border of the Dalradian terrane. Here, late last century, George Barrow first demonstrated that, on the scale of a few hundred square kilometers, regional metamorphism is a progressive phenomenon (Figure 10–11). And here, too, questions of general import were first raised, and today are actively pursued, regarding the possible relations of regional metamorphism to folding, emplacement of granite, orogeny, and time.

The Dalradian terrane, prior to deformation and metamorphism, was a pile of geosynclinal sediments and subordinate volcanic rocks some 10 km to 20 km in thickness. The period of sedimentation extended through the later part of Precambrian into earlier Cambrian time. The Caledonian orogeny, to which metamorphism is referred, was the last major tectonic cycle recorded in the rocks of Scandinavia and northwestern Britain. It was responsible for the folded condition of Ordovician and Silurian rocks in southern Scotland and Wales, but came to a close before the beginning of Devonian time; for the overlying Lower Devonian Old Red Sandstone everywhere is undisturbed.

Structural studies in the Dalradian and Moinian provinces have shown that the Caledonian orogeny was a protracted sequence of at least four episodes of folding and two distinct sets of plutonic events. These will be discussed in more detail later (page 565). Here we note that the climax of metamorphism followed the first two major folding episodes, and was accompanied by emplacement of the earlier granodiorite–granite bodies and migmatite complexes. These are termed Older Granites to distinguish them from Newer Granite plutons that later imprinted contact aureoles upon rocks affected by Dalradian regional metamorphism.

ZONES OF PROGRESSIVE METAMORPHISM   The grade of regional metamorphism in the southeastern Highlands rises northwestward from a strip of imperfectly reconstituted rocks that borders the Highland Boundary fault. In rocks of given composition successive stages of metamorphism can be recognized in the field as corresponding index minerals first appear in abundance, always in the same order (Figures 10–11 and 10–12). The sequence of Dalradian index minerals in pelitic schists (in order of increasing grade) is chlorite, biotite, almandine, staurolite, kyanite, sillimanite. A line connecting mapped points of first appearance of easily recognizable almandine is called the *almandine isograd*—signifying identity of metamorphic grade along its length. The mapped zone between the almandine isograd and that next in sequence (the staurolite isograd) is termed the *almandine zone*. Almandine is conspicuous, too, in pelitic schists of higher grade—those of the zones of kyanite and sillimanite. The configuration and sequence of metamorphic zones in parts of the Dalradian terrane, including Barrow's classic area, are shown in Figures 10–11 and 10–12.

It cannot be said that an isograd expresses precisely or completely some simple metamorphic reaction. Almandine occurs in small amounts in some rocks of the preceding biotite zone. It is absent or sparsely developed in others within the almandine zone. This is because almandine,

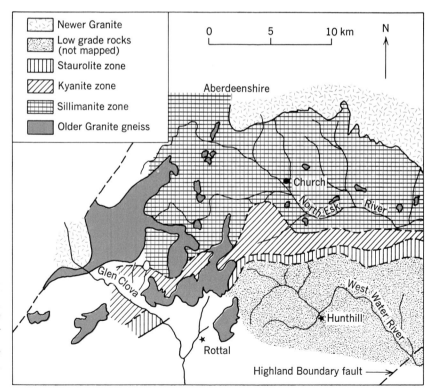

FIG. 10–11 Zones of progressive metamorphism, Dalradian of southeast Highlands, Scotland, as mapped by G. Barrow, 1893. (After F. J. Turner, ibid., p. 25, 1968. Copyright 1968. Used by permission of McGraw-Hill Book Co.)

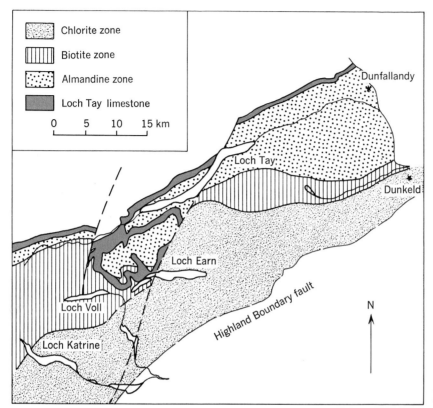

FIG. 10–12 Lower-grade zones of progressive regional metamorphism, Dalradian of southern Highlands, Scotland, as mapped by C. E. Tilley, 1925. (After F. J. Turner, ibid., p. 27, 1968. Copyright 1968. Used by permission of McGraw-Hill Book Co.)

though essentially an iron–aluminum garnet $Fe_3Al_2(SiO_4)_3$, always contains significant Mg^{2+} and Mn^{2+} substituting for Fe^{2+}; and rocks lumped together as pelitic vary appreciably in composition—for instance, with regard to the state of oxidation of iron and the relative proportions of Fe, Mg and Mn. Other, less obvious mineralogical changes occur at or close to the almandine isograd: for example, there are slight changes in the composition of biotite; chlorite diminishes in quantity; and some distance into the almandine zone plagioclase, which at lower grades is pure albite, suddenly develops a significant anorthite content (An_{20}-An_{30}). An isograd is generally based on some criterion that is easily recognized in the field—in this case the sudden development of plentiful garnet in most pelitic schists. Although its definition is to some degree subjective, most experienced workers will draw a given isograd at about the same place on the

map. What is important is that a mappable sequence of metamorphic zones, even though their boundaries (isograds) may not be so precisely located as a formation boundary or a fault, demonstrates the progressive character of metamorphism and the field pattern of changing metamorphic grade. It reveals the existence of a mineralogical gradient in essentially isochemical rocks; and this provokes the necessity of an explanation in terms of some corresponding physical gradient.

In the Dalradian, as elsewhere, isograds can be drawn for index minerals in rocks other than pelitic schists. The respective trends of the independent systems of isograds and zones so established are approximately parallel. In calcareous rocks calcium–aluminum silicates (garnets and members of the epidote family) first appear close to the almandine isograd as drawn for associated pelitic rocks. Plagioclase first becomes highly calcic (An_{80}) near the staurolite isograd, and pyroxene first appears at the sillimanite isograd as drawn for pelitic schists. The trend of metamorphic grade transverse to the isograds evidently expresses a trend in physical conditions, independent of rock composition.

MINERAL ASSEMBLAGES IN RELATION TO ROCK COMPOSITION Some typical mineral assemblages in the metamorphic zones of the southeastern Dalradian are presented in simplified form in Table 10–2. Again we find a close correlation between mineralogical and chemical composition among rocks of each zone.

To illustrate the mineral paragenesis of the commonest Dalradian rocks—those of pelitic composition—we may use a type of phase diagram designed for mineral assemblages containing a single calcium silicate. This, in the pelitic schists from the middle of the almandine zone to the sillimanite zone, is plagioclase (typically with composition not far from An_{30}). The three components for a triangular plot are: $A = Al_2O_3 - (K_2O + Na_2O + CaO)$; $K = K_2O$; $F = MgO + FeO + MnO$. All are expressed as molecular percentages. Additional possible (in fact almost universal) phases in every assemblage are quartz

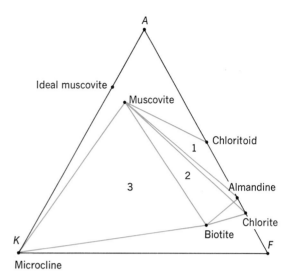

FIG. 10–13 *AKF diagram for pelitic mineral assemblages, high-grade part of almandine zone, Dalradian of southeastern Highlands, Scotland.*

and plagioclase. Figures 10–13 and 10–14 are *AKF* diagrams for pelitic and semipelitic rocks in the high-grade part of the almandine zone and in the zone of kyanite. Some of the associated minerals are the same as we encountered in pel-

TABLE 10–2   *Mineral assemblages in southeast Dalradian metamorphic zones*

Zonal Index (pelitic)	Rock Composition		
	Pelitic	Calcareous	Basic (basaltic)
Chlorite	muscovite–chlorite–quartz	calcite–mica–quartz	chlorite–albite–epidote–sphene–(–calcite)
Biotite	biotite–muscovite–chlorite–quartz		
Almandine	biotite–muscovite–almandine–quartz	garnet–epidote–hornblende	
Staurolite	biotite–muscovite–staurolite–almandine–quartz	garnet–anorthite–hornblende	hornblende–plagioclase (with epidote, almandine, or biotite)
Kyanite	biotite–muscovite–almandine kyanite–quartz		
Sillimanite	biotite–muscovite–almandine sillimanite–quartz (orthoclase)	garnet–anorthite–diopside	

itic hornfelses of the inner zone of the Inyo aureole. Other phases, not present in the Inyo hornfelses are

muscovite, $KAl_2(AlSi_3O_{10})(OH)_2$
chloritoid, $(Fe, Mg)_2(Al, Fe)Al_3O_2(SiO_4)_2$
    $(OH)_4$
almandine, $(Fe, Mg, Mn)_3Al_2(SiO_4)_3$
kyanite, Al_2SiO_5

The common pelitic assemblages in the two zones are set out in Table 10–3.

Only gross correlation between the mineralogical composition of metamorphic rocks and their chemistry can be expressed by *ACF* and *AKF* plots. More subtle and very consistent details of correlation appear when we assess the partition of elements between solid-solution series in terms of chemical controls. In any metamorphic zone we find a sympathetic relation between the Mg/Fe ratios of coexisting biotites and almandines. This is determined not so much by the corresponding ratio in the total-rock composition, as by the state of oxidation of iron (Figure 10–15). A low oxidation state, signified by the iron-oxide pair magnetite (Fe_3O_4) + ilmenite ($FeOTiO_2$), favors a low ratio MgO/FeO in associated ferrous silicates. This is illustrated in Figure 10–15 for high-grade rocks of the kyanite

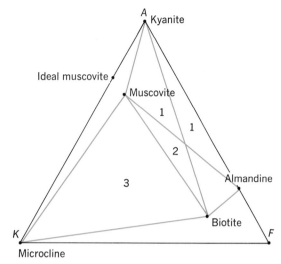

FIG. 10–14 *AKF diagram for pelitic assemblages, Kyanite zone, Glen Urquhart, southeastern Highlands, Scotland. (After G. N. Francis, Brit. Mus. (Nat. Hist.) Mineral Bull., vol. 1, 1964.)*

zone close to the sillimanite isograd. Rocks in which iron is more highly oxidized contain the oxide pair magnetite–hematite (Fe_3O_4-Fe_2O_3). In these rocks the total content of iron-oxide minerals is higher and the quantity of biotite and

TABLE 10–3   *Mineral assemblages of pelitic rocks, numbered to correspond with numbered fields of Figures 10–13 and 10–14, almandine and kyanite zones, southeastern Highlands, Scotland. Quartz, plagioclase, iron oxides, are additional phases*

Zone	Composition		
	(1) Aluminous	(2) Average	(3) Potassic
Almandine	muscovite–chloritoid–almandine–chlorite (biotite in some rocks)	muscovite–biotite–almandine	muscovite–biotite–microcline
Kyanite	kyanite–muscovite–biotite–almandine (almandine absent in some rocks)	muscovite–biotite–almandine	muscovite–biotite–microcline

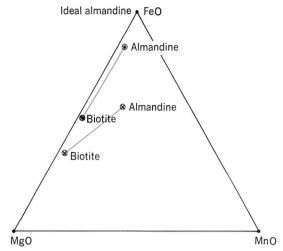

FIG. 10–15 *Fe-Mg-Mn plot of coexisting biotites and almandine; kyanite zone near sillimanite isograd, Glen Clova, southeastern Highlands, Scotland. (After data from G. A. Chinner, J. Petrol., vol. 1, pp. 178–217, 1960.) Circled points: low-oxidation assemblages with magnetite-ilmenite; circled crosses: high-oxidation assemblages with magnetite–hematite.*

almandine is correspondingly smaller. MgO/FeO is higher in both silicates, and MnO/FeO of almandine is much higher than in associated rocks in a lower state of oxidation. This is just one of many ways in which the mineral assemblages of associated rocks predictably reflect the overall chemical character of the system.

METAMORPHISM, FOLDING, PLUTONISM, AND TIME Structural analysis of complexly folded bedding and foliation in Dalradian rocks has unravelled a sequence of four distinct episodes of folding, respectively designated F_1, F_2, F_3, and F_4. The F_1 structures are large-scale recumbent folds and nappes that almost immediately became refolded on a smaller scale in the second major deformational event, F_2. These two episodes determined the geometry of outcrop and the regional trend of mapped formations. The isograd pattern within the area shown in Figure 10–12 is simple compared with the outcrop configuration of a stratigraphic formation, the Loch Tay Limestone. This kind of relation prevails throughout the whole southern Dalradian; indeed it is common though not universal in other areas of regional

metamorphism. For this reason, backed by microscopic structural evidence, Dalradian metamorphism (crystallization) is believed to have reached its culmination during and after F_2 folding.

Emplacement of foliated Older Granites is thought to have occurred at the peak of metamorphism; for the plutons are structurally similar, in some respects, to the enclosing metamorphic rocks. Radiometric evidence on the whole supports this correlation; but it also suggests that some of the Older Granites in Barrow's type sillimanite zone were emplaced a good deal later; probably during the F_3 folding event. Older Granites tend to be more conspicuous in the higher-grade zones. Could Dalradian metamorphism, then, have been a direct consequence of regional invasion of the crust by rising granitic magma? That was Barrow's interpretation. Alternatively, might the Older Granites have formed by fusion of Dalradian sediments virtually in place wherever metamorphic temperatures, induced by some unknown source of heat, rose above the necessary critical value? Strontium isotope analyses throw some light on this problem. The initial Sr^{87}/Sr^{86} values of Dalradian Older Granites are unusually high. Many lie in the range 0.715–0.719, consistent with origin by fusion of underlying sialic rocks in the crust. The latest of the Older Granites, including some near Glen Clova (Figure 10–11) give exceptionally high values, 0.728–0.733 consistent with direct melting of Dalradian rocks; for these have Sr^{87}/Sr^{86} values in the same range.

The third folding episode, F_3 had widespread small-scale effects and in parts of the Dalradian province structurally disturbed the previously imprinted isograd pattern. The general mineralogical response was incipient and patchy retrogressive adjustment, notably partial conversion of garnet and biotite to chlorite. Yet in the deepest zones now exposed, temperatures may have risen to the point where a second episode of highgrade metamorphism imprinted the sillimanite zone in the Glen Clova region and even culminated in local fusion to give the last of the Older Granite plutons.

The last major event in the Caledonian cycle was intrusion of numerous Newer Granite plutons—mainly of granodioritic composition. Their distribution (Figure 10–19) bears no relation to metamorphic grade or structure of the surrounding rocks. Low initial Sr^{87}/Sr^{86} values of some rocks—0.707 in the Lochnagar pluton cutting Barrow's sillimanite zone, 0.705 in several Irish plutons—indicate a primary deep-seated origin, perhaps beneath the crust. Plutons of the same age in the northern Dalradian terrane have higher values (0.715–0.717) consistent with origin by fusion of or reaction with crustal rocks.

The Caledonian cycle closed with local rather minor folding, F_4, unaccompanied by metamorphic effects or plutonism.

PATTERNS OF METAMORPHISM

ISOGRAD PATTERNS   *"Barrovian" patterns*   Part or the whole of Barrow's sequence of index minerals has now been recognized in metamorphic terranes of all ages in many parts of the world. It has even become customary to speak in such cases of *Barrovian zones*. And partly because this was the first pattern of progressive metamorphism to be recognized and mapped, it has come to be regarded by many geologists as "normal." With recognizable variations the "Barrovian" type of metamorphism has now been recognized in rocks of all ages from many regions—among them the Precambrian of eastern India, the early to mid-Paleozoic fold belts of Norway and eastern United States, a Permian to Jurassic geosynclinal filling in southern New Zealand (Figure 10–16), and the core of the European Alps where the climax of metamorphism came in mid-Tertiary times.

The supposedly uniform character of Barrovian metamorphism appears however, to have been overemphasized. The situation is akin to that relating to "standard" magma types (Chapter 6). No two regions of metamorphism are identical. The general pattern is recognizable, but so too are departures in detail from the unique Dalradian pattern of metamorphism.

In parts of New England the sillimanite zone is more extensive than "normal" and can be divided into a muscovite–sillimanite and an orthoclase–sillimanite zone. Plagioclase first becomes significantly calcic in the biotite zone of Vermont, but not until well beyond the almandine isograd in Scotland.

In the metamorphic belts of southern New Zealand, the biotite and almandine zones are much like those of Scotland; but they are not identical. For example, throughout the almandine zone two plagioclases, $An_{0=5}$ and $An_{20=30}$ coexist in quartz–feldspar–mica schists. Staurolite is absent, and kyanite rare in the high-grade schists, although this largely reflects predominance of sandstone over shale in the parent material. The chlorite zone of New Zealand is very extensive, covering some 20,000 km². Within parts of it (as represented in Figure 10–16), small amounts of biotite and almandine persistently occur in the chlorite-zone assemblage quartz–muscovite–chlorite–albite. It passes outward with decreasing grade into marginal zones whose mineral assemblages include distinctive hydrous Ca-Al silicates—zeolites, pumpellyite, lawsonite —unknown in Barrow's Dalradian zones. In the presence of lawsonite there is an unmistakable hint of affinity (though not identity) with yet another metamorphic pattern that is widely developed in many regions of geologically young metamorphism, such as Japan, the Alps, and California (see below).

Other patterns   It is recognized today that the Barrovian zones of the southeastern Highlands by no means provide a universally applicable standard picture of regional metamorphism. Elsewhere, the metamorphic pattern is very different but equally distinctive; one such is even developed in the northern segment of the Dalradian terrane itself. Here are some examples:

1. Along much of the length of Japan run two parallel contiguous metamorphic belts: the Ryoke belt on the continental side and the Sanbagawa belt facing east and southeast toward the Pacific (Figure 10–17). They are in fault contact along what is called the Median Line of Japan. Their respective metamorphic patterns are entirely different. In the Ryoke belt, isograds have been drawn for the following indices in pelitic rocks: chlorite, biotite–almandine, andalusite–cordierite–almandine, and sillimanite–cordierite–almandine. Andalusite- and cordierite-bearing assem-

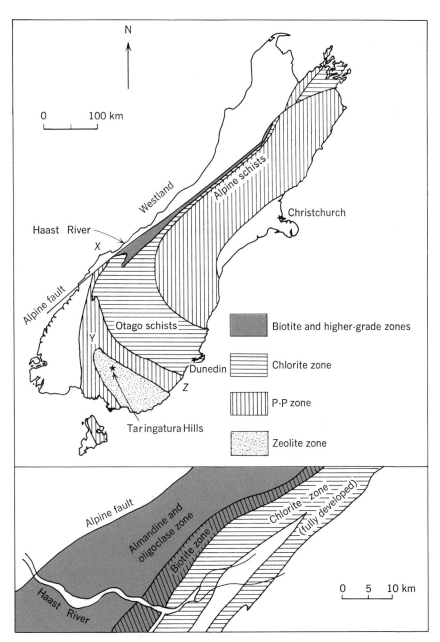

FIG. 10-16 *Metamorphic zones in the Alpine and Otago schists, New Zealand geosyncline. Blank area is the Tasman province with a metamorphic and plutonic history distinct from that of the New Zealand geosyncline.*

blages, common enough in contact aureoles, are not represented in the Barrovian zones. They do appear in Dalradian rocks, however, some 70 to 90 km north of the area mapped by Barrow in what has been termed the "Buchan pattern" of metamorphism (Figure 10-10). Japanese geologists ask, and with some justification: Which pattern is normal, Barrovian or Ryoke?

2. In the Sanbagawa belt of Japan the pattern of metamorphism of pelitic schists recalls that of

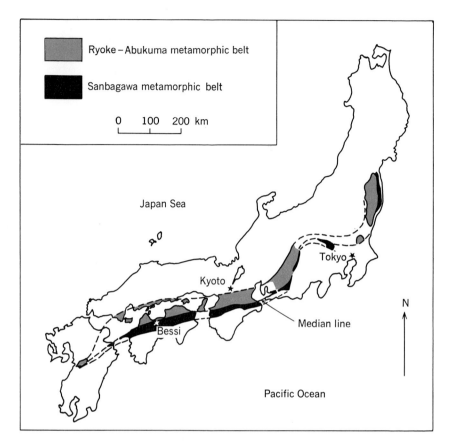

Ryoke–Abukuma metamorphic belt

Sanbagawa metamorphic belt

0   100   200 km

Japan Sea

Tokyo

Kyoto

Bessi

Median line

N

Pacific Ocean

FIG. 10–17 *Sanbagawa and Ryoke metamorphic belts of Japan. (Simplified after A. Miyashiro. Taken from F. J. Turner, Metamorphic Petrology, McGraw-Hill, p. 35, 1968. Copyright 1968. Used by permission of McGraw-Hill Book Co.)*

the lower grades of Barrow's Dalradian. But almandine tends to appear before biotite. Associated metamorphic basic rocks are represented in the chlorite zone (as defined for pelitic rocks) by assemblages that include mineral phases completely lacking in the Dalradian:

glaucophane, $Na_2(Mg, Fe)_3(Al, Fe)_2 Si_8O_{22}(OH)_2$

jadeite, $Na(Al, Fe)Si_2O_6$

omphacite, $(Ca, Na)(Mg, Al)Si_2O_6$

lawsonite, $CaAl_2Si_2O_7(OH)_2H_2O$

pumpellyite, complex hydrous (Ca, Al, Fe) silicate

stilpnomelane, complex hydrous (Fe, Mn) silicate

These same minerals appear in various combinations over a wide range of rock composition and metamorphic grade in rocks affected by relatively

young folding elsewhere: Californian coast ranges (Jurassic); Pennine Alps of Switzerland and Italy (Tertiary); New Caledonia (Tertiary). In these regions departure from the Barrovian zonal pattern is complete. In California for example, there is a general tendency for assemblages containing combinations of the following phases to appear in order of increasing grade:

albite–pumpellyite(–calcite)

albite–lawsonite(–aragonite)

quartz–lawsonite–jadeite–glaucophane (–aragonite)

omphacite–almandine–lawsonite– glaucophane(–argonite)

Biotite, universally present in Dalradian schists beyond the biotite isograd is completely lacking in Californian coast range assemblages.

3. Very different again are the isograd pat-

terns in many Precambrian terranes, where micaceous and hornblendic assemblages, such as those of Barrow's high-grade zones, give way with further increase in grade to almost anhydrous assemblages. Extreme products are granulites consisting of quartz–feldspar–almandine–sillimanite (pelitic) and plagioclase–diopside–hypersthene–almandine (basic). Cordierite is widespread in pelitic rocks of many granulite terranes. Isograd patterns have several variations. In one, that has been traced over an area of 3000 km² around the mining town of Broken Hill, central-east Australia, there are three mappable zones. The lowest grade corresponds pretty much to that of Barrow's sillimanite zone. Two isograds have been drawn where advancing metamorphic grade is indicated by the following mineralogical changes:

(a) Change from green to brown hornblende in amphibolites; appearance of sillimanite–orthoclase in place of muscovite–quartz in pelitic rocks.
(b) Appearance of diopside–hypersthene in place of hornblende in amphibolites; development of abundant cordierite in pelitic rocks.

Today, then, it has become fashionable to recognize half a dozen distinct "normal" patterns of regional metamorphism—Miyashiro's *facies series* (page 577). Nevertheless to these writers even this approach seems too rigid. Beneath the obvious features that conform to the general specifications of some recognized pattern, it is possible to see in any province of regional metamorphism a character that is peculiarly its own. To define and name specific metamorphic patterns may be useful in formalizing certain general aspects of regional metamorphism. But the same approach tends to obscure what may be the most significant quality of a particular metamorphic cycle in a particular region—its very uniqueness.

PATTERNS OF DEFORMATION AND PLUTONISM
Now generally established is a broad correlation, in space and in time, between regional metamorphism, orogeny, and granite plutonism. This we have already examined in the case of Dalradian metamorphism. In other regions some aspects of correlation are reminiscent of the Dalradian pattern, others not at all. As with isograd patterns the relation between metamorphism, plutonism and tectonism in each region appears to be unique.

Andean geosyncline, Chile A rather simple relationship is seen in the Jurassic–Cretaceous volcanic and sedimentary filling of the Andean geosyncline in Chile. These rocks were affected by low-grade regional (burial) metamorphism, the grade of which is related to stratigraphic depth. The pattern of subsequent folding is relatively simple. There is nothing comparable with the "Older Granites" of Scotland; but post-metamorphic granite plutons are synchronous with several phases of mid-Jurassic to early Tertiary orogeny.

Alpine metamorphism, New Zealand geosyncline In the South Island of New Zealand there are two independent older tectonic provinces, in mutual contact along major faults (Figure 10–16). The younger of the two, occupying the central and eastern part of the island, is the southern portion of part of the New Zealand geosyncline. This has a very thick filling of sediments deposited between the beginning of the Permian and late Jurassic times. In the lower levels basic volcanic rocks are profusely developed and there are extensive basic plutons and ultramafic sheets (page 309). Everywhere the rocks of the New Zealand geosyncline have been strongly affected by folding during a major tectonic convulsion, the Rangitatan orogeny. On stratigraphic evidence this has been placed in a short interval of 10 or 20 million years in latest Jurassic and early Cretaceous time. There are at least two major episodes of Rangitatan folding:

1. Development of major folds: a pile of recumbent folds and nappes in the axial zone (Otago and Alpine schists, Figure 10–16); a regional syncline in the border zone of weakly metamorphosed and nonmetamorphic rocks south of the Otago schist belt.
2. Widespread folding on a smaller scale. Over large areas the effects are so intense and so penetrative that the preceding major structures have been almost obliterated.

The axial zone of the geosynclinal province is occupied by a curved belt of completely metamorphosed rocks (Haast schist group) whose southern and northwestern segments, though mutually continuous, have long been respectively called the Otago and the Alpine schists. The whole metamorphism began in the lower levels of the geosyncline prior to the onset of folding; for here low-grade assemblages containing zeolites developed in Triassic volcanic sands, and the grade of metamorphism increases with stratigraphic depth in the section. This in fact is the site of Coombs' type area of burial metamorphism (Taringatura Hills). Deeper in the section Permian rocks show various stages of development of distinctive hydrous Ca-Al silicates (pumpellyite, lawsonite) that are found to be widely prevalent in other regions of burial metamorphism (for example, Chile, California, and New Caledonia).

Throughout the Otago and Alpine schist zones, metamorphism reached much higher grades, accompanying and outlasting the second folding event. The culmination of metamorphic crystallization and final imprinting of the isograds postdate both major episodes of Rangitatan folding.

Plutonic activity in the New Zealand geosyncline was limited to premetamorphic intrusion of basic and ultramafic bodies in the lower levels of the geosynclinal pile. Remarkable indeed in an area of such great extent and high relief is the complete absence of granitic plutons.

TIME PATTERNS   Of prime significance in our discussion of metamorphism in relation to orogeny and plutonism is the role of time. To speak of a metamorphic episode is to invoke an interval of time during which initially unaltered rocks became converted to their present mineralogical and structural condition. Structural evolution can be unraveled by mapping and analysis of folded once-planar structures (page 164). Microscopic study can tell much of the sequence of mineral crystallization in relation to episodes of deformation. Now, through radiometric dating of minerals and rocks, time limits may be set upon episodes of crystallization—metamorphic

and plutonic. Simultaneous pursuit of these three approaches in a number of regions has led to two general conclusions. The duration of a metamorphic cycle may be very long—ten to a hundred million years. The history of metamorphism in each region is unique.

In the case of progressive regional metamorphism the time–place problem that pervades all geology is acute indeed. A mapped sequence of isograds reveals a mineralogical (metamorphic) gradient in place. This presumably reflects a pre-existing gradient in physical conditions (temperature, pressure) that, as now seen, is also arrested in place. To what degree is this also a gradient in time? Were the zones of chlorite, biotite, almandine, and kyanite developed "synchronously"— that is, over one narrow time interval? Or could crystallization in the chlorite zone predate or postdate crystallization in the almandine zone by many million years, even by a geological period as measured on the stratigraphic time scale? Was metamorphism progressive? That is, was crystallization of almandine at a given locality preceded by earlier development of biotite, and by growth of chlorite and muscovite earlier still? And at what point in time, during the long interval encompassing burial, deformation, uplift and finally exposure by erosion, did the mineral assemblage as we now see it become established and "frozen in"? These are questions that must be answered individually for every metamorphic province. Some answers may prove applicable only to a single zone. We shall review briefly two well-documented examples.

Radiometric chronology of Dalradian metamorphism, Scotland   On geologic evidence Dalradian sedimentation is considered to have extended from later Precambrian into early Cambrian time. Local occurrence of Lower Cambrian fossils places a younger limit of between 550 m.y. and 540 m.y. on currently accepted time scales.

Earlier radiometric data include many K-A dates determined on micas from Dalradian schists and intrusive granites. Dates for schists and Older Granites show a wide spread, 490–380 m.y., with strong clustering at 450–430 m.y. Various thermal models have been proposed, all starting with culmination of metamorphism after the peak of the F_2 episode of Caledonian folding (page 565) at 500 m.y. or earlier. The dated event in any rock is viewed as the point at which post-metamorphic cooling had lowered temperatures below a critical value at which mica became sealed against argon loss. One model postulated a second event somewhat preceding 450 m.y., or spanning the interval 450–430 m.y.; and this was correlated with the third episode F_3 of Caledonian folding. Newer Granite plutons, the expression of a great upsurge of granodioritic magma from the deep crust, uniformly give K-A dates in the narrow range 410–390 m.y. Here is a postmetamorphic plutonic episode followed or accompanied by local postmetamorphic tectonic activity, F_4.

Newly available Rb-Sr data on Dalradian granites and schists on the whole confirm, sharpen, and amplify the picture based on K-A measurements. The Older Granites, it appears, were not emplaced during a single plutonic episode. Plutonism may have begun as early as 530 m.y., but

it may equally well have been concentrated in a major episode close to 500 m.y. (as inferred from K-A data), followed by later and more localized activity about 420 m.y. The 400 m.y. intrusive event (Newer Granites) of K-A chronology is confirmed by Rb-Sr data.

It is possible to construct various thermal models of Dalradian metamorphism and plutonism consistent with the radiometric data. One such, with the emphasis on variation of temperature with time in the southeastern Highlands, is presented graphically in Figure 10–18. It pictures two metamorphic episodes synchronous respectively with F_2 and F_3 folding. However it may be presented, the picture is in some significant respects the same. To the accompaniment of intermittent folding, some rocks may have been subjected to metamorphic temperatures for a period of at least 100 million years—more than one quarter of Paleozoic time. Maybe isograd patterns became "frozen in" early during a relatively brief interval, perhaps only 10 or 20 million years following the climax of F_2 folding. To most

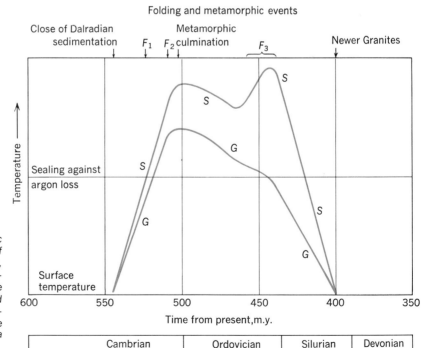

FIG. 10–18 Possible schematic model of thermal history of Dalradian metamorphism, southeast Highlands, Scotland. G—temperatures at some point on the garnet isograd in Figure 10–12; S—temperatures at some point in the sillimanite zone, Glen Clova (Figure 10–11).

writers this pattern has time implications to this extent: The course of mineralogical evolution at any site can be inferred from the sequence mapped in place in the direction of rising metamorphic grade. Metamorphism in other words was truly progressive. Over large areas of the sillimanite zone the final mineralogical event can be seen in an arrested state; sillimanite is crystallizing at the expense of muscovite in kyanite schists retaining the mineral assemblage typical of the immediately preceding stage.

We have not presented a complete picture of Dalradian metamorphism. Instead we have isolated one segment of the rocks affected—the one that includes Barrow's zones in the southeast Highlands. The same metamorphism affected the whole Dalradian terrane of Scotland and Ireland (Figure 10–19) and even the more ancient Moinian rocks farther northwest, where Rb-Sr dates as old as 740 m.y. record a Precambrian Moinian metamorphism that must later have been erased from the K-A memory of micas during Caledonian metamorphism.

Even Dalradian metamorphism did not every-

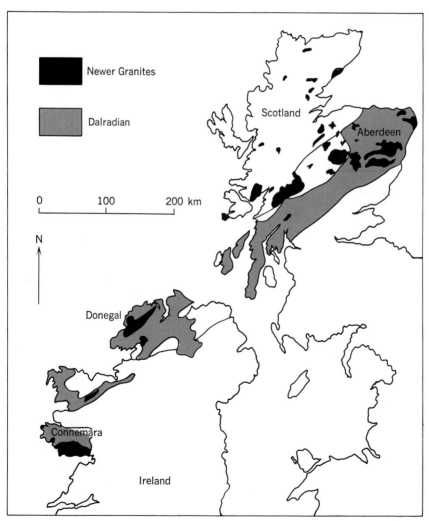

FIG. 10–19 *Distribution of Newer Granite plutons in relation to Dalradian schists, Scotland and Ireland. (After P. E. Brown, J. A. Miller, and R. L. Gastry, Yorkshire Geol. Soc. Proc., vol. 36, p. 252, 1968.)*

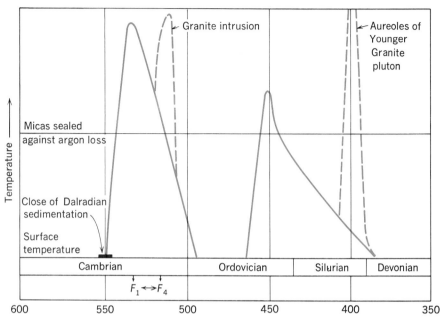

Temperature ——→

Granite intrusion

Aureoles of
Younger
Granite
pluton

Micas sealed
against argon loss

Close of Dalradian
sedimentation

Surface
temperature

| Cambrian | Ordovician | Silurian | Devonian |

$F_1 \leftrightarrow F_4$

600   550   500   450   400   350

Time from present, m.y.

FIG. 10–20 *Possible model of thermal history of Dalradian metamorphism in Connemara, Ireland.*

where follow an identical course. In Connemara, Ireland, development of the Barrovian isograd pattern was followed by several episodes of folding before intrusion of granite at 510 ± 35 m.y. Dalradian rocks here became stripped by erosion and then covered by marine sediments whose lowest members are dated by graptolite faunas as basal Ordovician (490 m.y.). These sediments contain detrital grains of staurolite worn from nearby Dalradian schists; and they themselves bear the imprint of weak regional metamorphism that must have been imprinted late in the Caledonian cycle. A possible thermal history for Dalradian metamorphism in Connemara is shown graphically in Figure 10–20.

Radiometric chronology of metamorphism, New Zealand geosyncline For rocks of the New Zealand geosyncline (page 569), a dozen K-A and two Rb-Sr dates are available, covering the surprising range 140 m.y. to 4 m.y. The pattern of chronological variation is related to grade of metamorphism and also to chronological provinces (Figure 10–21) delimited in large part by the Alpine fault zone—a spectacular transcur-

rent dislocation that has mutually displaced two segments of the geosynclinal filling (complete with matching stratigraphic sequences, low-grade metamorphic zones, and ultramafic intrusives) through some 480 km in the right-lateral sense. Briefly, the chronological provinces revealed by radiometric dates are as follows:

1. Northern province *west* of the Alpine fault. Permian and Triassic rocks in lowest grades of metamorphism, folded in the first Rangitatan episode. Four K-A dates for lawsonite-bearing rocks, 130 m.y. to 110 m.y.

2. Northwestern end of the Permian–Triassic border zone, immediately *east* of the southern end of the Alpine fault. Rocks similar to those of sector (1) but more tightly folded in the first Rangitatan event. Four K-A dates: one 106 m.y.; three 55 to 53 m.y.

3. Otago schist zone. Two K-A dates (141; 133 m.y.) from rocks of minimum chlorite-zone grade on coast south of Dunedin. One Rb-Sr date, 100 ± 10 m.y., from highest grade of chlorite zone near Cromwell.

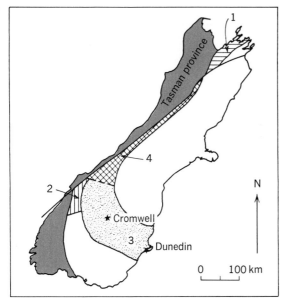

FIG. 10–21 *Chronological provinces for metamorphism in the New Zealand geosyncline, numbered as in text.*

4. Southern half of Alpine schist zone.

(a) Rocks of maximum grade close to Alpine fault: 5 K-A dates on metamorphic biotite, 8 to 4 m.y. Coarse micas of a single pegmatite secretion: biotite, K-A 25 m.y., Rb-Sr 26 m.y.; muscovite, Rb-Sr 60 m.y.

(b) Schist close to biotite isograd 20 km from Alpine fault, K-A 76 m.y. Fine phyllite of minimum grade 40 km from Alpine fault, K-A 133 m.y.

Each of these provinces has a different thermal history; but they start with a common event whose radiometric imprint is preserved unmodified in areas of minimal metamorphic grade. The date would seem to be 130–100 m.y.; the event is the first episode of folding in the Rangitatan orogeny. This is consistent with the evidence of stratigraphy and with the imprint of an early mid-Cretaceous event (120–100 m.y.) in the adjoining Tasman province. Younger K-A dates on biotite presumably reflect sealing of mica against argon loss during cooling from relatively high metamorphic temperatures. It is generally agreed that the very young dates obtained from high-grade rocks close to the Alpine fault were imprinted when postmetamorphic temperatures were quenched immediately following Pliocene elevation along the fault. In fact the event so dated is termed the Kaikoura orogeny.

There is no general consensus as to temperature gradients in the Alpine zone prior to Pliocene uplift, nor the related question of the magnitude of vertical displacement during the Kaikouran orogeny. Today the high-grade Alpine schists occupy a zone of presumably high thermal gradient dotted copiously with hot springs. To postulate a comparable gradient four or five million years ago—say 50°C/km—would place the minimum thickness of overburden

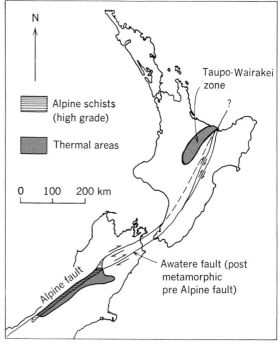

FIG. 10–22 *Recent thermal sites in relation to Alpine fault and Alpine zone of high-grade metamorphism, New Zealand. (Thermal zones from G. W. Grindley and G. J. Williams, in Economic Geology of New Zealand, G. J. Williams, ed., Australian Institute of Mining and Metallurgy, p. 234, 1965.)*

necessary to maintain biotite at 300°C at 6 km. About 350 km northeast along the extrapolated trend of the Alpine fault (Figure 10–22) is the eastern border of an elongate zone of much more intense thermal activity and volcanism. This is the Wairakei-Taupo belt, where geothermal power has been developed extensively for commercial use. Here temperatures of 250°C are maintained today over wide areas at depths of only 700 to 1500 meters. Here also from Pliocene times onward granitic magma formed by fusion of Jurassic sediments at comparatively shallow depth (Chapter 6) has repeatedly exploded through the surface. The volcanic products, largely rhyolitic debris (ignimbrite) aggregate 15 km³. Could this volcanism be a series of blowouts from a "Newer Granite" pluton, moving up—just as in the British Caledonian orogeny, 10^8 years after the climax of metamorphism? Before lateral displacement along th Alpine fault began, it is probable that the Wairakei–Taupo zone—not yet a volcanic area, but presumably already heating up—lay immediately west of the Alpine fault.

In conclusion we note that there is a possibility that high-grade metamorphism of the Alpine schists is directly connected with or at least was prolonged by movement along the Alpine fault and by Tertiary plutonism in the adjacent region (now the Taupo area) west of the fault. The style of folding is simpler here and the grade of metamorphism notably higher than in the Otago schist zone. The respective metamorphic histories of the Alpine and the Otago schists no doubt have much in common; but it is scarcely likely that they will prove to be identical. Students of Dalradian metamorphism postulate fluctuation of metamorphic temperatures over periods up to 100 million years, and find that thermal history was far from identical in different provinces. The main difficulty confronting acceptance of a model of similar dimensions for Alpine metamorphism in New Zealand is this: Tectonic events (Rangitatan and Kaikouran) conventionally considered to be unrelated have become telescoped into one cycle, and processes that have an "ancient" connotation (metamorphism and plutonism) are protracted into times disconcertingly close to those in which we live.

Metamorphic Facies

THE FACIES CONCEPT

REGULARITY OF METAMORPHIC PARAGENESIS   In spite of the wide total compositional range of metamorphic rocks, mineralogically they are surprisingly simple and regular. It is because of this that isograds and metamorphic zones may be mapped in the field, and that zonal patterns in different regions so often have much in common. For the same reason simple workable classifications of metamorphic rocks can be framed in terms of mineralogy and chemical composition. Much of petrological and geochemical research over the last half century has been concentrated on (1) exploring and formalizing the degree of correlation between the mineralogical composi- of metamorphic rocks, their overall chemistry, and their field setting; and (2) seeking to explain the resulting generalizations in terms of physical chemistry and geophysics.

In any metamorphic field situation (for example, within a given zone) there is an obvious correlation between each mineral assemblage and its total chemical composition. Rocks of identical composition from other situations (or zones) usually are mineralogically different. In the chlorite zone of southern New Zealand basaltic rocks have everywhere been converted to greenschists consisting of some combination of the minerals albite, epidote, chlorite, actinolite, calcite, and sphene. The associated pelitic assemblage is quartz–albite–muscovite–chlorite–epidote. Closely similar mineral assemblages are developed in rocks of comparable composition in low-grade zones of the Scottish Dalradian, the Appalachian fold belts of New England, and the Brisbane schist zone of Queensland in Australia. At higher grades of regional metamorphism in these and other regions, rocks of basaltic parentage are amphibolites (plagioclase–hornblende–epidote); associated pelites contain biotite, muscovite, almandine, quartz, and in many instances kyanite or sillimanite.

DEFINITION OF FACIES   Half a century age Eskola developed, on the basis of similar observations on European metamorphic rocks, his concept of *metamorphic facies*, which with slight modification may be stated thus: (Fyfe and Turner, 1966):

> A metamorphic facies is a set of metamorphic mineral assemblages, repeatedly associated in space and time, such that there is a constant and therefore predictable relation between mineral composition and chemical composition.

Note that a facies is defined, not in terms of a single index mineral, nor yet a single critical mineral assemblage, but by an entire natural association of mineral assemblages. Wherever they may occur, the associated mineral assemblages of the New Zealand chlorite zone, constitute one metamorphic facies. It has been named after one of the characteristic mineral assemblages, the *greenschist facies*.

NOMENCLATURE

Eskola named each facies after some characteristic rock type; and, in spite of its obvious disadvantages, this form of nomenclature is still universally followed. There is some confusion as

to the precise naming of certain well-recognized facies. For example, the glaucophane-bearing and associated lawsonite- and jadeite-bearing assemblages of regional metamorphism in the Alps, Japan, California, and elsewhere constitute Eskola's glaucophane–schist facies, now more generally named after the definitive widespread rock type glaucophane–lawsonite schist. Some writers call it the blueschist facies.

For each facies there is some latitude regarding mineralogical–chemical correlation, though still within strictly defined limits. Thus in the *amphibolite facies* of regional metamorphism, the definitive basic assemblage is always hornblende–plagioclase (with epidote or almandine as additional possible phases). In the Dalradian of Scotland it covers medium to high grades from the middle of the almandine to the sillimanite zone. Here local subfacies can be recognized, one for each zone (see Table 10–2). Rocks of the zones of chlorite and biotite in all parts of the world constitute the *greenschist facies* with pelitic chlorite–mica-bearing and basic albite–epidote-chlorite-bearing assemblages. Subfacies corresponding to the chlorite and biotite zones of different regions (for example, the Dalradian

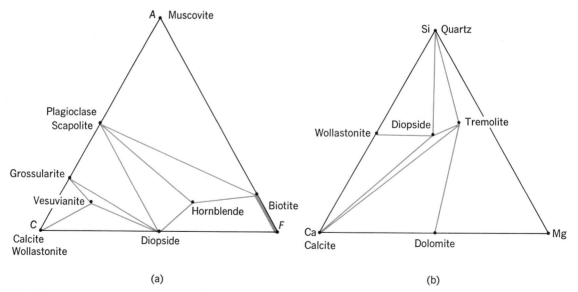

FIG. 10–23 *Hornblende–hornfels facies. Phase assemblages in pelitic and calcareous rocks, contact aureoles in roof pendants, Sierra Nevada batholith, California.*

versus southeastern New Zealand) have features in common, but are not identical.

Because metamorphism is a progressive field phenomenon, there must be facies transitions; and because every isograd pattern has some unique characters, corresponding transitional facies will tend to differ from one region to another. It has been found impracticable to set up any comprehensive and universally applicable schemes of transitional facies or subfacies.

We list below some of the more important of metamorphic facies and illustrate some of their characteristic mineralogical features by reference to phase-composition diagrams. Further details will be found in standard texts.

Hornblende–hornfels (Figures 10–5, 10–6, 10–23). This is the most widely developed facies of contact aureoles. The critical basic assemblage is hornblende–plagioclase(–diopside).

Pyroxene–hornfels. Confined to inner high-temperature zones of some contact aureoles. Highly characteristic are the basic assemblage diopside–hypersthene–plagioclase, and pelitic assemblages with quartz, orthoclase and andalu-site, sillimanite, or cordierite. These pelitic assemblages also occur with hornblende–plagioclase in rock associations transitional between the two hornfels facies.

Zeolite. Lowest grade of burial metamorphism. Mineral assemblages include zeolites coexisting with quartz, white micas, and chlorites. Commonly but not invariably, metamorphic recrystallization is incomplete or irregularly distributed through an outcrop.

Greenschist. The typical facies of low-grade metamorphism in the chlorite and biotite zones of the Scottish Dalradian, New England, southern New Zealand and elsewhere (Figures 10–24, and 10–25).

Glaucophane–lawsonite–schist. Low grades of regional metamorphism especially in certain young orogenic zones. Characteristic are various combinations of lawsonite, jadeite-quartz, stilpnomelane, albite, glaucophane, chlorite, muscovite, and garnet.

Amphibolite (Figures 10–13 to 10–15). Medium and high grades of regional metamorphism

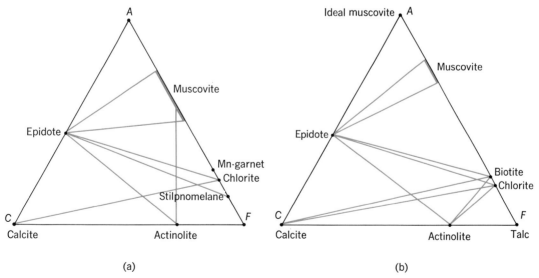

FIG. 10–24 Greenschist facies. ACF diagrams for assemblages with quartz and albite as possible additional phases. (a) Chlorite zone, east Otago, New Zealand (after data of E. H. Brown); (b) Biotite zone, Alpine schists, New Zealand. (After F. J. Turner, Metamorphic Petrology, McGraw-Hill, p. 276, 1968. Copyright 1968. Used by permission of McGraw-Hill Book Co.)

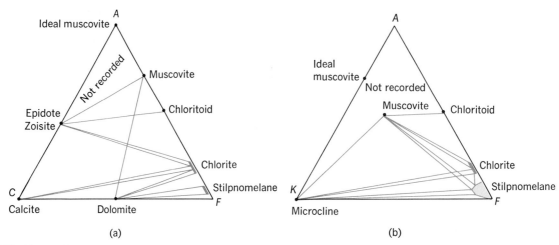

(a)   (b)

FIG. 10–25 *Greenschist facies, Castleton area, Vermont, U.S.A. Phase assemblages with quartz and albite as possible additional minerals. (Modified after E-an Zen; F. J. Turner, ibid., p. 278, 1968. Copyright 1968. Used by permission of McGraw-Hill Book Co.)*

in the Caledonian, Appalachian, and other fold zones; medium grades of Archaean shields, where this facies is very extensive.

Granulite (Figure 10–26). Maximum grades of regional metamorphism in certain regions, especially in Archaean shields.

Eclogite. Facies of very deep-seated metamorphism, in which basic rocks are represented by the two-phase assemblage Mg-Fe garnet plus Na-Ca-Mg-Al pyroxene.

PHYSICAL SIGNIFICANCE

EQUILIBRIUM IN METAMORPHIC ROCKS   From the outset Eskola viewed each metamorphic facies as the product of crystallization within some limited range of pressure and temperature. Moreover he and Goldschmidt developed the thesis that every critical assemblage is a heterogeneous physical system which reached stable divariant equilibrium under the *P-T* conditions of the facies to which it belongs. This proposition has stood up remarkably to critical examination in the light of the accumulated data of half a century's research.

The evidence for general approximation to stable equilibrium is of several independent kinds.

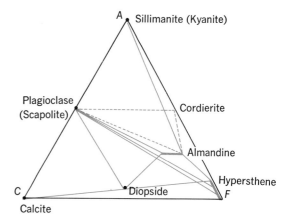

FIG. 10–26 *Granulite facies. Phase assemblages (generalized) in anhydrous rocks with quartz and potassium feldspar as possible additional minerals. (After P. Eskola; F. J. Turner, ibid., p. 329, 1968. Copyright 1968. Used by permission of McGraw-Hill Book Co.)*

1. General simplicity of assemblages, commonly consisting of no more than three to six principal phases.
2. Predictable correlation between rock composition and mineralogy in a given situation—the very essence of the facies concept.
3. Occurrence of facies in regular natural se-

quences, which in some instances can be correlated on geological grounds with depth (that is, increasing P and T) and in others with grade ($= T$ in contact aureoles).

4. Thermodynamic demonstration of stability of many natural carbonate–silicate assemblages (for example, calcite–diopside–wollastonite) in relation to demonstrably metastable chemically equivalent assemblages unknown in nature (for example, calcite–enstatite–wollastonite).

To these generalizations there are many exceptions. Simplicity of paragenesis is complicated by the presence of minor phases (tourmaline, apatite, sphene, iron ores, and so forth). Compositional correlation is never perfect; compositional gradients within crystals of isomorphous series, though by no means as obvious as in igneous rocks, are widespread in some metamorphic minerals (such as garnet or amphibole). Retrogressive effects such as partial chloritization of garnet mar the regularity of paragenesis and express incipient overprinting of one facies on another.

Nevertheless, the evidence of approximation to stable equilibrium is overwhelming. In two respects current interpretation of such equilibrium differs from that of Eskola and Goldschmidt. Both interpretations stem from the growing realization that most critical reactions of progressive metamorphism involve elimination of either water or carbon dioxide.

1. Where diffusion is slow, as it must be in rocks that have already become tightly recrystallized at lower grades, reaction may be constrained to procede strictly along the corresponding curve of univariant equilibrium. Thus the assemblage hornblende – diopside – hypersthene – plagioclase, typical of many granulites, could represent stable univariant equilibrium of the type

$$\text{hornblende} \rightleftarrows \text{pyroxenes} + H_2O$$

2. Equilibria in which either water or carbon dioxide participates will be strongly influenced by the partial pressure of H_2O, or of CO_2 in the gas phase. In a simplified model of ideal mixing of the gas component—justified by available experimental data—there are two independent variables: load pressure P_l, induced by the overlying column of rock, and fluid pressure P_f, maintained in the intergranular pore fluid. Metamorphism of common initially hydrous rocks such as shales approximates a very simple model, $P_l = P_f = P_{H_2O}$ (where P_{H_2O} is the partial pressure of water). In reactions involving carbonates the simplifying assumption is that H_2O and CO_2 are the sole components of the pore fluid, and that $P_f = (P_{H_2O} + P_{CO_2})$. But both in time and in place the relative values of P_{H_2O} and P_{CO_2} are subject to fluctuation. Herein lies the explanation of observed complexity and variability of phase assemblages in metamorphosed dolomitic limestones.

SURVIVAL OF HIGH-GRADE FACIES   In many areas of regional metamorphism, pelitic rocks change, with increasing grade, from chlorite–muscovite-biotite schist to garnet–muscovite–biotite schist to garnet–sillimanite–orthoclase–biotite schist. If each assemblage represents a stable equilibrium, listed in order of increasing temperature, how has the high-grade schist survived slow cooling and unloading without regression to the chlorite–muscovite–biotite assemblage? We have seen that temperatures may be maintained at low-grade levels for tens of millions of years after the isograd pattern became established (see Figure 10–18). This question is relevant to metamorphic rocks of all but the lowest grades. Three factors favor the survival of high-grade facies:

1. Once water has been expelled from the system during progressive metamorphism, the system becomes effectively sealed against backward diffusion of water that would be essential for subsequent retrogressive hydration reactions. In the same way, retrogressive carbonation reactions fail for lack of CO_2. Water, moreover, has a strong catalytic influence in accelerating reactions in which it takes no other part. Laboratory investigation of polymorphic transitions such as kyanite $\rightleftarrows$ sillimanite, became possible only through the development of high-pressure hydrothermal apparatus. Absence of water might slow reactions to a standstill.

2. In most well-documented cases of regional metamorphism, high-grade mineral assemblages began to crystallize early in the deformational history and continued to form, thus establishing the isograd pattern, after the main episodes of deformation recorded in the rock fabrics. Penetrative deformation by reducing grain size, renewing contacts between reactants, and facilitating diffusion of water, also strongly accelerates reaction rates. Indeed retrogressive mineralogical effects consistently occur in zones of strong deformation related to late tectonic episodes long after the culmination of progressive metamorphism.

3. Also significant may be a predictable tendency for reactions to proceed more rapidly in the sense of increasing entropy than in the reverse direction (Chapter 5). Most progressive metamorphism involves increase in entropy.

Temperature–Pressure Gradients of Metamorphism

PHYSICAL CALIBRATION OF ISOGRADS

THE GENERAL PROBLEM Any mapped sequence of metamorphic zones expresses the field distribution and mutual relations of subfacies and facies in some naturally developed series. Ideally, each isograd marks a metamorphic reaction leading to crystallization of the corresponding index mineral. But most of these reactions involve not just the index mineral, but in addition most or all of the closely associated phases, including a pore gas. Even on the assumption that stable equilibria are prevalent in metamorphic rocks, an isograd in many cases cannot be correlated precisely with a point on a linear P-T curve of univariant equilibrium. Instead, because members of isomorphous series almost invariably are among the participating phases, the corresponding equilibrium curve on a P-T diagram (even where $P = P_{H_2O}$) is a band rather than a line.

During the past two decades much effort has been concentrated—and a good deal of progress has been made—in experimental evaluation of the stability fields of critical metamorphic min-

erals. Precise application of experimental data to metamorphism tends, however, to be hindered by such factors as the following:

1. Experimentally investigated material consists largely of chemically pure phases. Most metamorphic minerals, on the other hand, are complicated by isomorphous substitution of two or more elements. Natural jadeite, for example, has a significant content of Fe^{3+}, substituting for Al^{3+} in the ideal composition $NaAlSi_2O_6$. Even calcite in a simple metamorphic assemblage such as calcite-tremolite-diopside may contain significant amounts of Mg.

2. The field of stability of a mineral phase may be reduced—though never extended—by the presence of additional phases. Thus at $T = 670°C$ and $P = P_{H_2O} = 2$ kb, muscovite and its breakdown products are in stable univariant equilibrium ($\Delta G_1 = 0$):

$$\underset{\text{muscovite}}{KAl_2(AlSi_3O_{10})(OH)_2} \rightleftarrows \underset{\text{K-feldspar}}{KAlSi_3O_8} + \underset{\text{corundum}}{Al_2O_3} + H_2O$$

$$(10\text{-}1)$$

Under the same conditions a second reaction tends to run from left to right (ΔG_2 negative):

$$\underset{\text{corundum}}{Al_2O_3} + \underset{\text{quartz}}{SiO_2} \rightarrow \underset{\text{andalusite}}{Al_2SiO_5} \qquad (10\text{-}2)$$

A coupled reaction (10-3), combining (10-1) and (10-2) will also have negative free energy ($\Delta G_3 = \Delta G_1 + \Delta G_2$) and so will also tend to run from left to right:

$$\underset{\text{muscovite}}{KAl_2(AlSi_3O_{10})(OH)_2} + \underset{\text{quartz}}{SiO_2} \rightarrow \underset{\text{K-feldspar}}{KAlSi_3O_8}$$

$$+ \underset{\text{andalusite}}{Al_2SiO_5} + H_2O \quad (10\text{-}3)$$

It can be shown by simple thermodynamic calculation that the equilibrium temperature of reaction (10-3) must be considerably lower than that of (10-1).

3. Some metamorphic assemblages have formed under conditions that differ significantly from simple experimental models such as $P_l = P_f = P_{H_2O}$.

4. Equilibria involving iron silicates and oxides are profoundly influenced by variation in

P_{O_2}. Thus the experimentally established equilibrium between anthophyllite and its dehydration products sets an upper limit to dehydration temperature of hornblende; for both yield (Mg, Fe) SiO_3. But in nature low values of P_{O_2} in contact aureoles would seem to reduce the stability field of hornblende by several hundred degrees below the dehydration temperatures of nonferrous amphiboles.

EXPERIMENTALLY REVERSED REACTIONS   The only satisfactory method by which to establish a *P-T* curve of univariant equilibrium is to reverse the corresponding reaction across narrow temperature intervals at a series of constant pressures. In a series of experiments on carbonate equilibria, Harker and Tuttle showed that the reaction

$$MgCO_3 \leftrightarrows MgO + CO_2$$
$$\text{magnesite} \quad \text{periclase}$$

runs from left to right at 830°C and in the reverse direction at 800°C, in both cases at $P_{CO_2} = 1.43$ kb. Univariant equilibrium at this pressure is thus fixed at 815° ± 15°C. Other points were determined by the same procedure over a convenient pressure range. The corresponding curve of equilibrium is *a* in Figure 10–27.

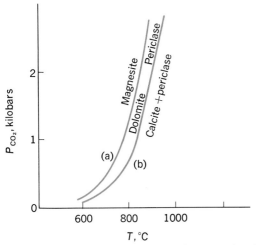

FIG. 10–27 *Experimentally determined curves for decarbonation reactions. (a) Univariant equilibrium: $MgCO_3 \rightleftarrows MgO + CO_2$. (b) Decomposition: $CaMg(CO_3)_2 \leftrightarrows CaCO_3 + MgO + CO_2$. (After R. I. Harker and O. F. Tuttle.)*

Simple though this method may seem, it is beset by experimental difficulties, even to the point where it may fail completely. Nevertheless it may still be possible, even then, to set limits on stability fields of certain phases by determining temperatures and pressures at which a reaction proceeds spontaneously in one direction (usually that of positive ΔS). Such is the curve (Figure 10–27, curve *B*) for decomposition of dolomite

$$CaMg(CO_3)_2 \rightarrow CaCO_3 + MgO + CO_2$$
$$\text{dolomite} \quad\quad \text{calcite} \quad \text{periclase}$$

To the right of curve *B*, dolomite clearly is unstable. Moreover, curve *B* in Figure 10–30, representing an equilibrium

$$CaAl_2Si_2O_7(OH)_2H_2O \rightleftarrows CaAl_2Si_2O_8 + 2H_2O$$
$$\text{lawsonite} \quad\quad\quad \text{anorthite}$$

that is metastable sets limits to temperatures beyond which lawsonite cannot be stable.

THERMODYNAMIC APPROACH   Given accurate thermal data for all mineral and gas phases involved in metamorphic reactions, it would be possible to define the stability field of every metamorphic phase assemblage. Unfortunately the required data are scanty and subject to significant error. Nevertheless the thermodynamic approach can give useful information applicable to metamorphic problems:

1. Since for equilibrium at a given temperature (T_e°K) and constant pressure (*P* kb)

$$\Delta G = \Delta H - T\Delta S = 0$$

then

$$T_e = \frac{\Delta H}{\Delta S}$$

In many cases, a good approximation to the equilibrium temperature can be obtained by using standard values $\Delta H°$ and $\Delta S°$ at 25°C. Temperatures (±40°) thus calculated for some possible carbonate equilibria (at $P_{CO_2} = 1$ bar) are as follows:

$$200°C$$
$$CaMg(CO_3)_2 + 2SiO_2 \rightleftarrows CaMgSi_2O_6 + 2CO_2$$
$$\text{dolomite} \quad\quad \text{quartz} \quad\quad \text{diopside}$$

$$\overset{270°C}{CaCO_3 + SiO_2 \rightleftarrows CaSiO_3 + CO_2}$$

calcite   quartz   wollastonite

$$\overset{290°C}{2CaMg(CO_3)_2 + SiO_2 \rightleftarrows Mg_2SiO_4 + 2CaCO_3}$$

dolomite   quartz   forsterite   calcite

$$+ 2CO_2$$

These data show that, in the absence of water, diopside should form in siliceous dolomites at temperatures considerably lower than those at which wollastonite first appears in siliceous limestones. Most geologists would agree with this on the basis of field evidence. It is also obvious that the third equilibrium must be metastable, and hence cannot account for the first appearance of forsterite in nature.

2. By locating approximate positions on an equilibrium curve, thermodynamic calculation limits the likely field of P and T for attempts at experimental reversal.

3. The slopes of equilibrium curves can be predicted from the Clausius-Clapeyron relation, equation (5-12):

$$\frac{dP}{dT} = \frac{\Delta S}{\Delta V}$$

There is a common inverse correlation between density and entropy in silicates; so that for solid $\rightleftarrows$ solid reactions involving significant volume change, the equilibrium curves have similar slopes—about 20 bars per degree at pressures of a few kb. Decarbonation curves in the range $P = 1$ to 2 kb, $T = 600°$ to $800°C$, slope at 12–15 bars per degree. The figure for silicate dehydration reactions is significantly greater: That calculated for dehydration of muscovite in the general range $P_{H_2O} = 1$–2 kb, $T = 650°$–$700°C$, is 28 bars per degree.

4. Thermodynamic data demonstrate the potentiality of coupled reactions for reducing the stability fields of simple mineral assemblages. Referring once more to the breakdown of muscovite, the first reaction

muscovite → K-feldspar + corundum + water

involves a large positive ΔS_1. The second reaction

corundum + quartz → andalusite

has a small negative ΔS_2 (as in most solid → solid reactions) and large negative ΔH_2 (typical of oxide → silicate reactions). So the third (coupled) reaction,

muscovite + quartz → K-feldspar
+ andalusite + water

has ΔS_3 slightly lower than ΔS_1 and ΔH_3 much lower than ΔH_1. Consequently at the equilibrium temperature T_1 of the simple muscovite breakdown

$$T_1 = \frac{\Delta H_1}{\Delta S_1} > \frac{\Delta H_1 + \Delta H_2}{\Delta S_1 + \Delta S_2} = \frac{\Delta H_3}{\Delta S_3} = T_3$$

Thus the equilibrium temperature of the muscovite breakdown is reduced in the presence of quartz by an amount somewhat smaller than $\Delta H_2 / \Delta S_1$.

5. The magnitude of reaction entropy ΔS for any reaction involving CO_2, H_2O, or both components, is determined largely by the high entropy of CO_2 and H_2O in the gaseous state. Reliable data are available for S_{CO_2} ($P = 0$ to 1.4 kb) and for S_{H_2O} ($P = 0$ to 5 kb) over the complete range of metamorphic temperatures. It is possible, therefore, to calculate with fair accuracy the value of ΔS for any such reaction at any given P and T within these limits. The equilibrium can be written in a general form

$$aA = bB + yCO_2 + zH_2O$$

with due regard to sign of y and z (for example, z positive in dehydration, negative in hydration), and putting $|y| + |z| = 1$; $y + z \gtrless 0$. For any fixed concentrations of $CO_2(X_{CO_2})$ and $H_2O(X_{H_2O})$ in the gas phase at any constant pressure P, the equilibrium temperature T_e is related to X_{CO_2} by the expression

$$\left(\frac{\partial T_e}{\partial X_{CO_2}}\right)_P = \frac{RT}{\Delta S}\left(\frac{y}{X_{CO_2}} - \frac{z}{X_{H_2O}}\right)$$

where $X_{CO_2} + X_{H_2O} = 1$. This expression prescribes the geometric form of any isobaric plot of T_e against X_{CO_2} for an equilibrium of this kind, as follows:

$$\tfrac{1}{2}CaMg(CO_3)_2 \rightleftarrows \tfrac{1}{2}CaCO_3 + \tfrac{1}{2}Mg(OH)_2$$

dolomite   calcite   brucite

$$+ \tfrac{1}{2}CO_2 - \tfrac{1}{2}H_2O$$

The value of ΔS clearly must be small. In fact as calculated for $P = 1$–500 bars it is zero, within limits of accuracy of the data. Thus, T_e at constant pressure is insensitive to complementary variation in X_{CO_2} and X_{H_2O}, and the equilibrium curve (Figure 10–28, curve a) is horizontal. Also, it must pass through an invariant point I at the intersection of the experimentally determined

curves for decarbonation of dolomite to periclase and hydration of periclase to brucite.

$$\tfrac{1}{4}Ca_2Mg_5Si_8O_{22}(OH)_2 + \tfrac{3}{4}CaCO_3 + \tfrac{1}{2}SiO_2 \rightleftarrows$$
$$\text{tremolite} \qquad\quad \text{calcite} \qquad \text{quartz}$$
$$1\tfrac{1}{4}CaMgSi_2O_6 + \tfrac{3}{4}CO_2 + \tfrac{1}{4}H_2O$$
$$\text{diopside}$$

The equilibrium curve (b in Figure 10–28) rises

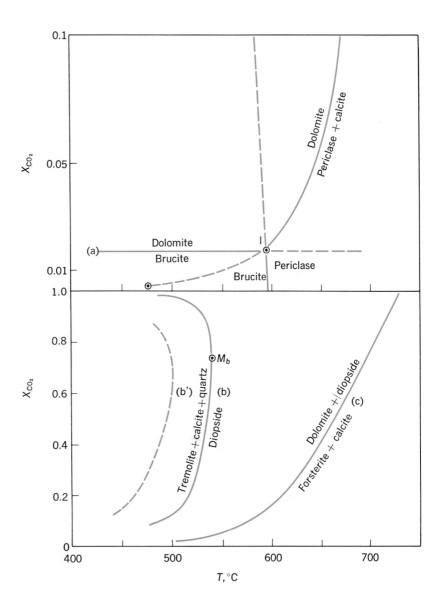

FIG. 10–28 Isobaric plot (at $P_f = 1$ kb) of equilibrium temperature T_e against molecular concentration of CO_2 in gas phase, X_{CO_2}, for some decarbonation and dehydration reactions. (a) ½ Dolomite ⇆ ½ Calcite + ½ Brucite + ½ CO_2 − ½ H_2O. Calculated. Broken curves show metastable equilibria. (b) ¼ Tremolite + ¾ Calcite + ½ Quartz ⇆ 1¼ Diopside + ¾CO_2 + ¼H_2O. Experimentally determined. (After P. Metz and H. G. F. Winkler.) (b') Same as (b). Calculated. (c) ½ Dolomite + 1½ Diopside ⇆ Forsterite + 2 Calcite + CO_2. Calculated.

to a maximum temperature at $X_{CO_2} = y = 0.75$; for here $(\partial T_e/\partial X_{CO_2})_P = 0$.

$$1\tfrac{1}{2}\underset{\text{dolomite}}{CaMg(CO_3)_2} + \tfrac{1}{2}\underset{\text{diopside}}{CaMgSi_2O_6} \rightleftarrows$$
$$\underset{\text{forsterite}}{Mg_2SiO_4} + \underset{\text{calcite}}{2CaCO_3} + CO_2$$

Here, as in all pure decarbonation reactions, the equilibrium temperature is maximal for $X_{CO_2} = 1$ and falls with decreasing X_{CO_2}, becoming asymptotic toward the zero line (curve C, Figure 10–28).

SOME CRITICAL EQUILIBRIA *Equilibria for pelitic assemblages* Figure 10–29 shows two sets of univariant equilibrium curves that have been applied to pelitic mineral assemblages. Each, of course, is subject to future modification. There

is still no general consensus regarding location of the triple point for Al_2SiO_5 polymorphs in Figure 10–29a; inversion is so slow that it is difficult to demonstrate experimental reversal. Only a few years ago some geochemists placed this value at about 8 kb, 400°C. This result posed almost insurmountable geological problems and was in direct conflict with reliable thermodynamic data. Some geochemists today accept as a "best" value Newton's experimentally determined point close to 4 kb, 550°C; others prefer a value of 5 kb. In Figure 10–29a we have shown two alternatives: Newton's value and one proposed by Fyfe at 2.8 kb, 480°C. With regard to other critical curves, such as that for dehydration of muscovite–quartz (Figure 10–29b), there is more general agreement. Since muscovite always

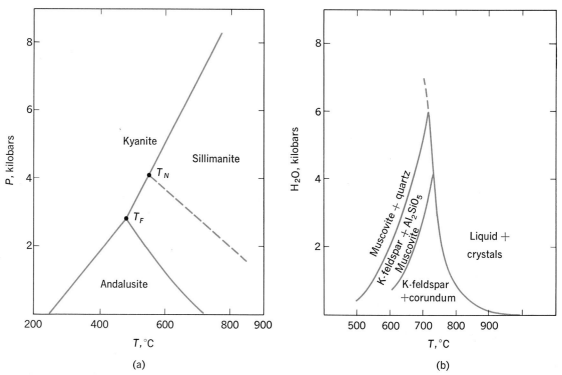

FIG. 10–29 *Experimentally based curves of univariant equilibrium for critical minerals of pelitic rocks. (a) Polymorphs of Al_2SiO_5. (After W. S. Fyfe, Chem. Geol., vol. 2, p. 74, 1967.) T_F is maximum pressure within limits of Fyfe's diagram. T_N is triple point as defined by R. C. Newton. (b) Dehydration of muscovite (after B. W. Evans, Am. J. Sci., vol. 263, p. 660, 1965) and melting of anhydrous products.*

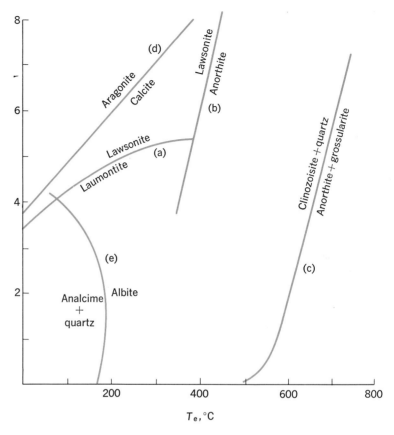

FIG. 10–30 *(a)–(c). Experimentally based curves of univariant equilibrium for some CaAl and NaAl silicates of metamorphic rocks: lawsonite, $CaAl_2Si_2O_7(OH)_2 \cdot H_2O$; laumontite, $CaAl_2Si_4O_{12} \cdot 4H_2O$; clinozoisite, $Ca_2Al_3Si_3O_{12}(OH)$; anorthite, $CaAl_2Si_2O_8$; grossularite, $Ca_3Al_2Si_4O_{12}$, albite, $NaAlSi_3O_8$; analcime, $NaAlSi_2 \cdot O_6 \cdot H_2O$. (a) Calculated from thermochemical data (after W. A. Crawford and W. S. Fyfe). (b) Experimentally determined (metastable) (after W. A. Crawford and W. S. Fyfe). (c) Experimentally determined (after M. J. Holdaway). (d) Calcite ⇌ aragonite inversion, experimentally determined (after W. L. Boettcher and P. J. Wyllie). (e) Experimentally determined at low pressure and thermodynamically extrapolated to high pressures (after A. S. Campbell and W. S. Fyfe).*

contains some Na^+ substituting for K^+, the breakdown curves for natural muscovites may be slightly to the left of those shown here.

Equilibria with Ca-Al Silicates   At all grades of metamorphism derivatives of basic igneous rocks, feldspathic sediments, and limestones with initial clay impurity are represented by assemblages that include one or more Ca-Al silicates. At the lowest grades these are typically hydrated phases, such as lawsonite or clinozoinite. The ultimate products of high-grade metamorphism are anhydrous silicates: anorthite (as a component of plagioclase) and grossularite. Some useful experimental data, together with the aragonite ⇌ calcite inversion curve are shown in Figure 10–30.

Carbonate equilibria   Progressive metamor-phism of limestones containing normal silica and clay impurities involves a succession of decarbonation reactions with calcite and dolomite as initial participants. Significant reactions between carbonates and silica in the absence of water (Figure 10–31) are:

(1) $\frac{1}{2}\underset{\text{dolomite}}{CaMg(CO_3)_2} + \underset{\text{quartz}}{SiO_2}$

$\rightleftarrows \frac{1}{2}\underset{\text{diopside}}{CaMgSi_2O_6} + CO_2$

(2) $\underset{\text{calcite}}{CaCO_2} + \underset{\text{quartz}}{SiO_2} \rightleftarrows \underset{\text{wollastonite}}{CaSiO_3} + CO_2$

(3) $\frac{1}{2}\underset{\text{diopside}}{CaMgSi_2O_6} + 1\frac{1}{2}\underset{\text{dolomite}}{CaMg(CO_3)_2}$

$\rightleftarrows \underset{\text{forsterite}}{Mg_2SiO_4} + 2\underset{\text{calcite}}{CaCO_3} + CO_2$

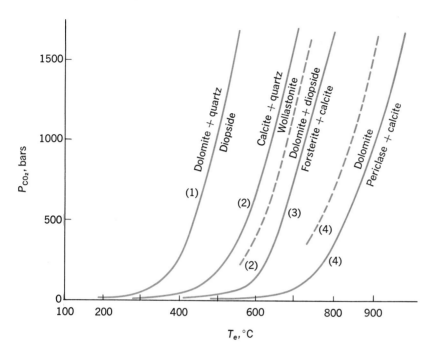

FIG. 10–31 Curves of univariant equilibrium for reactions involving dolomite, calcite, and quartz in the absence of water. Thermodynamically computed. Reactions numbered as in text. Dotted curves (2) and (4) experimentally determined by R. I. Harker and O. F. Tuttle.

(4) $CaMg(CO_3)_2 \rightleftarrows CaCO_3$
     dolomite   calcite
     $+ MgO + CO_2$
          periclase

At any given pressure P_f, the equilibrium temperature of any such reaction is lowered by addition of water to the gas phase—reduction of X_{CO_2}. Between X_{CO_2} values 1 and 0.8, the reduction must be small.

Presence of water, even at concentrations of

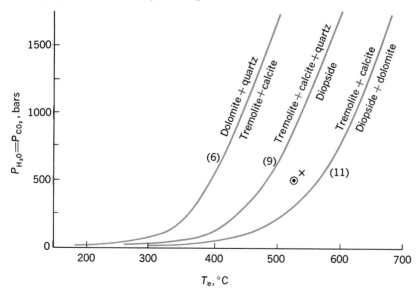

FIG. 10–32 Curves of univariant equilibrium for carbonate-quartz reactions involving water. X_{CO_2} constant at 0.5, thermodynamically computed. Point X experimentally determined for reaction (9) by P. Metz and H. G. F. Winkler.

this order $(X_{H_2O} = 0.05\text{--}0.2)$ introduces the possibility of combined hydration–decarbonation reactions (Figure 10–32), such as those that yield tremolite, and much more rarely talc, at low grades of metamorphism of siliceous dolomitic limestones. These hydrous phases tend to be eliminated with advancing temperature by reactions of combined dehydration and decarbonation.

SOME PARTICULAR GRADIENTS

CRITERIA EMPLOYED   The particular gradient that is recorded along a line transverse to the isograds of any individual area can be calibrated by using a number of independent criteria:

1. Stratigraphic depth as an index of load pressure P_l (especially useful in load and contact metamorphism).

2. Stratigraphic depth interval between isograds, as an index of pressure intervals between different grades of burial metamorphism. On these grounds it has been shown that in the low-grade metamorphic terrane of southern New Zealand, the zeolite and intermediate low-grade facies cover a pressure interval of at least 5 kb before the greenschist facies develops at still greater depth and pressure.

3. Pressure–temperature values on experimentally established curves of univariant equilibrium, with due regard to possible effects of coupled reactions, solid-solution effects (estimated according to solution theory), and reasonable ranges of P_{O_2}.

4. Estimates of isograd temperatures for which direct experimental evidence is meager or lacking. The first appearance of biotite, judging from field relations of the biotite to other isograds, must usually be in the range 350–400°C. Oxygen-isotope data indicate values at least as low as 400°C. Cordierite is a low-pressure phase compared with garnet. Hornblende gives way to pyroxenes only at temperatures higher than those on the dehydration curve for muscovite–quartz; for in some contact aureoles (Sierra Nevada, California) and in zones of transition from the amphibolite to the granulite facies, horn-

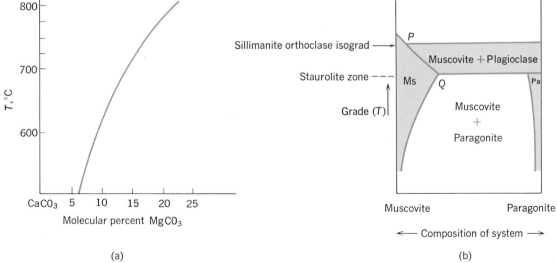

(a)   (b)

FIG. 10–33 *Composition of coexisting phases in solid-solution series with limited miscibility. (a) Magnesian calcite in equilibrium with dolomite, P_{CO_2} = 500–1500 kb. (After D. L. Graf and J. R. Goldsmith, Geochim. Cosmochim. Acta, vol. 7, p. 118, 1955.) (b) Coexisting muscovite and paragonite in pelitic schists, staurolite–kyanite and sillimanite zones, Maine and Nova Scotia. Observed compositions, PQ. Remainder of diagram inferred. (Simplified after B. W. Evans and C. V. Guidotti, Contrib. Mineral. Petrol., vol. 12, p. 53, 1963.)*

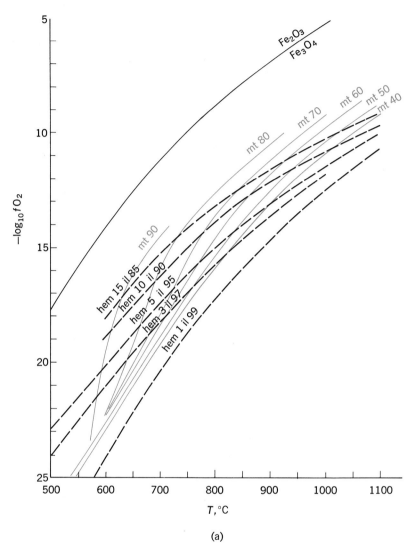

FIG. 10–34 (Left and facing) *Experimentally determined magnetite–hematite equilibria. (After A. F. Buddington and D. H. Lindsley, Jour. Petrol., vol. 5, pp. 315, 316, 1964.) (a) Compositions of magnetite–ulvospinel and hematite–ilmenite solid solutions as a function of temperature and oxygen fugacity f_{O_2}.*

blende–plagioclase assemblages are associated with quartz–sillimanite (or andalusite–orthoclase); see equation (10-3).

5. The past decade has seen rapid development and increased use of new instruments and techniques for mineral analysis, including the electron microprobe, the mass spectrometer, and X-ray and spectrographic techniques. In consequence it is relatively easy to obtain information regarding the distribution of common elements, and even of different isotopes of the same element (O, S), between coexisting phases in natural or experimentally formed phase assemblages. Such information will be increasingly used in the future to calibrate metamorphic temperatures and pressures.

(a) The simplest case is metamorphic crystallization of two phases in a solid-solution series of limited miscibility. Such is calcite–dolomite (Figure 10-33a). The calcite side of the solvus has been determined experimentally; and, because ΔV of solution is almost zero, this is a satisfactory

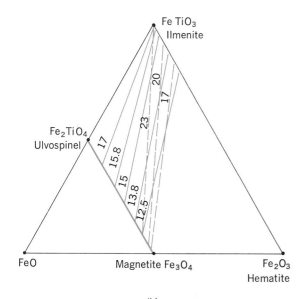

(b)

FIG. 10–34 *(b) Coexisting solid solutions at 800°C (full lines) and 600° (dashed lines). Values of ln f_{o_2} are shown on each tie.*

compositions of coexisting magnetite and ilmenite at a range of oxygen fugacities held constant in each experiment by a buffer such as Fe_3O_4–Fe_2O_3 or Fe_2SiO_4–Fe_3O_4–SiO_2. In Figure 10–34, the variable titanium content of magnetite, *mt*, Fe_3O_4 is expressed as molecular percentage of ulvospinel *usp*, Fe_2TiO_4. Similarly excess iron in ilmenite, *il*, $FeTiO_3$ is shown in terms of the hematite molecule, *hem*, Fe_2O_3.

(c) Most promising of all is the partition of oxygen isotopes between quartz, which has a relatively high O^{18}/O^{16} ratio at all temperatures, and various coexisting silicates. A well-established experimental standard is provided by the widely distributed metamorphic pair quartz–muscovite, which is especially sensitive in the low-temperature range (Figure 10–35).

potential geothermometer relatively insensitive to pressure. Its use is limited to calcite coexisting with dolomite; and since microscopically visible exsolution takes place above about 600°C, the composition of magnesian calcite is an index limited to the lower range of metamorphic temperatures. Much is already known as to the compositions of coexisting members of some solid-solution series in metamorphic rocks. Such data will be used in the future for estimation of *P-T* conditions of crystallization as soon as the temperature scale of the solvus has been established by experiment. A case in point concerns compositions of coexisting white micas—muscovite $KAl_2(AlSi_3O_{10})(OH)_2$ and its sodic analogue paragonite $NaAl_2(AlSi_3O_{10})(OH)_2$—in high-grade pelitic schists (Figure 10–33b).

(b) Already widely used are compositions of coexisting iron oxides. Postmetamorphic exsolution occurs here, too, but the individual crystals of the two phases are easily separated for analysis; and, provided there is no postmetamorphic oxidation or reduction, the individual mineral crystal retains its original total composition. There are experimental data for equilibrium

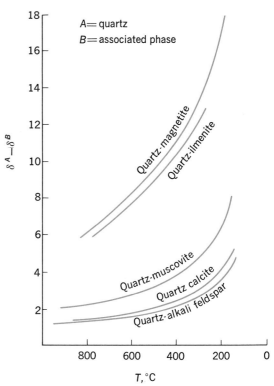

FIG. 10–35 *Experimentally determined standards for $\delta_{o_{18}}/_{o_{16}}$ in coexisting phases. (After H. P. Taylor, in Geochemistry of Hydrothermal Ore Deposits, Holt, Rinehart and Winston, Inc., p. 125, 1967.)*

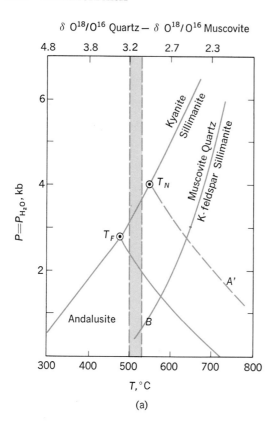

δ O^{18}/O^{16} Quartz $-$ δ O^{18}/O^{16} Muscovite

(a)

TEMPERATURE GRADIENT, SANTA ROSA AUREOLE, NEVADA Assuming constant pressure across the full width of a contact aureole it is possible to construct, on a mineralogical basis, a gradient for temperature decreasing outward from the contact. Figure 10–36b represents such a gradient in the aureole of the Santa Rosa grandiorite stock intrusive into pelitic phyllites with thin limestone interbeds, Santa Rosa Range, Nevada. The composition of the intrusive body is consistent with initial magmatic temperatures of 800°C to 900°C. Equilibria for evaluating T and P are shown in Figure 10–36a. Critical points are as follows:

1. Aureole temperatures of 510°–530° within a few centimeters of the contact, and 500° less than 1 meter away are indicated by respective values 3.1 and 3.2 for $\delta_{O^{18}/O^{16}}$ fractionation between muscovite and quartz.

2. At about 100 meters from the contact andalusite and muscovite, both widely prevalent further out in the aureole, begin to be eliminated:

andalusite → sillimanite
muscovite + quartz → K-feldspar + sillimanite + water

Curves A and B of Figure 10–36a, used in conjunction, give temperatures close to 500°C at pressures of 1–1.5 kb, if P_{H_2O} is somewhat less

FIG. 10–36 (Above and right) (a) Equilibrium curves used to estimate P–T conditions in a contact aureole. (b) Mineralogically calibrated temperature gradient (full line) contact aureole of Santa Rosa granodioritic stock, Nevada. Broken curves computed by H. P. Taylor for various heat-flow models. A—Intrusive infinite cylinder, square cross section 2.5 km × 2.5 km; initial temperature 700°C, initial country-rock temperature 100°C. B—Cylinder, dimensions 3.75 km × 3.75 km; initial magmatic temperature 900°C. C—Similar to A, but intrusive body is an infinite sheet 2.5 km wide.

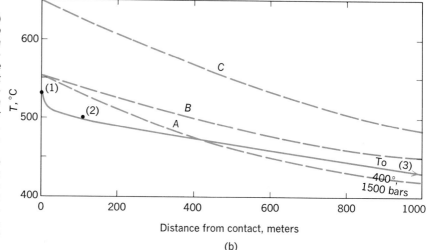

(b)

than total pressure.[2] Alternatively if the andalusite $\rightleftarrows$ sillimanite transition is defined by curve (A[1]), we must suppose either that temperature is impossibly high (620°C) compared with paragraph 1 above, or that total pressure is between 3 kb and 4 kb and P_{H_2O} is very much lower. Such high pressures are inconsistent with widespread crystallization of andalusite, not kyanite, far out from the contact. Pressures independently estimated on stratigraphic evidence relating to thickness of cover are 1–2 kb, with preference for the lower limit.

3. In the outer aureole the first sign of contact metamorphism is crystallization of biotite at about 1500 meters from the contact. This geologically obvious and almost universal index of increasing metamorphic grade has not yet been satisfactory calibrated by experiment. Oxygen-isotope fractionation between quartz and muscovite in metamorphic rocks that also contain biotite indicates temperatures down to 420° or 400°C. So in Figure 10–36 the first appearance of biotite is rather arbitrarily assigned the value 400°C; this temperature may well prove to be somewhat high.

Wollastonite has crystallized abundantly in impure limestone interbeds in the inner zone of the aureole. At temperatures around 500°C this implies P_{CO_2} values of only a few bars—that is, free escape of carbon dioxide under conditions in which, even in the limestone, P_{H_2O} was considerably higher than P_{CO_2}. This seems a rather common situation in contact metamorphism.

TEMPERATURE–PRESSURE GRADIENTS OF REGIONAL METAMORPHISM   The gradient expressed by a series of isograds in any province of regional metamorphism must involve significant variation

in both temperature and pressure. To construct a temperature–pressure gradient in such cases is obviously more difficult than to plot temperature against distance in a contact aureole. The mineral paragenesis of each zone represents a limited *P-T* span upon some gradient that existed over a limited period of time during the metamorphic cycle. If crystallization in the lower-grade and in the higher-grade zones covered time intervals that were mutually separated by tens of millions of years (see Figure 10–18), then the gradient expressed by the whole sequence of isograds must be compounded of two or more distinct *P-T* gradients. To draw a rectilinear gradient passing through the zero point of pressure and temperature (surface conditions) implies that metamorphic conditions were controlled by depth alone.

Theoretically it should be possible to establish points on a natural gradient by measuring temperatures on the oxygen-isotope geothermometer at isograds marked by pressure-dependent simple solid-solid reactions. Some that have obvious potentiality are

$$\text{kyanite} \rightleftarrows \text{sillimanite}$$
$$\text{andalusite} \rightleftarrows \text{sillimanite}$$
$$\text{jadeite} + \text{quartz} \rightleftarrows \text{albite}$$

Dehydration reactions will also be useful, provided it can be assumed that $P_{H_2O} = P_l$. Particularly important is

$$\text{muscovite} + \text{quartz} \rightleftarrows \text{orthoclase}$$
$$+ \text{Al}_2\text{SiO}_5 + \text{water}$$

There is still a good deal of uncertainty regarding the *P-T* conditions of all the foregoing and other critical equilibria. But a start has been made in applying them to evaluation of metamorphic gradients; and the results, though open to constant revision, are beginning to assume a state of internal consistency.

Some writers, following Miyashiro, have attempted to establish standard gradients of pressure and temperature defining standard *facies series*—for example, the Barrovian versus the Ryoke pattern. We tend to regard each gradient as unique; and on a pressure–temperature diagram surely there will be some gradients that in-

---

[2] A similar situation has been established by Sheih and Taylor from oxygen-isotope compositions in the inner part of the Birch Creek sector of the Inyo contact aureole (Figure 10–4). Temperature rises from 460°C at 400 meters from the contact to 535°C at the contact itself. At 300 meters from the contact andalusite gives way to sillimanite, and in the inner sillimanite zone muscovite has been elminated in quartz-bearing rocks (see *J. Petrol.*, vol. 10, pp. 307–331, 1969).

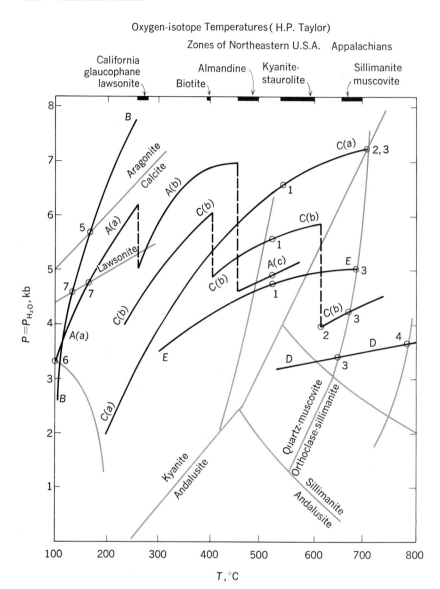

FIG. 10–37 *Some tentative temperature-pressure gradients of regional metamorphism.*
A—New Zealand geosyncline.
B—California coast ranges.
C—Barrow's zones, southeastern Dalradian, Scotland.
D—Broken Hill, Australia.
E—Lepontine Alps, Switzerland.

tersect. Figure 10–37 shows several highly tentative gradients corresponding to classic areas of regional metamorphism. Numbers on each curve refer to points annotated below; circled points have been calibrated with reference to experimentally based curves:

1. First appearance of kyanite, Al_2SiO_5. This must be at temperatures greater than 400°–

420°C, the upper limit of stability of the hydrous aluminum silicate pyrophyllite.

2. Kyanite stops; sillimanite comes in.

3. Quartz–muscovite gives way to orthoclase-sillimanite.

4. Hornblende in granulites becomes dehydrated to pyroxenes.

5. The high-pressure polymorph of $CaCO_3$,

aragonite, appears, and can survive without inversion to calcite on subsequent cooling, only from temperatures less than 200°–300°C.

6. The sodic zeolite analcime in the presence of quartz is dehydrated to albite.

7. Lawsonite forms from calcic zeolites.

The following lettered items refer to the corresponding curves of Figure 10–37:

A. (a) Burial metamorphism in marginal zone of New Zealand geosyncline.
    (b) Progressive metamorphism, chlorite and biotite zones, Otago schist zone, New Zealand.

(c) Progressive metamorphism, Alpine schist zone, New Zealand. Broken line represents unloading subsequent to the second episode of Rangitatan folding.

Possible change of temperature in time along each of these gradients is shown in Figure 10–38.

B. Burial metamorphism culminating in regional metamorphism in glaucophane–lawsonite–schist facies, Californian coast ranges.

C. Regional metamorphism, Barrovian zones, southeastern Dalradian, Scotland.

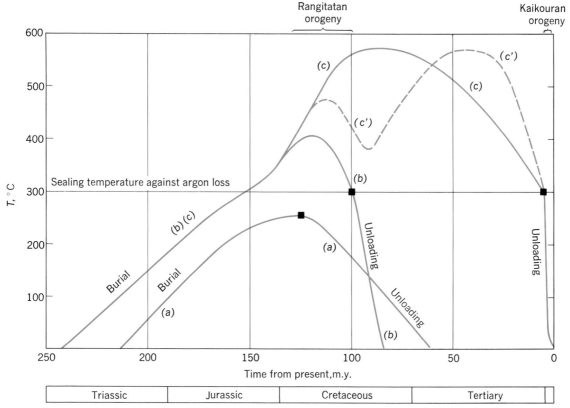

FIG. 10–38 Not impossible relations of temperature to time in three chronological provinces of metamorphism, New Zealand geosyncline (see page 569). Lettered to correspond with gradients A in Figure 10–37. (a) Marginal zone, purely burial metamorphism. (b) Maximum grade, chlorite zone, Otago schist. (c) Maximum grade, oligoclase zone Alpine schist near Alpine fault zone; (c') is a second alternative.

(a) Simple gradient
(b) Broken gradient showing two stages of reduction of pressure (erosion) following F_1 and F_2 folding episodes.
D. Regional metamorphism, Precambrian of Broken Hill mining region, Australia. Low pressure is inferred from abundance of cordierite in the high-grade rocks (granulite facies). Point 4 was determined experimentally for hornblende of Broken Hill amphibolite, but the reaction is sensitive to variation in P_{O_2}. Temperatures in the range $600°-670°C$ are indicated by compositions of coexisting iron-titanium oxide minerals in high-grade rocks (between points 3 and 4).
E. Leopontine Alps, Switzerland. Data are taken from work by E. Wenk, E. Niggli, and colleagues. The isograds were imprinted in a single Tertiary event of rather short duration.

Outstanding Problems

RELATION OF FACIES TO TEMPERATURE AND PRESSURE

Thirty years ago Bowen proposed the then almost abstract concept of a *petrogenic grid*—a network of intersecting univariant equilibrium curves for reactions significant in metamorphism, plotted in terms of P and T variables. Today this concept is abstract no longer. Many such curves, thanks to experimental geochemists and the growing data of thermodynamics, can be located with fair accuracy. On this grid we may now plot the distribution of index minerals and critical phase asssemblages typical of every metamorphic facies. In this way the facies themselves are calibrated in terms of pressure and temperature, and the physical significance of transitional facies, such as the amphibolite–granulite transition, also becomes apparent. Since the day a half-century ago when Goldschmidt calculated a curve for the calcite–wollastonite equilibrium (Figure 10–31, curve 2), much of the effort in metamorphic petrology has been directed to this general end.

A tentative version is given in Figure 10–39. The outstanding problem is to refine and modify the facies grid to meet the requirements of more reliable data, always remembering that the newest data are not necessarily the best.

WATER SOURCES

We have seen that a most important role in metamorphism must be assigned to water, and that where metamorphic reactions involve hydration or dehydration—as they commonly do—water must be able to diffuse into or from the reacting system. There are three obvious possible sources for such water: descending meteoric water, juvenile water ascending from the mantle or the deep crust, and water held in the parent rock (for example, in shale) prior to metamorphism. Oxygen-isotope and hydrogen-isotope data are beginning to eliminate some possibilities and to pose more concrete problems as to the sources of "metamorphic" waters and to systems of diffusion during a cycle of metamorphism.

In some contact aureoles that have been investigated, the consistent "shale values" of $\delta_{O^{18}}/\delta_{O^{16}}$ (16–18 per mil) displayed by pelitic metasediments, except at the immediate igenous contact, show that the shales themselves have supplied the metamorphic water. Isotopic fractionation during dehydration of shale appears to be negligible. The sense of diffusion of water expelled from the magma seems to be upward. Lateral diffusion, where effective, is an earlier process by which water from the metamorphic system may be transferred some distance into the still-molten magma body.

In the case of regional metamorphism the situation seems to be entirely different. Only exchange with an extensive external oxygen reservoir can account for systematic observed changes in the isotopic composition of oxygen. The value of $\delta_{O^{18}}/\delta_{O^{16}}$ in pelitic rocks of low grade (chlorite zone) is that typical of shales (15 to 18 per mil). It decreases steadily through the biotite, garnet, and staurolite–kyanite zones, to values in the range 9–13 for high-grade sillimanite schists. Taylor proposes continuous exchange, over very long intervals of time, between the metamorphic sys-

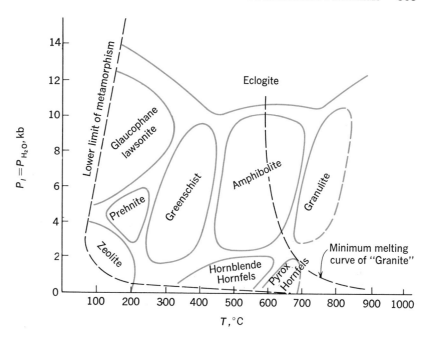

FIG. 10–39 *Tentative scheme of metamorphic facies in relation to* $P_1 (= P_{H_2O})$ *and T. All boundaries gradational. (Slightly modified from F. J. Turner, Metamorphic Petrology, McGraw-Hill, p. 366, 1968. Copyright 1968. Used by permission of McGraw-Hill Book Co.)*

tem and an oxygen reservoir of aqueous fluid rising from some kind of deep-seated, and necessarily extensive, igneous bodies. And he cites the well-known broad association in space and time between regional metamorphism and plutonism (emplacement of granites). But this relation, as we have seen, is somewhat capricious. Are these granites the source of the metamorphic oxygen reservoir? Or must we appeal to some other source?

HEAT SOURCES

To set up a tentative *P-T* gradient of metamorphism is to pose the vexing problem of a possible heat source.

1. It would seem intuitively that the source of heat for contact metamorphism must lie in the pluton itself. The thermal gradients constructed from geological data for individual aureoles on the whole fit remarkably well those predicted by Jaeger's model of heat flowing outward from a crystallizing and cooling intrusive body of once-liquid magma.

2. Some gradients of regional metamorphism leading from the zeolite to the glaucophane–

lawsonite–schist or to the greenschist facies are consistent with simultaneous rise in *P* and *T* on geothermal gradients that are less than average or normal respectively. This is the concept of burial metamorphism. Where reactions are endothermic (as in dehydration) there is still a problem of heat supply. But reactions such as hydration of basaltic tuff to greenschist would be exothermic and self-perpetuating. Herein may be a signficant heat source for low-grade regional metamorphism, for much of the original filling of geosynclines is anhydrous volcanic material.

3. High grades of regional metamorphism cannot be explained so simply. They demand a geothermal gradient much greater than that usually regarded as normal. In some areas uprise of granitic magma on a regional scale may possibly have accelerated heat flow in the overlying rocks. But the sequence of events in metamorphic–orogenic cycles as revealed by radiometric dating is not compatible with the once-favored view that temperature gradients of regional metamorphism are the direct consequence of regional invasion by subjacent granitic batholiths. In the classic Dalradian terrane of Scotland the great upsurge

of "granitic" magma came many millions of years after the culmination of metamorphism; and at least some of this magma seems to have come from very great depth. By contrast some granites seem to be the product of rock melting, almost in place, at foci of high-grade metamorphism. These can be regarded as the extreme products rather than the primary cause of metamorphism. A most convincing case, for example, has been made for development of Older Granite bodies by melting in place in the heart of Barrow's sillimanite zone at Glen Clova. There is a touch of irony in this; for Barrow's great classic of 1893— the first demonstration of the zonal pattern and progressive nature of regional metamorphism— bears this title: "On an intrusion of muscovite–biotite–gneiss [today called Older Granite] in the south-east Highlands of Scotland and its accompanying metamorphism."

And so we return to the question raised at the close of the preceding section: What is the deep plutonic source of metamorphic water? Not Older Granites, if they form as ultimate products of fusion in place. Not Younger Granites, since these are postmetamorphic in time. Perhaps the progressive change in oxygen composition with increasing grade of metamorphism is the only direct evidence of a continuous subcrustal disturbance, one aspect of which is sustained upward expulsion of primitive water throughout the whole duration of a cycle of regional metamorphism.

REFERENCES

Aronson, J. L.: Regional geochronology of New Zealand, *Geochim. Cosmochim. Acta*, vol. 32, pp. 669–697, 1968.

> Radiometric dating of metamorphic and plutonic events in southern New Zealand.

Barrell, J.: Relations of subjacent igneous invasion to regional metamorphism, *Am. J. Sci.*, vol. 1, pp. 1–19, 174–186, 245–267, 1921.

Bowen, N. L.: Progressive metamorphism of siliceous limestone and dolomite, *J. Geol.*, vol. 48, pp. 225–274, 1940.

> The classic theoretical discussion of steps in reaction between calcite, dolomite, and silica, with advancing temperature.

Brown, E. H.: The greenschist facies in part of eastern Otago, New Zealand, *Contrib. Mineral. Petrol.*, vol. 14, pp. 259–292, 1967.

> A study of progressive low-grade metamorphism.

Chinner, G. A.: Almandine in contact aureoles, *J. Petrol.*, vol. 3, pp. 316–340, 1962.

> Discussion of high-grade contact metamorphism superposed on regional metamorphism in the kyanite–sillimanite zones of Scotland.

Compton, R. R.: Contact metamorphism in the Santa Rosa range, Nevada, *Geol. Soc. Am. Bull.*, vol. 71, pp. 1383–1416, 1960.

Coombs, D. S.: Lower grade mineral facies in New Zealand, *Rept. Intern. Congr. 21st Session, Norden, 1960*, vol. 13, pp. 339–351, 1960.

Evans, B. W., and C. V. Guidotti: The sillimanite–potash feldspar isograd in western Maine, U.S.A., *Contrib. Mineral. Petrol.*, vol. 12, pp. 25–62, 1966.

Fyfe, W. S.: Hydrothermal synthesis and determination of equilibrium between minerals in the subsolidus region, *J. Geol.*, vol. 68, pp. 553–566, 1960.

> A critical discussion of experimental methods used to evaluate metamorphic equilibria.

———: Stability of Al_2SiO_5 polymorphs, *Chem. Geol.*, vol. 2, pp. 67–76, 1967.

———, Turner, F. J., and J. Verhoogen: Metamorphic reaction and metamorphic facies, *Geol. Soc. Am. Mem. 73*, 1958

Garlik, G. D. and S. Epstein: Oxygen isotope ratios in coexisting minerals of regionally metamorphosed rocks, *Geochim. Cosmochim. Acta*, vol. 31, pp. 181–214, 1967.

> Use of oxygen isotope data to calibrate temperatures of regional metamorphism.

Harker, A.: *Metamorphism*, Methuen, London, 1932.
> Classic text on petrography of metamorphic rocks.

Harker, R. I., and O. F. Tuttle: Studies in the system CaO-MgO-CO$_2$, Part I, *Am. J. Sci.*, vol. 253, pp. 209–224, 1955.

> Experimental studies of decarbonation of MgCO$_3$, CaMg(CO$_3$)$_2$, and CaCO$_3$.

Jaeger, J.: Temperatures outside a cooling sheet, *Am. J. Sci.*, vol. 257, pp. 44–54, 1959.

Johnston, J., and P. Niggli: The general principles underlying metamorphic processes, *J. Geol.*, vol. 21, pp. 481–516, 588–624, 1913.

> The first attempt to treat metamorphic reactions in terms of simple thermodynamics and kinetics.

Johnson, M. R. W.: Relations of movement and metamorphism in the Dalradians of Banffshire, *Trans. Edinburgh Geol. Soc.*, vol. 19, pp. 29–64, 1962.

> Study of relation between crystal growth and episodes of folding in Dalradian metamorphism.

Kretz, R.: Analysis of equilibrium in garnet–biotite–sillimanite gneisses from Quebec, *J. Petrol.*, vol. 5, pp. 1–20, 1964.

Miyashiro, A.: Evolution of metamorphic belts, *J. Petrol.*, vol. 2, pp. 277–311, 1961.

Newton, R. C.: Kyanite–sillimanite equilibrium at 750°C, *Science*, vol. 151, pp. 1222–1225, 1966.

————: Some calc-silicate equilibrium relations, *Am. J. Sci.*, vol. 264, pp. 204–222, 1966.

Sheih, Y. N. and H. P. Taylor: Oxygen and hydrogen isotope studies of contact metamorphism, *Contrib. Mineral. and Petrol.*, vol. 20, pp. 306–356, 1969.

Spry, A.: *Metamorphic Textures*, Pergamon Press, London, 1969.

> A well-illustrated comprehensive discussion of metamorphic textures and the processes connected with their origin.

Taylor, H. P.: Oxygen isotope studies of hydrothermal mineral deposits, in *Geochemistry of Hydrothermal Ore Deposits* (ed. by H. L. Barnes), Holt, Rinehart and Winston, Inc., New York, 1967, pp. 109–142.

————: and S. Epstein: Relationship between O^{18}/O^{16} ratios of coexisting minerals of igneous and metamorphic rocks, *Geol. Soc. Am. Bull.*, vol. 73, pp. 461–480, 675–694, 1962.

Tilley, C. E.: Contact metamorphism in the Comrie area of the Perthshire Highlands, *Geol. Soc. London Quart. J.*, vol. 80, pp. 22–71, 1924.

————: Metamorphic zones in the southern Highlands of Scotland, *Geol. Soc. London Quart. J.*, vol. 81, pp. 100–112, 1925.

Winkler, H. G. F.: *Petrogenesis of Metamorphic Rocks*, Springer, New York, 1965.

> The emphasis is on metamorphic assemblages and facies evaluated against the background of experimental data.

Zen, E-an: Metamorphism of lower Paleozoic rocks in the vicinity of the Taconic range in West-Central Vermont, *Am. Mineralogist*, vol. 45, pp. 129–175, 1960.

> A detailed study of low-grade regional metamorphism.

11

THE INTERIOR OF THE EARTH

PHYSICAL GEOLOGISTS are concerned mostly with processes they cannot directly observe, either because these processes occurred a long time ago, or because they occur too slowly, or because they occur at depths inaccessible to direct observation. This chapter is concerned mainly with the last of these three. What underlies the few kilometers of rocks that can be seen, or sampled in boreholes and mines? What happens inside the earth? What processes at depth can explain what we observe on the surface—the outpouring of lava, the uplift of mountains, the shaking of earthquakes, the movement of continents? The first problem, obviously, is to discover what makes up the earth.

Needless to say, we still do not know the exact answer. Very few categorical statements can be made about the interior of the earth—fewer certainly than physicists can make about the interior of an atom. The reason for this relative ignorance is that inferences about the earth must be drawn from observations made on its surface; one cannot split the earth to see what is inside. There are, of course, mathematical tools for relating observations on a surface to what goes on inside it; the divergence theorem (also called Gauss' theorem), for instance, states that the flux of any vector **F** across any closed surface S equals the integral of the divergence of **F** throughout the volume V enclosed by S

$$\int_S F_n \, dS = \int_V \text{div } \mathbf{F} \, dV$$

where F_n is the component of **F** along the normal to S at any point. Thus heat flow at the earth's surface is related to its divergence—that is, heat sources, inside; the gravitational force at the surface is related to the density, or mass, distribution, inside. But, clearly, there are an infinite number of ways in which sources can be distributed within S that would lead to the same value of the volume integral; they could, for instance, be uniformly distributed, or, on the contrary, be concentrated at a few points. This lack of "uniqueness" of the mathematical solutions is a characteristic, if annoying, feature of geophysics, in which one must generally resort to the inverse procedure: assume a distribution of sources (density, heat sources, and so on), calculate the effect of this distribution at the surface; compare it to observations. If calculations do not fit the observations, a new "model" must be devised and a new calculation made, until a good fit is obtained. But even if a good fit is obtained, there still is no assurance that the assumed model is the correct one, for possibly another, different, model could have given an even better fit. The choice of a model must then generally be made on other grounds: Model A is preferred to model B because it also fits other observations, or theories, or prejudices, better than B.

Most of our still somewhat subjective knowledge of the composition of the earth's interior comes from a study of its gravitational field and the propagation of seismic waves through it. Gravity gives information on the mass distribution that, when used in conjunction with the seismological information, allows limits to be set on the density distribution. The seismic velocities give additional information on elastic parameters from which some indications regarding the probable composition may be obtained.

Gravity

GRAVITATIONAL POTENTIAL AND GRAVITATIONAL ENERGY

Two point masses m_1 and m_2, separated by a distance r_{12}, attract each other with a force F

$$F = G \frac{m_1 m_2}{r_{12}^2} \qquad (11\text{-}1)$$

where G, the gravitational constant, is a fundamental constant of the universe. If masses are expressed in grams, distances in centimeters, and forces in dynes (g cm sec^{-2}), $G = 6.67 \times 10^{-8}$ g^{-1} cm^3 sec^{-2}. Place a mass m at the origin and a unit mass at point P with coordinates (xyz); see Figure 11–1. Then

$$F = G \frac{m}{r^2} = G \frac{m}{x^2 + y^2 + z^2} \qquad (11\text{-}2)$$

The attraction of an extended body is the sum of the attractions of all its parts. This sum is a vectorial sum, not an algebraic one, since the attractions are not all in the same direction. To calculate the total attraction, it is necessary to calculate separately the three components of it (components of a vector are scalar quantities that may be added algebraically). Such calculations are much simplified by use of U, the gravitational potential. U, a function of the coordinates, is defined by the relation

$$\mathbf{F} = -\operatorname{grad} U \qquad (11\text{-}3)$$

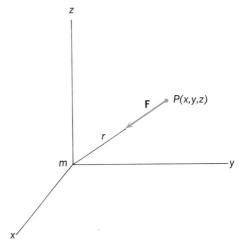

FIG. 11–1   The attraction at P due to a mass m at the origin.

that $\mathbf{F}$ is everywhere normal to a surface on which U is constant ("equipotential surface"), and its magnitude is $-dU/dn$, where dU is the change of U in a distance dn along the normal to the equipotential surface. Thus the component of $\mathbf{F}$ in the direction r (Figure 11–1) is, by equation (11-2)

$$F_r = -\frac{dU}{dr} = \frac{Gm}{r^2}$$

By integration,

$$U = \frac{Gm}{r} \qquad (11\text{-}4)$$

the value of the integration constant having been chosen so that U goes to zero when r goes to infinity.

U being a scalar quantity, the potential at P (xyz) for an extended body is the algebraic sum of the potentials of each of its parts

$$U_P = G \int_V \frac{dm}{h}$$

$$= G \int\int\int \frac{\rho \, dx' \, dy' \, dz'}{[(x - x')^2 + (y - y')^2 + (z - z')^2]^{1/2}}$$

where ρ is the density at the point Q $(x'y'z')$ where the mass dm is located (Figure 11–2); $dm = \rho \, dx' \, dy' \, dz'$. The calculation of U and of the corresponding attraction is relatively simple if the body has a simple shape; for instance, the attraction of an infinite plate with mass σ per unit area is everywhere the same and is $2\pi G\sigma$, this force having, by reason of symmetry, no component parallel to the plate. The potential and attraction of a homogeneous sphere of radius R are exactly as if the whole mass M of the sphere, where $M = (4/3)\pi\rho R^3$, were concentrated at its center, a result which is again obvious from the symmetry of the sphere: Where could the force point to, except to the center of the sphere, and how could equipotential surfaces fail to be concentric spheres centered at the center of the sphere?

Referring to Figure 11–1, it is easy to see that

$$\int_r^\infty \mathbf{F} \cdot d\mathbf{r},$$

which is the work (force × displacement) to lift a unit mass from P to infinity against the attraction of m, is precisely equal to $-U$, which dimensionally is equivalent to energy per unit mass. Conversely, U at a point P is the work gained (or energy released) when a unit mass falls from infinity to P under the effect of the attraction of m. Similarly, the gravitational potential U_g at the surface of the earth measures the work, or energy, necessary to remove a unit mass from the surface to infinity. To a first approximation, taking the earth to be a homogeneous sphere[1] of mass $M = 6 \times 10^{27}$ grams and radius $R = 6.37 \times 10^8$ cm, $U_g = GM/R = 6.28 \times 10^{11}$ ergs/g.

ESCAPE VELOCITY Any object moving away from the earth with velocity v and kinetic energy per unit mass $v^2/2$ larger than U will not fall back on it, since the object has enough energy to lift it to infinity and to escape the earth's gravitational attraction. The "escape" velocity for the earth $V_e = (2U_g)^{1/2} = (2GM/R)^{1/2}$ is about 11 km/

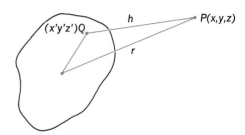

FIG. 11–2 The potential for an extended body. The origin is at the center of mass of the body.

sec. Now, molecules of mass m of a gas at (absolute) temperature T have a mean thermal velocity $(3kT/m)^{1/2}$, where k is Boltzmann's constant $= 1.38 \times 10^{-16}$ erg/deg. Half the molecules have a velocity greater than the mean, and a few molecules have a velocity greatly in excess of the mean. Those with velocity greater than V_e can escape from the earth's gravitational field. Thus the earth's atmosphere will evaporate into space at a rate which depends on its temperature (which is controlled by the radiation of the sun, and is very high at high levels), and on the mass of its molecules. Light molecules, such as hydrogen, evaporate rapidly, whereas heavier ones, such as oxygen or nitrogen, evaporate only very slowly. The gravitational potential thus sets limits on the chemical composition of the atmosphere that a planet can retain.

GRAVITATIONAL ENERGY The gravitational energy E of a body is defined as the sum of the gravitational potentials of all its parts—that is, the total amount of energy needed to remove every part of it to infinity against the attraction of all other parts. Conversely, it is also the energy released if the body forms by accretion of particles, initially at infinite separation, that fall toward each other under the effect of their mutual attraction. A simple calculation shows that for a homogeneous sphere of radius R and mass M,

$$E = \frac{3}{5}\frac{GM^2}{R}$$

The gravitational energy per unit mass, E/M, for a uniform earth would be $3U/5$ or, roughly, 4×10^{11} ergs/g. This energy, if released suddenly, would be sufficient to vaporize the earth

---

[1] The mass M of the earth (5.98×10^{27} g) is best determined from the motion of the moon or of artificial satellites. The angular velocity of the moon about the center of mass of the earth–moon system must be such that the corresponding centrifugal force balances the gravitational attraction of the earth, which is proportional to M. The angular velocity of the moon is determined from the length of the lunar month. The radius R of the earth is determined as explained subsequently.

and raise its temperature so that it would evaporate again. This sets a limit to the rate at which the earth, or any other planet, could have formed by accretion, the condition being that the rate of release of gravitational energy cannot much exceed the rate at which the heat generated can be radiated away into space.

Any change in the distribution of mass inside the earth is accompanied by a change in gravitational energy. Energy is required, and must be provided from some source, to uplift a mountain range or a continent. Energy is released when dense material settles toward the center, as in the formation of the core. If the earth loses more heat energy into space than is generated inside (see Chapter 12) it cools and contracts; this contraction decreases the radius and thus liberates gravitational energy, which compensates, in part, for the loss of heat that caused the shrinking in the first place.

THE SHAPE OF THE EARTH

Since force = mass × acceleration, the gravitational attraction that the earth exerts on a unit mass is referred to as the "acceleration of gravity," usually denoted by the letter g. On the surface of the earth, g is found to be generally close to, but slightly smaller than, the value 982.7 gals,[2] corresponding to a homogeneous sphere of mass $M = 5.98 \times 10^{27}$ g and radius $R = 6.371 \times 10^8$ cm; it varies from point to point for reasons that will soon become apparent. The variation at sea level is small, of the order of 0.5 percent, but of considerable interest, since several important facts may be learned from it.

A corollary of the definition of the potential is that **g** must everywhere be normal to a surface on which U is constant. In particular, the surface of a liquid (for example, the ocean) at rest must be an equipotential, or "level," or "horizontal," surface, for the force acting at any point of the free surface of a liquid must be normal to it if the liquid is at rest; otherwise, the component of the

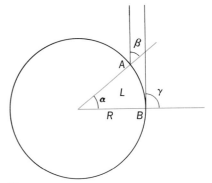

FIG. 11–3 *The determination of the radius of a homogeneous, nonrotating earth.*

force parallel to the surface would cause it to flow. The "shape" of sea level can thus be found by finding the shape of a surface on which U is constant. If the earth were a homogeneous nonrotating sphere, equipotential surfaces would be spherical, and so would the surface of the ocean. The radius of the earth could then easily be found as follows. The force of gravity—as indicated, say, by a mass hanging on a string ("plumb line")—would point everywhere to the center of the earth. If then (Figure 11–3) two telescopes at A and B point to the same point in the sky (and are therefore parallel), the difference $\gamma - \beta$ between the angles they make with the plumb line at B and A, respectively, is precisely equal to the angle α that subtends the arc AB. Let the length of this arc be L; then the radius R of the earth is $R = L/\alpha$, and R is found by measuring L by means of a tape or by triangulation.

As it turns out, the results of this experiment, first done by Eratosthenes[3] (276–196 B.C.), are slightly different depending on where the experiment is made. The distance L corresponding to an angle α of, say, one degree, is greater near the poles than at the equator. The earth's surface is thus more strongly curved at the equator than at the pole, and its shape is therefore that of a sphere flattened along the polar axis. There are two reasons for this. In the first place, the earth rotates. Because of this rotation, an object of unit

---

[2] The c.g.s. unit of acceleration is the gal (for Galileo); 1 gal = 1 cm sec^{-2} = 1000 milligals.

[3] In a slightly different form. Eratosthenes had no telescope.

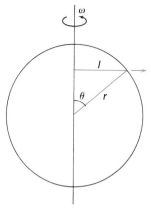

FIG. 11–4 *The centrifugal force per unit mass $\omega^2 l$ is perpendicular to the rotation axis.*

mass moving with the earth (that is, at rest with respect to rotating axes) experiences a centrifugal force per unit mass[4] of $\omega^2 l$, where ω is the angular velocity and l the distance from the rotation axis. As seen in Figure 11–4, $l = r \sin \theta$ where r is the distance from the center of the earth and θ, the "colatitude," is the complement of the latitude ϕ; $\theta = 90° - \phi$ is zero at the north pole and 180° at the south pole. The angular velocity ω is $2\pi/86{,}166 = 7.29 \times 10^{-5}$ rad/sec, since the earth makes one turn (2π radians) in one sidereal

---

[4] Newton's law, $\mathbf{F} = m\mathbf{a}$, or force = mass times acceleration, applies only in an "inertial" frame of reference—that is, one that is not rotated or accelerated in any way. If an object moves with velocity $\mathbf{v}$ and acceleration $\mathbf{a}$ with respect to axes rotating with angular velocity ω, its velocity $\mathbf{v}_0$ and acceleration $\mathbf{a}_0$ with respect to fixed axes are respectively

$$\mathbf{v}_0 = \mathbf{v} + (\omega \times \mathbf{r})$$
$$\mathbf{a}_0 = \mathbf{a} + \omega \times (\omega \times \mathbf{r}) + 2\omega \times \mathbf{v}$$

(From *Berkeley Physics Course*, vol. 1, pp. 84–86). This result follows simply from a transformation of coordinates. One may therefore still write, in the moving frame, that

$$m\mathbf{a} = \mathbf{F}$$

provided that one includes, among the forces on the right side of this equation, the "centrifugal force" $m(\omega \times \mathbf{r}) \times \omega$ and the "Coriolis" force $2m(\mathbf{v} \times \omega)$. Both the centrifugal and Coriolis forces are normal to the displacement and therefore do no work; no energy is involved. The Coriolis force is of course zero if the velocity is zero or if it is parallel to the angular-velocity vector.

day (86,166 sec). The centrifugal force is the gradient of a potential $U_c = (\omega^2 r^2 \sin^2 \theta)/2$, and it is the total potential $U = U_g + U_c$ that must be constant on the surface of an ocean at rest. Secondly, as the earth is not a uniform sphere, U_g is not simply GM/R; it departs from this value because (1) of the earth's nonspherical shape, and (2) masses on and in the earth are not uniformly distributed—that is, the earth does not have everywhere the same density.

If the earth were of uniform density, the effect of rotation considered alone would be relatively simple: to the gravitational attraction of a spherical, homogeneous sphere (therefore directed towards its center) add (Figure 11–5) everywhere the centrifugal force directed away from the rotation axis. The surface of an ocean covering this imaginary earth would have to be normal to the resultant of the two forces. The centrifugal force is zero at the poles and maximum at the equator, where it is directed outwards along a radius and thus directly opposed to the attraction. Thus the surface of the ocean remains normal to the radius at the poles or at the equator, but must become flattened, the equatorial radius a becoming larger than the polar radius c ("equatorial bulge"). The "flattening," or "ellipticity" e, of the equipotential surface, which is defined as $e = (a - c)/a$, will be rather small; one would expect it to be of the order of (but not exactly equal to) the ratio

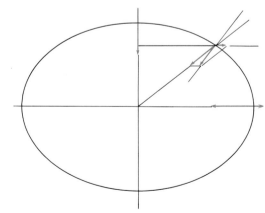

FIG. 11–5 *Shape of a uniform rotating earth. Equipotentials are everywhere normal to the resultant of gravitational attraction and centrifugal force.*

of the centrifugal force at the equator $\omega^2 a$ to gravity there (GM/a^2); this ratio, $\omega^2 a^3/GM$, which is 1/288.4, is indeed close to the observed flattening,[5] or 1/298.25. Gravity on the equipotential surface will also vary from equator to pole, for three reasons: (1) a point on the equator being farther from the center of the earth than the pole, the attraction should be less at the equator than at the pole; (2) the centrifugal force is opposed to gravity at the equator, and zero at the poles; and (3) the gravitational attraction at the equator is increased by the mass of the bulge. The third effect is opposite in sign to the other two.

The effect of nonuniformity in mass distribution, which is what geologists want to discover, is much more difficult to take into account. Suppose that we wish to determine, as before, the radius of a nonrotating earth, but that, unknown to us, a heavy mass m lies to north of A (Figure 11–6). Its attraction deflects the plumb line more at A, which is closer, than at B, and the angle α is no longer equal to $\gamma - \beta$, leading to an erroneous measurement of R. To correct for this effect, we must know where the masses m are. But how can the observer discover them? He could compare gravity at A and B and find that it differs at these two points, but it would differ even if $m = 0$ because gravity varies with latitude on a rotating, nonspherical homogeneous earth, as we have just seen. This variation, in turn, cannot be calculated until a and c have been determined, which cannot be done until the irregular mass distribution is known.

The problem calls obviously for a procedure of successive approximations, as follows: (1) Make many measurements of the radius at different latitudes, neglecting unknown inequalities of mass distribution, to find an approximate size and shape of the earth (that is, approximate values of a and c). (2) Calculate an approximate variation of gravity with latitude. (3) Compare calculated and observed value of g to obtain a

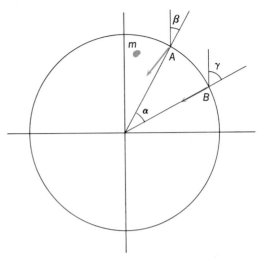

FIG. 11–6   Determination of the radius of a nonuniform earth.

preliminary estimate of the inequalities of mass. (4) Use these to correct the radii to get better estimates of a and c. (5) Repeat the procedure of calculating an improved mass distribution, and so on.

SPHEROID AND GEOID

It is convenient at this stage to define two surfaces.

1. The *spheroid* is the equipotential surface coinciding with mean sea-level on an imaginary rotating earth in which all masses are uniformly distributed laterally; that is, an earth on which all mountains and continents have been levelled and oceans have been filled to a uniform depth. This imaginary earth has the same total mass and size as the real earth.

2. The *geoid* is the equipotential surface that coincides with mean sea level on the real earth; it departs from the spheroid precisely because of the irregularities in mass distribution (mountains, continents, oceans, rocks of nonuniform density). In an oceanic area where there is less mass per unit area, seawater being less dense than continental rocks, the geoid would be expected to drop below the spheroid, while in a mountainous region, where there is more mass per unit area,

---

[5] The best available determinations of a and c are, respectively, 6378.163 km and 6536.177 km. The radius of a sphere of equal volume is 6371 km. The area of the surface is 5.1×10^8 km^2 = 5.1×10^{18} cm^2, and the volume is 1.083×10^{27} cm^3.

the geoid would rise above the spheroid (Figure 11–7).

The spheroid is an imaginary surface of no physical significance, which has the advantage of being easy to represent mathematically; it is essentially an oblate ellipsoid with a short polar axis and a circular equator. Gravity on the spheroid can be calculated as a function of latitude when the general dimensions of the spheroid have been agreed upon; this theoretical value of gravity g_0 on the spheroid, known as "standard gravity," serves as a reference for all actual gravity measurements; the formula that gives the dependence of g_0 on latitude by international agreement is known as the "International formula." The geoid, by contrast, is a surface of considerable physical significance, since it represents sea level, and all topographic elevations are distances to it. The plumb line, which defines the direction of the "vertical" at a point, is everywhere normal to it, the angle between the vertical and the normal to the spheroid being the "deflection of the vertical." It is not easy to represent the geoid mathematically (see below) as it is a rather irregular surface which rises and falls above and below the spheroid, reflecting irregularities in mass distribution. The total potential $U = U_g + U_c$ is, by definition, the same at every point of the geoid, but gravity is not constant on it, although the variation is small (about 0.5 percent).

ISOSTASY

The exact determination of the shape of the geoid, and of its distance to the spheroid, is a rather complicated process, which is not quite finished yet; new refinements, coming mainly from the observation of the motion of artificial satellites, are constantly being made. Measurements of the deflection of the vertical have, however, been made for a long time. In general, they tend to be much smaller than expected from the visible distribution of mass on the earth's surface, and generally do not exceed a half-minute of arc. This was first discovered in the first half of the eighteenth century by Pierre Bouguer who was attempting at that time to measure the equatorial radius of the earth in what was then called Peru and is now Ecuador. Ecuador has some very high mountains, including two large volcanoes (Cotopaxi and Chimborazo). Bouguer suspected that, as explained above, the mass of the mountains would deflect his plumb line and affect his measurements. To his surprise, he found that the results he got were independent of distance to the mountains, as if these did not exist at all, or at least were hollow, with no mass inside. A century later, Everest made a similar observation in India, where he found that the Himalayas produced a deflection only one third as large as could be expected from their visible mass. What could be the reason for this discrepancy?

Modern measurements are carried out as follows: A measurement g_A of gravity is made at A, the latitude of which is known; g_A is then compared to g_0, gravity on the spheroid at the same latitude, and generally found to be different—that is, $g_A \neq g_0$. Several obvious effects account for the difference.

1. In the first place, A is generally not on the

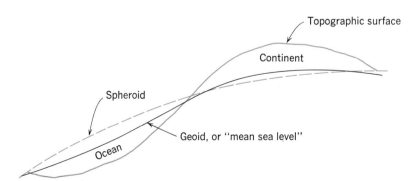

FIG. 11–7 *Topographic surface, spheroid, and geoid.*

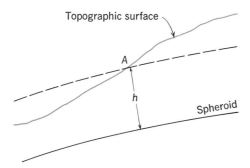

FIG. 11–8 *Procedure for reduction of gravity data.*

spheroid, but at some distance h above it (Figure 11–8). As gravity decreases approximately as the square of the distance to the center of the earth, g_0 should not be compared to g_A but to

$$g_A \left(\frac{R+h}{R}\right)^2 \cong g_A \left(1 + \frac{2h}{R}\right)$$

(Since h is much smaller than R, the term h^2/R^2 may safely be neglected.) The correction, called the "free-air" correction, amounts to adding to the observed gravity approximately 0.31 milligals per meter of elevation. We neglect at this stage the fact that the elevation h of A is measured with respect to the geoid, not to the spheroid; thus h is not exactly known. The quantity g_A + free-air correction $-$ g_0 is called the "free-air anomaly."

2. Gravity on the spheroid g_0 is calculated, as explained, for a uniform earth with all masses below sea level, and therefore neglects the mass of rocks situated between the spheroid and the topographic surface. This mass is allowed for by calculating its attraction, which can be found (with some labor) if topographic maps are available. An approximate correction, known as the Bouguer correction, can easily be made by assuming a flat topography such that the disturbing mass is simply a slab of uniform thickness h, the attraction of which is $2\pi G\rho h$, ρ being the density of the rocks. (A further correction, which is generally small, is made for departures of the topography from the flat surface assumed in the calculation of the Bouguer correction.) The quantity g_A + free-air correction $-$ $2\pi G\rho h$ $-$ g_0 is called the "Bouguer anomaly." Rather surprisingly, the Bouguer anomaly on land is usually

negative and numerically larger than the free-air anomaly, as if the slab had no mass.

This condition, which has been found to exist generally, is described as "isostasy," a statement of which is that the mass of a vertical column of given cross section in the earth is the same everywhere, regardless of topography and height, in oceans and continents alike. All masses above sea level must somehow be compensated by equivalent "negative" masses, such as rocks less dense than normal; and similarly, rocks below the sea floor must be denser than normal to compensate for the low density of seawater itself.

Isostasy implies a close approach to hydrostatic equilibrium. The condition for equilibrium in a liquid at rest is that the pressure be everywhere the same on a "level" or equipotential surface. Now at any depth h below the free surface of a liquid, the pressure (force per unit area) is g times the mass of a column of unit cross section, which in turn is simply ρh, ρ being the density of the liquid; $P = g\rho h$. Thus if all columns above a given level have approximately the same mass the pressure will be approximately the same everywhere on the level surface. If it were not, a liquid would flow from a point of high pressure toward points at lower pressure (Figure 11–9).

The equality of mass of different columns can, in principle, be achieved in a number of ways. For instance, column B, which is higher than column A, could consist of lighter rocks (Pratt model). Or both columns A and B could consist of two materials of different density in different proportions (Airy). Still other models are conceivable.

The Pratt model is not generally favored, for

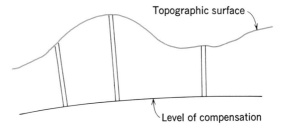

FIG. 11–9 *Illustration of the principle of isostasy. All columns above the level of compensation have the same mass per unit area, regardless of topography.*

the following reason. Erosion will occur at a high point such as B, and material will be deposited at a low point such as A. For isostasy to be maintained during this process, as it seems to be, the density of column B would have to increase progressively as it were being unloaded, while the density of column A would have to decrease while it were being loaded. There is no known mechanism for doing this.

The Airy model is somewhat easier to visualize. We now know (see below) that the mantle is denser than the overlying crust from which it is separated by the Mohorovičić discontinuity, which we shall call "Moho" for short. Equality of mass in columns A and B could thus be achieved if the crust were thicker at B than at A. Consider, for instance, three columns A, B, C in Figure 11–10. Column A consists of an ocean (density $\rho_0 = 1.03$ g/cm) overlying a thin light crust of density ρ_c (say, 2.8 g/cm) which itself overlies the mantle of density ρ_m (say, 3.3 g/cm). Column B is a continent at sea level of thickness H_2, while column C is a mountain range of mean elevation h_3. Equality of mass above level H_3 implies that

$$\rho_0 h_0 + \rho_c H_1 + \rho_m(H_3 - H_1 - h_0) =$$
$$\rho_c H_2 + \rho_m(H_3 - H_2) = \rho_c(H_3 + h_3)$$

which establishes a relation between the height of the topographic surface (above or below sea level) at any point, and the depth to Moho at that point. If, for instance, $H_2 = 30$ km, $h_3 = 3$ km, we find $H_3 = 46.8$ km.[6] Conversely, if the thickness of the crust can be determined seismically at points of known elevation, the density of the crust and mantle can be determined.

Suppose now that erosion at C removes material that is deposited in the ocean at A. The pressure increases under A because of increasing mass, and decreases below C. Flow of mantle material then occurs from A to C, and the sea floor sinks while column C rises. Equilibrium is restored when a mass of mantle equal to the mass of sediments has been transferred from A to C.

It seems likely that much of the recent rise of the Himalayan peaks may be due to recent erosion in that area.

On the whole, there does seem to be a correlation between topographic height and depth to Moho, as predicted. The greatest crustal thicknesses, about 70 km, have been observed seismologically beneath the Academy of Sciences Mountains of the U.S.S.R.[7] and the Altiplano of Chile, both with mean elevation of about 5000 meters. But the correlation of topographic height to crustal thickness is not perfect, indicating that the mechanism of isostatic compensation is not as simple as described. Conceivably, the density of the crust may be different in different places, and the density of the mantle is almost certainly not uniform. Much of the western United States, for instance, appears to be underlain by mantle of relatively low density.

ISOSTATIC ANOMALIES   Although a close approach to isostatic balance does seem to prevail in many parts of the world, some regions are known to depart from it, as shown by the existence of "isostatic anomalies." An isostatic anomaly exists wherever no reasonable allowance for variable crustal thickness or density will reduce the Bouguer anomaly to zero. A positive anomaly indicates an excess of mass. The positive anomaly at Hawaii, for instance, reflects the mass of the lava flows that recently (geologically speaking) accumulated on the sea floor to form the island. One would expect the sea floor to sink under such a load, which it will probably do in due course, as attested by the submarine extinct volcanoes that once stood at or above sea level ("guyots") and are now submerged below 0.5 to 1.5 km of water. (Note, however, that much of the southwest Pacific appears to have sunk as a unit, independently of the local loads.) Remarkable negative anomalies occur around island arcs (for example, Indonesia) and are associated with belts of intense seismicity, recent tectonic deformation, deep trenches, and volcanic activity, which agrees with the notion that if isostasy reflects

---

[6] The difference in crustal thickness $(H_3 - H_2)$ is referred to as the "root" of the mountain C.

[7] In the Pamir Range in the Tadzhik Republic of the U.S.S.R., northeast of the border of Afghanistan.

equilibrium, isostatic anomalies must reflect departures from it.

THE SHAPE OF THE GEOID: GRAVITY HARMONICS

The geoid is one of a family of equipotential surfaces (it is the one that coincides with mean sea level), the equation or description of which can be attained simply by setting U equal to a constant. Since U is a function of the coordinates, setting it equal to a constant constitutes a relation between these coordinates that defines an equipotential surface. To represent the geoid, all we need then is the proper representation of U as a function of r (distance to the center of mass of the earth), θ (colatitude, or $90° -$ latitude), and ψ (longitude). The centrifugal potential U_c is easily found, as

$$U_c = \frac{\omega^2 l^2}{2} = \frac{\omega^2 r^2 \sin^2 \theta}{2}$$

The general form of the gravitational potential is also known, because it follows from the definition of U_g and from the divergence theorem that at any point outside matter (that is, at the surface of the earth and above it), U_g must satisfy a differential equation known as Laplace's equation.[8] The general form of the solution of this equation is well known: It is a sum of terms of the form[9]

---

[8] Laplace's equation states that the Laplacian $\nabla^2 U$ of the potential is zero. The Laplacian $\nabla^2 U$ is the divergence of the gradient of U:

$$\nabla^2 U = \text{div grad } U$$

The expression for it in Cartesian coordinates is

$$\frac{\partial^2 U}{\partial x^2} + \frac{\partial^2 U}{\partial y^2} + \frac{\partial^2 U}{\partial z^2}$$

Laplace's equation is a particular case of Poisson's equation, $\nabla^2 U = -4\pi G\rho$, where ρ is the density at the point at which the Laplacian is to be measured. Outside matter, $\rho = 0$. A simple proof of Poisson's equation may be found in G. D. Garland, *The Earth's Shape and Gravity* (Pergamon Press, 1965, pp. 153–155).
[9] We neglect for the moment terms of the form $A_n r^n \cos m\psi P_n^m$ $(\cos \theta)$ which are also solutions of Laplace's equation [see equation (11-12)], but which arise from sources outside the earth. The gravitational potentials due to the sun and moon, and which produce tides, are of this form, but will be neglected here.

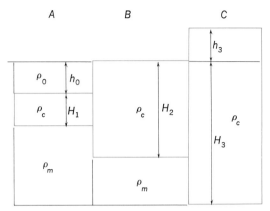

FIG. 11–10 *Isostatic balance between an oceanic column (A), a continental column at sea level (B), and a mountainous region (C).*

$$\frac{A_n}{r^{n+1}} \cos m\psi P_n^m(\theta) \quad \text{or} \quad \frac{B_n}{r^{n+1}} \sin m\psi \, P_n^m(\theta) \quad (11\text{-}5)$$

where A_n, B_n are numerical coefficients, n can be any positive integer, m is any positive integer equal to or less than n, and $P_n^m(\theta)$, an "associated Legendre polynomial of degree n and order m," is a specified function of θ; for example $P_2^0 = (3 \cos^2 \theta - 1)/2$, $P_2^2 = 3 \sin^2 \theta$, and so on. For the purpose of exposition, let us assume at this stage that U_g is independent of ψ, as would be the case if the earth were perfectly symmetrical about its rotation axis. Then the potential at any point (r, θ) could be written as

$$U_g = \frac{GM}{r} \left[1 - \sum_{n=2}^{\infty} \left(\frac{R}{r} \right)^n J_n P_n(\theta) \right] \quad (11\text{-}6)$$

where M is the mass of the earth; R is its mean radius; J_n is a numerical coefficient; and $P_n(\theta)$ is a Legendre polynomial of degree n of which the first four are:

$$P_0 = 1 \qquad P_1 = \cos \theta \qquad P_2 = \frac{3 \cos^2 \theta - 1}{2}$$

$$P_3 = \frac{5 \cos^3 \theta - 3 \cos \theta}{2}$$

Thus, in expanded form,

$$U_g = \frac{GM}{r} - \frac{GMR^2}{2r^3} J_2 \left(3 \cos^2 \theta - 1\right)$$

$$-\frac{GMR^3}{2r^4}\,J_3\,(5\cos^3\theta - 3\cos\theta) + \cdots$$

The first term is easily recognizable. At a large distance from the earth, such that $r \gg R$, the second and third terms on the right are much smaller than the first, and the potential looks like that of a *uniform* sphere of mass M, which is the same as if all its mass were concentrated at its center; the corresponding equipotential surfaces are spheres, where $GM/r = $ constant, or $r = $ constant, since G and M are constants. All the terms on the right except the first will thus measure departures of the earth from uniformity and sphericity. The second term, or "second harmonic," is symmetrical about the equator, since it takes the same value for $\theta = 0$ and $\theta = 180°$; $\theta = 30°$ or $\theta = 150°$; $\theta = 60°$ or $\theta = 120°$; and so forth. It has no minimum or maximum except at $\theta = 0°$, $\theta = 90°$, $\theta = 180°$, and must therefore represent the contribution to the potential of a feature that is symmetric about the equatorial plane, such as the equatorial bulge. An equipotential surface corresponding to the first two terms only is represented in Figure 11–11; it drops below the sphere $r = R$ at the pole by an amount RJ_2, and rises above it at the equator by $RJ_2/2$. J_2 thus measures the flattening or ellipticity of that surface, and when the centrifugal potential is included, gives the flattening of the geoid (1/298.25). The third

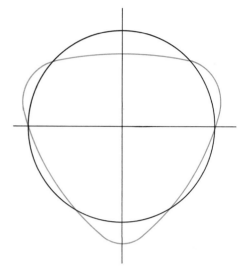

FIG. 11–12 *An equipotential surface containing the third harmonic ("pear shape").*

term, or "third harmonic," is antisymmetrical about the equator; by observing how the function $(5\cos^5\theta - 3\cos\theta)/2$ varies as a function of θ, it is seen that it deforms the spherical equipotential surface corresponding to the first term by adding to it bumps in the Northern Hemisphere and at the South Pole, and hollows at the North Pole and in the Southern Hemisphere as in Figure 11–12; this is known as the "pear shape" of the earth. The fourth harmonic adds a hollow at both poles and equator, and a bulge in between, and so forth.

The numerical values of the coefficients J_2, J_3, and so on, are best obtained from the observation of the motion of artificial satellites. If the earth were spherical and uniform, its gravitational effect would be the same as that of a point mass at its center, and a satellite would move around it on an invariable elliptic orbit of which the center of the earth is a focus (Kepler's laws). Departures from sphericity perturb this orbit in a calculable manner; the equatorial bulge, for instance, causes the normal to the plane of the orbit to precess (describe a cone) about the earth's axis at a rate which depends again on J_2, and from the observation of which J_2 may be determined. Very precise tracking of the satellite is required to determine the higher harmonics, particularly those

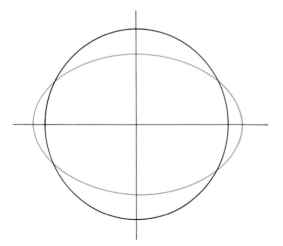

FIG. 11–11 *An equipotential surface corresponding to the second harmonic in the potential.*

FIG. 11–13 *Undulations of the geoid. Figures indicate the height in meters above or below the surface defined by J_2 and J_4; this surface is very close to an ellipsoid of flattening 1/298.3. (After W. H. Guier and R. R. Newton, J. Geophys. Res., vol. 70, 1966, p. 4621.)*

that depend on longitude, so that results to date are still in some respects preliminary. When observations on the ground, particularly of the free-air anomaly and deflection of the vertical are included, it becomes possible to draw maps, or contour lines, of the geoid, such as the one shown in Figure 11–13.

The map reveals several features of great interest. One of these is that the hills and hollows of the geoid do not coincide with obvious geological or topographical features; contour lines do not follow, for instance, the borders of continents. As shown in Figure 11–7, one would

expect the geoid to rise under land and to fall at sea, but this is not generally the case; and in fact, the sign of the J_3 coefficient, which turns out to be negative, indicates a rise of the geoid in the Arctic Ocean, and a drop over the land masses of the Northern Hemisphere and Antarctica. Thus the mass distribution that causes the undulations of the geoid is not that which we see and must therefore lie deeper; and from this we infer that the density in the mantle cannot be laterally uniform. The level of compensation for isostasy referred to in Figure 11–9 must lie much deeper than Moho.

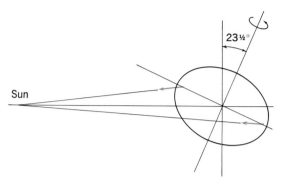

FIG. 11–14 *The attraction of the sun (or moon) on the earth's equatorial bulge produces a torque that causes the earth's axis to precess about the normal to the ecliptic.*

A second interesting observation is that the undulations of the geoid are as small as they are. The rise and fall of the geoid corresponding to the "pear-shaped" term J_3 is only about 15 meters, and the inequality of mass distribution needed to produce it is equivalent to a layer of rock of density 2.8 on the surface of the earth about 70 meters thick; the corresponding gravity perturbation is only about 10 milligals. The stress corresponding to an excess load of 70 meters of rock of density 2.8 is of the order of $g\rho h = 2 \times 10$ dynes/cm^2 = 20 bars, which is small compared to the crushing strength of rocks under normal conditions ($\sim 10^3$ bars). The earth is indeed very close to isostatic equilibrium. Note, however, that isostatic anomalies of small regional extent will not be reflected in the geoidal map (Figure 11–13) which represents only harmonics up to order 12; that is, features extending over distances of the order of 360/12, or 30°, in longitude or latitude.

MOMENTS OF INERTIA OF THE EARTH   The coefficient J_2 in the expression for the gravitational potential is, as we have seen, related to the equatorial bulge and the flattening of the earth, which may be derived from it. Still another interpretation of J_2 is possible, for it can be shown that $J_2 = (C - A)/Ma^2$, where C and A are, respectively, the moments of inertia of the earth about its polar axis and any axis in the plane of the

equator.[10] Now the ratio $H = (C - A)/C$ is well known from astronomical observations of the "precession of the equinoxes" —that is, the rate at which the axis of rotation of the earth moves about an axis normal to the plane of the ecliptic (the plane containing the sun and the earth's orbit around it). This, in turn, causes a gradual change in the time of the year at which seasons (for example, sowing time or harvest time) begin. [The precession of the equinoxes is caused by the attraction of the sun, and of the moon, on the earth's equatorial bulge, which does not lie in the plane of the ecliptic, but is inclined to it by 23½°; since this attraction is different in magnitude at A and B (Figure 11–14) there is a torque that tends to pull the bulge into the plane of the ecliptic. The gyroscopic effect due to the earth's rotation causes the earth's axis to describe a cone (or "precess") about the normal to the ecliptic with a period that depends on the nonsphericity of the earth—that is, ratio H.] H is found to be 1/305, a value which, when combined with that of J_2, yields $C = 0.3305Ma^2$.

---

[10]The moment of inertia of a body about an axis is $\int l^2\, dm$, where l is the perpendicular distance from an element of mass dm to the axis. The moment of inertia I_0 about the center of mass is $\int r^2 dm$, where r is the distance from dm to the center of mass. For a homogeneous sphere of radius R,

$$I_0 = \int_0^a 4\pi r^4 \rho\, dr = \frac{4\pi\rho R^5}{5} = \frac{3MR^2}{5}$$

where

$$M = \int_0^R 4\pi r^2 \rho\, dr = \frac{4\pi\rho R^3}{3}$$

It can be shown that it is always possible to find in a body three mutually perpendicular axes such that the moment about one of them is maximum, and the moment about another is minimum; these are the "principal" axes, and the corresponding moments are "principal moments." All diameters of a sphere are principal axes, by symmetry, and the three principal moments are equal, and equal to $(2/3)I_0 = (2/5)MR^2$.

In the flattened earth, the moment about the polar axis C is maximum, because the mass of the equatorial bulge is further away from it. The two other principal axes must lie in a plane perpendicular to the polar axis (equatorial plane) and are equal if, as is the case in the earth, the equator is circular. For an ellipsoid with semiaxes a and c, $C = (2/5)Ma^2$ and $A = M(a^2 + c^2)/5$.

For a homogeneous sphere, C would be $0.4Ma^2$. Since $A < C$, all three principal moments of the earth are smaller than those of a homogeneous sphere. This means that the earth cannot be homogeneous; there must be, in particular, a marked concentration of mass towards its center. The important result $C = 0.3305Ma^2$ will be used later in the determination of the density distribution within the earth; at the moment it is sufficient to remember that the density must somehow vary along a radius; that is, $\rho = \rho(r)$.

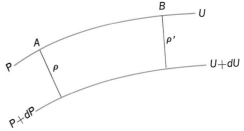

FIG. 11–15 In hydrostatic equilibrium, P and ρ are constant on an equipotential surface.

HYDROSTATIC EQUILIBRIUM WITHIN THE EARTH
The measured value of the flattening, $e = 1/298.25$, turns out to be very nearly, but not exactly, equal to the theoretical flattening that the earth should have if it were a liquid in hydrostatic equilibrium—that is, if no stress other than the hydrostatic pressure P due to gravity existed anywhere within it. In a liquid at rest (in equilibrium), the force of gravity must exactly balance the only other existing force, which is the gradient of the pressure; that is, $g = -(1/\rho)\,(dP/dr)$, where r is the distance from the center. Since g, the downward acceleration of gravity, is $-dU/dr$, $dP = \rho\,dU$, and P must be constant ($dP = 0$) on an equipotential surface where $dU = 0$. It follows that ρ must be also constant on an equipotential surface; if it were not ($\rho \neq \rho'$ in Figure 11–15), the change dP for given change dU would not be the same at points A and B, and P would not be constant on the lower equipotential surface $U + dU$ if it were constant on the upper one. Thus the shape, or flattening, of equipotential surfaces in a liquid at rest may be found from the condition that they must also be surfaces of constant density. The theoretical hydrostatic flattening of the external surface has recently been calculated using satellite data, and was found to be close to $1/300$; this value differs significantly from the actual flattening, which is $1/298.25$.

Undulations of the geoid described on page 609 imply, as we have seen, the existence of rather small nonhydrostatic stresses; the nonhydrostatic flattening implies somewhat larger

ones, which are of considerable theoretical interest. On the whole, the shape of the earth does indicate that it responds to its rotation much as a liquid would; the flattening it would have if it responded purely elastically to the centrifugal force can be calculated from the elastic coefficients provided by seismology (see below) and turns out to be much smaller than the observed one. If, then, the earth does behave like a liquid, why isn't its flattening equal to the theoretical value for a liquid? Several explanations have been proposed, one of which is based on the observation that the rate of rotation is slowly decreasing, at a known rate, because of tidal friction (see Chapter 12). Could the present flattening reflect a previous, higher, rate of rotation, the viscosity of the earth being such that it has not yet had time to adjust completely to its present rotation? The viscosity required by this explanation turns out to be quite high (10^{26} cm^2 sec^{-1}), much higher than that (10^{21}–10^{22}) deduced from the rate at which the surface rises in isostatic response to the recent removal of load, as in Scandinavia, where the land around the Baltic Sea is rising at about 1 cm/year, following the melting of the most recent icecap (Chapter 7). An explanation for the difference in viscosity may be that it increases with depth, the lower figure referring to the top layers of the mantle, where isostatic adjustments occur, and the higher figure applying to the lower mantle, or to most of the mantle, where the adjustment of the bulge to the changing rate of rotation must take place. The matter, though still under debate, has some bearing on our later discussion of convection in the mantle.

We note that the presently accepted value of hydrostatic flattening (1/300) is a calculated, not a measured, quantity; values ranging from 1/297 to 1/300 have been obtained in calculations involving slightly different but equally plausible assumptions. Further work may show that the actual and hydrostatic flattening do not differ significantly.

Propagation of Seismic Waves

ELASTIC WAVES

When a stress is suddenly applied to an elastic solid (as when it is hit with a hammer) or when the stress is suddenly changed (as when a previous state of stress is altered by fracturing), the corresponding change in strain is propagated outwards as an elastic wave, or vibration. Vibrations of the ground have many causes (traffic, surf beating on the coast, volcanic eruptions, and so on). The more intense ones are those associated with earthquakes, or with artificial underground explosions of sufficient magnitude. Earthquakes are generally thought to be caused by fracturing of rock masses along faults, and to be associated with sudden displacements along preexisting faults (see Chapter 9), although they may also have other causes. The "point" on the fault at which the displacement occurs is called the focus of the earthquake, and the point on the surface of the earth above the focus is the epicenter.

Vibrations of the ground are recorded by means of seismographs. A seismograph consists essentially of a mass attached by a spring to a support that moves with the ground. The mass remains nearly stationary, but the ground and support move; the relative motion of the mass and support is recorded. The instrument can be designed to record only vertical motion, or only horizontal motion in a particular direction, say north–south. In general, a seismographic station will have a set of instruments for measuring three components of motion (up–down, N–S, E–W) at different periods, the period T of a vibration being the time required for a complete cycle (maximum to maximum, or minimum to min-

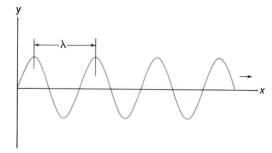

FIG. 11–16 A wave of wavelength λ propagating along the x-axis.

imum). The frequency ν is equal to $1/T$ (number of cycles per second). The circular frequency ω is $2\pi/T$ (radians per second). The motion in the y direction for a sinusoidal wave propagating in the x direction may be expressed as

$$y = A \sin (\omega t - kx) \qquad (11\text{-}7)$$

where A is the amplitude, t is time, and k, the wave number, is $2\pi/\lambda$, λ being the "wavelength." Figure 11–16 represents the wave at time $t = 0$, or at any time t that is an integer multiple of $2\pi/\omega$; the wave represented by equation (11-7) extends over all values of x and t. Equation (11-7) shows that at a given point ($x = $ constant), the motion is periodic with period $T = 2\pi/\omega$, since y assumes the same value at successive values of t differing by $2\pi/\omega$. At a given time ($t = $ constant), y is a periodic function of x, the distance between points of equal y being $\lambda = 2\pi/k$. The same value of y recurs for constant values of the argument $\omega t - kx$; hence $dx/dt = \omega/k$ represents the velocity v with which the wave propagates to the right. If the frequency ν is defined as $1/T = \omega/2\pi$, it follows that $v = \lambda\nu$. Any actual ground motion recorded on a seismograph can be represented by superposition of elementary sinusoidal waves of the type shown in equation (11-7), but of different wavelengths and frequencies. Periods of seismic waves generally fall between one tenth of a second and several minutes. The amplitude of the ground motion for a large earthquake may be of the order of half a millimeter for an epicenter several thousands of kilometers away, and is larger closer to it.

P- AND S-WAVES It can be deduced from the theory of elasticity that only two types of elastic waves can be transmitted through an isotropic solid, namely P- and S-waves. In an S-wave ("shear wave") the motion of a particle of the solid is transverse to the direction of propagation, as in Figure 11–16, or as in a ripple on the surface of a pond into which a stone has been thrown: the motion (up–down) propagates horizontally and outward from the point of impact.[11] The velocity V_S of an S-wave is $(\mu/\rho)^{1/2}$, where ρ is density and μ is the rigidity, or shear modulus— that is, the ratio of a shear stress to the corresponding shear strain (see Chapter 9). A P-wave is a compressional wave involving alternating expansion and contraction of the medium; the particle motion is along the direction of propagation, which may be determined by comparing the amplitudes of the three components of motion recorded simultaneously on three properly oriented seismographs. The velocity V_P of a P-wave is

$$V_P = \sqrt{\frac{K + (4/3)\mu}{\rho}}$$

where K is the bulk modulus defined in Chapter 2.

$$K = \rho \frac{dP}{d\rho}$$

Both V_P and V_S in rocks under ordinary conditions of pressure and temperature are of the order of a few kilometers per second. V_P is obviously greater than V_S, so that P arrives at a recording station before S, and the length of time separating the two arrivals is a measure of the distance to the source. The epicenter of an earthquake can be determined in this way from the arrival times of P and S at three stations, for there is only one point on earth that is located at given distances from three other points.

A third type of wave (Rayleigh wave) is propagated along the surface of a solid with an amplitude that decreases exponentially with depth below the surface. The velocity of a Rayleigh wave is about $0.9V_S$.

If a layer of medium 1 overlies a layer of medium 2, with higher velocities V_P, V_S—or more generally, if the velocity increases with depth in the body—a fourth type of wave, known as a Love wave, will propagate along the surface slightly more slowly than the Rayleigh wave. The particle motion in a Love wave is transverse to the direction of propagation and parallel to the surface—that is, horizontal for a layered earth.

REFLECTION AND REFRACTION In a homogeneous medium, P- and S-waves spread out equally in all directions from the source; wavefronts are spherical surfaces centered at the source, and normal to the direction of propagation. If the wavefront impinges on the boundary of a second medium with different elastic properties, both reflected and refracted waves are set up (Figure 11–17). The angle of reflection i_r equals the angle of incidence i_1, but the angle of refraction i_2 is given by Snell's law:

$$\sin i_2 = \frac{V_2}{V_1} \sin i_1$$

Snell's law follows directly from Figure 11–18. Consider two parallel rays impinging on the interface S–S. When ray 1 reaches O_1, the wavefront is O_1P_1. At a time dt later, the wavefront is

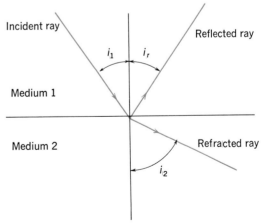

FIG. 11–17 Reflection and refraction of a wave at an interface.

[11]A wave on the surface of water is, however, a gravity wave, not a shear wave.

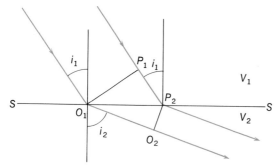

FIG. 11–18   *Illustration of Snell's law.*

at O_2P_2. Clearly, $P_1P_2 = V_1 \, dt$ and $O_1O_2 = V_2 \, dt$. But $P_1P_2 = O_1P_2 \sin i_1$, and $O_1O_2 = O_1P_2 \sin i_2$. Thus a ray is bent away from the normal when entering a medium where the velocity is greater. The relative amplitudes of the reflected and refracted waves depend on the densities and velocities in the two media.

From Snell's law it follows that when $\sin i_1 = V_1/V_2$, $i_2 = 90°$; a wave arriving at the "critical" angle $i_c = \sin^{-1} (V_1/V_2)$ does not penetrate into medium 2, but travels along the boundary. If the angle of incidence is greater than i_c, there is no penetration at all into medium 2 (since $\sin i_2$ can never be greater than 1); "total reflection" occurs.

Consider now an earthquake or an artificial explosion occurring at F in a layer 1 overlying layer 2 with different velocity $V_2 > V_1$ (Figure 11–19). A seismograph at R_0 may record a direct P-wave (or S-wave) traveling from F to R_0; it could also record, somewhat later, a reflected wave FAR_0. At a more distant point R_1 there will be, in addition to the direct arrival FR_1, another arrival corresponding to the path $FBCR_1$ where

B and C are located precisely so that the sine of the angle i_c, as shown, equals V_1/V_2; that wave will travel from B to C at the faster speed V_2 of the lower medium. At a sufficiently great distance from the epicenter, the refracted wave $FBCR_1$ will arrive before the direct one. From measured arrival times of the first disturbance at a number of recording stations at known distances from the epicenter, it is thus possible to determine V_1, V_2, and the thickness of the upper layer. It was essentially in this manner that Mohorovičić first demonstrated the existence of a "crust" overlying a "mantle" of higher velocity.

The actual picture is somewhat more complicated than this, as any P- or S-wave incident on a boundary at an angle other than $90°$ will generate *two* reflected (P and S) and *two* refracted (P and S) waves. The equality of the angles of incidence and reflection obtains only if the incident and reflected waves are of the same type. The angle i_r at which an S-wave is reflected from an incident P-wave is such that $\sin i_r = V_S^1/V_P^1 \sin i_1$, where V_S^1 and V_P^1 are, respectively, the velocities of S- and P-waves in medium 1.

DISPERSION   Dispersion is said to occur when the velocity of a wave depends on its frequency, or wavelength. P- and S-waves are not dispersive in a perfectly elastic medium. Love waves, on the other hand, are always dispersive, since their speed tends to approach that of S-waves in the upper medium for very short wavelengths (high frequency), whereas it approaches V_S in the lower medium for very long wavelengths (low frequency). Rayleigh waves on the surface of a homogeneous medium are not dispersive, but become so in a layered medium: If the velocity in-

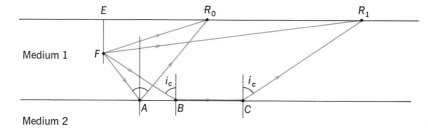

FIG. 11–19   *Wave paths in a two-layered medium.*

creases with depth, the longer waves, which also penetrate further down, travel faster and arrive first. The thickness of the earth's crust, for instance, can be determined from the observed dependence of velocity on wave length, or period.

PROPAGATION IN THE EARTH

Consider now waves propagated through a spherical earth, and neglect for the moment the thin (30–70-km) crust. If the earth were homogeneous, and V_P and V_S the same everywhere, the time it would take a wave to travel from the focus (assumed to be very close to the surface) to recording stations R_1, R_2, and so on. (Figure 11–20) would be proportional to the lengths of the chords FR_1, FR_2, which are proportional to the sine of one half the epicentral angles Δ_1, Δ_2. Observations show (Figure 11–21) that travel times increase less rapidly than predicted, as if the waves that traveled farther also traveled faster. But the body waves (P, S) that travel farther would also penetrate deeper into the earth, from which it is inferred that V_P and V_S both increase with depth. This introduces a serious complication, because waves do not travel in straight paths in heterogeneous media; if the velocity increases with depth, the path will be refracted upwards, as indicated by Snell's law. A wave emerging at R_1 will, in fact, have traveled along a curved path, as shown in Figure 11–22, which can be calculated given the variation of velocity with depth. Conversely, given travel–time curves such as in Figure 11–21, the velocity at each depth can be found.

Travel–time curves at epicentral distances greater than $100°$ turn out to be very complicated, revealing the complicated structure of the earth. At a depth of about 2900 km,[12] the velocity V_S suddenly falls to zero and V_P is considerably reduced. This is attributed to the existence of a "core" with a radius of some 3470–3480 km, which has zero rigidity and is therefore liquid.

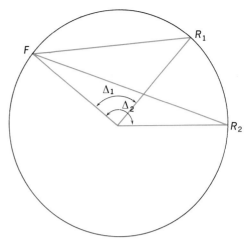

FIG. 11–20   Propagation of waves through a homogeneous earth.

But at depths of about 5100 km, V_P suddenly increases, perhaps in two or more steps, indicating the existence of an "inner core," which is presumably solid ($\mu > 0$), and may itself consist of two or more shells.

An actual seismogram (the recording at a distant station of all ground motion following an earthquake) appears rather confusing, because of the large number of different arrivals that are recorded (Figure 11–23). Indeed, at large distances, the direct P- and S-waves will be accompanied by a number of reflected waves bouncing off the core or the surface of the earth (Figure 11–24), or refracted through the core. Any P-wave (or S-wave) generates at an interface where it is reflected or refracted both P- and S-waves, which travel at different speeds and arrive therefore at different times. In addition, Rayleigh and Love waves, traveling along the surface of the earth in both directions and occasionally going several times around it, contribute to the total number of "phases," or arrivals, that the seismologist must properly identify. Following a large earthquake, wave after wave may continue to arrive for an hour or more after the first, direct, P-wave. Lateral variations in speed in the mantle add to the complication; it appears, for instance, that waves travel from Japan to Europe with a mean velocity somewhat

---

[12] This depth was determined by H. Jeffreys to be 2898 ± 3 km. Recent observations give 2885, or even 2878, km.

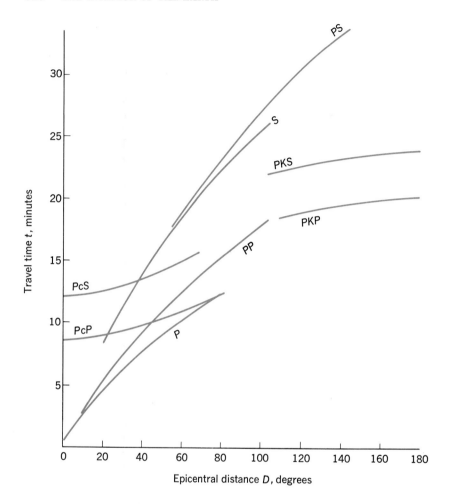

FIG. 11–21 *Travel times of seismic waves plotted against epicentral distance. For the meaning of symbols, see Figure 11–24.*

different from that of waves traveling eastward across and beneath the Pacific Ocean.

STRUCTURE OF THE EARTH

When all the information is pieced together, the following conclusions regarding the structure of the earth can be drawn:

1. Below a thin and local veneer of sedimentary rocks there is a crust, 30 to 70 km thick in continental areas, much thinner (6–8 km) in oceanic areas, in which V_P is generally between 5 and about 6.8 km/sec, increasing downward. A discontinuity ("Moho") separates the crust from the underlying mantle, at the top of which V_P is commonly about 8.1 km/sec, although this speed varies regionally (for example, about 7.7–7.9 km/sec under the western United States; about 8.2 km/sec under the Atlantic Coastal plain).

2. In the upper 200 km of the mantle, V_S seems to decrease with depth, at least locally ("low-velocity" layer). In general, V_P does not decrease with depth, although the rate of increase may be very small or zero; there are areas, however, where both V_P and V_S go through a minimum in the upper mantle (see Figure 12–14). Both V_P and V_S vary regionally, being somewhat different under oceans and continents.

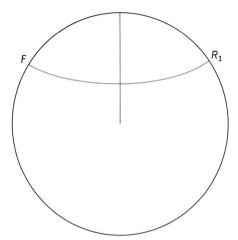

FIG. 11-22 *Upward refraction of ray resulting from increase in velocity with depth.*

3. Both V_P and V_S increase rapidly, but not uniformly, with depth, from about 200-km to 1000-km depths and more slowly thereafter; there may be two zones, around 400- and 600-km depths, respectively, where the rate of increase of V_P with depth is particularly large (see Figure 12–14).

4. There is a major discontinuity at a depth of approximately 2900 km, separating the mantle from the core. At the core boundary, V_P drops discontinuously from about 13.7 km/sec (mantle) to about 8.1, while V_S drops from 7.2 to 0.

5. In the outer core, from 2900 to about 5000 km, V_P increases slowly; the outer core is presumably liquid, with $V_S = 0$.

6. There is a small inner core (radius about 1200 km), which is probably solid; it may have a complex structure.

Density Distribution in the Earth

From the mass of the earth ($M = 5.98 \times 10^{27}$ g) and its mean radius R (6.37×10^8 cm), the average density ρ is easily found to be 5.517 g/cm³, much greater than the densities of most rocks, which usually lie between 2.5 and 3.4 g/cm³. We already know, from isostatic and seismic considerations, that the earth has a thin

crust, with density around 2.85 g/cm³ on the average, overlying a mantle, at the top of which the density must be about 3.3 or 3.4 g/cm³. The mean density of the earth, and its moment of inertia, imply that much denser matter must occur at greater depths. The present problem is to discover how density is distributed.

To the degree of approximation that the data warrant, it is permissible to neglect the very small effects of flattening and consider the earth to be a sphere in hydrostatic equilibrium. Since the total volume of the crust is small compared to that of the earth, any error made in estimating the density of the crust will not seriously affect our calculations; thus we subtract the approximate mass of the crust from that of the earth, and start our calculation at the top of the mantle, 6340 km from the center.

THE ADAMS-WILLIAMSON EQUATION

We recall that the density of a substance increases with increasing pressure at a rate measured by the bulk modulus (or incompressibility) $K = \rho \, dP/d\rho$, or $d\rho/\rho = dP/K$.[13] The pressure increases downward (or decreases outward) at the hydrostatic rate, $dP = -g\rho \, dr$; hence $d\rho/\rho = -g(\rho/K) \, dr$. But, from the definition of the seismic velocities V_P and V_S (page 613), $K/\rho = V_P^2 - 4V_S^2/3$; let us call this quantity ϕ. Since V_P and V_S are assumed to be known at all depths, ϕ is also known as a function of r; hence,

$$\frac{d\rho}{\rho} = \frac{-g}{\phi} \, dr \qquad (11\text{-}8)$$

This equation could, in principle, be integrated to find ρ as a function of r. The only difficulty is that g is also a function of ρ, which depends on r, as follows: Consider a point A inside the earth at a distance r from its center (Figure 11–25). What is g at that point? The mass $m(r)$ of the sphere of radius r contributes an attraction $Gm(r)/r^2$. The rest of the earth, between A and

---

[13] K, like most physical properties, varies with pressure and temperature. It generally increases roughly as the third or fourth power of the density.

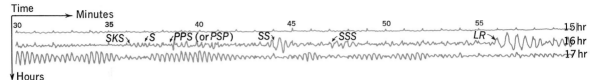

FIG. 11–23 (Above and facing) *Record at Berkeley (vertical instrument) of the earthquake of September 8, 1968, near the north coast of New Guinea, at an epicentral distance from Berkeley of 92°. The earthquake occurred at 15ʰ 12ᵐ 23ˢ.8 GCT. The first arrival (P) was recorded at Berkeley a few seconds before 15ʰ 26ᵐ. Indicated arrivals are: P, PP, SKS, PPS (or PSP), SS, SSS, and the surface (Rayleigh) waves beginning at 15ʰ 55ᵐ and lasting more than an hour. Love waves, in which the particle motion is parallel to the surface, are not recorded on a vertical instrument. The magnitude of the earthquake was 6.1. (Courtesy of B.A. Bolt.)*

the surface, contributes nothing, because the attraction of a spherical shell at a point inside it is zero everywhere. Thus,

$$g_r = \frac{Gm(r)}{r^2} = \frac{G}{r^2} \int_0^r 4\pi r^2 \rho(r)\, dr$$

Equation (11-8), known as the Adams-Williamson equation, can still be integrated by steps,

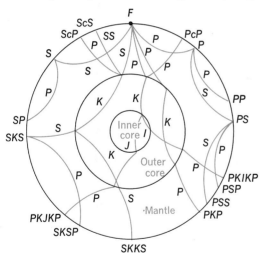

FIG. 11–24 *Possible seismic paths through the earth. The focus of the earthquake is at F. The symbol c designates a wave reflected at the core's surface; thus P_cP is a P-wave through the mantle reflected at the core; P_cS is a P-wave reflected as S. The symbols K and I refer, respectively, to waves that have traveled through the outer and inner core. The symbol SP designates an S-wave through the mantle reflected at the surface as P. PKS travels through mantle and core as P, and up through the mantle again as S. The ray marked PKJKP, which travels as S through the inner core, has not been observed. (After K. E. Bullen.)*

since we know g at the surface. We divide the earth into concentric thin layers. In the top layer we know g and ϕ, and can therefore calculate, by (11-8), the increment of density attributable to pressure; this gives the mass of the first layer, which, when subtracted from the mass of the earth, gives the mass of all the other layers (and therefore g at the top of the second layer), and so on. The result of this calculation depends on what density ρ_0 is assumed for the top of the first layer; as it turns out, there is no geologically reasonable value of ρ_0 that will give a density distribution which yields the correct moment of inertia $C = 0.33MR^2$. Thus at least one of our assumptions must be incorrect.

THE MANTLE–CORE MODEL

The assumption most likely to be wrong is that the density increases solely because of the increase in pressure, $d\rho/\rho = dP/K$. We recall that the seismic results clearly indicate that the earth consists of a mantle and a core in which V_P and V_S have very different velocities (V_S is zero in the outer part of the core), and therefore presumably also different densities and compositions. We thus repeat the calculation for the mantle as before, but when the depth of 2900 km is reached, we substitute a new density ρ_1, and continue to the center. The new density ρ_1 is chosen so as to give the correct value for the moment of inertia C for the whole earth.

This is, however, not the end of our troubles. Having found the density in the mantle, we can now calculate the moment of inertia of the mantle C_m and, by subtraction, that of the core $C_c =$

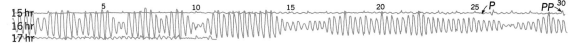

C − C_m. It now turns out that unless we take an improbably high value (about 3.7) for the density at the top of the mantle, C_c will be *greater* than $(2/5) M_c r_c^2$ (M_c is the mass of the core), implying that the density must decrease with depth in the core, which is physically most unlikely and contradicts our assumption. On the other hand, all gravity and seismic data on the upper mantle seem to preclude a density larger than about 3.4 except, perhaps, locally. No adjustment of density in the inner core will remove the discrepancy, essentially because the inner core contributes very little to the moment of inertia.

A HETEROGENEOUS MANTLE

An alternative assumption is that the mantle itself is not homogeneous, in the sense that its mineralogical composition changes with depth. Such mineralogical changes, which could reflect either changes in gross chemical composition or phase changes, or both, will be further discussed in the next section. The difficulty now is that one must more or less guess what these changes are, and where they occur, although the smooth variation of V_P and V_S between a depth of 900 km and the core boundary suggests that changes occur in the upper mantle rather than in its deeper

parts. The problem of the density distribution thus becomes somewhat indeterminate, and a number of distributions ("models" or "solutions") can be found that fit all known conditions; fortunately, the densities at a given depth predicted by different models generally do not differ by more than a few percent.

Birch has found a useful empirical relation, which seems to hold at pressures above a few kilobars for a wide variety of minerals and rocks, between the compressional velocity V_P and density ρ:

$$V_P = A + B\rho \qquad (11\text{-}9)$$

where A and B are constants; A depends on the mean atomic weight of the substance.[14] Conversely,

$$\rho = a + bV_P$$

where a and b are constants. Since V_P is known as a function of depth in the earth, this relation may be used to calculate a corresponding density distribution. Birch has calculated a possible density distribution using this relation down to 1000 km, and the Adams-Williamson equation below that level. The constant b used in this calculation $(0.328 \text{ g cm}^{-3} \text{ km}^{-1} \text{ sec}^{-1})$ is that appropriate for rocks of low mean atomic weight. A second solution (Table 11–1, Solution II) corresponds to choosing the constant a so as to give the correct V_P and a density of 3.32 g/cm³ at the top of the mantle; b is then adjusted to give the appropriate

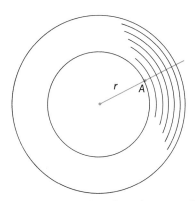

FIG. 11–25 *The acceleration of gravity at a point inside a sphere. Matter between A and the surface does not contribute to the attraction at A.*

---

[14] If x_i is the proportion by weight of oxide i (for example, SiO_2, Al_2O_3, MgO) in a rock, and m_i its mean atomic weight, the mean atomic weight m of the rock is

$$m = \left[\sum_i \frac{x_i}{m_i} \right]^{-1}$$

where the summation is over all oxides in the rock. The mean atomic weight of an oxide is its molecular weight divided by the number of particles in its stoichiometric formula. For SiO_2, for example, $m = 60.09/3 = 20.03$. For most common rocks, m is usually close to 21, but is somewhat higher (about 24) in rocks rich in iron.

TABLE 11-1   *Velocity, density, acceleration, and pressure, as functions of radius* (R_m = 6338 km, R_c = 3473 km)*

The Mantle

			Solution I			Solution II		
r/R_m	V_P, km/sec	V_S, km/sec	ρ, g/cm³	g, cm/sec²	P, Mb	ρ, g/cm³	g, cm/sec²	P, Mb
1.00	8.10		3.425	984	0.009	3.320	984	0.009
0.98	8.13		3.435	988	0.052	3.332	989	0.051
0.96	8.38		3.517	992	0.095	3.426	994	0.093
0.94	8.97		3.710	995	0.141	3.650	998	0.138
0.92	9.91		4.018	997	0.190	4.006	1001	0.186
0.90	10.55		4.228	997	0.242	4.248	1001	0.239
0.88	10.99		4.372	996	0.296	4.415	1000	0.294
0.86	11.29		4.471	995	0.352	4.529	998	0.350
0.84	11.50	6.40	4.540	994	0.409	4.608	997	0.408
0.82	11.67	6.48	4.613	993	0.466	4.681	995	0.467
0.80	11.85	6.56	4.684	993	0.525	4.752	994	0.526
0.78	12.03	6.64	4.755	993	0.584	4.823	994	0.586
0.76	12.20	6.71	4.824	994	0.645	4.892	994	0.648
0.74	12.38	6.77	4.892	995	0.705	4.960	995	0.710
0.72	12.54	6.83	4.958	997	0.768	5.026	996	0.773
0.70	12.71	6.89	5.023	1001	0.831	5.091	999	0.837
0.68	12.88	6.95	5.088	1005	0.896	5.156	1002	0.902
0.66	13.01	7.01	5.152	1011	0.961	5.220	1007	0.968
0.64	13.16	7.07	5.216	1018	1.028	5.284	1013	1.035
0.62	13.32	7.14	5.278	1027	1.096	5.346	1021	1.103
0.60	13.46	7.20	5.341	1039	1.165	5.409	1032	1.173
0.58	13.60	7.26	5.405	1053	1.236	5.473	1044	1.245
0.56	13.64	7.31	5.468	1069	1.310	5.536	1059	1.318
0.548	13.64	7.30	5.508	1081	1.354	5.576	1070	1.363

The Core

		Solution I			Solution II		
r/R_c	V_P, km/sec	ρ, g/cm³	g, cm/sec²	P, Mb	ρ, g/cm³	g, cm/sec²	P, Mb
1.0	8.10	10.05	1081	1.35	9.96	1070	1.36
0.9	8.53	10.59	999	1.73	10.49	989	1.73
0.8	9.03	11.05	909	2.08	10.94	899	2.08
0.7	9.44	11.45	811	2.42	11.33	802	2.41
0.6	9.78	11.78	706	2.73	11.66	698	2.71
0.5	10.10	12.05	596	3.00	11.92	589	2.97
0.4	10.44	12.27	482	3.22	12.13	476	3.20
0.3	11.20	(12.43)†	(364)	(3.40)	(12.29)	(360)	(3.37)
0.2	11.24	(12.53)	(244)	(3.54)	(12.39)	(241)	(3.50)
0.1	11.28	(12.60)	(122)	(3.62)	(12.46)	(121)	(3.58)
0	11.31	(12.62)	(0)	(3.64)	(12.48)	(0)	(3.61)

* From F. Birch, *J. Geophys. Res.*, vol. 69, p. 4381, 1964.
† Values in parentheses are in the region of the inner core, for which no special allowance has been made.

mass and moment of inertia. Note from Table 11–1 how little different these two solutions are.

FREE OSCILLATIONS OF THE EARTH

When a bell is struck, it rings. The tone of the bell, which is peculiar to it, consists of a particular combination of frequencies that depend on the size and shape of the bell and on the elastic constants of the material of which it is made. Similarly, a sudden and violent disturbance, such as an earthquake of sufficient magnitude, may cause the whole earth to vibrate. The vibrating motion of a particle consists of the superposition of a number of fundamental "modes," the frequency or period of which depends on the manner in which mass is distributed in the earth and on its elastic constants. Two of these modes are illustrated in Figure 11–26. Figure 11–26a represents a "torsional oscillation," in which the motion is purely tangential (normal to a radius) but of opposite sense in two hemispheres, a pole of which is at the point where the disturbance occurred. In Figure 11–26b ("spheroidal oscillation"), the motion is neither purely radial nor purely tangential. There is actually an infinite number of possible distinct torsional or spheroidal modes, differing as to the number of nodal lines on the surface (a nodal line connects points of no displacement, as the "equator" of Figure 11–26a).

Different spheroidal modes correspond, for instance, to the deformation of a sphere into a pear-shaped figure described by a Legendre polynomial of degree 3, or into a figure described by P_4 and so forth. Each mode has a number of "harmonics" or "overtones." For instance, an overtone of the motion represented in Figure 11–26a may be such that the outer half of the earth moves as shown and the inner half moves in opposite sense; the sphere with radius $r = R/2$ is then a "nodal" surface on which there is no motion.

Observed oscillations have an amplitude at the surface of the order of a micron (10^{-4} cm) or less; periods range from slightly less than an hour down to minutes.[15] These oscillations may

---

[15] An alternative representation of these oscillations is in terms of "standing" Rayleigh and Love waves of different wavelengths. A "standing" wave occurs by superposition of two traveling waves of the same amplitude, wavelength, and frequency, traveling in opposite directions; that is,

$$y = A \sin (\omega t - Kx) + A \sin (\omega t + Kx) = 2A \cos Kx \sin \omega t$$

which represents a standing (nonpropagating) wave of frequency ω, with an amplitude that is "modulated" (that is, depends on positions) though the factor $2 \cos Kx$. Love waves, in which the motion of particle is purely horizontal, correspond to torsional oscillation, whereas Rayleigh waves correspond to spheroidal oscillations.

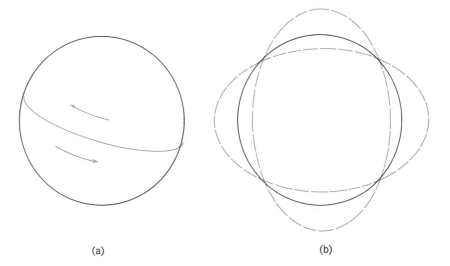

FIG. 11–26 Two modes of oscillation of the earth. (a) "Torsional" oscillation, in which the motion is tangential (that is, normal to a radius). (b) "Spheroidal" oscillation.

(a)   (b)

last for a day or two, and then gradually die down.

Given a density distribution, and corresponding distribution of the elastic parameters K and μ, as deduced from the velocity distribution of elastic waves, it is possible to calculate what the period of a given mode should be, and compare it to observations. The free oscillations thus provide a check on any assumed density distribution. The agreement is usually close for any distribution calculated from the seismic data as explained above; it is rarely perfect, however, since free oscillations are planetary phenomena in the sense that they involve the whole earth and therefore represent average properties, whereas the seismic velocities, as we have seen, vary slightly from region to region. A velocity and density distribution that fits exactly the free-oscillation data might not actually exist anywhere in the earth. It is also possible that the radius of the core deduced from travel times may be slightly in error, by a few kilometers or so, or that the surface of the core may be somewhat "rough" and irregular, the bumps and hollows of this surface being possibly reflected in some of the undulations of the geoid.

OTHER PARAMETERS IN THE EARTH

For any chosen density distribution, the seismic velocities V_P and V_S immediately give K and μ, the elastic coefficients. The variation of g with depth can also be found and is rather curious, for g remains nearly constant (within about 1 percent) in the mantle, while in the core it decreases linearly to zero at the center of the earth. [In a homogeneous sphere of density ρ, $g = (4/3)\,\pi G\rho r$.] From the value of g and ρ, the pressure at any depth can be found by integrating the hydrostatic equation $dP = -g\rho\,dr$. The pressure turns out to be about 1.4×10^{12} dynes/cm², or 1.4 megabars at the core boundary, and about 3.6 megabars at the earth's center. For a homogeneous earth of density $\bar{\rho} = 5.52$ g/cm³, the pressure P_c at the center would be

$$P_c = -\int_R^0 \frac{4\pi G\bar{\rho}r\bar{\rho}\,dr}{3} =$$

$$\frac{2\pi G\bar{\rho}^2 R^2}{3} = 1.7 \text{ megabars}$$

The high density of the core thus nearly doubles P_c with respect to what it would be if the earth were of uniform density.

EFFECTS OF TEMPERATURE; THE ADIABATIC GRADIENT

Nothing has yet been said of the temperature T, which affects density through the coefficient of thermal expansion $\alpha = -(1/\rho)(d\rho/dT)$ (ρ generally decreases with increasing T). The coefficient α is usually about 3×10^{-5} degree for silicates under normal conditions; (it generally increases with increasing T, but decreases with increasing P), so that a change in temperature of $1000°$C produces a change in density of 3 percent or so. Since the temperature in the mantle, which is solid, cannot anywhere exceed its melting point of a few thousand degrees, its effect on density is certainly much smaller than that of pressure, and in the opposite sense. It is therefore not likely to affect our calculations very much.

There is, however, a temperature effect concealed in the Adams-Williamson equation (11-8). The incompressibility K that controls the speed of P-waves is the adiabatic incompressibilty K_S defined on page 99; K_S is related to K_T through $K_S = K_T[1 + T\alpha\gamma]$ where γ, the Grüneisen ratio,[16] is a dimensionless parameter which, for most solids, lies between 1 and 2.5. The compression that accompanies the passage of a P-wave is so fast, as compared with the poor thermal conductivity of rocks, that practically none of the heat generated by the compression has time to escape; thus V_P is determined by K_S, not K_T, and the quantity that appears in the Adams-Williamson equation is K_S/ρ. Hence the increase in density with depth deduced from that

---

[16] The Grüneisen ratio may be defined as

$$\gamma = \frac{\alpha K_T}{\rho C_V} = \frac{\alpha K_S}{\rho C_P}$$

where C_P and C_V are, respectively, the specific heat at constant pressure and at constant volume.

equation also corresponds to adiabatic conditions: it is the increase in density induced by a change in pressure *and* temperature, the change in temperature being precisely that corresponding to the change in pressure under the assumption of no heat exchange, or "adiabaticity," or constant entropy. It can be shown from simple thermodynamics that

$$\left(\frac{\partial T}{\partial P}\right)_S = \frac{\alpha T}{\rho C_P} \qquad (11\text{-}10)$$

where the subscript S implies the constancy of entropy. Since $dP = -g\rho \, dr$, the corresponding "adiabatic gradient" is

$$\frac{dT}{dr} = -g\frac{\alpha}{C_P} = -g\frac{\gamma}{\phi} T \qquad (11\text{-}11)$$

This adiabatic gradient, as we shall see (Chapter 12), plays an important role in convection theory, since it determines the onset of instability in a fluid heated from below. Its value in the mantle is of the order of a fraction of a degree per kilometer.

Composition of Mantle and Core

Now that we have obtained approximate (that is, within a few percent) values of the density ρ, the incompressibility K_S, the rigidity μ, and the pressure P at any depth within the earth, what can we deduce regarding the composition?

The density of a substance is, to some extent, a diagnostic property; it helps, for instance, in the identification of minerals. The density determined at a point in the earth is, however, the density at the pressure and temperature prevailing there; the latter is essentially unknown, although its effects are unlikely to be large, as we have just seen. The first problem is then to somehow reduce the density at pressure P to the corresponding density ρ_0 at normal pressure (1 bar); or, conversely, start with a material of known initial density and determine what its density, incompressibility, and rigidity would be at P. Any material whose properties at P match the observed ones could represent the composition of the earth at that depth. So little is known

of the dependence of μ on pressure and temperature that most of the effort has gone, so far, into matching ρ and K only.

THE EQUATION OF STATE

The equation of state of a substance is the relation between density, pressure, and temperature, from which the density and its derivatives, such as K_T, can be computed for any given P and T. The perfect gas law $PV = RT$ (V, the volume per mole, is m/ρ, where m is the molecular weight) is an equation of state from which it is easily deduced that $K_T = P$, $\alpha = 1/T$; thus from the values of ρ and K_T of a perfect gas the values of P and T can be deduced, and conversely K_T and ρ can be calculated for any given P and T. But the earth is not a perfect gas; and the problem is to find an equation of state applicable to it.

In principle, an equation of state can be determined experimentally by measuring the density (or volume) of the substance under study at different pressures and temperatures. Unfortunately, the pressures that prevail inside the earth are, as we have seen, of the order of several megabars and are much higher than the pressures that can be created experimentally in a static apparatus. Very high pressures up to several megabars can be created by shock waves—that is, by impact of a high-speed projectile or by the use of explosives. By employing the equations of conservation of mass, momentum, and energy, the density and pressure behind the shock front can be calculated from the observed velocity of propagation of the front and from the observed particle velocity, which is essentially the rate of deformation of the body subjected to shock; but the experimental difficulties of measuring any other property in the very short time (milliseconds or microseconds) that the pressure pulse lasts are considerable. The temperature in the shocked material is usually quite high and can be evaluated precisely only if Grüneisen's ratio and its dependence on volume are known. Nevertheless, shock-wave experiments are our main source of information on the behavior of matter at pressures of several megabars, and some important geophysical results have been derived from them.

It is equally, or even more, difficult to derive the equation of state of a solid from theory. The change in density with pressure, or incompressibility, measures essentially the electrostatic repulsion between electrons of adjacent atoms or ions as they are squeezed together [the second term on the right in the equation (2-7) for the potential energy of an ionic crystal]. Since common atoms have many electrons, the calculation of the repulsion as a function of distance between nuclei is extremely difficult and has been attempted, without much success, only in very few relatively simple cases.

The device most commonly resorted to is that of successive approximations. Assume, for instance, that the effect of pressure on the isothermal incompressibility can be represented in a series:[17]

$$K = K_0 + bP + cP^2 + \cdots$$

where K_0 is the value of K at $P = 0$, and $b, c, \cdots$ are coefficients that depend on temperature only. Assume further, by reason of ignorance rather than for any theoretical reason, that c and all further coefficients are very small and can be neglected. Thus, at constant temperature

$$K = \frac{dP}{d\rho} = K_0 + bP \qquad \frac{dK}{dP} = b$$

which by integration, gives

$$\rho = \rho_0 \left(1 + b\frac{P}{K_0}\right)^{1/b}$$

from which the density ρ at any pressure P can be calculated, given the constants K_0 and b.

This empirical equation does represent rather well the experimental results for some substances. The constant b commonly turns out to be close to 4 for many oxides and silicates. There are indications, however, that dK/dP is not quite constant, but tends to decrease slightly with increasing pressure; its temperature dependence is not well known. Several other equations of

state have been proposed, which fit experimental data equally well; Birch, for instance, has proposed an equation of the form

$$P = \frac{3}{2}K_0\left[y^{7/3} - y^{5/3}\right]$$

where $y = \rho/\rho_0$.

COMPOSITION OF THE MANTLE

UPPER MANTLE   The composition of the upper mantle can be broadly determined from the fact that very few rocks have a density between about 3.2 and 3.4 (as determined from isostatic considerations) and a compressional velocity V_P near 8.1 km/sec. Only one common group of rocks, namely peridotites, satisfies these requirements; the less common eclogites also do. The large volume of peridotites found in the crust in tectonic settings (see Chapter 6), such that they could be chunks of the mantle brought up mechanically (that is, by faulting), confirms the impression that peridotites are indeed dominant constitutents of the upper mantle. So does the common occurrence in basaltic lavas of inclusions of peridotites, some of which may be fragments of the mantle, or of the residual mantle material left after partial melting (see Chapter 6).

Peridotites consist mostly of olivine and pyroxene, but as explained in Chapter 6, they vary a great deal in detail. Their pyroxenes vary in composition (alumina content, for instance); moreover, some peridotites contain garnet and a few contain feldspars. Since they all have similar mean atomic numbers, the density and seismic velocity give little information as to their mineralogical composition; see equation (11-9). Ringwood has proposed that the term "pyrolite" be used for the rock forming the upper mantle, the composition of pyrolite being defined by the property that when it is fractionally melted, it yields a basaltic melt and an unmelted refractory residue equivalent to an ordinary dunite (olivine) or an "alpine" (that is, tectonically emplaced) peridotite. The arguments are petrological rather than geophysical.

Regional differences in the properties of the upper mantle, as between western and eastern North America, for instance, or as between

---

[17] This is, in effect, the MacLaurin expansion of K as a function of P:

$$K(P) = K(0) + P\left(\frac{\partial K}{\partial P}\right)_0 + \frac{1}{2}P^2\left(\frac{\partial^2 K}{\partial P^2}\right)_0 + \cdots$$

oceans and continents in general, may be caused by differences in composition, or average temperature, or both. The mantle, as the crust, appears to be heterogeneous on all scales.

THE LOWER MANTLE   Whatever the density adopted for the lowermost mantle, and whatever the equation of state used to reduce the density to its value ρ_0 at ordinary pressure and temperature, it turns out that ρ_0 must be about 4–4.2 g/cm^3; it also appears that $\phi_0 = (K_S/\rho_0)$ at ordinary pressure and room temperature must be in the neighborhood of 55 or 60 km/sec^2. No common rock satisfies this condition, although a few minerals (corundum Al$_2$O$_3$, periclase MgO, rutile TiO$_2$) do; in general, ϕ_0 for minerals is much lower for a given density than the required value. Fayalite, for instance, has $\rho_0 = 4.07$ but $\phi_0 = 26$.

As mentioned on page 619, the evidence is very strong that the mantle is heterogeneous; the lower mantle must differ mineralogically from the upper mantle. The difference could, in principle, be either in the gross chemical composition or in crystal structure (polymorphism). To get the proper density ρ_0 by changing the chemical composition a great deal of iron would have to be added to upper mantle material, either as FeO (in silicates) or as metallic iron (in some meteorites). Addition of iron, however, decreases ϕ_0. The most probable alternative, therefore, is polymorphism.

THE TRANSITION ZONE (200–900 KM)   It seems likely that the phase changes occur mostly in the "transition" zone (also referred to as layer C) extending in depth roughly from 200 to 900 km, as this is also the region in which the density and seismic velocities increase most rapidly. The corresponding pressures are approximately 70 to 350 kb. We remember (Chapter 5) that the pressure P_e at which a polymorphic transition occurs depends on temperature as

$$\frac{dP_e}{dT} = \frac{\Delta S}{\Delta V}$$

where ΔS and ΔV are the changes in entropy and volume, respectively, at the transition.

A number of polymorphic transformations that could occur in the appropriate range have been suggested; some of these have been observed experimentally. For instance, coesite (a dense, four-coordinated form of silica SiO$_2$) transforms to stishovite, which is a six-coordinated polymorph with the structure of rutile (see Chapter 2). Fayalite (Fe$_2$SiO$_4$) undergoes a transition to a dense form with the spinel structure, and so do solid solutions of Fe$_2$SiO$_4$ and Mg$_2$SiO$_3$, and, as it is claimed, Mg$_2$SiO$_4$ (forsterite) itself. Pyroxenes, such as MgSiO$_3$ (coordination 6 for Mg, 4 for Si) could undergo a transition to a six-coordinated form with the structure of ilmenite or corundum. Finally, all magnesium silicates could break down to their constituent oxides in their dense form; for example,

$$\underset{\text{olivine}}{\text{Mg}_2\text{SiO}_4} \rightarrow \underset{\text{spinel}}{\text{Mg}_2\text{SiO}_4} \rightarrow \underset{\text{periclase}}{2\text{MgO}} + \underset{\text{stishovite}}{\text{SiO}_2}$$

or alternatively, Mg$_2$SiO$_4$ in the spinel form could transform to periclase plus MgSiO$_3$ in the ilmenite form. Any reaction or transformation that entails a decrease in volume will take place, of course, at a sufficiently high pressure; the only question is which of these reactions actually occur in the mantle. The fact that the transition zone in the mantle is spread over a pressure range of nearly 300 kb suggests that, in fact, several successive reactions occur at increasing depths. In Chapter 12, an attempt will be made to determine the temperature at a 400-km depth on the assumption that the rapid velocity increase that occurs there reflects the olivine–spinel transition.

A polymorphic transformation of a single, pure, substance occurs at a given P and T with a finite change in density. In the mantle, however, there is no clear-cut evidence of any sudden discontinuous change in density or seismic velocity. The reason may be that the upper mantle does not consist of a single, pure phase. In multicomponent systems, pressure-induced transitions will be spread over a pressure range, just as temperature-induced transitions (for example, melting) occur over a finite temperature range (see Chapters 5 and 6). A possible phase diagram for the olivine–spinel transition appears on page 657.

A plausible guess for the lower mantle, then, is that it consists of tightly packed oxides and silicates of magnesium and iron, and with minor amounts of such elements as Al, Ca, and others.

The possible crystal structures include those of periclase, stishovite, spinel, ilmenite (or corundum), and possibly still others. Iron in the low-spin state would probably occur in solid solution in magnesium compounds. It is unlikely to be distributed uniformly, because of gravity. As mentioned briefly in Chapter 5, the chemical potential depends on position (or height) in a gravitational field. The general condition for equilibrium, namely, that the chemical potential μ_i of any component i must be the same in all phases in which it is present, is replaced in a gravitational field by the condition that $\mu_i^\alpha + M_i\phi^\alpha$ be constant. In this expression M_i is the molecular weight of i and $-\phi^\alpha$ is the gravitational potential at the position of phase α, which appears in this expression because the work or energy to transfer one mole of i from position α to position β is

$$\int_\alpha^\beta M_i g dh = M_i(\phi^\beta - \phi^\alpha)$$

where h is height, measured positively upward. From this condition it is possible to calculate how the two components of an ideal binary system would distribute themselves.[18] It is not possible to make exact numerical calculations for the lower mantle, since neither the composition nor the densities of the relevant phases are known; approximate calculations do show, however, that the FeO content would increase downward over a distance of 1000 km or more by a very large factor, if gravitational equilibrium were attained. It probably would be attained if the mantle ever were completely molten, but diffusion is so slow in solids that the mantle may still be chemically far from gravitational equilibrium.

THE CORE

THE OUTER CORE   Since the mantle presumably has a composition not very different from that of some stony meteorites, it might be guessed that

---

[18] The calculation may be found in Chapter 11 of the book by Guggenheim, and in the book by Kern and Weisbrod, both of which are listed in the references for Chapter 5.

the core should correspond in composition to the iron meteorites which, as their name implies, consist mostly of iron with a few percent of nickel and other metals. The high density of the core (about 11 g/cm³, on the average) does indeed indicate that it must consist of elements much heavier than those that form the mantle; and since Fe is the only heavy element that seems to exist in the solar system in some abundance, there is a strong presumption that it is indeed an important constituent of the core.

The outer core is liquid, as shown by the fact that S-waves are not propagated through it. The velocity V_P of the compressional or "sound" wave in a medium with zero rigidity (liquid, gas) is simply $(K_S/\rho)^{1/2} = (\partial P/\partial\rho)_S^{1/2}$. This quantity or, rather, a quantity closely related to it can be determined from shock-wave experiments at very high pressure by plotting the pressure against the density, and taking the slope of the curve; this slope is not exactly equal to $(K_S/\rho)^{1/2}$, because conditions in a shock wave are not adiabatic, but the difference is not important here. Values of V_P determined in this manner are plotted against density in Figure 11–27, and compared to the seismic values of $(K_S/\rho)^{1/2}$ (the dotted lines indicate approximate limits arising from the uncertainty of the density distribution). Noting that the position on the plot of the experimental curve for an element seems to be determined primarily by its atomic number, Birch points out that the mean atomic number of the core must be (1) distinctly different from, and much higher than, that of the mantle, and (2) less than that of iron. The first remark effectively disposes of previous suggestions that mantle and core have the same composition, the boundary between them corresponding to a phase change. This is clearly not so; mantle material could not have a density comparable to that of the core at any pressure likely to exist in the earth. Birch's second remark implies that the core must consist of iron alloyed with some element, or elements, with atomic number appreciably less than 26. The atomic number of nickel, which is commonly associated with iron in meteorites, is 28. A direct comparison of the estimated density of the core to that of iron as obtained in shock-wave experiments, al-

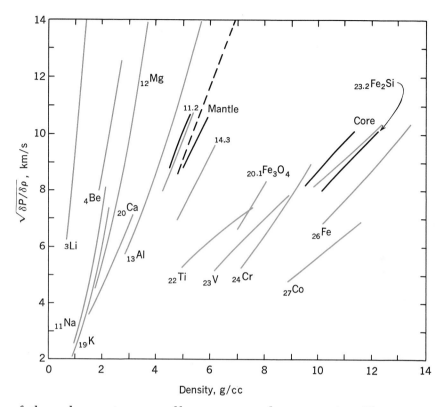

though difficult because of the unknown temperature of the core and high temperature developed in the shock experiment, leads to much the same conclusion: The core is probably too light to consist of pure iron, or of an iron–nickel alloy.

Since silicon is abundant in the mantle, and readily soluble in molten iron, it has been suggested that it is responsible for the low atomic number of the core (the atomic number of silicon is 14). If so, it is unlikely that the core could be in chemical equilibrium with the mantle (see Chapter 14). It has also been suggested by Alder that MgO and FeO may be sufficiently soluble in liquid iron to account for the density of the core. Sulfur, carbon, or hydrogen in solution in the core could also contribute to decreasing its mean atomic "number"; sulfur, with atomic number 16, is a particularly likely constituent of the core, as most rocks (and presumably also the mantle from which they derive) seem to be depleted in

sulfur as compared to meteorites. The missing balance of this element might well be in the core.

THE INNER CORE Very little can be said about the inner core, which appears to be solid. The simplest assumption is that it has essentially the same composition as the outer core, implying that the temperature at the inner–outer core boundary is precisely the melting point of the inner core at the pressure prevailing there. The density of the inner core is hard to determine exactly, because the inner core contributes very little either to the mass or moment of inertia of the earth; what is known of it does not preclude its consisting of roughly the same elements as the outer core, although its composition is not likely to be exactly the same, since the liquid in equilibrium with a solid phase in a multicomponent system usually does not have exactly the same composition as the solid. The seismic structure of the inner core appears to be complex; it consists perhaps of two or more concentric layers of slightly different composition. This layering could reflect changes in composition of the solids that crystallize, at progressively lower temperatures, from a multicomponent liquid.

The Earth's Magnetic Field

The geomagnetic field has no measurable effect on geological processes; accordingly, its study was considered until a few years ago to be unrelated to geology. It now appears that a great deal of useful geological information on the origin of the sea floor, displacements of and internal deformation in continents, rates of sedimentation, and so forth (see Chapter 13), can be obtained from the magnetic record as read from the "fossil" magnetization of rocks. This magnetization is related to the direction and intensity of the field when and where the rock formed; its interpretation thus requires some knowledge of the general features of the field. As the earth's field originates mostly in the core, and provides some information on it, it may be appropriate to discuss it here.

MAGNETIC FIELDS

All magnetic fields originate from electric currents. We recall that a current I in an infinite straight wire produces at a point P a field of intensity $2I/r$, where r is the perpendicular distance from P to the wire; this field lies in a plane normal to the wire and is everywhere tangent to a circle centered on the wire. The magnetic field of a circular loop is equivalent to that of a dipole (see below) of moment $m = IA$ normal to the plane of the loop, A being the area of the loop. The magnetic field of a magnet has its origin in the orbital and spin motions of some of the electrons in the atoms forming the magnet, which are equivalent to electric currents, since a current is, by definition, a moving electric charge.

A magnetic field can be measured by the force it exerts. For instance, two parallel wires at a distance r and carrying a current I in the same direction attract each other with a force $2I^2/r$

FIG. 11–28   *Parallel dipoles repel each other; antiparallel dipoles attract each other.*

per unit length of wire; they repel each other if the currents are in opposite senses. Similarly, two pieces of magnetized material, such as two compass needles, attract or repel each other with a force as though each needle carried on both ends "charges" of opposite sign ("dipole"); these charges repel each other (if they are of the same sign) or attract each other (if they are of the opposite sign) with a force inversely proportional to the square of the distance between them (Figure 11–28).

Since the two ends of a compass needle are not equivalent, one of them always pointing towards north and the other towards south, different signs have to be attached to them; by convention, the plus sign is assigned to the north-seeking end. Such magnetic charges do not actually exist, although it can be shown that the magnetic field of a body carrying a uniform magnetization J is formally the same as that of a surface charge density J_n over the surface of the body, J_n being the component of J along the outer normal to the surface of the body. The magnetic field of a rod magnetized parallel to its length is thus the same as that of a "charge" $+J$ at one end and $-J$ at the other; such a combination of $+$ and $-$ equal charges constitutes a "dipole," the lines of force[19] of which are shown in Figure 11–29. Note that these "charges" must necessarily go in pairs of opposite sign, so that the net magnetic charge is always zero.

Just as the gravitational attraction can be derived from a potential, the magnetic field at any point in space where there is no current (and hence no magnetic material) can be expressed as the gradient of a "magnetostatic" potential W:

---

[19] A line of force is a line in space that is tangent to the field at every point.

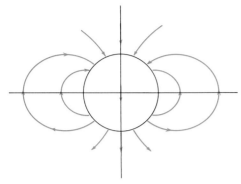

FIG. 11–29 Lines of force outside a sphere of a dipole at center of the sphere.

$$\mathbf{H} = -\,\mathrm{grad}\ W$$

where W is a function of the coordinates, and like the gravitational potential, satisfies Laplace's equation $\nabla^2 W = 0$.[20] As for U, this condition determines the general mathematical form of W.

DIPOLES AND MULTIPOLES

Consider first the relatively simple case of a potential (or field) symmetrical about an axis, such as the field of the dipole illustrated in Figure 11–30, for which it is sufficient to specify two coordinates r and θ, the potential and field being independent of the third. The function of r and θ that satisfies Laplace's equation is of the general form of equation (11-5).

$$W = A_0 + \frac{B_0}{r} + \left(A_1 r + \frac{B_1}{r^2}\right)\cos\theta +$$

$$\left(A_2 r^2 + \frac{B_2}{r^3}\right)\left(\frac{3\cos^2\theta - 1}{2}\right)+$$

$$\left(A_3 r^3 + \frac{B_3}{r^4}\right)\left(\frac{5\cos^3\theta - 3\cos\theta}{2}\right) + \cdots$$

$$(11\text{-}12)$$

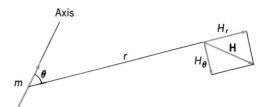

FIG. 11–30 Components of an axisymmetrical field.

where the functions of θ are the Legendre polynomials that appear in equation (11-6), and the coefficients $(A_0, A_1, \cdots B_0, B_1, \cdots,)$ are numerical constants appropriate to the particular problem. These constants may be determined by measuring the components of the field (Figure 11–29) $H_r = -(\partial W/\partial r)$, $H_\theta = -(1/r)\,(\partial W/\partial\theta)$ at a number of known points, and finding the values of the coefficients that best fit the observations. A_0 may be taken to be zero, since potentials, like energy, are measured from some arbitrary reference point. B_0 must also be zero, because the potential B_0/r is that of a single magnetic charge at the origin, and such charges do not exist. The second term is interesting: The first part of it, $A_1 r \cos\theta$, describes a uniform field of intensity A parallel to the axis of symmetry, whereas the second part $(B_1/r^2)\cos\theta$ describes the field that would be produced by a "dipole"— that is, a combination of + and − charges such as those shown in Figure 11–31; indeed, the potential at P due to these two charges would be $(+q/r_1) - (q/r_2) = q(r_2 - r_1)/r_1 r_2$. If a is much smaller than r, $r_2 - r_1 \simeq 2a\cos\theta$, $r_1 r_2 \simeq r^2$, so that $W = (2aq/r^2)\cos\theta$. The quantity $\mathbf{m} = 2aq$ is called the moment of the dipole and is a vectorial quantity, directed along the axis of the dipole. Similarly, the third term $(B_3/r^4)(5\cos^3\theta - 3\cos\theta)/2$ in equation (11-12) can be shown to be

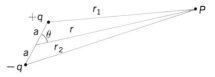

FIG. 11–31 Diagram illustrating the calculation of the magnetic potential of a dipole.

---

[20] The necessary and sufficient condition that a vector $\mathbf{F}$ be the gradient of a potential is that curl $\mathbf{F} = 0$. Since, according to Maxwell's law, curl $\mathbf{H} = 4\pi\mathbf{j}$, where $\mathbf{j}$ is the current density, $\mathbf{H}$ admits a potential wherever $\mathbf{j} = 0$. Laplace's equation follows from the fact that since magnetic charges do not exist, div $\mathbf{H} = 0$ outside magnetic matter; hence div grad $W = \nabla^2 W = 0$.

FIG. 11–32 *Axial quadrupoles.*

the potential of an "axial quadrupole"—that is, a combination of dipoles, as shown in Figure 11–32.

THE GEOMAGNETIC FIELD

Let us turn now to the earth's field. At any point O, its direction and magnitude can be specified by three components (for example, down, horizontal northward, horizontal eastward), or by a magnitude and two angles, declination δ and inclination i, as shown in Figure 11–33. The inclination i, which is generally downward in the Northern Hemisphere and upward in the Southern Hemisphere, varies from 0 near the equator to 90° near the geographic poles. The declination

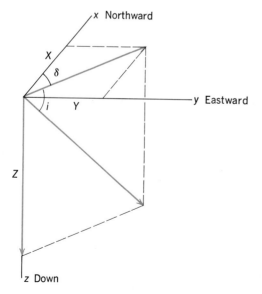

FIG. 11–33 *Components of the earth's field. The angle i is the inclination; the angle δ is the declination.*

δ (positive if eastward) is usually less than 20°. The intensity varies from about 0.3 oersted near the equator to 0.6–0.7 oersted near the poles. The points on the earth's surface where $i = 90°$ are called "magnetic poles"; the line where $i = 0°$ is called the "magnetic equator"; it does not quite coincide with the geographic equator about which it weaves back and forth from one hemisphere to the other.

The field at and above the surface may be described by a potential W, the form of which is more complicated than equation (11-12), because the field depends on longitude ψ as well as on colatitude θ and distance r from the earth's center; the geomagnetic field is decidedly less symmetric about the rotation axis than the gravitational field. The numerical constants are determined, as before, by measuring three components of the field (for example, X, northward $= + (1/r) (\partial W/\partial\theta)$; Y, eastward, $= -(1/r \sin\theta) (\partial W/\partial\psi)$; Z, downward $= +(\partial W/\partial r)$, at a number of points of known r, θ, ψ, and calculating the values of the numerical constants that best fit the observations ("spherical harmonic analysis"). When this is done, it appears that the coefficients of all terms containing positive powers of r (such as $A_2 r^2$) are much smaller than those containing negative powers (such as B_2/r^3). Since a magnetic field decreases with distance from the source, a term that increases with r must represent a source farther out from the origin than the earth's surface, where the measurements are made; thus the very small value of these terms implies that the earth's field originates almost exclusively inside the earth; the very small contribution from sources above the surface, such as electric currents in the ionosphere, may be neglected.

Using a nomenclature first used by Gauss, the remaining terms in the potential are commonly written out as follows:

$$W = W_1 + W_2 + \cdots W_n$$

$$W_1 = R \left(\frac{R}{r}\right)^2 [g_2^0 \cos\theta + (g_2^1 \cos\psi$$

$$+ \; h_1^1 \sin\psi) \sin\theta]$$

$$W_2 = R \left(\frac{R}{r}\right)^3 [\tfrac{1}{2}g_2^0 (3\cos^2\theta - 1)$$

$+ (g_2^1 \cos \psi + h_2^1 \sin \psi)3 \sin \theta \cos \theta$

$+ (g_2^2 \cos 2\psi + h_2^2 \sin 2\psi) \, 3 \sin^2 \theta] + \cdots$

where R is the radius of the earth, and where each term W_1, W_2, and so forth, satisfies Laplace's equation. Some of the Gaussian coefficients for the field as it existed in 1960 are given in Table 11–2. This table shows that the largest, by far, of the coefficients is g_1^0; the corresponding potential is $(g_1^0 R^3/r^2) \cos \theta$, which is that of a dipole of moment $M = g_1^0 R^3$ located at the center of the earth and directed along the rotational axis. (Since g_1^0 is negative, it is actually directed from north to south.) This means that, to a first approximation, the field of the earth is that of an axial, centered dipole.

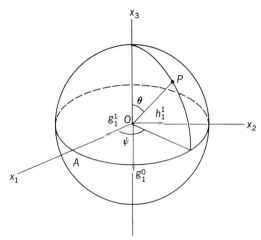

FIG. 11–34 *Components of a centered dipole that account for the potential* W_1

TABLE 11–2 *Some coefficients of the geomagnetic potential; epoch 1960.0*

$g_1^0 =$	-30426*	
$g_1^1 =$	$-\ 2174$	$h_1^1 = \quad\ 5761$
$g_2^0 =$	$-\ 1548$	
$g_2^1 =$	3000	$h_2^1 = -1949$
$g_2^2 =$	1574	$h_2^2 = \quad\ 201$
$g_6^0 =$	58	
$g_6^1 =$	71	$h_6^1 = \qquad 6$

* The unit is the gamma; one gamma $(1\ \gamma) = 10^{-5}$ oersted.

Take rectangular axes x_1, x_2, x_3 at the center of the earth (Figure 11–34) such that x_1 lies in the plane of the equator and in the Greenwich meridian ($\psi = 0°$), x_2 is also in the equatorial plane ($\psi = 90°$) and x_3 is the rotation axis ($\theta = 0$). It is seen that the potential $(R^3/r^2)g_1^1 \cos \psi \sin \theta$ is that of a dipole of moment $g_1^1 R^3$ along x_1, as indeed the cosine of the angle POA equals $\cos \psi \sin \theta$; similarly, the last term in W_1 is the potential of a dipole of moment $h^1 R^3$ along x_2. Thus the W_1 term arises from the contributions of three centered dipoles which can be thought of as the projections on the axes of a single moment

$$M = R^3[(g_1^0)^2 + (g_1^1)^2 + (h_1^1)^2]^{1/2}$$

$$= 8.03 \times 10^{26} \text{ oersted cm}^3$$

From the numerical values in Table 11–2, and paying due regard to signs, we calculate that this moment M is inclined to x_3 by $11°26'$ (Figure 11–35). The axis of M intersects the surface of the earth at two points located respectively at $290°40'$E, $78°34'$N; and $110°40'$E, $78°34'$S. These points, which are called "geomagnetic poles," are distinct from the magnetic poles, where $i = 90°$, with which they would coincide only if all the other terms ($W_2 \cdots W_n$) in the expansion of the potential were zero.

To the first approximation, then, the geomagnetic field is that of a centered, axial dipole; to a better approximation it is that of a centered inclined dipole, and to a still better approximation, it is a combination of a centered inclined dipole and various multipoles W_2, W_3, $\cdots$. (The first term in W_2 is easily recognized as the axial quadrupole mentioned on page 630; all the other terms in W_2 are similarly quadrupoles of various kinds in various orientations. The term W_3 corresponds to "octopoles"—that is, a combination of quadrupole and dipole; and so on.) Not much is gained by carrying the expansion much beyond the 6th term, the coefficients of which are already quite small (see Table 11–2).

The geomagnetic field described by the first 6, 8, or even 12, harmonics $W_1 \cdots W_{12}$ does not describe localized features of the field known as "magnetic anomalies." These anomalies are local fields, occasionally as intense as the geomagnetic field but generally much weaker (100–5000 γ), which clearly have their source in the earth, but

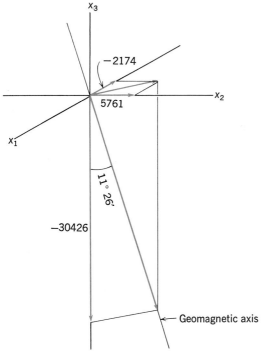

FIG. 11–35 *The three components of the earth's centered dipole are equivalent to a centered dipole inclined at 11°26′ to the rotation axis.*

very close to its surface; from their small horizonal extent it may be inferred that none of these anomalies had a source deeper than 30 km or so. They are caused by local variations in the intensity of magnetization of crustal rocks.

Still other representations of the geomagnetic field are possible. It can be shown, for instance, that the field of a uniformly magnetized sphere of radius a, with intensity of magnetization J,[21] is the same as that of a dipole of moment $(4/3)\pi a^3 J$ at the center of the sphere. Thus the moment M of the geocentric dipole is equivalent to a uniform magnetization of 0.074 oersted, which is much more than that of most surface rocks, and certainly much more than that of the mantle, most of which cannot be magnetized because of

---

[21] The intensity of magnetization is defined as the moment per unit volume; it is measured in oersteds or gammas.

its temperature and because iron, the principal contributor to the magnetization of rocks, is presumably in its low-spin, nonmagnetic state (see page 72). Alternatively, it can be shown that the field of an excentric dipole (that is, not at the center) is the same at the surface as that of a combination of centered dipoles and multipoles; conversely the observed multipoles could be due to excentric dipoles. One can, for instance, represent the earth's field rather well by superposition of a centered dipole and a small number (8 to 10) of smaller dipoles arranged radially on or near the surface of the core. We note, once more, the impossibility of finding uniquely the distribution of sources from measurements on the surface.

SECULAR VARIATION

The field changes rapidly, its variation being mostly regional. The declination at London is known to have changed gradually from 11½°E in 1580 A.D. to 24½°W in 1819; it is now a few degrees east. During the same time interval the field hardly changed at some other points. The intensity may increase, or decrease, again locally, by as much as 150 or 200 γ per year. These changes, known as the "secular variation," are in addition to much smaller changes, of the order of 10–15 γ, that occur daily and are related to tides in the upper atmosphere, and to rather sudden changes of the order of 1000 γ, known as magnetic storms, which are caused by solar events. Magnetic storms last for a day or two.

The first observations of the intensity of the field were made by Gauss around 1830, so that our records of intensity of the secular variation are relatively short. It appears that since that time the moment of the centered dipole has decreased by 6 or 7 percent. Paleomagnetic observations (see Chapter 13) indicate an intensity about 1.5 times the present one some 1500 years ago, and about half the present one 5500 years ago; thus the magnitude of M appears to fluctuate by a factor of 3 or so in the relatively short time of a few thousand years; it can even change sign, producing the "field reversals" discussed in Chapter 13. The geomagnetic pole has not moved noticeably since 1830 (the magnetic poles have); paleomagnetic data strongly suggest, however, that it does move around the geographical pole, so its mean position, when averaged over a few thousand years, is indistinguishable from the geographical pole.

The secular variation affects mostly the nondipole part of the field. Centers of most rapid changes are called "foci"; there are presently some six or eight such irregularly distributed foci, although it is difficult to describe them precisely, because all the elements of the field (vertical component, horizontal component, declination, and so on) do not change in the same manner or at the same rate. The maximum rate of change of an element at a focus waxes, then wanes; simultaneously, the foci move systematically westward ("westward drift") at a somewhat variable rate, which averages about 0.2° per year; at this rate, a pattern of disturbances would make a turn around the earth (360°) in about 1800 years. Secular variation seems to be such that, on the whole, the time average of the nondipole part of the field at any point is zero; in other words, it appears that the field, when averaged over a few thousand years, is essentially that of an axial centered dipole. Direct observations cannot prove this, simply because they do not extend over a sufficient period of time; however, paleomagnetic observations on Recent and Pleistocene rocks certainly bear it out. The observation is of fundamental importance in the interpretation of paleomagnetic data from older rocks (Chapter 13).

THE ORIGIN OF THE FIELD

We have seen that the magnetization of crustal rocks is too weak to account for the earth's main field, although it accounts for the local anomalies, and that most of the mantle cannot have any magnetization at all, because of its high temperature. Nor can the outer core be magnetized, because it is liquid; magnetization is a property of the solid state, which depends critically on the lattice structure and dimensions. It is unlikely that the inner core could be magnetized, as we presently know of no substance whatsoever that remains magnetic at temperatures of the order of those (about 4000–5000°) prevailing

there. Furthermore, any magnetic substance must be exposed to a magnetic field in order to become magnetized.[22] Finally, the hypothesis of a magnetic inner core does not explain why the field changes with time, nor how it could reverse its polarity.

The rate of change of the magnetic field is quite surprising. As we noted, substantial changes can occur within a few decades; the westward drift indicates periodicities of the order of a few thousand years, which is also the time it takes the field to reverse (Chapter 13). No geological phenomenon is known that occurs at comparable rates; the only geophysical phenomena with a similar time scale are irregular changes in the rate of rotation and, perhaps, the damping of the wobble of the earth about its axis of rotation (see variation of latitude, Chapter 4). The time scale of the secular variation has, in fact, long been considered sufficient evidence that the magnetic field of the earth must be unrelated to any geological processes occurring in the crust or mantle, for which the time scale is usually measured in millions rather than in thousands of years. This places the origin of the field in the core—which, being fluid, is likely to respond rapidly to any forces imposed on it. Since the core is not magnetic, the source of the magnetic field must lie in electric currents in it.

Electric currents, to be maintained, need a source of energy; if the source is disconnected, as when a battery is switched off, the current decays in a characteristic time t, which is proportional to (1) the electrical conductivity σ, and (2) the square of a characteristic length L of the system; that is, $t \sim \sigma L^2$. The electrical conductivity of the core is hard to evaluate, since we don't know precisely what its composition and temperature are, but a rough estimate can be made. Taking L to be the radius of the core, t turns out to be of the order of 10^4–10^5 years. Any electric currents

---

[22] The unmagnetized state is always that of lowest energy in the absence of an external field, because of the "demagnetizing" field that a magnetized body exerts on itself. A "permanently" magnetized body does, in the absence of an external field, gradually lose its magnetization, just as a glass tends in the long run to devitrify.

generated when the earth formed would have vanished long ago. Since, on the other hand, there is paleomagnetic evidence from the magnetization of old rocks that the field has existed for at least 2.5×10^9 years, it follows that there must be a source that continuously supplies the energy needed to maintain the currents.

An electric current can be generated by the thermoelectric effect: If two different substances are in contact at two points at different temperatures, an electromotive force will be generated and current will flow. One could easily imagine that the core–mantle contact might not have everywhere exactly the same temperature, and thus a weak current, and corresponding weak magnetic field, could be generated in this way. The problem is to find a mechanism by which such a weak magnetic field, or, alternatively, a weak magnetic field from a source outside the earth (for example, the sun), could be suitably amplified.

This is simple enough in principle. Whenever a conductor moves with velocity **v** in a magnetic field **H**, a current σ (**v** $\times$ **H**) is generated in it; this is essentially the principle of a dynamo. Any motion of the conducting liquid core in the presence of a weak magnetic field would induce currents and another magnetic field. The problem is to find a current distribution such that the new field will reinforce, not oppose, the weak field that caused it.

The core motions most commonly considered in this connection are convective motions induced by a vertical temperature gradient. However, a conductor carrying a current density **j** experiences in a magnetic field a force per unit mass that is equal to **j** $\times$ **H**; this is essentially the principle of the electric motor. Thus any field in the core exerts on the core fluid a force that affects the motion. The electromagnetic equations (Maxwell's equations) that govern the behavior of the magnetic field are thus coupled to the dynamical equations that govern the velocity of the fluid; in brief, one must know the velocity to find the field (dynamo), but one must know the field to find the velocity (motor). Magnetohydrodynamics (MHD) is the science of solving

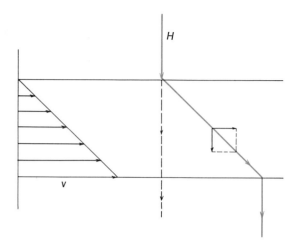

FIG. 11–36 *Deformation of a magnetic field by a velocity gradient in a conducting fluid. The lines of force are carried in the fluid and tend to become parallel to its motion. The velocity gradient is shown on the left. The magnetic field H acquires a component normal to the velocity gradient.*

the two sets of equations simultaneously, a rather complicated business.

It is not known at this moment whether or not the earth's field can be explained in this way; mathematical complications preclude any formal immediate solutions. It is known, however, from theory and experiments that some fields can indeed be amplified, and a number of simple physical models have been proposed. It can be shown, for instance, that in a perfect fluid conductor, $\sigma = \infty$, the lines of force of the magnetic field must move with the fluid, so that there is no relative displacement of the fluid with respect to the field. This implies that if there is a velocity gradient in the fluid, a component of the field must appear at right angles to the gradient (Figure 11–36). Now convective motion in the core must lead, by conservation of angular momentum, to a nonuniform rotation, as the rising masses (initially near the center, hence with low angular momentum) exchange position with descending masses, which carry with them their high initial momentum. Thus the outer part of the core will be slowed down, while the inner part speeds up.

(Incidentally, any magnetic field originating in the outer, slow part would appear to move westward with respect to a mantle moving at the average speed of the core; this is a possible explanation of the westward drift of the secular variation.) The angular velocity gradient will in turn produce a "toroidal" field, the lines of force of which will be perpendicular to the angular velocity gradient—that is, wrapped around the axis of rotation. This toroidal field could, in principle, grow in time to become very large, regardless of the magnitude of the initial field from which it grew. Presumably a large toroidal field could somehow interact with the convective motion to produce the observed dipolar field.

Whatever the details of the process may be, the large dimensions of the earth's core play an essential role. Amplification of a weak initial field requires that the field be produced faster than it decays. The rate of production, as we have just seen, is proportional to the velocity of the conductor, whereas the rate of decay is inversely proportional to the square of the linear dimension ($t \sim \sigma L^2$, see page 632). Thus amplification does not require very high velocities if L is sufficiently large. A second important conclusion seems to hold—namely, that the earth's magnetic field will be controlled to a large extent by the earth's rotation. It can be shown indeed that the Coriolis force (see page 632, footnote) is likely to be one of the dominant forces, the other being the $\mathbf{j} \times \mathbf{H}$ force. The Coriolis force leads in the first place to the nonuniform rotation and the toroidal field mentioned above; in the second place it would tend to align turbulent eddies in the core along the axis of rotation, and presumably would align the magnetic fields these eddies produce. This implies that the earth's field should, in the mean, be symmetrical around the rotation axis; that is, geomagnetic poles should coincide, in the mean, with the rotational pole; and the average of all nonaxisymmetric terms in the potential (for example, $g_1^1, h_1^1, g_2^1, h_2^1$) should be zero, as paleomagnetic data for Recent and Pleistocene rocks seem to indicate. The point is important when it comes to interpreting paleomagnetic results for older rocks.

HEAT SOURCES IN THE CORE

To summarize, the earth's magnetic field is believed to arise, by a MHD mechanism, from a combination of rotation and convective motion in the liquid, conducting, core. The sun, which has a magnetic field, rotates and convects; it consists of a highly ionized gas which is a good electrical conductor. The moon and Mars have no magnetic field (or only very small ones), probably because of the absence of a liquid core of sufficient size; Venus has no field, probably because it rotates too slowly. One remaining question is: Why does the earth's core convect, and what are the heat sources in it that maintain the motion and supply the energy to maintain the electric currents? As explained in Chapter 12, the heat that drives mechanical motion in the mantle presumably comes mostly from radioactivity; but common radioactive elements, such as uranium or potassium, are hardly soluble at all in liquid iron, and the radioactive content of iron meteorites, if typical also of the core, is much too small to maintain active convection.

Other sources of energy have been proposed. It is possible, for instance, that turbulent motion of some kind could be induced at the core–mantle boundary by the difference in the rate of precession of these two bodies for which the ratios $(C_m - A_m)/C_m$ and $(C_c - A_c)/C_c$ (where $c =$ core, $m =$ mantle) must be different. It is possible also that the core may be cooling very slowly. The depth in the core at which the actual temperature equals the melting temperature would decrease with time, and the inner core would grow. The latent heat of crystallization released in this process might be sufficient to drive the convection, even though the growth rate of the inner core must be very small. It may be possible in this way to set some limits on the thermal history of the core, and therefore of the earth in general.

REFERENCES

The following books cover most of the material in the present chapter: *The Physical Constitution of the Earth* by **J. Coulomb** and **G. Jobert** (Hafner, New York, 1963); **B. Gutenberg**, *Physics of the Earth's Interior* (Academic Press, New York, 1959); *Physics and Geology* by **J. A. Jacobs, R. D. Russell,** and **J. Tuzo Wilson** (McGraw-Hill, New York, 1959), and *The Earth* by **H. Jeffreys** (Cambridge, New York, 1963). The latter is very mathematical. A nonmathematical account by the same author is *Earthquakes and Mountains* (2d ed., Methuen, London, 1950).

On gravity there is an excellent short book by **G. D. Garland**, *The Earth's Shape and Gravity* (Pergamon, New York, 1965). On magnetism, the reader will find in **J. A. Jacobs**, *The Earth's Core and Geomagnetism* (Pergamon, New York, 1963) most of the information he may need. *Introduction to Geophysical Prospecting*, by **M. B. Dobrin** (McGraw-Hill, New York, 1960), has a simple and excellent account of seismic-wave propagation, and of the reduction and interpretation of gravity data.

On density distribution and composition of the mantle and core, we mention the following articles: **F. Birch**, "Density and composition of mantle and core" (*J. Geophys. Res.*, vol. 69, pp. 4377–4388, 1964); **S. P. Clark,** and **A. E. Ringwood**, "Density distribution and constitution of the mantle" (*Rev. Geophys.*, vol. 2, pp. 35–88, 1964; **A. E. Ringwood**, "Mineralogy of the mantle," in *Advances in Earth Sciences*, edited by **P. M. Hurley** (M.I.T. Press, Cambridge, Mass., 1966); and **P. G. Harris, A. Reay,** and **I. G. White**, "Chemical composition of the upper mantle" (*J. Geophys. Res.*, vol. 72, pp. 6359–6369, 1967).

Considerable work is going on at present on the application of shock-compression experiments to problems of the deep mantle and core. Experimental data are reproduced in the *Handbook of Physical Constants*, **S. P. Clark**, editor (Geological Society of America Memoir 97, 1966). See also **F. Birch**, "Some geophysical applications of high-pressure research," in *Solids under Pressure*, edited by **W. Paul** and **D. M. Warschauer** (McGraw-Hill, New York, 1963), and **B. J. Alder**, "Physics experiments with strong pressure pulses" in the same volume. The theory underlying the interpretation of such experiments, and the experimental techniques are described in **M. H. Rice, R. G. McQueen,** and **J. M. Walsh**, "Compression of solids by strong shock waves," in *Solid State Physics*, edited by **F. Seitz** and **D. Turnbull**, vol. 6, (Academic Press, New York, 1958).

12

HEAT SOURCES
AND THERMAL EVOLUTION
OF THE EARTH

This chapter is concerned with the heat sources within the earth and the manner in which heat is transferred. These matters are of fundamental importance. All geologic processes require a source of energy to drive them. Heat is needed to produce magma from an otherwise solid mantle; it is also needed in metamorphism. Uplift of a mountain range, or of a continent, entails an increase in potential energy, for which an appropriate source must exist. Earthquakes and faulting imply a previous accumulation of strain energy—which, again, must come from somewhere. What are the sources of energy in the earth, where are they, and how is the energy converted from, say, heat to mechanical energy, or vice versa? These are some of the questions that we shall now consider.

The concept of heat is, of course, intimately linked to temperature; the thermal state (that is, temperature distribution) and history of the earth are closely related to, and indeed determined by, the distribution and intensity, past and present, of heat sources. Actually, we know neither the temperature distribution nor that of the heat sources; both must be inferred from observations made on the surface of the earth. Here again the nonuniqueness of the solutions of the mathematical equations leads to considerable uncertainty; here again we must resort to the indirect method

of selecting "models" on the basis of circumstantial evidence of a somewhat subjective character. There is much about the earth's heat engine that remains uncertain.

The main datum is the surface heat flow, which we shall now proceed to examine.

Heat Flow, Heat Sources, and Heat Transfer

GEOTHERMAL GRADIENT AND HEAT FLOW

Almost everywhere, in boreholes or mines, the temperature of the ground is found to increase downward. The geothermal gradient, dT/dz (where z is depth), ordinarily varies between $8°K/km$ and $40°K/km$, on land, but is somewhat higher in deep-sea sediments. Thus heat must be flowing upward in the earth. Heat flow $\mathbf{q}$ is related to the temperature gradient by a conduction law similar to Ohm's law relating electric current flow to potential gradient:

$$\mathbf{q} = -K \operatorname{grad} T \qquad (12\text{-}1)$$

where K is the thermal conductivity already discussed in Chapter 2 (the minus sign indicates that heat flows down the gradient, from a high temperature to a lower one). Heat flow is commonly expressed in calories per cm² per second, in which case K must be expressed in calories per degree per cm per second. Alternatively, both K and **q** may be expressed in ergs or joules (1 joule $= 10^7$ ergs; 1 cal $= 4.187$ joules; 1 μcal $= 1 \times 10^{-6}$ cal). The conductivity K depends on the type of rock, and also on temperature, pressure, porosity, and water content of porous rocks; usual values lie between 4 and 10×10^{-3} cal cm^{-1} sec^{-1} deg^{-1} (somewhat less in deep-sea sediments of high porosity, in which pores are filled with water of low conductivity). Thus, on land, a typical value of the heat flow might be about 1.5 μcal cm^{-2} sec^{-1}, corresponding to measured values of $K = 5 \times 10^{-3}$, $dT/dz = 30°/$km $= 3 \times 10^{-4}$ deg/cm. The average of several thousand measurements of heat flow, on land and on the sea floor, is just about 1.5 (or roughly, 63 ergs cm^{-2} sec^{-1}) although it varies significantly from place to place (see below). The total heat output of the earth is thus about 2.4×10^{20} cal/yr, or roughly 10^{28} ergs/yr. (Area of the earth $= 5.1 \times 10^{18}$ cm²; 1 year $= 3.15 \times 10^7$ sec.)

SOLAR ENERGY   Large as this figure may seem by human standards, it is still very small compared to the heat the earth receives from the sun, which is about 1.36×10^6 ergs cm^{-2} sec^{-1} at normal incidence; this amounts, on the average, to 0.34×10^6 ergs cm^{-2} sec^{-1}. It is the solar heat that determines the surface temperature of the earth, and no climatic change in the past can be explained solely by changes in the internal heat flow, which is much too small, compared to the solar heat, to have any appreciable effect on the surface temperature.

It is interesting to stop for a moment to consider the fate of the incident solar energy. It follows directly from the laws of thermodynamics and radiation that a body[1] at absolute temperature T must emit, at equilibrium, an amount of

radiation $E = \sigma T^4$ where σ, the Stefan-Boltzmann constant, is 5.67×10^{-5} erg cm^{-2} sec^{-1} deg^{-4}. The spectral composition of the radiation depends on temperature; by Wien's law the wavelength λ_m at which most energy is emitted varies as $1/T$. At low temperatures the radiation is mostly in the very-far-infrared region, but as the temperature rises, the dominant wavelength shortens, and the object begins to glow, first in the infrared and then in the visible part of the spectrum.[2] At the temperature (about 6°C) at which a blackbody would radiate exactly the average amount of solar radiation it receives $(0.34 \times 10^6$ ergs cm^{-2} sec^{-1}) the dominant wavelength is at 10 microns, in the infrared part of the spectrum.

The fact that the average temperature of the ground (about 10°C) is not much greater than 6°C is a good indication that the earth eventually radiates back into space all the heat it receives from the sun. The details of the process are, however, enormously complicated. In the first place, not all the solar radiation reaches the surface; some of it (the ultraviolet radiation, for instance) is absorbed in the atmosphere, and some of it is reflected by the ground, or by clouds; what fraction of it is absorbed in the ground depends also on the nature of the surface (water, ice, vegetation, and so on). Much of the infrared radiation reemitted by the ground is reabsorbed by H_2O and CO_2 in the atmosphere, and particularly in clouds, which in turn reradiate partly upwards and partly downwards, thus raising the ground temperature (greenhouse effect). All other factors being constant, the incident radiation varies with time of the day and season; at times heat flows down from the surface into the earth, whereas at other times (night, winter) it flows up again. The depth of penetration of these fluctuations is limited by the poor conductivity of the ground and generally does not exceed a few feet, although long-period fluctuations corresponding to climatic changes penetrate deeper, in proportion to the square root of their period. All things considered,

---

[1] Strictly speaking, only a "blackbody" obeys this law. A blackbody is defined as one that absorbs completely the incident radiation, reflecting none. A body characterized by an emissivity coefficient b will radiate a fraction b of the blackbody radiation. The emissivity of highly polished silver is about 0.02, that of black paint about 0.95.

[2] This is how the temperature at the source of the solar, or of any stellar, radiation may be determined.

the earth does seem to be in equilibrium with the solar radiation; all heat (from any source) received at its surface and in its atmosphere is eventually radiated away. Thus the internal heat that flows to its surface is also dissipated by radiation into space, as is the heat liberated at the surface in volcanic eruptions, or the potential energy accumulated in the uplift of a mountain range, which ends up as frictional heat released in the turbulent motion of the streams that carry down the erosional debris of the mountain. Geological processes in general entail a loss of energy from the earth.

HEAT LOSSES FROM THE EARTH   It is difficult to evaluate just how much energy the earth loses in these processes. Volcanic eruptions on land may produce, on the average, perhaps as much as 1 km³ or 3×10^{15} grams of lava per year.[3] Since 1 gram of lava cooling and crystallizing from 1000°C would liberate about 400 cal/g, the heat discharged in this manner might amount to 1.2×10^{18} cal/yr, about one-half percent of the internal heat flow (2.4×10^{20} cal/yr). This figure, however, does not include submarine eruptions, of which we know very little. Menard estimates that some 10^4 volcanoes with a relief of more than 1 km exist in the Pacific Basin, far more than on land, and all formed probably within in the last 10^8 years or so; he estimates the rate of extrusion on the Pacific sea floor to be perhaps 0.24 km³/year. The formation of new crust postulated by the sea-floor-spreading hypothesis (Chapter 13) would entail a very large amount of volcanic activity, perhaps as much as 10^{16} g/yr. Uncertain as these figures may be, they seem to indicate that heat transfer to the surface by effusion of lava is still rather small compared to the conductive heat flow.

In some areas ("geothermal areas"), heat is brought to the surface by circulating water (hot springs, steam vents, geysers, fumaroles, and so forth) in such quantities that it can be used as a source of industrial power. The source of the heat is not obvious; it may be volcanic, although most of the water itself appears, from its isotopic composition, (deuterium/hydrogen and O^{18}/O^{16} ratios) to be ordinary ground (or rain) water. In most geothermal areas (for example, Larderello, Italy; Yellowstone, U.S.A.; Wairakei, New Zealand) the heat probably has its source in a shallow, cooling, intrusive body. It is difficult to evaluate precisely the amount of heat brought to the surface in geothermal areas, as large variations in heat flow can occur over very small distances; it would seem that locally the heat flow may be 10 to 100 times greater than normal over areas of the order of 100 to 1000 km²; but since such geothermal areas constitute much less than 1 percent of the total land area, their contribution to global heat flow remains small.

The energy required to build mountains is very difficult to evaluate because so little is known of the exact mechanism or of its rate. A very rough estimate of the potential energy required for uplift may be obtained on the assumption that, on the whole, the relief of the earth does not change very much; therefore, the rate of uplift must be, on the average, equal to the rate of denudation, which can itself be assessed from the rate of transport of sediments. Rates of denudation seem to be of the order of a few centimeters per thousand years, although locally they may be much larger, as in the Himalayas (100 cm per thousand years), or practically nil, as in areas lying near sea level. The total mass m of sediments so produced annually would then be of the order of the total land area (about 1.5×10^{18} cm²) times, say, 5×10^{-3} cm times density; and the energy mgh released by mass m falling from an average height h (which cannot be more than 1 km, since the average elevation of the continents is less than that) under the effect of gravity g cannot be more than about 10^{24} ergs/year, which is again very small compared to the 10^{28} ergs/year of the heat flow.

The energy involved in deformation, as distinct from uplift, is also very hard to estimate. An indication of its magnitude may be provided by the fact that the average annual release of energy in all earthquakes is of the order of 10^{26}

---

[3] At that rate, in 5×10^9 years, a total volume of 5×10^{24} cm³ would be produced, corresponding almost to the whole of the continental crust.

ergs; this energy is essentially elastic strain energy stored in rocks prior to the fracturing. The nonelastic energy of deformation is not likely to be very much greater.

It would thus seem that the heat flow is the largest item in the budget of the earth. If we could account for it, we would be well on our way toward understanding how the earth functions.

Heat Sources in the Earth

At first sight it does not seem difficult to find an adequate source for the heat flow. We now list some of the possible sources.

1. *Cooling of the earth from an original hot state.* The earth might conceivably have formed by condensation from a hot gas, although this now seems very unlikely, for a number of reasons. As mentioned in Chapter 11, formation of the earth by accretion of small, cold particles would release a very large amount of gravitational energy, most of which must have been radiated away; yet some of it might have remained.

2. *Separation of the core.* The difference in gravitational energy of a uniform earth and of an earth like the present one (with a heavy core and lighter mantle) is quite large—of the order of 10^{38} ergs. Release of this energy could have occurred at the time of formation of the earth itself, or shortly thereafter; alternatively, the core might have grown gradually by slow sinking of denser components towards the center of the earth.

3. *Tidal friction.* The gravitational potential of the moon and sun (the effect of the sun is about one half that of the moon) at any point in the earth varies with time as the positions of the sun and moon relative to that point change because of the rotation of the earth and the orbital motion of the moon. Equipotential surfaces, such as the surface of the oceans, are periodically deformed, leading to the familiar rise and fall of the tide. The body of the earth also deforms, and points on its surface move away from or toward its center with an amplitude of about 30 cm (earth tides). This deformation of the earth is

essentially elastic, although imperfections of elasticity (internal friction) and viscosity of the ocean water lead to dissipation (as heat) of the earth's kinetic energy of rotation[4]; the earth accordingly slows down. The deceleration $d\omega/dt$ is observed astronomically and is about 5×10^{-22} rad sec^{-2}. Since the kinetic energy of rotation is $E = C\omega^2/2$, where C is the moment of inertia around the rotational axis, the rate of dissipation of energy

$$\frac{dE}{dt} = C\omega \frac{d\omega}{dt}$$

is 3×10^{19} ergs/sec. A small fraction of this energy goes to "lift" the moon away from the earth; the rest, which is dissipated as heat, amounts to about 10 percent of the heat flow. It is not known precisely where the dissipation occurs; a large part of it presumably takes place in tidal currents in shallow seas, and therefore does not contribute to the heat flow measured on land or on the ocean floor; but part of it may occur in the earth itself, constituting a heat source that would have been appreciable in earlier times, when the moon was closer[5] and the earth's rotation more rapid.

4. *Radioactivity.* Radioactive nuclides decay by emitting α-particles (for example, U^{238}) or electrons (for example, Rb^{87}) at a very high speed (see Chapter 4). These particles are stopped by collision with surrounding atoms, and their kinetic energy is transformed into heat. Any γ radiation emitted by the decaying nuclide is also absorbed within a short distance of its source. Thus the decay energy of the unstable radioactive nuclide is converted into heat; one gram of U^{238}, for instance, generates 0.94 erg sec^{-1} and one gram of K^{40} generates 0.28 erg sec^{-1}. Given the amount of radioactive elements in a rock, it is

------

[4] If the earth did not rotate, the relative position, with respect to the moon, of a point on its surface, would change much more slowly, and much less energy would be dissipated. The dissipation mainly tends to slow down the rotation that causes it, although it also affects the motion of the moon.

[5] As the earth is losing angular momentum, the moon must gain an equal amount. This, by Kepler's laws, requires that the moon move away from the earth.

possible to calculate the rate of heat generation in it. Typical figures are given in Table 12–1. Small as these figures may be, they are significant. Imagine, for instance, that the crust, 30 km thick, consists of granite. A column with a cross section of 1 cm² would contain 3×10^6 cm³, or 8.1×10^6 grams, taking the density of granite to be 2.7 g/cm³. The heat generated in this column would thus be 2.1 μcal/sec, which is more than the normal heat flow. Or take the whole mantle with a mass of approximately 4×10^{27} grams and assume it to consist of material similar in composition to a chondritic meteorite: the heat generation in it would be about 5×10^{12} cal/sec, or two thirds of the earth's total heat flow. Radiogenic heat evidently must be an important source of internal heat.

TABLE 12–1   *Radiogenic heat production in rocks*

Type of Rock	Rate of Heat Generation, cal g⁻¹ sec⁻¹
Granite	2.6×10^{-13}
Basalt	3.8×10^{-14}
Peridotite	2.9×10^{-16}
Dunite	6.0×10^{-17}
Chondritic meteorite	1.2×10^{-15}
Iron meteorites	1.0×10^{-18}

Note the correlation, evident in Table 12–1, between heat generation and silica content. Apparently uranium and thorium behave geochemically very much like potassium, and tend to become more concentrated in acid rocks than in basic ones.

HEAT FLOW IN OCEANS AND CONTINENTS

Inasmuch as continents obviously contain large masses of granite, which is the most powerful heat producer of all rocks, it was long thought that the continental heat flow would necessarily be much larger than the heat flow in ocean basins, where granites do not occur. It came as a surprise when the first measurements in deep-sea sediments, around 1950, revealed a heat flow comparable to that on land. The average of all measurements in the oceans does not depart significantly from the average on land.

This extremely curious observation is generally explained by supposing that the total amount of radioactive matter is about the same in continental and oceanic areas, but distributed differently. Clearly, the oceanic heat flow must come from the mantle, for the oceanic crust is much too thin (see Chapter 11) to generate much heat. Suppose now that the mantle was originally of the same composition and radioactive content everywhere, but that in some areas (the present continents) a process of partial melting has excreted from the mantle and transferred upwards not only the material that now forms the continents, but also the major part of the radioactive elements originally present; this in effect simply assumes that uranium, thorium, and potassium move with the other "sialic" elements (silicon, aluminum, sodium, and so forth) in which the crust is enriched with respect to the mantle. The fact that the mantle below the continents would now be depleted of much of its heat sources leads, as we shall presently see, to interesting consequences regarding the temperature distribution.

The heat flow is far from uniform either in continents or oceans. The data in Table 12–2, taken from Lee and Uyeda, are instructive. As the figures for the standard deviation clearly indicate, heat flow varies greatly within any of the areas listed. Von Herzen has called attention, for instance, to a region in the western Pacific that straddles the equator and extends roughly from 115 to 135°W. In this deep basin the average heat flow at 39 stations is only 0.79 (standard deviation 0.57). Across the boundaries of this region, heat flow changes from low to average or high values in a distance of about 175 km. There are similar regions of abnormally high heat flow, far from any active ridges.

The correlation between heat flow and geological character of an area is interesting. The low heat flow in Precambrian shields—be they in Australia, Canada, India, South Africa, or the Ukraine—indicates that shields contain much less granite than they were once thought to; their mean composition must, in fact, be closer

TABLE 12–2   *Heat-flow values for typical geological features*

	Geological Feature of Area	Number of Measurements	Mean, μcal cm^{-2} sec^{-1}	Standard Deviation
Land:	shield	26	0.92	0.17
	Mesozoic–Cenozoic orogenic areas	19	1.92	0.49
	Cenozoic volcanic areas (excluding geothermal areas)	11	2.16	0.46
Ocean:	basins	273	1.28	0.53
	ridges	338	1.82	1.56
	trenches	21	0.99	0.61

to basalt than to granite (see Table 12–1). Shields are also stable areas, in which very little tectonic activity or uplift has occurred since Precambrian times; the high heat flow in more recent orogenic areas, by contrast, strongly suggests that orogeny is somehow related to large-scale thermal disturbances. Precisely where does this heat come from and how is it carried? How is the supply of heat related to uplift and deformation?

HEAT TRANSFER IN THE EARTH

The average intensity of heat sources, or radioactive content of the earth, cannot be obtained simply by dividing the total surface heat flow by the mass of the earth. Such a procedure would assume in the first place that the heat escaping per unit time is exactly equal to the heat generated per unit time, or, in other words, that the earth is neither heating up nor cooling down. We have no evidence to this effect. Furthermore, transfer of heat through the earth is not instantaneous; heat generated now at great depth may not reach the surface until some time later, and therefore does not contribute to the present heat flow. Obviously, the matter needs to be looked into more carefully.

EQUATION OF HEAT CONDUCTION   We first establish a general relation between heat generation, temperature distribution, and change in temperature with time. Imagine a medium containing uniformly distributed heat sources of intensity ε (cal cm^{-3} sec^{-1}). In Figure 12–1 is shown an arbitrary surface S enclosing a portion of the medium of volume V; let $\mathbf{q}$ be the heat flow at any point on this surface. The total heat Q escaping through the surface per unit time is

$$Q = \int_S q_n \, dS$$

where q_n is the component of the heat-flow vector along the outer normal to the element of surface dS. Conservation of energy requires that Q be equal to the sum of the heat generated per unit time inside the surface, $\int_V \varepsilon \, dV$, and of the heat released by cooling; if $\partial T/\partial t$ is the change in temperature T with time t, the corresponding

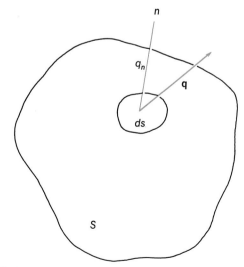

FIG. 12–1   *Heat flow through a closed surface S.*

change in heat content, or heat released, is, by definition of the specific heat c, $c(\partial T/\partial t)$ per unit mass, or $\rho c(\partial T/\partial t)$ per unit volume. Thus

$$\int_S q_n \, dS = \int_V \left(\varepsilon - \rho c \frac{\partial T}{\partial t}\right) dV \qquad (12\text{-}2)$$

where the sign preceding $\partial T/\partial t$ reminds us that heat is liberated only if the body cools—that is, if its temperature decreases with time.

The left-hand side of this equation is easily transformed by the divergence theorem

$$\int_S q_n \, dS = \int_V \operatorname{div} \mathbf{q} \, dV$$

but since, by equation (12-1), $\mathbf{q} = -K \operatorname{grad} T$, $\operatorname{div} \mathbf{q} = -K\nabla^2 T$, assuming that the thermal conductivity is uniform in the body. Thus, substituting in equation (12-2) and grouping terms,

$$\int \left(K\nabla^2 T + \varepsilon - \rho c \frac{\partial T}{\partial t}\right) dV = 0$$

Since this relation must hold for any arbitrary surface S and any volume V, it must hold at every point. Hence the integrand must be zero everywhere and

$$\rho c \frac{\partial T}{\partial t} = K\nabla^2 T + \varepsilon$$

or

$$\frac{\partial T}{\partial t} = h\nabla^2 T + \frac{\varepsilon}{\rho c} \qquad (12\text{-}3)$$

where $h = K/\rho c$ is called the "thermal diffusivity." Equation (12-3) is the desired relation.

STEADY-STATE SOLUTIONS   To see clearly some of the relations that exist between distribution of heat sources and temperature, let us examine first simple cases in which it is assumed that thermal equilibrium has been reached and temperature no longer changes with time; $\partial T/\partial t = 0$. In Figure 12–2 we consider in particular an infinite plate, of thickness H representing, say, a continent at the surface of which the heat flow q_0 is 1.5 μcal cm^{-2} sec^{-1}. What is the steady-state

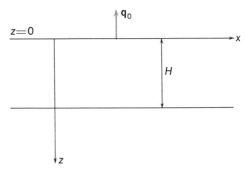

FIG. 12–2 Heat flow through a uniform, infinite plate.

temperature distribution in the continent? Since the plate is assumed to be uniform and of infinite extent, the temperature is independent of the coordinates x and y in the horizontal plane. Thus equation (12-3) reduces to

$$\frac{\partial^2 T}{\partial z^2} = -\frac{\varepsilon}{K}$$

By integration,

$$\frac{\partial T}{\partial z} = -\frac{\varepsilon}{K}z + c_1 \qquad (12\text{-}4)$$

and a second integration gives

$$T = -\frac{1}{2}\frac{\varepsilon}{K}z^2 + c_1 z + c_2 \qquad (12\text{-}5)$$

where c_1 and c_2 are constants, to be determined from the boundary conditions. Let the temperature at the surface $z = 0$ be T_0; then $c_2 = T_0$. The constant c_1 in (12-4) obviously equals the downward temperature gradient at the surface, $z = 0$, which equals the upward heat flow q_0 divided by K; hence $c_1 = q_0/K$ and

$$T = T_0 + \frac{q_0}{K}z - \frac{1}{2}\frac{\varepsilon}{K}z^2 \qquad (12\text{-}6)$$

The temperature at the base of the continent is therefore

$$T_H = T_0 + \frac{H}{K}\left[q_0 - \frac{1}{2}\varepsilon H\right] \qquad (12\text{-}7)$$

Suppose $K = 5 \times 10^{-3}$ cal cm^{-1} sec^{-1} deg^{-1}; then the gradient at the surface is 30°/km, or 3×10^{-4} deg cm^{-1}. If the continent contains no

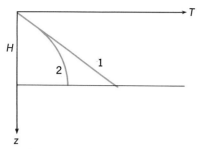

FIG. 12–3 *Steady-state temperature distribution in a continental plate (1) assuming no heat generation in the continent; (2) assuming that all the surface heat flow is generated in the continent.*

heat sources at all, $\varepsilon = 0$, and by equation (12-4) the gradient is everywhere the same; the temperature increases linearly downwards, and $T_H = T_0 + (Hq_0/K)$. For $H = 30$ km, this gives $T_{30} = T_0 + 900°C$. In this case, all the surface heat flow must enter the continental plate from below, and all the heat sources must be in the underlying mantle.

Suppose now that all the heat flow comes from the continent itself. This requires that no heat should be entering the continent from below, which in turn requires that the temperature gradient be zero at $z = H$. Hence, from equation (12-4),

$$0 = \left(\frac{\partial T}{\partial z}\right)_{z=H} = -\frac{\varepsilon}{K}H + c_1 = -\frac{\varepsilon}{K}H + \frac{q_0}{K}$$

or $\varepsilon = q_0/H$. Equation (12-7) then reduces to

$$T_H = T_0 + \frac{1}{2}H\frac{q_0}{K} = T_0 + 450°$$

Figure 12–3 illustrates a general feature: For a given rate of heat generation, or a given heat flow, the temperature at any depth increases with depth of burial of the sources. Placing the heat sources in the mantle rather than in the continent itself raises the temperature at the base of the continent from 450° to 900°C. If all the heat sources had been spread on the surface of the continent (a physically rather improbable assumption), the temperature everywhere would be just T_0; indeed, if the heat sources are on the surface, no heat need be moved through the

plate, and the temperature gradient is zero everywhere. The curvature of the temperature–depth curve at any point is a measure of the intensity of the heat sources at that point; with no heat sources, as in curve (1) of Figure 12–3, the curve is a straight line.

The same principle can be illustrated for a sphere. If the sphere of radius a is perfectly uniform, with a uniform distribution of heat sources (ε independent of r), the temperature depends only on r, the distance to the center. The solution[6] is easily found to be

$$T = T_0 + \frac{1}{6}\frac{\varepsilon}{K}(a^2 - r^2) \qquad (12\text{-}8)$$

where T_0 is the temperature at the surface. The surface heat flow q must be such, in the steady state, that all the heat generated in the sphere, $(4/3)\,\pi a^3\varepsilon$, equals the total flow on the surface, $4\pi a^2 q_0$; hence $q_0 = (1/3)\varepsilon a$. The temperature T_c at the center $r = 0$ is

$$T_c = T_0 + \frac{1}{2}\frac{q_0 a}{K}$$

For $q_0 = 1.5 \times 10^{-6}$, $a = 6 \times 10^8$ cm, $K = 6 \times 10^{-3}$ cal cm^{-1} sec^{-1} deg^{-1}, this gives $T_c = T_0 + 75,000°C$.

It is easy to see that if all the heat sources were concentrated at the very center of the sphere, the temperature there would be infinite. On the other hand, if all heat sources were on the surface $r = a$, the temperature everywhere would be simply T_0. This illustrates the futility of attempting to calculate temperatures inside the earth without knowing more precisely where the heat sources are.

TIME-DEPENDENT SOLUTIONS   We now assume that we start at some time $t = 0$ with a known temperature distribution, and wish to find the temperature at some later time. If there are no

---

[6] In spherical coordinates, r, θ, ψ, and for perfect spherical symmetry as assumed here, the Laplacian $\nabla^2 T$ reduces to the single term:

$$\frac{1}{r^2}\frac{\partial}{\partial r}\left(r^2\frac{\partial T}{\partial r}\right)$$

heat sources, equation (12-3) with $\varepsilon = 0$ would describe the cooling history of a body. Mathematical solutions are somewhat more cumbersome than in the steady-state case (except in cases of very simple geometry, such as a sphere) and it is actually not necessary at this stage to pursue them very far. The interesting feature of equation (12-3) is the relation it implies between cooling time and the dimensions of the body. The term at the left, $\partial T/\partial t$, obviously has the dimension of temperature over time (degrees per second, say). The diffusivity h has the dimensions of length² over time (cm² sec⁻¹); thus the Laplacian $\nabla^2 T$ must have the dimensions of temperature over length², as is obvious from its definition (temperature over a coordinate squared, $\partial^2 T/\partial z^2$ for instance). Thus one can predict, and all formal solutions bear this out, that cooling (or heating) or, more generally, transfer times will increase proportionally to the square of the linear dimensions of the body (a^2, for a sphere), and decrease proportionally to the diffusivity h; that is, $t \sim L^2/h$.[7]

For many rocks, the diffusivity at ordinary pressure and temperature is of the order of 0.01 cm² sec⁻¹. A typical transfer time for the earth (for example, the time required to move heat from the center to the surface) would thus be of the order of $(6.4 \times 10^8)^2/10^{-2} = 40 \times 10^{18}$ sec, or 10^{12} years, much more than the age of the earth! The earth is so large, and its thermal diffusivity so small (rocks are good insulators) that conduction alone could not cause appreciable cooling of its deeper parts (see below); correspondingly, if heat is transferred by conduction, as we have so far assumed, the heat escaping at the surface today cannot have traveled in the earth's life time much more than a few hundred kilometers; it follows that the heat generated today in the lower mantle, if any, is not contributing to the present surface heat flow.

The slowness with which heat is transferred through rocks has several consequences. Obviously, steady-state solutions are inapplicable

to the earth as a whole, since (1) the age of the earth is less than the time it needs to come to equilibrium, and (2) cooling (or heating) times for the earth are comparable to radioactive decay times. Since the half-life of U²³⁸ is of the order of 4.5×10^9 years, the amount of U²³⁸ present in the earth will change appreciably during the time it would take the earth to reach equilibrium, and therefore the heat-generating term ε in equation (12-3) must also be considered to be a function of time, which makes the formal solutions yet more complicated.

Heat-transfer times are thought to be of considerable geological significance, because they presumably determine the whole geological time scale—that is, the rate at which geological processes (igneous activity, deformation, orogeny) can occur. We noted the difference in heat flow between stable Precambrian shields and more recent orogenic areas. Since it takes about 3×10^8 years to transfer heat through 100 km of rock, such differences in heat flow cannot become established in much less than this; in other words, orogenic events, insofar as they reflect thermal disturbances in the crust and underlying mantle, must have characteristic time scales of the order of several hundred million years.

Equation (12-3) carries still another important implication. Because time enters it only as a first derivative, solutions of this equation are valid only for $t > 0$. Given a temperature distribution and heat sources at some initial time $t = t_0$, it is possible to calculate from (12-3) the temperature distribution at some *later* time, but the equation cannot be used to determine what happened before t_0. The reason for this is, fundamentally, the irreversibility of heat flow and related irreversibility of time (see Chapter 4). In any isolated body the temperature will tend to become uniform, regardless of the initial temperature distribution; conversely, a uniform temperature can correspond to an infinite number of prior nonuniform temperature distributions. We readily imagine heat spreading from an initial hot spot, but the reverse process is physically inconceivable because in an isolated system entropy must increase in any spontaneous process. What this implies is that even if we did know

---

[7] Note the similarity in form of this expression to the time of decay of electric currents or magnetic fields, page 633.

the present distribution of temperature and heat sources in the earth, we could still not work backward in time to calculate what these were at an earlier time. The initial temperature distribution must be assumed, or determined by an independent method.

IMPLICATIONS FROM THE TEMPERATURE DISTRIBUTION IN THE UPPER MANTLE   Although heat transfer by conduction in the earth appears to be very slow, there are some indications that, at least in the deeper parts of the earth, heat may be transferred somewhat faster than the value used here for the thermal diffusivity would predict. These indications come from a calculation of the temperature distribution in the upper mantle.

To avoid complications arising from the uncertain composition and radioactive content of the continental crust, consider an ocean basin with a thin (4–8 km) crust and a surface heat flow of, say, 1.3 μcal cm^{-2} sec^{-1}. Assume that the underlying mantle consists of peridotite, with the rate of heat generation indicated in Table 12–1; thus ε, the heat generation for unit volume is 10^{-15} cal cm^{-3} sec^{-1}. Take for K the rather high value of 10^{-2} cal cm^{-1} sec^{-1} deg^{-1}, and take $T_0 = 0°C$. Neglecting the curvature of the earth, equation (12-7) predicts a steady-state temperature T_{200} of 2600°C. The pressure at that depth is about 65 kilobars. At 65 kb and 2600°C, peridotite would be completely molten, which is clearly impossible, since the mantle at that depth transmits S-waves (Chapter 11), which cannot propagate through a liquid. If, on the other hand, we use equation (12-8) for a spherical earth, the temperature at a depth of 200 km is only 420°C, but the surface heat flow (1/3) εa is only 0.21 μcal cm^{-2} sec^{-1}. To get the proper heat flow we must assume the earth to consist of material several times more radioactive than peridotite, in which case the temperature at a 200-km depth again exceeds the melting point.

To avoid these inconsistencies, our model must be amended in one or both of the following ways:

1. Increase (by a factor of ten or more) the assumed rate of heat generation in the upper mantle, so as to increase the curvature of the temperature curve, and keep it everywhere below the melting-point curve. There is, however, as mentioned earlier, a correlation between radioactive content of a rock and silica content; it seems unlikely that any ordinary ultrabasic rock could generate enough radiogenic heat. We must assume then that the upper mantle consists of material somewhat richer in silica than peridotite, in which radioactive elements have become concentrated. This could be, for instance, the mixture ¼ basalt–¾ peridotite suggested and called "pyrolite" by Ringwood (see Chapters 6 and 11).

2. Increase the effective thermal conductivity so as to reduce the temperature gradient required to transfer a given amount of heat. This could conceivably happen in two ways: by radiative transfer or by convection.

RADIATIVE TRANSFER   The thermal conductivity coefficient K introduced in equation (12-1) describes the ordinary process by which heat is transferred through a solid. Heat, a form of energy, exists in a solid in the form of vibrational energy of its particles, which oscillate about their mean lattice position with a frequency that depends on the strength of the interatomic forces and an amplitude that depends precisely on the total heat content—that is, the temperature of the solid. When one end of the solid is heated, the amplitude of the lattice vibrations increases locally, the motion being gradually transferred from one particle to the next; one may think of the heat being propagated as elastic waves through the solid. The thermal conductivity is not very sensitive to pressure, but generally decreases with increasing temperature.

At high temperatures, however, the thermal conductivity of many electrically nonconducting substances (that is, nonmetals) is found to increase rapidly with increasing temperature (roughly as T^3), the transfer of heat being now by radiation. It was mentioned earlier that a body at temperature T radiates electromagnetic energy at a rate proportional to T^4. At low temperatures, the wavelength of this radiation is very long, and falls in a part of the spectrum in which most solids are nearly opaque; then the radiation emitted by a hotter portion of the body cannot travel very far without being reabsorbed, and the transfer of energy is limited. By Wien's displacement law, however, the wavelength λ_m at which most of the energy is radiated is $\lambda_m = 0.29/T$, where T is the absolute temperature; thus at $T = 2000°$ K, $\lambda_m = 1.45 \times 10^{-4}$ cm $= 14{,}500$ Å, and much of the energy is emitted in the near-infrared and visible parts of the spectrum, where many nonmetals, and particularly many silicates, are transparent. The radiation can therefore travel a long distance before being reabsorbed, and the rate of transfer of energy thus becomes rapid since the radiation itself travels at the velocity of light in the solid,[8] and is very much greater than the rate of propagation of the elastic waves involved in ordinary conduction. Many silicates do, of course, absorb light of certain wavelength in the visible range (corresponding to their color), as well as at the infrared wavelength corresponding to the frequency of lattice vibrations, but unless the crystal is perfectly black, the radiation transfer at high temperature exceeds the conductive transfer. Thus at depths in the mantle where the temperature is sufficiently high and approaches the melting point, radiative transfer may become sufficiently important to reduce the temperature gradient by a factor of, say 3 to 5. Exact calculations are impossible, because the "opacity"[9] of a substance is a function of temperature and pressure and also of physical state; large, clear, single crystals are obviously less opaque than aggregates of small grains, in which light is scattered at grain boundaries and at imperfections of any kind. Temperature calculations also become more complicated because K is now a function of T and depends therefore on position in the body,

---

[8] The velocity of light in a vacuum divided by the index of refraction.

[9] The opacity is defined as follows: If radiation of intensity I_0 is reduced to intensity I_x after traveling a distance x, the opacity α is such that

$$I_x = I_0 e^{-\alpha x} \quad \text{or} \quad \alpha = \frac{1}{x} \ln \frac{I_0}{I_x}$$

and div $\mathbf{q} = $ div $(-K \operatorname{grad} T) = -K\nabla^2 T + \operatorname{grad} K \cdot \operatorname{grad} T$; an additional term appears in equation (12-3).

The second way in which the rate of heat transfer in the mantle may be greatly increased is, as mentioned, convection. The subject is of sufficient importance to geology and geophysics to deserve separate treatment, to which we now proceed.

CONVECTION

DEFINITION   Convection refers to mass motion in a fluid produced by gravity acting on density differences produced by unequal temperatures. Imagine a fluid, all parts of which are not at the same temperature and have therefore different densities; in general, gravitational energy can be gained by moving the less dense parts upwards and the denser part downward. Heat is transferred as it moves with the hot masses that carry it.

Convection occurs on a large scale in the atmosphere and oceans; it is by convection that much of the solar heat received near the equator is transferred to higher latitudes. Convection presumably also occurs in the core, where the mass motions it produces may generate the electric currents that maintain the earth's magnetic field, and where the gravitational energy it releases provides the energy needed to maintain those currents (see Chapter 11). Convection in the mantle is thought to provide the means by which heat is converted to mechanical work as needed, for instance to move continents or make mountains.

It may at first appear paradoxical to talk about convection, which evokes the properties of a fluid, in connection with a mantle which otherwise displays, as in the transmission of seismic waves, extremely high rigidity. Clearly, the mantle may be considered, at best, only to consist of a substance with enormous viscosity; but we do not really know exactly how it responds to stresses of long duration, and accordingly cannot very well predict what the motions in the mantle will be or how fast they occur. It is interesting, nevertheless, to show that even at the very small rates of flow that might occur in a body so extremely viscous, heat transfer by convection is likely to be at least as important as transfer by conduction.

THE HEAT CONDUCTION EQUATION INCLUDING CONVECTION   First let us consider how the heat conduction equation (12-3) can be modified to include the effects of convection. Let x, y, and z be the coordinates of a moving portion of the fluid; thus x, y, and z change with time t. The components of the velocity v are $v_x = dx/dt$, and so forth. The temperature T changes with time t because the particular element of fluid we are considering may be gaining (or losing) heat as it moves into warmer (or colder) regions. Thus T is a function of x, y, z, and t; and

$$dT = \frac{\partial T}{\partial x} dx + \frac{\partial T}{\partial y} dy + \frac{\partial T}{\partial z} dz + \frac{\partial T}{\partial t} dt \quad (12\text{-}9)$$

Dividing both sides by dt, and substituting the components of velocity, equation (12-9) becomes

$$\frac{dT}{dt} = v_x \frac{\partial T}{\partial x} + v_y \frac{\partial T}{\partial y} + v_z \frac{\partial T}{\partial z} + \frac{\partial T}{\partial t}$$

or, in short

$$\frac{dT}{dt} = \frac{\partial T}{\partial t} + \mathbf{v} \cdot \text{grad } T \quad (12\text{-}10)$$

an important relation between the rate of change of temperature (or, for that matter, of any variable) with time at a fixed point ($\partial T/\partial t$), and its total change dT/dt in an element of the moving fluid. $\partial T/\partial t$ would represent, say, successive readings on a thermometer at a fixed point, around which the fluid flows, whereas dT/dt would represent successive readings on a thermometer attached to a particular element of the fluid moving with it.

Return now to the surface S considered in Figure 12–1. If the surface is fixed, but fluid flows in and out of it, a term should be added to the right side of equation (12-2) to measure the heat carried in and out of S by the fluid itself. Actually, it is easier to imagine that the surface S moves and deforms with the fluid, so no fluid either leaves or enters the enclosed volume. Thus

no provision need be made in equation (12-2) for the heat carried across S by the fluid, except that, as we are now considering the change in temperature with time of a moving element of fluid, the term $\partial T/\partial t$ that appears in (12-2) must be replaced by dT/dt as defined in (12-10). Thus convective transport of heat is simply taken care of by replacing $\partial T/\partial t$ in equation (12-3) by dT/dt or, by virtue of equation (12-10), by subtracting from the right side of equation (12-3) the convective term $\mathbf{v} \cdot \text{grad } T$. Thus,

$$\frac{\partial T}{\partial t} = h\nabla^2 T + \frac{\varepsilon}{\rho c} - \mathbf{v} \cdot \text{grad } T \ (12\text{-}11)$$

How fast does the mantle have to flow in order for the convection term to be important? Consider a simple case of perfect spherical symmetry (if such were physically realizable), so that

$$\nabla^2 T = \frac{\partial^2 T}{\partial r^2} + \frac{2}{r} \frac{\partial T}{\partial r}$$

(see footnote, page 644), and

$$\mathbf{v} \cdot \text{grad } T = v_r \frac{\partial T}{\partial r}$$

Compare now the first and last terms on the right of equation (12-11). Convection is important if $v_r \, (\partial T/\partial r)$ is of the same magnitude as, say,

$$h\frac{\partial^2 T}{\partial r^2} \qquad \text{or} \qquad \frac{2h}{r} \frac{\partial T}{\partial r}$$

The latter requirement is, simply,

$$v_r \geq \frac{2h}{r} \quad (12\text{-}12)$$

or, for $h = 10^{-2}$, $r = 4 \times 10^8$ cm, as might be the case in the mantle, $v_r > 5 \times 10^{-11}$ cm sec^{-1}, or roughly, 1.5×10^{-3} cm/yr. At that rate of upwelling, and even if the temperature gradient $\partial T/\partial r$ is only a fraction of a degree per kilometer, it is easy to show that the convective term will also be greater than the heat generation term $\varepsilon/\rho c$, if ε in the mantle is comparable to its value for ultrabasic rocks (Table 12–1). Deformational rates of the order of centimeters per year are observed on the surface; it is also inferred that continents must have moved at about that rate (Chapter 13).

According to equation (12-11) it is necessary to know **v**, a function of the coordinates and time, to solve for T. The velocity itself must be found by solving a dynamical equation (force $=$ mass times acceleration) appropriate to the fluid considered (for example, the so-called Navier-Stokes equation for a Newtonian fluid). This dynamical equation must, of course, specify the force at every point, which in this case is the gravitational force acting on the density perturbations produced by the unequal temperature; thus T appears in the dynamical equation, which must therefore be solved simultaneously with equation (12-1). By conservation of mass, it is necessary to specify also ("equation of continuity") that the change in mass in a given volume (or change in density) must equal what flows into that volume minus what flows out of it; and the manner in which density depends on pressure and temperature (equation of state) must also be specified. Thus four equations must be simultaneously satisfied. Complete mathematical solution is generally very difficult, except in a few cases of relatively simple geometry.

GEOPHYSICAL EFFECTS OF THE EARTH'S SIZE The condition described by equation (12-12) illustrates once more an important feature of the physics of the earth—namely, the relevance of the earth's size to the processes that can take place in it. An illustration may already have been noted in the discussion of the origin of the earth's magnetic field (page 635): The earth probably has a magnetic field only by virtue of the size of its core, which, being large, also has a sufficiently long decay time for electric currents and corresponding magnetic fields. Thus inductive processes have time to regenerate the currents before the magnetic field necessary to induce them has completely decayed. Similarly, convection becomes an important mechanism of heat transfer in the earth only because the great size of the earth specified by the value of r in equation (12-12) makes conductive transfer relatively inefficient.

This effect of size may be brought out in still another way. Suppose that the mantle, as might perhaps be the case, behaves as a plastic material which begins to flow only when stresses imposed on it exceed a certain yield point X_0. Suppose that a small temperature difference δT causes a small difference in density $\delta\rho$; then, if g is the acceleration of gravity, the buoyancy force would be of the order of $g\delta\rho V$, where V is the total volume affected by the temperature perturbation δT. Now stress is force per unit area. The force, as we have just seen, increases as the volume, or as the cube of the linear dimension L; the area, however, increases only as the square of the linear dimension, and the stress increases as L. Provided that L is large enough, the stress could exceed the yield point even though $\delta\rho$ and δT are very small; if for instance, L is of the order of 10^8 cm, a density perturbation $\delta\rho = 10^{-4}$ g cm^{-3} would suffice to produce a stress of the order of 10 bars; this density perturbation might be produced by a temperature perturbation of the order of $1°$.

CONVECTIONAL INSTABILITY; THE ADIABATIC GRADIENT As explained before (Chapter 11), a fluid can be in hydrostatic equilibrium only if both pressure and density are constant on equipotential (horizontal) surfaces. In a homogeneous fluid, density is a function of both pressure and temperature, so equilibrium also requires that temperature be constant on an equipotential surface. Thus a fluid in a tank that is heated on one side and cooled on the other (Figure 12–4) cannot be in equilibrium; temperature differences between the two sides will lead to density differences that will cause the hot fluid to rise on the left, spread along the surface while cooling, and sink on the right. If the supply of heat is continuous, the circulation will also be continuous, as the cold fluid moving along to the left at the bottom becomes

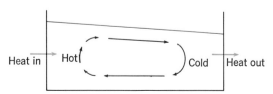

FIG. 12–4 Convection in a tank with a horizontal temperature gradient.

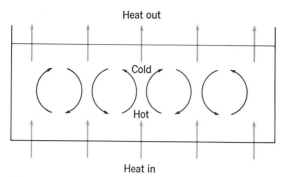

Heat out

Heat in

FIG. 12-5 *Convection in a tank with a vertical temperature gradient.*

heated, rises, and moves again to the right along the surface.

The situation is slightly more complicated if the temperature gradient is vertical—that is, if the fluid is heated from below (Figure 12-5). The bottom layer will be heated first and, becoming lighter, will rise by buoyancy, while the cold and denser fluid on the surface sinks. A pattern of rising and sinking currents may become established in this manner. It is interesting, though, that a compressible fluid may become unstable with respect to circulating motion even though the vertical temperature gradient is not sufficient to cause the density to decrease with depth. This may be shown as follows:

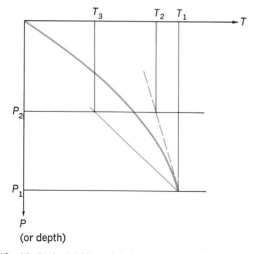

FIG. 12-6 *Instability related to the adiabatic gradient.*

Imagine a compressible, homogeneous, fluid in which the temperature increases with depth from the surface as shown in Figure 12-6, and remember that in a gravitational field, pressure and, therefore, density increase downward. Consider an element of fluid at pressure P_1, temperature T_1, and test its stability by imagining that it be given a small upward displacement; if the fluid so displaced continues to move up, it expands because it moves into a region of lower pressure, and cools; if it moves without exchanging heat with the surrounding fluid, the cooling is adiabatic and given by equation (11-10). Let the dashed line in Figure 12-6 represent the cooling, so that the temperature of the displaced fluid drops from T_1 to T_2 as the pressure drops from P_1 to P_2. Note, however, that at the level P_2, the temperature T_2 of the displaced fluid is higher than that of the fluid initially at P_2; the displaced fluid is therefore lighter than the ambient fluid, and will therefore continue to rise by buoyancy. The system is unstable.

The system would, on the other hand, be perfectly stable if the adiabatic cooling were represented by the thin solid line in Figure 12-6; in this case the temperature T_3 of the displaced fluid at level P_2 is less than that of the ambient fluid, which is therefore lighter; the displaced fluid, being denser, will sink back to its original level.

The system is thus unstable or stable according to whether the actual temperature gradient—that is, the slope of the solid line in Figure 12-6—is greater or less than the adiabatic gradient. The latter cannot be evaluated accurately for the mantle, since the temperature itself [see equation (11-11)] is not precisely known; yet it would seem that the adiabatic gradient in the mantle is unlikely to be much more than a fraction of a degree per kilometer, which makes it very likely that the mantle, or at least some parts of it, may be essentially unstable.

RAYLEIGH'S NUMBER   The conditions for the onset of convection can be studied somewhat more rigorously in specific cases in which the boundary conditions are adequately described. Rayleigh found, for instance, that in a convecting thin layer of fluid heated from below, motion will start if the dimensionless parameter R, Rayleigh's number, exceeds a certain value, which depends again on specific circumstances but is generally of the order of 1500. This dimensionless number, which is essentially a ratio of factors that tend to enhance convection to factors that tend to dampen or prevent it, is

$$R = \frac{g\alpha\beta d^4}{h\nu}$$

where g is the acceleration of gravity, α the coefficient of thermal expansion, β is the temperature gradient in excess of the adiabatic value, d is the thickness of the layer, h is the thermal diffusivity, and ν the kinematic viscosity (ratio of viscosity to density). Note again the importance of the linear dimensions of the system, which enter R as the fourth power of the thickness d; clearly, convection becomes possible in a system with very large viscosity and very low temperature gradient, provided that d is large enough. In the mantle $g = 10^3$ cm sec^{-2}, $\alpha = 2 \times 10^{-5}$ deg^{-1}, $h = 10^{-2}$ cm^2 sec^{-1}, say. Suppose $\beta = 0.1$ deg/km and $d = 10^8$ cm; then $R = 10^3$ for $\nu = 2 \times 10^{23}$, which is somewhat more than the viscosity deduced from the rate of isostatic recovery of Scandinavia, consequent on the melting of the latest Pleistocene icecap (see page 363). If, however, the viscosity of the lower mantle is as high as 10^{26} (see page 611), then much larger and in fact impossibly high values of the temperature gradient and of the thermal expansion would be required to maintain convection.

PATTERNS OF MOTION   Essentially, the pattern of motion must consist of localized upward currents of hot material and localized descending currents of colder material. Since matter must be conserved in the process, there must also be horizontal currents, as in Figure 12–7. Currents diverge at the top of the rising columns and bottom of the sinking columns, and converge at the top of the sinking and bottom of the rising ones. The exact pattern, however, cannot be easily predicted.

In experiments on thin layers of fluid heated from below, one generally observes that the distance between rising and sinking columns is

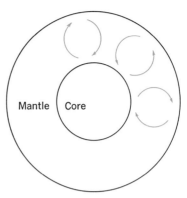

FIG. 12–7 Convection pattern in a spherical shell.

commensurate with the thickness of the convective shell. When the heat sources are within the fluid itself (as would be the case for radiogenic heat sources in the mantle), the pattern becomes elongated in the horizontal direction and considerable horizontal motion occurs. For a given stress, velocity gradients vary inversely as the viscosity (see page 226); if the latter is small, fluid motion may be rapid but restricted to relatively narrow sheets (Figure 12–8). At high Rayleigh numbers, the convective equivalent of turbulence may appear; the motion becomes somewhat disorganized, and very large fluctuations in temperature, density, and velocity may become apparent on horizontal surfaces. Discontinuous motion in the form of isolated and irregular blobs moving up and down may also occur.

Clearly, the pattern of convection in the mantle will depend on its rheological properties; one does not expect the same behavior in a fluid with Newtonian viscosity as in a plastic substance or in a substance in which the viscosity itself is a function of stress or strain rate. The pattern will also

FIG. 12–8 A convection pattern in which the upward motion is more localized than the descending motion.

reflect conditions at the surface as they affect the rate at which heat is discharged. Heat must be removed at the top by the relatively slow process of conduction through the crust; mantle motion will therefore presumably be quite different under continents, where the crust is thick, and oceans, where it is thin. Alternatively, heat may be removed by melting and transfer of magma to the surface.

Pekeris has done some calculations for a Newtonian liquid with a kinematic viscosity $\nu = 10^{22}$ cm^2 sec^{-1}, assuming a steady state in which the velocity at any point is independent of time. He finds velocities of the order of a few centimeters per year, as expected. At this rate the time required for a complete overturn of the whole mantle would be of the order of 10^8 years. Neither of Pekeris' assumptions is warranted without further study. The mantle is probably not exactly a Newtonian liquid, and the motion may not be steady; more probably, it consists of short and irregular pulses followed by periods of quiescence.

In summary, in a body of the size of the mantle, temperature (or density) perturbations inconsistent with hydrostatic equilibrium are likely to lead to convection. We recall in this connection that the odd-numbered harmonics of the gravitational potential (J_3, J_5, $\cdots$) testify unambiguously to the nonhydrostatic state of the earth,[10] as also perhaps does the difference between the observed and calculated values of the earth's flattening (see page 611). Thus internal motion must occur unless the mantle has sufficient strength (of the order of 10 bars) to support the nonhydrostatic component of stress. There is no evidence that any material would have such strength with respect to stresses of long duration; creep, for instance, seems to occur however small the stress, provided it is applied for a sufficient length of time. Convection would seem to be prohibited— or its rate would be so small as to be of no geo-

logical interest—if the equivalent "viscosity" of the mantle exceeds 10^{25}–10^{26} cm^2/sec; thus the lower mantle may be nonconvecting. The pattern of convection in the upper mantle, where the viscosity may be of the order of 10^{22}, is likely to be highly irregular.

SOME GEOLOGICAL EFFECTS OF CONVECTION Convective motion in the mantle, or parts of it, could affect the crust in the following ways:

1. *Heat flow.* A rising column consists of hotter, lighter stuff than a sinking one. Other things being equal, the heat flow through the crust should be higher above a rising column than above an area of downward motion.

2. *Uplift and downwarp.* For the same reason, one might expect the crust to be uplifted over an area of the mantle that is particularly hot; a downwarp could develop wherever the mantle cools and contracts, or over an area of descending currents.

3. *Horizontal movement.* In any region where the top of the mantle is moving horizontally, the crust could be dragged along with it. As a result, either tensional or compressional stresses could develop, the former over regions of diverging currents, the latter over regions of converging currents (Figure 12–9).

4. *Production of magma.* Suppose, as in Figure 12–10, that at some time the temperature gradient in the mantle exceeds the adiabatic value, and convection sets in. Material rising from A cools by expansion on the way up, following the adiabatic path AB, which intersects the incipient melting curve at B. As melting requires some latent heat, which must be supplied by the

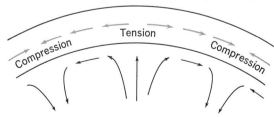

FIG. 12–9 *Stresses in a rigid crust overlying a convection cell.*

---

[10] These odd-numbered harmonics cannot arise from the rotation of the earth (as does J_2), because rotation about the polar axis cannot induce any effects that are not symmetric with respect to the plane of the equator.

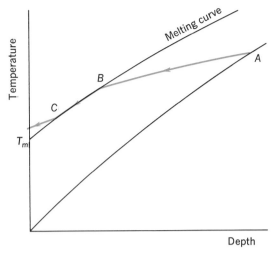

FIG. 12–10 *Diagram to explain the formation of magma in upward convective motion.*

material itself, it will follow the melting curve until cooling (from *B* to *C*) supplies the equivalent of the latent heat; molten material then moves up by buoyancy. This is one of two ways in which significant amounts of magma could be formed in the mantle, the other being downward motion of low-melting material (for example, crustal rocks) into deeper and warmer regions. In fact, production of magma can be taken to constitute substantial evidence that vertical (up or down) transfer of material does occur in the mantle.

CONVECTION AND HEAT FLOW THROUGH THE OCEANIC CRUST   We return now to a discussion of heat flow through the ocean floor, the singular pattern of which is thought to provide further evidence on the mechanism of heat transfer.

The average of 913 measurements of heat flow in oceans is 1.60 μcal cm^{-2} sec^{-1} (standard deviation = 1.18), and is not significantly different from that (1.43, s.d. = 0.56) of 131 measurements on land. Heat flow in the ocean is, however, far from uniform. The average for ocean basins, as shown in Table 12–2, is 1.28 $\pm$ 0.53, that for trenches is 0.99 $\pm$ 0.61, that for ridges is 1.82 $\pm$ 1.56. The difference between trenches and ridges is particularly notable. Very high values (up to 8 μcal) have been observed on the

crest of the Atlantic ridge and of the East Pacific rise; in both cases, as also in the mid-Indian ridge, there is a tendency for the heat flow to decrease gradually with increasing distance from the crest (Figure 12–11), although the data are scattered.

The following interpretation is possible: Upwelling currents in the mantle form vertical sheets, which intersect the earth's surface along the crest of the ridges. These upwellings account for both the high heat flow and the copious production of basaltic magma, which seems to form the bulk of the ridges themselves. Divergence at the top of the sheet (Figure 12–12) produces tension, which stretches and opens fractures in the crust; magma congealing in these cracks forms new crust, while the slightly older material is carried laterally away from the axis of the ridge. This lateral motion may extend some several thousand kilometers from the ridge axis; to the extent that the continents bordering the ocean are carried with it, the ocean itself will grow in width. On the other hand, trenches, with their low heat flow, are thought to represent areas of downward motion of cold material; the trenches that lie along the western coast of South America, for instance, are thought to be areas where the convection current that rises under the East Pacific rise and moves eastward turns downward under the continent in a sort of gigantic underthrust. This interpretation has been much reinforced by the discovery of the extraordinary pattern of magnetic anomalies described in Chapter 13 (sea-floor spreading hypothesis).

It may be too early to judge the merits of this hypothesis. Measurement of heat flow on the deep-sea floor is difficult; heat-flow values are exceedingly scattered, as shown by the very large standard deviations quoted above, and very high values occasionally turn up in immediate proximity to very low ones. This phenomenon is hard to understand on the basis of any mechanism. It suggests perhaps that measurements are occasionally disturbed by extraneous factors such as the relief of the sea floor, recent removal of sediments by water currents (which would tend to steepen the surface gradient and lead to spuriously high values of the heat flow) or local thick-

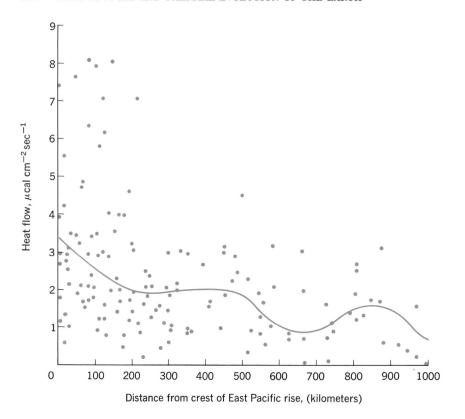

FIG. 12–11 *Heat flow values versus distance from the crest of the East Pacific rise between 50°S and 20°N. The 50-percentile line is such that half the points lie above it and half the points below it. (From W. H. K. Lee and S. Uyeda, in Terrestrial Heat Flow, American Geophysical Union Monograph No. 8, 1965.)*

ening of sediments by slumping, which would have the opposite effect. Be that as it may, it remains that the surface heat flow, at land as at sea, is far from uniform, and bears some relation to geological structure. This statement implies that heat sources are not uniformly distributed, and that rates of heat transfer are different in different places. It follows that the temperature cannot be a uniform function of depth. Figure 12–13, for instance, shows how the temperature distribution could differ below continents and oceans, given certain (to some extent arbitrary) values of the radiogenic heat and opacity. Such lateral variations in temperature at a given level (500°C at a depth of 300 km, in the case illustrated in Figure 12–13) are, of course, inconsistent with hydrostatic equilibrium. Even if they do not lead to convection because of the rheological properties of the mantle (they certainly would in a Newtonian fluid), they must lead to fairly large stresses, particularly at the junction between continents and oceans, which might account for much of the faulting and deformation observed on the surface.

These regional differences in temperature in the upper mantle must also lead, in material of uniform composition, to appreciable differences in density, which should be replicated in the gravitational picture. The undulations of the geoid described on page 609 could be attributable to such differences; the undulations themselves should therefore be correlated with fluctuations in heat flow, in the sense that where gravity is high and the geoid rises, heat flow should be low. The comparison cannot yet be made, because there are still too many vast regions for which we have hardly any heat-flow values at all—for example, almost the whole of Asia between the Urals and the Sea of Japan. The correlation, if it exists, could also be obscured by the fact that

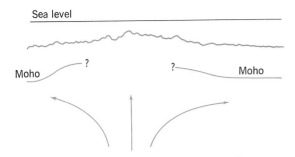

FIG. 12-12 *Flow pattern under an oceanic ridge.*

gravity represents the density distribution as it is today, whereas surface heat-flow values may represent, because of slowness of conduction through the crust, the temperature and heat-source distribution of some past time. Finally, density may vary laterally in the mantle because of lateral variation in composition rather than in temperature.

Temperature Distribution in the Earth

Heat generation, heat transfer, and temperature distribution are so fundamental to the dynamics of geology that any observation of the actual temperature now prevailing at any depth

in the earth would be of extraordinary interest. Attempts have been made, with uncertain success, to determine such temperatures. We shall now review some of the methods used, and some lines of attack on the problem that could be fruitful.

UPPER MANTLE

SEISMOLOGICAL EVIDENCE   It was mentioned in Chapter 11 that the shear velocity V_s appears to decrease slightly with depth in the upper mantle, reaching a minimum somewhere near a 100- or 200-km depth ("low-velocity layer"). The velocity profile varies locally, as between oceanic and some continental regions. The velocity V_p of the P-wave at these depths seems in general to increase only slightly or remain constant; there are, however, some areas (such as the western U.S.A.) where V_p may also decrease slightly with depth. It would indeed be surprising if V_p decreased with depth everywhere, since the correlation between V_p and density (see page 619) implies that density should also decrease with depth; the upper mantle would then be gravitationally unstable. This is unlikely to be a general and permanent feature of the earth, in view of the ease with which the mantle seems to adjust

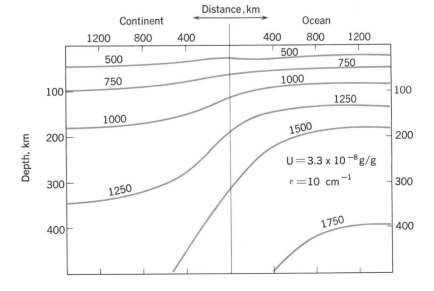

FIG. 12-13 *Temperature distribution under oceans and continents for a mantle having an average uranium content of 3.3 × 10⁻⁸ g/g. The opacity ε is assumed to be 10 cm⁻¹. (From G. J. F. MacDonald, in Terrestrial Heat Flow, American Geophysical Union Monograph No. 8, 1965.)*

to even slight loads; but gravitational instability could well exist temporarily in regions where the geological evidence (for example, recent orogeny) does imply absence of equilibrium.

Considering now a region where V_s decreases but V_p does not, and remembering that the rigidity μ is more sensitive to temperature than either the bulk modulus K or the density ρ (at the melting point μ decreases to zero whereas K and ρ vary by only a few percent), it is possible to interpret the low-velocity layer as a temperature effect and set limits to the temperature gradient: The temperature must increase with depth at a rate sufficient to overcome the effect of pressure on μ and cause it to decrease, but the gradient must not be so high as to cause ρ and V_p to decrease. Calculations at this stage of the art are perforce approximate, as we know neither the exact composition of the mantle nor the precise effect of T and P on μ, ρ, and K. By the use of what seem to be reasonable values, the temperature gradient comes out at about 10–15°/km in the suboceanic mantle, and 5–10°/km under the continents (the gradient would necessarily be steeper than this in continental areas where V_p also decreases with depth). The fact that these figures differ somewhat from those that can be deduced from Figure 12–13 is hardly surprising, considering the number of assumptions regarding heat generation, opacity, and other parameters necessary for the calculation. The method is, however, subject to improvement as more experimental results become available.

MELTING   Since the upper mantle transmits shear waves, it must be solid, and therefore its temperature cannot be much above that of incipient melting[11] at the prevailing pressure, except locally (in volcanic areas, which form at one time only a small fraction of the earth's total surface area) and momentarily (volcanic episodes in any one region do not seem to last much more

than 50 to 100 million years). Again, if the composition of the mantle were exactly known, experiments could tell what the melting range is at a given pressure, and set an upper limit to the actual temperature. As it is, the absence of large-scale melting in the mantle has been used to infer a change in the mechanism of heat transfer above 200 km (page 646). On the whole, from what is now known of the effect of pressure on the melting temperature of rocks such as might occur in the upper mantle, it would seem unlikely that the temperature could exceed 1300°C at a depth of 100 km, or 1600°C at 200 km.

PHASE CHANGES   Recent seismological work described in Chapter 11 suggests that the velocity of seismic waves in zone C of the mantle increases particularly rapidly with depth in two layers centered around depths of 400 and 650 km respectively. This is illustrated in Figure 12–14, which is based on recordings at stations in Arizona of earthquakes occurring within 30° of that area, and which describes therefore the mantle below the western half of the North American continent. These two layers of rapid velocity (and presumably density) increase may perhaps be interpreted as zones in which phase transitions occur. Fugisawa has suggested that the layer at 400 km depth corresponds to the olivine–spinel

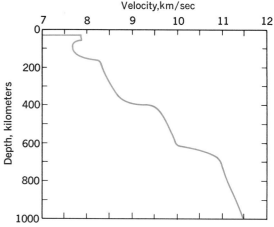

FIG. 12–14 *Velocity of P-waves in the upper mantle (From L. R. Johnson, J. Geophys. Res., vol. 72, p. 6318, 1967.)*

---

[11] Although it may be so close to it that a relatively small perturbation may cause local melting. The low velocity of S-waves (and locally also P-waves) in the "low-velocity" layer may perhaps be caused by the presence in that layer of small amounts of interstitial liquid, indicating incipient melting.

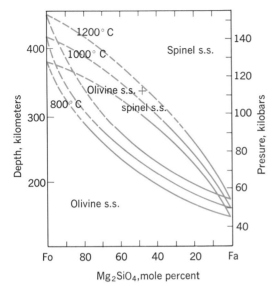

FIG. 12–15 *Phase diagram for the olivine-spinel transformation. (From H. Fujiyama, J. Geophys. Res., vol. 73, p. 3282, 1968.)*

transition. If so, the relevant phase diagram, determined experimentally, is as shown in Figure 12–15. There is, of course, some uncertainty as to the exact Fe/Mg ratio in olivines in the upper mantle. If the ratio is taken to be 1/9, and given the pressure (125 kb) at the top of the transition layer (370 km depth), the temperature is estimated to be in the range of 1150°C to 1530°C (the uncertainty is due mostly to the possible experimental errors). This result is mentioned here mainly to illustrate an approach that may be very useful.

In Figure 12–16 we reproduce the result of some calculations by Clark and Ringwood. These calculations are based on heat-flow measurements and assumed values of the radiogenic heat production and of the conductivity and its dependence on temperature (transfer by radiation included). A noteworthy feature of these temperature–depth curves (or geotherms) is the difference between oceanic areas and stable shield areas of low heat flow (see page 642), as illustrated already in Figure 12–13. The strong curvature of the oceanic geotherm reflects the importance of radiative transfer in reducing the

gradient to avoid crossing the melting curve. The curves of Figure 12–16 extrapolated to a depth of 400 km indicate temperatures well above those deduced from the olivine–spinel transition. These geotherms, however, are calculated on the assumption of a steady state; but the large horizontal gradients between oceans and continents that they predict would almost certainly be sufficient to induce vigorous convective motions, which are not allowed for in the calculations. These curves cannot therefore be accepted without reservations.

LOWER MANTLE AND CORE-MANTLE BOUNDARY

Since the mantle is solid and the outer core is liquid, the temperature at the interface must exceed the melting point of core material, and be less than that of mantle material, at the relevant pressure (about 1.4 Mb). No melting point has yet been measured at such a high pressure, and theories of melting are somewhat uncertain. The dependence of the melting point T_m on pressure is, of course, given by the Clausius-Clapeyron relation (Chapter 5)

$$\frac{dT_m}{dP} = \frac{\Delta V}{\Delta S}$$

where ΔV and ΔS are, respectively, the volume and entropy changes on melting; the problem is to determine how these quantities vary with temperature and pressure. ΔS is not likely to vary a great deal with pressure, but ΔV presumably does. Since, in addition, the composition of neither core nor mantle is exactly known, a considerable amount of guessing is unavoidable at this stage. All that can be said at present is that the temperature at the core boundary is likely to be between 2500°C and 5000°C.

Temperature could, in principle, be determined accurately if the equation of state for mantle (or core) material were exactly known (see Chapter 11). If the density and its first and second derivatives with respect to P and T [that is, K_T, $(\partial K_T/\partial P)_T$, $(\partial K_T/\partial T)_P$, α, $(\partial \alpha/\partial T)_P$] were known, the knowledge of density and seismic velocity at any depth would suffice to determine T, since P can be calculated if the density distri-

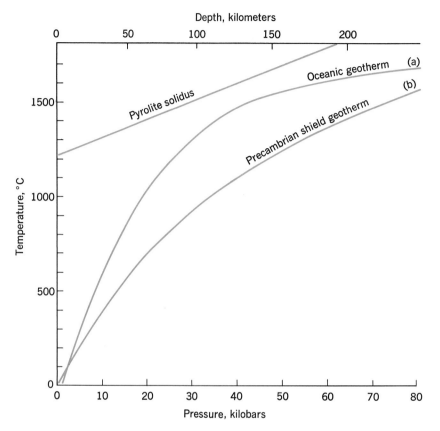

FIG. 12–16 *Calculated temperature distributions (a) under an oceanic area, and (b) under a stable shield area with low heat flow. (After A. E. Ringwood, in* Advances in Earth Sciences, *edited by P. M. Hurley, by permission of The M.I.T. Press, Cambridge, Massachusetts. Copyright © 1966 by The M.I.T. Press.)*

bution is known. As things now stand, the effect of T on ρ or K in the mantle and core appears to be of the same order as the uncertainty on the effect of P alone; thus T cannot be determined accurately. All that can be said at the moment is that a value of about 3000°C at the core boundary is not incompatible with the data. More theoretical and experimental work at very high pressures is needed.

THE CORE

If the inner core is solid and, as has been suggested, of the same general composition as the liquid outer core, the temperature at the interface must be precisely equal to the melting point at the pressure prevailing there (about 3.2 Mb). Various extrapolations of the melting point of pure iron to that pressure yield values ranging from 2500°C to 6000°C; since the core does not consist of pure iron, its melting point is presumably less than that.

If the outer core is in convective motion, as is generally assumed in theories of the origin of the earth's magnetic field, the temperature gradient in it must be higher than the adiabatic value, but probably not much higher, since the viscosity is very low. On the other hand, the temperature gradient must be less than the melting-point gradient if the inner core is to be solid, since the temperatures of outer core and inner core are respectively higher and lower than the temperature of melting (Figure 12–17). Since the adiabatic gradient is itself proportional to T, from equation (11-11), it may be possible to set limits on the actual temperature distribution.

On general grounds, it seems unlikely that the temperature of the core could be very high, for the following reason. The outer core is the main source of the earth's magnetic field. If convec-

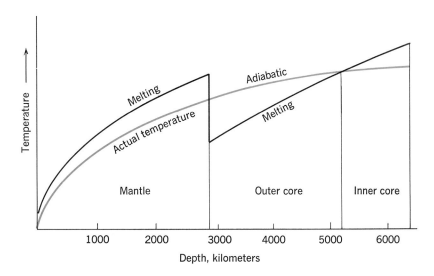

FIG. 12–17 *Melting curve and adiabatic curve in the core.*

tion is needed to produce that field, the thermal conductivity K must be rather low (refer to Rayleigh's number, page 651); indeed, if it were high, weak heat sources could not maintain a gradient in excess of the adiabatic value. On the other hand, the core must have a large electrical conductivity σ in order to allow large currents to flow and to minimize their dissipation as heat. In metals, electrons are the carriers for both electric current and heat; the ratio of K to σ turns out to be proportional to the absolute temperature T (Wiedemann-Franz ratio). Thus small K and large σ require a small T. Temperatures high enough to affect the density by more than a few percent appear to be ruled out.

Thermal History of the Earth

The thermal history of the earth is closely linked to its structural evolution. Surface heat flow and temperature distribution strongly depend, as we have seen, on the intensity and distribution of the heat sources and on the mechanism of heat transfer. Any major event that redistributes or alters the heat sources or affects in some way the rate of transfer of heat must necessarily leave its record in the temperature distribution.

We noted, however, that the very nature of

the equation of heat transfer—with or without convection—precludes the possibility of working backward in time; past history cannot be unambiguously reconstructed from the present state of the earth. The best that can be done is to devise a number of models by means of assumptions regarding the initial temperature of the earth at the time of its formation, its initial radioactive content, its thermal conductivity, and so forth, and to calculate for each model what the present temperature distribution and heat flow would be. Models that fail to predict correct values may then be discarded.

Surface geology has little to say on the matter. It was once thought that orogeny could be readily explained if the earth were cooling at a sufficient rate, but other explanations of orogeny have been found that do not involve cooling (Chapter 13). The intensity of orogenic deformation at any time must of course be related to the rate of heat transfer as measured, say, by the intensity of the convective circulation, but there is no clear-cut evidence as yet that this intensity has increased or decreased with time; the best guess at the moment is that orogenic activity has remained roughly constant for the past two or three billion years. The common occurrence in Precambrian formations—and only in Precambrian formations—of metamorphic rocks of a particular type (cordierite granulites) that implies high temperatures *and* low pressure (that is, shallow depth) at the time of recrystallization suggests that, in some areas at least, the rate of heat flow may have been greater in the past than it is now. Yet at present heat flow varies by a large factor (2 or 3) from one geological province to the next, so that it would be unsafe to conclude from the occurrence of these cordierite granulites that the average heat flow was indeed greater. The only geological datum that may be significant in the present context is that no rocks have yet been found that are older than about 3.5×10^9 years, whereas the earth itself seems to be 4.5×10^9 years old (see Chapter 4). What happened during that first billion years?

Birch has recently put forth some "speculations" that deserve close attention.[12] His arguments are mainly geochemical. Birch envisages that the earth formed by accretion of cold particles at a rate such that the gravitational energy could be dissipated by radiation from the surface; the initial temperature was probably nowhere greater than 1000°C, and so the earth was warm rather than hot. Radioactive elements were necessarily more abundant then than they are now, because of decay, so that the rate of heat generation probably was several times what it is now. This radiogenic heat and perhaps also the heat generated by tidal friction (if the moon already was in orbit around the earth or was captured at that time and was closer to the earth than it is now) would have been sufficient to raise the internal temperature within 500 million years to the melting point of iron; thus iron, assumed to be originally distributed uniformly through the earth, began to move down because of its greater density and condensed to form the core some 4.5 billion years ago; gravitational energy released in the process was sufficient to cause fractional melting of the mantle; the low-melting fraction containing all of the original potassium and uranium moved up, leaving a lower mantle devoid of radioactivity. Formation of a stable continental crust became

[12] F. Birch, Speculations on the earth's thermal history, *Geol. Soc. Am. Bull.*, vol. 76, pp. 133–154, 1965.

possible after this upward concentration and further decay of radioactivity, some 3.5 billion years ago. An interesting conclusion of Birch is that the original earth could not have had the composition of ordinary chondrites; for the latter contains too much K in relation to U. A chondritic earth would in fact barely provide enough U to account for the present abundance of that element in the crust; and the Sr^{86}/Sr^{87} is too high, as compared to basalt, to allow basalts to be derived from a chondritic mantle. The only meteoritic material that seems to have the proper K-U and Th-U ratios and abundances is the meteorite Orgueil, a representative of the relatively rare carbonaceous chondrites. [Carbonaceous chondrites are characterized, however, by a rather high state of oxidation, as they contain Fe_3O_4 (magnetite) rather than metalic iron. If the primitive earth had exactly the composition of a carbonaceous chondrite, a mechanism for reducing the iron and disposing of the corresponding amount of oxygen would have to be found.] The equality of heat flow in continents and oceans is accounted for, in Birch's model, by the fact that the total amount of radioactive material in a vertical column is presumably the same everywhere, the only difference being that in oceanic areas it still resides entirely in the upper mantle, whereas in continental areas much of it has become concentrated in the crust. This difference leads to differences in temperature as shown in Figures 12–13 and 12–16. No allowance is made in this model for lateral convective transport of heat in the upper mantle.

Perhaps the only firm statement that can be made at this time is that we are still far from a complete understanding of the earth's thermal history. The formation of the earth, and its separation into core, mantle, and crust, must have been rather complicated events, the details of which are not entirely understood. What is clear is that the earth is not, and presumably never has been, in a thermal steady state; yet thermal conditions in the upper few hundred kilometers may, on the average, not have changed very much in the past two billion years, except locally. Prior to that, conditions may have been rather different.

REFERENCES

The standard text on heat conduction is **H. S. Carslaw** and **J. C. Jaeger**, *Conduction of Heat in Solids* (2d ed., Oxford, New York, 1959).

Brief treatments of the subject matter of this chapter may be found in **J. Coulomb**, and **G. Jobert**, *The Physical Constitution of the Earth* (Hafner, New York, 1963, Chap. 6, pp. 240–280) and in **J. A. Jacobs, R. D. Russel**, and **J. T. Wilson**, *Physics and Geology* (McGraw-Hill, New York, 1959, Chap. 5, pp. 101–116). An excellent popular account may be found in Chapter 6 of *Debate about the Earth*, by **H. Takeuchi, S. Uyeda**, and **H. Kanamori** (Freeman, San Francisco, 1967). See also: *Physics of the Earth*, by **F. D. Stacey** (Wiley, New York, 1969).

A comprehensive treatment of the earth's thermal state, not including convection, is that of **E. A. Lubimova**, "Theory of thermal state of the earth's mantle," Chapter 10 in *The Earth's Mantle*, edited by **T. F. Gaskell** (Academic Press, New York, 1967).

Heat-flow data and related calculations are to be found in *Terrestrial Heat Flow*, edited by **W. H. K. Lee** (American Geophysical Union Monograph No. 8, Washington, D.C., 1965), and also in an article by **R. P. von Herzen**, "Surface heat flow and some implications for the mantle," Chapter 9 in *The Earth's Mantle*, edited by **T. F. Gaskell** (Academic Press, New York, 1967).

The following two articles deal mainly with the composition of the mantle but also contain temperature calculations: **S. P. Clark** and **A. E. Ringwood**, "Density distribution and constitution of the mantle" (*Rev. Geophys.*, vol. 2, pp. 35–88, 1964) and **A. E. Ringwood**, "Mineralogy of the mantle," in *Advances in Earth Sciences*, edited by **P. M. Hurley** (M.I.T. Press, Cambridge, Mass., 1966).

On the subject of convection, it is suggested that the student read the following: **W. M. Elsasser**, "Thermal structure of the upper mantle and convection," in *Advances in Earth Sciences*, edited by **P. M. Hurley** (M.I.T. Press, Cambridge, Mass., 1966); **J. W. Elder**, "Convection—the key to dynamic geology" (*Sci. Prog.*, vol. 56, pp. 1–33. 1968), and **D. C. Tozer**, "Towards a theory of thermal convection in the mantle," in *The Earth's Mantle*, edited by **T. F. Gaskell** (Academic Press, New York, 1967).

A series of short articles on convection also appeared in Section IX of *Mantles of the Earth and Terrestrial Planets*, edited by **S. K. Runcorn** (Interscience, New York, 1967).

One of the first quantitative treatments of convection was given by **C. L. Pekeris**, "Thermal convection in the interior of the earth" (*Monthly Notices Roy. Astron. Soc. (Geophys. Suppl.)*, vol. 3, pp. 343–367, 1935).

Estimates from seismic velocities of the temperature gradient in the upper mantle are given by **L. Thomsen** in "On the distribution of density and temperature in the low-velocity zone (*J. Geophys. Res.*, vol. 72, pp. 5649–5653, 1967).

13

STRUCTURAL EVOLUTION
OF CONTINENTS
AND OCEANS

THE PURPOSE of this chapter is to examine some evidence regarding processes by which continents and oceans have attained their present configurations. Have continents always been where they are today? Have they always had their present size and shape? To what extent have they been internally deformed? What mechanisms could account for their evolution?

To these, and to many other similar questions, there is no definite answer as yet. Different geologists may hold quite different views as to, for instance, the relative importance in continental mechanics of vertical (up and down) versus horizontal (compression and extension) deformation. Nor is it surprising that they should hold such different views. Here, as in many other geological inquiries, the evidence is mostly circumstantial, and observations are generally open to several interpretations. The geological record is nowhere complete. All one sees of it are scattered bits that must somehow be patched together, but to do so requires a mastery of an enormous amount of detail (stratigraphic, for example) that very few geologists can even hope to attain. Only the barest outline can be presented here.

Much geological thought seems to revolve about a few cardinal problems, as follows:

1. The growth of continents.

2. The mechanics of intracontinental deformation.
3. Continental drift.
4. The origin of the sea floor.

The related problem of the growth of the oceans and the origin of seawater will be discussed in the next chapter. We begin by examining some features of the present distribution of continents.

Distribution of Continents

Continents, with their adjacent continental shelves (Figure 1–1) and bordering shallow seas, occupy a little more than one third of the earth's surface, the rest of which consists of oceans, about 4.8 km deep on the average. The present distribution of continents is odd, for most of them are concentrated in approximately one hemisphere. Only about 4 percent of the earth's surface is occupied by land that has land opposed to it at its antipodes. If the distribution were random, a radius drawn at random would have a probability of one third of hitting land, and the combined probability that both ends of a diameter hit land would therefore be $\frac{1}{3} \times \frac{1}{3} = 0.11$, instead of 0.04 as observed. The difference, however, may not be significant, inasmuch as we have only one earth and therefore no statistical test of randomness can be applied.

The distribution of continents reflects none of the symmetry (expressed by the spherical harmonic P_2, see Chapter 11) inherent in the earth's rotation. Rotational symmetry would require the continents to be distributed uniformly in longitude and symmetrically with respect to the equator, which is conspicuously not true.[1]

There is now a substantial body of evidence, outlined later in this chapter, to show that continents have moved relative to each other (continental drift). Reconstructions of their past locations, which are not precisely known as yet, suggest that at one time, possibly as late as early Mesozoic, they all were part of a single large mass ("Pangea"), or perhaps of two large masses ("Laurasia" and "Gondwana"), the dispersed fragments of which form the continents of today. There are also suggestions, still rather imprecise, that these primitive continents may have formed by coalescence of earlier continents not identical with the present ones. It is hard to see what determined the sense and amplitude of these movements. Even if one accepts the view that the opening of the Atlantic and the relative movements of the continents bordering on it are determined by the upwelling of mantle material along the crest of the Atlantic ridge (see Chapter 3), the location and shape of the ridge itself remain to be accounted for. One can only venture to guess that what we now see is a consequence of an original heterogeneity of the mantle. Perhaps nothing like what has happened would have occurred if the mantle had originally been spherically symmetrical, in the sense that its properties at any point depended only on distance from the center of the earth and not on latitude and longitude. Differences in chemical composition and physical properties may have been originally rather small, but they would tend to become enhanced rather than destroyed by the very geological processes to which they give rise. Should melting, for instance, start at one particular point in an otherwise homogeneous mantle, the fractional melting and the upwelling of magma would permanently disturb the thermal regime, the distribution of heat sources (K^{40}), the density, and the mass distribution—not only at the source but also on the surface. Geological and geophysical heterogeneity must therefore tend to increase with time. The present surface heterogeneity and, in particular, the present distribution of continents may be the result of a rather trivial original heterogeneity, perhaps of the kind that determines where the first bubbles will form in a liquid when brought to its boiling point.

PERMANENCY OF CONTINENTS

Sedimentary rocks on land are generally different from the muds that presently cover the deep-ocean floor. Nowhere in the oceans have we yet found a crust resembling in thickness or composition the continental crust.[2] Thus oceans and continents are presumably not interchangeable; the ocean floor does not rise above sea level like the floor of the epicontinental seas, and continents do not simply sink into the oceanic depths. It was therefore once generally thought that oceans and continents were permanent features.

Some observations, however, contradict this view of permanency. The great thickness of sediments that accumulated in Paleozoic times in what now forms the Appalachian Mountains seems to have been derived from erosion of a

---

[1] There is a force, generally known by its German name of "Polfluchtkraft" (= "flight from the Pole"), that tends to push continents toward the equator. This force arises as follows. Equipotential surfaces are not exactly parallel; they are more closely spaced at the poles (where g is greater) than at the equator (where g is smaller). A high-riding or "floating" continent is subject to two forces: a downward gravitational force acting at its center of mass, and an upward buoyancy force exerted, by Archimedes' principle, at the center of mass of the fluid that the floating body displaces. The center of mass lies above the center of buoyancy. Both the gravitational and buoyancy forces are normal to different equipotential surfaces which are not parallel, as we have just seen. The two forces are therefore not exactly antiparallel, and their resultant, the Polfluchtkraft, is directed toward the equator; it is, however, very small and believed to be geologically insignificant.

---

[2] However, some oceanic islands (for example, the Seychelles Islands in the northwestern Indian Ocean) do have a continental structure.

land mass lying to the southeast in what is now the Atlantic Ocean. Similarly, the late-Mesozoic sediments of the coast of California ("Franciscan") seem partly to have come from the west, and the nature of their metamorphism suggests that they may possibly have accumulated in what was once an oceanic trench. Still other land masses may have existed where we now find oceans. Paleontologists attempting to explain the similarity of terrestrial fossil faunas and floras on widely separated lands (for example, Africa and South America) have postulated the former existence of land, or chains of islands ("land bridges"), over which new forms of terrestrial life could spread from one place to another across what are now impassable oceanic barriers.

Rates of sedimentation on the ocean floor have been estimated by measuring the thickness of sediments between layers that could be dated either by changes in the character of the fossil fauna related to dated Pleistocene climatic events, or by changes in the polarity of the earth's magnetic field (see page 688), or by still other methods involving short-lived radioactive decay products of uranium or thorium precipitated with sediments from seawater. Rates of sedimentation so determined appear to be rather variable, both in time and space, but are generally of the order of a few millimeters per thousand years. If the average rate is, say, 0.5 cm per 1000 years, the total thickness of sediments accumulated through geologic time ($\sim 4 \times 10^9$ years) in a permanent ocean should be of the order of 20 kilometers; yet seismic exploration of the ocean floor rarely reveals much more than a kilometer of material that could be interpreted, from its characteristic seismic velocity, to be sedimentary. The discrepancy is so great that it seems safe to conclude that sediments have not accumulated on the ocean floor for very long; in other words, the ocean floor must be relatively young. No rocks recognizably older than late Jurassic have yet been recovered from the ocean floor.

CONTINENTAL GROWTH

Volcanic action continuously adds to the continents material that presumably originates in the upper mantle (see Chapter 6). Erosion, on the other hand, continuously removes material from land; part of this comes to rest on the continental shelf (and therefore remains within the continental realm), but part of it finishes up in the ocean or on the ocean floor and is therefore lost to the continents. It is not clear whether continents on the whole gain or lose in these processes.

THE STRUCTURE OF CONTINENTS   The structure of North America and Eurasia (Europe + Asia) has suggested to some geologists that perhaps continents do grow. As described in Chapter 3, continents consist of shields, platforms, and mountain belts.

1. Shields are areas underlain by Precambrian metamorphic rocks that have remained essentially stable since their last episode of metamorphism, one billion or more years ago; because of this apparent stability, they are thought to be extremely rigid and undeformable. They almost certainly were at one time areas of sedimentation and volcanism, which later were intensely deformed (orogeny) and metamorphosed, with contemporary intrusion of magma, mostly granitic. Such shields may have a rather complex structure and consist of several units of different age; the units forming the several "provinces" of the Canadian shield are described in Chapter 4. In the Canadian shield, the age of the units decreases radially outward from one or two very ancient nuclei. In Eurasia, there are three such shields: around the Baltic Sea,[3] in the Ukraine, and in north-central Siberia.

2. Platforms are areas presently covered with flat-lying sediments of post-Precambrian age. They differ from shields only in having been below sea level during part or most of the time since their latest metamorphism, but apart from broad warping they seem to have suffered no recent deformation. An example is the Russian platform, encompassing most of the European part of the U.S.S.R. and extending roughly from the Arctic

---

[3] Also called the Fennoscandian shield (Finland + Scandinavia + northwestern Russia).

to the Caucasus and from longitude 30°E to the Urals.

3. Mountain belts of post-Precambrian age appear in general as if wrapped around the shields and platforms, as the Appalachians (late Paleozoic) on the eastern side of the North American continent, and the Cordilleras on the west.

In Europe, three major episodes of post-Precambrian deformation can be clearly recognized. They are, respectively, the Caledonian (early to middle Paleozoic), the Hercynian–Variscan (late Paleozoic), and the Alpine (Cenozoic) orogenies. The first is seen (Figure 3–64) on the western edge of the Baltic shield in Norway, and in Great Britain. The Hercynian mountain belt extends roughly east–west from western Europe to the Pacific, with a notable north–south appendix in the Ural Mountains. The Alpine range, also trending east–west, lies mainly to the south of the Hercynian belt which it partly overlaps. In Siberia, there is a similar arrangement around the Siberian shield, with orogenic belts of these same ages arranged more or less concentrically around the shield, the age of the belts decreasing radially outward.

CONTINENTAL ACCRETION   This somewhat over-simplified picture of successive fold belts has been interpreted by many geologists to indicate that continents grow from an initial nucleus by accretion of successive orogenic belts. According to these views, each belt started out as a sedimentary basin or geosyncline, which then became folded. Most of the folded sediments were later removed by erosion, leaving a metamorphic core with numerous plutonic intrusions which somehow became incorporated into the adjoining growing shield. It is around this enlarged shield that the next orogeny would develop. Volcanic contributions from the mantle, particularly during the early (sedimentary) stage of the process, would account for the ever-increasing volume of the continents.

This hypothesis, which probably carries some element of truth, is also hard to substantiate. Although it is true that orogenic belts tend to

occur on the oceanic edges of continents (perhaps because that is where we expect, from the discussion of Chapter 12, the greatest intensity of thermal stresses), the picture of continental growth presented above lacks generality. In the first place, it is clear that successive orogenies overlap: the Hercynian belt of western Europe, for instance, includes Lower Paleozoic rocks previously deformed in the Caledonian orogeny, and the core of the central Alps includes rocks metamorphosed in the Hercynian episode and remetamorphosed in the Alpine orogeny (Chapter 10). There is evidence of a mid-Paleozoic orogeny in northern California, and of a late-Paleozoic orogeny in Nevada; both areas lie within a belt of later (Jurassic) orogeny and to the west of, and therefore outwards from, the late-Mesozoic orogenic belt of the Rocky Mountains. Where relatively recent orogenies have occurred, the older basement is rarely exposed; thus it is impossible to affirm that the Cenozoic Cordilleras of western North America, for example, are not underlain by rocks as old as, or older than, the most ancient rocks exposed in the Canadian shield. Radiometric ages of about 1.5 b.y. have in fact been obtained for rocks in Texas and on the western coast in the San Gabriel Mountains of California. Along the Pacific coast of Chile Paleozoic metamorphic rocks and granite plutons form the western (outer) border of the Andean geosyncline which was filled with lavas, volcanic debris, and sediment during the Jurassic and Cretaceous. Very old ages appear in the Lewisian of Scotland, at the westernmost edge of Europe. If a recent radiometric determination of the age of the Stillwater ultramafic intrusion in Montana is correct, this peripheral body is, in fact, the oldest rock known (3.6 b.y.) on the North American continent. Clearly also, the most recent episode of metamorphism tends to erase in rocks all features by which earlier events could be dated. Thus it is difficult to decide on this basis whether continents have grown in size by accretion as suggested.

Yet it does seem that the volume of the continents must either remain constant or grow. In recent years volcanoes have discharged on the average about 1 km³ (10^{15} cm³) per year of material, part of which may be the product of re-melting of the continental crust, but part of which must have come from the mantle. At this rate, the whole volume of the continental crust ($\sim 10^{24}$ cm³) could have been erupted in a few billion years. At the present rate of sedimentation losses from the continents to the ocean floor can hardly exceed this figure.[4] Furthermore, since the total volume of sediments actually present on the ocean floor is relatively small (see page 664), sediments removed from it are presumably some-how reincorporated in or under the continental crust by the process of sea-floor spreading, which will presently be described (see page 683). The uncertainty affecting most of the numbers quoted here is very large, so that no formal conclusions can be reached; yet the impression remains that the total volume of the continental crust has not decreased through geologic time and may have substantially increased.

Intracontinental Deformation

VERTICAL DISPLACEMENTS

Perhaps the easiest generalization that any student of geology can make is that any part of the earth's surface has, in the course of time, repeatedly moved up and down. Some relevant evidence has been given in Chapter 8, and more will be given below, but not before it is pointed out that although relative movement is easily detected, the magnitude and sense of the motion are actually very hard to determine for lack of suitably accessible reference points. The center of mass of the earth would be a suitable reference point from which to measure changes in radial distance to a point on the surface, but it is not

accessible. Ordinarily vertical heights or distances are measured with respect to sea level (the geoid), but sea level is itself likely to change. Water may be added to the oceans by volcanic action, thereby raising their level, or may be withdrawn and stored in icecaps. Sea level might also drop or rise as a result of displacements of the sea floor in some distant part of the ocean; as mentioned on page 606 there is evidence that large areas of the sea floor in the southwestern Pacific may have subsided. Changes in sea level can, however, be separated, at least in theory, from other vertical movements since sea level, if it changes at all, must change everywhere by the same amount. An apparent uplift (relative to sea level) that is localized cannot be the result of falling sea level. Some of the evidence for vertical displacement is as follows:

1. *Changes in sedimentary pattern.* Transgression of the sea (that is, lowering of the land) results in the deposition of marine sediments on an erosional land surface. Regression (rising) is marked by the change from marine to terrestrial sedimentation, or by the cessation of marine sedimentation as it is succeeded by erosion. The stratigraphic record is replete with evidence of this kind. Not only once, but at dozens of times, the sea has come in, only to go out again at some later time.

Maximum amplitude of the vertical motion, as recorded in the maximum thickness of marine sediments deposited on a sunken land surface, may be of the order of 20 km or more.

2. *High-angle dip-slip faulting* (normal and high-angle reverse faults). Any fault with a dip-slip component of motion (see Chapter 3) implies vertical displacement. The displacement is relative, and there is generally no evidence of its absolute sense: Did both sides of the fault move up, or down, by different amounts? Or did one side move up and the other down? Or was one side stationary? If so, which side?

Normal faulting is extremely common. Maximum relative displacement on a single fault may be of the order of a kilometer.

3. *Uplift.* It is not uncommon to find marine sediments in high mountains. These sediments,

---

[4] The area of the ocean floor is about 3×10^{18} cm²; if the present rate of sedimentation were as high as 5×10^{-4} cm/year, on the average, the volume of sediments deposited annually would be 1.5×10^{15} cm³. The density of deep-sea sediments is considerably less than that of lava, and part of the deep-sea sediments may be derived from noncontinental sources (for example, volcanic eruptions on the sea floor). Thus the total mass of deep-sea sediments deposited annually is probably less than the mass added to the crust by volcanic action.

originally deposited below sea level, have been somehow pushed up to where we now find them. Displacements involved may amount to approximately 10 km.

4. *Metamorphism.* One commonly finds at the surface metamorphic rocks, which, judging from the minerals they contain, must have recrystallized at pressures up to 10 kb or more, which implies burial to depths of the order of 20 to 30 km. Such is the case for the rocks of the glaucophane–lawsonite-schist facies (Chapter 10). Following recrystallization, these rocks that we now see at the surface must have been stripped of their cover by erosion; this implies uplift by 20 to 30 km.

There is no obvious rule relating vertical displacement to other geological processes. In some instances, slow sinking and accumulation of a thick sequence of sediments, as in a geosyncline, is accompanied by extensive volcanism and followed by intense deformation, but this is not an invariable rule. Upward motion frequently occurs during deformation. In other instances, uplift occurs without deformation, as in the area that now forms the Colorado Plateau and which was the scene of quiet sedimentation throughout the Paleozoic and Mesozoic eras; uplift of several kilometers occurred in early-Cenozoic time without any noticeable deformation of the sediments, which can still be seen to lie perfectly flat in the Grand Canyon of the Colorado. Uplift also occurs in mountain ranges long after any obvious tectonic activity has ceased. The Precambrian shield of western Australia has been uplifted along a spectacular fault that runs along the western edge of that continent; this fault is marked by a continuous scarp and is seismically active. It is, in fact, surprising how few areas of the world today lie at the level (near sea level) to which erosion should reduce them; it seems that continents now stand higher than they stood during most of geologic time (see Chapter 7). Uplift is a general and widespread phenomenon.

Surprisingly, and perhaps because vertical movement is so common, it attracts relatively little attention, and relatively little thought has been given to its causes. Some vertical displacement may be caused by a tendency to isostatic adjustment. If, for instance, erosion removes part of the load in a mountain range, the rest of the range will rise, and if sediments are poured into the sea, the sea floor may sink under the load. It is easy to see, however, by comparing the density of the surface material moved with that of the underlying mantle, where the compensating flow takes place, that isostatic adjustments of this kind can explain but a small part of the observed displacements.

HORIZONTAL STRAINS

COMPRESSION   Folded sedimentary strata that are so conspicuous in deformed areas such as fold mountain ranges imply shortening in the horizontal dimension perpendicular to the fold axes. On the assumption that shortening implies compression, it has often been accepted that stresses in the earth's crust are mostly compressive. Because there seemed to be an easy explanation for them, their importance has tended to be exaggerated; the mechanics of extension, on the other hand, have been given relatively less attention by geophysicists. The explanation for compression was based on the observation that the earth is losing heat and may therefore be cooling; since cooling implies contraction, the earth was also thought to be contracting. This contraction must take place at depth, since that is where the heat comes from. The crust, assumed to be at nearly constant temperature, thus becomes too large to fit the shrinking interior and must therefore be shortened.

This simple idea must now be carefully reexamined. In the first place, as noted in Chapter 12, it is impossible to assert that the earth is cooling without further evidence on the distribution and intensity of internal heat sources and on the earth's initial temperature. It may be cooling, or it may be warming up, or it may be doing both at different depths. In the second place, crustal shortening explains neither local extension, nor vertical displacements, nor any of the tangential movements to be covered later in discussions of continental drift and sea-floor spreading. Finally it is now generally accepted that folds and "nappe" structures in sedimentary layers that were once thought to indicate a general compressional state of stress in the crust may have resulted instead from essentially vertical movements and consequent sliding of large sedimentary blocks that became crumpled in the process ("gravity" tectonics). That some compression and crustal shortening attends the formation of a fold mountain range such as the Alps seems clear from the thickening of the crust necessary to produce the "roots" mentioned in Chapter 11. It appears, nevertheless, that crustal shortening in a fold mountain range may be considerably less than the crumpling of the sedimentary cover would indicate. It also appears, as we shall presently see, that the earth may not be contracting at all.

AN EXPANDING EARTH?   It has indeed been suggested from several quarters that, far from contracting, the earth is actually expanding. This view contends that continents with essentially the same total area as the present ones initially covered the whole of a smaller earth with a radius R_0 approximately 0.57 times the present one. (If continents now occupy 1/3 of the surface of an earth with radius R, R_0 must have been such that $4\pi R_0^2 = 4\pi R^2/3$; hence $R_0 = 0.57R$.) As the earth expands, the continental crust becomes too small to cover the whole surface, and gaps represented by the present oceans must open up. The idea is attractive in that it disposes of the problem of explaining how the continents happened to become distributed unsymmetrically; for what could be more symmetrical than a uniform continental crust covering the whole earth? At the same time, it avoids the mechanical problems implied in moving continents around, since continents would become separated without moving with respect to the underlying mantle.

If the assumption is made that the size of a continent does not change during expansion of the earth, it should be possible to determine its ancient radius from paleomagnetic measurements, since the inclination i of the field at a point on the surface is a simple function of the angular distance p to the pole: $\tan i = 2 \cot p$

(see page 678). Suppose that the inclination has been measured on rocks of a given age at two points on the same continent, L being the (magnetic) north–south distance between these two points. The difference in inclination measures the difference in angular distance to the magnetic pole, whereas L measures the difference in linear distance. Linear distance on a sphere of radius R is R times the corresponding angular distance; hence R can be found.[5] Present paleomagnetic indications are that the radius has not changed by a significant amount since the Permian, although the data are not sufficiently precise to rule out a change of a few percent in the earth's radius since that time.

Another argument makes any large change, by a factor of 2 or so, most unlikely. If the radius shrinks by a factor of 2, while the mass of the earth is kept constant, the average density must increase by a factor of 8. Any change in radius and density affects g, and therefore the pressure inside the earth; for a homogeneous earth one calculates by the argument on page 622 that the pressure at the center increases by a factor of $2^4 = 16$. Solids are so incompressible, particularly at the high pressures involved, that a sixteenfold increase in pressure could not cause an eightfold increase in density, unless phase changes of a totally unknown and unpredictable nature took place. Again, a small change in radius cannot be excluded, although the problem of supplying the gravitational energy required for the expansion may be serious.

It has been suggested that expansion of the earth could result from a decrease in time of the gravitational constant G, to which g is proportional. The cosmological arguments on which this is based appear rather weak, and there are sound reasons, mostly from astronomy, for believing that if G has changed at all, it must have done so at an extremely slow rate, the total change through geological time being of the order of a

---

[5] For example, a difference in inclination of 90°, as between equator and pole, corresponds on the present earth to a linear distance of $\pi R/2$ or 10,000 km. If a difference of inclination of 90° were found in old rocks at points 5000 km apart, the ancient radius would have been one half the present one.

few percent. Such a change could alter the earth's radius, but only by a very small amount.

There is a possibility, based on the coral growth rings mentioned on page 218, to estimate possible changes in G and mean radius R since Devonian times. The growth mechanism of coral seems to be somehow affected by both sunlight and moonlight, so the thickness of daily growth rings varies with a yearly and a lunar monthly period. From the count of the number of rings between successive maxima it is possible to deduce the number of days in a Devonian lunar month (30.59 ± 0.13), and in a Devonian year (398 ± 7). The length of the day may change because of tidal friction, or because of a change in the radius and moment of inertia of the earth, or both. In the first case, there must be a corresponding change in the length of the lunar month, since the effect of tidal friction is to transfer angular moment from the rotation of the earth to the orbital motion of the moon. The angular momentum of the rotation of the earth is, as we recall, $C\omega$, where C is the moment of inertia about the rotation axis, and $\omega = 2\pi/T$ is the angular velocity corresponding to a day of length T seconds. Thus if C changes while angular momentum remains constant, ω must change, but the length of the month and year are unaffected. A change in G affects the length of both the year and the lunar month. The problem has recently been considered by R. R. Newton, who finds that if G is assumed to have remained constant, the moment of inertia and therefore presumably also the radius of the earth has also remained essentially unchanged. If, on the other hand, G is allowed to vary, the coral data together with the earth's deceleration calculated from historically recorded times of occurrence of ancient eclipses and by the perturbation of satellite motion, allow an estimate to be made of changes in both C and G. Newton finds that the data are consistent with an increase in C (by some 10 percent) and a decrease in G (at the rate of 1 part in 10^{10} per year) since Devonian time. Uncertainties in the calculation arise not only from the uncertainty in the coral data themselves and their interpretation but also from several perturbing factors such as planetary disturbances

of the motion of the moon, the ratio of the tidal retardations due to the sun and the moon, and the possible effect of atmospheric tides in changing the earth's rotation rate. We note that a decrease in G would decrease g everywhere inside the earth, thereby reducing the internal pressure and the density; this would in itself lead to a small expansion of the earth's radius. The calculated change in G, however, is too small to account for all of the change in C; thus mass must have been transferred radially outwards. We conclude that there is at present no evidence that the earth is shrinking, as demanded by the contraction theory of orogeny; there is on the contrary some tenuous evidence that its radius may be expanding at a rate of not more than about 0.1 cm per year.

EXTENSION   By extension of the crust we mean the kind of tectonic deformation predominantly associated with normal faulting, as seen in rift valleys or in block-mountain structures, as in the western United States and in many other parts of the world. Normal faulting does not necessarily imply a tensional stress, but only that the stress component normal to the earth's surface is the largest of the principal stresses, all three of which may be compressions. There is invariably a component of vertical displacement associated with extension.

The amount of extension can, in some instances, be measured. The flood basalts of the Paraná Basin, in southern Brazil and adjoining countries, cover an area of more than 10^6 km^2. Around the margins of the basin thousands of vertical feeder dikes are exposed. They average 50 meters in width; some are as wide as 100 meters and extend over 1000 km. They collectively cover 5 percent of the total outcrop. This implies a lateral expansion (normal to the strike of the dikes) of 5 percent during the period of basaltic eruption—a span of some 25 m.y. in early Cretaceous time. Similarly, Iceland, which lies on the crest of the Atlantic ridge, consists of a thick accumulation of lava flows fed from numerous dikes; as many as 1000 having a total thickness of 3 km have been counted in one 53-km section. From a comparison of the total thickness of these dikes with the volume of lava erupted from them, it has been calculated that if the total thickness of the lava pile is 30 km, a lateral extension of Iceland by as much as 400 km may have occurred. Here is perhaps an indication of the process by which new crust forms at the crest of an oceanic ridge, as demanded in sea-floor spreading; that is, extension opens fissures through which a great volume of basaltic magma rises to form dikes and flows. But extension is not necessarily limited to regions of active volcanism.

It is again very difficult to make any general statement as to where and when this type of deformation occurs. The rift valleys of Africa seem not to be associated with any other kind of deformation. Volcanism has occurred along them, but although the rifts are still seismically active, and therefore presumably still developing, there are only a few active volcanoes scattered along their great length. In western Europe, the great Hercynian orogeny of fold-mountain type was followed in the Permian by normal faulting on a large scale. Whether the block mountains of the western Cordillera of the U.S. are related in the same way to the Laramide (late Cretaceous) orogeny of the Rocky Mountains is not known.

A similar pattern of extension and normal faulting seems to be typical of oceanic ridges. In many places along the crest of a ridge there exists a narrow trough reminiscent in size and shape of the rift valleys of Africa which, like their counterpart in the oceanic ridge, occur at the crest of a very broad rise (Figure 3–71). The analogy between oceanic ridges and the African rift valleys, however, does not seem to be so striking as to require these valleys to be part of the world-wide system of oceanic ridges, as they are shown to be on some maps; for example, the oceanic ridges are characterized (see the section on sea-floor spreading below) by large-scale lateral spreading of which the African rifts show but little sign; if these rifts are spreading like ocean ridges, they are doing so at a much slower rate.

TRANSCURRENT FAULTING   It is only in recent years that geologists have been able to demonstrate that large horizontal displacements, of the order of several hundred kilometers, have oc-

curred along transcurrent faults, the best known of which is the San Andreas fault in California. Displacement along this fault, or parts of it, is presently at an average rate of a few centimeters per year, so this fault must presumably have been active for some 10^8 years. Similar faults are the Alpine fault of New Zealand, the Atacama fault in Chile, and the Philippine fault (Figure 3–73), all of which run nearly parallel to the border of the Pacific. Displacement along the Mendocino fracture zone, on the floor of the northeastern Pacific, is thought to amount to more than 1000 km. The direction of motion at many earthquake foci, as deduced from seismic first-motion studies (Chapter 9), suggest that strike-slip displacement may indeed be a very common feature of many presently active faults.

Compression and extension of the crust may perhaps be accounted for in terms of the drag produced by mantle convection, with compression occurring above converging descending and extension above diverging upwelling currents (Figure 12–9). One might then guess that transcurrent faulting would occur near the boundary between horizontal currents of opposite sense. This oversimplified picture may, however, be difficult to reconcile with other features. For instance, the Atacama fault implies, on this mechanism, flow parallel to the Pacific border; but the Peru–Chile trench, which runs parallel to and only a short distance from, the Atacama fault, is usually attributed to a current moving at a right angle to the axis of the trench, from the East Pacific rise towards the South American continent.

Horizontal displacements on a scale even larger than that observed on transcurrent faults are believed to have occurred in the form of "continental drift" and "sea-floor spreading." We now examine the evidence for these displacements.

Continental Drift

THE FIT OF THE ATLANTIC

The idea that continents, or some continents, have moved relative to each other is not new; it was in fact already suggested in the seventeenth century. The first comprehensive statement of what has become known as the theory of continental drift was enunciated by A. Wegener in 1911.

What started the idea is the extraordinary similarity in shape of the eastern and western coasts of the Atlantic Ocean. A glance at a map will suffice to show that these two coasts, both of which are roughly shaped as an "S," can be made to coincide by shifting the American continents eastward or, equivalently, shifting Europe and Africa westward. The bulge of Brazil, for instance, can be fitted into the Gulf of Guinea, while the bulge of Africa may fit against the southeastern coast of North America. It looks much as if the continental masses were originally joined and had later split along an S-shaped fracture following perhaps the axis of the Atlantic ridge; they then moved in opposite sense to open a gap now filled by the Atlantic Ocean floor.

When such a reconstruction is made on a suitable map projection that avoids angular distortions, it is found that the two coastlines do not coincide exactly. Nor should they be expected to do so, for the split, if it occurred, must have occurred some time ago (sediments of Cretaceous and late-Jurassic age are known to exist on the Atlantic floor), and coastlines do not remain unchanged very long. Because of wave erosion and sedimentation the present and initial coastlines might differ appreciably.

But continents do not stop at the coastline; the geophysical evidence indicates that continental crust extends seaward at least to the edge of the continental shelf and slope. Thus the fit of opposite sides of the Atlantic should be judged by comparing the edge of the continental shelf, or the base of the continental slope, or some intermediate contour, rather than the present coastline, since these are presumably less subject to change than the coastline itself. Carey showed how well Africa and South America fit together along the 200-meter contour (depth below sea level).

Bullard, Everett, and Smith have recently reexamined the fit in slightly different terms. There is a theorem of geometry known as the fixed-point theorem, to the effect that any displacement of a spherical surface over itself leaves one

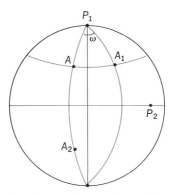

FIG. 13–1 *Translation of A to A_1 is equivalent to a rotation of ω around P_1. Translation of A to A_2 is equivalent to rotation about P_2.*

point fixed, so that any such displacement can be thought of as a rotation about some point on the surface. For instance, translation of point A in Figure 13–1 to A_1 along a parallel of latitude is equivalent to rotating it by an angle ω around P_1; and translation from A to A_2 is equivalent to a rotation about P_2. By trial and error, Bullard, Everett, and Smith determined the rotations that would best bring into coincidence the 500-fathom contour lines on opposite sides of the Atlantic. The fit so produced is indeed extraordinarily good (Figure 13–2). A noteworthy detail of the reconstruction is that Spain must first be rotated with respect to the rest of Europe; otherwise it overlaps North Africa. As we shall see, there is independent geological and paleomagnetic evidence for this displacement of Spain.

THE GEOLOGICAL ARGUMENT

If a continent splits, geological structures and events older than the split should match on opposite sides of the fracture. Thus, if Africa and South America are pieces of the same continent, the geology of the American side should match that of the African side up to the time of separation. For instance, ancient metamorphic provinces or igneous intrusions of the same age should be found at corresponding points, for which the geological history should be identical up to the time of their separation. The test is easier to apply negatively: If two areas have very different geological histories, it seems reasonable to

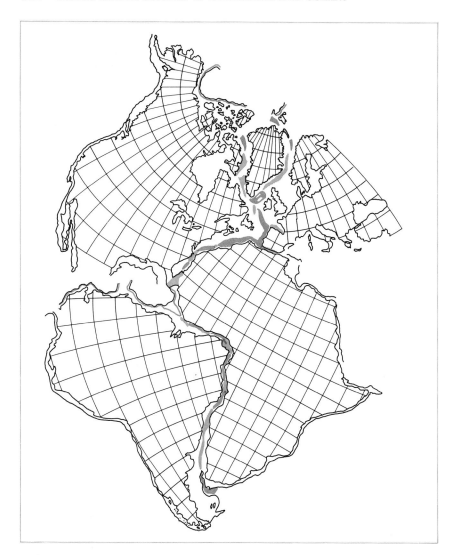

FIG. 13–2 *Fit of continents on opposite sides of the Atlantic Ocean. Black indicates areas where the 500-fathom contour lines on opposite sides of the Atlantic overlap, whereas in color-shaded areas the two do not quite touch. (After E. C. Bullard, J. E. Everett, and A. G. Smith, Phil. Trans. Roy. Soc. London, vol. A258, p. 41, 1965.)*

assume that they never were contiguous. If they have similar histories, they may or may not have been contiguous, for the same kind of igneous activity can occur simultaneously in very distant parts of the world, and similar sediments, similar deformation, or similar metamorphism may commonly be found in places that were never close together. To prove that two areas were once contiguous requires an overwhelming abundance of matching features, none of which should be ubiquitous, and all of which should be of corresponding ages.

Detailed matching of this kind has been found at some points on opposite shores of the South Atlantic. In northeastern Brazil, above and below the eastward coastal bulge at Recife, the almost continuously exposed rocks of the Precambrian shield yield two distinct patterns of radiometric dating. One event, almost limited to the northern part of the coast, is dated at 2000 m.y. The other event, which is uniformly displayed along the southern coastal sector, is late Precambrian. It is represented by ages, varying regularly according to the nature of the dated material (hornblende, biotite, whole rock) between 700 and 450 m.y. Precisely the same age pattern characterizes the opposite coast of West Africa; and in the rotated model of Figure 13–2, the Brazilian and African lines of junction between the two age provinces match perfectly. Structural trends in the Precambrian match equally well.

Similar matching of geological structures and ages can be made for the land masses bordering on the northern Atlantic (North America, Greenland, Europe, North Africa). The trend and structural histories of the Paleozoic fold mountain belts of eastern North America fit perfectly those of the corresponding belts in Europe and North Africa; dates of metamorphism and intrusion in Greenland fit equally well those of corresponding events in North America and northwestern Europe.

THE GONDWANA FORMATIONS AND LATE-PALEOZOIC GLACIATIONS   There occurs in India a thick sedimentary sequence, known as the Gondwana system, ranging in age from late Paleozoic to late Mesozoic. It consists mostly of nonmarine sediments, including coal; a few intercalated marine beds indicate deposition near sea level. The system has a distinctive fossil flora, known as the *Glossopteris* flora from a typical genus of seed fern. Similar formations with similar floras have been found in Australia, Madagascar, Africa (where they are known as the Karroo formation), Antarctica, the Falkland Islands, and portions of South America (mainly southern Brazil and northern Uruguay); these areas are known collectively as "Gondwanaland." Contemporaneous floras in other parts of the world are completely different.

Wherever it is found, the base of the Gondwana sequence includes thick tillites; in many places these tillites can be seen to rest on a striated, ice-grooved pavement of Precambrian rocks. These glacial deposits, locally interbedded with marine deposits, extend over very large areas, north and south of the present equator (up to 30°N in India) (Figure 13–3). Their age is hard to establish accurately, precisely because the associated flora and fauna are peculiar to these areas and difficult to place in the stratigraphic

column based on the nonglacial faunas of the rest of the world. It is generally agreed that the glacial episode or episodes started in middle-Carboniferous time and extended into the Permian.

The distribution of these glacial deposits is indeed peculiar with respect to present geography. If the climate were cold and wet enough to allow the development of glaciers at sea level on both sides of the equator, it should a fortiori be sufficiently cold and wet to allow a similar development of glaciers at mid-latitudes in the Northern Hemisphere, as in North America, Europe, and central Siberia, where Permian sediments (evaporites, red beds) indicate on the contrary dry and warm and locally desert-type conditions.

Present climatic zoning is roughly concentric about the poles and symmetrical with respect to the equator. The late-Paleozoic zoning is quite different; it has been suggested that the difference might have been caused by a displacement of the earth as a whole with respect to its rotation axis ("polar wandering"). One could perhaps imagine that in late-Paleozoic time the poles were displaced from their present position, so as to bring one of them close to the glaciated areas and to move the equatorial and adjacent arid regions northward into Europe and North America. While something of the sort may indeed have happened (the mechanics of polar wandering will be discussed on page 681), it remains true that the glaciated areas are spread over such enormous distances—from Antarctica to 30°N of the equator in India—that the glaciers must have spread at least 60° from one pole. Symmetry requires an equal spread around the other pole, of which there is no sign at all. The only sensible explanation proposed so far is that the glaciated areas were at that time much closer, together forming perhaps a single continent of Gondwana. This continent presumably was much closer to one pole than the Gondwanalands are today. Lack of symmetry could be explained if the other pole fell into what was then an oceanic area. It is interesting that the glacial evidence definitely requires continental displacement not only for continents bordering on the Atlantic Ocean, but also for Australia, Antarctica, and India. We also

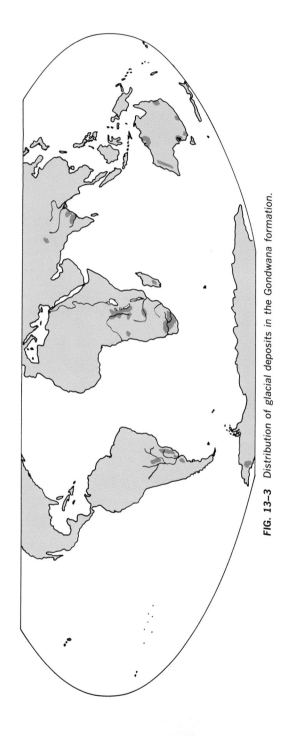

FIG. 13–3 *Distribution of glacial deposits in the Gondwana formation.*

note that these displacements must have occurred after deposition of the glacial formations and must therefore be of very late Paleozoic, Mesozoic, or Cenozoic age.

THE DISTRIBUTION OF AMPHIBIANS AND REPTILES
The similarity in terrestrial faunas and flora between distant land masses has been, on the whole, rather difficult to account for in the absence of continental drift. It is generally held that a new species appears by random mutation at one and only one point, from which it spreads out. Floating or free-swimming marine animals (for example, fishes) spread without difficulty and without particular regard to the geography of the coastlines, but the spreading of nonswimming terrestrial forms is not so easy to explain. The fauna of an isolated land mass tends to evolve in its own peculiar way. The indigenous mammalian fauna of Australia, for example, consists almost entirely of marsupials. This may reflect the fact that placental mammals, which evolved outside Australia, were unable to reach it because of the isolation of that continent. A case in point is that of Mesosaurus, a swimming reptile of fresh or brackish waters that has been found so far in the Gondwana formations of South America and Africa only; it has no close relatives anywhere. How did it ever get from one place to the other across the deep and wide Atlantic Ocean? If it could swim that distance, why isn't it also found elsewhere?

The paleontological argument for or against (mainly against) continental drift has, however, never been very conclusive, since it depends on assessing the differences or similarities between faunas at distant points. Such faunas are never identical even today, on the same continent. The problem is then to decide whether two fossil faunas are sufficiently close to demand land connections between the points where they are found, or whether they are sufficiently different not to require such connections.

The matter has recently been examined in a different context by Brown. It is well known that present-day faunas are distributed with greater abundance and more variety within tropical latitudes than elsewhere; for instance, many more species and genera of mollusks occur in the tropics than at high latitudes. This is also true of terrestrial faunas.

Brown has pointed out that the distribution of late-Paleozoic and early-Mesozoic amphibia and reptiles from all continents does not show this feature, as illustrated in Figure 13–4a, which gives as a histogram the number of genera plotted against present latitude of the fossil sites. On this

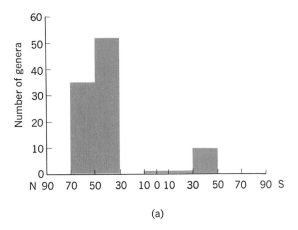

(a)

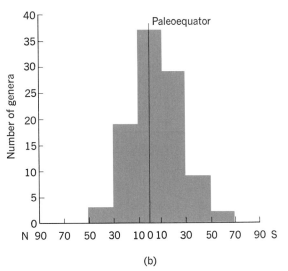

(b)

FIG. 13–4 Diversity of late-Paleozoic amphibia plotted against (a) present latitude of sites of occurrence, and (b) paleomagnetic latitudes of these sites. (After D. A. Brown, Australian J. Sci., vol. 30, p. 439, 1968.)

plot, diversity is clearly not maximum near the equator, nor is the distribution symmetrical with respect to the equator. If, on the other hand, the number of genera is plotted against the paleo-latitude,[6] the histogram (Fig. 13–4b) shows the expected maximum between 10°N and 10°S, and approximate symmetry of the two hemi-spheres. Such data provide convincing evidence that the sites where these fossil amphibians are found were *not* at their present latitude in late-Paleozoic time. Large amounts of drift are clearly implied.

Triassic reptiles (Figures 13–5a and b) show similar features in their distribution; plotted against present latitudes, diversity is again mini-mum at the equator, contrary to the expectation of nondrifters. The plot against paleomagnetic latitude does not show a maximum near the paleoequator, but does show a greatly increased diversity between 30°N and 30°S. When late-Paleozoic reptiles and Triassic amphibians are also considered,[7] the percentage of genera found between 0° and 30° rises from 17 (when plotted against present latitude) to 71 (when plotted against paleolatitude).

DISTRIBUTION OF SEDIMENTARY-ROCK TYPES Irving has assembled much evidence regarding the distribution of sedimentary rocks that are affected by climate and, hence, by latitude. Evaporites, for instance, are forming today only between latitudes of 10° and 50°. Carbonate rocks in general are thought to represent warm conditions; modern coral reefs, in particular, are restricted to latitudes of less than 30°, with 75 percent of them in latitudes of less than 20°. Fossil coral reefs, on the contrary, occur between

40°S and 80°N, with a maximum frequency of occurrence near 60°N. When plotted against paleolatitude, however, 90 percent of the occur-rences fall between 20°S and 30°N, and only 10 percent between 30°N and 50°N. Similarly, the paleodistribution of other carbonate rocks, and of evaporites, red beds, and desert sands, becomes more restricted in latitude, more symmetrical with respect to the equator, and thus easier to understand, when plotted against paleolatitude rather than present latitude. Here again we find strong indications that continents have not always been at their present latitudes.

PALEOMAGNETIC EVIDENCE

MAGNETIZATION OF ROCKS Some rocks acquire at the time of their formation a permanent, or "remanent," magnetization, the direction of which is, if the rock is magnetically isotropic, parallel to the earth's field at that place and time. The magnetization resides in a few magnetic minerals, mostly iron–titanium oxides such as magnetite (Fe_3O_4) and solid solutions of magne-tite and ulvospinel (Fe_2TiO_4), hematite (α-Fe_2O_3) and solid solutions of hematite and ilmenite ($FeTiO_3$), maghemite (γ-Fe_2O_3), goethite (α-Fe-OOH), and still other minerals. Remanent magne-tization may be acquired by several different processes, some of which are not completely un-derstood. Thermal remanent magnetization, for instance, is acquired during initial cooling of an igneous rock. Its intensity and stability (that is, resistance to demagnetization) depend on the occurrence, within the magnetic grains, of defects of various kinds and particularly of highly strained regions surrounding dislocations.

In addition to the original remanence, most rocks carry other components of magnetization acquired later, such as a "viscous" magnetization acquired in geologically recent times by expo-sure to the earth's present field. These subsidiary magnetizations are usually less resistant to arti-ficial demagnetization than the original reman-ence, so it is often possible to eliminate them by careful treatment in the laboratory and retrieve what is believed to be the original direction of the field. Measurements are carried out on specimens

---

[6] The paleolatitude is 90° minus the paleocolatitude p which is calculated from the paleomagnetic inclination i by the re-lation $\tan i = 2 \cot p$ (see page 678).

[7] But excluding Therapsids, which are advanced mammal-like forms of reptiles that may have had their own good reasons for preferring less tropical temperatures, as do present-day pen-guins. It must also be remembered that statistics of this kind may be biased by the fact that sampling is not uniform. Fos-siliferous formations of a given age do not occur everywhere and at all latitudes; where they occur they have not been searched for fossils with uniform thoroughness.

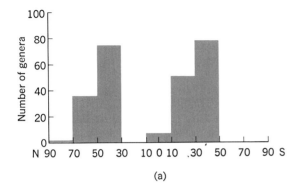

(a)

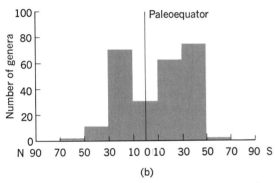

(b)

FIG. 13-5 *Diversity of Triassic reptiles plotted against (a) present latitude of sites of occurrence, and (b) paleomagnetic latitudes of these sites. (After D. A. Brown, Australian J. Sci., vol. 30, p. 440, 1968.)*

that have been collected with care and whose orientation with respect to geographical coordinates is known, so it is possible to determine from the measurements the inclination i and declination δ of the ancient field at the collecting site. Measurements are repeated on a large number of specimens (for example, eight or ten specimens from each lava flow, or from each sedimentary layer), and the mean direction is determined by a suitable averaging procedure, whereas the scatter of the observations may be described by an angle α_{95} such that there is a 95 percent probability that the true direction of the ancient field lies within the angle α_{95} from the observed mean. The angle α_{95} is small when directions of magnetization in the several specimens agree closely.

Directions of the field determined from lava flows erupted in recent years at sites where the direction of the field is known usually agree with the latter within less than 5°.

VIRTUAL GEOMAGNETIC POLES   At present, we recall, the direction of the field at any point on the earth's surface is approximately that of the field of a dipole located at the center of the earth and inclined at 11½ degrees to the rotation axis; the points where the dipole axis intersects the earth's surface are the geomagnetic poles. The actual direction of the field differs from that corresponding to the inclined dipole only by a small angle (everywhere less than 25°) which varies in time (secular variation). This variation is such as to suggest that the field, when averaged over a few thousand years, may perhaps be exactly dipolar; the average dipole itself appears, furthermore, to be aligned along the earth's rotation axis ("axial" dipole). There is at present no formal proof that this is always so, except that a spherical harmonic analysis of the Quaternary paleomagnetic data yields, for the nonaxial components of the dipole and nondipole terms, values that are small and statistically not significant.

We recall here an interesting feature of a dipole field (Figure 13-6). The corresponding magnetic potential W is

$$W = \frac{m \cos \theta}{r^2}$$

where **m** is the moment of the dipole. The components H_r and H_θ of the field are, respectively,

$$H_r = -\frac{\partial W}{\partial r} = \frac{2m \cos \theta}{r^3}$$

$$H_\theta = -\frac{1}{r}\frac{\partial W}{\partial \theta} = \frac{m \sin \theta}{r^3}$$

FIG. 13-6 *The field of a dipole of moment **m** is such that tan i = 2 cot θ.*

Hence the angle i that the field **H** makes with the normal to the radius vector **r** is

$$\tan i = \frac{H_r}{H_\theta} = 2 \cot \theta$$

Paleomagnetic directions for a given time are usually determined by sampling sedimentary formations in which the rate of deposition is relatively slow, or a sequence of lava flows erupted over an interval of time, or on slowly cooled igneous bodies. Thus the average direction of the field determined from the sampling has the character of a time average; it is, ideally, the average direction for the span of time involved in the accumulation of the sediment, or of the lava flows, or in the cooling of the pluton. If the time average of the earth's field is indeed dipolar, paleomagnetic data may be interpreted in the same way. Thus if δ and i are, respectively, the measured declination and inclination at site S_1, draw a great circle through S_1 making an angle δ with a meridian, and measure an arc p such that $\tan i = 2 \cot p$ (Figure 13–7). The point P_1 so determined is the intersection on the earth's surface of the axis of the centered dipole that would produce at S_1 a field with declination δ and inclination i; it is called the "virtual geomagnetic pole for S_1."

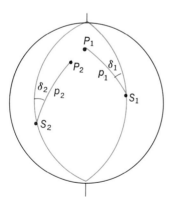

FIG. 13–7 *Virtual geomagnetic pole P_1 corresponding to a measured declination δ_1 and inclination i_1 at site S_1 (tan $i_1 = 2 \cot p_1$). The virtual geomagnetic pole P_2 corresponding to declination δ_2 and inclination i_2 measured at S_2 on rocks of the same age should coincide exactly with P_1 if the field is dipolar and no errors of any kind occur in the measurements.*

The assumption that the earth's field was dipolar can be tested by sampling at a second site S_2 of the same age, which, should yield a virtual pole P_2 coinciding with P_1. Virtual poles rarely do coincide exactly, for several reasons.

1. In the first place, measurements at S_1 and S_2 are affected by errors of various kinds (in the orientation of the specimens, in the determination of the direction of magnetization of each specimen, in the elimination of unwanted viscous components of magnetization, and so forth) so that the mean directions determined at S_1 and S_2 are somewhat uncertain. The scatter of individual measurements at a site is measured by, say, the angle α_{95} to which corresponds a probable error in the position of the virtual pole; thus one can draw around it an "oval of confidence" such that there is certain probability (say 95 percent) that the virtual pole corresponding to the true direction at the site will fall within the oval. If the ovals of confidence for P_1 and P_2 overlap, there is a finite probability that P_1 and P_2 do, in fact, coincide.

2. Apart from experimental errors, P_1 and P_2 might not coincide because sampling at S_1 and S_2 may not cover exactly the same span of geologic time and, conceivably, the earth's field may have changed in between.

3. Finally, the time span covered at S_1 or S_2, or both, may not be sufficient to average out completely the nondipole components of the field or, conceivably, the average field may not be exactly dipolar. As it turns out, virtual poles for the same geologic period usually agree within $10°$ or $12°$, when determined from sites on the the same continent.

DISTRIBUTION OF VIRTUAL POLES AND EVIDENCE FOR CONTINENTAL DISPLACEMENTS   Virtual geomagnetic poles determined for Quaternary rocks from all parts of the world cluster around, and close to, the present geographical pole, as if the average geomagnetic field for that period were indeed indistinguishable from that of an axially centered dipole. As mentioned above, a spherical harmonic analysis of the data that does not assume the dipolar nature of the field leads to the same conclusion.

The fact that the average Quaternary geomagnetic pole coincides with the geographic pole rather than with the present geomagnetic pole which, as we recall, lies 11½ degrees from the former, is of considerable theoretical interest. As pointed out in Chapter 11, of all the forces that may act on the fluid in the earth's core and determine its motion, forces (for example, Coriolis force) derived from the earth's rotation are likely to be among the largest; one expects therefore that if the motion, and the magnetic field induced by it, have any symmetry at all, they should be symmetrical about the axis of rotation. The Quaternary paleomagnetic data suggest that the geomagnetic pole averaged over a sufficient length of time is, in fact, indistinguishable from the pole of rotation.

Late Tertiary paleomagnetic data, although still relatively scanty, confirm the same general picture but data for earlier times show quite different features, perhaps best illustrated by the results for the late Mesozoic shown in Figure 13–8. These poles generally depart significantly from the present geographic pole; in addition, significant differences appear between poles from different continents. Figure 13–8 for instance, shows how poles determined from North America, Africa, and Australia[8] differ as to their grouping around significantly different mean poles.[9] These differences are unlikely to arise from a failure of the dipolar hypothesis on which the concept of virtual poles is based, for virtual poles from the same continent continue to agree among themselves as they could not if the field were multipolar. The simplest explanation for the intercontinental discrepancy is that some or all of the continents involved have moved since

their rocks became magnetized in a dipolar field. It is easy to see how continental displacement could lead to scatter of the poles determined for separate continents: Since the inclination at a site is a measure of the angular distance of the site to the pole at the time of magnetization, any displacement of the site toward or away from the pole will displace its virtual pole by an equal amount.

A substantial number of paleomagnetic results are available for sedimentary red beds and igneous rocks of Permian age. The scatter of virtual poles from single continents (intracontinental dispersion) is somewhat larger than the corresponding scatter of Cretaceous poles, but it is significantly less than the scatter that is observable when poles from several continents (intercontinental scatter) are compared (Figure 13–9a).

The Permian data for continents bordering on the Atlantic offer the possibility of a significant test. We recall that the glacial evidence requires much, if not all, of the continental displacements to have occurred since the Permian. Suppose that the post-Permian displacements are precisely those (although of opposite sense) calculated by Bullard, Everett, and Smith (Figure 13–2), and apply to the Permian virtual poles these same reverse rotations. If the hypothesis of opening of the Atlantic by continental displacement (or rotation) is correct, the intercontinental scatter should be appreciably reduced by the rotation. As it turns out, these reverse rotations do reduce the intercontinental scatter to the level of the intracontinental one (Figure 13–9b). It is difficult to believe that this result could be purely coincidental; the authors of this book prefer to interpret it as confirmation of the hypothesis of continental drift.

A further point of interest may be noted. The reconstruction shown in Figure 13–2 requires that Spain be rotated with respect to the rest of Europe, so as to close the Bay of Biscay by bringing the northern Atlantic coast of Spain close to the southern coast of Brittany. A similar rotation of Spain had previously been deduced by Carey on purely tectonic grounds. What few paleomagnetic data exist for the Permian of Spain confirm

[8] There is yet a regrettable lack of paleomagnetic data for Europe and South America. Unmetamorphosed Cretaceous rocks in Europe are mostly limestones and chalk, which carry little or no stable remanence.

[9] An interesting exception occurs for the single virtual pole for Madagascar, which falls in the North American group rather than in the African group. This may suggest that in Cretaceous times Madagascar was already separated from Africa and has moved independently from it.

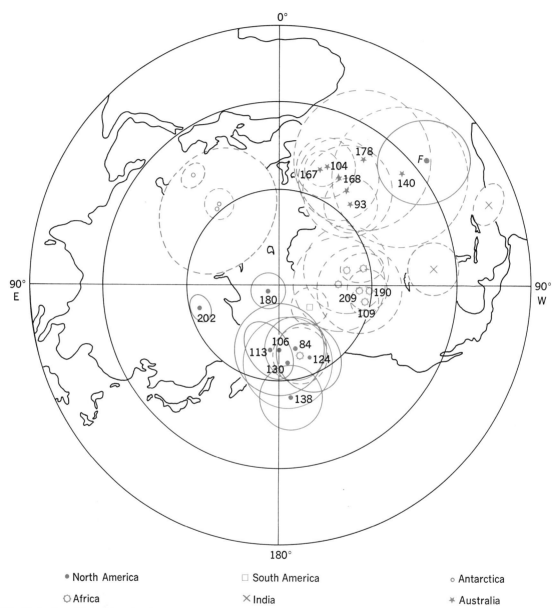

FIG. 13–8 *Late Mesozoic poles from several continents. Radiometric ages (in millions of years) are given when available. Circles and ovals around each pole are such that there is a 95 percent probability that the true pole lies within the circle or oval. Where circles overlap it cannot be assumed that the corresponding poles differ significantly. The pole marked F, which departs significantly from the other results from North America, is from the Franciscan formation of California; the corresponding sites are in a tectonically much disturbed area. (From C. S. Grommé, R. T. Merrill, and J. Verhoogen, J. Geophys. Res., vol. 72 pp. 5661–5177, 1967.)*

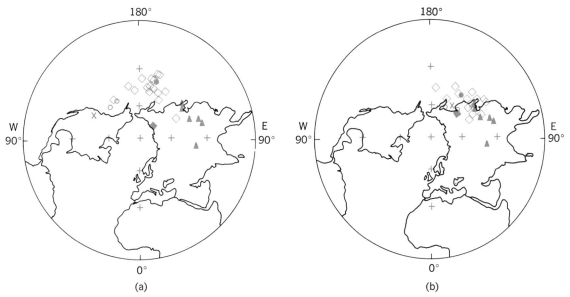

FIG. 13–9 (a) Permian virtual geomagnetic poles. (b) Permian poles after rotation of continents as required to close the Atlantic (see Figure 12–2). Symbols are as follows: open diamond, Europe and Asia, except Spain; open circle, Spain; solid triangle, North America; solid diamond, South America; solid circle, Greenland; cross, Africa. (After J. M. Wells and J. Verhoogen, J. Geophys. Res., vol. 72, pp. 1777–1781, 1967.)

this movement: Virtual poles for Spain, which disagree with other European poles before rotation (see Figure 13–9a), agree better with other poles after this additional rotation. It would thus seem that paleomagnetic data can be used also to determine intracontinental deformation. A similar result has been obtained in Japan, where some Cretaceous and earlier paleomagnetic results from the southwestern part of the main island of Honshu seem to disagree with those determined from the northeastern end of the same island, as if the island itself had been bent into its present arcuate shape in post-Cretaceous times.

Note that the reconstruction shown in Figure 13–9b assumes that North America remained fixed, all other continents moving in relation to it. This is only one among an infinite number of possibilities, for if all continents have moved, it is unlikely that North America did not move also. The region in the western Pacific into which poles from all continents seem to cluster after the in-

verse rotation is therefore not necessarily where the geomagnetic pole happened to lie at that time.

Polar Wandering

As shown in Figure 13–8, and in striking contrast to results for the Quaternary, none of the late Mesozoic poles coincides with the geographic pole. The discrepancy may have two causes. (1) It is possible that the late Mesozoic geomagnetic pole was indeed close to the present geographic pole, but that all continents have moved; North America, for instance, could have moved so as to carry its virtual pole some 30° to the south to where we now find it. (2) Alternatively, it is possible that the late-Mesozoic geomagnetic pole was displaced from the present rotational axis. This alternative is known as "polar wandering." Since it is unlikely that the rotation axis and dipolar axis differed by more than a few degrees, this alternative requires displacement of the rotational axis as well.

If polar wandering has occurred, all continents but one must necessarily have moved (since they show different virtual poles), and they may all have moved. This makes it impossible, in the absence of further information, to discover where the pole was.

MECHANICS OF POLAR WANDERING

Whether polar wandering is mechanically possible or not is still being debated. The argument centers on the rheological properties of the earth. We now give an elementary discussion of the subject.

As long as no external torque is applied to the earth, the angular-momentum vector, which for all practical purposes is indistinguishable from the axis of rotation, remains fixed in space.[10] The orientation of the body relative to that fixed axis may, however, change. It is useful to remember that polar wandering refers to a movement of the whole earth relative to its axis of rotation, which remains fixed in space.

A rigid body can rotate stably around a principal axis of inertia; for given angular momentum kinetic energy is minimum when the rotation is about the axis of maximum inertia; that is, the axis from which the masses forming the body are, on the whole, more distant (C-axis). The "pole of figure" is, by definition, the intersection of the C-axis on the earth's surface.

Any displacement of mass (for example, uplift of a mountain range or displacement of a continent) in or on the earth may change the position of the C-axis, which will no longer coincide with the rotational axis. It can then be shown that the C-axis will describe a cone in space about the rotation axis,[11] corresponding to a "wobble" of the earth, until dissipation of energy by internal friction brings the new C-axis back to the axis of rotation. Theoretically, this wobble could have any amplitude; conceivably the earth could topple over by 90°, if the change in mass distribution were large enough and such as to make the old axis of minimum inertia become the new axis of maximum inertia.

It is unlikely, however, that this would ever happen, for the following reason: The position of the present C-axis is overwhelmingly determined by the earth's flattening and equatorial bulge. As long as the bulge remains fixed, no conceivable geological change is likely to be large enough to move the C-axis by more than a fraction of a degree. (Compare the additional mass on the earth's surface represented by an ordinary mountain range to the mass of the equatorial bulge itself.) The equatorial bulge, by its sheer size, stabilizes the earth's rotation about its present axis. But the equatorial bulge is itself a result of centrifugal force (this is, of the earth's rotation); and if the earth wobbles with respect to its axis of rotation, the direction and magnitude of the centrifugal force at any point will change. Suppose that a very small displacement of C has taken place, so that when C has fallen back on R (the axis of rotation), the earth has turned very slightly with respect to R. The direction of the centrifugal force at every point (always directed outwards from R) has also changed very slightly. If the earth were completely rigid and undeformable, nothing more would happen, but if the earth is easily deformed, the equatorial bulge will respond to the slight change in centrifugal force and also move, so its stabilizing influence vanishes and the earth behaves as if the bulge were not there at all. In such a case, a relatively small displacement of mass on the earth's surface could entail a relatively large displacement of the earth with respect to R, which, as we recall, remains fixed in space.

Polar wandering on a large scale (tens of degrees) is thus virtually impossible on a rigid undeformable earth, but possible on an earth sufficiently weak and inviscid to permit its bulge to adjust to the instantaneous position of the rotation axis.

---

[10] This is a consequence of Newton's laws, for the rate of change in time of the angular momentum equals the applied torque, just as the rate of change of the linear momentum equals the applied force.

[11] Equivalently, the pole of figure circles about the pole of rotation. A motion of this kind is observed as the "variation of latitude" (see Chapter 4).

How does the earth effectively behave? Controversy on this matter has raged back and forth. At the present time, there seems to be a consensus of opinion that polar displacement on a large scale is improbable because of the very high apparent viscosity of the lower mantle inferred from the difference between the actual flattening of the earth and a calculated hydrostatic flattening; but, as noted on page 612, other interpretations are possible.

The paleomagnetic data themselves may offer some confirmation of the stability of the earth's axis. It turns out that all Australian rocks from Permian to early Cenozoic in age tested so far have a very steep and nearly constant inclination. If the pole moved during that interval of time, Australia must have moved at precisely the same rate and in a direction such as to remain at the same angular distance from it. African data (Figure 13–8) also indicate a nearly constant inclination from Triassic, or earlier, to late-Cretaceous times; and a similar constancy in the apparent position of the pole for North America seems to have prevailed throughout Cretaceous time (140–80 m.y.). Rather than assume that, by an extraordinary coincidence, all three continents were moving at the right speed in the right direction to keep up with the polar displacement, it seems simpler to infer that neither the pole nor the continents moved during the indicated spans of time. Since, however, the pole did move relative to North America between the Permian and the Cretaceous, whereas the Australian data require it to be fixed in that interval of time, the former displacement must be entirely due to motion of the North American continent. Thus continents certainly move while poles possibly do not. If indeed poles do not move, rates of motion of continents towards and away from the poles can be determined from paleomagnetic data; they usually turn out to be of the order of a fraction of a degree per million years, or a few centimeters per year. The general agreement as to order of magnitude between this rate of drift determined from paleomagnetic data and that determined from other data (for example, the present width of the Atlantic Ocean) is encouraging. It also appears as if separate continents moved at different times and intermittently, with episodes of relatively rapid motion alternating with periods of rest. Australia, for instance, seems to have moved significantly in the lower Carboniferous, and then again in the Cenozoic, but not between those times; and Africa also appears to have remained fixed for some 150 m.y. in the Mesozoic. Much more information will be needed before a consistent picture of continental displacement can be pieced together; yet it appears that paleomagnetic studies may provide the necessary data.

Much paleomagnetic work remains to be done on the history of the several continents prior to the breakup of Gondwanaland in late-Permian or post-Permian times and to the opening of the North Atlantic. Paleomagnetic data indicate considerable movement of Africa with respect to the pole (or vice versa) throughout the Precambrian. It will be interesting to see if the movement pattern for Africa agrees with that of the other fragments of Gondwanaland; if not, it will be necessary to conclude that the present continents, or parts of them, moved independently prior to their coming together. Wilson has indeed suggested on geological grounds that an ancestral Atlantic Ocean may have closed before reopening along slightly different lines. In this manner, North America may have carried off fragments of what was once Europe, and North Africa may now encompass land that was previously attached to North America.

Sea-Floor Spreading

MAGNETIC ANOMALIES ON THE OCEAN FLOOR

The recent discovery of a regular pattern of magnetic anomalies on the ocean floor has added much weight to the suggestion, originally put forth by Holmes, Hess, and Dietz, that the ocean floor generally moves away from the axis of an oceanic ridge where new crust is forming.

A magnetic anomaly, like a gravity anomaly, is the difference between the observed value of the field and a predicted value. The predicted value of the magnetic field at a point may be calculated from the spherical harmonic coefficients (Chapter 11) derived from worldwide measurements, or interpolated smoothly from these measurements. An anomaly is therefore a local feature. It is said to be positive if the local field is stronger than the predicted field, and negative otherwise. Anomalies are due to local causes, such as local variation in the intensity or direction of magnetization of crustal rocks.

The anomaly pattern along the oceanic ridges consists of a number of bands that run parallel to the ridge crest on either side of it and are alternatively positive and negative (Figure 13–10). Differences in intensity of the field between adjacent belts are generally of the order of a few hundred gammas at sea level. The anomalies appear to be caused by the juxtaposition of elongated blocks or zones where crustal rocks (basaltic lava flows or dikes) are magnetized alternatively in the sense of the present earth's field and in the opposite sense (Figures 13–11 and 13–12). This pattern is very widespread. It extends, for instance, throughout the Atlantic Ocean on both sides of the central ridge almost

(but not quite) to the base of the continental slope. It is also found along the East Pacific rise, the Pacific–Antarctic ridge, in the Indian Ocean, and in the northeastern Pacific where it appears along the Juan de Fuca and Gorda ridges. The pattern shows extraordinary regularity and continuity, as successive magnetic highs and lows can be correlated over long distances and from one ocean ridge to another. In many instances, the pattern is extraordinarily symmetrical about the ridge axis; peaks of equal height and equal width are found at equal distances on both sides of the axis. Clearly some global process of great regularity must be involved. The probable explanation of this pattern has come from unrelated observations of reversals of the earth's field.

FIELD REVERSALS

A fundamental assumption of paleomagnetism, well supported by laboratory experiments and by measurements on lavas erupted in recent years, is that the remanent magnetization of rocks is parallel to the field that induced it. Yet

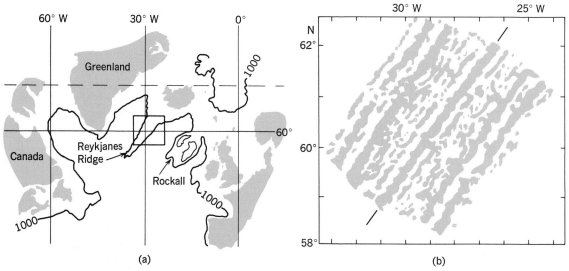

FIG. 13–10 *The sketch map on the left shows the location of the Reykjanes ridge, a portion of the North Atlantic ridge southwest of Iceland. The magnetic pattern is shown on the right. Dark areas indicate positive magnetic anomalies. Straight lines indicate the axis of the ridge and the central positive anomaly. (From F. J. Vine, Science, vol. 154, p. 1407, 1966. Copyright 1966. American Association for the Advancement of Science.)*

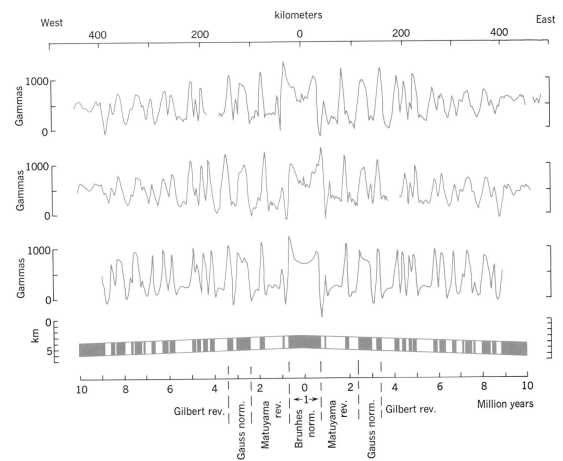

FIG. 13-11 *Interpretation of magnetic anomalies. The* **middle** *curve shows a magnetic profile across the Pacific–Antarctic ridge (the south-western extension of the East Pacific rise) near 50°S, 120°W. The intensity of the anomalous field is plotted against distance from the axis of the ridge. The scale is at the top; east is on the right. The* **top** *curve is the same profile reversed; that is, west is on the right. A comparison of these two profiles shows that the magnetic pattern is nearly perfectly symmetrical about the Ridge axis. The* **bottom** *curve is the calculated anomaly profile that would be produced by parallel strips of the oceanic crust that alternatingly carry normal and reversed remanant magnetizations. Normal blocks are shown in dark shading. The axis of the ridge corresponds to a wide block normally magnetized. By comparison with Figure 13-13, the Jaramillo and Olduvai events are readily recognized in the magnetic profiles. The time scale at the bottom corresponds to a spreading rate of 4.5 cm/year. (After W. C. Pitman III and J. R. Heirtzler, Science, vol. 154, p. 1166, 1966. Copyright 1966. American Association for the Advancement of Science.)*

it was found as early as 1906 by Brunhes,[12] and later by Matuyama, that some rocks may carry a remanence directed at about 180° to the expected direction. Such "reversely" magnetized rocks have now been found to occur abundantly in formations of almost all geological ages.

The simplest explanation for such reversals is that the earth's field occasionally reverses its polarity; that is, the electric currents in the core that produce it occasionally flow, so to speak,

---

[12] Alexander von Humboldt described in 1797 the reversed magnetization of a mountain in the Fichtelgebirge of Germany.

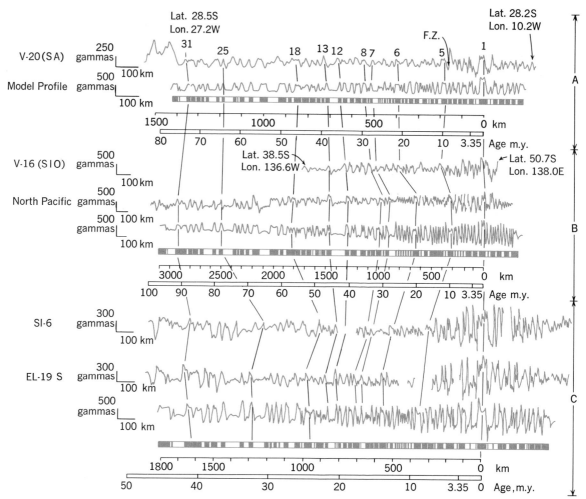

FIG. 13–12 *A comparison of magnetic profiles across several ridges. The top profile SA is across the South Atlantic. SIO means South Indian Ocean. The bottom profile EL-19S is the one shown in Figure 13–11; the profile SI-6 is in the same area. The ridge axis is indicated by the dashed vertical line on the right. The pattern of normally and reversely magnetic blocks, 2 km thick, is the same in all cases, except that the horizontal scale differs because of different spreading rates. The recurrence in all observed and calculated profiles of certain conspicuous features is easily noted. Broken lines indicate some possible correlations. (From J. R. Heirtzler, G. O. Dickson, E. M. Herron, W. C. Pitman III, and X. LePichon, J. Geophys. Res., vol. 73, p. 2120, 1968.)*

backwards relative to their present sense. However, it can be shown experimentally that some materials may acquire a magnetization directed at 180° to the ambient field; a rock (a dacite from Mt. Haruna, in Japan) was indeed found which has this property of "self-reversal." A large

number of mechanisms may theoretically lead to self-reversal; some of these require the presence of two magnetic phases (or minerals) with somewhat different properties (for example, Curie points). Others depend intricately on the distribution of magnetic ions (Fe^{2+}, Fe^{3+}) among different types of lattice sites in a magnetic phase, and on the relative strength of the magnetic interactions between ions on different sites. For instance, solid solutions of α-Fe_2O_3 (hematite) and $FeTiO_3$ (ilmenite) in a certain compositional range turn out to be self-reversing, to a degree that depends on their degree of ordering with respect to Fe and Ti.

There is an elegant method of demonstrating that all reversed rocks are not self-reversing and that field reversals do occur. A field reversal is a phenomenon that must affect the whole earth; thus all rocks (except self-reversing ones) that become magnetized at a time when the field is reversed should be reversed, regardless of where they occur. Since, on the contrary, self-reversal is a property that depends on the physical and chemical state of the rock and on its thermal history (as it affects the degree of ordering, for instance), there is no reason why all rocks of the same age should be reversed. Synchroneity of reversed rocks would be a sufficient proof of field reversal.

Experimentally, the proof of synchroneity is difficult, because it requires extremely precise dating. Paleomagnetic data show that if the field has reversed once, it has done so many times. The evidence is that in a vertical section through a thick pile of superposed lava flows, one generally finds several zones, consisting each of one or more flows, in which the polarity is alternatively normal and reversed. The time represented by all flows in one zone is not exactly known, but may be very short, of the order of 10^5 years or less. Thus to prove synchroneity of reversed flows in different parts of the world one has to date these flows within 10^5 years or better. The best accuracy attainable by the K-A method in radiometric dating of young rocks is only about 3 percent. It is also difficult to find rocks that are at once suitable for precise dating (that is, unweathered) and for the determination of their original remanence—rocks that are magnetically "hard," and unlikely, judging from their composition and magnetic behavior, to be self-reversing.

Much painstaking work has produced some remarkable results, however, and demonstrated the occurrence of field reversals. It turns out, for

instance, that all rocks younger than 7×10^5 years have normal polarity[13]; all those of age between 1.0 and 1.6×10^6 years are reversed, and so on. It has, in fact, been possible to establish a chronology of reversals, as shown in Figure 13–13.

It will be noted from Figure 13–13 that the length of time during which the field maintains a given polarity is variable: there are relatively long "epochs," of the order of 10^6 years (e.g., the Brunhes normal epoch), and relatively short "events," of the order of 10^4-10^5 years (e.g., the Jamarillo event). Needless to say that events of much shorter duration may go unrecorded, merely because suitable rocks of the right age have not yet been found. As seen in Figure 13–13, the field has reversed its polarity about 20 times in the past 3 million years; but the frequency of reversals does not appear constant. For about 50 million years, starting in the Upper Carboniferous, as far as we know the field maintained the same polarity.

The time it takes for the field to switch from one polarity to the other appears to be very short (of the order of 10^3-10^4 years)—so short, in fact, that flows erupted during a switch are relatively rare. Such flows generally show very scattered directions and a greatly reduced intensity of magnetization. Thus, during the switch the main dipole moment of the earth actually appears to go to zero before changing sign, leaving only an irregular multipole field, which is, however, probably more intense than the multipolar (or nondipolar) part of the present field.

The cause of the field reversals is not understood any more than we understand the origin of the field itself (see Chapter 11). On general grounds, one can say from the nature of the equations that govern the field (Maxwell's equations, as applied to the particular case of the core) that the field could be of either sign: If $H(x, y, z, t)$ is a solution of the equations, so is $-H$. Since both polarities are, at least in theory, equally probable, it is perhaps not too surprising

---

[13] With the possible exception of a very short interval of time some 30,000 years ago.

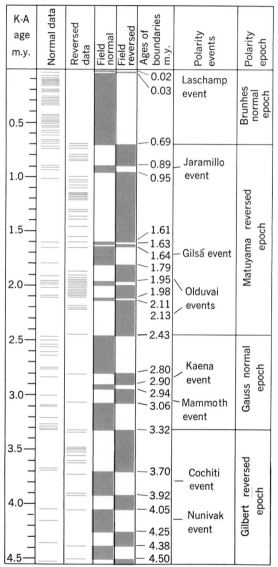

K-A age m.y.	Normal data	Reversed data	Field normal	Field reversed	Ages of boundaries m.y.	Polarity events	Polarity epoch
					0.02 0.03	Laschamp event	Brunhes normal epoch
0.5					0.69		
1.0					0.89 0.95	Jaramillo event	Matuyama reversed epoch
1.5					1.61 1.63 1.64 1.79	Gilsá event	
2.0					1.95 1.98 2.11 2.13	Olduvai events	
2.5					2.43		Gauss normal epoch
3.0					2.80 2.90 2.94 3.06	Kaena event Mammoth event	
3.5					3.32		Gilbert reversed epoch
4.0					3.70 3.92 4.05 4.25	Cochiti event Nunivak event	
4.5					4.38 4.50		

FIG. 13–13 *Time scale for reversals of the earth's field. (From Allan Cox, Science, vol. 163, p. 240, 1969. Copyright 1969. American Association for the Advancement of Science.)*

that both should occur. One can construct simple electrical machinery to produce a field that oscillates between two opposite polarities.

The chronology of reversals deduced from recent lava flows and shown in Figure 13–13 has

been confirmed in all essential aspects by the study of the magnetization of deep-sea sediments. In drill cores brought up from the ocean bottom one can see a succession of zones of alternatingly normal and reversed polarity. Some cores confirm exactly the succession of epochs and events of Figure 13–13, whereas in other cores some of the events seem to be missing, perhaps because of interrupted sedimentation. In still other cores there may be evidence for short events still unrecorded on land. The dating of deep-sea sediments is notoriously difficult but, for what paleontological evidence there is (for example, succession of "warm" and "cold" faunas corresponding to climatic changes), the sedimentary time scale for reversals seems to be approximately right. Conversely, the time scale of Figure 13–13 can be used to date sediments if the correlation of epochs and events is clear. Since the thickness of the magnetic zones is easily measured, rates of sedimentation can be obtained. They appear to be irregular, changing by a factor of 2 or 3 from core to core, or within a single core.

SPREADING OF THE OCEAN FLOOR

We now return to the magnetic-anomaly pattern of the ocean floor. Suppose that highs and lows are caused by and represent, respectively, strips of normally and reversely magnetized blocks of oceanic crust. The succession of highs and lows along a profile perpendicular to the ridge axis thus represents a succession in space of N (normal) and R (reversed) rocks. The magnetic stratigraphy of Figure 13–13 represents such a succession in time. Vine and Matthews suggested in 1963 that the two might be correlated in the following fashion.

Suppose that hot mantle material rises to the surface at the crest of the ridge, where it cools and acquires a remanence corresponding to the polarity of the field at the time, say N. Suppose that this material is then pushed aside, on both sides, by new material that is continuously coming up. If at time T_0 the field reverses, all material erupted after T_0 will be R; a later switch at time T_1 to normal polarity produces again normally magnetized rocks. At some still later time, the reversed material produced from T_0 to T_1 will find itself at some distance from the ridge axis, and cause a negative band of magnetic anomaly, the width of which will, if the rate of motion is steady, be proportional to $T_0 - T_1$.

This is, in fact, what is generally observed (Figures 13–11 and 13–12). The anomaly over the crest of the ridge is positive $(+)$ corresponding to the N polarity of the present field. On either side of it occurs a narrow negative band that could well correspond to the short Jamarillo event. Next to this on the outward side is a narrow $(+)$ band, followed by a wide $(-)$ band that could represent the Matuyama epoch. The N polarity of the Olduvai event is again conspicuous; and so on. The similarity of the temporal and spatial distributions of N and R polarities is very striking indeed.

The hypothesis assumes, essentially, that new oceanic crust is continuously being formed at the crest of a ridge and is continuously being pushed or pulled aside. The rate of motion can be found from the magnetic chronology: If an event that occurred t years ago is now found at a distance x from the ridge axis, the rate of motion is x/t. The rate of spreading so found turns out to be of the order of a few centimeters per year although it varies from ridge to ridge and along the same ridge. It is about 1.0 cm/year in the North Atlantic, about 6 cm/year for the East Pacific rise.

The magnetic pattern extends much farther out from the ridge axis than would correspond to the 3×10^6 years of the magnetic stratigraphy; in some instances it has been followed over distances of several thousand kilometers. If the rate of spreading has been constant in time, as it appears to have been in the Quaternary, the ocean floor offers a complete magnetic record of reversals for the past 10^8 years or so—that is, back into the Cretaceous. The assumption of constant spreading rate cannot, however, be strongly supported without additional proof.

Formation of new crust at the crest of oceanic ridges implies that either the earth is expanding or equivalent amounts of old crust are destroyed elsewhere. The former alternative is unlikely, judging from the present asymmetry in the dis-

tribution and activity of the ridges. The total length of the ridges, and their rate of motion, is much greater in the Southern Hemisphere than in the Northern Hemisphere; furthermore, the motion away from the ridge axis is dominantly east–west. Thus all great circles do not increase in length at the same rate, and the earth would be distorted assymetrically with respect to the plane of the equator. It thus seems preferable to assume that crustal material also moves downward at approximately the rate at which new crust forms. Loci of sinking or downward motion may be regions of compression (as in recent fold mountain belts) where downward moving convection currents converge, or the fracture zones (also called "Benioff" and "Gutenberg" zones) on which intermediate and deep earthquake loci lie. These zones, as will be recalled, dip at approximately 45° below continents or island areas; their updip extension intersects the surface approximately at the position of oceanic trenches.

Trenches, or fold mountain belts parallel to the coastline are conspicuously absent on both sides of the Atlantic (with the exception of the Puerto Rico trench). This suggests, but doesn't prove, the absence of downward motion of the sea floor in the Atlantic. Continents bordering on it appear therefore to be carried or rafted along with the sea floor itself, accounting thus for continental drift and the progressive widening of the Atlantic Ocean. Alternatively, it is possible that one side of the Atlantic (for example, the eastern side) remains stationary while the axis of the ridge itself migrates westward at precisely the rate at which new crust spreads out on its eastern side. By both of these hypotheses, North and South America would presently be rafted westward over the floor of the Pacific. This suggests that continental motion is not limited to the continental crust itself; more probably an appreciable thickness (100 or 200 kilometers or more) of the upper mantle participates in the motion.

The hypothesis of continuous creation of oceanic crust accounts for the small thickness of sediments on the ocean floor. Accumulating sediments, in this hypothesis, are continuously carried away by the moving crust which has been aptly described as a "conveyor belt with a built-in magnetic tape recorder." The thickness of sediments, and the age of the oldest sediments should gradually increase with distance from the axis of the nearest ridge. This is roughly what is observed, although the rather sudden increase in sediment thickness at a short distance from the axis of the Atlantic ridge may suggest discontinuous rather than continuous motion. It is also remarkable that the motion of the crust could occur without any visible distortion of the sediments it carries and which are everywhere found to lie perfectly flat, even in the Peru–Chile trench, where the crust is assumed to be thrust under South America.

A striking picture of what may be happening has recently been presented by Morgan, and by Le Pichon. Both these authors assume that an outer shell[14] of the earth can be divided into a small number (six, according to Le Pichon) of rigid blocks that move more or less independently as they are rafted along; these blocks are jostled about much as gigantic ice floes. Where two blocks move apart, an oceanic ridge forms and new crust is produced; where two blocks move towards each other, either shortening and compression produce a fold mountain belt, or crust is destroyed as one block is thrust under the other. Outlines of these blocks are shown in Figure 13–14. The geometry of the motion is worked out as follows: We recall that any displacement in a sphere is equivalent to a rotation about a vertical or radial axis intersecting the surface of the sphere at a point called a center of rotation. If two blocks move apart, their relative motion can be described as a rotation of one block with respect to the other, or as a rotation of the two blocks in opposite sense. The center of rotation corresponding to the motion that opens an oceanic ridge may be found in two ways: (1) Since the transform faults that intersect the ridge represent the direction of spreading away from the ridge axis, all such faults must lie on small circles centered on the center of rotation. (2) The rate of spreading at a point along the

ridge must vary as the sine of the angular distance from the center of rotation to that point. Wherever spreading rates, determined from the chronology of magnetic reversals, are sufficiently well-known, centers of rotation determined by these two methods agree rather well. Rates of angular rotation of blocks found in this manner are of the order of one degree or less per million years.

Having determined thus the angular rate at which the Pacific block, say, moves away from the American block, and the rate at which the latter moves away from Eurasia, it is a relatively simple matter to determine, by vector addition, the rate at which Eurasia and the Pacific block move toward each other; and the same procedure can be used for all the other blocks. The directions of relative motion at a few points are shown in Figure 13–14, where the length of each arrow is proportional to the calculated present displacement rate; these rates all fall between 1 and 10 cm/year.

Starting from these data it should be possible to work backward in time and infer the relative positions of the blocks at some time in the past. This backward extrapolation is somewhat hazardous because, as it turns out, sea-floor spreading appears to be somewhat episodic, as already deduced from the distribution of sediments and the episodic character of continental drift (page 683). Centers of rotation also appear to move; the pattern of fracture zones in the northeast Pacific, for instance, seems to imply that the pattern of spreading has changed in the past ten million years. Le Pichon infers that during early Cenozoic time the main Pacific trenches were along the west coast of America and not along the coast of eastern Asia, where they are now.

Clearly, the validity of the results shown in Figure 13–14 is contingent on the validity of the initial assumption regarding the number of blocks and their boundaries; future work will probably reveal a somewhat more complicated pattern differing in many details from the present one. The assumption was also made that there is no internal deformation of the blocks themselves. Although it is true that large areas of the ocean floor are covered by flat-lying, undisturbed,

---

[14] We purposely avoid the term "crust," as the shell envisaged here may include a substantial part of the upper mantle.

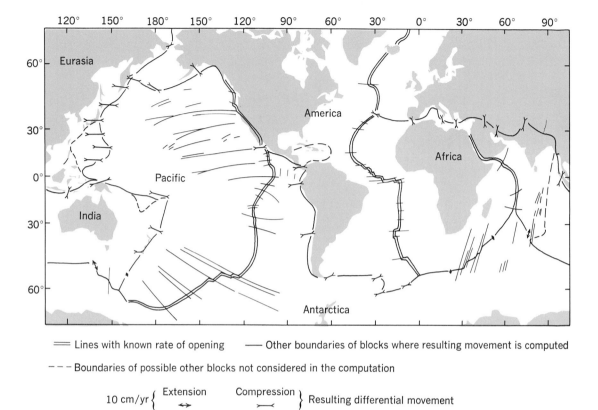

FIG. 13–14   *The boundaries of six blocks whose relative movements account for the opening of the oceanic ridges. The length of the arrows across the boundaries are proportional to the calculated rate of displacements, in cm/year. (From X. LePichon, J. Geophys. Res., vol. 73, p. 3675, 1968.)*

Cenozoic sediments, it would be difficult to assert that visible intracontinental deformation (for example, the African rift system) is unrelated to the displacement of the corresponding block.

This method of analysis, however, has two outstanding merits. In the first place, it forms a coherent frame in which continental drift, sea-floor spreading, and orogeny (for example, the genesis of the Alpine–Himalayan mountain belt) appear as different aspects of the same process. Secondly, it clearly shows in a global pattern how events at one place are related to events at all other places. Indeed, the amount and rate of compression at one point is related to the rate of spreading along all oceanic ridges; conversely, the rate of spreading at a particular point as a ridge is affected by the amount of compression, or crustal shortening, or destruction of crust, and the rate of production of new crust, everywhere else. The location of a rise, as in this model, is no longer necessarily fixed by some localized, deep-seated, thermal source, but is a concise statement of all relevant properties of the whole earth. Figure 13–15 clearly shows how most of what has happened in the past ten million years can be considered to be a general counterclockwise drift of the whole crust, relative to Antarctica.

The force that drives the plates is still unknown. Clearly, convection is involved: Hot material rises from the mantle to form new crust along a ridge, while old crust moves down somewhere into the mantle. But does this convection

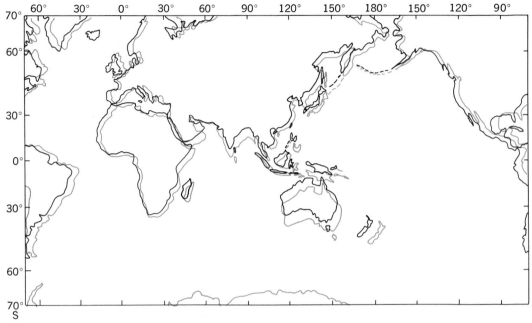

FIG. 13–15 *The lines in color show the position of the continents ten million years ago, assuming Antarctica has not moved. The reconstruction is based on the assumption that blocks have moved as shown in Figure 13–14, and that magnetic anomaly shown as No. 5 in Figure 13–12 is ten million years old. (From X. LePichon, J. Geophys. Res., vol. 73, p. 3682, 1968.)*

drive the motion of the plates, or is it driven by it? Does material rise along a ridge because that is where plates move apart and provide an opening, or is it the rising material that forces the plates apart? No detailed analysis has yet been made of the possible origin of forces other than thermally-driven convection.

Summary

We now attempt to summarize some features of the structural evolution of the earth's surface. It is a recurring theme of this book that each rock, each mountain range, and each continent is unique, in the sense that it has had its own peculiar and individual history. Generalizations are therefore difficult to make, and can be stated only in very broad terms. It is perhaps appropriate to repeat here the warning of Chapter 1 regarding the degree of certainty (or uncertainty) inherent in all, or most, geological statements.

The whole argument for continental drift would collapse if drilling into the Atlantic sea floor revealed the presence of extensive early-Paleozoic sediments. The case for ocean-floor spreading is largely based on the assumption that magnetic anomalies along the ridges are caused by rocks of alternating polarity whose ages fit the magnetic chronology of reversals; yet no samples of these rocks have yet been obtained and tested for polarity. The provisional nature of our conclusions must be clearly recognized; they should all be prefaced with the words "in the present state of our knowledge, it appears that . . ."

1. There is no clear-cut evidence that the total area of the continents has increased in time, although it appears likely that they have grown in volume. Additions from the mantle by volcanism and intrusion probably exceed the loss (by erosion) from the continents to the deep-sea floor.

2. Vertical displacements of small amplitude (~1 km) are ubiquitous in space and time. Dis-

placements of large amplitude (~ 10 km) are less common—or, at least, less commonly observed. They occur over limited areas and are generally associated with other modes of deformation.

3. Compression, once thought to be the dominant mode of deformation and the most important cause of structural evolution, is probably neither more widespread nor more frequent than extension or uplift.

4. It is still difficult, for lack of adequate data, to draw synoptic charts showing for the whole earth what was happening at each point at a given time. In some regions, as in Europe, periods of intense compressional deformation (fold mountain ranges) alternate with periods of quiescence. In other regions, such as along the west coast of North America, severe deformation of all types has occurred almost continuously, at least since the end of the Paleozoic. There is no clear-cut evidence for worldwide synchronous disturbances, even though a late-Paleozoic episode of orogeny affects very large areas of several continents. There is still no quantitative scale to measure the intensity of deformation at a given time; there is still no recognizable periodicity (see Chapter 4).

5. The most striking feature of the structural evolution of the earth's crust is the recurrence of very large (10^2–10^3-km) horizontal displacements. Large-scale transcurrent faulting, continental drift (now well-demonstrated), and seafloor spreading—all mutually related—are presumably different aspects of a single underlying planetary pattern of deformation.

6. The case for polar wandering is still not clear. Apparent displacements of the magnetic poles may be caused by displacements of the continents with respect to which they are observed. We still have no invariant frame of reference for the continents and poles.

THE SEARCH FOR A MECHANISM

There is abundant evidence that structural evolution is linked to heat flow. The association of high heat flow with the crestal areas of active oceanic ridges is striking. We mentioned in Chapter 12 the inverse correlation between high heat flow and time elapsed since the last major episode of deformation, as exemplified by a comparison of the low heat flow of the Canadian shield to the high heat flow of the western Cordillera. Regional metamorphism, which is mainly a thermal phenomenon (Chapter 10) is almost invariably associated with deformation. It is reasonable to conclude that deformation is related to thermal events.

Two mechanisms come to mind. In any medium with nonvanishing thermal expansion, temperature differences must create differential strains. Uplift, for example, could be expected above a region of the mantle that is warming up and therefore expanding. Differences in temperature distribution between suboceanic and subcontinental portions of the mantle could create large stresses at the continental margins. It is difficult to see, however, how these localized thermal stresses could lead to large-scale horizontal displacements, as in continental drift.

Alternatively, we recall from Chapter 11 that hydrostatic equilibrium in a homogeneous medium requires that both pressure and density —and therefore, also, temperature—be constant as an equipotential surface. If this condition is not satisfied, nonhydrostatic stresses must arise and may lead, in a medium with suitable mechanical properties, to convection. One often tends to think of convection only in terms of a steady-state continuous circulation of fluid in a geometrically well-defined and constant pattern. Such regular motion does occur when the Rayleigh number that describes the system falls within a certain range. Under different experimental conditions other behaviors can be observed which range from the discontinuous rise of single bubbles or drops—as perhaps in the ascent of a lump of liquid magma—to continuous but highly irregular and turbulent motions in which the velocity at a point in the fluid is a fluctuating and unpredictable function of coordinates and time. As, furthermore, the mantle is probably heterogeneous and becoming more and more so in the course of time, it is perhaps not surprising that we should still be unable to relate every observed motion of the surface to specific events at depth. To do this will require (1) a better knowledge of the physical properties, and particularly of the mechanical properties of the mantle; and (2) a much more accurate picture, on a worldwide and synoptic scale, of just what does happen on the surface, and of the time constants relevant to each process. (See Chapter 4.)

One more curious feature of crustal evolution that is worth mentioning is its low symmetry. Structural patterns on the continents do not conspicuously reflect the symmetry evident in the earth's shape or inherent in its rotation.[15] We have already noted that the distribution of continents and oceans shows a singular disregard for symmetry with respect to the equator. Yet one would expect on theoretical grounds that the

flattening of the earth and its equatorial bulge would exert a major control on internal convective patterns. In a homogeneous but flattened rotating body with internal heat sources, internal isothermal surfaces cannot everywhere coincide with equipotential (or isobaric) surfaces, and hydrostatic equilibrium would be impossible; the resulting convecting motion would, however, be symmetrical with respect to the equator, which it does not seem to be. Perhaps all this means is that the earth has not rotated about the present axis for very long; if indeed polar wandering has occurred on a large scale, there would be no reason to expect symmetry about the present axis. Polar wandering requires, however, an asymmetrical cause; we are thus forced back to the not implausible assumption of a heterogeneous earth that formed asymmetrically. Or perhaps there is, as in Figure 13–15, some indication of a generalized pattern of deformation (in this case, dominantly east–west motion) that conforms with rotational symmetry. We must conclude once more that we still do not understand very well either why or how the earth deforms.

---

[15] Except perhaps in the case of island arcs, which are convex to the earth, northeast, or south, but not to the west. As the physical distinction between east and west arises solely from the sense of the earth's rotation, one might find here a tenuous suggestion that the earth's rotation may exert some slight control on structure.

REFERENCES

The reader is referred first to an excellent short summary by **J. Tuzo Wilson**, "Theories of building of continents," Chapter 14 in *The Earth's Mantle*, edited by **T. F. Gaskell**, (Academic Press, New York, 1967).

Information on the structure and evolution of continents is dispersed in many books and publications, too numerous to list. We cite, for instance, **A. J. Eardley**'s *Structural Geology of North America* (Harper & Row, New York, 1962). Brief accounts are given in books on historical geology, such as **A. O. Woodford**, *Historical Geology*, 1965, and **B. Kummel**, *History of the Earth*, 1961 (both published by W. H. Freeman, San Francisco).

Numerous paleographic and structural maps for all continents may be found in **H. Termier** and **G. Termier**, *Histoire Géologique de la Biosphere* and *L'Evolution de la Lithosphere*, vol. 2, parts 1 and 2, (both in French, published by Masson et Cie, Paris, 1952 and 1956).

A book by **V. V. Beloussov**, *Basic Problems in Geotectonics* (McGraw-Hill, New York, 1962) presents much not readily accessible material on the geology of the U.S.S.R., but is out of date in some respects.

There is an enormous literature on continental drift, starting with **A. Wegener**, *Die Enstehung der Kontinente und Ozeane;* first edition, 1915. The third edition (1922) was translated into English as *The Origin of Continents and Oceans* (Methuen, London, 1924). The reader is also referred to **A. L. Du Toit**, *Our Wandering Continents* (Oliver & Boyd, Edinburgh, 1937), and to **S. W. Carey**, The tectonic approach to continental drift, in *Continental Drift—a Symposium* (University of Tasmania, Hobart, 1956). The paleomagnetic evidence is clearly presented in **E. Irving**, *Paleomagnetism and Its Application to Geological and Geophysical Problems* (Wiley, New York, 1964).

A collection of articles examining various aspects of the topic appeared in *Continental Drift*, edited by **S. K. Runcorn** (Academic Press, New York, 1962) and "A symposium on continental drift," edited by **P. M. S.**

Blackett, E. Bullard, and S. K. Runcorn (*Phil. Trans. Roy. Soc. London,* vol. 258, 1965). An excellent, more popular treatment is given by H. Takeuchi, S. Uyeda, and H. Kanamori in *Debate about the Earth* (Freeman, Cooper and Co., San Francisco, 1967).

The reader interested in sea-floor spreading should read first the paper by H. H. Hess, "History of ocean basins," in *Petrologic Studies: a volume to honor A. F. Buddington,* edited by A. E. J. Engel, H. L. James, and B. F. Leonard, and published by the Geological Society of America, 1962. The suggestion that magnetic anomalies along oceanic ridges could be related to the spreading mechanism was made by F. J. Vine and D. H. Matthews, in "Magnetic anomalies over oceanic ridges," in *Nature,* vol. 199, p. 947, 1963. See also F. J. Vine, "Spreading of the ocean floor: new evidence" (*Science,* vol. 154, pp. 1405–1415, 1966). Since then a large number of articles describing recent discoveries have appeared mostly in *Nature, Science,* and the *Journal of Geophysical Research.* In the latter publication, there is a good summary by J. R. Heirtzler, G. O. Dickson, E. M. Herron, W. C. Pittman, III, and X. Le Pichon (vol. 73, 1968, pp. 2119–2136, 1968). Block movements as described in this chapter were first suggested by W. Jason Morgan in "Rises, trenches, great faults, and crustal blocks" (*J. Geophys. Res.,* vol. 73, pp. 1959–1982, 1968), and by X. Le Pichon in "Sea-floor spreading and continental drift" (*ibid.,* pp. 3661–3698). On the chronology of reversals, the reader is referred to articles by A. Cox and G. B. Dalrymple, "Statistical analysis of geomagnetic reversal data and the precision of K. A. dating" (*J. Geophys. Res.,* vol. 72, pp. 2603–2614, 1967) and by Allan Cox, "Geomagnetic reversals" (*Science,* vol. 163, pp. 237–245, 1969.)

A recent book, *The History of the Earth's Crust, A Symposium,* edited by R. A. Phinney (Princeton University Press, Princeton, N.J., 1968), contains important contributions on all aspects of the subject.

A paper by R. R. Newton, "Experimental evidences for a secular increase in the gravitational constant G" (*J. Geophys. Res.,* vol. 73, pp. 3765–3772, 1968) is also recommended.

14

SOME ASPECTS OF
THE CHEMICAL EVOLUTION
OF THE EARTH

IN THIS CHAPTER we examine briefly a few topics relating to the chemical composition and evolution of the earth. Uncertainty is perhaps even greater here than in other aspects of geology, for tracing the flow of chemical elements through space and time is not easy. The complexity of this flow may perhaps be illustrated by considering the history of atoms of carbon now bound as carbonate in, say, the fossil shell of a marine organism. As we shall presently see, these atoms may have been born a few billion years ago in a distant star. They may have traveled, perhaps as graphite, perhaps as solid grains of CO_2 or CH_4, in a cloud of cosmic dust; fallen into the earth at the time of its formation; risen from the deep mantle to the atmosphere as CO_2 in volcanic gas; gone through many cycles of fixation in the living matter of plants and animals and return to the atmosphere by decay of this matter; become attached to sodium in a weathered igneous rock and carried to sea; precipitated as calcium carbonate in limestone only to be later returned to the atmosphere by weathering or metamorphism; and dissolved once more in seawater before incorporation into the shell in which we now find them. Some of the steps in this complicated history have been examined in previous chapters; we now consider briefly other less-well-understood, and more speculative, aspects of the earth's chemistry.

Chemical Composition of the Earth

Geophysical data outlined in Chapters 11 and 12 lead to the following conclusions:

1. The crust, hydrosphere, and atmosphere together constitute only a small fraction (less than one percent) of the total mass of the earth. The gross chemical composition of the earth is therefore essentially determined by that of the mantle and core. The mass of the mantle is about two thirds that of the earth.

2. The core, with a mean atomic number close to, or slightly less than, that of iron (26) is metallic. It presumably consists dominantly of iron with accessory amounts of nickel and of some lighter elements, such as carbon, silicon, or sulfur. It has also been suggested that the core might contain dissolved MgO as well. Not enough is known of the properties of iron under pressures such as those existing in the core to allow a precise determination of its composition.

3. The mantle, with a mean atomic number close to 12, almost certainly consists dominantly of silicates and oxides of Mg and Fe, with subor-

dinate amounts of Al, Ca, Na, K, and so forth. Minerals in the mantle probably occur in several polymorphic forms. The most distinctive character of the mantle, as contrasted with the core, is its much higher content of oxygen. The upper mantle must have a composition such that it could yield, by partial or total melting, liquids of basaltic composition. The density and elastic properties of the upper mantle are matched only, among common rocks, by those of peridotites and eclogite.

4. The mantle contains radioactive elements (mainly U, Th, K), the abundance and distribution of which must be consistent with what little we know of the temperature distribution within the earth, and of heat flow at its surface.

Some information regarding the probable gross composition of mantle and core may be gathered from what is known of the composition of extraterrestrial matter.

"COSMIC ABUNDANCES"

Information on the chemical composition of matter outside the earth accrues from a number of sources:

1. Spectroscopic studies of the sun, stars, the interstellar medium, comets, and atmospheres of other planets.
2. Determination by means of high-altitude balloons of the nature of the heavy particles present in cosmic rays and in the streams of matter ("solar wind") ejected from the sun in solar eruptions ("flares").
3. Analysis of meteorites.
4. Studies of the moon's surface.
5. Theoretical calculations, based mainly on nuclear binding energies and the kinetics of nuclear reactions, of the relative abundances in which elements may be formed in nuclear processes of fusion (nucleosynthesis).

"Cosmic" abundances are somewhat subjective averages of information derived from these sources. Abundance is usually expressed as the number of nuclei of an element relative to a fixed number of nuclei of an element selected as a standard, such as Si or H. Tables of abundances appear in the *Handbook of Physical Constants* and in the book by Kaula cited at the end of this chapter.

The apparently uniform abundance of some elements throughout the universe is striking. On a scale where the abundance of Si is taken as 10^6, the logarithm of the abundance of Mg is 6.49 in the hot stars, called B stars; 6.1 in the solar wind; 6.1 in the sun's photosphere; 6.02, 5.97, and 5.93 in three different types of meteorites; 5.2 on the moon's surface; and 4.9 in the earth's crust. This latter figure suggests that inside the earth the Mg/Si ratio may be greater than 1, as it would be in, say, olivine (Mg_2SiO_4). The cosmic abundance of Mg calculated by Suess and Urey is 5.96.

Other elements show greater variation; figures for hydrogen, for instance, are 10.0 for the sun, 6.7 for meteorites known as carbonaceous chondrites, and 4.5 for the earth's crust. As is well known, hydrogen and helium are by far the most abundant elements in most stars; elements heavier than iron are relatively sparse. In series of elements such as O-F-Ne, or V-Cr-Mn-Fe-Co-Ni, abundance varies irregularly with atomic number. Elements with even atomic numbers tend to be more abundant than their odd-numbered neighbors in the Periodic Table; nuclei with even numbers of protons and neutrons are more abundant than those with even–odd combinations, and odd–odd combinations are even rarer. Models of nucleosynthesis that account for these features have been proposed.

METEORITES

Meteorites, as mentioned in Chapter 1, are grouped into two great classes, "irons" and "stones." Irons consist dominantly of metallic iron, with 4 to 20 percent of alloyed nickel, small amounts of other metals, a few percent of sulfide (mostly iron sulfide troilite), some iron carbide (Fe_3C), and graphite. Irons form about 5 percent of observed falls. Ninety percent of the stones are chondrites, which consist of approximately 40 percent olivine, 30 percent pyroxenes, 10 percent plagioclase, 6 percent troilite, and 10 to 20 percent iron–nickel; the remaining 10 percent of the stones are achondrites, which consist mostly of pyroxenes and plagioclase, with minor amounts of olivine (about 10 percent) and iron–nickel. There is also a minor, but significant, group—carbonaceous chondrites—whose composition differs from that of ordinary chondrites. The main constituents of carbonaceous chondrites are serpentine or chlorite, with some olivine, iron oxides, carbonates, sulfates, and "organic" carbon compounds; characteristically, carbonaceous chondrites contain no reduced iron. There is still another class of objects, completely different from meteorites in composition, to which most geologists ascribe a meteoric origin. These are the tektites, rounded buttonlike glass bodies highly localized in their distribution; many have been collected, for example, from the central Australian desert. Tektites resemble, yet are distinct from, terrestrial obsidians.

POSSIBLE COMPOSITION OF THE EARTH

The broad, but not exact, resemblance between stony meteorites and some terrestrial rocks (such as peridotites) and the analogy between the inferred properties of the core and those of iron meteorites led long ago to the suggestion that the composition of the earth might perhaps be similar to that of the "unsuccessful planet" (as Birch calls it), of which meteorites may be fragments. Mason has computed a possible composition of the earth on the assumptions that (1) the core has the composition of an average metallic meteorite, (2) the mantle consists of peridotite, and (3) the earth contains 8 percent of sulfides similar to meteoritic troilite. As shown in Table 14–1, such an earth would be broadly similar to an average chondrite. Yet, as noted by Birch, an earth with the composition of a chondrite would not contain enough uranium to account for the amount of that element that occurs in the earth's crust alone; the K/U ratio in ordinary chondrites (about 7×10^4) is also quite different from what

TABLE 14–1 *Average composition of chondrites and hypothetical composition of the earth (after Mason)*

Element	Chondrites, weight percent	Earth, weight percent
O	33.24	29.5
Fe	27.24	34.6
Si	17.10	15.2
Mg	14.29	12.7
S	1.93	1.93
Ni	1.64	2.39
Ca	1.27	1.13
Al	1.22	1.09
Na	0.64	0.57
Cr	0.29	0.26
Mn	0.25	0.22
P	0.11	0.10
Co	0.09	0.13
K	0.08	0.07
Ti	0.06	0.05

it is in most terrestrial rocks (1×10^4). Carbonaceous chondrites might be more suitable than ordinary chondrites with respect to uranium content and K/U ratio, but the former are highly oxidized bodies from which it would be difficult to form a reduced, metallic, iron core (see below). No single type of meteorite appears to fit the earth in all respects (ratios of K to U, of K to Rb, of Rb to Sr, isotopic composition of carbon, rate of radioactive heat generation, and so on). Thus we may conclude only that the earth's gross composition is likely to be similar to that of a mixture, in uncertain proportions, of the various types of meteorites. As explained in Chapter 11, difficulties in determining composition from geophysical data (for example, density, velocity of seismic waves) are that (1) measurable physical properties of the earth's interior, such as seismic velocities, are not sensitive to slight variations in chemical composition; (2) these physical properties depend also on pressure and temperature in a manner that it not precisely known, particularly at the very high pressures that prevail inside the earth; and (3) very little is known of the physical properties of the high-pressure polymorphs of common minerals that probably form the bulk of the mantle.

Distribution of Elements in the Earth

What determines the distribution of elements in the earth as, for example, between mantle and core? In 1922 Goldschmidt proposed an empirical geochemical classification of the elements deduced from their actual occurrence and association in rocks, meteorites, and industrial slags. "Siderophile" elements (such as Co, Ni, Mo, Pt, Os, and Au) generally accompany iron. "Chalcophile" elements (such as Zn, Pb, and Hg) accompany sulfur. "Lithophile" elements (Na, K, Rb, Mg, Ca, Al, Si, and others) accompany oxygen. As would be expected, these geochemical groups correspond roughly with chemical properties; siderophile elements, for instance, mostly belong to the same groups of the Periodic Table. The geochemical classification may lead to interesting predictions; for example, the cosmic abundance of gold is much greater than its crustal abundance, and the metal phase of meteorites is much richer in gold than the silicate phase and thus, presumably, much terrestrial gold is in the core. The usefulness of the classification is limited, however, in that the chemical behavior of an element depends not only on its own electronic structure, but also on its chemical environment. Thus some elements belong to more than one of Goldschmidt's groups; chromium, for instance, is a lithophile element where oxygen is abundant, but occurs as a sulfide where oxygen is deficient, as in some meteorites. Meteorites also contain unusual minerals such as oldhamite [CaS], osbornite [TiN], sinoite [Si_2N_2O] and djerfisherite [$K_3(Na, Cu) (Fe, Ni)_{12}S_{14}$]; the association of K and S in the latter would not have been predicted by Goldschmidt's rules.

THERMODYNAMIC DATA

To some extent, it is possible to predict the distribution of some elements in the earth from thermodynamic data. Consider, for instance, the standard free energy of oxidation, at $25°C$, of the following elements:

	$\Delta G°$, kcal
$Fe + \frac{1}{2}O_2 = FeO$	-58.7
$Ni + \frac{1}{2}O_2 = NiO$	-50.6
$Mn + \frac{1}{2}O_2 = MnO$	-86.7
$Mg + \frac{1}{2}O_2 = MgO$	-136.1
$\frac{2}{3}Al + \frac{1}{2}O_2 = \frac{1}{3}Al_2O_3$	-126.0
$\frac{1}{2}Si + \frac{1}{2}O_2 = \frac{1}{2}SiO_2$	-102.3
$2Na + \frac{1}{2}O_2 = Na_2O$	-90.0
$2K + \frac{1}{2}O_2 = K_2O$	-76.3
$\frac{1}{2}U + \frac{1}{2}O_2 = \frac{1}{2}UO_2$	-123.2

Clearly, it is easier to reduce FeO or NiO than MgO or SiO_2. Elements that would be left in the metallic state if there were a deficiency of oxygen would be Ni and Fe. Conversely, if there is enough oxygen for Fe to occur as Fe^{2+}, as it probably does in silicates in the lower mantle, it seems unlikely that silicon could occur in the reduced state in the core,[1] if the latter is in equilibrium with the mantle.

The positive free energy of reactions such as

$$Na_2SiO_3 + FeS = FeSiO_3 + Na_2S$$
$$\Delta G° = +21 \text{ kcal}$$
$$Na_2CO_3 + FeS = FeCO_3 + Na_2S$$
$$\Delta G° = +37 \text{ kcal}$$

indicates that terrestrial sulfur is more likely to be bound to iron than to sodium. Sulfides are generally soluble in molten metals at high temperature, so that one might expect much terrestrial sulfur to occur in the core.

GRAVITATIONAL EQUILIBRIUM

We noted in Chapter 5 that the chemical potential μ_i of a chemical species i depends on height h in a gravitational field:

---

[1] The reaction

$$SiO_2 + 2Fe = 2FeO + Si$$

has a free energy of $+87.2$ kcal under standard conditions. The pressure at the core–mantle boundary, which is about 1.4 megabars, would make the reduction of SiO_2 even less likely, since the volume change for this reaction is positive. However, the actual volume change at a pressure of 1.4 Mb is not known.

$$\left(\frac{\partial \mu_i}{\partial h}\right)_{PT} = M_i g$$

where M_i is its molecular weight. In a binary ideal solution at constant temperature, the mole fraction N_1 of component 1 will vary as

$$\frac{dN_1}{dh} = \frac{N_1(\overline{v}_1 \rho - M_1)g}{RT}$$

where $\overline{v}_1$ is the partial molar volume of 1 and ρ is the density of the solution. Thus if component 1 is heavier than the average, its molar fraction will decrease with height. One would expect, for instance, that the high molecular weight of uranium would cause its concentration to increase downward. However, in a multicomponent solution of $j + 1$ components with j independent molar fractions $(N_1 \cdots N_k \cdots N_j)$, the general condition for equilibrium with regard to any component i is

$$d\mu_i = 0 = \left(\frac{\partial \mu_i}{\partial T}\right)_{P,h,N} dT + \left(\frac{\partial \mu_i}{\partial P}\right)_{T,N,h} dP +$$

$$\left(\frac{\partial \mu_i}{\partial h}\right)_{T,P,N} dh + \sum_j \left(\frac{\partial \mu_i}{\partial N_j}\right)_{P,T,N_k,h} dN_j$$

where the last term on the right represents chemical interactions of i with all other components. Brewer has called attention to the importance of this term. In a solution containing uranium and oxygen, for instance, the affinity of uranium for oxygen will be more important than its molecular weight in determining its distribution; thus in the earth, where oxygen concentration is greater in the crust than in the core, uranium will also tend to be concentrated in the crust. The distribution of uranium therefore seems to be governed by both the gravitational field, which determines the distribution of oxygen, and the chemical affinity of uranium for oxygen.

The question remains, of course, as to whether gravitational equilibrium is fully attained in the earth. Diffusion rates in solids are so slow that in the absence of melting, equilibrium is unlikely to have been reached within the lifetime of the earth. But was the earth ever molten? We now turn to geochemical evidence bearing on the formation of the earth and its early history.

Early History of the Earth

COLD ACCUMULATION

It is generally agreed that the earth could not have been very warm at the time of its formation. The basis for this statement is found in a comparison of terrestrial and cosmic abundances of some elements. It was noted above that the Mg/Si ratio in the earth does not differ much from the cosmic ratio, and the same is true for a number of other elements, including Al, Na, Fe, and Ca. On the other hand, rare gases (such as He, A, Kr, and Xe) are much less abundant (by a factor of 10^{14} for He and 10^7 for Kr) on earth than in the cosmos. Loss of these gases after formation of the earth is not likely; for if heavy Kr (molecular weight 83) could escape, all other volatile components (CO_2 H_2O, N_2, O_2, and so on) now present in the atmosphere would have escaped even faster. The earth does indeed appear to be slightly depleted with regard to C, N, F, O, and Cl but the depletion factor is very much smaller for these elements than for the rare gases. Remembering that rare gases do not readily form solid compounds, it has been inferred from the terrestrial low abundance of rare gases that the earth must have accumulated at a temperature sufficiently low for all elements except the rare gases to be present in *solid* form, such as oxides of Si, Mg, Al, Na, and others, solid CO_2, CH_4, or NH_3; and water as ice or as hydration water attached to oxides, silicates, or carbonates. Even taking into account the heat generated by compression of the growing earth, it seems unlikely that the internal temperature could have much exceeded 1000°C or 1500°C. The large amount of gravitational energy released at the time of accumulation must have been dissipated away quickly and efficiently, probably by radiation from the surface.

SEPARATION OF THE CORE

It does seem, however, that there must have been an important early thermal event, leading to partial melting. This is implied by the very existence of a liquid metallic core. It is difficult to see how reduction of the iron that now forms the core could have occurred after formation of the earth, for there is no obvious mechanism by which the enormous amount of H_2O and CO_2 so formed could escape. Thus the iron that now forms the core must have been present in reduced but solid form in the original dust cloud; this would be chemically possible if the ratio of oxygen to hydrogen in the dust cloud were no greater than is now seen in the sun (about 10^{-3}). But why would only iron particles accumulate at first to form the core, leaving silicates and oxides to accumulate in a second, later stage? More probably, metal and stone accumulated together to form a grossly homogeneous undifferentiated earth. Elsasser has suggested that separation of the core from the mantle took place some time after accumulation, when the temperature inside the earth had risen (see below) to the melting point of iron;[2] drops of iron then coalesced to a size sufficient to permit them to sink readily and form the liquid core.

Melting could have been induced by a number of causes, already briefly outlined in Chapter 12:

1. *Radiogenic heat.* Shortly after formation of the earth, some 4.5 billion years ago, important heat-generating radioactive elements were more abundant than they are now; K^{40}, in particular, must have been about eight times more abundant than today, for its half-life is only 1.3×10^9 years. Thus the rate of heat production must have been considerably greater. In addition, short-lived radioactive elements with half-lives of the order of 10^5–10^7 years (Be^{10}, Al^{26}, and so forth) may still have been present in notable amounts. Anomalous amounts of Xe^{129} in meteorites imply that its parent element, radioactive I^{129}, must indeed have been present when these meteorites formed; the isotopic composition of terrestrial xenon similarly suggests accumulation of the earth sufficiently shortly after nucleosyn-

thesis for survival of some Pu^{244}. Birch estimates that radiogenic heat from these short-lived elements and from U, Th, and K^{40} may have caused partial melting within half a billion years of the earth's formation.

2. *Gravitational energy.* Formation of a dense core would release enough gravitational energy, as shown by Birch, to raise the internal temperature by some $1500°$. This heating would produce more melting, including partial fusion of the silicate phases. The low-melting silicate fraction, containing much of the alkalis, alumina and silica, would rise, carrying with it uranium and thorium, which tend in general to follow potassium. The residual lower mantle, presumably depleted of most of its radiogenic heat sources, would consist of refractory silicates and oxides of magnesium and iron.

Crystallization of the solid inner core may have started at about that time, and proceeded from the center outwards because of the effect of pressure on melting. Even though the melting temperature of the core is not exactly known, it is very likely that the melting-point gradient exceeds the adiabatic gradient. The temperature in the core must be such that it exceeds the melting point in the outer core, but is less than the melting point in the inner core.

3. *Lunar effects.* The moon is now moving away from the earth, because of tidal friction. At some time in the past it must have been much closer to the earth, thus raising bigger tides and dissipating more energy. Although it is not yet clear just how the moon–earth system came into existence, it is not unlikely that a catastrophic event, such as the capture of the moon by the earth, may have occurred shortly after formation of the earth itself. This catastrophic event may have generated enough heat in the earth to cause partial melting.

The Crust

Differentiation of the earth into core, mantle and crust seems to have been a relatively early event in the earth's history. The oldest known

---

[2] Since the outer core is now liquid while the lower mantle is solid, the melting point of iron must be lower than that of the mantle at the pressure prevailing at the mantle-core boundary. Hence the first particles to melt inside the earth would consist of iron (and, presumably, iron sulfide).

crustal rocks have an age of about 3.5 b.y.; this date presumably marks the time when the heat flow from the interior had sufficiently diminished to allow the existence of a solid crust more than a few kilometers thick. We recall that a surface temperature gradient of 100°/km, roughly three times the present one, would cause melting below a depth of 10 km or less. It is not known by what amount the mass of the crust has actually increased, if it has changed at all, since that early time; as mentioned in Chapter 13, it is probable that the rate at which new crust is produced matches the rate at which old crust is destroyed.

The average chemical composition of the continental crust is not easily determined. Sampling is perforce restricted to the relatively small depth accessible by means of drill holes; we still know only very little of the nature of the lower part of the crust. Tens of thousands of chemical analyses of near-surface rocks are available, however, from which a broad picture of the average composition may be obtained. Two estimates are given in Table 14–2. A comparison of the two values for an element indicates roughly the uncertainty.

The crustal abundance of elements not listed in Table 14–2 is less than 10 g/ton; among these are, for instance, Sn (3), U (1.8), Hg (0.08), Pt (0.01). Note that oxygen, forming 47 percent of the crust by weight, represents 62.5 percent of all atoms. Because O^{2-} has a larger ionic radius than the other common elements, oxygen ions form 93.7 percent of the volume of the crust, which, to a first approximation, can thus be described as solid oxygen.

Whatever the process may be by which crust forms (or formed), it implies efficient fractionation of at least some elements. Although the mass of the present crust is only about 0.6 percent of the mass of the present mantle, it contains as much uranium as would the whole earth if it had the composition of an average chondrite; Ba, Rb, and, to a lesser degree, Sr also show a high degree of crustal concentration. On the other hand, iron and magnesium are less abundant, and nickel and sulfur are much less abundant, in the crust than they probably are in the earth as a whole. The distribution of elements is, in general, consistent with the conjecture that the crust represents the most easily fusible fraction of the mantle.

By far the most copious magma to rise from the mantle is basalt; we would thus expect the crust to have essentially a basaltic composition, which is indeed consistent with its average density (2.85 g/cm). The present upper crust, however, contains much granitic material in the form of large intrusions and extrusions. A small amount

TABLE 14–2 *Average compositions of the crust, grams per metric ton (or parts per million)*

Element	1*	2†	Element	1*	2†	Element	1*	2†
O	466,000	470,000	Li	20	32	Zn	70	83
Si	277,200	295,000	B	10	12	Ga	15	19
Al	81,300	80,500	C	200	230	Rb	90	150
Fe	50,000	46,500	N	20	19	Sr	375	340
Ca	36,300	29,600	F	625	660	Y	33	29
Na	28,300	25,000	S	260	470	Zr	165	170
K	25,900	25,000	Cl	130	170	Nb	20	20
Mg	20.900	18,700	Sc	22	10	Ba	425	650
Ti	4,400	4,500	V	135	90	La	30	29
H	1,400	—	Cr	100	83	Ce	60	70
P	1,050	930	Co	25	18	Nd	28	37
Mn	950	1,000	Ni	75	58	Pb	13	16
			Cu	55	47	Th	7.2	13

*After B. Mason, *Principles of Electrochemistry*, 3d ed. (Wiley, New York, 1966).
† After A. P. Vinogradov (*Geokhemiya*, pp. 555–571, 1962; translated from the Russian in *Geochemistry*, pp. 641–664, 1962).

of granitic liquid can be derived by fractional crystallization of a basaltic melt, but fractional crystallization cannot account for crustal granitic bodies that are not accompanied by any visible intrusion of basalt or gabbro. It seems more likely that many granitic bodies in metamorphic terranes are derived by partial fusions of sediments previously transformed to high-grade metamorphic rocks. The process may perhaps be understood by referring first to weathering of basalt. Residual sediments, after removal of soluble carbonates and bicarbonates would, after high-grade metamorphism, be transformed to the assemblage amphibole + iron oxides + feldspar + biotite + quartz. Partial melting in the presence of a small amount of water would then produce a granodioritic melt plus amphibole + iron oxides. Thus from an originally basaltic crust weathering, metamorphism, and partial fusion could form an upper crust of granodioritic composition, and a lower crust consisting of amphibolite somewhat less siliceous than the original basalt.

The distribution of chemical elements in the crust raises interesting problems. Some elements of low abundance, such as gallium, are distributed rather uniformly. Gallium is generally found in all minerals containing aluminum, but it does not form minerals of its own; in no mineral does its concentration exceed a small fraction of one percent. Similarly, rubidium accompanies potassium, but does not form separate mineral phases; nowhere do we find, for instance, a pure rubidium feldspar comparable to potassium feldspar. Zirconium, on the contrary, occurs mostly in the mineral zircon ($ZrSiO_4$), which is sparsely though widely distributed in granitic rocks; but copper, which is four times less abundant than zirconium (Table 14–2), occurs locally in high concentration (several percent) in deposits containing millions of tons of that element. Thousands of tons of nearly pure gold have been mined in some localities even though the average concentration of gold in the crust is only about 4×10^{-9} g/ton. Such differences in the distribution pattern of the elements are determined by a very large number of factors, some of which have been mentioned in Chapter 2: electronegativity

of the element; size and charge of its ions; availability and distribution of other elements (oxygen, sulfur, and so on) with which it readily forms stable chemical compounds; solubility of the element in aqueous solutions in which it can be carried and become locally concentrated (see Chapter 5); participation of the element (for example, phosphorus) in biological processes through which it can be selectively extracted from a dilute solution (for example, seawater); and so on. Much remains to be done, however, to account in detail for observed distributions.

The Origin of Seawater and the Atmosphere

The composition of seawater is given in Table 8–3; the major constituents of the atmosphere are listed in Table 14–3. In addition to these constituents, the atmosphere also contains very small amounts of H_2, CH_4, N_2O, NO_2, O_3, SO_2. The total mass of the atmosphere is about 5.1×10^{21} grams.

The amount of sodium dissolved in seawater corresponds very nearly to the amount of chlorine, as if the main dissolved salt were NaCl. This is surprising, for sodium is continuously brought into the sea by rivers, which carry Na mainly as carbonate or bicarbonate; what little chlorine (Table 7–1) rivers contribute to the oceans comes from sea salt carried by winds, from the weathering of salt beds (themselves derived by evaporation of seawater) and from the weathering of igneous rocks. The amount of chlorine in ocean water is in fact many times greater than the total amount of this element that could be released by weathering of igneous rocks throughout the

TABLE 14–3 *Major constituents of the atmosphere*

Constituent	Volume Percentage
Nitrogen	78.1
Oxygen	20.9
Argon	0.9
CO_2	0.03
Rare gases (He, Ne, Kr, Xe)	0.02

TABLE 14–4 *Balance of volatile materials now near the earth's surface (after Rubey) (in units of 10^{20} grams)*

	H_2O	Total C as CO_2	Cl	N	S	H, B, Br, A, F, etc.
In present atmosphere, hydrosphere, and biosphere	14,600	1.5	276	39	13	1.7
Buried in ancient sedimentary rocks	2,100	920	30	4.0	15	15
Total	16,700	921.5	306	43	28	16.7
Supplied by weathering of crystalline rocks	130	11	5	0.6	6	3.5
"Excess" volatiles unaccounted for by rock weathering	16,600	910	300	42	22	13

whole of geologic time. Where does oceanic chlorine come from?

Discrepancies are also observed for other constituents of seawater and of the atmosphere. The amount of CO_2 now locked in carbonate sediments is several hundred times greater than the amount of CO_2 now present in the atmosphere and the hydrosphere combined; it is also very much greater than the amount of CO_2 that could be released into the atmosphere by weathering of igneous rocks, some of which contain small amounts of calcite and other carbonates. Similar statements, summarized in Table 14–4, can be made about other "volatiles," such as boron, bromine, fluorine, nitrogen, sulfur, and water itself.

Rubey has carefully examined possible sources of these "excess volatiles," as he calls them. He points out that only two sources are possible: Either (a) they are largely or entirely residual from a "primitive" atmosphere or ocean; or (b) they have risen to the surface from the earth's interior in the course of geologic time.

The "primitive atmosphere" hypothesis can probably be rejected on the following grounds: Had all the excess volatiles, including water, been initially present in the atmosphere, the primitive ocean would have been extremely acid (*p*H less than 1). In this environment CO_2 would react with the bare rocks at the earth's surface to produce enormous amounts of carbonates; HCl would produce silica by reactions such as

$$M \text{ silicate} + \text{HCl} = M \text{ halide} + SiO_2 + H_2O$$

where M stands for Mg, Ca, Fe, Na, etc. Weathering of this kind would produce vast amounts of carbonate sediment and silica. No such sediments are found in the earliest Precambrian record; a number of compilations suggest, on the contrary, that the proportion of limestone to other types of sediments has remained approximately constant throughout geologic time.

The alternative hypothesis that excess volatiles have been continuously supplied to the surface from the interior appears much more likely, as this is precisely what volcanoes do. Volcanic eruptions (Chapter 6) release into the atmosphere gases that consist dominantly of H_2O, CO_2, HCl, HF, N_2, H_2S, and SO_2. The average composition of volcanic gases is not exactly known, because it fluctuates from one volcano to another, from one eruption to the next at the same volcano, and even during the course of a single eruption. Yet, as Rubey pointed out, there is a remarkable resemblance between the "excess volatiles" and the gases collected at volcanic vents and fumaroles and those released by heating volcanic rocks *in vacuo*.

It thus appears likely that the mass of the hydrosphere and atmosphere has grown continuously through geologic time, whereas the composition of seawater must have remained nearly constant. Nowhere do we find sedimentary deposits of brucite [$Mg(OH)_2$] that would form if the oceanic pH were to increase much above its present value; nor do we find evidence that oceans of the past ever were much more acid than they are today. Volcanic activity and the supply of volatiles must, on the whole, have proceeded at a rather uniform rate.

Evidence that the solid earth is losing gas to the atmosphere also comes from a different source. Argon is much more abundant in the atmosphere than any other of the rare gases (Table 14–3), and it consists mostly of the radiogenic isotope A^{40}. The conclusion seems clear that atmospheric argon is mostly argon produced by radioactive decay of K^{40}. There is, however, more argon in the atmosphere than could be produced in the crust during the lifetime of the earth; thus the mantle, too, must be losing some of its radiogenic argon to the atmosphere. Turekian, assuming that the rate of loss of argon from the mantle is proportional to the amount present in the mantle, has calculated the fractional loss to be 2.8×10^{-11}/year. It is interesting that the same factor applied to water (assuming that the whole of the hydrosphere has come from the mantle) implies a water content of the mantle similar to that of meteorites. Turekian's calculations suppose a mantle of chondritic composition and thus probably overestimate its potassium content; Gast finds that a mantle with a K content about one seventh of that of chondrites would by now have lost to the atmosphere about 70 percent of its radiogenic argon. Such figures seem to imply that a very large fraction of the mantle has undergone partial melting and release of argon.

ATMOSPHERIC OXYGEN AND THE ORIGIN OF LIFE

Free oxygen, as we well know, is an important constituent of the present atmosphere, whereas oxygen in volcanic gases is bound as H_2O, CO_2, CO, or SO_2. Where does free oxygen come from? A small amount of it may be produced in the upper atmosphere by photodissociation of water followed by escape of H_2, but most of it appears to come from photosynthesis, the complicated process by which plants use atmospheric carbon dioxide, water, and sunlight to synthesize the

organic compounds of which they are made. For instance, the reaction by which glucose ($C_6H_{12}O_6$) is formed may be summarized as

$$6CO_2 + 6H_2O + h\nu = C_6H_{12}O_6 + O_2$$

where $h\nu$ represents a quantum of solar radiation of frequency ν. Notice that oxygen is released in the process. From the amount of vegetation now present on land and in the sea it has been calculated that oxygen is now produced at a rate sufficient to supply the whole present amount of atmospheric oxygen in about 3000 years; all atmospheric CO_2 would be used up in an even shorter time if it were not replenished by respiration, decay, and other sources. Some of the oxygen produced in photosynthesis is, of course, used up when decaying vegetal matter is once more converted to CO_2 and H_2O; yet some vegetal matter escapes oxidation, as by burial in sediments where it forms, for instance, deposits of coal and petroleum. Rubey estimates from the amount of organic carbon (excluding carbonates) buried in sediments that a net amount of 1.8×10^{22} grams of oxygen has been added to the atmosphere by photosynthesis[3] in geologic time; Abelson gives a higher figure of 2.3×10^{22}. One would thus expect the amount of atmospheric oxygen to have increased through time roughly in proportion to biological activity. But when, and how, did life start?

Following the experimental demonstration that organic compounds essential to life, such as amino acids, could be produced by passing an electric discharge (equivalent, perhaps, to lightning?) through a gaseous mixture of water, ammonia, and methane, it has commonly been assumed that the earth had once a primitive atmosphere consisting of these gases. This hypothesis, however, seems hardly tenable, for several reasons. It was mentioned earlier that the very low abundance on earth of rare gases such as He, Ne, A, Kr, and Xe strongly suggests that the earth formed by accretion of solid particles, and thus

---

[3] There is now only about 1.2×10^{21} grams of O_2 in the atmosphere; the difference represents oxygen fixed in oxidation of iron during weathering, or combined with H_2 and CO supplied by volcanic activity.

without an atmosphere; the early atmosphere that formed by partial melting and degassing of the interior must have consisted of those gases that are released by fusion of rocks and meteorites, mostly H_2O and CO_2. It also seems unlikely that ammonia (NH_3) could survive very long in the atmosphere where it is subject to photodissociation by solar radiation; the hydrogen so produced could escape from the earth's gravitational field in a matter of 30,000 years. Nor do the most ancient sediments afford any evidence of an early atmosphere differing in composition from the present one, as, for example, by unusual abundance of carbon or organic chemicals. The earliest atmosphere, produced by melting and degassing of the earth's interior, presumably consisted mainly of H_2O, CO_2, and N_2, with some CO and H_2.[4] Abelson has shown that photochemical processes in such an atmosphere could lead to the formation of a wide range of organic compounds. An important step seems to be the formation of hydrogen cyanide (HCN), from which a number of amino acids can be produced by polymerization.

A further constraint on the origin of life arises from the fact that ultraviolet solar radiation of very short wavelength is lethal to most organisms. At the present time the surface of the earth is shielded from this radiation by atmospheric ozone (O_3) which could not be present in an early atmosphere devoid of oxygen; thus it would seem that life, which produces oxygen, cannot start unless oxygen is present. It is possible, however, that a small amount of O_2 and O_3 produced in the upper atmosphere by photodissociation of H_2O may have played a crucial role. It also seems possible that life may have started under a cover of a few meters of water, sufficient to absorb ultraviolet radiation but still sufficiently thin to allow penetration of light indispensable to the basic photosynthetic process. Thus enough oxygen could be gradually produced to build up the ozone content of the atmosphere, and this in

turn would allow life to move first to the surface of the water, and then onto land. The process has been followed in some detail by Berkner and Marshall, who have attempted to account by the increase in atmospheric oxygen for the great expansion of life that occurred towards the end of the Precambrian, and its emergence on land in mid-Paleozoic times.

Fascinating research, well summarized by Hoering, is now being pursued on the small amounts of organic compounds that can be found in very old sediments. Evidence for life on earth now goes back to about 3 billion years; early biological processes seem to have been very much as those found in simple organisms (bacteria) today.

Trends in Chemical Evolution

We may perhaps summarize the chemical evolution of the earth by pointing once more to two distinct and opposite trends in geochemical processes: (1) a trend towards differentiation, diversification, or purification; and (2) a trend towards mixing and homogenization.

We have repeatedly described examples of the first trend. Thermal gradients existing in the earth must lead, as mentioned in Chapter 5, to concentration gradients (Soret effect). The earth's gravitational field sorts out elements by weight, pushing the heavy ones (such as iron) towards the center of the earth, and concentrating the lighter ones (such as oxygen) toward the surface. Differentiation of the earth into core, mantle, and crust appears to be mainly an effect of gravitation. Molten fractions of the mantle, which rise because they are lighter than the unmelted residue, proceed to split by fractional crystallization, or otherwise, into groups of related rocks, each of which has a distinct chemical and mineralogical composition. The last residue of crystallization of a magma is commonly an aqueous hydrothermal solution in which some of the less abundant elements (such as lithium, beryllium, fluorine, boron, tantalum, and others) become notably concentrated, as in pegmatites. Weathering, as we have seen, is an effective agent of chemical

---

[4] Hydrogen in volcanic gases is mostly bound as H_2O or H_2S; but at high temperature H_2 may be formed by dissociation of water or by reaction between H_2S and CO_2.

separation; some elements (such as Na) are carried to the sea where they remain in solution, and others (such as K) become concentrated in newly formed minerals such as clays. We noted that residual soils are occasionally so enriched in aluminum that they become economically important ores of that metal (bauxite). Sedimentary processes, including biological activity, carry this separation still further: Carbonates and phosphate are deposited selectively under certain conditions; chlorides and sulfates become separated in salt deposits; there are sediments (cherts) consisting of almost pure silica; calcium and magnesium follow on the whole somewhat different geochemical paths. Separation and purification occasionally go so far as to fractionate isotopes; we noted, for instance, that the O^{18}/O^{16} ratio is noticeably higher in igneous rocks than in fresh waters. The ratio S^{34}/S^{32} appears to be different in rocks formed through purely inorganic processes from that typical of rocks formed by biological agents.

This trend toward chemical separation and differentiation is, however, opposed by powerful mixing processes and agents—for instance, the ocean. Lead from highly concentrated deposits of lead sulfide may be leached in weathering and enormously diluted in ocean water where it mixes with leads of various isotopic compositions from many other sources. Sediments derived from weathering of igneous rocks of contrasted types cropping out at different places are mixed in transportation and deposition. Sediments appear further to become grossly homogenized during metamorphism. On an even broader scale, mixing of crust and mantle is implied by continuous formation of new crust and downward transport of old crust back into the mantle. Convection in a heterogeneous mantle must necessarily entail some mixing on a large scale.

Given these two opposing trends, the question arises as to whether they have attained some kind of balance. Is the earth becoming more uniform, or more differentiated, or has it reached a steady state? No definite answer can be given, because the processes themselves are not completely understood, and we know very little of their rates; the evidence, on the whole, is ambiguous. The oldest known sedimentary and igneous rocks are not markedly different from more recent ones, and a continental crust chemically similar to the present crust seems to have existed for a very long time. Yet some signs of change can be found in the record. Precambrian sedimentary iron ores that occur in most continents have no modern equivalent on a comparable scale. Nor in younger rocks are there comparable equivalents to the great Precambrian anorthosite batholiths or to extensive metamorphic cordierite-bearing granulites, which perhaps indicate unusually steep geothermal gradients at the time and place of their formation. We have just seen evidence that the mass of the hydrosphere has probably increased significantly through geologic time, and the composition of the atmosphere has changed by gradual accretion of oxygen.

It would, in fact, be surprising if the earth had reached a steady chemical state. Much of its chemical evolution is related to, and determined by, its thermal evolution: Addition to the hydrosphere and atmosphere occur through volcanism, which is a thermal event; mixing of crust and mantle is presumably also a thermally driven process. But, as pointed out in Chapter 12, time constants for heat transfer and radioactive heat generation are of the order of, or greater than, the age of the earth, which cannot therefore have yet reached a steady thermal state.

Thus, the earth presumably is still evolving, as are stars and the rest of the universe around us. Hutton once wrote[5]: "The result, therefore, of our present enquiry is that we find no vestige of a beginning—no prospect of an end." We now know that the earth had a beginning; but what will be the nature, what the timing, of the end?

---

[5] James Hutton, "Theory of the earth" (*Trans. Roy. Soc. Edinburgh*, vol. 1, p. 304). The paper was read in 1785.

REFERENCES

STANDARD TEXTS ON GEOCHEMISTRY

Goldschmidt, V. M.: *Geochemistry* (A. Muir, editor), Oxford, New York, 1958.

Krauskopf, K.: *Introduction to Geochemistry*, McGraw-Hill, New York, 1967.

Mason, B., *Principles of Geochemistry* (3d ed.), Wiley, New York, 1966.

On nuclear abundances, nucleosynthesis, and meteorites, we recommend the following:

Goles, G. G.: Cosmic abundances, in *Handbook of Geochemistry*, Part I, Springer, Berlin (to appear in 1969).

Kaula, W. M.: *An Introduction to Planetary Physics* (Chapters 8 and 9), Wiley, New York, 1968.

Keil, K.: Meteorite composition, in *Handbook of Geochemistry*, Part I, Springer, Berlin (to appear in 1969).

Mason, B.: *Meteorites*, Wiley, New York, 1962.

COLLECTIONS OF DATA

Clark, S. P. (editor): *Handbook of Physical Constants*, Geological Society of America, Memoir 97, 1966.

Valley, S. L.: *Handbook of Geophysics and Space Environments*, McGraw-Hill, New York, 1965.

The Data of Geochemistry, U.S. Geological Survey Professional Papers 440A through W, 1963–1966.

THERMODYNAMIC TREATMENTS OF EQUILIBRIUM IN A GRAVITATIONAL FIELD

Guggenheim, E. A.: *Thermodynamics*, North-Holland, Amsterdam, 1950.

Kern, R., and A. Weisbrod: *Thermodynamics for Geologists*, Freeman, Cooper and Co., San Francisco, 1967.

ADDITIONAL REFERENCES

Abelson, P. H.: Chemical events on the primitive earth, *Proc. Natl. Acad. Sci.*, vol. 55, pp. 1365–1372, 1966.

Berkner, L. V., and L. C. Marshall: History of major atmospheric components, *Proc. Natl. Acad. Sci.*, vol. 53, pp. 1215–1226, 1965.

Birch, F.: Speculations on the earth's thermal history, *Geol. Soc. Am. Bull.*, vol. 76, pp. 133–154, 1965.

Brewer, L.: The equilibrium distribution of the elements in the earth's gravitational field, *J. Geol.*, vol. 59, p. 490–497, 1951.

Clark, S. P., and A. E. Ringwood: Density distribution and constitution of the mantle, *Rev. Geophys.*, vol. 2, pp. 35–88, 1964.

Clayton, D. D.: Cosmoradiogenic chronologies of nucleosynthesis, *Astrophys. J.*, vol. 139, pp. 637–663, 1964.

Cloud, P. E.: Atmospheric and hydrospheric evolution on the primitive earth, *Science*, vol. 160, pp. 729–736, 1968.

Davidson, C. F.: Geochemical aspects of atmospheric evolution, *Proc. Natl. Acad. Sci.*, vol. 53, pp. 1194–1204, 1965.

Elsasser, W. M.: Early history of the earth, in *Earth Science and Meteorites*, J. Geiss and E. D. Goldberg, editors, North-Holland, Amsterdam, 1963, pp. 1–30.

Gast, P. W.: Upper mantle chemistry and evolution of the earth's crust, in *The History of the Earth's Crust*, R. A. Phinney, editor, Princeton University Press, Princeton, N.J., 1968, pp. 15–27.

Hoering, T. C.: The organic geochemistry of Precambrian rocks, in *Researches in Geochemistry*, vol. 2, P. H. Abelson, editor, Wiley, New York, 1967, pp. 87–111.

Lowenstam, H. A.: Biologic problems relative to the composition and diagenesis of sediments, in *The Earth Sciences*, T. W. Donnelly, editor, University of Chicago Press, Chicago, 1963, pp. 137–195.

Rubey, W. W.: Geologic history of sea water, *Geol. Soc. Am. Bull.*, vol. 62, pp. 1111–1147, 1951.

———, Development of the hydrosphere and atmosphere, in *The Crust of the Earth*, Geol. Soc. Am. Spec. Paper 62, pp. 631–650, 1955.

Turekian, K. K.: The terrestrial economy of helium and argon, *Geochim. et Cosmochim. Acta*, vol. 17, pp. 37–43, 1959.

APPENDIX: REPRESENTATION OF STRUCTURE

A PROBLEM constantly facing the geologist in general and the structural geologist in particular is the clear and accurate representation in two dimensions of a three-dimensional part of the earth's crust. The simplest and most universally employed representation is the geologic map, the main function of which is to show the outcrop patterns of formations on a topographic base map of suitable scale. Geometrically the map is of a surface, and, even where symbols are added to indicate the orientation of planar and linear structures, its capacity to represent structure in three dimensions is limited. Geologists employ several standard techniques to add "depth" to a geologic map and to facilitate three-dimensional interpretation. In the absence of comprehensive data from mines, boreholes, or geophysical explorations, these techniques involve extrapolation from surface data. To determine the structure of a small region may require extrapolation only to a few hundred meters; but extrapolations to depths of many kilometers may be necessary to give a three-dimensional picture of some of the larger crustal structures.

Without some previous familiarity with the geometric problems of intersecting surfaces it is difficult for a student to read a geologic map or study rock structure in the field with understanding. We depart in this Appendix, therefore, from our stated intention of avoiding discussion of investigative techniques and review briefly some of the peculiarly geologic problems of geometry facing the field geologist. We introduce also some of the geometric methods of representation upon which the geologist depends to "see" into the crust.

Outcrop Patterns on Geologic Maps

A contact placed on a geologic map is the line of intersection of two generally curved surfaces: (1) the contact surface, separating two formations, and (2) the topographic surface. The pattern of a contact on a map depends upon the scale and complexity of the curvatures of the two surfaces and it can be very complicated and difficult to interpret by inspection. The possible complexity of the contact between two formations depends upon its character. The contacts can be sedimentary, either conformable or unconformable; igneous, either volcanic or plutonic; or tectonic, generally faults or thrusts. The topographic surface can show almost limitless variety, from the smooth level surface of a plain or plateau to the intricate ruggedness of many mountain ranges. To illustrate the factors that control outcrop patterns we consider some of the simplest relationships.

OUTCROP PATTERN OF A PLANE LAYER

Many rock formations (for example, sedimentary beds, igneous sills or dikes, tectonic thrust slices) are essentially plane parallel-sided layers. The outcrop patterns on a simple topographic surface of such layers with

709

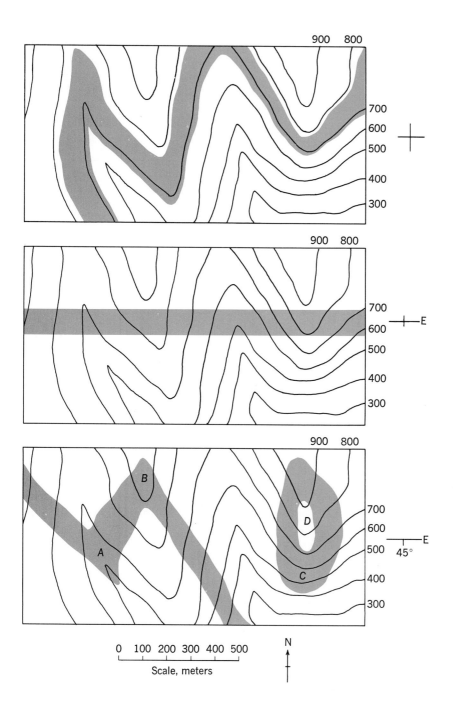

FIG. A–1 *Outcrop patterns of a layer (color) on a topographic surface: upper, horizontal layer; center, vertical layer; lower, layer striking due east and dipping 45° south (contour interval 100 meters).*

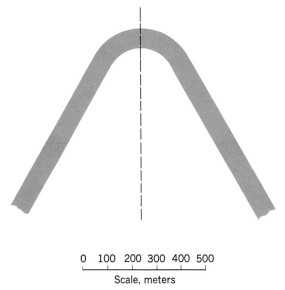

0   100   200   300   400   500

Scale, meters

FIG. A–2 *Profile of a plane cylindrical fold; broken line is trace of axial plane.*

various orientations are shown in color in Figure A–1. The contacts of a horizontal layer (upper diagram) follow contours on the topographic surface; those of a vertical layer (center diagram) cut across contours with no deflection. A dipping layer (lower diagram) striking across a valley or a ridge forms a V-shaped outcrop, pointing respectively in the direction of dip (locality A) or in the opposite direction (locality B). Where the strike of the dipping layer is the same as that of the topographic surface, the contacts follow contours (locality C). If the dip of the layer is less than the average dip of the topographic surface, the contacts can form closed loops and appear in several places on the map (locality D).

OUTCROP PATTERN OF A CYLINDRICALLY FOLDED LAYER

Planar limbs of folds act in the same way as the planar layers just described. The outcrop pattern of a hinge zone depends upon the orientations of the fold axis and axial plane, the shape of the hinge, and the tightness of folding. Consider, as an example, a plane cylindrical fold with true profile given in Figure A–2. Possible outcrop patterns of such a fold with three

different orientations are given in Figure A–3. In the upper diagram the fold is horizontal with a vertical axial plane and the hinge would appear on the map only if the topographic surface reached a sufficient elevation to cut the horizontal hinge. In the center diagram the fold is vertical and the outcrop pattern is the same as the true profile. In the lower diagram the general case of a plunging fold with dipping axial surface is shown. There are no horizontal attitudes of the folded surface on such a fold, and for the orientation shown (with one "overturned" limb) the layer becomes vertical somewhere in the hinge zone (locality A). The strike of the layer at this point coincides with the trend of the fold axis. The dip of that part of the layer striking perpendicular to the vertical segment (locality B) gives the plunge of the fold axis.

In regions of cylindrical folding, therefore, much can be learned about the orientation of the folds by study of their outcrop patterns and of the variation in orientation of the folded surface at various points. In particular, any vertical segment on the folded surface permits the trend of the fold axis to be determined, and horizontal attitudes are possible only on folds with horizontal axes. Particular care must be taken not to confuse the direction of the lines AA' in Figure A–4 (showing the outcrop pattern of a plunging inclined fold on a level, smooth topographic surface) with the trend of the fold axis. This line joins the "apparent" hinge points on the folded surface (remember that the map is *not* a true profile) and can be inclined at any angle to the trend of the axis. In "reclined folds," for example, this line and the trend are subperpendicular. In folds with very sharp hinges (such as chevron or certain types of similar folds) the line AA' corresponds to the trace of the axial plane on the topographic surface so that if the orientation of the fold axis is known the orientation of the axial plane can be found. In folds with rounded hinges (see, for example, Figure A–4) the axial trace TT' and the "apparent" axial trace AA' are not in the same direction.

OUTCROP PATTERN OF NONCYLINDRICALLY FOLDED LAYERS

In many regions of the crust folding cannot be considered cylindrical. This is particularly true where the rocks have been repeatedly deformed so that more than

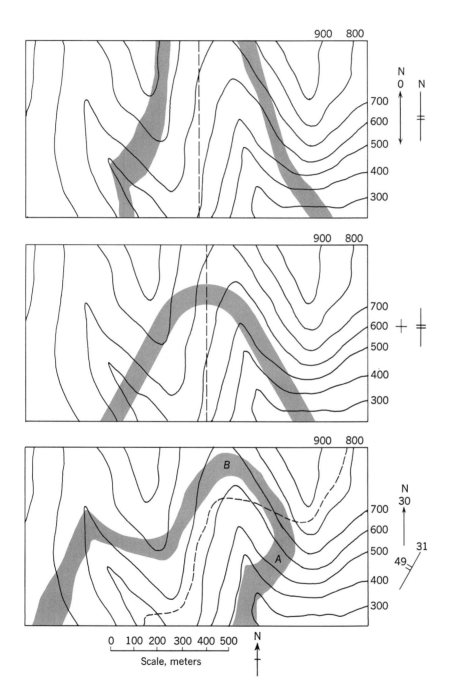

FIG. A–3 *Outcrop patterns of fold in Figure A–2 on a topographic surface: upper, horizontal axis, vertical axial plane; center, vertical axis and axial plane; lower, axis plunges 30° due north, axial plane strikes N31°E and dips 49° northwest (contour interval 100 meters). Broken lines are traces of axial planes.*

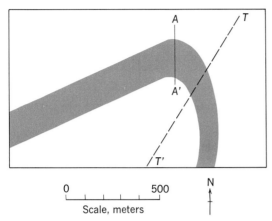

FIG. A-4 *Outcrop pattern of fold in lower diagram of Figure A–3 on a horizontal plane surface. AA′ is "apparent" axial-plane trace; TT′ is true axial-plane trace.*

one generation of folds is present. But it is true also of many areas of simple folding in which folds were formed initially with trend and plunge that varied from place to place. No general rules governing interpretation of the outcrop patterns of such complexly folded boundaries of any kind can be given, except to say that they commonly contain closed ringlike outcrops resulting from the presence of domelike and basinlike structures. Also, the axial traces of folds are themselves seen to be folded in suitable outcrops.

An example of a typical outcrop pattern from an area of interfering fold systems in the Scottish Highlands is shown in Figure A–5. Three sets of folds, the approximate axial traces of which are as shown, interfere to form tight domelike structures, the three-dimensional form of which is represented diagrammatically in Figure A–6. In other regions of noncylindrical folding the outcrop patterns may clearly indicate the presence of two sets of axial planes, even where no ring-shaped outcrops are present. An example is given in Figure A–7, in which the apparent axial traces of early folds are clearly crossed by those of a later generation. The form of the folded surfaces in three dimensions is represented diagrammatically in Figure A–8. Detailed geometric analysis of such large-scale structures formed by superposition of folds is made possible by dividing the mapped areas into small domains in which the folding is essentially cylindrical. The change in orientation of folds from place to place can then be determined.

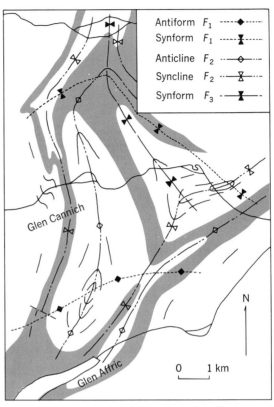

FIG. A-5 *Ring-shaped outcrops formed by basins and domes at Glen Cannich, Scottish Highlands. F_1, F_2, and F_3 are folds of three successive generations the approximate axial plane traces of which are shown. (After O. T. Tobisch, Large-scale basin and dome pattern resulting from the interference of major folds, Geol. Soc. Am. Bull., 1966.)*

Many types of irregular geologic boundaries occur other than those resulting from noncylindrical folding. The boundaries of most plutons, for example, are complex (refer to Figure 3–18), and fault contacts, particularly those of low-angle thrusts, can be extremely intricate on a map. No standard methods of geometric projection exist by which such nonsystematic outcrop patterns can be interpreted. Each example is unique and requires a fresh exercise of ingenuity and perception by the geologist. But the source of all interpretation is the geologic map, and much can be read from outcrop patterns, particularly in areas of rugged topography where some view of the third dimension of the crust is exposed. If the earth's surface were everywhere smooth

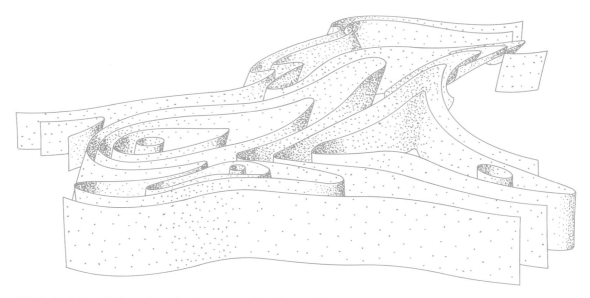

FIG. A–6 *Schematic three-dimensional representation of part of the structure shown in Figure A–5. (After O. T. Tobisch, Large-scale basin and dome pattern resulting from the interference of major folds, Geol. Soc. Am. Bull., 1966.)*

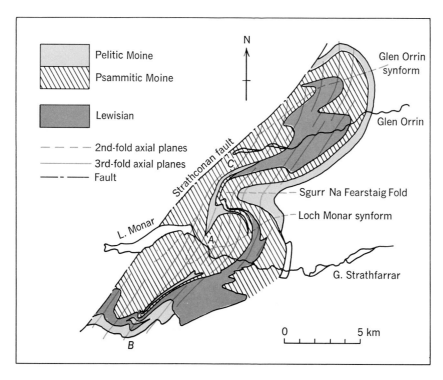

FIG. A–7 *Map of region of superposed folding around Loch Monar, Scottish Highlands: Two generations of folds shown. (After J. G. Ramsay, in The British Caledonides, M. R. W. Johnson and F. Stewart, eds., Oliver & Boyd, 1963.)*

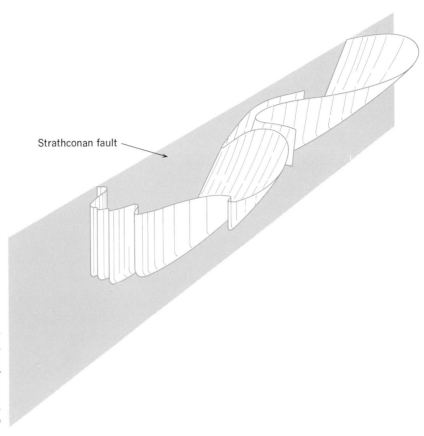

FIG. A–8 *Schematic three-dimensional representation of the structure shown in Figure A–7 showing small late folds formed on the limbs of early large folds. (After J. G. Ramsay, in The British Caledonides, M. R. W. Johnson and F. Stewart, eds., Oliver & Boyd, 1963.)*

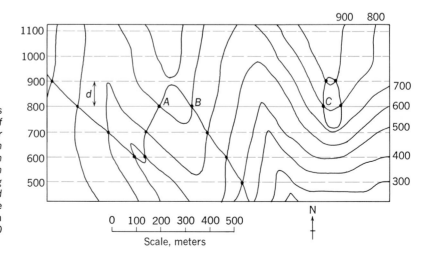

FIG. A–9 *Structure contours drawn on the upper surface of the layer in Figure A–1 (lower diagram). Control points (such as A, B, and C) where elevation of surface is accurately known are given by dots. The spacing of the contours is given by d and the dip of the surface δ can be found as $\delta = \tan^{-1} h/d$ where h is the contour interval (100 meters).*

and level, outcrop patterns alone would tell almost nothing of its internal structure.

Structure Contours

One of the most useful means of adding "depth" to a geologic map is by the construction, where possible, of structure or stratum contours—that is, of contours drawn upon a geologic interface of some kind. If underground data from boreholes or mines are available, a map of spot elevations on a particular surface can be prepared, and sketch "form lines" interpolated as for a topographic contour map. In general, only the outcrop pattern on the topographic surface is available and a structure contour map must be prepared from known elevations on contacts. In the presence of moderate topographic relief, such a map can commonly be made, provided that the form of the surface to be contoured is not too complex.

STRUCTURE CONTOURS ON A UNIFORMLY DIPPING SURFACE

Consider the upper surface of the layer in Figure A–1 (lower diagram). Elevations on such a surface are known at all points along the mapped contact, particularly where this crosses known topographic contours (values can be interpolated for intermediate points). Because the surface has uniform dip and strike points of the same elevation, such as A, B, and C in Figure A–9, can be joined by a straight line, which can then be projected laterally as shown. Once the direction and position of any one contour and the interval between any pair are determined the complete set of contours on the surface can be constructed over the whole area of the map (broken lines in Figure A–9). Some of the contours lie on the buried part of the surface and would be important, for example, in determining the depth at which the layer would be uncovered in a borehole drilled at a given point. Other contours are above the ground surface and represent a part of the surface removed by erosion.

The strike of the surface is given by the direction of the contours and the dip δ can be found from their spacing d on the map from the relationship $\delta = \tan^{-1} h/d$ where h is the contour interval. In practice, contours (even on planar geologic boundaries) are rarely perfectly straight and uniformly spaced, and an average attitude for the surface is best calculated from a number of contours in several places.

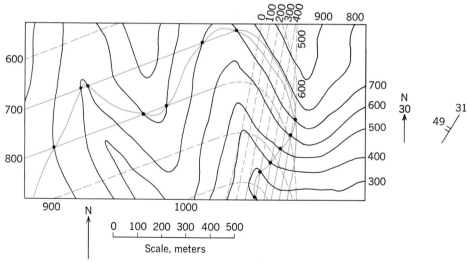

FIG. A–10 *Structure contours drawn on the upper surface of the fold in Figure A–3 (lower diagram). Points of known elevation on the contact are given by dots. Extrapolated contours are shown as broken lines. Note that because one limb of the fold is overturned, the contours cross one another.*

STRUCTURE CONTOURS ON A CYLINDRICAL FOLD

Contours drawn on a cylindrical fold are ideally congruent curves displaced uniformly according to the trend and plunge of the fold axis. In contrast to topographic surfaces, folded surfaces are commonly vertical or "overhanging," so contours on them meet and cross one another. In Figure A–10 contours are drawn by the method outlined above on the upper surface of the folded layer in Figure A–3 (lower). From the segments of contours (solid lines) that can be sketched through points of known elevation on the contact, other contours (broken lines) can be extrapolated up and down the plunge of the fold axis. The actual form of each contour in the hinge zone cannot be accurately determined; but because the limbs are essentially planar, a "constructed hinge line" can be found by projecting the contours on each limb until they meet, as shown in Figure A–11. The trend of the fold axis is then given by the azimuth of the line LL' joining the points of intersection, and the plunge α can be found from the relationship $\alpha = \tan^{-1} h/t$, where h is the contour interval and t is the spacing of the intersection points along line LL'.

Where a planar fault cuts and displaces a cylindrical fold hinge, a unique solution for the direction and amount of relative displacement can sometimes be obtained with the aid of structure contours. For example, the hinge zone of a fold in a surface (heavy line) is repeated on opposite sides of a fault FF' (broken line) as shown in the map in Figure A–12. Construction of structure contours on one surface of the folded layer on the opposite sides of the fault yields two constructed hinge lines as shown by the dotted lines. The elevations on these lines are known at every point and they must impinge on the fault surface at points P_1 and P_2, where spot elevations on the hinge lines and structure contours on the fault agree. Points P_1 and P_2 must have coincided before faulting, so the projection of the relative displacement vector on a horizontal surface is given by d, the separation of P_1 and P_2 as seen on the map. The trend of the displacement direction is given by the azimuth of the line through P_1 and P_2 and its plunge α can be found as $\alpha = \tan^{-1}(h/d)$, where h is the difference in elevation between P_1 and P_2 (found from the structure contours on the fault) and d is the separation of these points measured on the maps. The relative displacement t in this direction can be found at $t = d/\cos \alpha$.

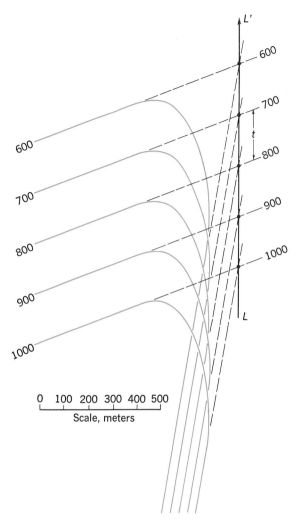

FIG. A–11 "Constructed" hinge line LL' for fold in Figure A–10. Contours on planar limbs are projected until they intersect in the line LL'. The azimuth of this line is the trend of the fold axis and the plunge α can be found as α = tan⁻¹ (h/t) where t is the spacing of the intersection points along LL' and h is the contour interval (100 meters).

STRUCTURE CONTOURS ON IRREGULARLY CURVED SURFACES

Many geologic boundaries (such as noncylindrically folded surfaces) are neither plane nor cylindrically curved and have no straight lines of constant orientation

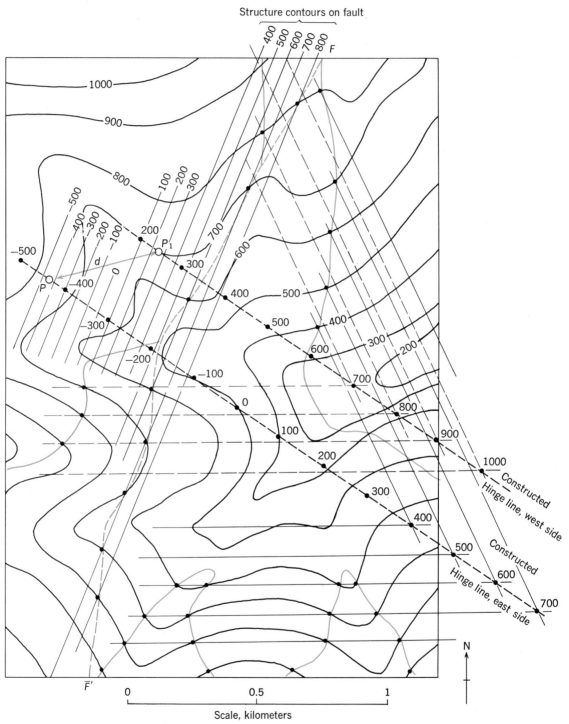

Structure contours on fault

F

−500

200
P₁
d
P

−400

−300

−200

−100

0

100

200

300

400

500

600

700

800

900

1000

100
200
300

700

600

500

400

300

200

100

0

800

900

1000

Constructed
Hinge line, west side

Constructed
Hinge line, east side

700

N

F̄′

0   0.5   1

Scale, kilometers

FIG. A–12

lying within them. The outcrop patterns of such surfaces cannot be linearly projected in any direction; and although a few contours can generally be sketched on such surfaces through known spot elevations, the shape of contours above and below the immediate vicinity of the contact is a matter of conjecture. Without underground data, for example, the forms of most plutonic bodies, salt domes, and "dome and basin" folds in sediments are imperfectly known. In some instances, unusually perfect exposure in rugged topography permits the contouring of even the most complexly shaped surfaces. In some regions structure contours can be drawn even on transposed contacts located by detailed mapping.

Cross Sections, Profiles, and Block Diagrams

Geologists conventionally provide a view of a geologic body other than that given by the map. The simplest such representation is the vertical cross section (see, for example, Figures 3–1 and 3–2), which is a view of the internal structure as seen on a hypothetical vertical cut. There are various ways of preparing such sections. The most accurate technique, which involves the use of subsurface data, is much used by petroleum geologists working in bedded, simply folded, and faulted rocks. But most such sections must be prepared by projection of surface data. For example, a cross section is constructed of a dipping layer in the following way. The

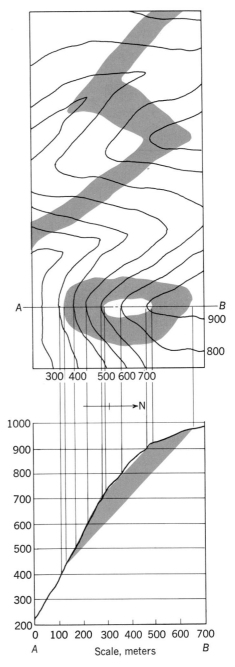

FIG. A–12 *Solution for relative motion on a fault displacing the hinge of a cylindrical fold. The folded surface is the continuous color line and the fault the broken color line FF'. Contours are drawn on the folded surface on the west side (fine broken lines) and on the east side (fine continuous lines) of the fault. Constructed hinge lines (dashed black lines) for the west and east sides projected up and down plunge impinge on the projected fault surface (given by contours on the fault surface) at points P_1 and P_2 respectively. Line P_1P_2 in the fault surface is the relative displacement of the fault. The trend of this line can be measured directly from the map: The plunge α can be found as $\alpha = \tan^{-1}(h/d)$ where d is the distance P_1P_2 projected onto a horizontal surface and h is the difference in elevation between P_1 and P_2 found from contours on fault.*

FIG. A–13 *Vertical cross section along line AB across the dipping layer in Figure A–1 (lower).*

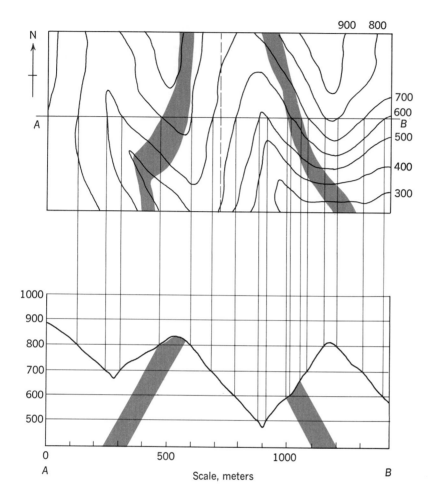

FIG. A–14 *Vertical cross section along line AB across the horizontal fold in Figure A–3 (upper).*

plane of section is chosen perpendicular to the strike so that the true dip of the layer is shown. The line of section in Figure A–13 is chosen as *AB*, and a topographic profile is constructed along it as shown (a vertical exaggeration can be included if desired), and the outcrop points of the upper and lower surfaces of the layers are plotted on this profile. The dip is known and the layer can be drawn in on the profile and projected to depth. For a horizontal upright anticline the same procedure can be adopted for each limb (Figure A–14); but a difficulty arises in drawing the shape of the fold hinge if, as in the example shown, the hinge does not appear on the map. Various techniques are used to form the fold hinges, but they all depend upon a preconceived notion

of the shape of an eroded or buried fold. Some possible shapes—all reasonable—are shown in Figure A–15.

In spite of this disadvantage, vertical cross sections are useful and are often employed to show the approximate subsurface form of simple structures, such as open folds with subhorizontal axes, intrusive bodies, and fault systems. They are less useful, perhaps even useless or misleading, in regions of complex structure with no linear continuity of form in any direction. Even in regions of moderately plunging cylindrical folds, a vertical cross section has no particular merit since, like the map, it shows a view of the fold forms that is to some degree distorted. For such bodies a nonvertical cross section or profile should be constructed by orthographic

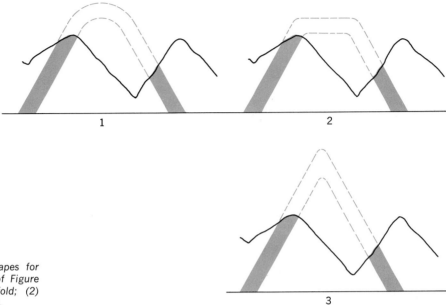

FIG. A-15 *Possible shapes for the eroded fold hinge of Figure A-14: (1) concentric fold; (2) box fold; (3) similar fold.*

projection[1] of the outcrop pattern of the folded layers onto a plane perpendicular to the fold axis. To make such a projection two types of distortion present in the

_____

[1] An orthographic projection of a body onto a given plane is made by projecting every point on the body onto the plane along lines perpendicular to the plane.

outcrop pattern of the fold must be removed. First is homogeneous distortion resulting from the fact that the fold axes plunge. Second is heterogeneous distortion resulting from topography. To illustrate the geometric procedure involved we take the map of the plunging fold in Figure A-3 (lower). First we assume that the ground surface is smooth and level and that the observed outcrop pattern can be projected orthograph-

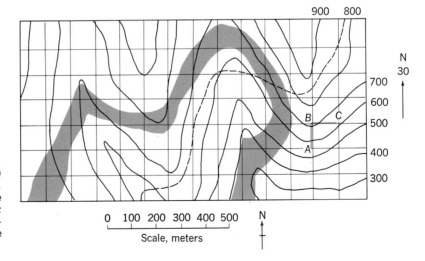

FIG. A-16 *Figure A-3 (lower) with square grid superposed. Grid lines parallel to AB have the same trend as the fold axis: grid lines parallel to BC are perpendicular to the trend of the fold axis.*

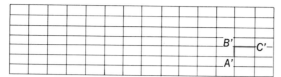

FIG. A–17 *Grid shown in Figure A–16 distorted to allow for the plunge of the fold axis (30°). This distorted grid is the orthographic projection of the square grid on a plane perpendicular to the fold axis.*

ically along the fold axial direction. By this process all lines on the map in the direction of the fold-axial trend, such as AB in Figure A–16, are shortened in projection to length $A'B'$ given by $A'B' = AB \sin \alpha$, where α is the plunge. All lines on the map perpendicular to the trend, such as BC in Figure A–16, remain the same length in projection. Thus an orthogonal grid with intervals AB and BC on the map becomes distorted into an orthogonal grid with intervals $A'B'$ and $B'C'$ on the projection (Figure A–17), and the simplest means of transposing the outcrop pattern to the projection is to sketch it in by hand on the distorted grid (other, more elegant methods can be used).

The second correction involves determination of the elevation of points such as A, B, and C to be transferred to the distorted grid. For example, the positions of A and B as seen on the map correspond respectively to two points a and b on the topographic surface (Figure A–18). The first projection given above transfers points A and B on the map to $A'B'$ in the projection; whereas projection of points a and b (of different elevation) would give respectively points a' and b'. The position of A' must therefore be moved to a' where $A'a' = h_a \cos \alpha$ and h_a is the elevation of a above a chosen base line (generally chosen lower than any point on the map). The position of B' is correspondingly corrected to b', where $B'b' = h_b \cos \alpha$.

By a combination of these two distortions the pattern on the map in Figure A–16 is transformed into the true profile of Figure A–19, which shows the forms of the cylindrical fold as viewed along the fold axis. The advantage of this method over conventional methods of constructing cross sections is that no line appears on the profile that is not a contact on the map, so that no assumptions about the shapes of fold hinge zones need be made. This technique of axial projection of folds played an important part in determining the structure of parts of the Swiss Alps in which great plunging cylindrical folds are locally present in regions of high relief. Even where fold axes curve, combination of successive profiles from essentially cylindrical segments can give a reasonably accurate representation of structure.

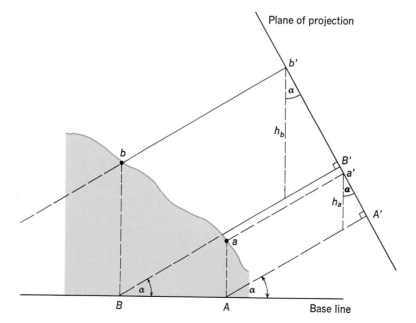

FIG. A–18 *Topographic correction for points of different elevation to be applied in profile. Vertical section is along AB with α the plunge of the fold axis. Point A on the map projects to A' in the profile and must be moved to a' where a'A' = h_a cos α and h_a is the elevation of a above a chosen base line. A similar correction moves B' to b'.*

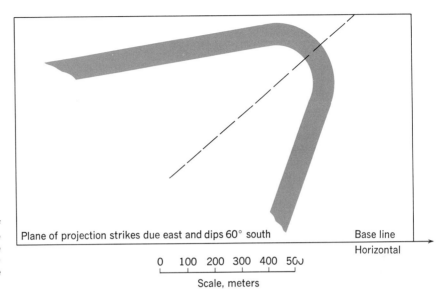

Plane of projection strikes due east and dips 60° south   Base line

Horizontal

0   100 200 300 400 500

Scale, meters

FIG. A–19 *True profile of fold in Figure A–16. Plane of projection strikes due east and dips 60° south and is viewed down the plunge of the fold axis.*

In regions of complex noncylindrical folding or otherwise complex structure, cross sections and profiles are of little use. The construction of such sections is generally highly subjective and generally nonquantitative. To depict the structure of such regions use is sometimes made of block diagrams, which show sections through a body on three or more planes (one usually corresponds to the map). Many varieties have been used for different purposes; some are accurately constructed, even from subsurface data, but most are purely qualitative attempts to represent very complex structures and, as such, are often dramatically successful (see, for example, Figure A–20).

Stereographic and Equal-Area Projections

The stereographic projection is used by crystallographers and structural geologists alike; use of the equal-area projection is confined to structural geology. Both projections are projections of a sphere onto a plane and are generally employed as "nets," which are projections of a sphere inscribed with great circles of longitude and small circles of latitude. Two forms of each net are in use:

1. Equatorial or meridional nets, in which the plane of projection is a great circle of longitude and is thus perpendicular to the equatorial plane (see Figure A–21).

2. Polar nets in which the plane of projection is the equatorial plane and is thus perpendicular to the polar axis (see Figure A–22).

Equatorial nets are most commonly used because only these can be used to draw great circles obliquely inclined to the plane of projection.

The nets are three-dimensional protractors by means of which angles between lines and planes can be simply represented and measured in two dimensions. In crystallography, for example, face poles and zone circles can be plotted and interfacial angles and interzone angles measured. In structural geology, on the other hand, the attitude of the line of intersection of a fault and a bedding plane can be found.

Plotting and manipulation of data are exactly the same for both nets and will be found described in the references at the end of this Appendix.

In stereographic projection, surfaces on the projection sphere appear as circles and are easy to construct; in the equal-area projection, such circles are ellipses and no simple geometric construction is possible. The only advantage of the equal-area projection that makes it preferred in structural geology is that equal areas on the projection sphere project as equal areas. This feature is not found in the stereographic projection in which

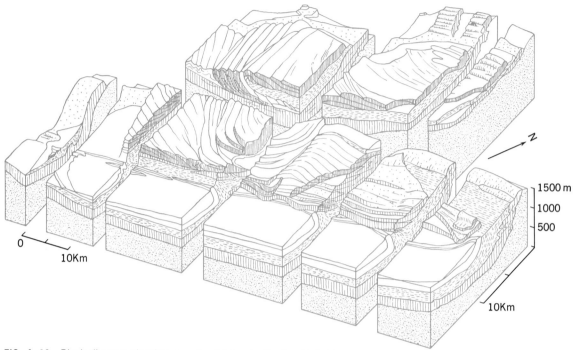

FIG. A–20   *Block diagram showing complex folding in the Naukluft Mountains of southwest Africa. (After H. Korn and H. Martin, Gravity Tectonics in the Naukluft Mountains of South West Africa. Geol. Soc. Am. Bull., 1963.)*

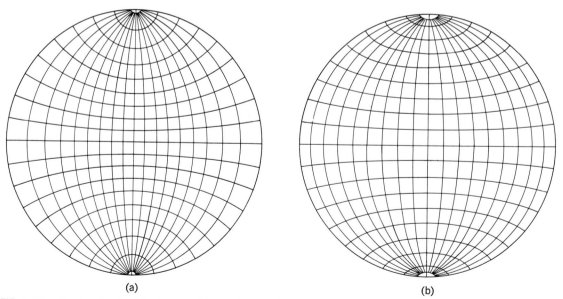

(a)   (b)

FIG. A–21   *Meridional nets: (a) stereographic net; (b) equal-area net. (Meridians and parallels at 10° intervals.)*

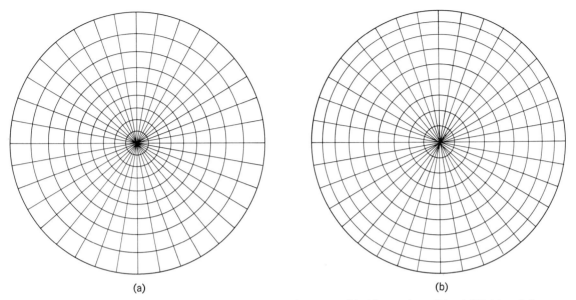

(a)   (b)

FIG. A–22 *Polar nets: (a) stereographic net; (b) equal-area net. (Meridian and parallels at 10° intervals.)*

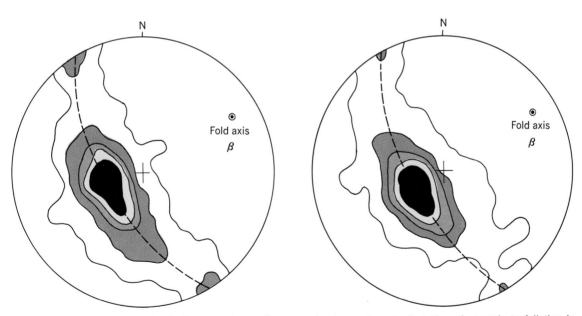

FIG. A–23 *Contoured lower-hemisphere equal-area diagrams showing preferred orientation of normals to foliation in Precambrian metamorphic rocks in southern Kenya. Left, 429 measurements from northern half of region; right, 573 measurements from southern half of region; contours 9, 7, 5, 3, and 1 percent per 1 percent area.*

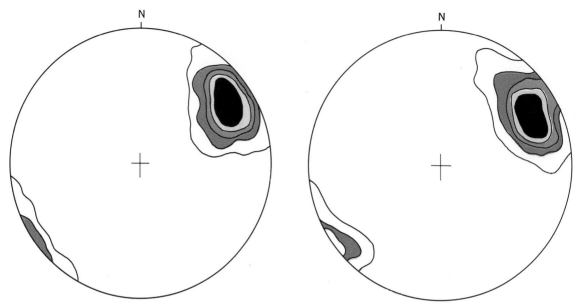

FIG. A–24   *Contoured lower-hemisphere equal-area diagrams showing preferred orientation of lineations in Precambrian rocks in southern Kenya (same region as in Figure A–23). Left, 284 lineations from northern part of the region; right, 502 lineations from southern part of the region; contours 9, 7, 5, 3, and 1 percent per 1 percent area.*

centrally situated areas are diminished with respect to peripheral areas of equal size on the projection sphere. Because of this property, density distribution of points on the equal-area projection faithfully represents the preferred orientation of structural lines and the projection can be contoured for density distribution of points to yield an image of preferred orientation. Procedures

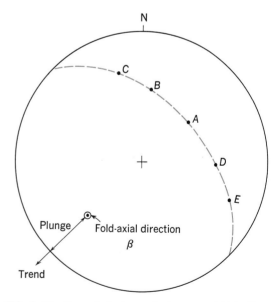

FIG. A–26   *Normals to tangent planes on fold in Figure A–25 plotted in lower-hemisphere equal-area projection on a horizontal plane. The points all lie on a single great circle (broken line), the normal to which is the fold-axial direction β.*

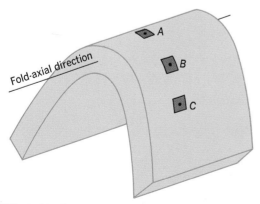

FIG. A–25   *Perfectly cylindrical fold with tangent planes A, B, C, and so on.*

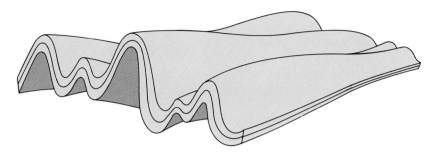

FIG. A–27 *Group of nat-ural cylindrical folds.*

for contour are outlined in the last reference at the end of this Appendix.

The main use of the equal-area projection by the structural geologist is to represent internal structure. We have already noted its use in representing preferred orientations of mineral grains in rocks. But it can be used similarly to show patterns of orientation of structural surfaces and lines on a larger scale, particularly pervasive structures such as foliations and lineations. For example, the preferred orientation of the normals to foliation measured in a particular area can be plotted in equal-area projection on a horizontal plane to give an "orientation diagram" of the kind shown in Figure A–23. A single maximum concentration of points is present which can be emphasized by contouring as shown. The "mean orientation" of the regional foliation can be simply found as the centroid of the area within the highest contour.

Plotting of orientation data for internal structures can be used also as a test for structural homogeneity in a body. For example, in Figure A–23 are shown orientation diagrams for foliation-poles measured in two distinct parts of the same body of deformed rock; in Figure A–24 are shown diagrams for lineations in the same two areas. The similarity of the diagrams for the two samples confirms that the internal structure as represented by orientation foliation and lineation is essentially homogeneous, and is highly symmetric.

The most important use of such techniques in recent years has been in the geometric analysis of complexly folded rocks. The principle that forms a basis for such analysis is that tangent planes at any points on a cylindrically folded surface are cozonal with the fold axis or zone axis. For example, consider the perfectly cylindrical fold in Figure A–25. Poles to tangent planes at a number of points on the folded surface (such as A, B, C, . . ., and so on) when plotted in projection (Figure A–

26) lie on a great circle of the projection (called the S-pole circle) the normal to which is the geometrically constructed fold axis, generally given the symbol β. For a real cylindrical fold or system of folds (such as, for example, that shown diagrammatically in Figure A–27), the poles to the folded surface similarly plotted lie in a broad band or "girdle" across the projection (Figure A–28: see also Figure A–23). The compactness of this girdle is a measure of the "cylindricality" of the folding,

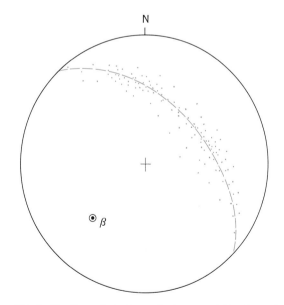

FIG. A–28 *Normals to tangent planes on folds shown in Figure A–27 plotted in lower-hemisphere equal-area pro-jection on a horizontal plane. The points lie in a broad band or "girdle" across the projection; the broken line shows the great circle of best fit to this girdle. The direction normal to this great circle can be taken as the fold-axial direction for the group of cylindrical folds.*

and the normal to the great circle of best fit (placed by inspection or by a method of least squares) is taken as the statistically defined fold axis β.

By use of this simple technique the trend and plunge of individual cylindrical folds or cylindrical fold systems can be rapidly determined from measured attitudes on the folded surface, and a region of noncylindrical folding can be separated into domains in which the folding is essentially cylindrical. Thus the variation in fold-axial directions from place to place can be determined and the presence of superposed fold systems detected and their properties established. Many studies of complex folding using this procedure have been made by geologists in recent years and equal-area projections are playing an increasingly important part in the study of preferred orientations on a regional scale of a large variety of structural features in metamorphic, igneous, and sedimentary rocks.

REFERENCES

Badgley, P. C.: *Structural Methods for the Exploration Geologist,* Harper & Row, New York, 1959, pp. 187–242.

Bishop, A. C.: *An Outline of Crystal Morphology,* Hutchinson, London, 1967.

Bucher, W. H.: The stereographic projection, a handy tool for the practical geologist, *J. Geol.,* vol. 52, pp. 191–212, 1944.

Dennison, J. M.: *Analysis of Geologic Structures,* Norton, New York, 1968.

Haman, P. J.: *Manual of Stereographic Projection,* West Canadian Research Publications, Calgary, pp. 1–67, 1961.

Higgs, D. V., and G. Tunell: *Angular Relations of Lines and Planes,* William C. Brown Company, Dubuque, Iowa, 1959.

Phillips, F. C.: *Stereographic Projection in Structural Geology,* E. Arnold, London, 1954.

————: *An Introduction to Crystallography,* 3d edition, Longmans, London, 1963.

Ragan, D. M.: *Structural Geology: An Introduction to Geometrical Techniques,* Wiley, New York, 1968.

Terpstra, P., and L. W. Codd: *Crystallometry,* Longmans, London, 1961.

Turner, F. J., and L. E. Weiss: *Structural Analysis of Metamorphic Tectonites,* McGraw-Hill, New York, 1963.

INDEX